PRENTICE HALL
CUSTOM BUSINESS RESOURCES

Compiled by

San Jose State University
Business Statistics
Custom Edition

PEARSON Custom Publishing

PEARSON Prentice Hall

Director of Database Publishing: Michael Payne
Senior Sponsoring Editor: Robin J. Lazrus
Development Editor: Catherine O'Keefe
Marketing Manager: Amy Dawson
Assistant Editor: Ana Díaz-Caneja
Operations Manager: Eric M. Kenney
Production Product Manager: Jennifer Berry
Cover Designer: Renée Sartell

Cover Art: Courtesy of EyeWire/Getty Images and PhotoDisc/Getty Images. Photodisc, "Globe surrounded by business people on computer monitors," courtesy of Photodisc/Getty Images. Dave Cutler (Artist), "Man Dropping Coins Into Glass Jar," courtesy of David Cutler/Images.com. Dave Cutler (Artist), "Three Coins in Glass Jar," courtesy of David Cutler/Images.com.

This special edition published in cooperation with Pearson Custom Publishing.

Printed in the United States of America.

Please visit our web site at *www.pearsoncustom.com*

Attention bookstores: For permission to return unused stock, call 800 777-6872.

ISBN–13: 9780536889164

ISBN–10: 0536889163

Package ISBN–13: N/A

Package ISBN–10: N/A

PEARSON
Custom Publishing

PEARSON CUSTOM PUBLISHING
501 Boylston Street, Suite 900
Boston, MA 02116

Editorial Advisory Board

Contents

Introduction and Data Collection

USING STATISTICS: Good Tunes—Part I

LEARNING OBJECTIVES

- To understand how statistics is used in business
- To identify sources of data
- To distinguish between different survey sampling methods
- To understand the different measurement scales

USING STATISTICS

Good Tunes—Part I

Good Tunes, a privately held online retailer of top-quality stereo systems and other consumer electronics items, is seeking to expand its business by opening its first retail location. To obtain the financing necessary to underwrite this expansion, Good Tunes needs to apply for loans at local area banks. The managers of the firm agree to develop an electronic slide show that will explain their business and state the facts that will convince the bankers to loan Good Tunes the money it needs. You have been asked to assist in the process of preparing the slide show. What facts would you include? How would you present those facts?

1 WHAT IS STATISTICS

For a business to thrive, it must collect and generate facts that reflect its current status. These facts, or **data**, need to be changed into **information**, in order to best support rational management decision making. Today, many of the ways used to change data into information are applications of **statistics**, the branch of mathematics that focuses on processing and analyzing data.

Statistics, itself, is divided into two branches, both of which are applicable to managing businesses. **Descriptive statistics** focuses on the collection, summarization, and characterization of a set of data. **Inferential statistics** estimates a characteristic of a set of data, or help uncover patterns in data sets that are unlikely to occur by chance.

Descriptive statistics has its roots in the recordkeeping needs of large political and social organizations. For example, since 1790, the United States has conducted a decennial census that collects and summarizes data about its citizens. Through the years, the U.S. Census Bureau has been one of the many groups that have refined the methods of descriptive statistics.

The mathematics of probability theory form the foundations of inferential statistics. Inferential methods select **samples**, portions of an entire set of data, rather than the complete set itself, which is known as the **population** or **universe**. Inferential methods use the sample data to calculate summary measures called **statistics** that decision-makers can use to estimate the **parameters** characteristics of the entire population.

Today, applications of statistical methods can be found in the different functional areas of business. Accounting uses statistical methods to select samples for auditing purposes and to understand the cost drivers in cost accounting. Finance uses statistical methods to choose between alternative portfolio investments and to track trends in financial measures over time. Management uses statistical methods to improve the quality of the products manufactured or the services delivered by an organization. Marketing uses statistical methods to estimate the proportion of customers who prefer one product over another and why they do, and to draw conclusions about what advertising strategy might be most useful in increasing sales of a product.

Sample
A sample is the portion of the population that is selected for analysis.

Population (universe)
A population (or universe) is the totality of items or things under consideration.

Statistic
A statistic is a summary measure computed from sample data that is used to describe or estimate a characteristic of the entire population.

Parameter
A parameter is a summary measure that describes a characteristic of an entire population.

2 THE GROWTH OF STATISTICS AND INFORMATION TECHNOLOGY

During the past century, statistics has played an important role in spurring the use of information technology and, in turn, such technology has spurred the wider use of statistics. At the beginning of the 20th century, the expanding data-handling requirements associated with the decennial census led directly to the development of tabulating machines that were the forerunners of today's business computer systems. Statisticians, such as Pearson, Fisher, Gosset, Neyman, Wald, and Tukey, established the techniques of modern inferential statistics in response to the need to analyze large sets of population data that had become increasingly costly, time-consuming, and cumbersome to collect. The development of early computer systems permitted others to develop computer programs to ease the calculational and data processing burdens imposed by those techniques. These first programs, in turn, allowed greater use of statistical methods by business decision-makers. This greater use, as well as more recent advances in information technology, have completed the cycle by spurring the development of even more sophisticated statistical methods.

Today, when you hear of retailers investing in a "customer-relationship management system" or a packaged goods producer engaging in "data mining" to uncover consumer preferences, you should realize that statistical techniques form the foundations of such cutting-edge applications. While such applications might require special programming, for many years businesses have used **statistical packages** to help managers use a wide range of statistical techniques by automating the data processing and calculations such techniques require. These standardized sets of programs that include the products Minitab, SAS®, and SPSS®, were once available only in corporate computing centers. However, the increasing power and connectivity of personal computers have brought the statistical power of these packages to the desktop, where they have joined such familiar tools as word processing, spreadsheet, and Web browser programs.

3 MICROSOFT EXCEL: SOLUTION TO A PROBLEM OR A PROBLEM ITSELF?

The leasing and training costs associated with statistical applications of information technology, particularly those associated with statistical packages, have caused some managers to look elsewhere on their desktops for easier-to-use and cheaper statistical functionality. Many have discovered the graphical and statistical functions of Microsoft Excel. Microsoft Excel seems like an attractive alternate because:

- Excel is already installed on the typical business desktop, so no added software costs are incurred.
- Most business users already have some familiarity with Excel.
- For casual users, Excel seems easy-to-use and easy-to-learn.
- The graphical and statistical functions of Excel operate on the same handy worksheet-based data that users create for other business purposes.
- Some graphical functions of Excel produce more vivid visual output than some statistical packages.

While all of these *are* attractive features, many managers choosing Microsoft Excel have not considered the accuracy and completeness of the statistical results that Excel produces. Unfortunately, some investigators have determined that certain Microsoft Excel statistical capabilities contain flaws that can lead to invalid results, especially when data sets that are very large or that have unusual statistical properties are used (see reference 7). Even using Microsoft Excel with small data sets to produce simple descriptive statistics can lead to nonstandard results. Clearly, when you use Microsoft Excel, you must be careful about the data and the analysis you are conducting. Whether this complication outweighs the benefits of Excel's attractive features is still an unanswered question in business today.

Besides this issue of accuracy, Microsoft Excel has one unfortunate feature that it shares with all easy-to-use programs (including some desktop statistical packages): It is just as easy to *misuse* Excel as it is to use properly! For example, every day, some use the Chart Wizard (introduced in section EP6 of the Excel Primer) to produce charts that we may consider to be "chartjunk." Users who produce such charts show that while they may know how to *operate* Microsoft Excel, *they do not know how to use Excel as a statistical tool.*

Using Microsoft Excel (or any other program) for statistics requires being fully aware of the appropriateness of your selection as well as the requirements or assumptions an analysis makes. Only by understanding the application of statistical concepts to a particular problem can you avoid performing inappropriate analyses or the common mistake of relying on overly simplified decision-making processes that are solely based on a few easily calculated statistics. Proper use also requires knowing about a program's limitations, such as the accuracy of Excel's results mentioned earlier in this section. In contrast, focusing solely on learning keystroke and menu sequences—the operational mechanics of Microsoft Excel—gains you very little, or nothing, if you are not also *knowledgeable* about statistics.

4 LEARNING ABOUT BUSINESS STATISTICS

The primary goal of this text is helping you learn to be *knowledgeable* about business statistics, that is, understanding how the methods of statistics can be applied successfully to decision-making processes. For managers, being knowledgeable about business statistics includes being able to:

- Properly present and describe business data and information.
- Draw conclusions about large populations based solely on information obtained from samples.
- Improve business processes.
- Obtain reliable forecasts about business trends.

How statistics educators can best help you learn to be knowledgeable about business statistics is a source of debate today.

As section 2 notes, programs that incorporate statistical methods have greatly affected the acceptance of statistical methods in business. When such programs began to be used, statistics educators began to debate whether lessons written in the past that emphasized manual calculation and the use of simple calculating devices should be reconsidered. Some educators insisted that such lessons were basic to understanding statistics, while others pointed out the new opportunities to emphasize the application of statistics in business that statistical programs created.

This debate continues today, with both sides making valid points and striving to identify how using such programs affect the definition of being knowledgeable about statistics. In this text, you will find a middle ground: While the text extensively uses Microsoft Excel to illustrate the application of statistics to specific business problems, the text also presents the calculational basics of key statistical procedures. Moreover, the Microsoft Excel-based solutions presented in each chapter almost always allow you to discover more about the calculational foundations of a statistical method, even when those aspects are not emphasized in a particular chapter. You and your instructor can choose to explore these foundations while simultaneously learning about the application of statistics in business.

Because learning in context enhances comprehension, each chapter begins with a Using Statistics scenario, such as the "Good Tunes—Part I," that identifies a business problem in which statistics can be applied to change data into the useful information required for a rational decision. Questions raised in the scenarios lead to answers in the form of statistical methods presented in subsequent sections of the text. By thinking about these questions, you will gain an appreciation of how business managers are using statistics today to solve problems and improve the quality of their products and services.

For the "Good Tunes—Part I" scenario, selecting what to present would be just as important as selecting the proper method for presentation and summarization. In this case, presumably the bankers themselves would demand some of the data, the "financials" of the business. But what other data could you collect and present that would help win the approval of the loans? (See "Good Tunes—Part II" further on.) Of course, having presented your data, you would hope that the bankers could make the right inferences. That is, you would hope that the bankers were knowledgeable about the appropriate inferential methods that assist in the loan-making decision!

5 LEARNING STATISTICS WITH MICROSOFT EXCEL

As section 2 explains, the growth of statistics during the past century has led to the increasing use of programs that automate the data processing and calculations of statistical analyses. If this text only covered statistical concepts and did not illustrate the use of a computer program that generates statistical information, your education would be incomplete.

The ideal program to use in this text would be widely available in business, easy for you to use, not too difficult or time-consuming for you *to learn to use*, and would always produce accurate statistical information. Unfortunately, no such program exists today! In place of an "ideal" program, the text uses Microsoft Excel. You will discover that despite the concerns raised in section 3, Microsoft Excel provides an excellent way to introduce you to basic statistical methods, and to demonstrate the application of those methods in business decision making.

Of course, the concerns raised earlier are real, so the data used in this text have been carefully chosen to minimize or eliminate the statistical flaws researchers have uncovered. When you use Microsoft Excel with any of the data sets of this text, you will always be able to draw the correct inference or conclusion from the results produced by Microsoft Excel. (This may not be true for other data sets you decide to use, so you need to be aware of the accuracy issue raised in section 3 if you use such other data.)

6 USING MICROSOFT EXCEL IN THE BEST WAY POSSIBLE

This text uses Microsoft Excel to help you learn about business statistics. Similar to the debate about the best way to learn statistics noted in section 4, statistics educators differ in their approach over the best way to "use" Microsoft Excel while learning about business statistics. Some educators want to use Microsoft Excel as a tool that can conveniently illustrate applications of statistics. Others, concerned that their students might be using Microsoft Excel as a primary tool for statistical analysis in later years, believe using Excel must include more formal technical learning of the special Excel instructions and worksheet entries needed to produce statistical results.

This debate means that there cannot ever be a single best way for *all* students in *every* introductory business statistics course to "use" Microsoft Excel. As a practical matter, other issues such as the amount of training, experience, and level of technology required for a particular approach, as well as the quality of technical support available, and the length of the course affect the debate as well and your instructor may want to use a mix of both approaches.

For these reasons, this text uses in-chapter **Excel Strategies** sections that first state, in a short executive summary how to apply Microsoft Excel to a specific statistical method and then presents detailed instructions for *both* those who want to use Excel in the most convenient way as well as those who want a more in-depth technical way. By avoiding a "one way fits all" approach, this text gives you and your instructor the flexibility to tailor your Microsoft Excel usage while learning introductory business statistics. Even if you are a committed user of a single approach, seeing the other approach in the same context can enhance your learning and give you the opportunity to deepen or broaden your awareness of Microsoft Excel.

To help you use Microsoft Excel in the best way possible (whichever way that may be), this text has these additional unique set of features:

- **Numerous examples of worksheet and chart results generated by Microsoft Excel.** These examples appear both as chapter figures and as sheets in chapter Excel workbooks. You can see how you can use Excel even if you do not have time to produce your own results while learning a particular statistical method.
- **Full integration with PHStat2, Prentice Hall's supplemental program for Microsoft Excel that is bundled free with this text.** Using PHStat2 minimizes the tedious and error-prone tasks that are associated with *operating* Microsoft Excel as well as making Microsoft Excel a more convenient tool for statistical analysis by lessening the need for formal technical learning about Excel. (If you plan to use PHStat2, see the appendix for the user's guide to this program.)
- **Ready-to-use worksheet templates and macro workbooks for selected statistical methods.** These worksheets and workbooks allow you to generate certain results that would be otherwise

hard to achieve in Microsoft Excel. This allows you to benefit from PHStat2 technology without having to set up or use that program or any other macros.

- **"Excel Handbook" sections that walk you through detailed procedures for manually generating your own statistical results or revising results generated by standard Microsoft Excel commands.** These sections are particularly useful if you are interested in the more formal technical instruction about Microsoft Excel or if you want to learn more about the methods that PHStat2 uses to generate worksheets and charts.
- **A "Preparing Data for Reports and Presentations Using Microsoft Office" appendix that explains techniques for integrating Microsoft Excel results in Microsoft Word documents and Microsoft PowerPoint presentations and for retrieving data from the World Wide Web for use by Microsoft Excel (see the appendix).**

Because both ways of using Microsoft Excel require that you are familiar with the basics of operating Microsoft Windows and Microsoft Excel, this text includes an Excel Primer (consult your instructor if you require this item). The primer reviews the basics of using Microsoft Excel and presumes no prior experience using Microsoft Excel. Before jumping to the primer, continue with the rest of this chapter to understand the overall organization of the text and to learn some of the foundational concepts of statistics.

7 LEARNING BUSINESS STATISTICS USING THIS TEXT

To help you become knowledgeable about business statistics, this text uses the four tasks listed at the beginning of section 4 as its organizing principle. Figure 1 represents a structure chart that shows how individual concepts relate to these tasks. You will explore the methods involved in the collection, presentation, and description of information in the remaining portion of this chapter.

USING STATISTICS

Good Tunes—Part II

The owners of Good Tunes have decided to supplement the financial data in their loan application with data concerning customer perceptions about Good Tunes. To help assess these perceptions, Good Tunes has been asking its customers to complete and promptly return a customer satisfaction survey that is included in every order. The survey includes the following questions:

- How many days did it take from the time you ordered your merchandise to the time you received it? __________
- How much money (in U.S. dollars) do you expect to spend on stereo and consumer electronics equipment in the next twelve months? __________
- How do you rate the overall service provided by Good Tunes with respect to your recent purchase?

Much better than expected	☐	Worse than expected	☐
Better than expected	☐	Much worse than expected	☐
About as expected	☐		

- How do you rate the quality of the items you recently purchased from Good Tunes?

Much better than expected	☐	Worse than expected	☐
Better than expected	☐	Much worse than expected	☐
About as expected	☐		

- Are you likely to buy additional merchandise through Good Tunes in the next twelve months? Yes __________ No __________

You have been asked to review the survey. What type of data does the survey seek to collect? What type of information can be generated from the data of the completed survey? How can Good Tunes use that information to improve the perceived quality of the service and merchandise? How can Good Tunes use that information to increase its chance of getting a loan approval? What other questions would you suggest be included in the survey?

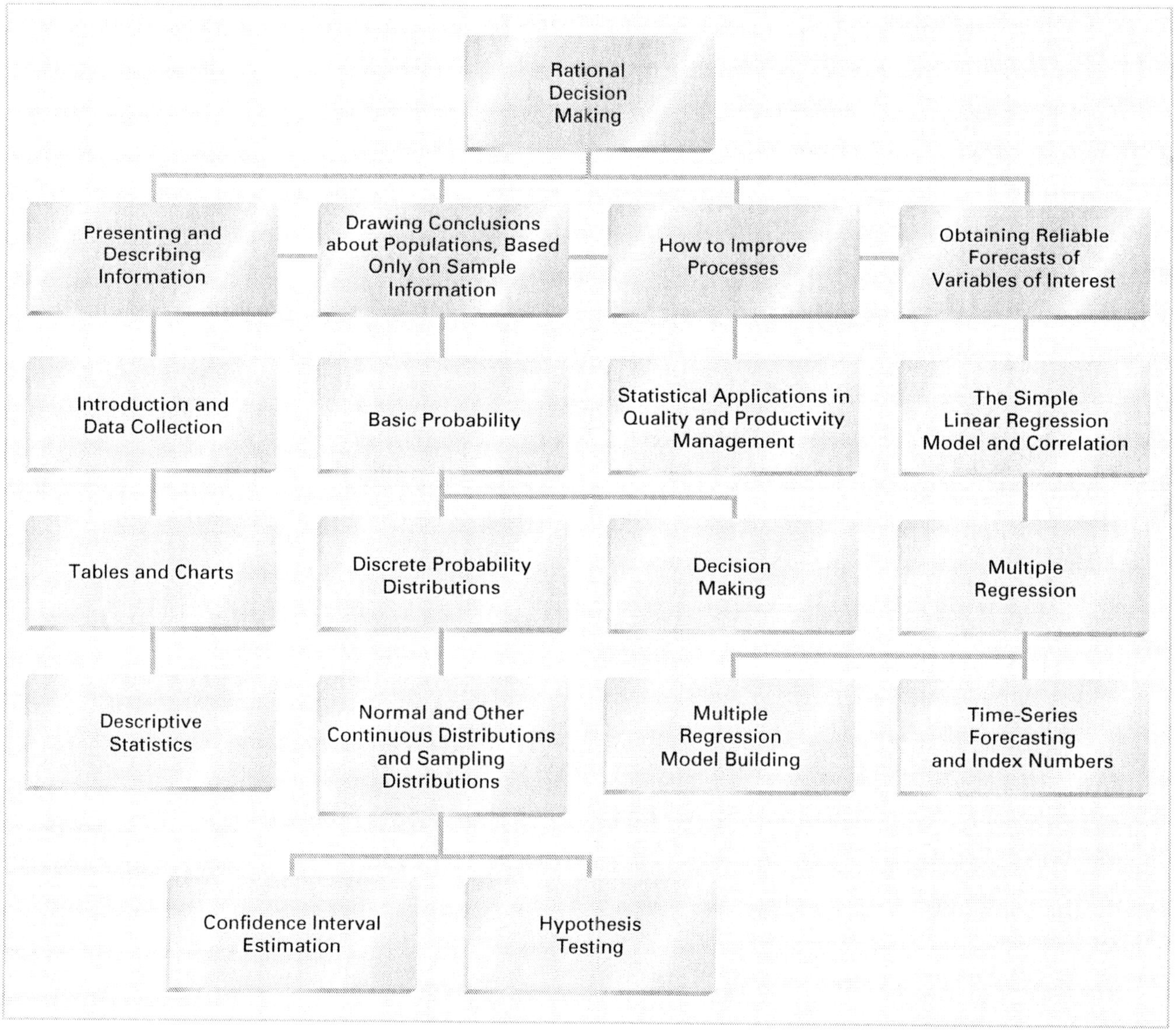

FIGURE 1
Structure chart for this text

8 THE IMPORTANCE OF COLLECTING DATA

Collecting the appropriate data is essential to managing a business effectively. There are many different types of circumstances that require the collection of data:

- A market researcher needs to assess product characteristics to distinguish one product from another.
- A pharmaceutical manufacturer needs to determine whether a new drug is more effective than those currently in use.
- An operations manager wants to monitor a production process on a regular basis to find out whether the quality of product being produced is conforming to company standards.
- An auditor wants to review the financial transactions of a company in order to determine whether or not it is in compliance with generally accepted accounting principles.
- A potential investor wants to determine which firms within which industries are likely to have accelerated growth in a period of economic recovery.
- A student wants to get data on classmates' favorite rock groups to satisfy a curiosity.

Six general reasons can be identified for collecting data. These reasons are listed in Exhibit 1.

EXHIBIT 1 REASONS FOR COLLECTING DATA

1. To provide the necessary input to a survey.
2. To provide the necessary input to a study.
3. To measure performance of an ongoing service or production process.
4. To evaluate conformance to standards.
5. To assist in formulating alternative courses of action in a decision-making process.
6. To satisfy our curiosity.

The customer satisfaction survey in the Using Statistics scenario, "Good Tunes—Part II," illustrates reasons 1, 3, 4, and 5. For example, after Good Tunes collects the data from the surveys, the company could analyze the data to measure the performance of its customer service functions and evaluate its customer service standards. The data could also be used to help formulate alternatives to current customer service practices and might also be used to influence the loan-approval process.

9 IDENTIFYING SOURCES OF DATA

Identifying the most appropriate source of data must be the starting point of any statistical analysis. If biases, ambiguities, or other types of errors flaw the data being collected, even the most sophisticated statistical methods will not be able to produce accurate information. Exhibit 2 lists the four important sources of data.

EXHIBIT 2 IMPORTANT DATA SOURCES

1. Data may already be distributed by an organization or an individual.
2. An experiment may be designed to obtain the necessary data.
3. A survey may be conducted.
4. An observational study may be conducted.

Data sources are classified as being either **primary sources** or **secondary sources**. A source is primary if the data collector is the one using the data for analysis. A source is secondary if one organization or individual has compiled the data to be used by another organization or individual.

Organizations and individuals that publish data typically are collectors of data that use that data as a primary source and that let others use it as a secondary source. For example, the United States government collects and distributes data in this way for both public and private purposes. The Bureau of Labor Statistics collects data on employment as well as distributing the monthly *Consumer Price Index*. The Census Bureau oversees a variety of ongoing surveys regarding population, housing, and manufacturing and undertakes special studies on topics such as crime, travel, and health care.

Market research and trade publications also distribute data pertaining to specific industries or markets. Investment services such as Mergent's provide financial data on a company-by-company basis. Syndicated services such as A. C. Nielsen provide clients with data enabling the comparison of client products with those of their competitors. Daily newspapers are filled with numerical information regarding stock prices, weather conditions, and sports statistics.

As listed in Exhibit 2, conducting an experiment is another important data collection source. In an experiment, strict control is exercised over the treatments. For example, in a study testing the effectiveness of laundry detergent, the researcher determines which brands in the study are more effective in cleaning soiled clothes by actually washing dirty laundry instead of asking customers which brand they believe to be more effective. Proper experimental designs are usually the subject matter of more advanced texts, because they often involve sophisticated statistical procedures.

Conducting a survey is a third important data source. Here no control is exercised over the behavior of the people being surveyed. They are merely asked questions about their beliefs, attitudes, behaviors, and other characteristics. Responses are then edited, coded, and tabulated for analysis.

Conducting an observational study is the fourth important data source. In a study, a researcher observes the behavior directly, usually in its natural setting. Most knowledge of animal behavior has been collected in this way, and in other fields, such as the social sciences, observational studies are commonly used. Observational studies take many forms in business. One example is the **focus group**, a market research tool that is used for eliciting unstructured responses to open-ended questions. In a focus group, a moderator leads the discussion, and all the participants respond to the questions asked. Other, more structured types of studies involve group dynamics and consensus building and use various organizational behavior/industrial psychology tools such as brainstorming, the Delphi technique, and the nominal-group method. Observational study techniques are also used in situations in which enhancing teamwork, or improving the quality of products and service are management goals.

10 TYPES OF SURVEY SAMPLING METHODS

As defined in section 1, a sample is the portion of the population that has been selected for analysis. Rather than taking a complete census of the whole population, statistical sampling procedures focus on collecting a small representative group of the larger population. The resulting sample provides information that can be used to estimate characteristics of the entire population.

The sampling process begins by defining the frame. The **frame** is a complete or partial listing of items comprising the population. The frame can be data sources such as population lists, directories, or maps. Samples are drawn from these frames. If the frame is inadequate because certain groups of individuals or items in the population were not properly included, then the samples will be inaccurate and biased. Using different frames to generate data can lead to opposite conclusions, as illustrated in Example 1.

EXAMPLE 1

A CASE OF OPPOSING CONCLUSIONS

The following headline appeared in a suburban New York newspaper over a decade ago: "Off, With a Head Count: Is Suffolk More Populous Than Nassau? LILCO and the Census Bureau Disagree" (*Newsday*, April 25, 1988). Given Suffolk's survey data, the Suffolk county executive felt it was more populous, whereas the Nassau county executive disagreed, citing Nassau's own survey data. Who was right?

SOLUTION

The differences in the two estimates come from the fact that the Census Bureau and the Long Island Lighting Company (LILCO) used different frames and formulas to estimate population in the two counties. The Census Bureau used birth and death rates, migration patterns as shown on income tax returns, and a demographic formula that estimates that the average number of people per household had been shrinking in the past several years. For its definition, LILCO used the number of year-round electric and gas meters, building permits, and a factor for the number of people in each house.

There are three main reasons for drawing a sample, as depicted in Exhibit 3.

EXHIBIT 3 REASONS FOR DRAWING A SAMPLE

1. A sample is less time-consuming than a census.
2. A sample is less costly to administer than a census.
3. A sample is less cumbersome and more practical to administer than a census.

As depicted in Figure 2, there are two kinds of samples: the nonprobability sample and the probability sample.

FIGURE 2
Types of samples

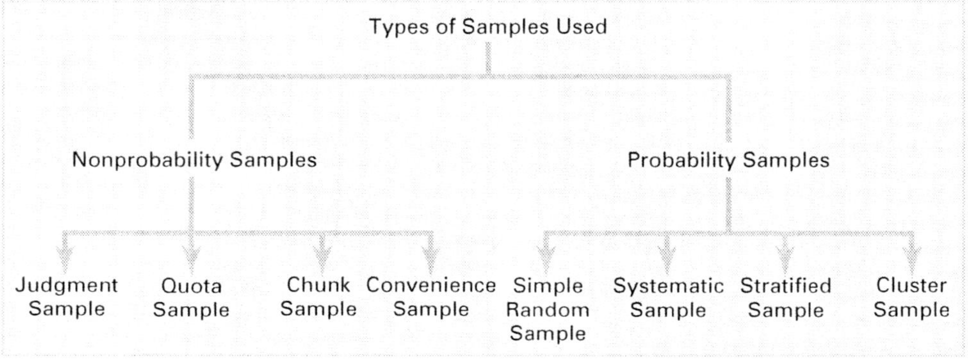

Nonprobability Sample
A nonprobability sample is one in which the items or individuals included are chosen without regard to their probability of occurrence.

A **nonprobability sample** (see definition at left) chooses participants without knowing their probabilities of selection, and in some cases participants are self-selected. Thus, the theory that has been developed for probability sampling cannot be applied. A common type of nonprobability sampling is convenience sampling. Here items are selected into the sample based only on the fact that they are easy, inexpensive, or convenient to sample. For example, many companies conduct surveys by giving visitors to their World Wide Web site the opportunity to complete survey forms and submit them electronically. The response to these surveys can provide large amounts of data in a timely fashion, but the sample is composed of self-selected Web users. For many studies, only a nonprobability sample such as a judgment sample is available. In these instances, the opinions of preselected experts in the subject matter are obtained in order to make changes in a process. Some other common procedures of nonprobability sampling are quota sampling and chunk sampling; these are discussed in detail in specialized books on sampling methods (see references 1 and 2).

Nonprobability samples can have certain advantages such as convenience, speed, and lower cost. On the other hand, two major disadvantages—a lack of accuracy due to selection bias and a lack of generalizability of the results—more than offset the advantages. Therefore, you should restrict the use of nonprobability sampling methods to situations in which you want to obtain rough approximations at low cost in order to satisfy your curiosity about a particular subject or to small-scale initial or pilot studies that will later be followed up by more rigorous investigations.

Probability Sample
A probability sample is one in which the subjects of the sample are chosen on the basis of known probabilities.

A **probability sample**, as defined on the left, should be used whenever possible. Probability sampling methods allow you to infer unbiased generalizations upon the population of interest. In practice, a true probability sample is often difficult or impossible to obtain. However, you should work toward achieving a probability sample and acknowledge any potential biases that might exist. The four types of probability samples most commonly used are simple random, systematic, stratified, and cluster samples. These sampling methods vary from one another in their cost, accuracy, and complexity. A discussion of these sampling methods follows.

Simple Random Sample

A **simple random sample** is one in which every individual or item from a frame has the same chance of selection as every other individual or item. In addition, every sample of a fixed size has the same chance of selection as every other sample of that size. Simple random sampling is the most elementary random sampling technique. It forms the basis for the other random sampling techniques.

With simple random sampling, n is used to represent the sample size and N is used to represent the frame size. Every item or person in the frame is numbered from 1 to N. The chance that any particular member of the frame is selected on the first draw is $1/N$.

There are two basic methods by which samples are selected: with replacement and without replacement.

Sampling with replacement means that after a person or an item is selected, it is returned to the frame, where it has the same probability of being selected again. Imagine a fishbowl with N business cards. On the first selection, suppose the name Judy Craven is selected. Pertinent information is recorded, and the business card is replaced in the bowl. The cards in the bowl are then well shuffled and the second card is drawn. On the second selection, Judy Craven has the same probability of being selected again, $1/N$. The process is repeated until the desired sample size n is obtained. However, it is generally considered more desirable to have a sample of different people or items than to permit a repetition of measurements on the same person or item.

Sampling without replacement means that a person or item, once selected, is not returned to the frame and therefore cannot be selected again. As before, in sampling with replacement the chance that any particular member in the frame, say Judy Craven, is selected on the first draw is $1/N$. The chance that any individual not previously selected will be selected on the second draw is now 1 out of $N - 1$. This process continues until the desired sample of size n is obtained.

Regardless of whether the sample is taken with or without replacement, such "fishbowl" methods for sample selection have a major drawback—the ability to thoroughly mix the cards and randomly pull the sample. As a result, fishbowl methods are not very useful. Less cumbersome and more scientific methods of selection are desirable.

One such method uses a **table of random numbers** (see the table in the appendix—consult your instructor if you require this item) for obtaining the sample. A table of random numbers consists of a series of digits randomly generated and listed in the sequence in which the digits were generated (see reference 12). Because the numeric system uses 10 digits (0, 1, 2, . . . , 9), the chance of randomly generating any particular digit is equal to the probability of generating any other digit. This probability is 1 out of 10. Hence, if a sequence of 800 digits were generated, you would expect about 80 of them to be the digit 0, 80 to be the digit 1, and so on. In fact, researchers who use tables of random numbers usually test out such generated digits for randomness before employing them. The table of random numbers has met all such criteria for randomness. Because every digit or sequence of digits in the table is random, the table can be read either horizontally or vertically. The margins of the table designate row numbers and column numbers. The digits themselves are grouped into sequences of five to make reading the table easier.

To use such a table instead of a fishbowl for selecting the sample, it is first necessary to assign code numbers to the individual members of the frame. Then the random sample is obtained by reading the table of random numbers and selecting those individuals from the frame whose assigned code numbers match the digits found in the table. To better understand the process of sample selection from its inception, consider Example 2.

EXAMPLE 2

SELECTING A SIMPLE RANDOM SAMPLE USING A TABLE OF RANDOM NUMBERS

A company wants to select a sample of 32 full-time workers out of a population of 800 full-time employees in order to obtain information on expenditures from a company-sponsored dental plan. The company assumes that not everyone will be willing to respond to the survey, so they must have a larger mailing than 32 to get the desired 32 responses. Assuming that 8 out of 10 full-time workers are expected to respond to such a survey (that is, a rate of return of 80%), a total of 40 such employees must be contacted to obtain the desired 32 responses. Therefore, the survey will be distributed to 40 full-time employees drawn from the personnel files of the company. How will the simple random sample actually be drawn?

SOLUTION

To select the random sample, you use a table of random numbers. The frame consists of a listing of the names and company mailbox numbers of all $N = 800$ full-time employees obtained from the company personnel files. Thus, the frame is an accurate and complete listing of the population. Because the population size (800) is a three-digit number, each assigned code number must also be three digits, so that every full-time worker has an equal chance for selection. A code of 001 is given to the first full-time employee in the population listing, a code of 002 is given to the second full-time employee in the population listing, and so on, until a code of 800 is given to the Nth full-time worker in the listing. Because $N = 800$ is the largest possible coded value, all three-digit code sequences greater than N (i.e., 801 through 999 and 000) are discarded.

To select the simple random sample, a random starting point for the table of random numbers is chosen. One such method is to close your eyes and strike the table of random numbers with a pencil. Suppose such a procedure is used and row 06, column 05, of Table 1 (which is extracted from the table in the appendix), is selected as the starting point. Although you can go in any direction, in this example the table will be read from left to right in sequences of three digits without skipping.

TABLE 1

Using a table of random numbers

		Column							
		00000	*00001*	*11111*	*11112*	*22222*	*22223*	*33333*	*33334*
	Row	*12345*	*67890*	*12345*	*67890*	*12345*	*67890*	*12345*	*67890*
	01	49280	88924	35779	00283	81163	07275	89863	02348
	02	61870	41657	07468	08612	98083	97349	20775	45091
	03	43898	65923	25078	86129	78496	97653	91550	08078
	04	62993	93912	30454	84598	56095	20664	12872	64647
	05	33850	58555	51438	85507	71865	79488	76783	31708
Begin	06	97340	03364	88472	04334	63919	36394	11095	92470
selection	07	70543	29776	10087	10072	55980	64688	68239	20461
(row 06, column 05)	08	89382	93809	00796	95945	34101	81277	66090	88872
	09	37818	72142	67140	50785	22380	16703	53362	44940
	10	60430	22834	14130	96593	23298	56203	92671	15925
	11	82975	66158	84731	19436	55790	69229	28661	13675
	12	39087	71938	40355	54324	08401	26299	49420	59208
	13	55700	24586	93247	32596	11865	63397	44251	43189
	14	14756	23997	78643	75912	83832	32768	18928	57070
	15	32166	53251	70654	92827	63491	04233	33825	69662
	16	23236	73751	31888	81718	06546	83246	47651	04877
	17	45794	26926	15130	82455	78305	55058	52551	47182
	18	09893	20505	14225	68514	46427	56788	96297	78822
	19	54382	74598	91499	14523	68479	27686	46162	83554
	20	94750	89923	37089	20048	80336	94598	26940	36858
	21	70297	34135	53140	33340	42050	82341	44104	82949
	22	85157	47954	32979	26575	57600	40881	12250	73742
	23	11100	02340	12860	74697	96644	89439	28707	25815
	24	36871	50775	30592	57143	17381	68856	25853	35041
	25	23913	48357	63308	16090	51690	54607	72407	55538

Source: Partially extracted from The Rand Corporation, *A Million Random Digits with 100,000 Normal Deviates* (Glencoe, IL: The Free Press, 1955) and displayed in the appendix of this book.

The individual with code number 003 is the first full-time employee in the sample (row 06 and columns 05–07), the second individual has code number 364 (row 06 and columns 08–10), and the third individual has code number 884. Because the highest code for any employee is 800, this number is discarded. Individuals with code numbers 720, 433, 463, 363, 109, 592, 470, and 705 are selected third through tenth, respectively.

The selection process continues in a similar manner until the needed sample size of 40 full-time employees is obtained. During the selection process, if any three-digit coded sequence repeats, the employee corresponding to that coded sequence is included again as part of the sample if sampling with replacement; however, the repeating coded sequence is discarded if sampling without replacement.

Systematic Sample

In a **systematic sample**, the N individuals or items in the frame are partitioned into k groups by dividing the size of the frame N by the desired sample size n. That is,

$$k = \frac{N}{n}$$

where k is rounded to the nearest integer. To obtain a systematic sample, the first individual or item to be selected is chosen at random from the k individuals or items in the first partitioned group in the frame, and the rest of the sample is obtained by selecting every kth individual or item thereafter from the entire frame.

If the frame consists of a listing of prenumbered checks, sales receipts, or invoices or if the frame pertains to club membership listings, student registration listings, or a preset number of consecutive items coming off an assembly line, a systematic sample is faster and easier to obtain than a simple random sample. In such situations, the systematic sample is a convenient mechanism for obtaining the data.

If you wanted to take a systematic sample of 40 from the population of $N = 800$ employees, the frame of 800 would be partitioned into $800/40 = 20$ groups. A random number would be selected from the first 20 individuals, and every twentieth individual after the first selection would be included in the sample. For example, if the first number selected was 008, the subsequent selections would be 028, 048, 068, 088, 108, . . . , 768, and 788.

Although they are simpler to use, simple random sampling methods and systematic sampling methods are generally less efficient than other, more sophisticated, probability sampling methods. This means that for any one sample obtained by either simple random sampling or systematic sampling, the data obtained may or may not be a good representation of the population's underlying characteristics (parameters). Although most simple random samples are representative of their underlying population, it is not possible to know if the particular sample taken is in fact representative.

Even greater possibilities for selection bias and lack of representation of the population characteristics occur from systematic samples than from simple random samples. If a pattern were to exist in the frame, severe selection biases could result. To overcome the potential problem of disproportionate representation of specific groups in a sample, either stratified sampling methods or cluster sampling methods can be used.

Stratified Sample

In a **stratified sample**, the N individuals or items in the frame are first subdivided into separate subpopulations, or **strata**, according to some common characteristic. A simple random sample is conducted within each of the strata, and the results from the separate simple random samples are then combined. Such sampling methods are more efficient than either simple random sampling or systematic sampling because they ensure representation of individuals or items across the entire population, which ensures a greater precision in the estimates of underlying population parameters. The homogeneity of individuals or items within each stratum, when combined across strata, provides precision.

EXAMPLE 3

SELECTING A STRATIFIED SAMPLE

A company wants to select a sample of 32 full-time workers out of a population of 800 full-time employees in order to obtain information on expenditures from a company-sponsored dental plan. If an (overall) 80% response rate is assumed, the survey will be distributed to 40 full-time employees taken from the personnel files of the company to obtain the desired 32 responses. How will the stratified sample actually be selected?

SOLUTION

The population frame consists of a listing of the names and company mailbox numbers of all $N = 800$ full-time employees obtained from the company personnel files. Since 25% of the full-time employees are managerial, the first step is to separate the population frame into two strata: a subpopulation listing of all 200 managerial-level personnel and a separate subpopulation listing of all 600 full-time nonmanagerial workers. Since the first stratum consists of a listing of 200 managers, three-digit code numbers from 001 to 200 are assigned. Since the second stratum contains a listing of 600 nonmanagerial-level workers, three-digit code numbers from 001 to 600 are assigned.

To obtain a stratified sample proportional to the sizes of the strata, 25% of the overall sample is drawn from the first stratum and 75% of the overall sample is taken from the second stratum. Two separate simple random samples are drawn, each of which is based on a distinct random starting point from a table of random numbers. The first sample selects 10 managers from the listing of 200 in the first stratum, and the second sample selects 30 nonmanagerial workers from the listing of 600 in the second stratum. The results are then combined to reflect the composition of the entire company.

The Cluster Sample

In a **cluster sample**, the N individuals or items in the frame are divided into several clusters so that each cluster is representative of the entire population. A random sampling of clusters is then taken, and all individuals or items in each selected cluster are then studied. **Clusters** can be naturally occurring designations, such as counties, election districts, city blocks, apartment buildings, or families.

Cluster sampling methods can be more cost-effective than simple random sampling methods, particularly if the population is spread over a wide geographic region. However, cluster sampling methods tend to be less efficient than either simple random sampling methods or stratified sampling methods and often require a larger overall sample size to obtain results as precise as those that would be obtained from the more efficient procedures.

A detailed discussion of systematic sampling, stratified sampling, and cluster sampling procedures is found in references 1 and 2.

PROBLEMS FOR SECTION 10

Learning the Basics

1 For a population containing $N = 902$ individuals, what code number would you assign for

a. the first person on the list?
b. the fortieth person on the list?
c. the last person on the list?

2 For a population of $N = 902$, verify that by starting in row 05 of the table of random numbers in the appendix, only six rows are needed to draw a sample of size $n = 60$ *without* replacement.

3 Given a population of $N = 93$, starting in row 29 of the table of random numbers (Table E.1), and reading across the row, draw a sample of size $n = 15$

a. *without* replacement.
b. *with* replacement.

Applying the Concepts

4 For a study that consists of personal interviews with participants (rather than mail or phone surveys), explain why a simple random sample might be less practical than some other methods.

5 You want to select a random sample of size 1 from a population of three items (which are called A, B, and C). The rule for drawing the sample is: Flip a coin; if it is heads, pick item A; if it is tails, flip the coin again; this time, if it is heads, choose B; if it is tails, choose C. Explain why this is a random sample but not a simple random sample.

6 A population has four members (call them A, B, C, and D). You would like to draw a random sample of size 2, which you decide to do in the following way: Flip a coin; if it is heads, the sample will be items A and B; if it is tails, the sample will be items C and D. Although this is a random sample, it is not a simple random sample. Explain why. (If you did problem 5, compare the procedure described there with the procedure described in this problem.)

7 The registrar of a college with a population of $N = 4,000$ full-time students is asked by the president to conduct a survey to measure satisfaction with the quality of life on campus. The following table contains a breakdown of the 4,000 registered full-time students by gender and class designation:

	Class Designation				
Gender	**Fr.**	**So.**	**Jr.**	**Sr.**	**Total**
Female	700	520	500	480	2,200
Male	560	460	400	380	1,800
Total	1,260	980	900	860	4,000

The registrar intends to take a probability sample of $n = 200$ students and project the results from the sample to the entire population of full-time students.

a. If the frame available from the registrar's files is an alphabetical listing of the names of all $N = 4{,}000$ registered full-time students, what type of sample could be taken? Discuss.
b. What is the advantage of selecting a simple random sample in (a)?
c. What is the advantage of selecting a systematic sample in (a)?
d. If the frame available from the registrar's files is a listing of the names of all $N = 4{,}000$ registered full-time students compiled from eight separate alphabetical lists based on the gender and class designation breakdowns shown in the table above, what type of sample should be taken? Discuss.
e. Suppose that each of the $N = 4{,}000$ registered full-time students lived in one of the 20 campus dormitories. Each dormitory contains four floors with 50 beds per floor, and therefore accommodates 200 students. It is college policy to fully integrate students by gender and class designation on each floor of each dormitory. If the registrar is able to compile a frame through a listing of all student occupants on each floor within each dormitory, what type of sample should be taken? Discuss.

8 Prenumbered sales invoices are kept in a sales journal. The invoices are numbered from 0001 to 5,000.

a. Beginning in row 16, column 1, and proceeding horizontally in the table of random numbers in the appendix, select a simple random sample of 50 invoice numbers.
b. Select a systematic sample of 50 invoice numbers. Use the random numbers in row 20, columns 5–7, as the starting point for your selection.
c. Are the invoices selected in (a) the same as those selected in (b)? Why or why not?

9 Suppose that 5,000 sales invoices are separated into four strata. Stratum 1 contains 50 invoices, stratum 2 contains 500 invoices, stratum 3 contains 1,000 invoices, and stratum 4 contains 3,450 invoices. A sample of 500 sales invoices is to be selected.

a. What type of sampling should be done? Why?
b. Explain how you would carry out the sampling according to the method stated in (a).
c. Why is the sampling in (a) not simple random sampling?

11 TYPES OF DATA

Statisticians develop surveys to deal with a variety of **random variables**. The data, which are the observed outcomes of these random variables, will virtually always differ from item to item (or person to person), since no two things are exactly alike. As illustrated in Figure 3, there are two types of random variables that yield the observed outcomes or data: categorical and numerical.

FIGURE 3
Types of data

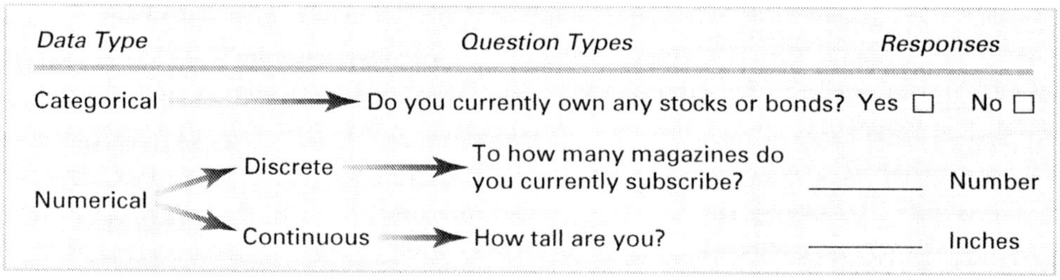

Categorical random variables yield categorical responses, such as yes or no answers. An example is the response to the question "Do you currently own any stocks or bonds?" because it is limited to a simple yes or no answer. Another example is the response to the question on the Good Tunes survey, "Are you likely to buy additional merchandise through Good Tunes in the next 12 months?" Categorical variables can also yield more than two possible responses. For example, "Which day of the week are you most likely to eat dinner in a restaurant?"

Numerical random variables yield numerical responses such as your height in inches. Other examples are how much money you expect to spend on stereo equipment in the next 12 months, from the Good Tunes customer satisfaction survey, or the response to the question "To how many magazines do you currently subscribe?" There are two types of numerical variables: discrete and continuous.

Discrete random variables produce numerical responses that arise from a counting process. "The number of magazines subscribed to" is an example of a discrete numerical variable, because the response is one of a finite number of integers. You subscribe to zero, one, two, and so on, magazines.

Continuous random variables produce numerical responses that arise from a measuring process. Your height is an example of a continuous numerical variable, because the response takes on any value within a continuum or interval, depending on the precision of the measuring instrument. For example, your height may be 67 inches, $67\frac{1}{4}$ inches, $67\frac{7}{32}$ inches, or $67\frac{58}{250}$ inches, depending on the precision of the available instruments.

Theoretically, no two persons could have exactly the same height, because the more precise the measuring device used, the greater the likelihood of detecting differences between their heights. However, most measuring devices are not sophisticated enough to detect small differences. Hence, *tied observations* are often found in experimental or survey data even though the random variable is truly continuous.

Levels of Measurement and Types of Measurement Scales

Data can also be described in terms of the level of measurement attained. There are four widely recognized levels of measurement: nominal, ordinal, interval, and ratio scales.

Nominal and Ordinal Scales Data obtained from a categorical variable are considered to be measured on a nominal scale or on an ordinal scale. A **nominal scale** (Figure 4) classifies data into various distinct categories in which no ordering is implied. In the Good Tunes customer satisfaction survey, the answer to the question "Are you likely to buy additional merchandise through Good Tunes in the next 12 months?" is an example of a nominally scaled variable, as is your favorite soft drink, your political party affiliation, and your gender. Nominal scaling is the weakest form of measurement because no attempt can be made to account for differences within a particular category or to specify any ordering or direction across the various categories.

Categorical Variable	*Categories*
Personal Computer Ownership ⟷	Yes ☐ No ☐
Type of Stocks Owned ⟷	Growth ☐ Value ☐ Other ☐ None ☐
Internet Provider ⟷	Microsoft Network ☐ AOL☐ Other ☐

FIGURE 4
Examples of nominal scaling

An **ordinal scale** classifies data into distinct categories in which ordering is implied. In the Good Tunes survey, the answers to the question "How do you rate the overall service provided by Good Tunes with respect to your recent purchase?" represents an ordinal scaled variable because the responses much better than expected, better than expected, about as expected, worse than expected, and much worse than expected are ranked in order of satisfaction level. Other examples of ordinal scaled variables, such as bond ratings and grades, are depicted in Figure 5.

Categorical Variable	*Ordered Categories*
	(Lowest-Highest)
Student class designation ⟷	Freshman Sophomore Junior Senior
Product satisfaction ⟷	Very Unsatisfied Fairly Unsatisfied Neutral Fairly Satisfied Very Satisfied
Faculty rank ⟷	Professor Associate Professor Assistant Professor Instructor
Standard & Poor's bond ratings ⟷	AAA AA A BBB BB B CCC CC C DDD DD D
Student grades ⟷	A B C D F

FIGURE 5
Examples of ordinal scaling

Ordinal scaling is a somewhat stronger form of measurement, because an observed value classified into one category possesses more of a property being scaled than does an observed value classified into another category. Nevertheless, ordinal scaling is still a relatively weak form of measurement because no attempt is made to account for differences *between* the classified values. This is because no meaningful numerical statements can be made about differences between the categories. The ordering implies only *which* category is "greater," "better," or "more preferred"—not by *how much*.

Interval and Ratio Scales An **interval scale** (Figure 6) is an ordered scale in which the difference between measurements is a meaningful quantity that does not involve a true zero point. For example, a noontime temperature reading of 67 degrees Fahrenheit is 2 degrees Fahrenheit warmer than a noontime reading of 65 degrees Fahrenheit. In addition, the 2 degrees Fahrenheit difference in the noontime temperature readings is the same quantity that would be obtained if the two noontime temperature readings were 74 and 76 degrees Fahrenheit, so the difference has the same meaning anywhere on the scale.

FIGURE 6
Examples of interval and ratio scales

Numerical Variable		*Level of Measurement*
Temperature (in degrees Celsius or Fahrenheit)	→	Interval
Standardized exam score	→	Interval
Height (in inches or centimeters)	→	Ratio
Weight (in pounds or kilograms)	→	Ratio
Age (in years or days)	→	Ratio
Salary (in American dollars or Japanese yen)	→	Ratio

A **ratio scale** is an ordered scale in which the difference between the measurements involves a true zero point as in height, weight, age, or salary measurements. In the Good Tunes customer satisfaction survey, the amount of money (in U.S. dollars) you expect to spend on stereo equipment in the next 12 months is an example of a ratio scaled variable. As another example, a person who is 76 inches tall is twice as tall as someone who is 38 inches tall. Temperature is a trickier case: Fahrenheit and Celsius (centigrade) scales are interval but not ratio scales; the "zero" value is arbitrary, not real. You cannot say that a noontime temperature reading of 76 degrees Fahrenheit is twice as hot as a noontime temperature reading of 38 degrees Fahrenheit. But a Kelvin temperature reading, which involves a scientifically set absolute zero tied to molecular speed, is ratio scaled, in contrast to the Fahrenheit and Celsius scales, which involve scientifically arbitrary zero-degree beginning points.

Data obtained from a numerical variable are usually assumed to have been measured either on an interval scale or on a ratio scale. These scales constitute the highest levels of measurement. They are stronger forms of measurement than an ordinal scale, because you can determine not only which observed value is the largest but also by how much.

PROBLEMS FOR SECTION 11

Learning the Basics

10 Three different beverages are sold at a fast-food restaurant—soft drinks, tea, and coffee.

a. Explain why the type of beverage sold is an example of a categorical variable.

b. Explain why the type of beverage sold is an example of a nominal scaled variable.

11 Soft drinks are sold in three sizes in a fast-food restaurant—small, medium, and large. Explain why the size of the soft drink is an ordinal scaled variable.

12 Suppose that you measure the time it takes to download an MP3 file from the Internet.

a. Explain why the download time is a numerical variable.

b. Explain why the download time is a ratio scaled variable.

Applying the Concepts

13 For each of the following random variables, determine whether the variable is categorical or numerical. If the variable is numerical, determine whether the variable of interest is discrete or continuous. In addition, determine the level of measurement.

a. Number of telephones per household
b. Type of telephone primarily used
c. Number of long-distance calls made per month
d. Length (in minutes) of longest long-distance call made during a month
e. Color of telephone primarily used
f. Monthly charge (in dollars and cents) for long-distance calls made
g. Ownership of a cellular phone
h. Number of local calls made per month
i. Length (in minutes) of longest local call during a month
j. Whether there is a telephone line connected to a computer modem in the household
k. Whether there is a fax machine in the household

14 The following information is obtained from students upon exiting the campus bookstore during the first week of classes:
a. Amount of money spent on books
b. Number of textbooks purchased
c. Amount of time spent shopping in the bookstore
d. Academic major
e. Gender
f. Ownership of a personal computer
g. Ownership of a DVD player
h. Number of credits registered for in the current semester
i. Whether or not any clothing items were currently purchased at the bookstore
j. Method of payment

Classify each of these variables as categorical or numerical. If the variable is numerical, determine whether the variable is discrete or continuous. In addition, determine the level of measurement.

15 For each of the following random variables, determine whether the variable is categorical or numerical. If the variable is numerical, determine whether the variable of interest is discrete or continuous. In addition, determine the level of measurement.
a. Name of Internet provider
b. Monthly charge for Internet service
c. Amount of time spent surfing the Internet per week
d. Primary purpose for surfing the Internet
e. Number of e-mails received in a week
f. Number of online purchases made in a month
g. Total amount spent on online purchases in a month
h. Whether the personal computer has a DVD drive

16 For each of the following random variables, determine whether the variable is categorical or numerical. If the variable is numerical, determine whether the variable of interest is discrete or continuous. In addition, determine the level of measurement.
a. Amount of money spent on clothing in the last month
b. Number of winter coats owned
c. Favorite department store
d. Amount of time spent shopping for clothing in the last month
e. Most likely time period during which shopping for clothing takes place (weekday, weeknight, or weekend)
f. Number of pairs of winter gloves owned
g. Primary type of transportation used when shopping for clothing

17 Suppose the following information is obtained from Robert Keeler on his application for a home mortgage loan at the Metro County Savings and Loan Association:
a. Place of Residence: Stony Brook, New York
b. Type of Residence: Single-family home
c. Date of Birth: April 9, 1962
d. Monthly Payments: $1,427
e. Occupation: Newspaper reporter/author
f. Employer: Daily newspaper
g. Number of Years at Job: 14
h. Number of Jobs in Past 10 Years: 1
i. Annual Family Salary Income: $86,000
j. Other Income: $26,000
k. Marital Status: Married
l. Number of Children: 2
m. Mortgage Requested: $120,000
n. Term of Mortgage: 30 years
o. Other Loans: Car
p. Amount of Other Loans: $8,000

Classify each of the responses by type of data and level of measurement.

18 One of the variables most often included in surveys is income. Sometimes the question is phrased "What is your income (in thousands of dollars)?" In other surveys, the respondent is asked to "Place an X in the circle corresponding to your income level" and gives a number of ranges to choose from.
a. For each of the two formats, state whether the measurement level for the variable is nominal, ordinal, interval, or ratio.
b. In the first format, explain why income might be considered either discrete or continuous.
c. Which of these two formats would you prefer to use if you were conducting a survey? Why?
d. Which of these two formats would likely bring you a greater rate of response? Why?

19 If two students score a 90 on the same examination, what arguments could be used to show that the underlying random variable—test score—is continuous?

20 The director of market research at a large department store chain wanted to conduct a survey throughout a metropolitan area to determine the amount of time working women spend shopping for clothing in a typical month.
a. Describe both the population and the sample of interest, and indicate the type of data the director might wish to collect.
b. Develop a first draft of the questionnaire needed in (a) by writing a series of three categorical questions and three numerical questions that you feel would be appropriate for this survey.

12 EVALUATING SURVEY WORTHINESS

Nearly every day, you read or hear about survey or opinion poll results in newspapers, on the Internet, or on radio or television. Clearly, advances in information technology have led to a proliferation of survey research. Not all this research is good, meaningful, or important.

To avoid surveys that lack objectivity or credibility, you must critically evaluate what you read and hear by examining the worthiness of the survey. First, you must evaluate the purpose of the survey, why it was conducted, and for whom it was conducted. An opinion poll or survey conducted to satisfy curiosity is mainly for entertainment. Its result is an end in itself rather than a means to an end.

The second step in evaluating the worthiness of a survey is to determine whether it was based on a probability or a nonprobability sample (as discussed in section 10). Recall that the only way to make correct statistical inferences from a sample to a population is through the use of a probability sample. Surveys employing nonprobability sampling methods are subject to serious, perhaps unintentional, biases that may render the results meaningless, as illustrated in the following box.

A NONPROBABILITY SAMPLING DISASTER

In 1948, major pollsters predicted the outcome of the U.S. presidential election between Harry S. Truman, the incumbent president, and Thomas E. Dewey, then governor of New York, as going to Dewey. The *Chicago Tribune* was so confident of the polls' predictions that it printed its early edition based on the predictions rather than waiting for the ballots to be counted.

An embarrassed newspaper and the pollsters it had relied on had a lot of explaining to do. How had the pollsters been so wrong? Intent on discovering the source of the error, the pollsters found that their use of a nonprobability sampling method was the culprit (see reference 9). As a result, polling organizations adopted probability sampling methods for future elections.

Survey Errors

Even when surveys use random probability sampling methods, they are subject to potential errors. As illustrated in Exhibit 4, there are four types of survey errors. Good survey research design attempts to reduce or minimize these various survey errors, often at considerable cost.

EXHIBIT 4 SURVEY ERRORS

1. Coverage error or selection bias
2. Nonresponse error or nonresponse bias
3. Sampling error
4. Measurement error

Coverage Error The key to proper sample selection is an adequate frame or up-to-date list of all the subjects from which the sample will be drawn. **Coverage error** occurs if certain groups of subjects are excluded from this frame listing so that they have no chance of being selected in the sample. Coverage error results in a **selection bias**. If the listing is inadequate because certain groups of subjects in the population were not properly included, any random probability sample selected will provide an estimate of the characteristics of the frame, not the *actual* population.

Nonresponse Error Not everyone is willing to respond to a survey. In fact, research has indicated that individuals in the upper and lower economic classes tend to respond less frequently to surveys than do people in the middle class. **Nonresponse error** arises from the failure to collect data on all subjects in the sample and results in a **nonresponse bias**. Because it cannot be generally assumed that persons who do not respond to surveys are similar to those who do, it is extremely important to follow up on the nonresponses after a specified period of time. Several attempts should be made, either by mail or by telephone, to convince such individuals to change their minds. Based on these results, the estimates obtained from the initial respondents are subsequently tied to those obtained from the follow-ups so that the inferences made from the survey are valid (reference 1).

The mode of response affects the rate of response. The personal interview and the telephone interview usually produce a higher response rate than does the mail survey—but at a higher cost. The following box provides a famous example of coverage error and nonresponse bias.

A CASE OF COVERAGE ERROR AND NONRESPONSE ERROR

In 1936, the magazine *Literary Digest* predicted that Governor Alf Landon of Kansas would receive 57% of the votes in the U.S. presidential election and overwhelmingly defeat President Franklin D. Roosevelt's bid for a second term. However, Landon was soundly defeated when he received only 38% of the vote. Such an unprecedented error by a magazine with respect to a major poll had never occurred before. As a result, the prediction devastated the magazine's credibility with the public, eventually causing it to go bankrupt.

Literary Digest thought it had done everything right. It had based its prediction on a huge sample size, 2.4 million respondents, out of a survey sent to 10 million registered voters. What went wrong? There are two answers: selection bias and nonresponse bias.

To understand the role of selection bias, some historical background must be provided. In 1936 the United States was still suffering from the Great Depression. Not accounting for this, the *Literary Digest* compiled its frame from such sources as telephone books, club membership lists, magazine subscriptions, and automobile registrations (reference 3). Inadvertently, it chose a frame primarily composed of the rich and excluded the majority of the voting population who, during the Great Depression, could not afford telephones, club memberships, magazine subscriptions, and automobiles. Thus, the 57% estimate for the Landon vote may have been very close to the frame but certainly not the total U.S. population.

Nonresponse error produced a possible bias when the huge sample of 10 million registered voters produced only 2.4 million responses. A response rate of only 24% is far too low to yield accurate estimates of the population parameters without some mechanism to ensure that the 7.6 million individual nonrespondents have similar opinions. However, the problem of nonresponse bias was secondary to the problem of selection bias. Even if all 10 million registered voters in the sample had responded, this would not have compensated for the fact that the frame differed substantially in composition from the actual voting population.

Sampling Error There are three main reasons for drawing a sample rather than taking a complete census: It is more expedient, less costly, and more efficient. However, chance dictates who will or will not be included in the sample. **Sampling error** reflects the heterogeneity, or "chance differences," from sample to sample based on the probability of particular individuals or items being selected in the particular samples.

When you read about the results of surveys or polls in newspapers or magazines, there is often a statement regarding margin of error or precision. For example, "the results of this poll are expected to be within ±4 percentage points of the actual value." This margin of error is the sampling error. Sampling error can be reduced by taking larger sample sizes, although this also increases the cost of conducting the survey.

Measurement Error In the practice of good survey research, a questionnaire is designed with the intent that it will allow meaningful information to be gathered. But there is a dilemma here—obtaining meaningful measurements is often easier said than done. Consider the following proverb:

> A man with one watch always knows what time it is;
> A man with two watches always searches to identify the correct one;
> A man with ten watches is always reminded of the difficulty in measuring time.

Unfortunately, the process of obtaining a measurement is often governed by what is convenient, not what is needed. And the measurements obtained are often only a proxy for the ones really desired. Much attention has been given to measurement error that occurs because of a weakness in question wording (reference 4). A question should be clear, not ambiguous. It should be objectively presented in a neutral manner; "leading questions" must be avoided.

Measurement Error
Measurement error refers to inaccuracies in the recorded responses that occur because of a weakness in question wording, an interviewer's effect on the respondent, or the effort made by the respondent.

There are three sources of **measurement error**: ambiguous wording of questions, the halo effect, and respondent error. As an example of ambiguous wording, several years ago the Department of Labor reported that the unemployment rate in the United States had been underestimated for more than a decade because of poor questionnaire wording in the Current Population Survey. In particular, the wording led to a significant undercount of women in the labor force. Because unemployment rates are tied to benefit programs such as state unemployment compensation systems, it was imperative that government survey researchers rectify the situation by adjusting the questionnaire wording.

The "halo effect" occurs when the respondent feels obligated to please the interviewer. This type of error can be minimized by proper interviewer training.

Respondent error occurs as a result of overzealous or underzealous effort by the respondent. This type of error can be minimized in two ways: (1) by carefully scrutinizing the data and calling back those individuals whose responses seem unusual and (2) by establishing a program of random callbacks in order to ascertain the reliability of the responses.

Ethical Issues

Ethical considerations arise with respect to the four types of potential errors that can occur when designing surveys that use probability samples: coverage error or selection bias, nonresponse error or nonresponse bias, sampling error, and measurement error. Coverage error or selection bias becomes an ethical issue only if particular groups or individuals are *purposely* excluded from the frame so that the survey results are skewed, indicating a position more favorable to the survey's sponsor.

In a similar vein, nonresponse error or nonresponse bias becomes an ethical issue only if particular groups or individuals are less likely to respond to a particular survey format and the sponsor knowingly designs the survey in a manner aimed at excluding such groups or individuals. Sampling error becomes an ethical issue only if the findings are purposely presented without reference to sample size and margin of error so that the sponsor can promote a viewpoint that might otherwise be truly insignificant. Measurement error becomes an ethical issue in one of three ways: (1) A survey sponsor may purposely choose loaded, lead-in questions that would guide the responses in a particular direction; (2) An interviewer, through mannerisms and tone, may purposely create a halo effect or otherwise guide the responses in a particular direction; (3) A respondent having a disdain for the survey process may willfully provide false information.

Ethical issues also arise when the results of nonprobability samples are used to form conclusions about the entire population. When a nonprobability sampling method is used, the sampling procedures must be clearly explained and it must be noted that the results cannot be generalized beyond the sample.

PROBLEMS FOR SECTION 12

Applying the Concepts

21 A survey indicates that the vast majority of college students owned their own personal computers." What information would you want to know before you accepted the results of this survey?

22 A simple random sample of $n = 300$ full-time employees is drawn from a company list containing the names of all $N = 5{,}000$ full-time employees in order to evaluate job satisfaction.

a. Give an example of possible coverage error.
b. Give an example of possible nonresponse error.
c. Give an example of possible sampling error.
d. Give an example of possible measurement error.

23 According to a survey of 1,000 AOL subscribers (Harry Berkowitz, "Screen Name Loyalty," *Newsday*, December 1, 2002, A42), 92% of the AOL subscribers gave "don't want to change e-mail address" as a reason for sticking with the online service. What information would you want to know before you accepted the results of the survey?

24 According to a survey of online shoppers conducted by Forrester Research Inc. (Michael Totty, "The Masses Have Arrived," *Wall Street Journal*, January 27, 2003, R8), for those shoppers who have been buying online for less than one year, 39% have a college degree, 57% are women, and the average annual income of these shoppers is $52,300. What information would you want to know before you accepted the results of this survey?

25 According to a Maritz poll of 1,004 adult drivers ("Snapshots," *USA Today*, October 23, 2002), 45% admit to eating or drinking while driving and 36% admit to talking on a cell phone. What information would you want to know before you accepted the results of this survey?

26 A survey conducted by Career Builder indicates that some workers take longer than others to adjust to their normal work routine after taking vacations ("Snapshots," *USA Today*, July 18, 2001). The survey results indicated that 19% responded that it takes no time, 40% responded one day, 34% responded a few days, and 7% responded that it takes a week or longer. What information would you like to know before you accepted the results of this survey?

27 According to a survey conducted by Opinion Research Corporation for Cingular Wireless, 67% of Americans say it is annoying to hear ringing cellphones or cellphone chatter in certain public places ("Snapshots," *USA Today*, August 13, 2001). What information would you like to know before you accepted the results of this survey? How could Cingular Wireless make use of information gained from analyzing this survey?

28 The *Wall Street Journal* reported that among Americans who get their music on the Internet, the overwhelming majority use only free services ("Low on the Charts," May 7, 2002, A1). Specifically, 92% responded that they only use free services, 1% responded that they only use pay services, and 7% responded that they use both. These findings were part of a survey conducted by eMarketer during February 2002. What information would you like to know before you accepted the results of this survey?

SUMMARY

As you can see in the summary flowchart, this chapter provides an introduction to statistics and discusses data collection. You have studied various types of data, and different ways of selecting random samples. In addition, you have examined several aspects of survey worthiness.

In the Using Statistics scenario in this chapter you were asked to review the customer survey used by the Good Tunes company. You should observe that the first two questions shown will produce numerical data and the last three will produce categorical data. The responses to the first question (number of days) are discrete, and the responses to the second question (amount of money spent) are continuous. After the data have been collected, they must be organized and prepared in order to make various analyses.

KEY TERMS

categorical random variables
cluster sample
clusters
continuous random variables
coverage error
data
descriptive statistics
discrete random variables
focus group
frame
inferential statistics
information
interval scale
measurement error
nominal scale
nonprobability sample
nonresponse bias
nonresponse error
numerical random variables
ordinal scale
parameter
population
primary sources
probability sample
random variables
ratio scale
sample
sampling error
sampling with replacement
sampling without replacement
secondary sources
selection bias
simple random sample
statistic
statistics
statistical packages
strata
stratified sample
systematic sample
table of random numbers
universe

Chapter summary flowchart

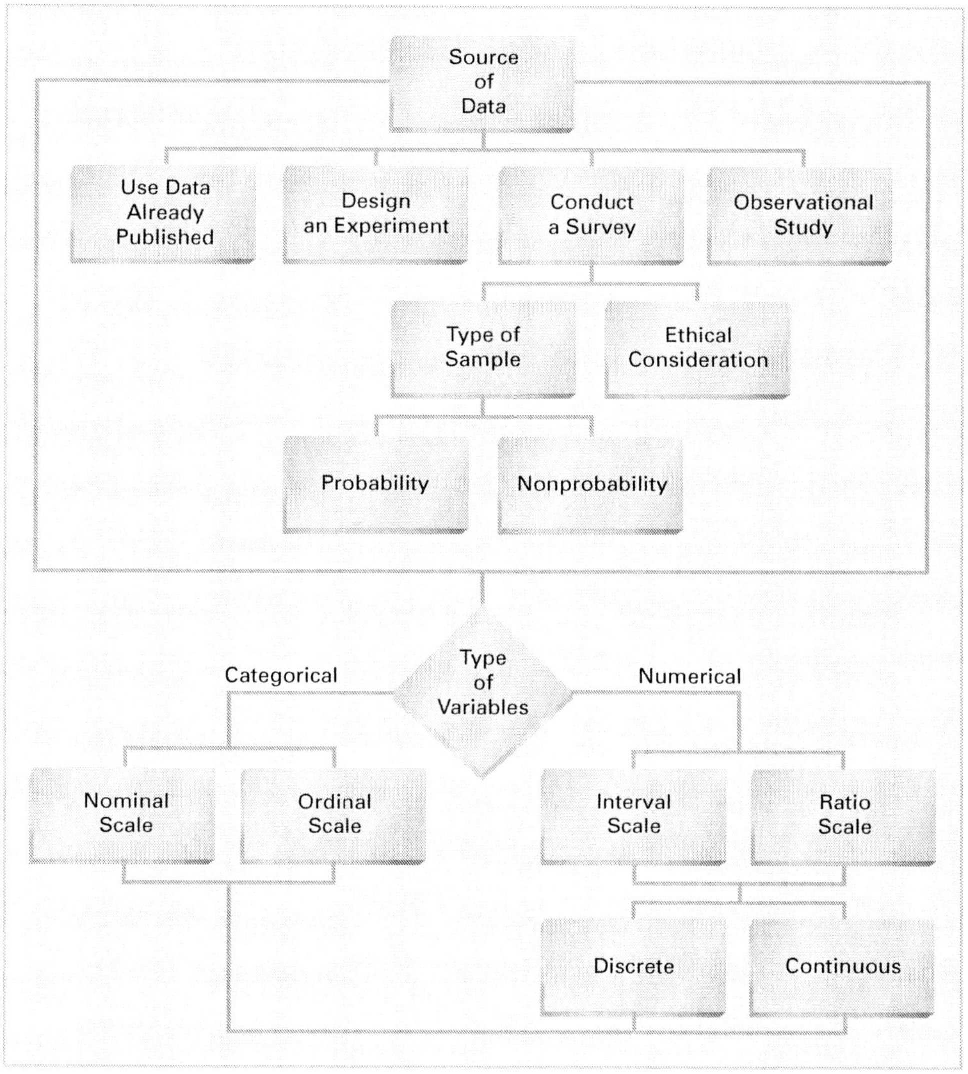

CHAPTER REVIEW PROBLEMS

Checking Your Understanding

29 What is the difference between a sample and a population?

30 What is the difference between a statistic and a parameter?

31 What is the difference between descriptive and inferential statistics?

32 What is the difference between a categorical and a numerical random variable?

33 What is the difference between discrete and continuous data?

34 What is the difference between a nominal and an ordinal scale?

35 What is the difference between an interval and a ratio scale?

36 What are the main reasons for obtaining data?

37 What is the difference between probability and nonprobability sampling?

38 What are some potential problems with using "fishbowl" methods to draw a simple random sample?

39 What is the difference between sampling *with* replacement versus *without* replacement?

40 What is the difference between a simple random sample and a systematic sample?

41 What is the difference between a stratified sample and a systematic sample?

42 What is the difference between a stratified sample and a cluster sample?

43 What distinguishes the four potential sources of error when dealing with surveys designed using probability sampling?

Applying the Concepts

44 The Data and Story Library (**lib.stat.cmu.edu/DASL**) is an online library of data files and stories that illustrate the use of basic statistical methods. Each data set has one or more associated stories. The stories are classified by method and by subject. Go to this World Wide Web site and, after reading a story, summarize how statistics have been used in one of the subject areas.

45 Go to the official Microsoft Excel Web site (**www.microsoft.com/office/excel**). Explain how you think Microsoft Excel could be useful in the field of statistics.

46 The Gallup organization presents the results of recent polls at its Web site **www.gallup.com**. Go to this site and click on Business and the Economy. For the survey indicated:

a. give an example of a categorical random variable found in this survey.

b. give an example of a numerical random variable found in this survey.

c. develop three questions that could be used in this survey.

47 The U.S. Census Bureau (**www.census.gov**) maintains a large Web site with links to many types of data. The site contains information on people, business, geography, and other categories. Go to the site and locate the description of the American Housing Survey in the People section.

a. Briefly describe the American Housing Survey.

b. How large is the sample, and what type of sampling method is used?

c. Give an example of a categorical random variable found in this survey.

d. Give an example of a numerical random variable found in this survey.

e. What types of businesses can benefit from the information gathered by the American Housing Survey? Explain.

f. Go to the link to business, and locate the section devoted to the manufacturing sector. Describe the Annual Survey of Manufacturers.

g. How large is the sample, and what type of sampling method is used?

h. Give an example of a categorical random variable found in this survey.

i. Give an example of a numerical random variable found in this survey.

j. How can an executive of a manufacturing company benefit from the information gathered by the Annual Survey of Manufacturers?

48 Political polling has traditionally been accomplished through telephone interviews. Researchers at Harris Black International Ltd. argue that Internet polling is less expensive, faster, and offers higher response rates than telephone surveys. Critics are concerned about the scientific reliability of this approach (*Wall Street Journal*, April 13, 1999). Even amid this strong criticism, Internet polling is becoming more and more common. What concerns, if any, do you have about Internet polling?

49 A study by Rajesh Mirani and Albert Lederer ("An Instrument for Accessing the Organizational Benefits of IS Projects," *Decision Sciences*, Vol. 29, 1998, 803–838) discusses the organizational benefits of information systems (IS) projects. The researchers mailed 936 questionnaires to randomly selected members of a large nationwide information systems organization. Two hundred valid responses were received, for a response rate of 21%. Of the 200 respondents, 190 answered questions concerning a recently completed IS project. The average budget for these projects was $3.8 million with a range of $4,000 to $100 million. Of these 190 responses, 45% indicated that the CEO was required to give approval before starting the projects.

a. What was the source of the data used in this study?

b. Name a categorical random variable discussed in this article.

c. Name a numerical random variable discussed in this article.

d. Discuss the sampling method used in this study.

e. What types of survey errors do you think the researchers are most likely to encounter?

50 According to a Taylor Nelson Sofres Intersearch study of 703 respondents ("Snapshots," *USA Today*, February 3, 2002, A1) the following is a partial listing of how workers found their latest jobs.

Category	%
Networking/word of mouth	61
Newspaper ad	16
Walk in/applied in person	9
Newspaper Web site	5
Internet job site	4
Employment agency/recruiter	2
Through school	1

a. Describe the population for this survey.

b. Describe how a frame for this survey could have been constructed.

c. Describe how a sample could have been drawn for this survey.

d. Is the response to the question "How did you find your latest job?" categorical or numerical?

e. Sixty-one percent of the respondents said that they found a job from Networking/word of mouth. Is this a parameter or a statistic? Why?

51 A survey of online retailers were asked what measures they use to gauge the success of their sites (Michael Totty,

"So much information," *Wall Street Journal*, December 9, 2002, p. R.4)

a. Describe the population for this survey.
b. Describe how a frame for this survey could have been constructed.
c. Describe how a sample could have been drawn for this survey.
d. Is the response to the question "Do you use site traffic to gauge the success of your site?" categorical or numerical?
e. Why is the response to the question "Do you use session length to gauge the success of your site?" categorical and not numerical?

52 As part of a mediation process overseen by a federal judge to end a lawsuit that accuses Cincinnati, Ohio, of decades of discrimination against African Americans, surveys on how to improve Cincinnati police-community relations were taken. One survey was sent to the 1,020 members of the Cincinnati police force. The survey included a cover letter encouraging participation by the chief of police and president of the Fraternal Order of Police. Respondents could either return a hard copy of the survey or complete the survey online. To the researchers' dismay, only 158 surveys were completed ("Few Cops Fill Out Survey," *The Cincinnati Enquirer*, August 22, 2001, B3).

a. What type of errors or biases should the researchers be especially concerned with?
b. What step(s) should the researchers take to try to overcome the problems noted in (a)?
c. What could have been done differently to improve the survey's worthiness?

53 According to a survey conducted by International Communications Research for Capital One Financial, 24% of teens ages 13 to 19 own a cell phone and 10% own a beeper ("USA Snapshots," *USA Today*, August 16, 2001, A1).

a. What other information would you want to know before you accepted the results of this survey?
b. Suppose that you wished to conduct a similar survey for the geographic region you live in. Describe the population for your survey.
c. Explain how you could minimize the chance of a coverage error in this type of survey.
d. Explain how you could minimize the chance of a nonresponse error in this type of survey.
e. Explain how you could minimize the chance of a sampling error in this type of survey.
f. Explain how you could minimize the chance of a measurement error in this type of survey.

54 According to Dr. Sarah Beth Estes, sociology professor at the University of Cincinnati, and Dr. Jennifer Glass, sociology professor at the University of Iowa, working women who take advantage of family-friendly schedules can fall behind in wages. More specifically, the sociologists report that in a study of 300 working women who had children and returned to work and opted for flextime, telecommuting, and so on, these women had pay raises that averaged between 16% and 26% less than other workers ("Study: 'Face Time' Can Affect Moms' Raises," *The Cincinnati Enquirer*, August 28, 2001, A1).

a. What other information would you want to know before you accepted the results of this survey?
b. If you were to perform a similar study in the geographic area where you live, define a population, frame, and sampling method you could use.

55 A study published by the U.S. Department of Transportation reports that 27% of passenger vehicles have at least one substantially underinflated tire. The results were based on 11,530 passenger vehicles stopping at gas stations across the country ("Many Drivers Risk Blowouts," *The Cincinnati Enquirer*, August 30, 2001, A1).

a. Define the population, frame, and sample used in this study.
b. Is 27% a parameter or a statistic? Explain.

56 According to a study by the National Association of Colleges and Employers (NACE) college students are facing a dismal job market (Stephanie Armour, "Job Market Bleak for Grads," *USA Today*, May 2, 2002). Employers were expected to hire 36% fewer college graduates in 2001–02 than they hired in 2000–01. More than 20% of graduating students cited lack of experience as their biggest barrier to finding a job and another 20% blamed the economy. The article also reports that starting salaries were lower than in years past.

a. What other information would you like to know before accepting the results of this survey?
b. Give an example of a categorical variable discussed in the article.
c. Give an example of a numerical variable discussed in the article. Determine the level of measurement for this variable.
d. Twenty percent of the students stated that the economy was their biggest barrier to finding a job. Is this number a statistic or a parameter? Explain.
e. If you were to perform a survey to gather data on this topic, what type of sampling method would you use and why?

57 The manager of the customer service division of a consumer electronics company was interested in determining whether customers who had purchased a DVD player over the past 12 months were satisfied with their products. Using the warranty cards submitted after purchases, the manager was planning to survey these customers.

a. Describe the population.
b. Describe the frame.
c. What differences are there between the population and the frame? How might these differences affect the results?
d. Develop three categorical questions that you feel would be appropriate for this survey.
e. Develop three numerical questions that you feel would be appropriate for this survey.
f. How could a simple random sample of warranty cards be selected?
g. If the manager wanted to select a sample of warranty cards for each brand of DVD player sold, how should the sample be selected? Explain.

58 Political polls are taken to try to predict the outcome of an election. The results of such polls are routinely reported in newspapers and on television prior to an election. For a specific election, such as for U.S. president,

a. what is the population to which we usually want to generalize?
b. how might we get a random sample from that population?
c. what might be some problems with the sampling in these polls?

59 The following questionnaire is placed in each room of a well-known and widely respected hotel. The intent of management is to evaluate guest satisfaction.

How well did we serve you?				
Reservations				
Doorman				
Front desk				
Room				
Cleanliness				
Restaurant				

a. Do you think that this four-category device with faces provides management with enough information on each service or facility being rated? Discuss.
b. Would the addition of another frown face to balance the two smile faces improve this questionnaire instrument? Discuss.
c. Of what value are such self-selecting surveys? Can they be used to project the opinions of all guests during a particular interval of time (say, a week or a month)? Discuss.
d. How could a random sample of guests be selected?
e. What categorical question would you add to the survey?
f. What numerical question would you add to the survey?

60 A manufacturer of cat food was planning to survey households in the United States to determine purchasing habits of cat owners. Among the questions to be included are those that relate to:

1. where cat food is primarily purchased.
2. whether dry or moist cat food is typically purchased.
3. the number of cats living in the household.
4. whether or not the cat is pedigreed.

a. Describe the population.
b. Define the frame.
c. Indicate the type of sampling that you would use and why you would select it.
d. For each of the four items listed, indicate whether the variable is categorical or numerical.
e. Develop five categorical questions for the survey.
f. Develop five numerical questions for the survey.

Internet Exercises

61 Go to the Web site for this text

www.prenhall.com/levine

Select Chapter 1 and click Internet Exercises.

WEB CASE

People use statistical techniques to help communicate and present important information to others both inside and outside their businesses. And every day, people misuse these techniques:

- A sales manager working with an "easy-to-use" charting program chooses an inappropriate chart that obscures data relationships.
- The editor of an annual report presents a chart of revenues with an abridged *Y*-axis that creates the false impression of greatly rising revenues.
- An analyst generates meaningless statistics about a set of categorical data using analyses designed for numerical data.

Although much of the misuse of statistics is unintentional, you need to be able to identify all such misuses in order to be an informed manager. The primary goal of the Web Cases throughout this text is to help you develop this type of skill.

Web Cases ask you to visit the Web sites that are related to the companies and issues raised in the Using Statistics scenario that starts each chapter or a Web page that supports the continuing story of the *Springville Herald*, a small-city daily newspaper. You review internal documents as well as publicly stated claims, seeking to verify conclusions. Unlike a traditional text case study, but much like real-world situations, not all of the information you encounter will be relevant to your task and you may occasionally discover conflicting information that you need to resolve before continuing with the case.

To assist your learning, the Web Case for each chapter begins with the learning objective and a synopsis of the scenario under consideration. You will be directed to a specific Web site or Web page and given a set of questions that will guide your exploration of the Web site. If you prefer, you can also explore the Web pages for the Cases by linking to the Springville Chamber of Commerce page (**www.prenhall.com/Springville/SpringvilleCC.htm**).

Complementing the Web Case in most chapters is a traditional case study exercise in which you are asked to apply your knowledge of statistics to a statistical topic problem being faced by the management of the *Springville Herald*.

To illustrate how to use a Web Case, link to the Web site for Good Tunes (**www.prenhall.com/Springville/Good_Tunes.htm**), the online retailer mentioned in the Using Statistics scenarios for this chapter. Recall that the privately held Good Tunes is seeking financing to expand its business by opening its first retail location. Since it is in management's interest to show that Good Tunes is a thriving business, it is not too surprising to discover the "our best sales year ever" claim in the "Good Times at Good Tunes" entry at the top of their home page.

The claim is also a hyperlink, so click "our best sales year ever" to display the page that supports the claim. How would you support such a claim? With a table of numbers? A Chart? Remarks attributed to a knowledgeable source? Good Tunes has used a chart to present "two years ago" and "latest twelve month's" sales data by category. Are there any problems with the choices made on this Web page? *Absolutely*!

First, note that there are no scales for the symbols used, so it is impossible to know what the actual sales volumes are. In fact, charts that incorporate symbols in this way are considered examples of *chartjunk* and would never be used by people seeking graphical excellence.

This important point aside, another question that would arise would be whether the sales data represent the number of units sold or something else. The use of the symbols *creates the impression* that unit sales data are being presented. If the data are unit sales, does such data best support the claim being made—or would something else, such as dollar volumes—be a better indicator of sales at Good Tunes?

Then there are those curious chart labels. "Latest twelve months" is ambiguous—it could include months from the current year as well as months from one year ago and therefore may not be an equivalent time period to "two years ago." Since the business was established in 1997, and the claim being made is "best sales year ever," why hasn't management included sales figures for *every year since* 1997?

Is Good Tunes management hiding something or are they just unaware of the proper use of statistics? Either way, they have failed to properly communicate a vital aspect of their "story."

In subsequent Web Cases, you will be asked to provide this type of analysis, using the open-ended questions presented in this text as guidance. Not all the cases will be as straightforward as this example and in some cases what has been done may include perfectly appropriate applications of statistics.

REFERENCES

1. Cochran, W. G., *Sampling Techniques*, 3rd ed. (New York: Wiley, 1977).
2. Deming, W. E., *Sample Design in Business Research* (New York: Wiley, 1960).
3. Gallup, G. H., *The Sophisticated Poll-Watcher's Guide* (Princeton, NJ: Princeton Opinion Press, 1972).
4. Goleman, D., "Pollsters Enlist Psychologists in Quest for Unbiased Results," *The New York Times*, September 7, 1993, C1 and C11.
5. Kendall, M. G., and R. L. Plackett, eds., *Studies in the History of Statistics and Probability*, vol. 2 (London: Charles W. Griffin, 1977).
6. Kirk, R. E., ed., *Statistical Issues: A Reader for the Behavioral Sciences* (Monterey, CA: Brooks/Cole, 1972).
7. McCullough, B. D., and B. Wilson, "On the Accuracy of Statistical Procedures in Microsoft Excel 97," *Computational Statistics and Data Analysis*, 31 (1999), 27–37.
8. *Microsoft Excel 2002* (Redmond, WA: Microsoft Corporation, 2001).
9. Mosteller, F., et al., *The Pre-Election Polls of 1948* (New York: Social Science Research Council, 1949).
10. Pearson, E. S., ed., *The History of Statistics in the Seventeenth and Eighteenth Centuries* (New York: Macmillan, 1978).
11. Pearson, E. S., and M. G. Kendall, eds., *Studies in the History of Statistics and Probability* (Darien, CT: Hafner, 1970).
12. Rand Corporation, *A Million Random Digits with 100,000 Normal Deviates* (New York: The Free Press, 1955).
13. Walker, H. M., *Studies in the History of the Statistical Method* (Baltimore: Williams & Wilkins, 1929).
14. Wattenberg, B. E., ed., *Statistical History of the United States: From Colonial Times to the Present* (New York: Basic Books, 1976).

Answers to Selected Even-Numbered Problems

For more detailed solutions including explanations, interpretations, and Excel output, see the *Student Solutions Manual*.

2 338 505 855 551 438 ~~855~~ 077 186 579 488 767 833 170 897 340 033 648 847 204 334 639 193 ~~639~~ 411 095 ~~924~~ 707 054 329 776 100 871 007 255 ~~980~~ 646 886 823 ~~920~~ 461 893 829 380 900 796 ~~959~~ 453 410 181 277 660 ~~908~~ 887 237 818 721 426 714 050 785 223 801 670 353 362 449 406. *Note:* All sequences above 902 are discarded.

4 A simple random sample would be less practical for personal interviews because of travel costs (unless interviewees are paid to attend a central interviewing location).

6 Here all members of the population are equally likely to be selected and the sample selection mechanism is based on chance. But selection of two elements is not independent; for example, if A is in the sample, we know that B is also, and that C and D are not.

8 (a) 2323 ~~6737~~ ~~5131~~ ~~8888~~ 1718 0654 ~~6832~~ 4647 ~~6510~~ 4877 4579 4269 2615 1308 2455 ~~7830~~ ~~5550~~ ~~5852~~ ~~5514~~ ~~7182~~ 0989 3205 0514 2256 ~~8514~~ 4642 ~~7567~~ ~~8896~~ 2977 ~~8822~~ ~~5438~~ 2745 ~~9891~~ 4991 4523 ~~6847~~ ~~9276~~ ~~8646~~ 1628 3554 ~~9475~~ 0899 2337 0892 0048 ~~8033~~ ~~6945~~ ~~9826~~ ~~9403~~ ~~6858~~ ~~7029~~ ~~7341~~ 3553 1403 3340 4205 0823 4144 1048 2949 ~~8515~~ ~~7479~~ ~~5432~~ ~~9792~~ ~~6575~~ ~~5760~~ 0408 ~~8112~~ 2507 3742 1110 0023 4012 ~~8607~~ 4697 ~~9664~~ 4894 3928 ~~7072~~ ~~5815~~ 3687 1507 ~~7530~~ ~~5925~~ ~~7143~~ 1738 1688 ~~5625~~ ~~8533~~ ~~5041~~ 2391 3483 ~~5763~~ 3081 ~~6090~~ ~~5169~~ 0546. *Note:* All sequences above 5000 are discarded. There were no repeating sequences. **(b)** 089 189 289 389 489 589 689 789 889 989 1089 1189 1289 1389 1489 1589 1689 1789 1889 1989 2089 2189 2289 2389 2489 2589 2689 2789 2889 2989 3089 3189 3289 3389 3489 3589 3689 3789 3889 3989 4089 4189 4289 4389 4489 4589 4689 4789 4889 4989. **(c)** With the single exception of invoice #0989, the invoices selected in the simple random sample are not the same as those selected in the systematic sample. It would be highly unlikely that a random process would select the same units as a systematic process.

10 (a) The types of beverages sold yield categorical or "qualitative" responses. **(b)** The types of beverages sold yield distinct categories in which no ordering is implied.

12 (a) The time it takes to download an MP3 file from the Internet yields numerical or "quantitative" responses. **(b)** The download time is a ratio scaled variable because the true zero point in the measurement is zero unit of time.

For problems **14–16,** money may be considered discrete by some, since it can be counted to the nearest penny.

14 (a) numerical, continuous, ratio scale **(b)** numerical, discrete, ratio scale **(c)** numerical, continuous, ratio scale **(d)** categorical, nominal scale **(e)** categorical, nominal scale **(f)** categorical, nominal scale **(g)** categorical, nominal scale **(h)** numerical, discrete, ratio scale **(i)** categorical, nominal scale **(j)** categorical, nominal scale

16 (a) numerical, continuous, ratio scale **(b)** numerical, discrete, ratio scale **(c)** categorical, nominal scale **(d)** numerical, continuous, ratio scale **(e)** categorical, nominal scale **(f)** numerical, discrete, ratio scale **(g)** categorical, nominal scale

18 (a) In the first format, the measurement level is a ratio scale. In the second format, the measurement level is in ordinal scale. **(b)** Income may be considered discrete if we "count" our money. It may be considered continuous if we "measure" our money; we are only limited by the way a country's monetary system treats its currency. **(c)** The first format is preferred because the responses represent data measured on a higher scale. **(d)** The second format is less threatening to a respondent and likely leads to a greater response rate.

20 (a) The population is all working women who shop at the department store. A systematic or random sample could be taken of women making purchases during a particular time period, such as a month.

22 (a) Only employees in a specific division of the company were sampled. **(b)** No attempt is made to contact nonrespondents to urge them to complete the evaluation of job satisfaction. **(c)** The sample statistics obtained from the sample will never be equal to the parameters of interest in the population. **(d)** There was ambiguous wording in questions asked on the questionnaire.

24 Who funded the study? Why was it conducted? What was the population from which the sample was selected? What was the sample size? What sampling design was used? What mode of response was used: a personal interview, a telephone interview, or a mail survey? Were interviewers trained? Were survey questions field-tested? What other questions were asked? Were they clear, accurate, unbiased, and valid? What was the response rate?

26 Who funded the study? Why was it conducted? What was the population from which the sample was selected? What was the sample size? What sampling design was used? What mode of response was used: a personal interview, a telephone interview, or a mail survey? Were interviewers trained? Were survey questions field-tested? What definition of "adjusting to normal work routine" was used? What questions were asked? Were they clear, accurate, unbiased, and valid? What was the response rate?

28 Who funded the study? Why was it conducted? What was the population from which the sample was selected? What was the sample size? What sampling design was used? What mode of response was used: a personal interview, a telephone interview, or a mail survey? Were interviewers trained? Were survey questions field-tested? What definition of "free services" was used? What questions were asked? Were they clear, accurate, unbiased, and valid? What was the response rate?

48 Even though Internet polling is less expensive, faster, and offers higher response rates than telephone surveys, it is a self-selection response method. Because respondents who choose to participate in the survey do not usually represent the view of the public, the data collected are not appropriate for making inference about the general population.

50 (a) The population for this survey will be all workers. **(b)** A frame for this survey could have been constructed using the list of employees from the human resource division of a company. **(c)** A simple random sample could have been drawn for this survey. **(d)** The response is categorical. **(e)** This is a statistic because it measures the percent of the respondents in the sample who said they found a job from networking/word of mouth.

52 (a) Given the low response rate, the researchers should be especially concerned with nonresponse bias. The low response rate will also increase the sampling error. **(b)** Researchers can follow up on the nonresponses by mail or telephone to encourage or remind those who have not returned the survey to complete the survey. **(c)** The researchers can enlist the chief of police and the president of the fraternal order of police to mobilize the supervisors of various units to convey to their subordinates the importance of completing the survey. Reminder memos can also be sent from the supervisors. Verbal reminders from the supervisors during weekly meetings will also serve the same purpose.

54 (a) Before accepting the results of this survey, one would like to know (i) what is the purpose of the survey, (ii) what sampling method is being used, (iii) what is the response rate, (iv) what is the frame used in the survey, and (v) how are the questions being phrased. **(b)** The population will be all the working women, which includes those who take advantage of family-friendly schedules and those who do not in the geographic region. The frame can be compiled from the list of the women who file income tax returns in the region. Since there are two natural strata in the population, those who take advantage of family-friendly schedules and those who do not, a stratified sampling method should be used to better represent the population.

56 (a) Before accepting the results of this survey, one would like to know (i) what is the purpose of the survey, (ii) what sampling method is being used, (iii) what is the response rate, (iv) what is the frame used in the survey, and (v) how are the questions being phrased. **(b)** An example of a categorical variable: "Do you blame the economy?" **(c)** An example of numerical variable: starting salaries. Level of measurement: ratio. **(d)** This is a statistic because it summarizes the feature in the sample. **(e)** A stratified sampling method should be used. The employers should be divided into strata according to the different industries. Students should be divided into strata according to their gender and graduating status.

58 (a) The population to which we want to generalize consists of citizens who are registered to vote and who will actually vote in the election of interest. **(b)** We could take a random sample of voters as they exit the polls. **(c)** Some of the problems might be that it may not be possible to sample all counties so there may be coverage error, or there could be nonresponse bias if people who voted a particular way tend to not respond, so it does not help predict the outcome of an election prior to the election.

60 (a) Population: Cat owners **(b)** Sample frame: Households in the United States **(d)** (1) categorical (2) categorical (3) numerical (4) categorical

Excel Primer

EP1 INTRODUCTION TO MICROSOFT EXCEL.
Introduces you to the operation of Microsoft Excel and other Microsoft Windows-based programs. Assumes no prior experience working with Microsoft Windows and Excel.

EP2 THE MICROSOFT EXCEL USER INTERFACE.
Covers the concepts and procedures you need to know in order to operate the Excel program successfully.

EP3 COMMON WORKBOOK OPERATIONS.
Reviews the basic file operations of opening, saving, and printing workbooks.

EP4 BASIC WORKSHEET CONCEPTS AND OPERATIONS.
Explains how to make entries into worksheet cells as well as how to enhance the appearance of worksheets.

EP5 ADVANCED WORKBOOK OPERATIONS.
Discusses the commands and procedures you need if you plan to construct, modify, or copy worksheets, in whole or part.

EP6 USING THE MICROSOFT EXCEL CHART WIZARD.
Provides an overview to operating the Chart Wizard, including the information you need to supply.

EP7 USING THE MICROSOFT EXCEL PIVOTTABLE WIZARD.
Provides an overview to operating the PivotTable Wizard, including the information you need to supply.

EP8 UNDERSTANDING AND USING ADD-INS.
Explains what add-ins are and how they are used in Microsoft Excel.

This primer discusses the concepts and reviews the operational skills you need in order to use Microsoft Excel effectively with this text. Because each reader's previous experience and chosen method for learning more about Microsoft Excel is different, you may not need to study all sections with equal attention. As a minimum, you should take some time to review the primer, if for no other reason than to discover the conventions and vocabulary that the authors use in the in-chapter Excel and Excel Handbook sections.

EP1 INTRODUCTION TO MICROSOFT EXCEL

Microsoft Excel is the worksheet component of the Microsoft Office suite of personal productivity programs. While not specifically designed for statistical analysis, Excel does contain basic statistical functions and includes the Data Analysis ToolPak, a limited set of advanced statistical routines. Microsoft Excel also contains **wizards**, a series of linked dialog boxes, that guide you through the process of creating charts and summary tables that can also be useful for statistical analyses. To compensate for Microsoft Excel's limited statistical procedures and to simplify the operation of Excel and its wizards, many procedures in this text use PHStat2, the Prentice Hall statistical add-in for Microsoft Excel.

In Microsoft Excel, you create or open and save files called **workbooks**. Workbooks are collections of **worksheets** and related items such as charts that contain the original source data as well as the results of an analysis and the intermediate calculations necessary for those results. Worksheets, in turn, are empty arrays of lettered columns and numbered rows, the intersections of which form **cells**. When you select an Analysis ToolPak or a PHStat2 procedure (see section EP8), or certain Excel menu choices, additional worksheets containing the results of an analysis are added to the opened workbook.

Microsoft Excel's ubiquity, it is found in almost every office and the program is readily available, makes this program a great tool for learning statistics. When combined with PHStat2, Microsoft Excel includes statistical procedures for just about every statistical topic discussed in this text, although you should be aware of the limits of its numerical accuracy. If you are using Microsoft Excel on a computer system that you maintain, you should read the technical information and instructions in the appendix containing the PHStat2 User's Guide (and the PHStat2 readme file on the CD-ROM that accompanies this text, if applicable) before using Microsoft Excel with this text.

EP2 THE MICROSOFT EXCEL USER INTERFACE

EP2.1 Basic Mouse Operations

You use a pointing device such as a mouse as the primary means by which to communicate selections and choices to Microsoft Excel. Moving your pointing device moves the onscreen symbol known as the **mouse pointer**, allowing you to interact with the visual objects on the screen. As with other programs for Microsoft Windows, pointing devices for Microsoft Excel must contain two buttons, one designated as the primary button, the other as the secondary button. You move the pointing device and press and release one of these buttons to execute one of four basic **mouse operations** (see Exhibit EP1).

EXHIBIT EP1 BASIC MOUSE OPERATIONS

Click: Move the mouse pointer over an object and press the primary button. In some contexts, the verbs **select** and **clear** are used to describe this action, for example, as in the phrases "select PHStat from the Excel menu" and "clear the Formulas check box."

Drag: Move the mouse pointer over an object. Then, while pressing and holding down the primary button, move the mouse pointer somewhere else on the screen and release the primary button. Dragging either moves objects to another position on the screen or allows you to select multiple items.

Double-click: Move the mouse pointer over an object and click the primary button twice in rapid succession.

Right-click: Move the mouse pointer over an object and click the secondary button.

Note: the Mousing Practice workbook (**Mousing Practice.xls**) in the Instructional Files folder on the CD-ROM that accompanies this text allows you to practice these operations.

By default, Microsoft Windows and Microsoft Excel define the left mouse button as the primary button and the right button as the secondary button (this is the derivation of the phrase "right-click"), but the definitions can be swapped by changing the appropriate Microsoft Windows user settings.

EP2.2 Opening the Microsoft Excel Application Window

You open Microsoft Excel from the Microsoft Windows desktop in one of three ways (see Exhibit EP2). Which way you choose is partly personal preference, although the authors note that using the first or second method *always* allows you to verify program settings before you use your data.

EXHIBIT EP2 METHODS OF OPENING PROGRAMS IN MICROSOFT WINDOWS

Program icon click: Double-click the Windows desktop icon representing the program (in some Windows versions requires only a single click).

Start Menu entry selection: Press the Windows key (or click the onscreen Start button) and select the "Programs" or "All Programs" choice. From the menu list that appears, select the entry for the program. Sometimes, you will find the program entry on a submenu, so several selections may be required.

File icon click: Double-click the Windows desktop icon representing a file of a type that Windows associates with a specific program. For example, if you click an icon for an .xls workbook file, both Microsoft Excel and the (Excel) workbook opens.

When you open Microsoft Excel, Microsoft Windows opens an **Excel application window**, the content of which is customizable by the user. This customizable window contains a title bar that identifies the current workbook in use, system buttons that appear on the top right edge of the window, a menu bar containing Excel commands, toolbars that contain icons that represent menu bar shortcuts, and a worksheet area of rows and columns that form cells into which data entries are made directly. Figure EP1 and Exhibit EP3 identify the components of the Excel 2002 application window of most relevance to this text. (If you want to customize your Excel application window so that it looks similar to Figure EP1, see the instructions in the appendix on Configuring and Customizing Microsoft Excel for Use with This Text.)

FIGURE EP1
The Microsoft Excel 2002 application window

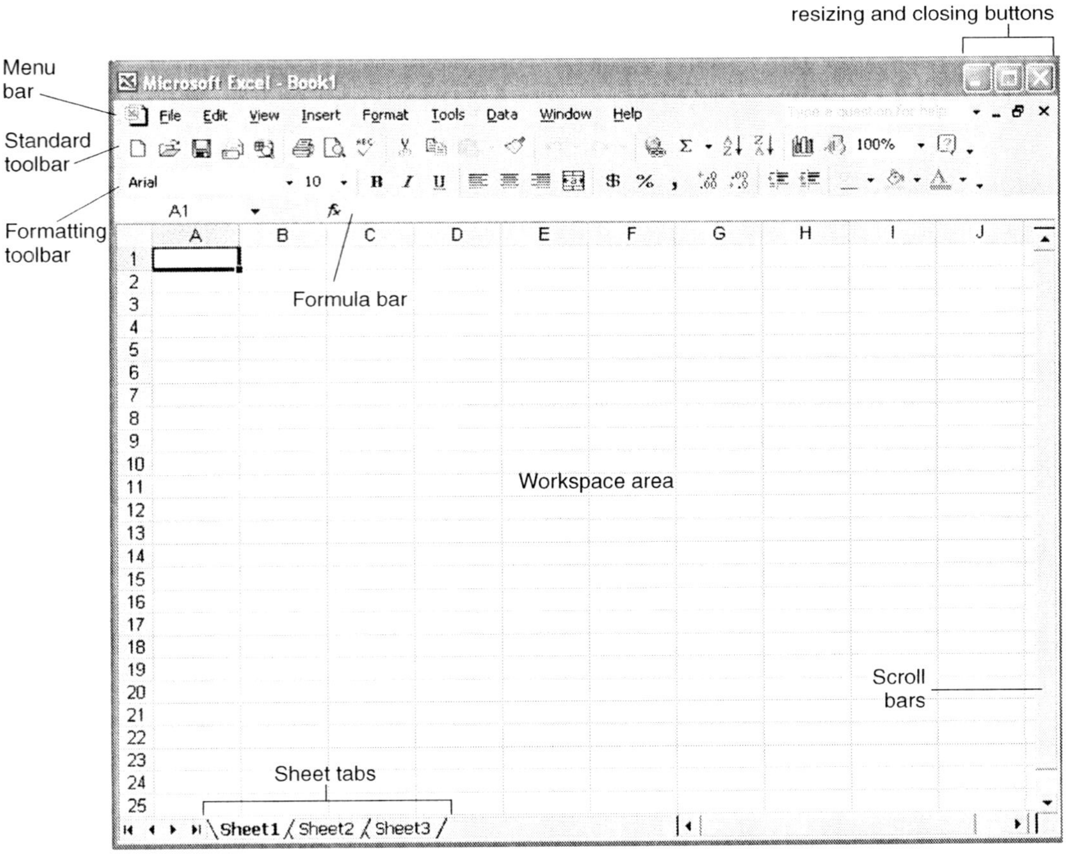

EXHIBIT EP3 IMPORTANT COMPONENTS OF THE EXCEL APPLICATION WINDOW

System minimize, resize, and **close buttons**. Buttons that minimize (hide) the Excel application window, resize the Excel window, and close Microsoft Excel, respectively.

Menu bar, the horizontal list of words that represent sets of pull-down menu command choices.

Standard toolbar, the toolbar that contains shortcuts to many file-oriented commands, including the common workbook operations discussed in section EP3.

Formatting toolbar, the toolbar that contains shortcuts for many formatting commands (see section EP4.3).

Formula bar, the area that identifies the currently selected worksheet cell (see section EP4) and its contents.

Workspace area, the area that contains the currently open workbook or workbooks. (Typically, only one workbook is opened at a time, but it is possible to open more than one and switch between them by selecting choices from the Window menu.)

Sheet tabs that display the names of the individual sheets that comprise a workbook. Clicking a sheet tab selects a sheet and makes it the currently active sheet. Double-clicking a sheet tab provides an easy way to rename a sheet.

Scroll bars that provide horizontal or vertical navigation to parts of the worksheet currently off-screen, for example, row 100 or column T in Figure EP1.

EP2.3 Standard Features of Microsoft Excel Menus and Dialog Boxes

You operate Microsoft Excel in the application window by making entries and selecting choices from the pull-down menus of the Excel menu bar or from **shortcut menus** that appear when certain objects are right-clicked. Figure EP2 shows several standard menu features, or conventions, that are helpful to know. These conventions are:

- Displaying underlined accelerator keys that can be used as a keyboard shortcut to select certain menu choices.

FIGURE EP2
The Microsoft Excel File Menu

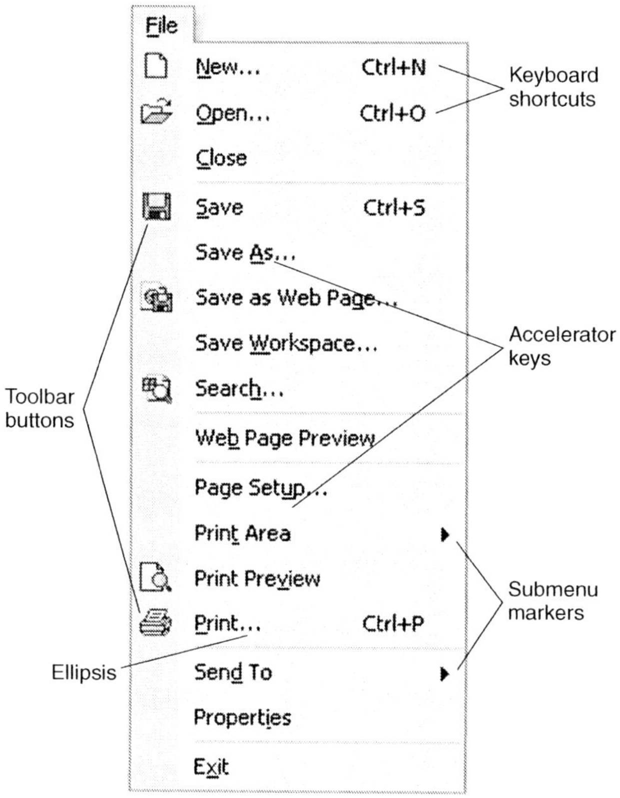

- Using an ellipsis to indicate that a menu choice leads to a dialog box.
- Using a triangular marker to indicate that menu choice leads to another menu of choices.
- Displaying the toolbar button that is the shortcut for a menu choice to the left of the menu choice.
- Listing the keyboard shortcut for a menu choice to the right of the menu choice.

Some menu selections directly perform a function or task, but many more lead to **dialog boxes** in which you enter information and settings for a procedure. The Open and Print dialog boxes from Microsoft Excel 2002 contain the types of objects commonly found in the dialog boxes of all programs (see Figure EP3). Exhibit EP4 explains each of the dialog box objects identified in Figure EP3.

FIGURE EP3

Microsoft Excel 2002 Open and Print dialog boxes

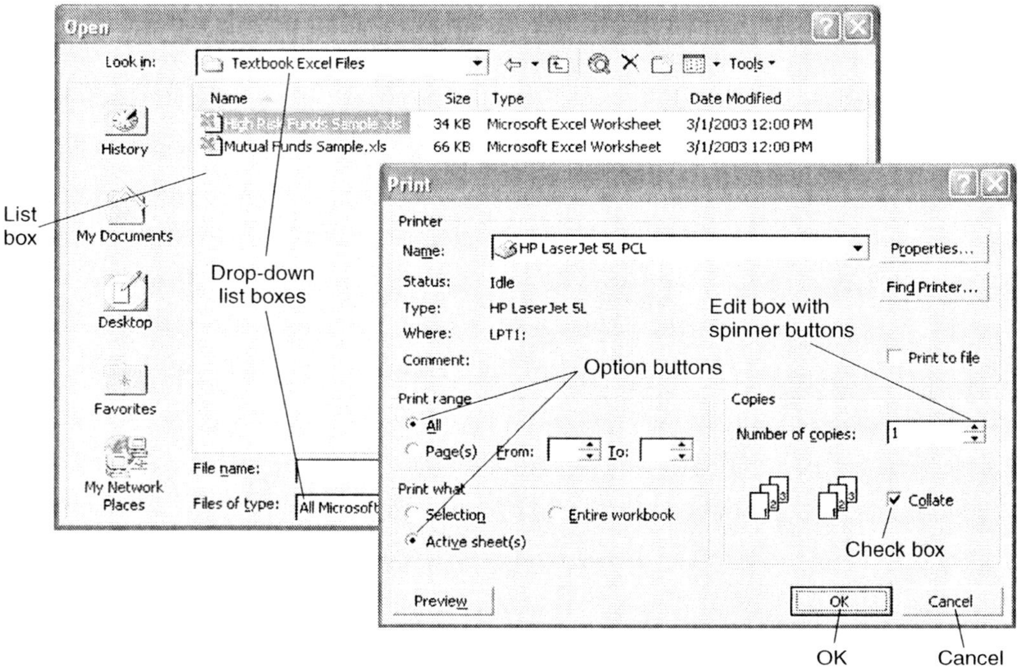

EXHIBIT EP4 COMMON DIALOG BOX OBJECTS

Drop-down list box: Displays a list of choices when the drop-down button, located on the right edge of the box, is clicked.

List box: Displays a list of choices for selection. Should the list exceed the dimensions of the list box, the list box will include **scroll buttons** and a **slider** that you can click to display the other choices of the list.

Edit box: Contains an area into which a value can be edited or typed. Edit boxes are often combined with either a drop-down list or **spinner buttons** to provide alternatives to the direct typing of a value. Edit boxes can include a button inside the right edge that allows you to enter a range by dragging your pointing device through a worksheet *cell range*.

Option buttons: Represent a set of mutually exclusive choices. Selecting an option button always clears the other option buttons in the set, thereby permitting only one choice to be made for that set at any given time.

Check box: Allows the selection of optional actions. Unlike option buttons, more than one check box can be selected at a time. If a check box is already checked, selecting the check box clears the check box of its check.

OK button: Causes the program to execute some action using the current values and settings of the dialog box. As in the File Open dialog box shown in Figure EP3, this button sometimes contains a different label such as Open (in Panel A), Save, or Finish.

Cancel button: Closes a dialog box and cancels the operation represented by the dialog box. In most contexts, clicking the Cancel button is equivalent to clicking the **Close button** on the title bar.

Question-mark button: Displays a context-sensitive help message for a selected object (see section EP2.5). Many dialog boxes contain a **Help button** that performs a similar function.

EP2.4 Correcting Mistakes and Data Entries

If you make an error in selecting a menu choice or clicking a command button that performs a task, selecting the Undo choice from the Edit pull-down menu will, in many cases, completely undo the action. If you make an error while entering data, you can usually do one of the following three things to correct the error.

- Press the Escape key to cancel the current entry.
- Press the Backspace key to erase typed characters to the left of the cursor one character at a time.
- Press the Delete key to erase characters to the right of the cursor one character at a time.

For errors made in the middle of an entry, you can also drag the mouse over the in-error text and then type the replacement text. Selecting Undo from the Edit menu will undo any typing as well. Should you change your mind after undoing a selection or entry, selecting Redo from the Edit menu will restore the program to the prior action.

HOW THIS TEXT REPRESENTS MULTIPLE MENU SELECTIONS

From this point forward in the text, when instructions call for two or more consecutive menu selections, the menu selections will appear chained together with the vertical slash character |. For example, the phrase "selecting Undo from the Edit menu" in the previous paragraph will be written as "select Edit | Undo" if found in later pages.

EP2.5 Using the General Help System

In Microsoft Excel 2003, the Help browser appears as part of the task pane (see section EP3.4).

You can get either general or context-sensitive help when you use Microsoft Excel. To get general help, including information about a Microsoft Excel feature, menu command, worksheet function (see section EP3.2), or Excel object, select **Help | Microsoft Excel Help**. Depending on Microsoft Office settings, you will then see the Microsoft Excel help browser (see Figure EP4) or the **Office Assistant** with its comics-like help balloon (see Figure EP5).*

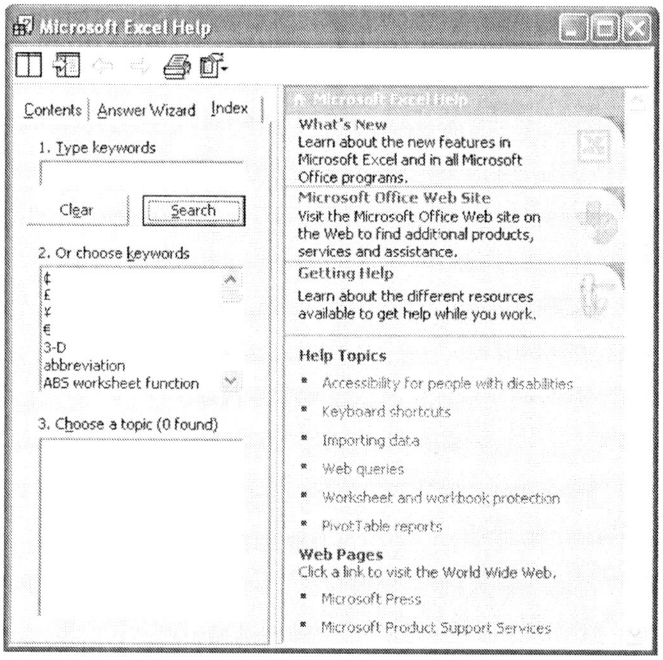

FIGURE EP4
Microsoft Excel 2002 Help browser

FIGURE EP5
Office Assistant with Help balloon

The Microsoft Excel Help browser, the design of which varies in the different versions of Excel, allows you to search on any word or phrase or select keywords from an alphabetized list. To perform a free-text search in the Excel 2002 Help browser, do the following:

Select the **Index** tab.

Type your word or phrase of interest in the **Type keywords** edit box and click the **Search** button.

Select the entry (or entries) or interest in the left pane of the browser to display the text for the entry in the right pane.

If applicable, you can click the hyperlinks in the right pane for additional help information. To perform another search, click the **Clear** button and repeat steps 1 and 2. In lieu of doing step 1, you can scroll and select from the list that appears in the **Or choose keywords** list box to retrieve appropriate entries for display.

You use the Office Assistant in a similar way, except that you type your search phrase in its help balloon and then click the **Search** button in the balloon to display a set of help choices. Because the help choices displayed are typically fewer in number than that displayed in the help browser, and because the Office Assistant animation can prove distracting, most users opt for turning off the Assistant and working with the browser. If the Office Assistant appears on your screen and you would like to turn it off to use the help browser, do the following:

Right-click on the Office Assistant when it appears onscreen.

Select **Options** from the shortcut menu.

In the Options tab of the Office Assistant dialog box that appears, click the **Use the Office assistant** check box to clear it and then click the **OK** button.

The Office Assistant will remain hidden and you will always get the help browser when you select Help | Microsoft Excel Help until you either select the Use the Office Assistant check box or select **Help | Show the Office Assistant**.

SPECIAL NOTES FOR MICROSOFT EXCEL 97 USERS

If you are using Microsoft Excel 97, the help browser is of an older design than the one for Excel 2002 illustrated in Figure EP4. You can perform a free-text search in that older help browser by first clicking the **Index** tab in the help browser window. You can also always avoid the display of the Office Assistant by always selecting **Help | Contents and Index** when you need to use Microsoft Excel help.

EP2.6 Getting Context-Sensitive Help

You can get context-sensitive help displays without searching for most onscreen objects in Microsoft Excel by using either the tool tips or "what's this?" help features.

Tool tips are context-sensitive pop-ups that identify elements of the Excel application window such as toolbar buttons or parts of other onscreen objects such as charts. To display a tool tip, pause the mouse pointer over an onscreen object and wait for the tool tip to be displayed. For example, Figure EP6 shows the tool tip text for a chart axis.

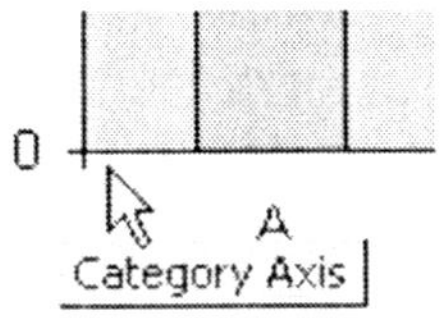

FIGURE EP6
Tool tip for a chart axis

"What's this?" help displays provide a context-sensitive message about an element of the Excel application window. To use this type of help, first select **Help | What's This?** to change the normal mouse pointer into the special question-mark pointer (see Figure EP7 top). Then click an onscreen object to display the help message for that object (see Figure EP7, inset). To remove the message from the screen, click anywhere in the application window. (You can also get "what's this?" help by clicking on the question-mark button of a dialog box, if the button is included in the top border of the dialog box.)

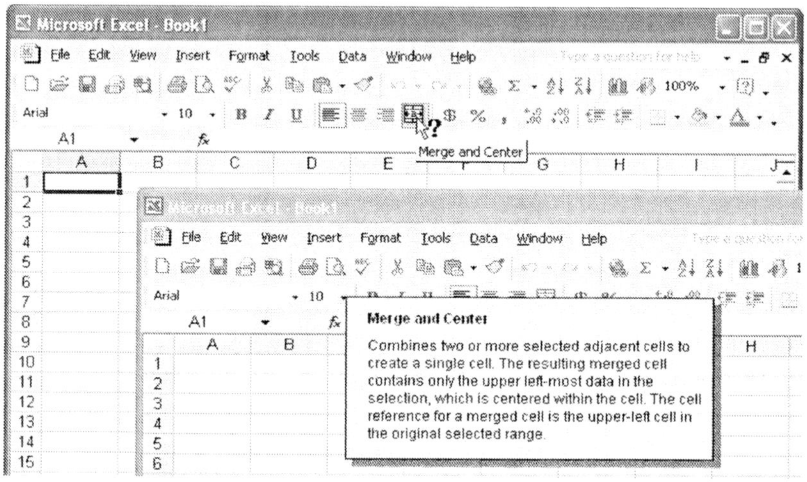

FIGURE EP7
What's This?" mouse pointer (top) and "What's This?" context-sensitive message (inset) for the Merge and Center button

EP3 COMMON WORKBOOK OPERATIONS

This section discusses basic file operations, using the dialog boxes and associated displays from Microsoft Excel 2002. If you are using another version of Microsoft Excel, some of the details of these displays will be different, but the basic operations described will be exactly the same or very similar.

EP3.1 Opening Workbooks

You open workbooks to use data and results that have been created by you or others at an earlier time. To open a Microsoft Excel workbook, select **File** | **Open**. In the Open dialog box that appears (see Figure EP3):

Select the appropriate folder (also known as a directory) from the **Look in** drop-down list box.

Check, and select, if necessary, the proper **Files of type** value from the drop-down list at the bottom of the dialog box. Typically, you will not need to change this selection as the default choice will list all Microsoft Excel files. However, to list all text files, select Text Files; to list every file in the folder, select All Files.

If necessary, change the display of files in the central files list box by clicking the rightmost (**Views**) button on the top row of buttons and selecting the appropriate view from the Views drop-down list.

Select the file to be opened from the files list box. If the file does not appear, review the previous steps changing the folder or file type as is necessary.

Click the **OK** button.

EP3.2 Saving Workbooks

You save a workbook to assure its future availability and to protect yourself against a system failure. To save a workbook, select **File** | **Save As**. In the Save As dialog box that appears (see Figure EP8):

Select the appropriate folder from the **Save in** drop-down list box.

Check, and select, if necessary, the proper **Save as type** value from the drop-down list at the bottom of the dialog box. Typically, you will want to accept the default choice, Microsoft Excel Workbook, but "Text (Tab delimited)" or "CSV (Comma delimited)" are useful choices to save data to be used by other programs that cannot open Excel workbooks.

Enter (or edit) the name of the file in the **File name** edit box.

Click the **OK** button.

You can repeat this procedure and save the workbook using a second name as an easy way to create a backup copy that can be used should some problem make your original workbook unusable.

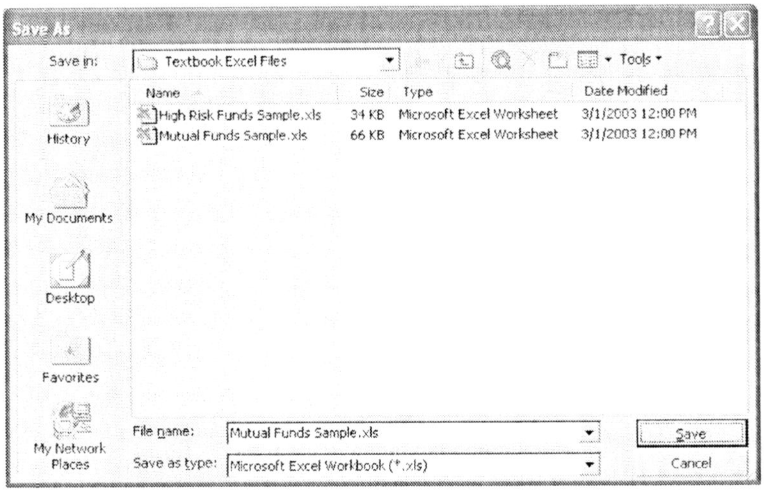

FIGURE EP8
Microsoft Excel 2002 Save As dialog box

If you retrieve a workbook directly from the CD-ROM that accompanies this text, Microsoft Excel will mark the workbook as "read-only" and not allow you to save the workbook under its original name. (You can save it under a second name in the Save As dialog box.)

EP3.3 Printing Worksheets

Printing workbooks gives you a means to study and review results away from the computer screen. At any one time, you generally should print individual worksheets and not the entire workbook. To print a specific worksheet, first select the worksheet and then select **File | Print Preview** to preview the output (see Figure EP9). If the preview contains errors or displays the worksheet in a manner not

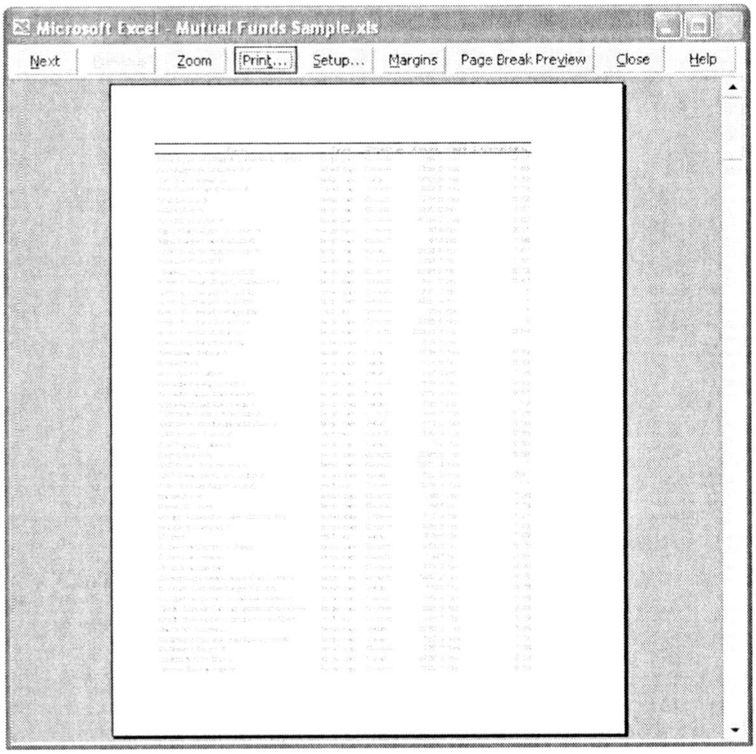

FIGURE EP9
Print Preview screen

desired, click the **Close** button, make the changes necessary, and reselect File | Print Preview. When you are ready to print, click the **Print** button in the Print Preview window. If the Print Preview Window is not opened, select **File** | **Print**. In either case, in the Print dialog box that appears (see Figure EP3):

Select the printer to be used from the **Name** drop-down list box.

Select the **All** option button under the "Print range" heading.

Select the **Active sheet(s)** option button under the "Print what" heading. (It is a good idea to avoid selecting the **Entire workbook** option button.)

Set the **Number of copies** to the proper value.

Click the **OK** button.

After printing, you should verify the contents of your printout. Most printing problems or failures will trigger the display of an informational dialog box. Click the OK button of any such dialog box and correct the problem noted before attempting a second print operation. You can customize printouts by selecting **File** | **Page Setup** (or clicking the **Setup** button in the Print Preview window) and making the appropriate entries in the Page Setup dialog box. For example, to print your worksheet with gridlines and numbered row and lettered column headings (similar to the appearance of the worksheet onscreen), select the **Sheet** tab in the Page Setup dialog box, then select the **Gridlines** and **Row and column headings** check boxes and click the **OK** button (see Figure EP10). (Additional information about using the Page Setup dialog box can be found in section F4 of the appendix on Configuring and Customizing Microsoft Excel for Use with This Text.)

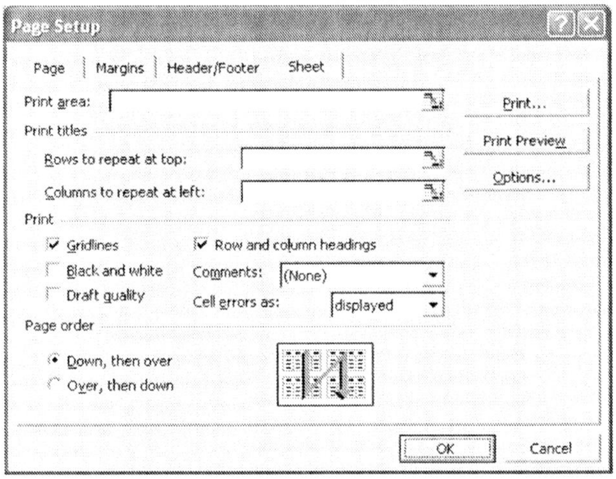

FIGURE EP10
The Sheet tab of the Page Setup dialog box

EP3.4 Using the Task Pane to Open Workbooks (Excel 2002 and later)

Beginning with Microsoft Excel version 2002, you can use the **task pane** to open workbooks and perform selected other operations. Figure EP11 shows the task pane with the New Worksheet panel as a window floating above the workspace area. To open a specific workbook, you click a hypertext blue entry, for instance, PHStat2.xla to open the PHStat2 add-in. You can also click **More workbooks** to display the standard file open dialog box discussed in section EP3.1. Because the task pane obscures the workspace area without adding much new functionality, many users hide this pane when they use Microsoft Excel. To hide the pane, either click the system close button on the title bar of the pane or select **View** | **Task Pane** to toggle off the display of the pane. Before hiding the pane, you can also clear the **Show at startup** check box (as is shown in Figure EP11) to prevent its display when you next open Excel.

FIGURE EP11
Microsoft Excel 2002 task pane

EP4 BASIC WORKSHEET CONCEPTS AND OPERATIONS

EP4.1 Using Microsoft Excel Worksheets

As mentioned in section EP1, in Microsoft Excel you enter data into worksheets that are comprised of lettered columns and numbered rows, the intersections of which form cells. Typically, you enter data for variables in separate columns, reserving the cells in row 1 for variable labels. Although each worksheet has many rows and columns and therefore can accommodate many data values, you should enter only one data set per worksheet.

You use the cursor keys, the Tab key, or your pointing device to move the **cell pointer** to navigate around a worksheet. You use a *Sheetname!ColumnRow* notation to refer to a specific cell. For example, Data!A2 refers to the cell in column A and row 2 in the Data worksheet. To refer to a specific **cell range**, a group or two or more cells, you use a *Sheetname!Upperleftcell:Lowerrightcell* notation. For example, Data!A2:B11 refers to the twenty cells that are in rows 2 through 11 in columns A and B of the Data worksheet.

Each Microsoft Excel worksheet has its own name. By default, Microsoft Excel names worksheets serially in the form of Sheet1, Sheet2, and so on. Better names are ones that reflect the content of the worksheets, such as Data for a worksheet that contains the data to be analyzed and Calculations for a sheet that holds the necessary calculations for an analysis. To give a sheet a descriptive name, double-click the **sheet tab** of the sheet to be renamed, type the descriptive name, and press the Enter key.

EP4.2 Using Formulas in Excel Worksheets

Besides data values, you can enter **formulas**, or instructions to perform a calculation or some other task, in worksheet cells. You enter formulas by typing the equal sign symbol (=) followed by some combination of mathematical or other data processing operations.

For simple formulas, the symbols +, –, *, /, and ^ are used for the operations addition, subtraction, multiplication, division, and exponentiation (a number raised to a power), respectively. For example, the formula =Data!B2 + Data!B3 + Data!B4 + Data!B5 adds the contents of the cells B2, B3, B4, and B5 of the Data worksheet and displays the sum as the value of the cell containing the formula. You can also use Microsoft Excel **functions** in formulas to simplify formulas. For example, the formula =SUM(Data!B2:B5) that uses the Excel SUM() function is a shorter equivalent to the prior example. You can also use cell or cell range references that do not contain the *Sheetname!* part, such as B2 or B2:B5. Such references *always* refer to the worksheet in which the formula has been entered.

You can distinguish between two similarly located cells on two similarly named worksheets in two different workbooks, by using the form '[*Workbookname*]*Sheetname*'!*ColumnRow*. For example, '[Chapter1]Data'!A1, refers to the upper-left corner cell on the Data worksheet in the Chapter1 workbook.

Formulas allow you to create generalized solutions and give Excel its distinctive ability to automatically recalculate results when you change the values of the supporting data. Some Excel procedures and most PHStat2 procedures add formulas to worksheets. To view the formulas in a worksheet, select **Tools | Options** and in the View tab of the Options dialog box that appears, select the **Formulas** check box under the "Windows options" heading, and click the **OK** button. (To restore the original view, clear the Formulas check box.)

If you use the "Excel Handbook" sections to construct your own worksheets, you should always take the time to turn on the display of the formulas in order to help you review your entries.

EP4.3 Enhancing the Appearance of Worksheets

You can use any number of formatting commands to enhance the appearance of your worksheets. Many of these commands are represented by button icons on the **formatting toolbar**, although you can also select **Format | Cells** and make the appropriate selections and choices in the Format Cells dialog box, if you prefer. Figure EP12 shows the Excel formatting toolbar with the icons of the commands used to format examples in this text. Exhibit EP5 lists eight common formatting operations that were frequently used to prepare the worksheet examples of this text.

FIGURE EP12
Formatting toolbar

EXHIBIT EP5 COMMON FORMATTING OPERATIONS

- To display cell values using boldface type, select the cell (or cell range) containing the values to be boldfaced and click the **Boldface** button on the formatting toolbar.
- To display a cell value centered in its column, select the cell (or cell range) containing the values to be centered and click the **Center** button on the formatting toolbar. (The **Align Left** and **Align Right** buttons to either side of the Center button similarly left justify or right justify values in a column.)
- To center a long cell entry, such as a title, over a range of columns, select the cell row range over which the entry is to be centered (this range must include the cell containing the title) and click the **Merge and Center** button on the formatting toolbar.
- To adjust the width of a column to completely display all the cell values in that column, select the column to be formatted by clicking its column heading in the border of the worksheet, and then select **Format | Column | AutoFit Selection**.
- To display numeric values as percentages, select the cell range containing the numeric entries to be displayed as percentages and click the **Percent** button on the formatting toolbar.
- To align the decimal point in a series of numeric entries, select the cell range containing the numeric entries to be aligned and click either the **Increase Decimal** or **Decrease Decimal** button on the formatting toolbar until the desired decimal alignment occurs.
- To change the background color, select the cell range containing the cells to be changed and click the **Fill Color** drop-down list button. In the **Fill Color** palette dialog box that appears (see Figure EP13), select the new background color. (Many worksheet examples in this text use the Windows color "Light Turquoise" to tint areas that contain user-changeable data values and the color "Light Yellow" to tint areas that contain results. Light Turquoise and Light Yellow are the fifth and third choices, respectively, on the bottom row of the standard palette.)
- To change the cell border effect, select the cell range containing the cells whose borders are to be changed and click the Borders drop-down list button. In the **Borders** palette dialog box that appears (see Figure EP14), select the new border effect. (Many of the worksheets illustrated in this text use a variety of border effects, including those identified by their tool tips as All Borders, Outside Borders, and Top Border.)

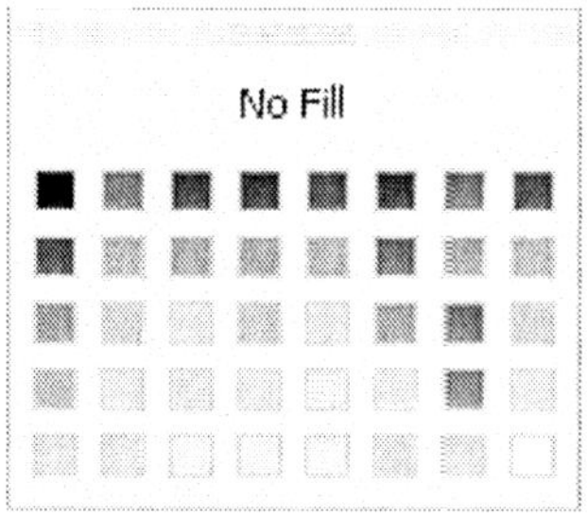

FIGURE EP13
Fill Color palette dialog box

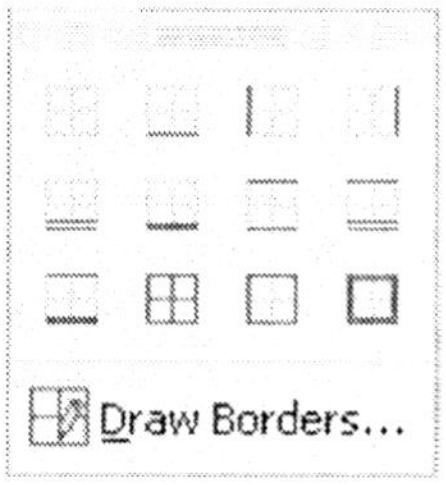

FIGURE EP14
Borders palette dialog box

EP5 ADVANCED WORKSHEET OPERATIONS

EP5.1 Copying Cell Entries and Formulas in a Worksheet

Many times when you add a calculation to a worksheet, you need to add the calculation to an entire column or row. Instead of entering the formula that represents the calculation numerous times, you can enter the formula once and then use the copy operation to copy the entry to the other cells.

Generally, copying a cell entry to another cell involves the simple procedure of selecting the cell with the entry to be copied, then selecting **Edit | Copy**, then selecting the cell to receive the copy, and then selecting **Edit | Paste**. Copying entries that contain formulas requires extra attention because exact duplicates may or may not result, depending on how cell references have been entered. If you have entered cell references in the form *ColumnletterRownumber*, such as A1 or any of the cell references used in section EP4.1, the cell references are considered **relative references** and will be changed to reflect their new, relative positions. For example, when you copy a cell C2 formula =A2+B2 down to cell C3, the formula will be changed to =A3+B3 to reflect its new relative position one row down from the original. Likewise, a cell A5 formula =SUM(A1:A4) when copied across to cell B5 will be changed to =SUM(B1:B4).

When you do not want this automatic adjustment, you enter the reference as an **absolute reference**, using the form $*Columnletter*$*Rownumber*. For example, if you enter the formula =$A$2+$B$2 and then copy it to another cell, the formula will always sum the contents of the row 2 cells in the first and second columns, regardless of the cell to which it is copied. Note that the dollar sign symbol does not imply currency values; it is used solely to prevent the changing of a cell reference during a copy operation. Formulas that mix relative and absolute cell references are allowed. For example, a cell C2 formula =A2/$B$10 when copied to cell C3 will be changed to =A3/$B$10. This mixing of cell reference types often simplifies the implementation of sets of worksheet formulas and you will find it used in many of the worksheet designs presented in the Excel Handbook sections in this text.

EP5.2 Copying Formulas and Transferring Information Between Worksheets

You can copy formulas between cells of different worksheets using a procedure similar to the Edit | Copy and Edit | Paste procedure discussed in the previous section. However, when you copy between worksheets, you should make sure that all cell references contain a worksheet name and are absolute references, such as Data!$A$1:$A$12, in order to get consistent results.

If you need only to transfer the calculated results from one sheet to another, for example, to create your own summary or report worksheet, consider using one of two methods to transfer information between worksheets. If you need to transfer the contents of only one or a few cells, consider entering formulas in the form =*Sourcesheetname*!*Cellreference* to transfer the information into the second worksheet. For example, if you want to transfer the results of the formula found in cell B10 of the worksheet named Results to cell A5 in the worksheet named Summary, you can enter the formula =Results!B10 in cell A5 of the Summary sheet in lieu of copying the original formula. You can also use this technique to transfer column headings or other labeling information between worksheets in order to maintain consistency across worksheets.

If you need to transfer the contents of a large cell range, consider using the Edit | Paste Special command. To use this command, first select the cell range to be copied and select **Edit | Copy**. Then select the cell range in the second worksheet to receive the copied information and select **Edit | Paste Special**. In the Paste Special dialog box (see Figure EP15), select the **Values and number formats** option button and click the **OK** button. Selecting this option button places the current values of all formulas in the second worksheet, so if you change the underlying data, you would need to repeat this procedure to update the values shown on the second worksheet.

FIGURE EP15
Excel Paste Special dialog box

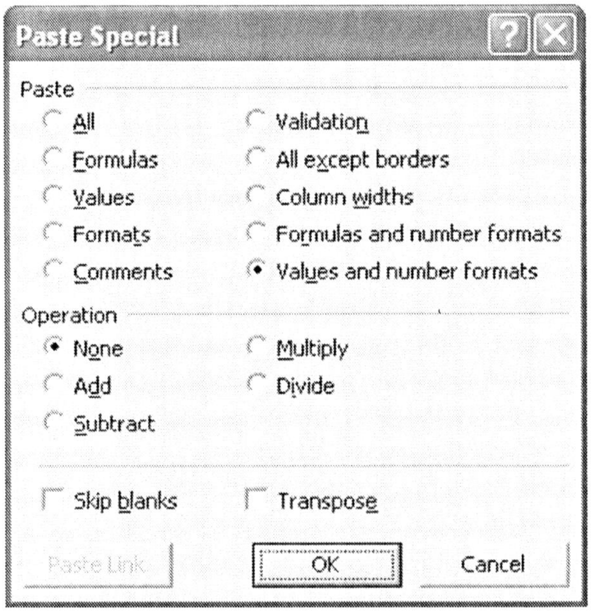

TRANSFERRING INFORMATION BETWEEN MICROSOFT OFFICE DOCUMENTS

Section 1 and 2 of the appendix, Preparing Data for Reports and Presentations Using Microsoft Office, discuss similar procedures for transferring information from Excel worksheets to other types of Microsoft Office documents.

EP5.3 Copying Worksheets

You copy entire worksheets when you need the same information formatted in two different ways or when you want to show the formulas contained in a worksheet separately from the results those formulas produce. To copy a worksheet, first select the worksheet by clicking on its sheet tab. Then select **Edit | Move or Copy Sheet**, and in the Move or Copy dialog box (see Figure EP16):

Select the **Create a copy** check box.
Select (new book) from the **To book** drop-down list if the worksheet copy is to be placed in a new workbook (shown in Figure EP16), or, if the copy is to be placed in the same workbook, specify the position of the copy in the opened workbook by selecting the appropriate choice from the **Before sheet** list box.
Click the **OK** button.

Microsoft Excel assigns the copied worksheet the name of the original sheet, plus a number in parentheses. For example, if you copy a sheet named Calculations, the copied sheet will be named Calculations (2). You should consider renaming copied worksheets to give them more descriptive names, such as "Calculations in Report Format," using the procedure discussed in section EP 4.1.

FIGURE EP16
Move or Copy dialog box

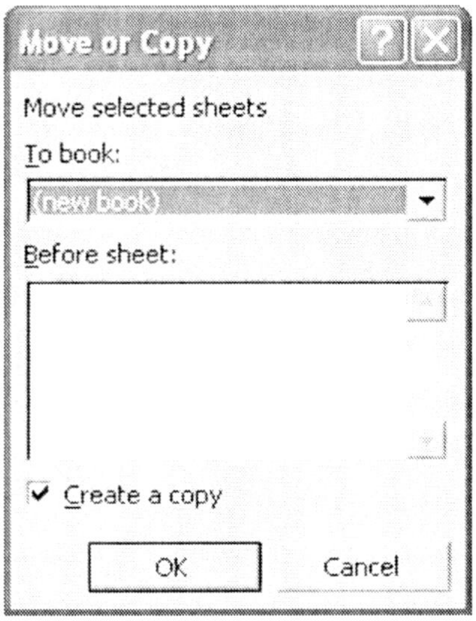

EP6 USING THE MICROSOFT EXCEL CHART WIZARD

Wizards are a series of linked dialog boxes that guide you, step-by-step, through the task of generating some Microsoft Office object. You make selections and enter information about the object as you step through the dialog boxes clicking **Next** buttons. Clicking a **Finish** button, typically done in the last dialog box, generates the object. At any point, you can cancel the operation of the wizard by clicking a **Cancel** button, or move to a previous dialog box by clicking **Back**.

You use the Microsoft Excel **Chart Wizard** to generate a wide variety of charts. You begin this wizard by selecting **Insert | Chart** from the Excel menu bar and making these entries in the Chart Wizard dialog boxes (see Figure EP17):

Step 1: Choose the chart type.

Step 2: Enter the workbook locations of the source data for the values to be plotted and the source data for chart labeling information (if any).

Step 3: Specify the formatting and labeling options for the chart. Exhibit EP6 contains guidance about many of these settings, the automatic settings of which lead to inferior charts.

Step 4: Choose the workbook location of the chart. You will always create a better-scaled chart if you choose the **As new sheet** and not the **As object in** (a worksheet) option.

FIGURE EP17
Chart Wizard dialog boxes as they appear in Microsoft Excel 2002

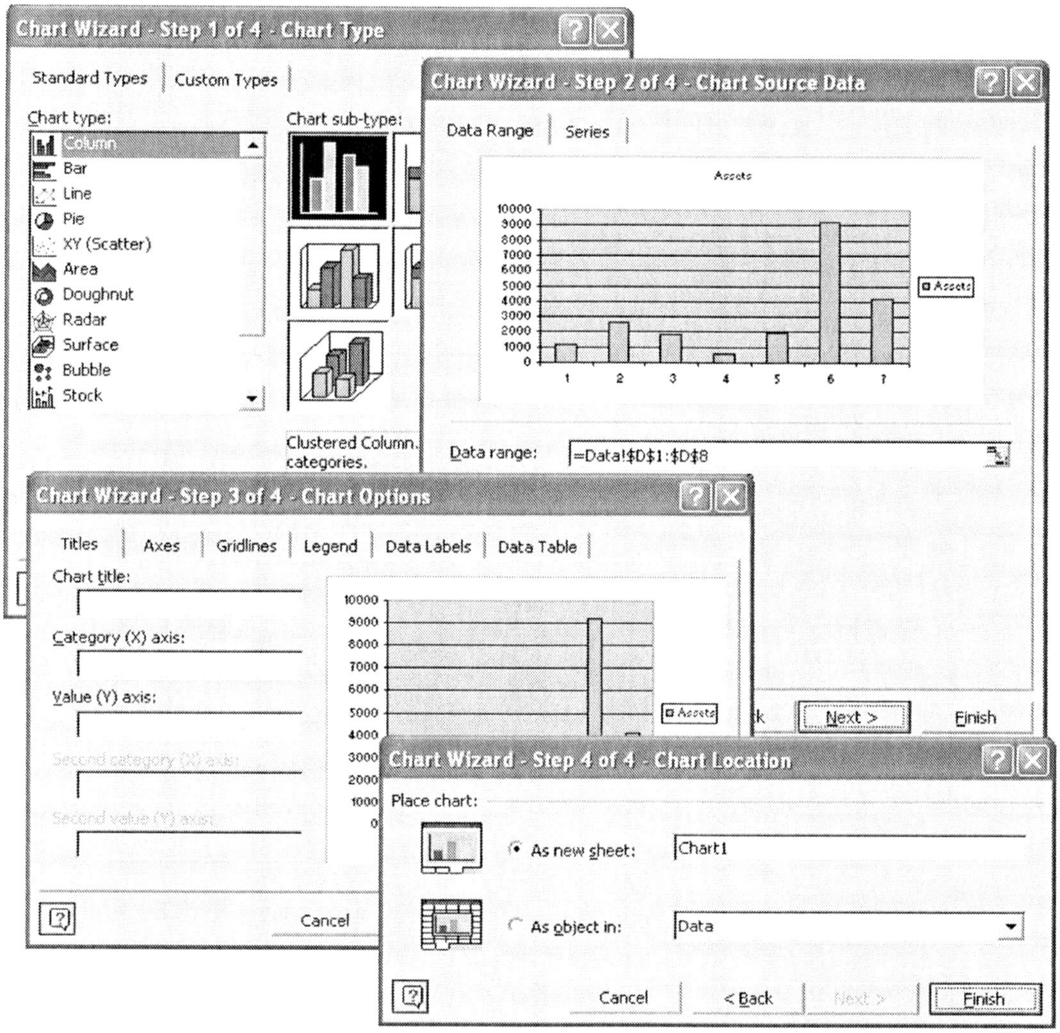

EXHIBIT EP6 CHOOSING THE BEST CHART OPTIONS

The Step 3 dialog box of the Chart Wizard (see Figure EP18) allows you to format and label a chart. Unless otherwise instructed in specific sections, always apply the following instructions when generating a chart for a text example or problem:

Select the **Titles** tab and enter a title and axis labels, if appropriate.

Select the **Axes** tab and then select both the (X) axis and (Y) axis check boxes. Also select the **Automatic** option button under the (X) axis check box.

Select the **Gridlines** tab and deselect (uncheck) all the choices under the (X) axis heading and under the (Y) axis heading.

Select the **Legend** tab and deselect (uncheck) the **Show legend** check box.

Select the **Data Labels** tab and select the **None** option button under the "Data Labels" heading.

Note that some instructions turn off the display of options that the wizard would otherwise (mistakenly) include and that some tabs will not appear for certain types of charts. Should you discover a mistake in your chart options after the chart is finished, right-click on the chart and select **Chart Options** from the shortcut menu to return to the Chart options (Step 3) dialog box.

FIGURE EP18
Microsoft Excel 2002 Step 3 dialog box

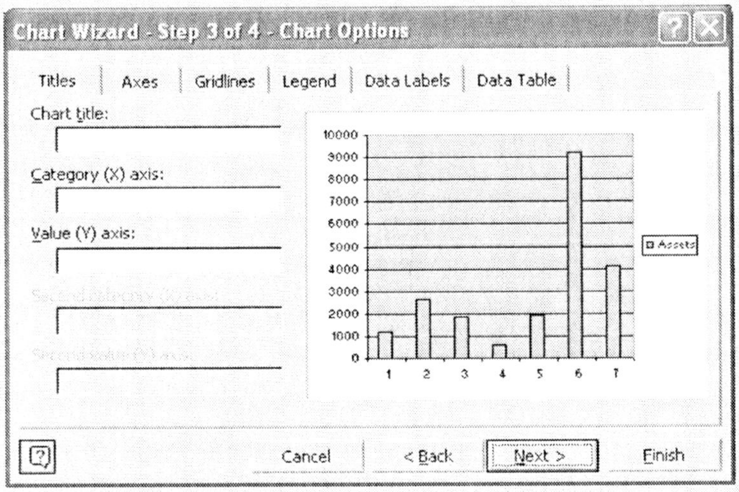

EP7 USING THE MICROSOFT EXCEL PIVOTTABLE WIZARD

You use the **PivotTable Wizard** to generate interactive tables of summary data, known as PivotTables, that can update themselves as their underlying raw data changes. In this text, you use the wizard to generate one-way and two-way frequency distribution tables for categorical data, although other applications, such as exploring your data dynamically by adding or removing variables or adding or removing levels of a table are possible.

To learn more about dynamically exploring your data with PivotTables, open the Exploring PivotTables workbook (**Exploring PivotTables.xls**) in the Instructional Files folder of the CD-ROM that accompanies this text.

In Microsoft Excel 97, you select* ***Data | PivotTable Report* *and supply information to a four-step wizard, in which the extra step is the Layout dialog box (see Figure EP20) described as part of the Step 3 dialog box.*

To use the PivotTable wizard in Microsoft Excel 2000 or later, select **Data | PivotTable and PivotChart Report** from the Excel menu bar* and make these entries in the PivotTable Wizard dialog boxes.

Step 1 dialog box: (see Figure EP19). Select the source for the data for the PivotTable and the type of report to be produced in the Step 1 dialog box. (For problems in this text, the source will always be **Microsoft Excel list or database** and the type of report will be always a **PivotTable**.)

FIGURE EP19
PivotTable Wizard as it appears in Microsoft Excel 2002

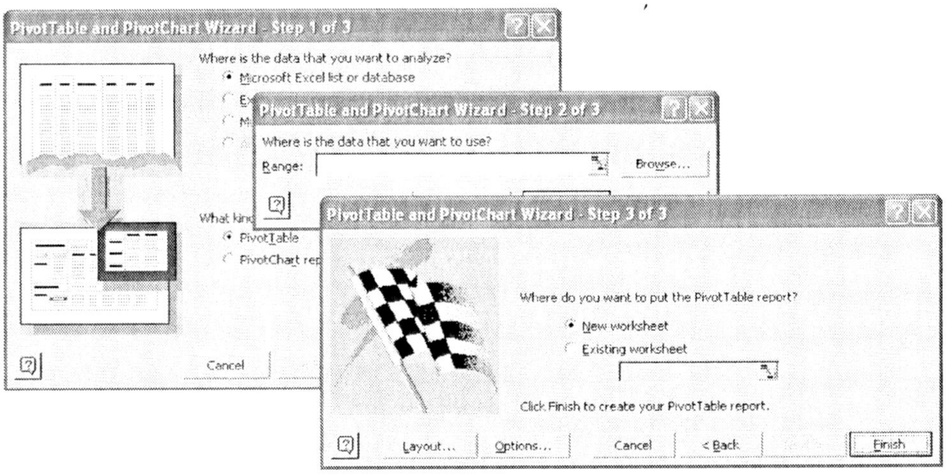

Step 2 dialog box: Enter the cell range of the set of data to be summarized. (The first row column headings in this cell range will become the names of the variables.)

Step 3 dialog box: Choose the location of the PivotTable. (For problems in this text, you should always choose the **New worksheet** option.) Specify the contents and design of the table by clicking the **Layout** and **Options** buttons.

Clicking the Layout button in Step 3 displays the Layout dialog box. In this dialog box, you drag name labels from a list of variables (slightly obscured in Figure EP20) into a PivotTable template that contains page, row, column, and data areas. (The page area is not used in this text.) Some users find this dragging task confusing, and if you prefer, you can have PHStat2 do this task for you as part of its one-way and two-way tables and charts procedures.

Clicking the Options button in Step 3 displays the Options dialog box. For most problems and examples in this text, you enter a self-descriptive name in the **Name** edit box, **0** in the **For empty cells, show** edit box, and leave the rest of the default settings, shown in Figure EP20, as is.

FIGURE EP20

PivotTable Layout (slightly obscured) and Options dialog boxes

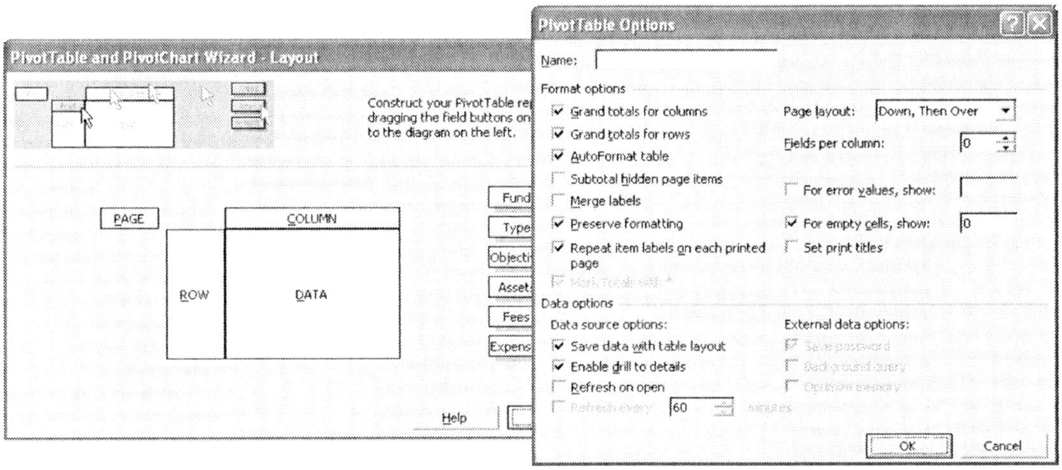

EP8 UNDERSTANDING AND USING ADD-INS

Add-ins are optional components of Microsoft Office that you use to enhance the functionality of Microsoft Excel. Some add-ins, such as the Analysis ToolPak, are included on the Microsoft Office set-up disks, while others, such as Prentice Hall's PHStat2 add-in system for Microsoft Excel, are supplied by third parties.

Add-ins modify Microsoft Excel in a variety of ways, usually by altering the Excel menu bar. For example, the Analysis ToolPak adds the Data Analysis choice into the Tools menu that, when selected, allows you to display the Data Analysis dialog box (see Figure EP21) that gives you access to a number of statistical procedures that otherwise would be very difficult to create through simple worksheet formulas. Prentice Hall's PHStat2 add-in extends the Analysis ToolPak by inserting a PHStat menu (see Figure EP22) that contains choices that give you added statistical functionality while simplifying the operations of certain Analysis ToolPak procedures.

Because add-ins are packaged as a special type of workbook, you can open add-ins through the File Open dialog box as you would any other workbook. However, if you prefer, you can "install" add-ins in Microsoft Excel so that they are opened automatically every time Excel itself is opened. You install an add-in—not to be confused with running a setup program—by first selecting **Tools | Add-Ins** and then, in the Add-Ins dialog box (see Figure EP23), selecting the check box of the **Add-Ins available** list that corresponds to the add-in to be installed. (When using this text, the authors suggest that you install the Analysis ToolPak to open automatically, but that you open the PHStat2 add-in manually.)

When you open add-ins such as PHStat2 that are not supplied by Microsoft, the add-in is subjected to a security screen in Microsoft Excel version 2000 SR-1 or later. You control this security screen by selecting **Tools | Macro | Security** and then selecting one of three levels of security (see Figure EP24). To allow add-ins such as PHStat2 to open, set the security level to **Medium**, and not to High, which would silently prevent PHStat2 from opening. Setting the security to Medium poses no threat to your system and gives you full control over enabling or disabling all add-ins and macros. (The authors advise that you never set security to Low, which, nevertheless, would allow add-ins such as PHStat2 to open.)

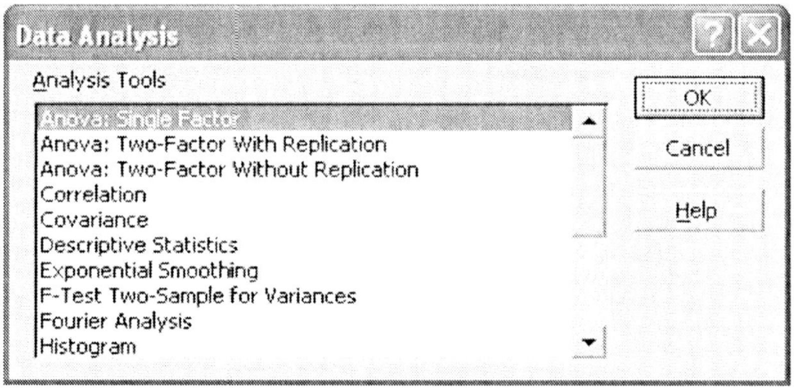

FIGURE EP21
Data Analysis dialog box

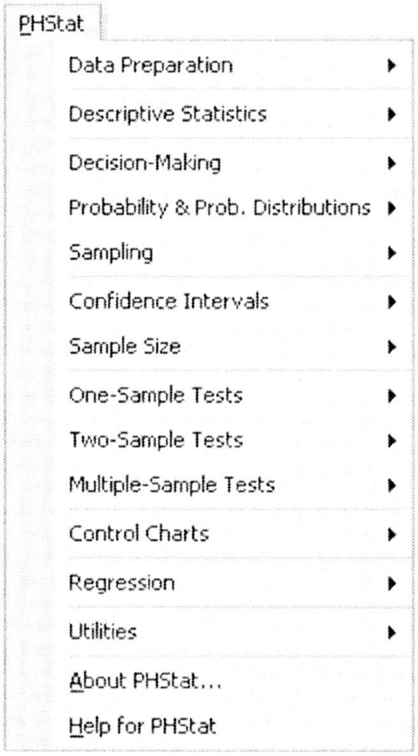

FIGURE EP22
PHStat menu

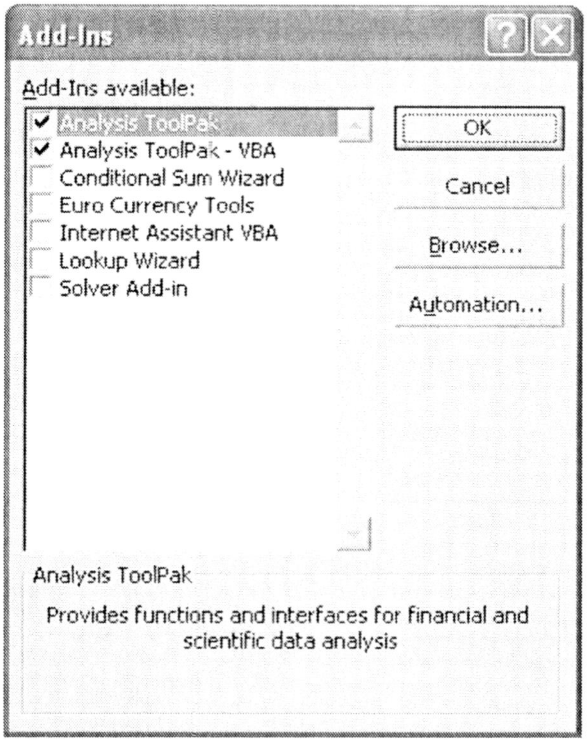

FIGURE EP23
Add-Ins dialog box

FIGURE EP24
Security dialog box

FIGURE EP25
Macro virus warning dialog box for Excel 2002 (dialog boxes for other versions of Excel are similar)

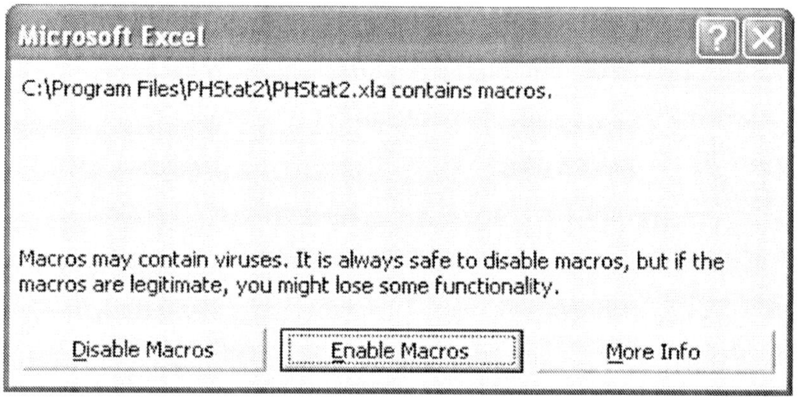

When you set the security level to Medium and then open an add-in such as PHStat2, you trigger the display of the "macros may contain viruses" dialog box (see Figure EP25) that warns you that certain types of Excel files, including add-in files, *could* contain computer viruses. Click the **Enable Macros** button to allow virus-free add-ins, such as PHStat2, to be opened and used.

KEY TERMS

absolute references
add-ins
Cancel button
cells
cell range
Chart Wizard
check box
clear
click
close button
dialog box
double-click
drag
drop-down list box
edit box
Excel application window
formatting toolbar
formulas
formula bar
functions
Help button
list box
menu bar
mouse pointer
mouse operations
Office Assistant
OK button
option buttons
PivotTable Wizard
question-mark button
relative references
right-click
scroll bars
scroll buttons
select
sheet tabs
shortcut menus
slider
spinner buttons
standard toolbar
System minimize, resize, and close buttons
task pane
tool tips
"what's this?" help
wizards
workbooks
worksheets
workspace area

Presenting Data in Tables and Charts

USING STATISTICS: Comparing the Performance of Mutual Funds

LEARNING OBJECTIVES

- To organize numerical data
- To develop tables and charts for numerical data
- To develop tables and charts for categorical data
- To understand the principles of proper graphical presentation

USING STATISTICS

Comparing the Performance of Mutual Funds

In recent years millions of individuals have invested billions of dollars in a variety of mutual funds. When an investor buys shares (partial ownership) of a stock mutual fund, he or she is buying stock in all of the companies that are part of the fund's portfolio. In this Using Statistics scenario, you will play the role of a financial advisor responsible for making recommendations to customers concerning which funds they should invest in. Different mutual funds have different objectives. Often, specific funds are made up of stocks from companies with similar characteristics. For example, a mutual fund may specialize in large companies (large cap), midsize companies (midcap), or small companies (small cap). Mutual funds also vary with regard to the degree of risk involved in the companies they invest in. They are categorized as very high-risk, high-risk, average-risk, low-risk, or very low-risk.

Your task is to advise your client about how best to invest in mutual funds. One place to begin your investigation is to analyze past performance of different types of mutual funds. Have growth funds outperformed value mutual funds? Has the performance of growth mutual funds shown more variability than value funds? How might you use tables and charts to investigate the past performance of these different types of funds?

INTRODUCTION

As a general rule, tables and charts should be constructed whenever a set of data contains about 20 or more observations. The important features or characteristics of the data from these tables and charts can then be determined. In this chapter large sets of data are organized and presented in the form of tables and charts in order to enhance data analysis and interpretation.

1 ORGANIZING NUMERICAL DATA

MUTUAL FUNDS.xls

One of the ways you can answer the questions raised in the Using Statistics scenario is by obtaining past data on the performance of mutual funds. The data relating to a sample of 259 mutual funds can be found in the **Mutual Funds.xls** file on the companion CD that accompanies this text.

One way to compare the performance of the funds in the sample is to look at the 5-year annualized rate of return for different types of funds. In the **Mutual Funds.xls** data file, there are two types of funds, growth and value. Growth funds are those whose stocks have higher price-to-earning ratios as compared to typical stocks of similar size companies. Value funds are those whose stocks have lower price-to-earning ratios as compared to typical stocks of similar size companies. You can answer such questions as "how did the performance of growth funds compare to that of value funds?" by examining the 5-year annualized rates of return for the two groups. (The sample in the **Mutual Funds.xls** data file includes 158 growth funds and 101 value funds.) The 5-year annualized rate of return for each fund is for the period January 1, 1997 through December 31, 2001, a period of time in which there was a great deal of fluctuation in the return of mutual funds. (For a complete description of the **Mutual Funds.xls** workbook, see the appendix on CD-ROM Contents)

The major features in a set of data become more difficult to focus on as the number of observations gets large. To better understand the information the data are conveying, ways to organize the observations are needed. Two commonly used methods for accomplishing this are the *ordered array* and the *stem-and-leaf display*.

The Ordered Array

An **ordered array** consists of an ordered sequence of the raw data in rank order from the smallest observation to the largest observation. Beginning the analysis with the growth funds, Table 1 indicates the 5-year annualized returns achieved by the 158 sampled growth funds. The ordered array makes it easier to pick out extremes, typical values, and where the majority of the values are concentrated.

TABLE 1

Ordered array of 5-year annualized returns achieved by the 158 growth funds (values given are the average annualized return for the 5-year period from January 1, 1997 to December 31, 2001)

MUTUAL FUNDS.xls

−6.1	−2.8	−1.2	−0.7	0.5	1.8	1.9	2.5	2.8	3.3
3.5	3.8	3.8	4.0	4.2	4.3	4.5	4.6	5.0	5.1
5.2	5.4	5.5	5.8	5.9	6.0	6.2	6.3	6.5	6.5
7.0	7.1	7.1	7.2	7.2	7.3	7.5	7.6	7.6	7.8
7.8	7.8	7.9	8.1	8.1	8.2	8.3	8.3	8.4	8.5
8.5	8.5	8.6	8.8	8.8	8.8	9.0	9.0	9.1	9.1
9.1	9.2	9.3	9.3	9.5	9.5	9.5	9.5	9.6	9.6
9.7	9.8	9.9	9.9	9.9	9.9	10.1	10.1	10.1	10.1
10.2	10.3	10.3	10.4	10.5	10.5	10.5	10.5	10.5	10.5
10.6	10.7	10.7	10.8	10.9	11.0	11.0	11.1	11.1	11.1
11.2	11.2	11.3	11.3	11.3	11.3	11.4	11.5	11.5	11.5
11.6	11.7	11.7	11.9	11.9	12.2	12.2	12.3	12.3	12.4
12.5	12.7	12.9	12.9	12.9	13.0	13.1	13.2	13.4	13.4
13.7	13.7	13.9	14.1	14.7	14.8	14.9	15.0	15.7	15.8
15.8	16.0	16.9	17.0	17.0	17.6	17.8	18.1	18.1	18.2
18.5	18.5	18.7	18.9	21.4	22.0	22.9	26.3		

The ordered array shows that the lowest 5-year annualized return was a loss of 6.1% a year and the highest or best return was a gain of 26.3% a year. In addition, a large number of funds had an annualized return between 5% and 15%. Before developing summary tables and charts of the data or computing descriptive summary measures, the data set can be organized into a stem-and-leaf display in order to study its characteristics (see references 9 and 10).

Excel Strategy Generating Ordered Arrays

Use the Microsoft Excel **Sort** command to sort the contents of a worksheet or cell range to generate an ordered array in either ascending or descending order. For example, to generate the ordered array of Table 1 above, open the **Growth Funds Sample.xls** workbook to the **Data** worksheet and: Select **Data | Sort**. In the Sort dialog box (shown at right), select **5-Yr Return** from the **Sort by** drop-down list and leave the first **Ascending** option button and the **Header row** option button selected. Click the **OK** button.

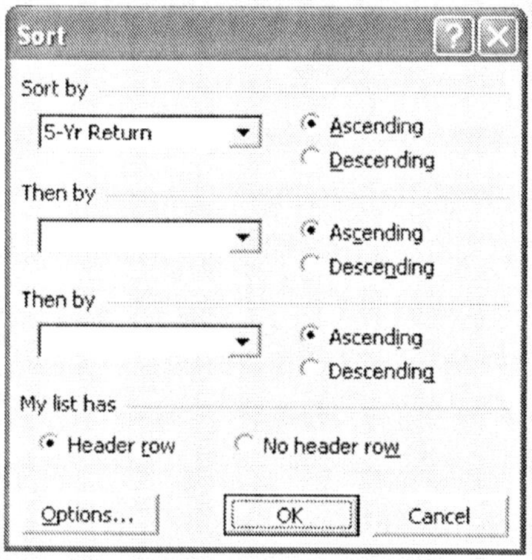

You can optionally drag the mouse pointer through the 5-Yr Return cell range (I1:I159) and copy and paste the range (see section EP5.1) to a new worksheet.

The Stem-and-Leaf Display

The stem-and-leaf display is a valuable tool for organizing a set of data and understanding how the values distribute and cluster over the range of the observations in the data set. A **stem-and-leaf display** separates data entries into leading digits, or stems, and trailing digits, or leaves. In this stem-and-leaf display, an entry of 10.9 (corresponding to a 5-year annualized return of 10.9%) has a stem of 10 and a trailing digit, or leaf, of 9.

Figure 1 depicts the stem-and-leaf display obtained from Microsoft Excel of the 5-year annualized returns achieved by the 158 growth mutual funds. The first two columns of numbers is the stem, or leading digits, of the data. The leaves, or trailing digits, branch out to the right of these numbers.

FIGURE 1

Stem-and-leaf display obtained from Microscft Excel of the 5-year annualized returns achieved by the 158 growth funds

	A	B
1	Stem-and-Leaf Display	
2		
3	Stem unit:	1
4		
5	-6	1
6	-5	
7	-4	
8	-3	
9	-2	8
10	-1	2
11	-0	7
12	0	5
13	1	8 9
14	2	5 8
15	3	3 5 8 8
16	4	0 2 3 5 6
17	5	0 1 2 4 5 8 9
18	6	0 2 3 5 5
19	7	0 1 1 2 2 3 5 6 6 8 8 8 9
20	8	1 1 2 3 3 4 5 5 5 6 8 8 8
21	9	0 0 1 1 1 2 3 3 5 5 5 5 6 6 7 8 9 9 9 9
22	10	0 1 1 1 2 3 3 4 5 5 5 5 5 5 6 7 7 8 9
23	11	0 0 1 1 1 2 2 3 3 3 3 4 5 5 5 6 7 7 9 9
24	12	2 2 3 3 4 5 7 9 9 9
25	13	0 1 2 4 4 7 7 9
26	14	1 7 8 9
27	15	0 7 8 8
28	16	0 9
29	17	0 0 6 8
30	18	1 1 2 5 5 7 9
31	19	
32	20	
33	21	4
34	22	0 9
35	23	
36	24	
37	25	
38	26	3

Some conclusions about the 5-year annualized returns of the growth funds can be made from Figure 1. Among the conclusions reached from the stem-and-leaf display are the following:

1. The lowest 5-year annualized return is −6.1.
2. The highest 5-year annualized return is 26.3.
3. The returns of the 158 growth funds are spread out between the lowest and highest returns, with concentration between 1.8 and 18.9 and very few values near the extremes.
4. Only four of the mutual funds had a negative annualized return and only four of the mutual funds had an annualized return exceeding 20.

To understand how the stem-and-leaf display is constructed, refer to Example 1.

Excel Strategies Generating Stem-and-Leaf Displays

You generate stem-and-leaf displays by first sorting the data into an ordered array and then making cell entries in two consecutive columns that represent the stems and the leaves. These tasks can be done for you in PHStat2, or you can do them yourself, although be aware that constructing leaves can be an error-prone manual process.

CHAPTER 2.xls

Retrieve the Figure 1 worksheet of the ***Chapter 2.xls*** *workbook to view a stem-and-leaf display in Microsoft Excel similar to the one in Figure 1.*

For example, to generate the stem-and-leaf display shown in Figure 1, open the **Growth Funds Sample.xls** workbook to the **Data** worksheet and use one of these strategies:

Using Excel with PHStat2

Use the PHStat2 Stem-and-Leaf Display procedure to generate a stem-and-leaf display using the rounding method.

Select **PHStat | Descriptive Statistics | Stem-and-Leaf Display**.

In the Stem-and-Leaf Display dialog box (shown at right):

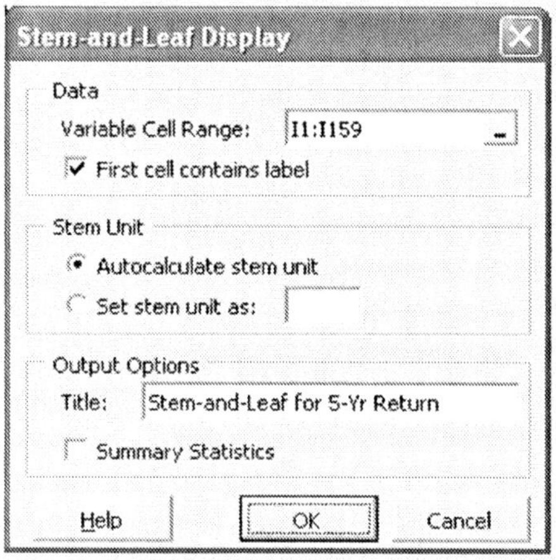

Enter **I1:I159** in the **Variable Cell Range** edit box.

Select the **First cell contains label** check box.

Select the **Autocalculate stem unit** option button.

Enter a title in the **Title** edit box.

Click the **OK** button.

To generate a table for your data that contains the same descriptive summary measures you will study in other chapters, select the ***Summary Statistics*** *check box.*

Using Excel

Copy the cell range containing the values to be sorted to column A of a blank worksheet. Select **Data | Sort** to order your values. Build the leaves in column B by manual inspection and begin all column B leaf entries with apostrophes to prevent Microsoft Excel from misinterpreting the string of digits as a very long number. Change the values in column A to stem values and delete duplicate stems.

EXAMPLE 1

CONSTRUCTING A STEM-AND-LEAF DISPLAY

The following raw data represent the amount spent by 15 students for lunch at a fast food restaurant.

5.35 4.75 4.30 5.47 4.85 6.62 3.54 4.87 6.26 5.48 7.27 8.45 6.05 4.76 5.91

Construct the stem-and-leaf display.

SOLUTION

To form the stem-and-leaf display, put the values in ascending order first, then use the units column as the stems and round the decimals to one decimal place:

3	5
4	83998
5	4559
6	631
7	3
8	5

PROBLEMS FOR SECTION 1

Learning the Basics

1 Form an ordered array given the following raw data from a sample of $n = 7$ midterm exam scores in accounting:

68 94 63 75 71 88 64

2 Form a stem-and-leaf display given the following raw data from a sample of $n = 7$ midterm exam scores in finance:

80 54 69 98 93 53 74

3 Form an ordered array given the following raw data from a sample of $n = 7$ midterm exam scores in marketing:

88 78 78 73 91 78 85

4 Form an ordered array given the following stem-and-leaf display from a sample of $n = 7$ midterm exam scores in information systems:

5	0
6	
7	446
8	19
9	2

Applying the Concepts

5 The following is a stem-and-leaf display representing the amount of gasoline purchased in gallons (with leaves in 10ths of gallons) for a sample of 25 cars that use a particular service station on the New Jersey Turnpike:

9	147
10	02238
11	125566777
12	223489
13	02

a. Place the data into an ordered array.
b. Which of these two displays seems to provide more information? Discuss.
c. What amount of gasoline (in gallons) is most likely to be purchased?
d. Is there a concentration of the purchase amounts in the center of the distribution?
e. Do you think these 25 purchase amounts are representative of a larger population? Explain.

6 The data file **PE.xls** contains a random sample of 30 stocks traded on the New York Stock Exchange. For each of the stocks, the ticker symbol and price-to-earnings ratio as reported in the *Wall Street Journal* on January 2, 2003 is given. The price-to-earnings ratio, commonly called the P/E ratio, is determined by dividing the closing market price by the company's diluted per-share earnings for the past four quarters. Stocks with extremely high P/E ratios are typically called overvalued stocks, and stocks with unusually low P/E ratios are often called undervalued stocks.
a. Place the data into an ordered array.
b. Set up a stem-and-leaf display for these data.
c. Which of these two displays seems to provide more information? Discuss.
d. Does there seem to be more undervalued stocks than overvalued stocks? Explain.
e. Using a current listing of stocks in the *Wall Street Journal*, *USA Today*, or some other source, collect your own random sample of size 30 and compare your results to the sample taken on January 2, 2003.
f. Using a current listing of stocks in the *Wall Street Journal*, *USA Today*, or some other source, collect a random sample of size 30 from the NASDAQ listings and compare your results to the sample you took from the New York Stock Exchange.

7 The following data represent the bounced check fee in dollars for a sample of 23 banks for direct-deposit customers who maintain a $100 balance. **BANKCOST1.xls**

26 28 20 20 21 22 25 25 18 25 15 20
18 20 25 25 22 30 30 30 15 20 29

Source: "The New Face of Banking." Copyright © 2000 by Consumers Union of U.S., Inc. Adapted from Consumer Reports, *June 2000, by permission of Consumers Union U.S., Inc., Yonkers, NY 10703–1057.*

a. Place the data into an ordered array.
b. Set up a stem-and-leaf display for these data.
c. Which of these two displays seems to provide more information? Discuss.
d. Around what value, if any, do the bounced check fees seem to be concentrated? Explain.

8 The following data represent the monthly service fee in dollars if a customer's account falls below the minimum required balance for a sample of 26 banks for direct-deposit customers who maintain a $1,500 balance. **BANKCOST2.xls**

12 8 5 5 6 6 10 10 9 7 10 7 7 5 0 10 6 9 12 0 5 10 8 5 5 9

Source: "The New Face of Banking." Copyright © 2000 by Consumers Union of U.S., Inc. Adapted from Consumer Reports, *June 2000, by permission of Consumers Union U.S., Inc., Yonkers, NY 10703–1057.*

a. Place the data into an ordered array.
b. Set up a stem-and-leaf display for these data.
c. Which of these two displays seems to provide more information? Discuss.
d. Around what value, if any, do the monthly service fees seem to be concentrated? Explain.

9 The following data represent the total fat for burgers and chicken items from a sample of fast-food chains. **FASTFOOD.xls**

Burgers

19 31 34 35 39 39 43

Chicken

7 9 15 16 16 18 22 25 27 33 39

Source: "Quick Bites." Copyright © 2001 by Consumers Union of U.S., Inc. Adapted from Consumer Reports, *March 2001, 46, by permission of Consumers Union U.S., Inc., Yonkers, NY 10703–1057.*

For the burgers and chicken items separately:
a. Place the data into an ordered array.
b. Set up a stem-and-leaf display for these data.
c. Which of these two displays seems to provide more information? Discuss.
d. Compare the burgers and chicken items in terms of the total fat. What conclusions can you make?

2 TABLES AND CHARTS FOR NUMERICAL DATA

The Frequency Distribution

When there are a large number of observations in a data set, it is not easy to present, analyze, and interpret the findings using an ordered array or a stem-and-leaf display. For large data sets, summary tables created by arranging the data into **class groupings** (or categories) provide a more effective presentation. This arrangement of data in tabular form is called a frequency distribution.

Frequency Distribution
A frequency distribution is a summary table in which the data are arranged into numerically ordered class groupings or categories.

When the observations are grouped or condensed into a frequency distribution, the process of data analysis and interpretation becomes more manageable. In constructing a frequency distribution, attention must be given to selecting the appropriate *number* of class groupings for the table, obtaining a suitable *class interval*, or *width* of each class grouping, and establishing the *boundaries* of each class grouping to avoid overlapping.

Selecting the Number of Classes

The number of class groupings used depends on the number of observations in the data. Larger numbers of observations allow for a larger number of class groups. In general, the frequency distribution should have at least five class groupings but no more than 15. If there are insufficient class groupings or if there are too many, little new information is learned.

Range
The range of the data is the numerical difference between the largest value and the smallest value.

Obtaining the Class Intervals

When developing the frequency distribution, each class grouping should have the same width. To determine the **width of a class interval**, the range of the data is divided by the number of class groupings desired.

DETERMINING THE WIDTH OF A CLASS INTERVAL

$$\text{Width of interval} \cong \frac{\text{range}}{\text{number of desired class groupings}} \tag{1}$$

Because there were 158 growth funds sampled, eight class groupings are sufficient. From the ordered array in Table 1, the range is computed as 26.3 – (–6.1) = 32.4. Using Equation (1), the width of the class interval is approximated as follows:

$$\text{Width of interval} \cong \frac{32.4}{8} = 4.05$$

Since it is desirable to have an interval width in units of 5 or 10, the selected interval or width of each class grouping is rounded to 5.0.

Establishing the Boundaries of the Classes

To construct the frequency distribution table, clearly defined **class boundaries** for each class grouping should be established so that the observations can be tallied into the classes. Overlapping of classes must be avoided.

Because the width of each class interval for the 5-year annualized return data has been set at 5.0%, the boundaries of the various class groupings must be established so as to include the entire range of observations. Whenever possible, these boundaries should be chosen to simplify the reading and interpretation of data. Thus, the first class-interval ranges from –10.0% to less than –5%, the second from –5.0% to less than 0.0%, and so on, until they have been tallied into eight classes, each having an interval width of 5.0%, without overlapping. By establishing these boundaries, all 158 observations can be tallied into eight classes as shown in Table 2.

TABLE 2

Frequency distribution of 5-year annualized returns achieved by 158 growth funds

5-Year Annualized Percentage Return	Number of Funds
–10.0 but less than –5.0	1
–5.0 but less than 0.0	3
0.0 but less than 5.0	14
5.0 but less than 10.0	58
10.0 but less than 15.0	61
15.0 but less than 20.0	17
20.0 but less than 25.0	3
25.0 but less than 30.0	1
Total	158

Source: Data are taken from Table 1.

The main advantage of using this summary table is that the major data characteristics can become immediately clear to the reader. For example, Table 2 shows that the *approximate range* in the 5-year annualized returns achieved by these 158 sampled growth funds is from –10.0% to 30.0% and the 5-year annualized returns tend to cluster between 5% and 15%.

Class Midpoint
The class midpoint is the point halfway between the boundaries of each class and is representative of the data within that class.

On the other hand, the major disadvantage of this summary table is that the distribution of the individual values within a particular class interval is unknown without access to the original data. Thus, the three funds in Table 2 whose 5-year annualized returns are between 20.0% and 25.0% could have values distributed throughout the interval, clustered near 20.0%, or clustered near 25.0%. The *class midpoint* (22.5%) is the value used to represent the 5-year annualized returns for all three funds contained in the particular interval. The class midpoint for the interval "−10.0 but less than −5.0" is −7.5%. (The other class midpoints are, respectively, −2.5, 2.5, 7.5, 12.5, 17.5, 22.5, and 27.5%.)

Subjectivity in Selecting Class Boundaries

The selection of class boundaries for frequency distributions is highly subjective. For data sets that do not contain many observations, a particular set of class boundaries may provide a different picture than another set. For example, for the 5-year annualized return data, using a class-interval width of 4.0 instead of 5.0 (as was used in Table 2) may cause shifts in the way in which the observations distribute among the classes. This is particularly true if the number of observations in the data set is not very large.

Such shifts in data concentration do not occur only because the width of the class interval is altered. The interval width may stay at 5.0%, but different lower and upper class boundaries can be chosen. Changing these boundaries can also cause shifts in the way in which the data distribute—especially if the size of the data set is not very large. Fortunately, as the number of observations in a data set increases, alterations in the selection of class boundaries affect the concentration of data less and less.

The Relative Frequency Distribution and the Percentage Distribution

To enhance the analysis of a frequency distribution, either the relative frequency distribution or the percentage distribution can be developed, depending on whether you prefer proportions or percentages. These two equivalent distributions are shown in Table 3.

TABLE 3

Relative frequency distribution and percentage distribution of 5-year annualized returns achieved by 158 growth funds

5-Year Annualized Percentage Return	Proportion of Funds	Percentage of Funds
−10.0 but less than −5.0	0.006	0.6
−5.0 but less than 0.0	0.019	1.9
0.0 but less than 5.0	0.089	8.9
5.0 but less than 10.0	0.367	36.7
10.0 but less than 15.0	0.386	38.6
15.0 but less than 20.0	0.108	10.8
20.0 but less than 25.0	0.019	1.9
25.0 but less than 30.0	0.006	0.6
Total	1.000	100.0

Source: Data are taken from Table 2.

The **relative frequency distribution** is formed by dividing the frequencies in each class of the frequency distribution (see Table 2) by the total number of observations. A **percentage distribution** is then formed by multiplying each relative frequency or proportion by 100.0. Thus, the proportion of growth funds that achieved 5-year annualized returns of 10.0 to under 15.0 is 0.386, and the percentage is 38.6%.

Working with a base of 1 for proportions or 100.0 for percentages is usually more meaningful than using the frequencies themselves. In fact, the use of the relative frequency distribution or percentage distribution becomes essential whenever one set of data is being compared with other sets of data, especially if the number of observations in the sets differ.

To illustrate such a situation, recall that in the Using Statistics scenario at the beginning of the chapter, you wanted to compare the 5-year annualized returns for growth and value mutual funds. Table 4 depicts both the frequency distribution and the percentage distribution of the 5-year annualized returns achieved by the 101 value funds. Note that the class groupings selected in Table 4 match, where possible, those selected in Table 3 for the growth funds.

TABLE 4
Frequency distribution and percentage distribution of 5-year annualized returns achieved by 101 value funds

5-Year Annualized Percentage Return	Number of Funds	Percentage of Funds
−10.0 but less than −5.0	0	0.0
−5.0 but less than 0.0	0	0.0
0.0 but less than 5.0	3	3.0
5.0 but less than 10.0	34	33.7
10.0 but less than 15.0	41	40.6
15.0 but less than 20.0	20	19.8
20.0 but less than 25.0	2	2.0
25.0 but less than 30.0	1	1.0
Total	101	100.0*

*Result differs slightly from 100.0 due to rounding.

With the use of the percentage distributions of Tables 3 and 4, the differences in the 5-year annualized returns achieved by growth funds versus value funds can be compared. There is a difference in the manner in which the two sets of data have distributed based on the following:

1. 10.8% of the growth funds have 5-year annualized returns between −5% and 5%, while 3.0% of the value funds have 5-year annualized returns between −5% and 5%.
2. Only 10.8% of the growth funds have 5-year annualized returns between 15% and 20% as compared to 19.8% of the value funds that have a 5-year annual return between 15% and 20%.

The Cumulative Distribution

A table of cumulative percentages, known as a **cumulative percentage distribution**, is another useful technique for tabulating data. The cumulative distribution and its associated cumulative polygon provide information about sets of data that cannot be obtained from the frequency distribution itself.

Example 2 demonstrates how the cumulative percentage distribution is constructed by using the percentage distribution of 5-year annualized returns achieved by the 158 growth funds.

EXAMPLE 2

FORMING THE CUMULATIVE PERCENTAGE DISTRIBUTION

Using the percentage distribution of Table 3, form the cumulative percentage distribution.

SOLUTION

From Table 5, observe that 0.0% of the 5-year annualized returns in growth funds are less than −10.0%, 0.6% are less than −5.0%, 2.5% are less than 0.0%, and so on, until all (100.0%) of the 5-year annualized returns are less than 30.0%.

TABLE 5
Developing the cumulative percentage distribution

5-Year Annualized Return (in %)	Percentage of Funds in Class Interval	Percentage of Funds Less Than Lower Boundary of Class Interval
−10.0 but less than −5.0	0.6	0.0
−5.0 but less than 0.0	1.9	0.6
0.0 but less than 5.0	8.9	2.5 = 0.6 + 1.9
5.0 but less than 10.0	36.7	11.4 = 0.6 + 1.9 + 8.9
10.0 but less than 15.0	38.6	48.1 = 0.6 + 1.9 + 8.9 + 36.7
15.0 but less than 20.0	10.8	86.7 = 0.6 + 1.9 + 8.9 + 36.7 + 38.6
20.0 but less than 25.0	1.9	97.5 = 0.6 + 1.9 + 8.9 + 36.7 + 38.6 + 10.8
25.0 but less than 30.0	0.6	99.4 = 0.6 + 1.9 + 8.9 + 36.7 + 38.6 + 10.8 + 1.9
30.0 but less than 35.0	0.0	100.0 = 0.6 + 1.9 + 8.9 + 36.7 + 38.6 + 10.8 + 1.9 + 0.6

Table 6 summarizes the cumulative percentages for the 158 growth mutual funds and the 101 value mutual funds.

TABLE 6

Cumulative percentage distributions of 5-year annualized returns achieved by 101 value funds and 158 growth funds

5-Year Annualized Return	Growth Percentage of Funds Less Than Indicated Value	Value Percentage of Funds Less Than Indicated Value
−10.0	0.0	0.0
−5.0	0.6	0.0
0.0	2.5	0.0
5.0	11.4	3.0
10.0	48.1	36.7
15.0	86.7	77.3
20.0	97.5	97.1
25.0	99.4	99.1
30.0	100.0	100.0

Source: Data are taken from Tables 3 and 4.

From Table 6, observe that more of the growth funds have lower 5-year annualized returns than the value funds. Specifically, 48.1% of the growth funds had an annualized return of less than 10%, as compared to 36.7% of the value funds.

Excel Strategies Generating Frequency Distributions for Numerical Data

CHAPTER 2.xls

*Retrieve the Table 2.2 worksheet of the **Chapter 2.xls** workbook to view the frequency distribution similar to one in Table 2.*

You generate frequency distributions for numerical data by using the Data Analysis Histogram procedure and then revising the results to correct for certain errors that the procedure produces. PHStat2 can run this procedure and make the necessary revisions for you as well as offering you extended input options.

One complication using Microsoft Excel is that Excel uses "bins," groups formed from the ordered list of maximum class values placed in a "bins cell range." To create class boundaries in the form *a* but less than *b*, used in Table 2 and throughout this text, you must place values in the bins cell range that are slightly less than the *b* values. For example, for the interval "5.0 but less than 10.0," you would enter a value such as 9.99 in order to approximate the interval. For the interval "−10.0 but less than −5.0," you would enter a value such as −5.01.

Values to produce a frequency distribution similar to Table 2 have already been placed in column C of the **5YrData worksheet.*

For example, to generate a frequency distribution shown in Table 2, open the **Growth Funds Sample.xls** workbook to the **5YrData** worksheet* and use one of these strategies:

Using Excel with PHStat2

Use the PHStat2 Frequency Distribution procedure to generate a frequency distribution on a new worksheet for the data of the **5YrData** worksheet.

Select **PHStat | Descriptive Statistics | Frequency Distribution**.

In the Frequency Distribution dialog box (shown at right):

Enter **B1:B159** in the **Variable Cell Range** edit box.

Enter **C1:C10** in the **Bins Cell Range** edit box.

Select the **First cell in each range contains label** check box.

Select the **Single Group Variable** option button.

Enter a title in the **Title** edit box.

Click the **OK** button.

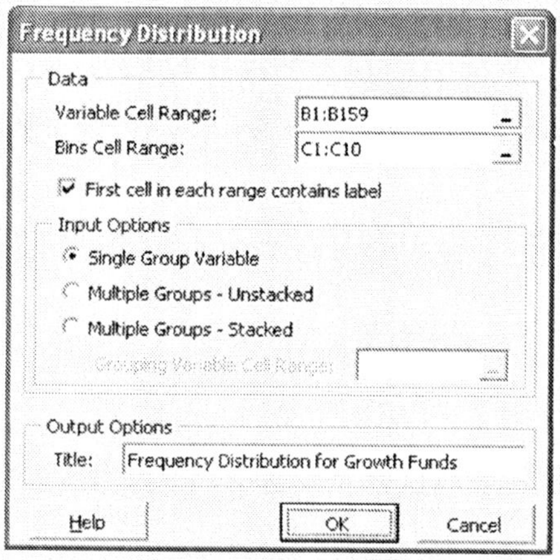

Using Excel
Select **Tools | Data Analysis** and then select **Histogram** from the list box in the Data Analysis dialog box and click the **OK** button to begin the procedure. In the Histogram dialog box that appears, enter **B1:B159** as the **Input Range** and **C1:C10** as the **Bin Range**. Select the **Labels** check box and **New Worksheet Ply** option button and enter a new worksheet name. Select the **Cumulative Percentage** check box to add cumulative percentages. Click the **OK** button. To correct the mistakes Excel makes, follow the instructions of section EH1 of the Excel Handbook at the end of this chapter. (Section EH1 also presents a design for a frequency distribution worksheet that dynamically changes the frequency counts as the underlying raw data change.)

The Histogram

Histogram
A histogram is a chart in which the rectangular bars are constructed at the boundaries of each class.

Consistent with the saying "a picture is worth a thousand words," graphic techniques are often used instead of tables to describe sets of data. One type of graph, the histogram, is used to describe numerical data that have been grouped into frequency, relative frequency, or percentage distributions.

FIGURE 2
Histogram obtained from Microsoft Excel of the 5-year annualized return of growth funds

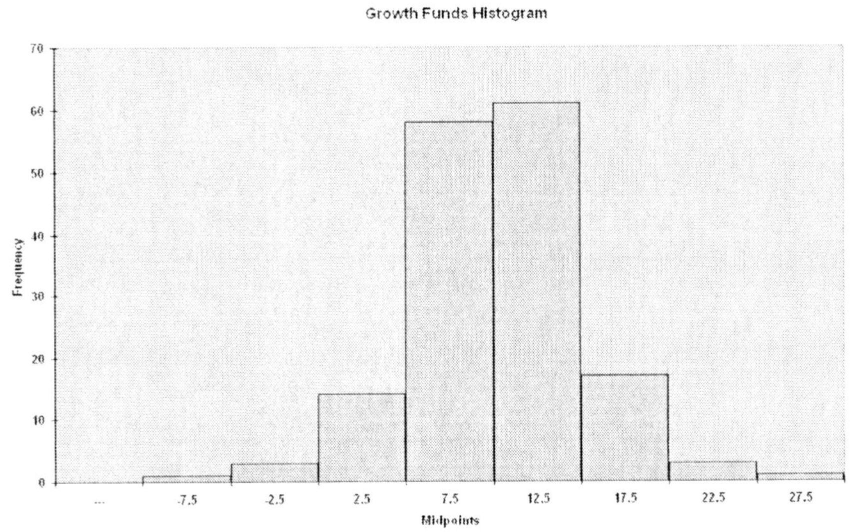

When plotting a histogram, the variable of interest is displayed along the horizontal (X) axis. The vertical (Y) axis represents the number, proportion, or percentage of observations per class interval.

A frequency histogram obtained from Microsoft Excel of the 5-year annualized returns achieved by the 158 growth funds is presented in Figure 2. Note that there is a strong concentration of funds with a return between 5% and 15% and little concentration of funds in the other class groupings.

When comparing two or more sets of data, constructing stem-and-leaf displays or histograms on the same graph is difficult and confusing. For a histogram, superimposing the vertical bars of one histogram on another histogram would cause difficulty in interpretation. For cases where there are two or more groups to compare, constructing relative frequency or percentage polygons is necessary.

The Polygon

As with histograms, when plotting polygons, the variable of interest is displayed along the horizontal axis. The vertical axis represents the number, proportion, or percentage of observations per class interval.

Percentage Polygon
The percentage polygon is formed by having the midpoint of each class represent the data in that class and then connecting the sequence of midpoints at their respective class percentages.

Figure 3 shows the percentage polygons obtained from Microsoft Excel for the 5-year annualized returns achieved by the 158 growth funds and the 101 value funds. The differences in the structure of the two distributions, previously discussed when comparing Tables 3 and 4, are indicated here. Although both the growth and value funds have annualized returns that are concentrated between 5% and 15%, observe that there is a much greater percentage of value funds between 15% and 20%. In contrast, the growth funds are spread out over a wider range of the distribution.

FIGURE 3
Percentage polygons obtained from Microsoft Excel of the 5-year annualized return of growth and value funds

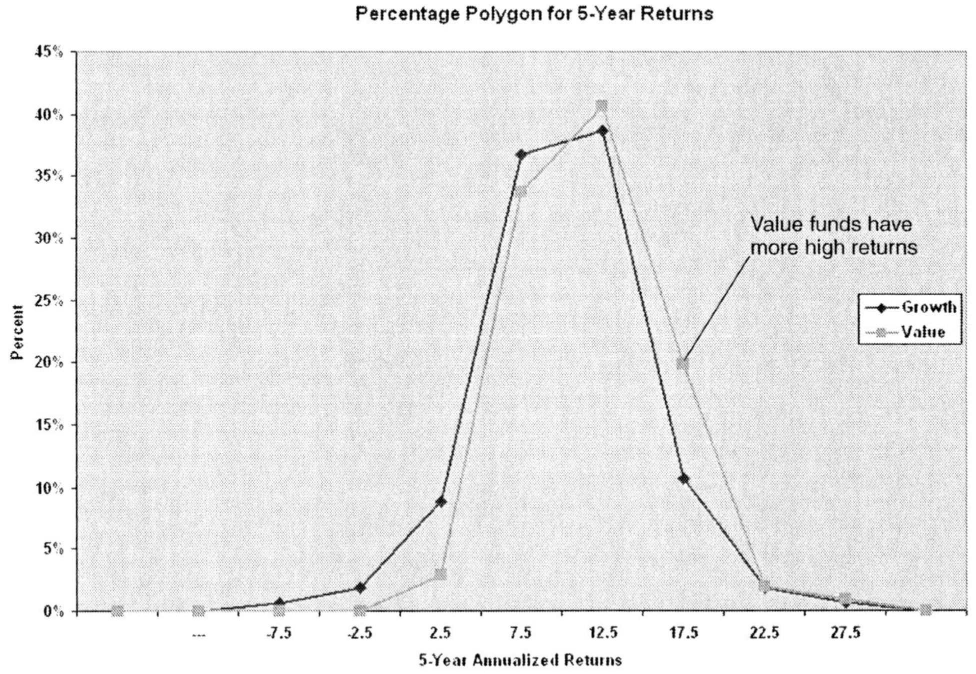

Polygon Construction Notice that the polygon in Figure 3 has points whose values on the X axis represent the midpoint of the class interval. For example, observe the points plotted on the X axis at 17.5%. The point for the value funds (the higher one) represents the fact that 19.8% of these funds have 5-year annualized percentage returns between 15% and 20%. The point for the growth funds (the lower one) represents the fact that 10.8% of these funds have 5-year annualized returns between 15% and 20%. Notice, too, that when polygons or histograms are constructed, the vertical axis should show the true zero or "origin" so as not to distort or otherwise misrepresent the character of the data. Depending on the data, the horizontal axis, however, does not need to specify the zero point for the variable of interest. For aesthetic reasons, the range of the variable should constitute the major portion of the chart.

The Cumulative Percentage Polygon (Ogive)

The **cumulative percentage polygon**, or **ogive**, is a graphic representation of a cumulative percentage distribution. When plotting cumulative polygons, the variable of interest is displayed along the X axis, and the Y axis represents the percentage of cumulated observations.

To construct a cumulative percentage polygon (also known as an ogive), note that the variable of interest—5-year annualized returns—is plotted on the horizontal axis, while the cumulative percentages (from the "less than" column) are plotted on the vertical axis.

Figure 4 illustrates the cumulative percentage polygons obtained from Microsoft Excel of the 5-year annualized returns achieved by the 158 growth funds and the 101 value funds. The lower limits of the classes are noted on the X axis. Thus, for example, for the growth funds, 48.1% had a 5-year annualized return of less than 10%, while for the value funds the percentage was 36.7%. Note that for a 5-year annualized return up to 20%, the growth funds curve is to the left of the value funds ogive. However, similar percentages of the two types of funds appear to have returns greater than 20%.

FIGURE 4
Cumulative percentage polygons obtained from Microsoft Excel of the 5-year annualized returns of growth and value funds

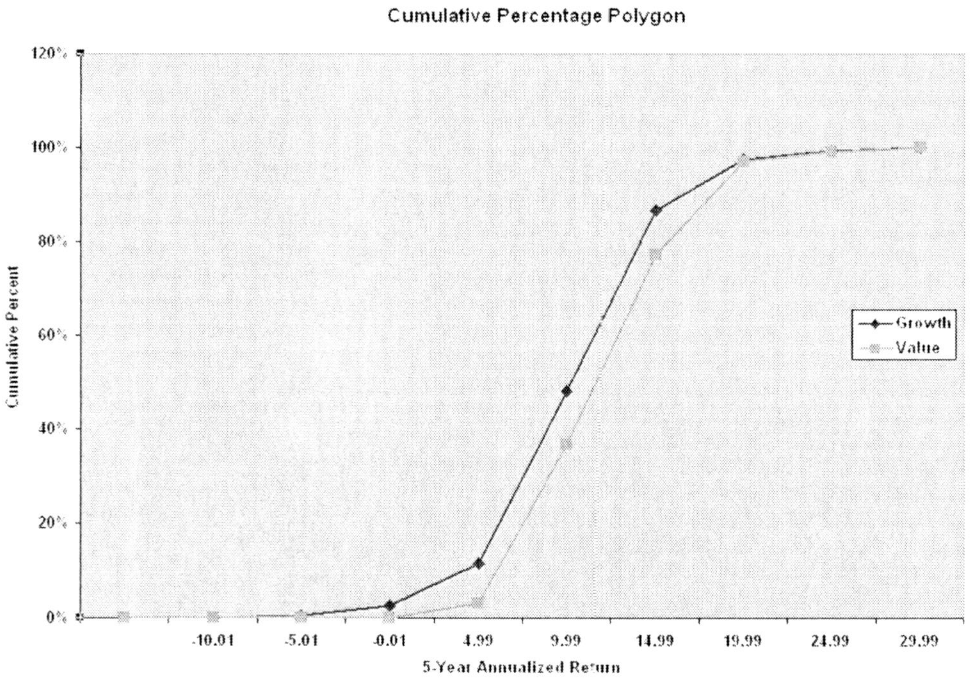

Excel Strategies Generating Histograms and Polygons for Numerical Data

CHAPTER 2.xls

Retrieve the Figure 2.2, Figure 2.3, and Figure 2.4 chart sheets of the ***Chapter 2.xls*** *workbook to view the graphs shown in Figures 2, 3, and 4.*

You generate histograms and polygons, along with their supporting frequency distributions, by using the combination of the Data Analysis Histogram procedure and the Chart Wizard and then revising the results to correct for certain errors that Excel makes. PHStat2 can execute this combination and make the necessary revisions for you as well as generate polygons for different groups in one step. (If necessary, review the "Excel Strategies" for generating frequency distributions to understand the differences between classes and bins before continuing.)

For example, to generate histograms and polygons for the growth and value funds, similar to Figures 2 through 4, and above, open the **Chapter 2.xls** workbook to the **ComparativeData** worksheet and use one of these strategies:

Using Excel with PHStat2

Use the PHStat2 Histogram & Polygons procedure to generate a histogram and polygons on new sheets.

Select **PHStat | Descriptive Statistics | Histogram & Polygons**.

In the Histogram & Polygons dialog box (shown at right):

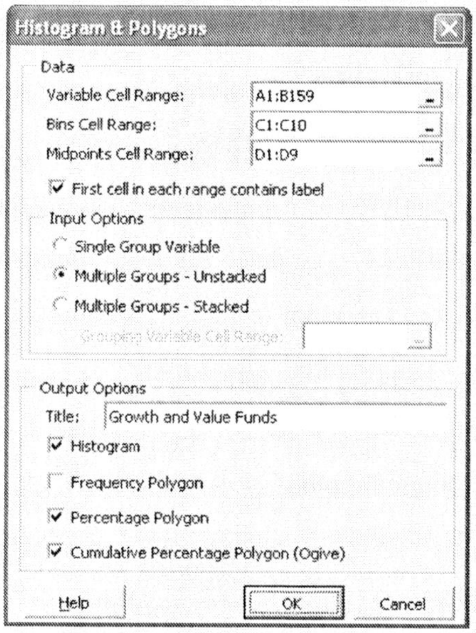

Enter **A1:B159** in the **Variable Cell Range** edit box.

Enter **C1:C10** in the **Bins Cell Range** edit box.

Enter **D1:D9** in the **Midpoints Cell Range** edit box.

Select the **First cell in each range** contains label check box.

Select the **Multiple Groups-Unstacked** option button.

Enter a title in the **Title** edit box.

Leave selected the **Histogram** check box.

Select the **Percentage Polygon** and **Cumulative Percentage Polygon (Ogive)** check boxes. Click the **OK** button.

Using Excel

Generate Histogram Task. Use the Histogram procedure twice to generate histograms for the growth and value funds. Select **Tools | Data Analysis** and then select **Histogram** from the list box in the Data Analysis dialog box and click the **OK** button to begin the procedure. In the Histogram dialog box that appears, enter **A1:A159** as the **Input Range** and **C1:C10** as the **Bin Range**. Select the **Labels** check box and **New Worksheet Ply** option button and enter a new worksheet name. Select the **Cumulative Percentage** and **Chart Output** check boxes. Click the **OK** button. Repeat instructions for the Value funds, using **B1:B102** as the **Input Range**.

Finish this task by applying the instructions of section EH3 to both pairs of frequency distributions and histograms generated by the Histogram procedure. *Note:* If you have already created a frequency distribution table, use the instructions of section EH4 to generate a histogram.

Generate Polygons Task. Use the instructions of section EH5 at the end of this chapter to use the Chart Wizard to produce frequency, percentage, or cumulative percentage polygons.

PROBLEMS FOR SECTION 2

Learning the Basics

10 The values for a set of data vary from 11.6 to 97.8.

a. Indicate the class boundaries of nine classes into which these values can be grouped.

b. What class-interval width did you choose?

c. What are the nine class midpoints?

11 In constructing an ogive (i.e., a cumulative percentage polygon) pertaining to the GMAT scores from a sample of 50 applicants to an MBA program, it was noted from a previously obtained frequency distribution that none of the applicants scored below 450 and that the frequency distribution was formed by choosing class intervals 450 to 500, 500 to 550, and so on, with the last class grouping, being 700 to 750. If two applicants scored in the interval 450 to 500 and 16 applicants scored in the interval 500 to 550:

a. What percentage of applicants scored below 500?

b. What percentage of applicants scored below 550?

c. What percentage of applicants scored between 500 and 550?

d. How many applicants scored between 500 and 550?

e. What percentage of applicants scored below 750?

Applying the Concepts

Problems 12–16 can be solved manually or by using Microsoft Excel.

12 The data displayed here represent the electricity cost during the month of July 2003 for a random sample of 50 one-bedroom apartments in a large city. **UTILITY.xls**

Raw Data on Utility Charges ($)

96	171	202	178	147	102	153	197	127	82
157	185	90	116	172	111	148	213	130	165
141	149	206	175	123	128	144	168	109	167
95	163	150	154	130	143	187	166	139	149
108	119	183	151	114	135	191	137	129	158

a. Form a frequency distribution that has
(1) five class intervals.
(2) six class intervals.
(3) seven class intervals.

(*Hint:* To help decide how best to set up the class boundaries, you should first place the raw data either in a stem-and-leaf display (by letting the leaves be the trailing digits) or in an ordered array.)

b. Form a frequency distribution that has seven class intervals with the upper class limits $99, $119, and so on.
c. Form the percentage distribution from the frequency distribution developed in part (b).
d. Plot the percentage histogram.
e. Plot the percentage polygon.
f. Form the cumulative frequency distribution.
g. Form the cumulative percentage distribution.
h. Plot the ogive (cumulative percentage polygon).
i. Around what amount does the monthly electricity cost seem to be concentrated?
j. Which of the graphs do you think is best for presenting the distribution of electricity cost? Explain.

13 The ordered arrays in the accompanying table deal with the lengths of life (in hours) of a sample of forty 100-watt lightbulbs produced by manufacturer A and a sample of forty 100-watt lightbulbs produced by manufacturer B: **BULBS.xls**

Manufacturer A					Manufacturer B				
684	697	720	773	821	819	836	888	897	903
831	835	848	852	852	907	912	918	942	943
859	860	868	870	876	952	959	962	986	992
893	899	905	909	911	994	1,004	1,005	1,007	1,015
922	924	926	926	938	1,016	1,018	1,020	1,022	1,034
939	943	946	954	971	1,038	1,072	1,077	1,077	1,082
972	977	984	1,005	1,014	1,096	1,100	1,113	1,113	1,116
1,016	1,041	1,052	1,080	1,093	1,153	1,154	1,174	1,188	1,230

a. Form the frequency distribution for each brand using the following class-interval widths of 100 hours for each distribution.
(1) Manufacturer A: 650 but less than 750, 750 but less than 850, and so on.
(2) Manufacturer B: 750 but less than 850, 850 but less than 950, and so on.
b. Change the class-interval width in (a) to 50 so that you have intervals from 650 to under 700, 700 to under 750, 750 to under 800, and so on. Comment on the results of these changes.
c. Form the percentage distributions from the frequency distributions developed in (a).
d. Plot the percentage histograms on separate graphs.
e. Plot the percentage polygons on one graph.
f. Form the cumulative frequency distributions.
g. Form the cumulative percentage distributions.
h. Plot the ogives on one graph.
i. Which manufacturer has bulbs with a longer life—manufacturer A or manufacturer B? Explain.

14 Given the following stem-and-leaf display representing the amount of gasoline purchased in gallons (with leaves in 10ths of gallons) for a sample of 25 cars that use a particular service station on the New Jersey Turnpike:

9	147
10	02238
11	135566777
12	223489
13	02

a. Construct a frequency distribution and a percentage distribution.
b. Form the cumulative frequency distribution and the cumulative percentage distribution.
c. Plot the percentage histogram.
d. Plot the percentage polygon.
e. Plot the ogive (cumulative percentage polygon).
f. Around what amount of gasoline do most of the purchases seem to be concentrated?

15 The following data represent the amount of soft drink in a sample of 50 consecutive 2-liter bottles. The results, listed horizontally in the order of being filled, were: **DRINK.xls**

2.109	2.086	2.066	2.075	2.065	2.057	2.052	2.044	2.036	2.038
2.031	2.029	2.025	2.029	2.023	2.020	2.015	2.014	2.013	2.014
2.012	2.012	2.012	2.010	2.005	2.003	1.999	1.996	1.997	1.992
1.994	1.986	1.984	1.981	1.973	1.975	1.971	1.969	1.966	1.967
1.963	1.957	1.951	1.951	1.947	1.941	1.941	1.938	1.908	1.894

a. Construct a stem-and-leaf display.
b. Construct the frequency distribution and the percentage distribution.
c. Plot the frequency histogram.
d. Plot the percentage polygon.

e. Form the cumulative percentage distribution.
f. Plot the cumulative percentage polygon.
g. On the basis of the results of (a) through (f), does there appear to be any concentration of the amount of soft drink filled in the bottles around specific values?
h. If you had to make a prediction of the amount of soft drink filled in the next bottle, what would you predict? Why?

16 One operation of a mill is to cut pieces of steel into parts that will later be used as the frame for front seats in an automotive plant. The steel is cut with a diamond saw and requires the resulting parts to be within ±0.005 inch of the length specified by the automobile company. The data in the file **STEEL.xls** comes from a sample of 100 steel parts. The measurement reported is the difference in inches between the actual length of the steel part, as measured by a laser measurement device, and the specified length of the steel part. For example, the first observation, –0.002, represents a steel part that is 0.002 inch shorter than the specified length.
a. Construct the frequency distribution and the percentage distribution.
b. Plot the percentage histogram.
c. Plot the percentage polygon.
d. Plot the cumulative percentage polygon.
e. Is the steel mill doing a good job in meeting the requirements set by the automobile company? Explain.

17 The data in the file **ENERGY.xls** contains the per capita energy consumption in kilowatt hours for each of the 50 states and the District of Columbia during a recent year.
a. Construct the frequency distribution and the percentage distribution.
b. Plot the percentage histogram.
c. Plot the percentage polygon.
d. Construct the cumulative percentage distribution.
e. Plot the cumulative percentage polygon.
f. Around what amount does the per capita energy consumption seem to be concentrated?
g. Which of the graphs do you think is best in presenting the distribution of per capita energy consumption? Explain.

3 GRAPHING BIVARIATE NUMERICAL DATA

Bivariate Numerical Data Bivariate numerical data consists of paired observations taken from two numerical variables.

When analyzing a numerical variable such as 5-year annualized returns, the histogram, the polygon, and the cumulative percentage polygon developed in section 2 are the appropriate graphical tools to use. When working with bivariate numerical data, a **scatter diagram** is a graphical tool used to examine possible relationships between the two numerical variables. For example, a marketing analyst could study the effectiveness of advertising by comparing weekly sales volumes and weekly advertising expenditures. Or, a human resources director interested in the salary structure of the company could compare the employees' years of experience with their current salaries.

To demonstrate a scatter diagram, the relationship between mutual fund returns in 2001 and the 5-year returns can be studied. For each mutual fund, the 5-year return is plotted on the vertical Y axis, and the 2001 return is plotted on the horizontal X axis. Figure 5 represents output obtained from Microsoft Excel for these two variables.

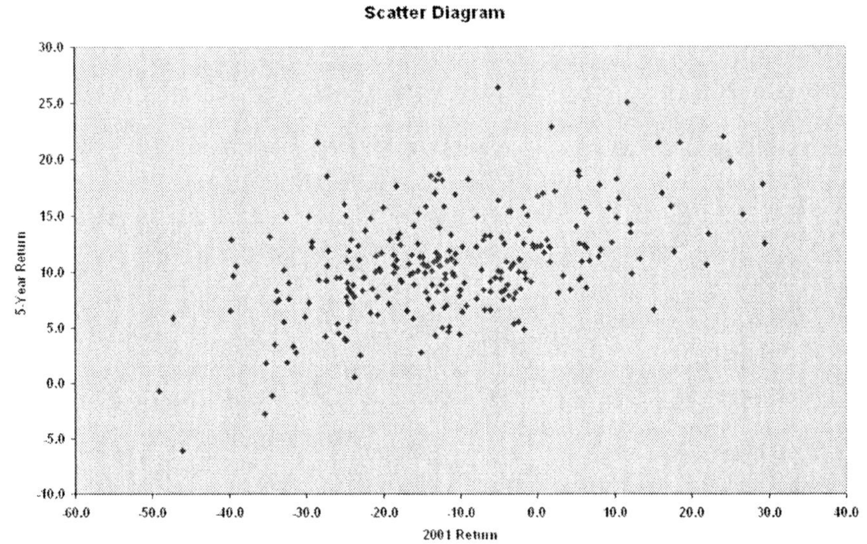

FIGURE 5
Scatter diagram obtained from Microsoft Excel of 5-year returns and returns during 2001

Although there is a great deal of variation in the returns of the mutual funds, there appears to be an increasing (positive) relationship between the 2001 return and the 5-year return. In other words, funds that provided higher returns in 2001 appear to also provide higher 5-year returns. Other pairs of variables may have a decreasing (negative) relationship in which one variable decreases as the other increases. The scatter diagram will be revisited when the coefficient of correlation is considered, and when regression analysis is developed.

Excel Strategy Generating Scatter Diagrams

CHAPTER 2.xls

*Retrieve the Figure 2.5 worksheet of the **Chapter 2.xls** workbook to view the scatter diagram similar to the one in Figure 5.*

Use the Chart Wizard to generate a scatter diagram on a new chart sheet. For example, to generate the scatter diagram shown in Figure 5, open the **Mutual Funds.xls** workbook to the **Data** worksheet, select **Insert | Chart** and make these entries in the Chart Wizard dialog boxes:

Step 1 dialog box. (shown at right) Select the **Standard Types** tab and then select **XY (Scatter)** from the **Chart type** list box. Select the first (top) **Chart sub-type** choice, labeled as **Scatter. Compares pairs of values.** And click the **Next** button.

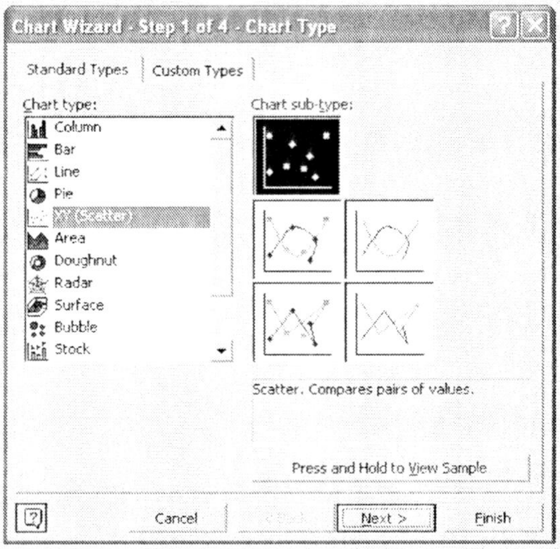

Step 2 dialog box. Select the **Data Range** tab. Enter **G1:G260, I1:I260** in the **Data range** edit box. Select the **Columns** option button in the **Series in** group and click **Next**.*

When you enter the cell range **G1:G260, I1:I260, be sure to include the comma as part of your entry.*

Step 3 dialog box. Select the **Titles** tab. Enter **Scatter Diagram** as the **Chart title**, **2001 Return** in the **Value (X) axis** edit box, and **5-Year Return** in the **Value (Y) axis** edit box. Select, in turn, the **Axes**, **Gridlines**, **Legend**, and **Data Table** tabs and adjust settings as discussed in Exhibit EP2 in the Excel Primer. Click **Next**.

Step 4 dialog box. Select the **As new sheet** option button, enter a descriptive chart sheet name, and click the **Finish** button to generate the chart.

The scatter diagram generated has axes drawn over data points and not on the edges of the graph as shown in Figure 5. To relocate the axes, follow the instructions of section EH6 at the end of this chapter.

The Chart Wizard assumes that the first column of the cell range entered in the Step 2 dialog box is the X variable data. Should you have other data in which the Y variable data appears first, rearrange your data by copying and pasting the columns, in the proper order, to a new worksheet before using the Wizard.

PROBLEMS FOR SECTION 3

Learning the Basics

18 The following is a set of data from a sample of $n = 11$ items:

X	7	5	8	3	6	10	12	4	9	15	18
Y	21	15	24	9	18	30	36	12	27	45	54

a. Plot the scatter diagram.
b. Is there a relationship between X and Y? Explain.

19 The following is a series of real annual sales (in millions of constant 1995 dollars) over an 11-year period (1992 to 2002):

Year	1992	1993	1994	1995	1996	1997	1998	1999	2000	2001	2002
Sales	13.0	17.0	19.0	20.0	20.5	20.5	20.5	20.0	19.0	17.0	13.0

a. Construct a scatter diagram with year as the X axis.
b. Does there appear to be any change in real annual sales over time? Explain.

Applying the Concepts

We recommend that Microsoft Excel be used to solve Problems 20–26.

20 The data in the file **REFRIGERATOR.xls** represent the approximate retail price (in $) and the energy cost per year (in $) of 15 top-freezer refrigerators.

Source: "Refrigerators." Copyright © 2002 by Consumers Union of U.S., Inc. Adapted from Consumer Reports, *August 2002, 26, by permission of Consumers Union U.S., Inc., Yonkers, NY 10703–1057.*

a. With energy cost on the X axis and price on the Y axis, set up a scatter diagram.
b. Does there appear to be a relationship between price and energy cost? If so, is the relationship positive or negative?
c. Would you expect the higher-priced refrigerators to have the greatest energy efficiency? Is this borne out by the data?

21 The following data **SECURITY.xls** represent the turnover rate of pre-boarding screeners at airports in 1998–1999 and the security violations detected per million passengers.

City	Turnover	Violations
St. Louis	416	11.9
Atlanta	375	7.3
Houston	237	10.6
Boston	207	22.9
Chicago	200	6.5
Denver	193	15.2
Dallas	156	18.2
Baltimore	155	21.7
Seattle/Tacoma	140	31.5
San Francisco	110	20.7
Orlando	100	9.9
Washington-Dulles	90	14.8
Log Angeles	88	25.1
Detroit	79	13.5
San Juan	70	10.3
Miami	64	13.1
New York-JFK	53	30.1
Washington-Reagan	47	31.8
Honolulu	37	14.9

Source: Alan B. Krueger, "A Small Dose of Common Sense Would Help Congress Break the Gridlock over Airport Security," The New York Times, *November 15, 2001, C2.*

a. Set up a scatter diagram with turnover rate of pre-boarding screeners on the X axis and security violations detected on the Y axis.
b. What conclusions can you reach about the relationship between the turnover rate of pre-boarding screeners and the security violations detected?

22 The following data **CELLPHONE.xls** represents the digital-mode talk time in hours and the battery capacity in milliampere-hours of cellphones.

Talk Time	Battery Capacity	TALK Time	Battery Capacity
4.50	800	1.50	450
4.00	1500	2.25	900
3.00	1300	2.25	900
2.00	1550	3.25	900
2.75	900	2.25	700
1.75	875	2.25	800
1.75	750	2.50	800
2.25	1100	2.25	900
1.75	850	2.00	900

Source: "Service Shortcomings." Copyright © 2002 by Consumers Union of U.S., Inc. Adapted from Consumer Reports, *February 2002, 25, by permission of Consumers Union U.S., Inc., Yonkers, NY 10703–1057.*

a. Set up a scatter diagram with battery capacity on the X axis and digital-mode talk time on the Y axis.
b. What conclusions can you reach about the relationship between the battery capacity and the digital-mode talk time?
c. You would expect the cellphones with higher battery capacity to have a higher talk time. Is this borne out by the data?

23 The data in the file **BATTERIES2.xls** represent the price and cold-cranking amps (which denotes the starting current the battery can deliver) of automobile batteries.

Source: "Leading the Charge." Copyright 2001 by Consumers Union of U.S., Inc. Adapted from Consumer Reports, *October 2001, 25, by permission of Consumers Union U.S., Inc., Yonkers, NY 10703–1057.*

a. Set up a scatter diagram with cold-cranking amps on the X axis and price on the Y axis.
b. What conclusions can you reach about the relationship between the cold-cranking amps and the price?
c. You would expect the batteries with higher cold-cranking amps to have a higher price. Is this borne out by the data?

24 The S&P 500 Index attempts to track the overall movement of the stock market by considering the stock price of 500 large corporations. The data file **STOCKS02.xls** contains weekly data for this index as well as the weekly closing stock price for three companies during 2002. The variables included are:

WEEK = Week ending on date given
S&P = Weekly closing value for the S&P 500 Index
SEARS = Weekly closing stock price for Sears, Roebuck and Company
TARGET = Weekly closing stock price for the Target Corporation
SARA LEE = Weekly closing stock price for the Sara Lee Corporation

Source: ***www.finance.yahoo.com/?u***

a. Plot the weekly closing values of the S&P 500 index on the Y axis in a scatter diagram with week on the X axis.
b. Explain any patterns present in the plot.
c. Plot the weekly closing stock prices for Sears, Roebuck and Company on the Y axis in a scatter diagram with week on the X axis.
d. Explain any patterns present in the plot. Compare your results to (b).
e. Plot the weekly closing stock prices for the Target Corporation on the Y axis in a scatter diagram with week on the X axis.
f. Explain any patterns present in the plot. Compare your results to (b).
g. Plot the weekly closing stock prices for the Sara Lee Corporation.
h. Explain any patterns present in the plot. Compare your results to (b).
i. Write a short summary of your findings.

25 The U.S. Bureau of Labor Statistics compiles data on a wide variety of workforce issues. The following table gives the monthly seasonally adjusted civilian unemployment rate for the United States from 1997 to 2002. **UERATE.xls**

Seasonally Adjusted U.S. Unemployment Rate (in %)

Month	1997	1998	1999	2000	2001	2002
January	5.3	4.7	4.3	4.0	4.2	5.6
February	5.3	4.6	4.4	4.1	4.2	5.6
March	5.2	4.7	4.2	4.0	4.3	5.7
April	5.0	4.3	4.3	4.0	4.5	5.9
May	4.9	4.4	4.2	4.1	4.4	5.8
June	5.0	4.5	4.3	4.0	4.5	5.8
July	4.8	4.5	4.3	4.0	4.5	5.8
August	4.8	4.5	4.2	4.1	4.9	5.8
September	4.9	4.5	4.2	3.9	4.9	5.7
October	4.7	4.5	4.1	3.9	5.4	5.8
November	4.6	4.4	4.1	4.0	5.6	5.9
December	4.7	4.4	4.1	4.0	5.8	6.0

Source: ***www.fedstats.gov.***

a. Plot the U.S. unemployment rate on the Y axis in a scatter diagram with month (in sequential order) on the X axis.
b. Does there appear to be any pattern?

26 The following data **DRINK.xls** represent the amount of soft drink filled in a sample of 50 consecutive 2-liter bottles. The results, listed horizontally in the order of being filled, were:

2.109	2.086	2.066	2.075	2.065	2.057	2.052	2.044	2.036	2.038
2.031	2.029	2.025	2.029	2.023	2.020	2.015	2.014	2.013	2.014
2.012	2.012	2.012	2.010	2.005	2.003	1.999	1.996	1.997	1.992
1.994	1.986	1.984	1.981	1.973	1.975	1.971	1.969	1.966	1.967
1.963	1.957	1.951	1.951	1.947	1.941	1.941	1.938	1.908	1.894

a. Plot the amount of soft drink on the Y axis and the bottle number (going consecutively from 1 to 50) on the X axis.
b. What pattern, if any, is present in the data?
c. If you had to make a prediction of the amount of soft drink filled in the next bottle, what would you predict?
d. Compare your prediction in (c) to the prediction made in problem 15 (h). Which one do you think is most likely to be correct? Why?

4 TABLES AND CHARTS FOR CATEGORICAL DATA

Thus far in this chapter, tables and charts have been used to organize and present numerical data. Often, however, the data collected are categorical, not numerical. In this and the following section, the organization and presentation of categorical data in the form of tables and charts will be studied.

Suppose once again that various features of the set of mutual funds are to be evaluated. In addition to annualized returns, the data set contains information on the risk of the mutual fund, classified either as very low, low, average, high, and very high. When dealing with categorical variables, first the observations are tallied into summary tables and then they are graphically displayed as bar charts, pie charts, or Pareto diagrams.

The Summary Table

A **summary table** for categorical data is similar to a frequency distribution table for numerical data (see section 2). To illustrate the development of a summary table, consider the data obtained on the risk level of a fund. When tallying the data, observe that of the 259 mutual funds, 6 are very low-risk funds, 76 are low-risk funds, 82 are average-risk funds, 80 are high-risk funds, and 15 are very high-risk funds (see Table 7).

TABLE 7
Frequency and percentage summary table pertaining to risk level for 259 mutual funds

Fund Risk Level	Number of Funds	Percentage of Funds %
Very low	6	2.32
Low	76	29.34
Average	82	31.66
High	80	30.89
Very high	15	5.79
Total	259	100.00

The Bar Chart

To express the risk level information provided in Table 7 graphically, a frequency bar chart is displayed. Figure 6 depicts a frequency bar chart obtained from Microsoft Excel for data presented in Table 7. In a **bar chart**, each category is depicted by a bar, the length of which represents the frequency or percentage of observations falling into a category. From Figure 6, observe that the bar chart allows the direct comparison of the number of funds in terms of the level of risk. Note that 82 of the funds have an average risk level and 80 of the funds have a high-risk level. Only six funds have a very low-risk level.

FIGURE 6
Bar chart obtained from Microsoft Excel of risk level

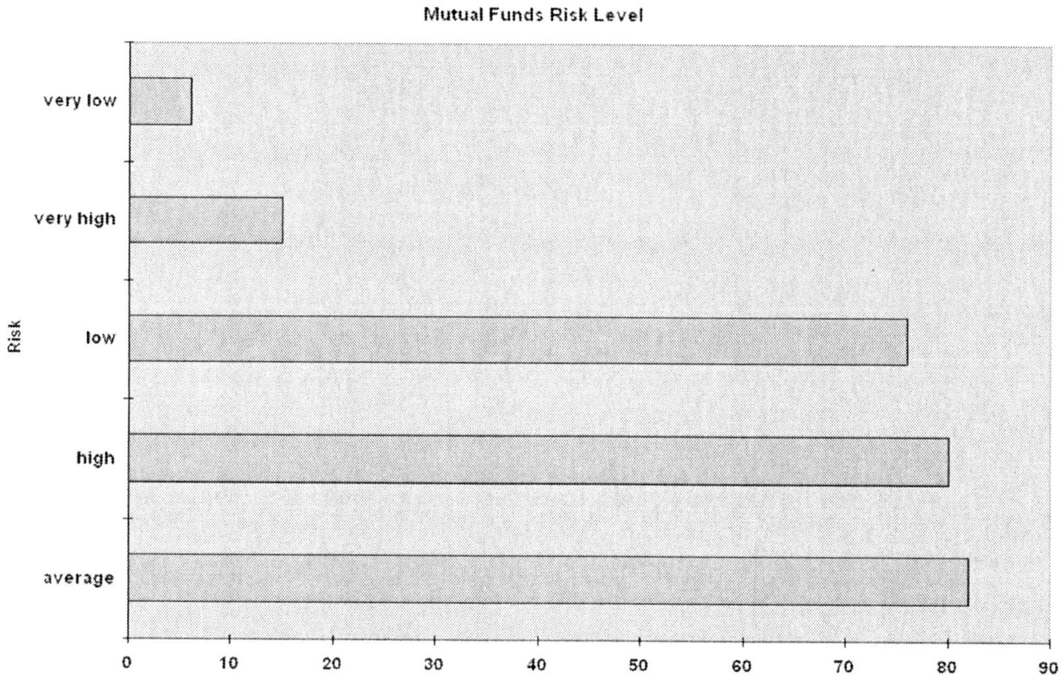

The Pie Chart

Another widely used graphical display to visually express categorical data from a summary table is the **pie chart**. Figure 7 depicts a pie chart for the risk level data presented in Table 7.

The pie chart is based on the fact that the circle has 360°. The pie is divided into slices according to the percentage in each category. As an example, in Table 7, 29.34% of the mutual funds sampled are classified as low-risk funds. Thus, in constructing the pie chart, 360° is multiplied by 0.2934, resulting in a sector that takes up 105.6° of the 360° of the circle. From Figure 7, observe that the pie chart lets you visualize the portion of the entire pie that is in each category. Observe that average-risk funds take more than 30% of the pie and very high-risk funds comprise only 6%.

The purpose of graphical presentation is to display data accurately and clearly. Figures 6 and 7 attempt to convey the same information with respect to fund risk level. Whether these charts succeed, however, is a matter of much concern (see references 1–3, 6, 7). In particular, some research in the human perception of graphs (reference 3) concludes that the pie chart presents a weaker display.

The bar chart is preferred to the pie chart because it has been observed that the human eye can more accurately judge length comparisons against a fixed scale (as in a bar chart) than angular measures (as in a pie chart). Note that in Figure 7 it is not easy to determine whether the low, average, or high risk category is bigger, whereas in Figure 6 you can see that the average-risk category is larger than either the low-risk or high-risk categories.

FIGURE 7

Pie chart obtained from Microsoft Excel of risk level

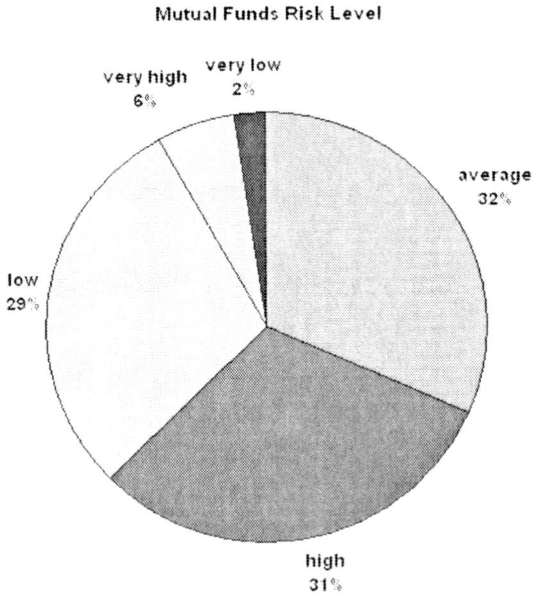

On the other hand, the pie chart clearly shows that the total for all categories adds to 100%. Thus, the selection of a particular chart is subjective and is often dependent on the intention of the user. If a comparison of categories is most important, it is best to use a bar chart. If observing the portion of the whole that is in a particular category is most important, it is best to use a pie chart.

The Pareto Diagram

A graphical device for portraying categorical data that often provides more visual information than either the bar chart or the pie chart is the Pareto diagram. This is particularly true as the number of classifications or groupings for the categorical variable of interest increases. The **Pareto diagram** is a special type of vertical bar chart in which the categorized responses are plotted in the descending rank order of their frequencies and combined with a cumulative polygon on the same graph. The main principle behind this graphical device is its ability to separate the "vital few" from the "trivial many," enabling you to focus on the important categories. Thus, the Pareto diagram achieves its greatest utility when the categorical variable of interest contains many categories. The Pareto diagram is widely used in analyzing process and product quality.

To illustrate the Pareto diagram, observe that in Figure 6 the bar chart presents the categories in terms of risk level. A Pareto diagram is formed by ordering the funds according to the most frequently occurring risk level. The Pareto diagram obtained from Microsoft Excel is depicted in Figure 8. From the lengths of the vertical bars, observe that about 32% of the funds are classified as average risk. From the cumulative polygon, note that 62.55% of these funds are classified either as average-risk or high-risk funds.

In the construction of a Pareto diagram, the vertical axis on the left contains the frequencies or percentages, the vertical axis on the right contains the cumulative percentages (from 100 on top to 0 on bottom), and the horizontal axis contains the categories of interest. The equally spaced bars are of equal width. The point on the cumulative percentage polygon for each category is centered at the midpoint of each respective bar. When studying a Pareto diagram, the focus is on two things: the magnitudes of the differences in bar lengths corresponding to adjacent descending categories and the cumulative percentages of these adjacent categories.

FIGURE 8
Pareto diagram obtained from Microsoft Excel of risk level

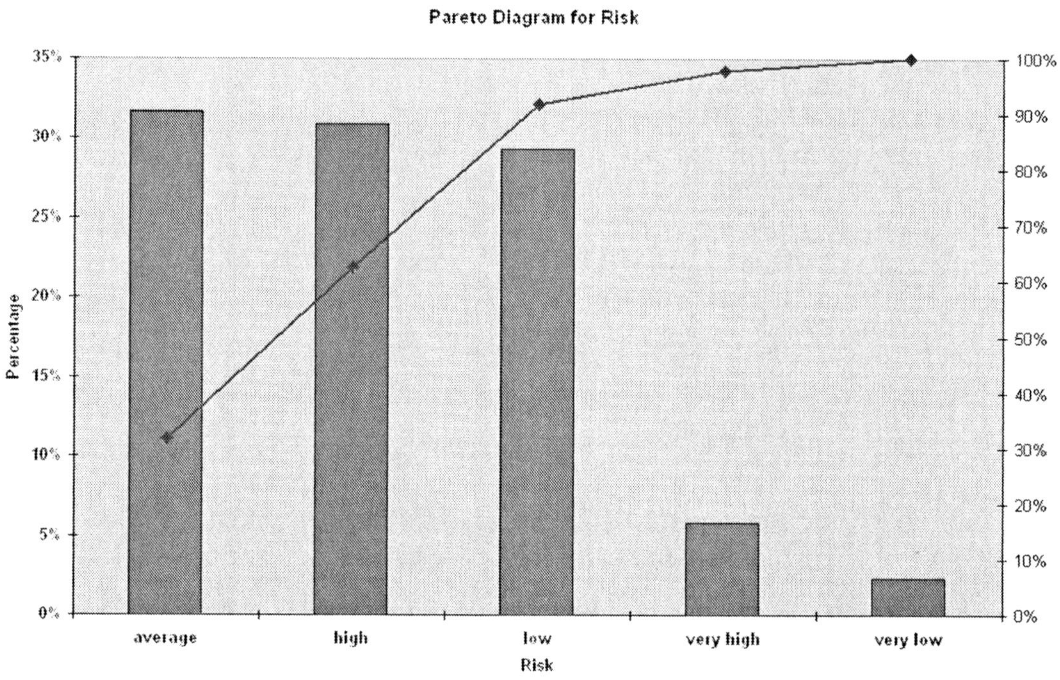

Pareto Principle
The Pareto principle exists when the majority of items in a set of data occur in a small number of categories, and the few remaining observations are spread out over a large number of categories.

The Pareto diagram is a very useful tool for presenting categorical data, particularly when the number of classifications or groupings increases. It can identify situations where the **Pareto principle** occurs. In situations where the data involved concern defective or nonconforming items, the Pareto diagram becomes a powerful tool for prioritizing improvement efforts. To further demonstrate its value in these situations, Example 3 provides an application in operations management.

EXAMPLE 3

USING THE PARETO DIAGRAM FOR PROCESS IMPROVEMENT

Data were obtained from a large injection-molding company that manufactures plastic molded components used in computer keyboards, washing machines, automobiles, and television sets. Table 8 presents the causes of defects in all computer keyboards produced during a three-month period.

TABLE 8
Summary table of causes of defects in computer keyboards in a 3-month period

Cause	Frequency	Percentage
Black spot	413	6.53
Damage	1,039	16.43
Jetting	258	4.08
Pin mark	834	13.19
Scratches	442	6.99
Shot mold	275	4.35
Silver streak	413	6.53
Sink mark	371	5.87
Spray mark	292	4.62
Warpage	1,987	31.42
Total	6,324	100.00*

*Result differs slightly from 100.0 due to rounding.
Source: U. H. Acharya and C. Mahesh, "Winning Back the Customer's Confidence: A Case Study on the Application of Design of Experiments to an Injection-Molding Process," *Quality Engineering*, 11, 1999, 357–363.

In order to obtain a Pareto diagram, a summary table is developed in which the categories are ordered based on the percentage of defects present (rather than being arranged alphabetically). Table 9 presents such a table for the computer keyboard defects data. The cumulative percentages for the ordered categories are also included as part of the table.

TABLE 9
Ordered summary table of causes of defects in computer keyboards in a 3-month period

Cause	Frequency	Percentage	Cumulative Percentage
Warpage	1,987	31.42	31.42
Damage	1,039	16.43	47.85
Pin mark	834	13.19	61.04
Scratches	442	6.99	68.03
Black spot	413	6.53	74.56
Silver streak	413	6.53	81.09
Sink mark	371	5.87	86.96
Spray mark	292	4.62	91.58
Shot mold	275	4.35	95.93
Jetting	258	4.08	100.00
Total	6,324	100.00*	

*Result differs slightly from 100.0 due to rounding.

Observe that in Table 9 warpage is the first category listed (with 31.42% of the defects) followed by damage (with 16.43%), followed by pin mark (with 13.19%). The two most frequently occurring categories—warpage and damage—account for 47.85% of the defects; the three most frequently occurring categories—warpage, damage, and pin mark—account for 61.04% of the corrections, and so on. The results displayed in tabular form in Table 9 are plotted in the Pareto diagram obtained from Microsoft Excel in Figure 9.

FIGURE 9
Pareto diagram obtained from Microsoft Excel for defects in computer keyboards
Source: *Data are taken from Table 9 above.*

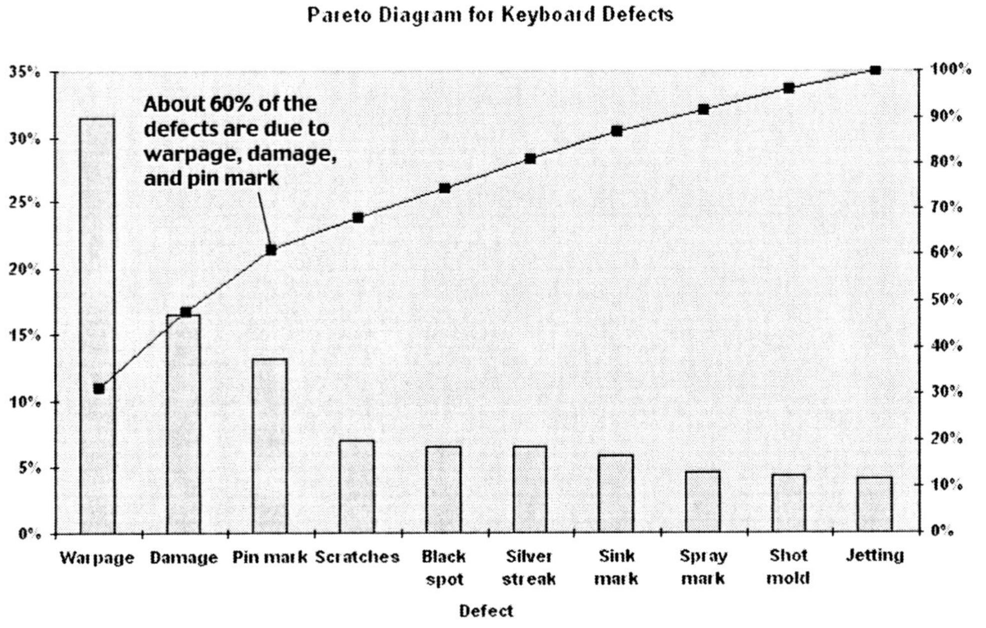

In Figure 9, the bars are presented vertically along with a cumulative percentage line for viewing clarity. If you follow the cumulative line, which is plotted at the category midpoint at a height equal to the total cumulative percentage, you see that these first three categories account for about 60% of the corrections. Since the Pareto diagram has ordered the categories by frequency of occurrences, concentrating process improvements on reducing defects due to warpage, damage, and pin marks results in the greatest payoff in reduction of defects, followed by scratches and black spots.

In order for categories to be collectively exhaustive, in some situations a category labeled *Other* or *Miscellaneous* is necessary. In these situations the bar representing these categories is placed to the right of the other bars, which are ordered by frequency.

Excel Strategies Generating Tables and Charts for Categorical Data

You generate a summary table for categorical data by using the PivotTable Wizard and then, after modifying the table, you use the Chart Wizard to generate bar and pie charts and a Pareto diagram. PHStat2 can do all these tasks for you in one step.

To generate a summary table similar to Table 7 and bar chart, pie chart, and a Pareto diagram similar to the ones shown in Figures 6 through 8, open the **Mutual Funds.xls** workbook to the **Data** worksheet and use one of these strategies:

CHAPTER 2.xls

Retrieve the Table 2.7 and Figure 2.6, Figure 2.7 and Figure 2.8 sheets of the ***Chapter 2.xls*** *workbook to view a summary table and charts similar to Table 7 and Figures 6, 7, and 8.*

Using Excel with PHStat2

Use the PHStat2 One-Way Tables & Charts procedure to generate a summary table and charts on individual sheets.

Select **PHStat | Descriptive Statistics | One-Way Tables & Charts**.

In the One-Way Tables & Charts dialog box (shown at right):

Leave selected the **Raw Categorical Data** option button.

Enter **K1:K260** in the **Raw Data Cell Range** edit box.

Select the **First cell contains label** check box.

Enter a title in the **Title** edit box.

Select the **Bar Chart**, **Pie Chart**, and **Pareto Diagram** check boxes.

Click the **OK** button.

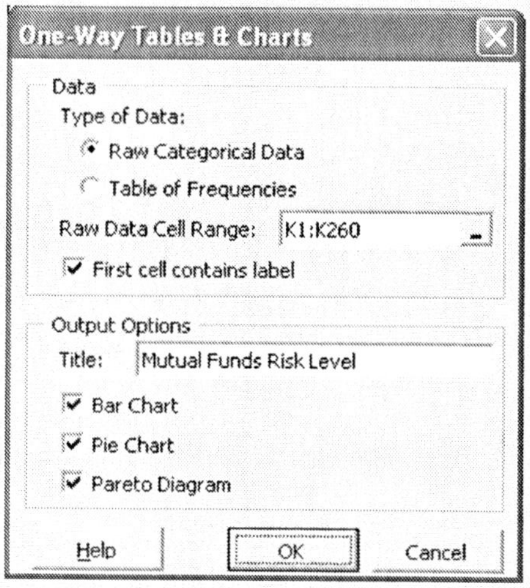

If you have data already in a frequency distribution table, you can also use the One-Way Tables & Charts procedure to produce bar and pie charts and Pareto diagrams. In the One-Way Tables & Charts dialog box, select the ***Table of Frequencies*** *option button and enter the table cell range in the edit box renamed as the* ***Freq. Table Cell Range****. (This edit box reverts back to the* ***Raw Data Cell Range*** *if the original* ***Raw Categorical Data*** *option is reselected.)*

Using Excel

Generate Summary Table Task. Follow the instructions of section EH7 at the end of this chapter to use the PivotTable Wizard to generate a summary table.

Generate Bar and Pie Charts and Pareto Diagram Task: Follow the instructions of section EH8 to generate bar and pie charts from a summary table. Follow the instructions of section EH9 to generate a Pareto diagram from an expanded summary table.

PROBLEMS FOR SECTION 4

Learning the Basics

27 A categorical variable had three categories with the following frequency of occurrence:

Category	Frequency
A	13
B	28
C	9

a. Compute the percentage of values in each category.
b. Construct a bar chart.
c. Construct a pie chart.
d. Form a Pareto diagram.

28 A categorical variable had four categories with the following percentages of occurrence:

Category	Percentage	Category	Percentage
A	12	C	35
B	29	D	24

a. Construct a bar chart.
b. Construct a pie chart.
c. Form a Pareto diagram.

Applying the Concepts

29 A network analyst has recorded the root cause of network crashes during the past six months.

Reason for Failure	Frequency
Physical connection	1
Power failure	3
Server software	29
Server hardware	2
Server out of memory	32
Inadequate bandwidth	1

a. Form a Pareto diagram.
b. Discuss the "vital few" and "trivial many" reasons for the root causes of network crashes.

30 Americans paid for more than 50 billion dollars in transactions online via credit card in 2000 (Byron Acohido, "Microsoft, Banks Battle to Control Your e-info," *USA Today*, August 13, 2001, 1B–2B). These transactions were broken down as follows:

Credit Card	Amount ($ billions)	%
American Express	8.04	15.6
Discover	1.97	3.8
MasterCard	15.57	30.2
Visa	25.96	50.4

a. Construct a bar chart.
b. Construct a pie chart.
c. Form a Pareto diagram.
d. Which of these charts do you prefer to use here? Why?

31 RHI Management Resources conducted a survey of 1,400 chief financial officers. When asked how much an impact interest rates have on the purchasing decisions they make for their company, 672 reported that they have little or no impact, 700 financial officers stated that interest rates have a significant impact or somewhat significant impact, and 28 reported that they were unsure ("*USA Today* Snapshots," *USA Today*, August 27, 2001, A1).

a. Construct a frequency and percentage summary table for the survey.
b. Form a bar chart for the responses to the survey.
c. Form a pie chart for the responses to the survey.
d. Which of these charts do you prefer to use here?

32 The results from an Internet survey taken by **Monster.com** on May 21–24, 2001 are given below. A total of 13,199 Internet users responded to the question "Would you be willing to relocate for a better job?" Each user was allowed only one vote.

Answer Given	Frequency
Yes, if the price is right	8,183
Yes, but only for a dream job	2,772
No, there are good jobs here	792
No, relocation isn't an option	1,452

Source: Extracted from USA Today, *June 26, 2001, A1.*

a. Construct a percentage summary table for the survey.
b. Form a bar chart for the responses to the survey.
c. Form a pie chart for the responses to the survey.
d. Which of these charts do you prefer to use here?

33 A *USA Today* article (Peter McMahon, "'Green Power' Gets Second Wind," *USA Today*, August 16, 2001, 3A) discussed the renewed interest in wind power in the United States. The following table represents the U.S. sources of electricity in 2000:

Source	%
Coal	51.8
Hydropower	7.3
Natural gas	15.7
Nuclear	19.8
Petroleum	2.9
Wind	0.1
Other	2.4

Source: U.S. Department of Energy.

a. Form a Pareto diagram.
b. What percentage of electricity is derived from coal, nuclear energy, or natural gas?
c. Construct a pie chart.
d. Which chart do you prefer to use, the Pareto diagram or the pie chart? Why?

34 A survey of 150 executives were asked what they think is the most common mistake candidates make during job interviews. The results reported (*USA Today Snapshots*, November 19, 2001) were as follows:

Reason	%
Little or no knowledge of company	44
Unprepared to discuss career plans	23
Limited enthusiasm	16
Lack of eye contact	5
Unprepared to discuss skills/experience	3
Other reasons	9

a. Form a bar chart.
b. Form a pie chart.
c. Form a Pareto diagram.
d. Which graphical method do you think is best to portray these data?
e. If you were a candidate interviewing for a job, which mistakes might you try hardest to avoid?

35 The following data represent daily water consumption per household in a suburban water district during a recent summer.

Reason for Water Usage	Gallons Per Day
Bathing and showering	99
Dishwashing	13
Drinking and cooking	11
Laundering	33
Lawn watering	150
Toilet	88
Miscellaneous	20
Total	414

a. Form a Pareto diagram.
b. If the water district wants to develop a water reduction plan, which reasons for water usage should it focus on?

36 A patient-satisfaction survey conducted for a sample of 210 individuals discharged from a large urban hospital during the month of June led to a list of 384 complaints in the following categories:

Reason for Complaint	Number
Anger with other patients/visitors	13
Failure to respond to buzzer	71
Inadequate answers to questions	38
Lateness for tests	34
Noise	28
Poor food service	117
Rudeness of staff	62
All others	21
Total	384

a. Form a Pareto diagram.
b. Which reasons for complaint do you think the hospital should focus on if it wishes to reduce the number of complaints? Explain.

5 TABULATING AND GRAPHING BIVARIATE CATEGORICAL DATA

The contingency table and the side-by-side bar chart are often used to study bivariate categorical data, the joint responses to two categorical variables.

The Contingency Table

In order to simultaneously study the responses to two categorical variables, a two-way table of cross-classification known as a **contingency table** or **cross-classification table** must be formed. For example, you might be interested in examining whether or not there is any pattern or relationship between level of risk and whether the fund has a fee. Table 10 depicts this information for all 259 sampled mutual funds.

TABLE 10
Contingency table displaying fund risk and fees

	Fund Level of Risk					
Fee	**Very High**	**High**	**Average**	**Low**	**Very Low**	**Total**
Yes	4	35	23	31	2	95
No	11	45	59	45	4	164
Total	15	80	82	76	6	259

To construct this contingency table, the joint responses for each of the 259 mutual funds with respect to risk and fee are tallied into one of the 10 possible cells in the table. Thus, the first fund listed (Amro Montag & Colwell Growth I) is classified as an average-risk fund, which has no fee. This joint response is tallied into the cell that is the intersection of the second row and third column. The remaining 258 joint responses are recorded in a similar manner.

In order to explore any possible pattern or relationship between fund risk and fee schedule, these results are first converted into percentages based on the following three totals:

1. The overall total (i.e., the 259 mutual funds)
2. The row totals (i.e., funds with fees and funds without fees)
3. The column totals (i.e., the five levels of risk)

This is accomplished in Tables 11, 12, and 13, respectively.

TABLE 11

Contingency table displaying fund risk and fees based on percentage of overall total

	Fund Level (Percentages Based on Overall Total)					
Fee	Very High	High	Average	Low	Very Low	Total
Yes	1.54	13.51	8.88	11.97	0.77	36.68*
No	4.25	17.37	22.78	17.37	1.54	63.32
Total	5.79	30.89*	31.66	29.34	2.32*	100.0

*Result differs slightly due to rounding.

TABLE 12

Contingency table displaying fund risk and fee based on percentage of row total

	Fund Level of Risk (Percentages Based on Row Total)					
Fee	Very High	High	Average	Low	Very Low	Total
Yes	4.21	36.84	24.21	32.63	2.11	100.0
No	6.71	27.44	35.98	27.44	2.44	100.0*
Total	5.79	30.89	31.66	29.34	2.32	100.0

*Result differs slightly from 100.0 due to rounding.

TABLE 13

Contingency table displaying fund risk and fee based on percentage of column total

	Fund Level of Risk (Percentages Based on Column Total)					
Fee	Very High	High	Average	Low	Very Low	Total
Yes	26.67	43.75	28.05	40.79	33.33	36.68
No	73.33	56.25	71.95	59.21	66.67	63.32
Total	100.00	100.00	100.00	100.00	100.00	100.00

Table 11 shows that 30.89% of the mutual funds sampled are high risk, 63.32% have no fee, and 17.37% are high-risk funds that have no fees. Table 12 shows that 36.84% of the funds with fees are high risk and 2.11% are very low risk. Table 13 shows that 43.75% of the high-risk funds, and only 28.05% of the average-risk funds have fees. The tables reveal some patterns; high-risk and low-risk funds are more likely to have fees, and average-risk and very high-risk funds are less likely to have fees.

The Side-by-Side Bar Chart

A useful way to visually display bivariate categorical data when looking for patterns or relationships is by constructing a **side-by-side bar chart**. Figure 10, which uses the data from Table 10, is a side-by-side bar chart obtained from Microsoft Excel that enables a comparison of the five fund risk levels based on whether they have a fee. An examination of Figure 10 reveals results consistent with those obtained from Tables 11, 12, and 13. High-risk and low-risk funds are more likely to have fees, while average-risk and very high-risk funds are less likely to have fees.

FIGURE 10
Side-by-side bar chart obtained from Microsoft Excel showing fees by fund risk

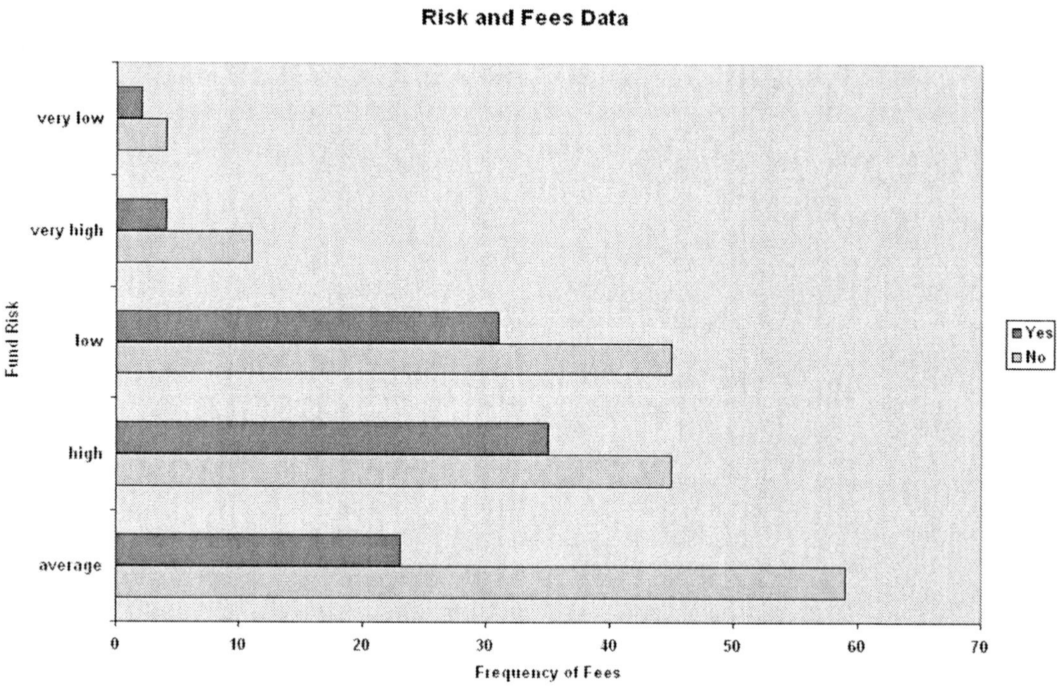

Excel Strategies Generating Tables and Charts for Bivariate Categorical Data

Generate a contingency table and a side-by-side chart for bivariate categorical data by using the combination of the PivotTable Wizard and the Chart Wizard. PHStat2 can do all these tasks for you in one step. (If your data is already in a contingency table, follow the Using Excel instructions for generating a side-by-side bar chart.)

CHAPTER 2.xls

Retrieve the Table 2.10 and Figure 2.10 sheets of the ***Chapter 2.xls*** *workbook to view a contingency table and side-by-side charts similar to Table 10 and Figure 10.*

To generate a contingency table similar to Table 10 and a side-by-side chart similar to Figure 10 above, open the **Mutual Funds.xls** workbook to the **Data** worksheet and use one of these strategies:

Using Excel with PHStat2

Use the PHStat2 **Descriptive Statistics | Two-Way Tables & Charts** procedure to generate a contingency table and side-by-side chart on individual sheets.

Select **PHStat | Descriptive Statistics | Two-Way Tables & Charts**.

In the Two-Way Tables & Charts dialog box (shown at right):

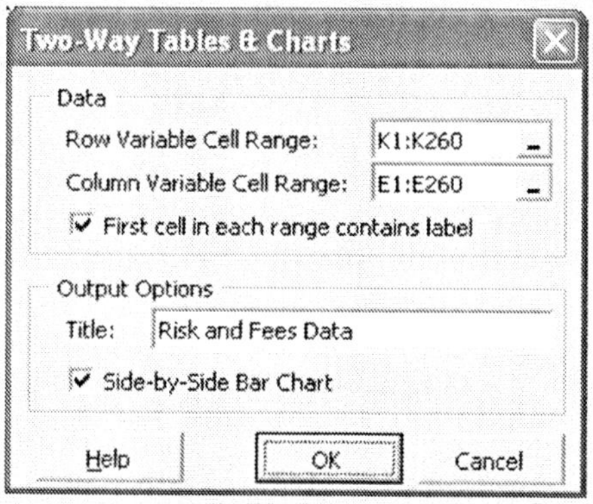

Enter **K1:K260** in the **Row Variable Cell Range** edit box.

Enter **E1:E260** in the **Column Variable Cell Range** edit box.

Select the **First cell in each range contains label** check box.

Enter a title in the **Title** edit box.

Select the **Side-by-Side Bar Chart** check box.

Click the **OK** button.

PHStat2 (and the PivotTable Wizard) uses the row variable to establish categories for the groups of bars on the side-by-side chart. In this example, using K1:K260 as the row variable cell range results in a chart similar to Figure 10, but a table in which the fees and risk data are transposed from their positions in Table 10. To produce a table that is similar to Table 10, swap the two cell ranges in the instructions.

Using Excel

Generate Contingency Table Task. Follow the instructions of section EH10 at the end of this chapter to use the PivotTable Wizard to generate a contingency table.

Generate Side-by-Side Bar Chart Task. If your contingency table is a PivotTable, use a Chart Wizard shortcut to generate your chart. Right-click your table and select **PivotChart** from the shortcut menu. Right-click the *background* of the new chart generated and select **Chart Type** from this second shortcut menu. In the Chart Type dialog box, make the selections for the Chart Wizard Step 1 dialog box given below and click the **OK** button. Right-click the new chart background a second time and select **Chart Options**. In the Chart Options dialog box, make the selections for the Chart Wizard Step 3 dialog box given below and click the **OK** button. Finally, right-click the **Fees** (or Risk) drop-down list and select **Hide PivotChart Field Buttons** for the shortcut menu to eliminate some clutter.

If your contingency table is not also a PivotTable, or if you are using Microsoft Excel 97, you cannot use the previous shortcut. Open to your contingency table and use the Chart Wizard to generate a side-by-side bar graph. For example, to generate a chart similar to Figure 10, open to the new PivotTable worksheet generated in the previous step (or the Table 2.10 worksheet of the **Chapter 2.xls** workbook), select **Insert | Chart** and make these entries in the Chart Wizard dialog boxes:

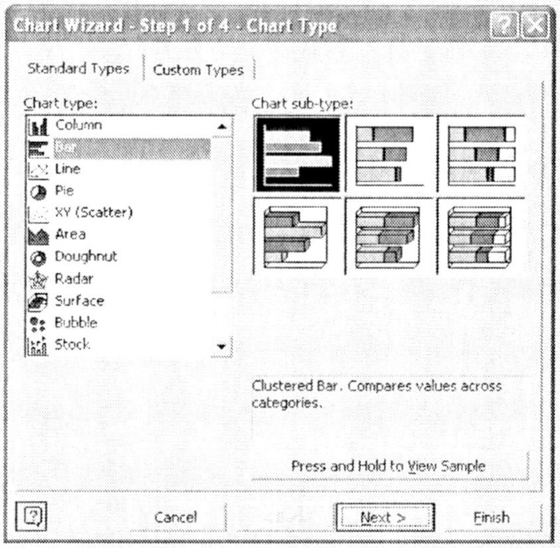

Step 1 dialog box (shown at right). Select the **Standard Types** tab and then select **Bar** from the **Chart type** list box. Select the first **Chart sub-type** choice, labeled as **Clustered Bar** when selected, and click the **Next** button.

Step 2 dialog box. Select the **Data Range** tab. Enter **A4:D9** in the **Data** range edit box. Select the **Rows** option button in the **Series in** group and click **Next**.

Step 3 dialog box. Select the **Titles** tab. Enter a title as the **Chart title**, Fund Risk in the **Category (X) axis** edit box, and **Frequency of Fees** in the **Value (Y) axis** edit box. Select, in turn, the **Axes**, **Gridlines** and **Data Table** tabs and adjust settings as discussed in Exhibit EP6 of the Excel Primer—consult your instructor if you require this item. Select the **Show Legend** check box in the **Legend** tab and click **Next**.

Step 4 dialog box. Select the **As new sheet** option button, enter a descriptive and unique sheet name, and click the **Finish** button to generate the chart.

PROBLEMS FOR SECTION 5

Learning the Basics

37 The following data represent the bivariate responses to two questions asked in a survey of 40 college students majoring in business—What is your gender (Male = M; Female = F) and What is your major (Accountancy = A; Computer Information Systems = C; Marketing = M):

Gender:	M M M F M F F M F M F M M M M F F M F F
Major:	A C C M A C A A C C A A A M C M A A A C
Gender:	M M M M F M F F M M F M M M M F M F M M
Major:	C C A A M M C A A A C C A A A A C C A C

a. Tally the data into a contingency table where the two rows represent the gender categories and the three columns represent the academic-major categories.
b. Form a contingency table based on percentages of all 40 student responses.
c. Form a contingency table based on row percentages.
d. Form a contingency table based on column percentages.
e. Using the results from (a), construct a side-by-side bar chart of gender based on student major.

38 Given the following two-way cross-classification table, construct a side-by-side bar chart comparing *A* and *B* for each of the three-column categories on the vertical axis.

	1	2	3	Total
A	20	40	40	100
B	80	80	40	200

Applying the Concepts

39 The results of a study made as part of a yield improvement effort at a semiconductor manufacturing facility provided defect data for a sample of 450 wafers. The following table presents a summary of the responses to two questions: Was a particle found on the die that produced the wafer? and Is the wafer good or bad?

	Condition of Die		
Quality of Wafer	**No Particles**	**Particles**	**Totals**
Good	320	14	334
Bad	80	36	116
Totals	400	50	450

Source: Hall, S. W., Analysis of Defectivity of Semiconductor Wafers by Contingency Table. Proceedings Institute of Environmental Sciences, *Vol. 1 (1994), 177–183.*

a. Construct a table of total percentages.
b. Construct a table of row percentages.
c. Construct a table of column percentages.
d. Construct a side-by-side bar chart of quality of wafer based on condition of die.
e. What conclusions do you draw from these analyses?

40 Retail sales in the USA for April 2002 were slightly higher than April 2001. Discounters such as Wal-Mart, Costco, Target, and Dollar General all had increased sales of 9% or more. Retail sales in the apparel industry, however, were mixed (Ann Zimmerman, "Retail Sales Grow Modestly," *Wall Street Journal*, May 10, 2002, B4). The following table presents total retail sales in millions of dollars for the leading apparel companies during April 2001 and April 2002.

	Total Sales in Millions $$$	
Apparel Company	**April 01**	**April 02**
Gap	1,159.0	962.0
TJX	781.7	899.0
Limited	596.5	620.4
Kohl's	544.9	678.9
Nordstrom	402.6	418.3
Talbots	139.9	130.1
AnnTaylor	114.2	124.8

Source: Extracted from the Wall Street Journal.

a. Construct a table of column percentages.
b. Construct a side-by-side chart to visually highlight the information gathered in (a).
c. Discuss the changes in retail sales for the apparel industry between April 2001 and April 2002.

41 International hotel chains including Marriott International and Holiday Inn Resorts are rapidly adding hotels in the Asian-Pacific market. This increase continued into 2002 even though occupancy and revenue-per-room rates declined in 2001 (Zach Coleman, "Hotel Groups Bolster Presence in Asia," *Wall Street Journal*, May 8, 2002, D10). The following table presents occupancy rates and revenue rates (reported here as the revenue generated per available hotel room) for five Asian cities in 2000 and 2001.

	Revenue Per Room		Occupancy Rate	
City	**2000**	**2001**	**2000**	**2001**
Tokyo, Japan	$132.63	$116.98	80.9%	78.9%
Hong Kong Island, China	$112.89	$103.29	82.6%	73.2%
Shanghai, China	$ 53.44	$ 58.25	69.7%	69.2%
Beijing, China	$ 49.57	$ 48.53	73.5%	73.0%
Bangkok, Thailand	$ 45.63	$ 44.95	67.8%	65.8%

Source: Extracted from the Wall Street Journal.

a. Construct a side-by-side chart for the revenue-per-room variable that allows you to visualize changes from 2000 to 2001.

b. Construct a side-by-side chart for the occupancy rates that allows you to visualize changes from 2000 to 2001.
c. Summarize the information that can be gathered from interpreting the charts constructed in (a) and (b).

42 Each day at a large hospital, several hundred laboratory tests are performed. The rate at which these tests are done improperly (and therefore need to be redone) seems steady, at about 4%. In an effort to get to the root cause of these nonconformances (tests that need to be redone), the director of the lab decided to keep records over a period of one week of the laboratory tests subdivided by the shift of workers who performed the lab tests. The results were as follows:

	Shift		
Lab Tests Performed	Day	Evening	Total
Nonconforming	16	24	40
Conforming	654	306	960
Total	670	330	1,000

a. Construct a table of row percentages.
b. Construct a table of column percentages.
c. Construct a table of total percentages.
d. Which type of percentage—row, column, or total—do you think is most informative for these data? Explain.
e. What conclusions concerning the pattern of nonconforming laboratory tests can the laboratory director reach?

43 A savings bank conducted a customer satisfaction survey on a monthly basis to measure satisfaction with several areas of services offered by a branch office. The results from a sample of 200 customers were as follows:

Area of Service	Number Satisfied	Number Dissatisfied
Waiting time for tellers	123	65
Automatic teller machine (ATM)	73	7
Investment advisement	43	6
Traveler's check service	25	11
Safe deposits	24	5
Account maintenance services	46	4

Note: Because all customers did not use each service, the number of responses for each area of service is different.

a. Construct a table of row percentages.
b. Construct a table of column percentages.
c. Construct a table of total percentages.
d. Which type of percentage—row, column, or total—do you think is most helpful in understanding these data? Why?
e. Construct a side-by-side bar chart of customer satisfaction by area of service.
f. Do customers seem equally satisfied with all areas of service? Which areas seem to need improvement more than others? Discuss.

6 GRAPHICAL EXCELLENCE

Among the methods for describing and communicating statistical information, well-designed graphical displays are usually the simplest and the most powerful. Good graphical displays reveal what the data are conveying. Tables and charts need to be presented clearly and carefully to enhance an analysis of the data. Frills must be eliminated from tables so as not to cloud the message given by the data with unnecessary adornments (references 4, 6–8).

The widespread use of spreadsheet and graphics software has led to a proliferation of graphics in recent years. While many of the graphics presented have served as useful presentations of the data involved, unfortunately the inappropriate and improper nature of many presentations has compounded the impression that the only purpose of statistics is to use numbers to lie.

Principles of Graphical Excellence

Perhaps the most well-known proponent of the proper presentation of data in graphs is Professor Edward R. Tufte, who has written a series of books that are devoted to proper methods of graphical design (see references 6–8). The work of Tufte is the focus of this section.

Exhibit 1 lists the essential features of graphical data. Tufte suggested five principles of graphical excellence (see reference 6). These principles are listed in Exhibit 2.

EXHIBIT 1 FEATURES OF GRAPHICAL DATA

The basic features of an ideal graph include the following:

1. Showing the data
2. Getting the viewer to focus on the substance of the graph rather than on how the graph was developed
3. Avoiding distortion
4. Encouraging comparisons of data
5. Serving a clear purpose
6. Being integrated with the statistical and verbal descriptions of the graph

EXHIBIT 2 PRINCIPLES OF GRAPHICAL EXCELLENCE

1. Graphical excellence is a well-designed presentation of data that provides substance, statistics, and design.
2. Graphical excellence communicates complex ideas with clarity, precision, and efficiency.
3. Graphical excellence gives the viewer the largest number of ideas in the shortest time with the least ink.
4. Graphical excellence almost always involves several dimensions.
5. Graphical excellence requires telling the truth about the data.

There are several ways in which the excellence of a graph can be evaluated. One important measure is the **data–ink ratio**.

DATA–INK RATIO

The data–ink ratio is the proportion of the graphic's ink that is devoted to nonredundant display of data information.

$$\text{Data–ink ratio} = \frac{\text{Data–ink}}{\text{Total ink used to print the graphic}} \quad \textbf{(2)}$$

Chartjunk
Chartjunk is decoration that is non-data–ink or redundant data–ink.

Lie Factor
The lie factor is the ratio of the size of the effect shown in the graph to the size of the effect in the data.

The objective is to maximize the proportion of the ink used in the graph that is devoted to the data. Within reasonable limits, non-data–ink and redundant data–ink should be eliminated. Non-data–ink includes aspects of the graph that do not relate to the substantive features of the data as well as grid lines that may be imposed on the graph. **Chartjunk** is defined on the left. In its extreme form, chartjunk represents self-promoting graphics that focus the viewer on the style of the graph, not on the data presented in the graph.

A central feature of graphical excellence is the importance of not using a graph to distort the data that it represents. A graph does not distort if its visual representation is consistent with its numerical representation. The amount of distortion can be measured by the **lie factor**. Any variation in the design of a graph must be consistent with the variation that exists in the data. Often changes in the graph are not consistent with variations in the data, producing a distortion between what the data represent and what the graph is showing.

In order to better understand these principles, several examples of graphs that lack graphical excellence will be examined. Figure 11 represents a graph printed in *Time* magazine as part of an article on the increasing exports of wine from Australia to the United States.

FIGURE 11
"Improper" display of Australian wine exports to the United States in millions of gallons
Source: *Adapted from* Time, *November 22, 1999, 68.*

In Figure 11, the wineglass icon representing the 6.77 million gallons for 1997 does not appear to be three times the size of the wineglass icon representing the 2.25 million gallons for 1992, nor does the wineglass icon representing the 2.25 million gallons for 1992 appear to be twice the size of the wineglass icon representing the 1.04 million gallons for 1989. Part of the reason for this is that a three-dimensional icon, the wineglass, is being used to represent the two dimensions of exports and time. Such an illustration may catch the eye, but its data could be presented better in a summary table or a plot of the data over time.

In addition to this type of visual distortion, if the zero point on the vertical axis is not shown, a set of data can be improperly displayed. This occurred in another graph in the same article from *Time* magazine, which is presented in Figure 12 below. There are several problems with this figure. First, there are no values shown on the horizontal X axis. Since Figure 12 is a plot of the amount of land planted over time, the years should be plotted on the X axis. Instead, this graph shows the year (in correct time order) next to the amount of land planted for grapes. Second, and perhaps more seriously, the points plotted contain distortions and inaccuracies. The acreage of 135,326 for 1949 to 1950 is plotted above the acreage of 150,300 for 1969 to 1970! In addition, the difference between 1979 to 1980 and 1997 to 1998 does not appear to be approximately three times the difference between 1979 to 1980 and 1969 to 1970 as it should be. Finally, the values for the time dimension do not appear to be properly spaced along the X axis; 1979 to 1980 is much closer to 1989 to 1990 than it is to 1969 to 1970 and 1997–1998 is much too far away from 1989–1990.

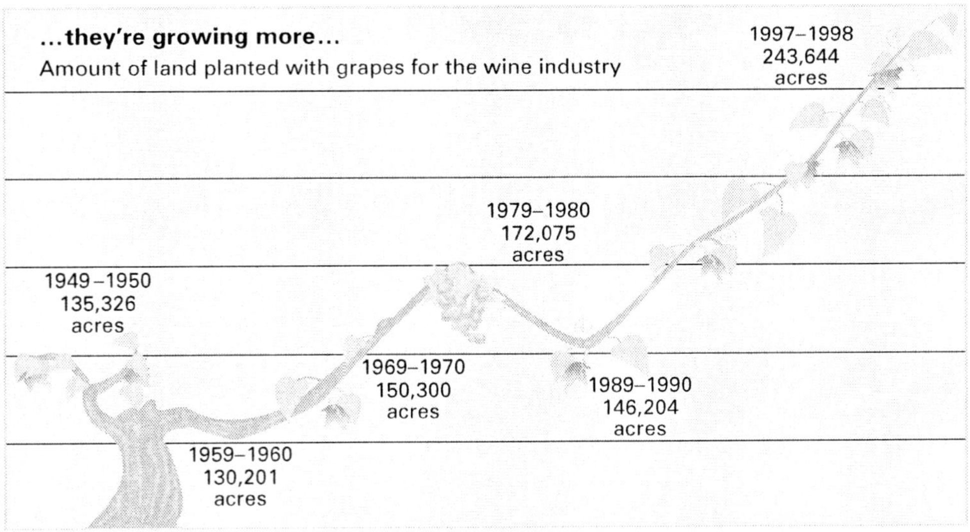

FIGURE 12
"Improper" display of amount of land planted with grapes for the wine industry
Source: *Adapted from S. Watterson, "Liquid Gold—Australians are Changing the World of Wine. Even the French Seem Grateful."* Time, *November 22, 1999, 68–69.*

Other types of eye-catching displays that we typically see in magazines and newspapers often include information that is not necessary and just add excessive data–ink. Figure 13 is an example of one such display. The graph in Figure 13 shows those products with the largest market share for soft drinks in 1999. Although the point of the graph is to show the differences in market share among the soft drinks, the graph suffers from excessive chartjunk. The amount of ink used to display the amount of fizz for each soft drink is much too large relative to the data–ink. The same information could have been conveyed with a bar chart or pie chart.

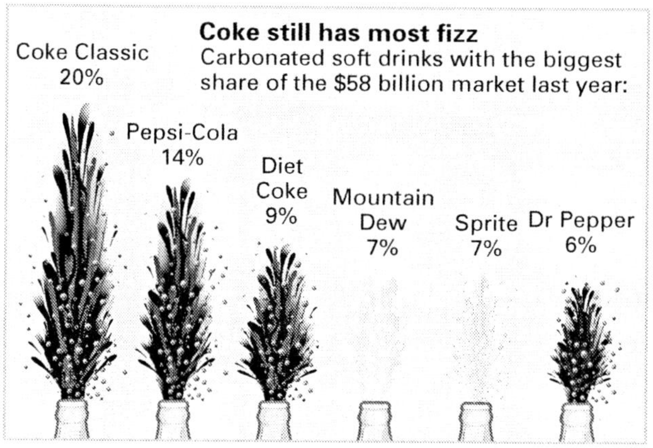

FIGURE 13
Plot of market share of soft drinks in 1999
Source: *Adapted from Anne B. Carey and Sam Ward, "Coke Still Has Most Fizz,"* USA Today, *May 10, 2000, 1B.*

To summarize, everyone actively consumes information daily through the various media. Because much of what is heard or read is junk, one must learn to evaluate critically and discard that which has no real value. One must also keep in mind that sometimes the junk provided is based on ignorance; other times, it is planned and malicious. Therefore it is important to be critical and skeptical of information provided.

According to Tufte (reference 6), for many people the first word that comes to mind when they think about statistical charts is "lie." Too many graphics distort the underlying data, making it hard for the reader to learn the truth. Ethical considerations arise when one decides what data to present in tabular and chart format and what not to present. When presenting data, both good and bad results should be documented. When making oral presentations and presenting written reports, the results need to be given in a fair, objective, and neutral manner. One must try to distinguish between poor data presentation and unethical presentation. Again, the key is *intent*. Often, fancy tables and chartjunk are presented or pertinent information is omitted simply out of ignorance. However, unethical behavior occurs when an individual willfully hides the facts by distorting a table or chart or by failing to report pertinent findings.

PROBLEMS FOR SECTION 6

Applying the Concepts

44 **(Student Project)** Bring a chart to class from a newspaper or magazine that you believe to be a poorly drawn representation of some numerical variable. Be prepared to submit the chart to the instructor with comments as to why you believe it is inappropriate. Also, be prepared to present and comment on this in class.

45 **(Student Project)** Bring a chart to class from a newspaper or magazine that you believe to be a poorly drawn representation of some categorical variable. Be prepared to submit the chart to the instructor with comments as to why you consider it inappropriate. Also, be prepared to present and comment on this in class.

46 **(Student Project)** Bring a chart to class from a newspaper or magazine that you believe to contain too much chartjunk that may cloud the message given by the data. Be prepared to submit the chart to the instructor with comments about why you think it is inappropriate. Also, be prepared to present and comment on this in class.

47 The following visual display contains an overembellished chart that appeared in *USA Today* dealing with the number of deaths from lightning strikes in the United States.

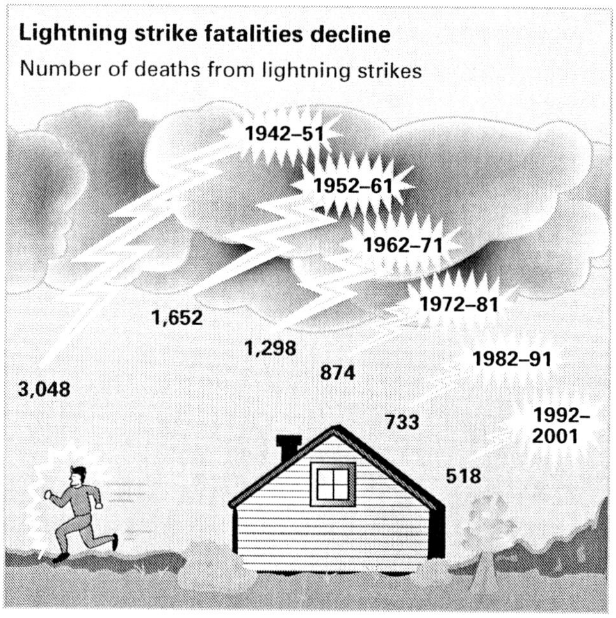

Source: *Adapted from* USA Today, *November 12, 2002.*

a. Describe at least one good feature of this visual display.
b. Describe at least one bad feature of this visual display.
c. Redraw the graph, using the principles of graphical excellence.

48 The visual display below appeared in *USA Today* and permits a comparison of the relative size of police departments in major U.S. cities.

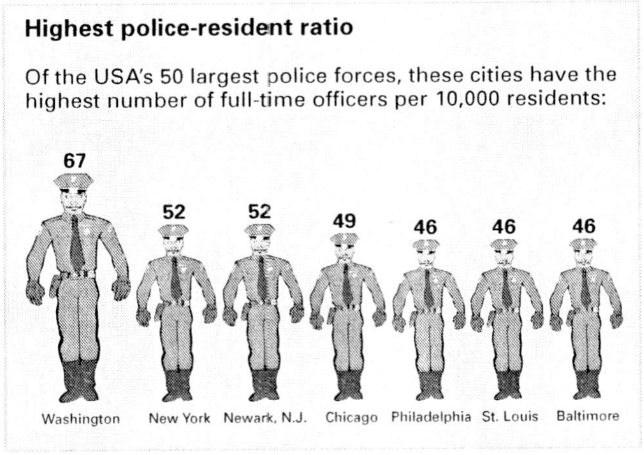

Source: *Adapted from* USA Today, *February 2000.*

a. Indicate a feature of this chart that violates Tufte's principles of graphical excellence.
b. Set up an alternative graph for the data provided in this figure.

49 The visual display on the right contains an overembellished chart that appeared in *USA Today* dealing with where the United States gets its electricity.
a. Describe at least one good feature of this visual display.
b. Describe at least one bad feature of this visual display.
c. Redraw the graph using the principles of graphical excellence.

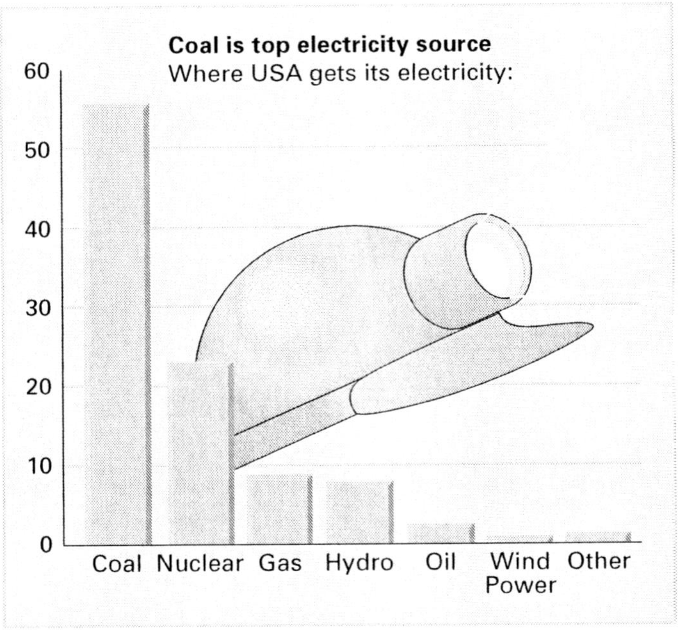

Source: *Adapted from* USA Today, *January 30, 2002.*

50 An article in the *New York Times* (Donna Rosato, "Worried about the Numbers? How about the Charts?" *The New York Times*, September 15, 2002, 7) reported on research done on annual reports of corporations by Professor Deanna Oxender Burgess of Florida Gulf Coast University. Professor Burgess found that even slight distortions in a chart changed readers' perception of the information. The article displayed sales information from the annual report of Zale Corporation and showed how results were exaggerated.

Go to the World Wide Web or the library and study the most recent annual report of a selected corporation. Find at least one chart in the report that you think can be improved and develop the improved chart. Explain why you believe the improved chart is better than the one included in the annual report.

SUMMARY

As you can see in the summary flowchart, this chapter is about data presentation. You have used various tables and charts to draw conclusions about the set of mutual funds that were first introduced in the Using Statistics scenario at the beginning of the chapter. Once the collected data have been presented in tabular and chart format, a variety of descriptive summary measures useful for data analysis and interpretation can be developed.

KEY TERMS

bar chart
bivariate numerical data
chartjunk
class boundaries
class groupings
class midpoint
contingency table
cross-classification table
cumulative percentage distribution
cumulative percentage polygon
data–ink ratio
frequency distribution
graphical excellence
histogram
lie factor
ogive (cumulative percentage polygon)
ordered array
Pareto diagram
Pareto principle
percentage distribution
percentage polygon
pie chart
range
relative frequency distribution
scatter diagram
side-by-side bar chart
stem-and-leaf display
summary table
width of a class interval

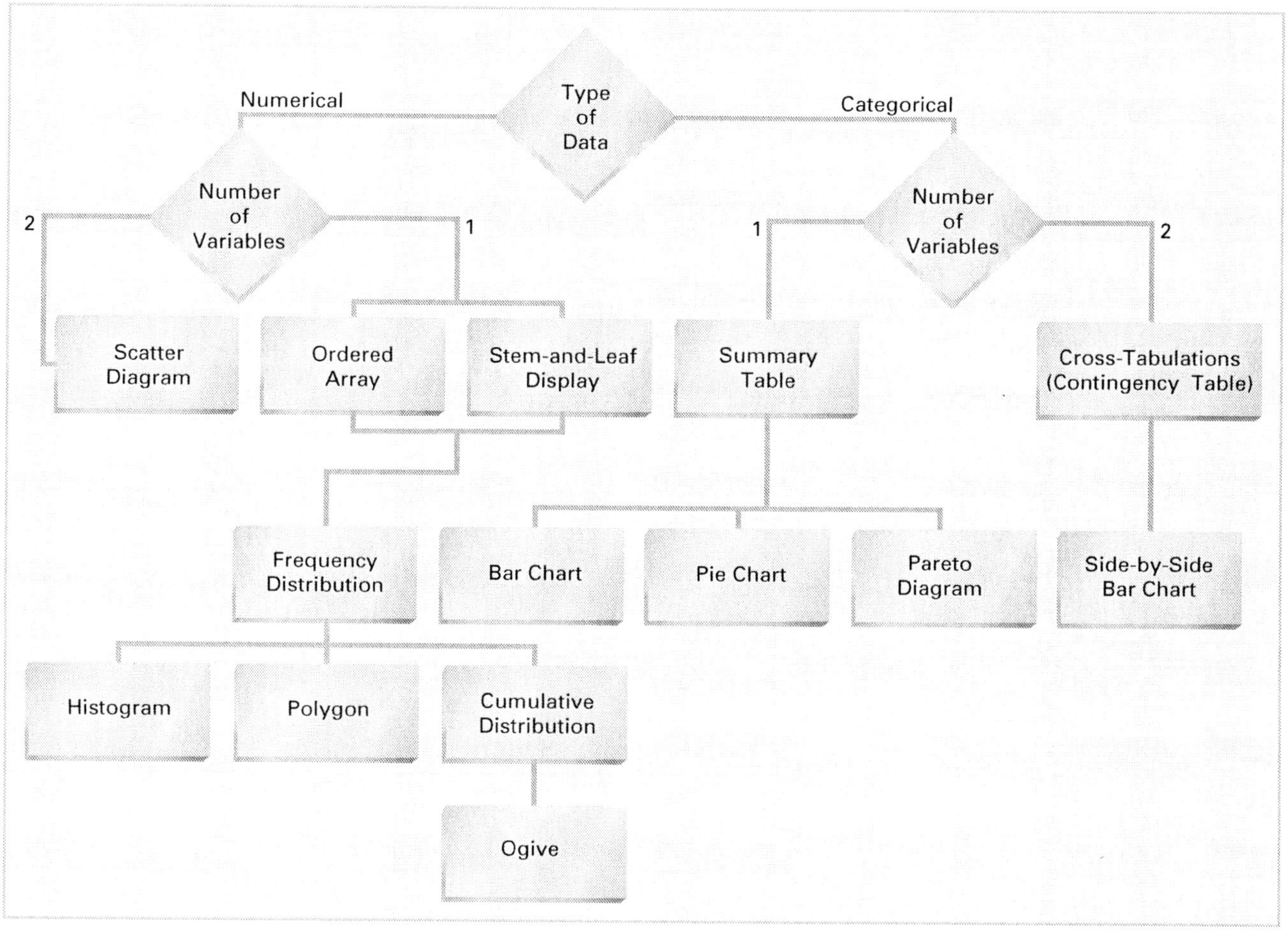

Chapter summary flowchart of tables and charts

CHAPTER REVIEW PROBLEMS

Checking Your Understanding

51 Why is it necessary to organize a set of numerical data that you collect?

52 What are the main differences between an ordered array and a stem-and-leaf display?

53 How do histograms and polygons differ with respect to their construction and use?

54 Why is the cumulative percentage polygon such a useful tool?

55 Why would you construct a frequency and percentage summary table?

56 What are the advantages and/or disadvantages of using a bar chart, a pie chart, or a Pareto diagram?

57 Compare and contrast the bar chart for categorical data with the histogram for numerical data.

58 Which of the following graphical displays are most similar in format to the Pareto diagram—the stem-and-leaf display, the histogram, the polygon, the ogive, the bar chart, and/or the pie chart? Discuss.

59 Why is it said that the main feature of the Pareto diagram is its ability to separate the "vital few" from the "trivial many"? Discuss.

60 What kinds of percentage breakdowns can help you interpret the results found through the cross-classification of data based on two categorical variables?

61 What are some of the ethical issues to be concerned with when presenting data in tabular or chart format?

Applying the Concepts

We recommend that Problems 62–80 be solved using Microsoft Excel.

62 One of the major measures of the quality of service provided by any organization is the speed with which the organization responds to customer complaints. A large family-held department store selling furniture and flooring including carpet had undergone a major expansion in the past several years. In particular, the flooring department had expanded from 2 installation crews to an installation supervisor, a measurer, and 15 installation crews. During a recent year the company got 50 complaints concerning carpet installation. The following data represent the number of days between the receipt of the complaint and the resolution of the complaint. **FURNITURE.xls**

54	5	35	137	31	27	152	2	123	81	74	27	11
19	126	110	110	29	61	35	94	31	26	5	12	4
165	32	29	28	29	26	25	1	14	13	13	10	5
27	4	52	30	22	36	26	20	23	33	68		

a. Form the frequency distribution and percentage distribution.
b. Plot the histogram.
c. Plot the percentage polygon.
d. Form the cumulative percentage distribution.
e. Plot the ogive (cumulative percentage polygon).
f. On the basis of the results of (a) through (e), does there appear to be a great deal of variation in the time it takes to resolve complaints? Explain.
g. On the basis of the results of (a) through (e), if you had to tell the president of the company how long a customer should expect to wait to have a complaint resolved, what would you say? Explain.

63 For a sample of 36 pizza products, the data in the file **PIZZA.xls** represent cost of a slice in dollars, number of calories per slice, and amount of fat in grams per slice for three types of products—supermarket cheese, pizza-chain cheese, and supermarket pepperoni.

Source: "Frozen Pizza on the Rise." Copyright © 2002 by Consumers Union of U.S., Inc. Adapted from Consumer Reports, *January 2002, 40–41, by permission of Consumers Union, U.S., Inc., Yonkers, NY 10703–1057.*

a. For each of the three numerical variables in the data set (cost, calories, and fat), develop the ordered array and form the stem-and-leaf display.
b. On the basis of whether the pizza product is classified as either supermarket or chain cheese versus supermarket pepperoni, for each of the three numerical variables in the data set (cost, calories, and fat), develop the ordered array and form the stem-and-leaf display.
c. Construct frequency distributions and percentage distributions for weight, cost, and calories.
d. Form cumulative percentage distributions for weight, cost, and calories.
e. Plot percentage polygons for weight, cost, and calories.
f. Plot ogives (cumulative percentage polygons) for weight, cost, and calories.
g. Construct scatter diagrams of cost and calories, cost and fat, and calories and fat.
h. Based on (a) through (g), what conclusions can you reach about the cost, fat, and calories of these pizza products?

64 In an article in *Quality Engineering*, the viscosity (resistance to flow) of a chemical product produced in batches was examined. Assume that the viscosity of the chemical needs to be between 13 and 18 to meet company specifications. The data for 120 batches are in the data file. **CHEMICAL.xls**

Source: D. S. Holmes and A. E. Mergen, "Parabolic Control Limits for the Exponentially Weighted Moving Average Control Charts," Quality Engineering *1992, 4(4): 487–495.*

a. Develop the ordered array.
b. Construct a frequency distribution and a percentage distribution.
c. Plot the percentage histogram.
d. What percentage of the batches is within company specifications?

65 Studies conducted by a manufacturer of "Boston" and "Vermont" asphalt shingles have shown product weight to be a major factor in the customer's perception of quality. Moreover, the weight represents the amount of raw materials being used and is therefore very important to the company from a cost standpoint. The last stage of the assembly line packages the shingles before the packages are placed on wooden pallets. Once a pallet is full (a pallet for most brands holds 16 squares of shingles), it is weighed, and the measurement is recorded. The company expects pallets of their "Boston" brand-name shingles to weigh at least 3,050 pounds but less than 3,260 pounds. For the company's "Vermont" brand-name shingles, pallets should weigh at least 3,600 pounds but less than 3,800. The data file **PALLET.xls** contains the weights (in pounds) from a sample of 368 pallets of "Boston" shingles and 330 pallets of "Vermont" shingles.

a. For the "Boston" shingles, form a frequency distribution having eight class intervals, using 3,015, 3,050, 3,085, 3,120, 3,155, 3,190, 3,225, 3,260, and 3,295 as the class boundaries.
b. Form the percentage distribution from the frequency distribution developed in (a).
c. Form the percentage histogram from the percentage distribution in (b).
d. Comment on the distribution of pallet weights for the "Boston" shingles. Be sure to identify the percentage of pallets that are underweight and overweight.
e. For the "Vermont" shingles, form a frequency distribution having seven class intervals, using 3,550, 3,600, 3,650, 3,700, 3,750, 3,800, 3,850, and 3,900 as the class boundaries.
f. Form the percentage distribution from the frequency distribution developed in (e).
g. Form the percentage histogram from the percentage distribution in (f).
h. Comment on the distribution of pallet weights for the "Vermont" shingles. Be sure to identify the percentage of pallets that are underweight and overweight.

66 Do marketing promotions, such as bobble-head give-aways, increase attendance at Major League Baseball games? An article in *Sport Marketing Quarterly* reported on the effectiveness of marketing promotions (T. C. Boyd and T. C. Krehbiel, "Promotion Timing in Major League Baseball and the Stacking Effects of Factors that Increase Game Attractiveness," *Sport Marketing Quarterly*, 12, March 2003). The data file **ROYALS.xls** includes the following variables for the Kansas City Royals during the 2002 baseball season:

GAME = Home games in the order they were played
ATTENDANCE = paid attendance for the game
PROMOTION (Y = a promotion was held; N = no promotion was held)

a. Construct a percentage histogram for the attendance variable. Interpret the histogram.
b. Construct a percentage polygon for the attendance variable. Interpret the polygon.
c. Which graphical display do you prefer, the one in (a) or (b)? Explain.
d. Construct a graphical display containing two percentage polygons for attendance—one for the 43 games with a promotion and the second for the 37 games without a promotion. Compare the two attendance distributions.

67 The data in the file **PROTEIN.xls** indicate fat and cholesterol information concerning popular protein foods (fresh red meats, poultry, and fish).

Source: United States Department of Agriculture.

For the data relating to the number of calories and the amount of cholesterol for the popular protein foods:
a. Construct the stem-and-leaf display.
b. Construct the frequency distribution and the percentage distribution.
c. Plot the percentage histogram.
d. Plot the percentage polygon.
e. Form the cumulative percentage distribution.
f. Plot the cumulative percentage polygon.
g. What conclusions can you draw from these analyses?

68 Suppose that you wish to study characteristics of the model year 2002 automobiles in terms of the following variables: horsepower, miles per gallon, length, width, turning circle requirement, weight, and cargo volume. **AUTO2002.xls**

Source: "The 2002 Cars." Copyright © 2002 by Consumers Union of U.S., Inc. Adapted from Consumer Reports, *April 2002, 22–71, by permission of Consumers Union U.S., Inc., Yonkers, NY 10703–1057.*

For each of these variables:
a. Construct the stem-and-leaf display.
b. Construct the frequency distribution and the percentage distribution.
c. Plot the percentage histogram.
d. Plot the percentage polygon.
e. Form the cumulative percentage distribution.
f. Plot the cumulative percentage polygon.
g. What conclusions can you draw concerning the 2002 automobiles?
h. Suppose that you want to compare front-wheel drive cars with rear-wheel drive cars. Redo (a) through (g) for each of these groups. What conclusions can you reach concerning differences between front-wheel drive cars and rear-wheel drive cars?
i. Form a contingency table cross-classifying type of drive with type of gasoline.
j. Plot a side-by-side bar chart of type of drive with type of gasoline.
k. Based on the results of (i) and (j), does there appear to be a relationship between type of drive with type of gasoline?

69 The data in the file **STATES.xls** was obtained from the American Community Survey a sampling of households taken in all states during the 2000 U.S. Census. For each of the variables of average travel-to-work time in minutes, percentage of homes with eight or more rooms, median household income, and percentage of mortgage-paying homeowners whose housing costs exceed 30% of income:
a. Form the frequency distribution and the percentage distribution.
b. Plot the percentage histogram.
c. Plot the percentage polygon.
d. Construct the cumulative distribution.
e. Form the cumulative percentage distribution.
f. Plot the cumulative percentage polygon.
g. Which of the graphs do you think is best in presenting the different variables? Explain.
h. What conclusions about these four variables can you make based on the results of (a) through (f)?

70 The economics of baseball has caused a great deal of controversy with owners arguing that they are losing money, players arguing that owners are making money, and fans complaining about how expensive it is to attend a game and watch games on cable television. In addition to data related to team statistics for the 2001 season, the file **BB2001.xls** contains team-by-team statistics on ticket prices; the fan cost index; regular season gate receipts; local television, radio, and cable receipts; all other operating revenue; player compensation and benefits; national and other local expenses; and income from baseball operations. For each of these variables:
a. Form the frequency distribution and the percentage distribution.
b. Plot the percentage histogram.
c. Plot the percentage polygon.
d. Construct the cumulative distribution.
e. Form the cumulative percentage distribution.
f. Plot the cumulative percentage polygon.
g. Which of the graphs do you think is best in presenting the different variables? Explain.

h. Set up a scatter diagram to predict the number of wins on the Y axis from the player compensation and benefits on the X axis.
i. What conclusions can you reach from the scatter diagram in (h)?
j. What conclusions about these variables can you reach based on the results of (a) through (f)?

71 The data in the file **AIRCLEANERS.xls** represent the price, yearly energy cost, and yearly filter cost of room air cleaners.
a. Set up a scatter diagram with price on the Y axis and energy cost on the X axis.
b. Set up a scatter diagram with price on the Y axis and filter cost on the X axis.
c. What conclusions about the relationship of energy cost and filter cost to the price of the air cleaners can you make?

Source: "Portable Room Air Cleaners." Copyright © 2002 by Consumers Union of U.S., Inc. Adapted from Consumer Reports, *February 2002, 47, by permission of Consumers Union U.S., Inc., Yonkers, NY 10703–1057.*

72 The data in the file **PRINTERS.xls** represent the price, text speed, text cost, color photo time, and color photo cost of computer printers.
a. Set up a scatter diagram with price on the Y axis and text speed on the X axis.
b. Set up a scatter diagram with price on the Y axis and text cost on the X axis.
c. Set up a scatter diagram with price on the Y axis and color photo time on the X axis.
d. Set up a scatter diagram with price on the Y axis and color photo cost on the X axis.
e. Based on the results of (a) through (d), do you think that any of the X variables might be useful in predicting printer price? Explain.

Source: "Printers." Copyright © 2002 by Consumers Union of U.S., Inc. Adapted from Consumer Reports, *March 2002, 51, by permission of Consumers Union U.S., Inc., Yonkers, NY 10703–1057.*

73 Brazil is the second-largest coffee consuming country in the world. Unlike most major markets where a handful of corporations dominate the coffee roasting and selling market, over 2,000 small roasters are active in Brazil. The Sara Lee Corporation has become the leading coffee retailer in Brazil by acquiring several Brazilian coffee roasters (Miriam Jordan, "Sara Lee Wants to Percolate through All of Brazil," *Wall Street Journal*, May 8, 2002, A14). Consumption by the seven largest coffee-consuming nations and a breakdown of the market leaders in Brazil are given at the top of the next column.

Coffee Consumption in Major Markets in 2000

Country	Consumption (in Millions of 60-kg Bags)
USA	18.6
Brazil	12.8
Germany	9.2
Japan	6.7
France	5.4
Netherlands	1.8
Finland	0.9

Source: Extracted from the Wall Street Journal.

Leading Coffee Brands in Brazil

Brand	Market Share
Sara Lee owned brands	27.6%
Nescafe	6.1%
Tres Coracoes	4.8%
Melitta	4.0%
All Others	57.5%

Source: Extracted from the Wall Street Journal.

a. Construct a graph for the data concerning the major coffee-consuming countries. Which type of graph is most appropriate? Explain.
b. Construct a graph for the data concerning the market share of coffee in Brazil. Which type of graph is most appropriate? Explain.

74 The following data represent proven conventional oil reserves in billions of barrels, subdivided by region and country.

Region and Country	Proven Conventional Reserves (Billions of Barrels)	
North America	54.8	
Mexico		28.3
U.S.		21.8
Canada		4.7
Central and South America	95.2	
Venezuela		76.9
Brazil		8.1
Other Central and South America		10.2
Western Europe	17.2	
Norway		9.5
Britain		5.0
Other Western Europe		2.7

Region and Country	Proven Conventional Reserves (Billions of Barrels)	
Africa	74.9	
Libya		29.5
Nigeria		22.5
Algeria		9.2
Angola		5.4
Other Africa		8.3
Middle East	683.6	
Saudi Arabia		259.2
Iraq		112.5
United Arab Emirates		97.8
Kuwait		94.0
Iran		89.7
Qatar		13.2
Oman		5.5
Other Middle East		11.7
Far East and Oceania	44.0	
China		24.0
Indonesia		5.0
India		4.7
Other Far East and Oceania		10.3
Eastern Europe and Former USSR	59.0	
Russia		48.6
Kazakhstan		5.4
Other Eastern Europe and Former USSR		5.0

Source: United States Department of Energy.

Using the set of countries:
a. Form a bar chart.
b. Form a pie chart.
c. Form a Pareto diagram.

Using the set of regions:
d. Form a bar chart.
e. Form a pie chart.
f. Form a Pareto diagram.
g. Which graphical method do you think is best to portray these data?
h. Based on the results of (a) through (f), what conclusions can you make concerning the proven conventional oil reserves for the different countries and regions?

75 In the aftermath of the attacks of September 11, 2001, statisticians at the National Center for Health Statistics became more concerned with their ability to track and classify victims of terrorism (E. Weinstein, "Tracking Terror's Rising Toll," *Wall Street Journal*, January 25, 2002, A13). The following data represent deaths due to terrorism on U.S. soil from 1990 to 2001 and also the deaths in the United States in 2000 due to various causes.

Year	Deaths Due to Terrorism in the U.S.
1990	0
1991	0
1992	0
1993	6
1994	1
1995	169
1996	2
1997	0
1998	1
1999	3
2000	0
2001	2,717

Cause	Deaths in Thousands
Smoke and fire	3.3
Accidental drowning	3.3
Alcohol-induced deaths	18.5
Alzheimer's disease	49.0
Assault by firearms	10.4
Assault by non-firearms	5.7
Asthma	4.4
Cancer	551.8
Strokes and related diseases	166.0
Emphysema	16.9
Diabetes	68.7
Heart diseases	710.0
Falls	12.0
HIV	14.4
Influenza and pneumonia	67.0
Injuries at work	5.3
Motor vehicle accidents	41.8
Suicide	28.3
Drug-related deaths	15.9

Source: Federal Bureau of Criminal Justice Statistics, National Center for Health Statistics, National Highway Transportation Safety Administration, Department of Defense.

a. Set up a scatter diagram with deaths due to terrorism on U.S. soil on the Y axis and year on the X axis.
b. Based on the results of (a), is there any pattern to the deaths due to terrorism on U.S. soil between 1990 and 2001?

For the deaths in thousands due to different causes:
c. Form a bar chart.
d. Form a pie chart.
e. Form a Pareto diagram.
f. Which graphical method do you think is best to portray these data?
g. Based on the results of (c) through (e), what conclusions can you make concerning the deaths in the United States in 2000 due to various causes?

76 In a *Wall Street Journal* article, Forrester Research, Inc., claims that 19% of all Internet users play games online. Offering free games can dramatically increase traffic to a company's site and thus increase a company's exposure to Web users and/or allow companies to charge higher rates for Internet advertising. The eight leading game sites according to PC Data, Inc., for March 2000 are listed in the following table.

Site	Unique Users (Thousands)	Web Audience Reached (%)
freelotto.com	12,901	19.1
AOLGames.com	9,416	13.9
uproar.com	8,821	13.1
webstakes.com	7,499	11.1
iwin.com	7,410	11.0
speedyclick.com	6,628	9.8
shockwave.com	5,582	8.3
prizecentral.com	4,899	7.3

Source: Dean Takahashi, "Don't Shoot," Wall Street Journal, *April 17, 2000, R53.*

a. Construct a bar chart for the number of unique users.
b. Construct a bar chart for the percentage of total Web audience reached.
c. Compare the two charts. Which of these charts do you prefer? Why?

77 The owner of a restaurant serving Continental-style entrées was interested in studying patterns of patron demand for the Friday to Sunday weekend time period. Records were maintained that indicated the number of entrées ordered for each type. The following data were obtained:

Type of Entrée	Number Served
Beef	187
Chicken	103
Duck	25
Fish	122
Pasta	63
Shellfish	74
Veal	26

a. Construct a bar chart for the types of entrées ordered.
b. Construct a Pareto diagram for the types of entrées ordered.
c. Construct a pie chart for the types of entrées ordered.
d. Do you prefer a Pareto diagram or a pie chart for these data? Why?
e. What conclusions can the restaurant owner draw concerning demand for different types of entrées?

Suppose that the owner was also interested in studying the demand for dessert during the same time period. She decided that two other variables, along with whether a dessert was ordered, were to be studied: the gender of the individual, and whether a beef entrée was ordered. The results were as follows:

	Gender		
Dessert Ordered	Male	Female	Total
Yes	96	40	136
No	224	240	464
Total	320	280	600

	Beef Entrée		
Dessert Ordered	Yes	No	Total
Yes	71	65	136
No	116	348	464
Total	187	413	600

For each of the two cross-classification tables:
f. Construct a table of row percentages.
g. Construct a table of column percentages.
h. Construct a table of total percentages.
i. Which type of percentage (row, column, or total) do you think is most informative for each gender? for beef entrée? Explain.
j. What conclusions concerning the pattern of dessert ordering can the owner of the restaurant reach?

78 AT&T is the number one long-distance telephone service provider in the United States in terms of revenues and in total number of households. In January 2002, Verizon was fourth in both measures, trailing AT&T, MCI, and Sprint. Using an aggressive marketing strategy and by lowering prices, Verizon surpassed Sprint in household market share by the third quarter of 2002.

Long-Distance Provider	Household Market Share (in %)	Revenue Market Share (in %)
AT&T	33.8	33.0
MCI	15.8	19.4
Verizon	10.6	5.9
Sprint	8.3	9.1
VarTec	6.3	3.7
Others	25.2	28.9

Source: Adapted from S. Backover, "Verizon Tops Sprint in Long-distance," **usatoday.com**, *January 8, 2003.*

a. Construct pie charts for both household market share and revenue market share.
b. Construct a side-by-side bar chart for the data.
c. Which type of graphical display is more helpful in depicting the data? Explain.
d. What conclusions can you draw concerning household and revenue market share?

79 An article in the *New York Times* (William McNulty and Hugh K. Truslow, "How It Looked Inside the Booth," *The New York Times*, November 6, 2002) provided the following data on the method for recording votes in 1980, 2000, and 2002, broken down by percentage of counties in the United States using each method and percentage of registered voters using each method. The results were as follows:

Percentage of Counties Using

Method	1980	2000	2002
Punch cards	18.5	18.5	15.5
Lever machines	36.7	14.4	10.6
Paper ballots	40.7	11.9	10.5
Optical scan	0.8	41.5	43.0
Electronic	0.2	9.3	16.3
Mixed	3.1	4.4	4.1

Percentage of Registered Voters Using

Method	1980	2000	2002
Punch cards	31.7	31.4	22.6
Lever machines	42.9	17.4	15.5
Paper ballots	10.5	1.5	1.3
Optical scan	2.1	30.8	31.8
Electronic	0.7	12.2	19.6
Mixed	12.0	6.7	9.3

a. Set up separate pie charts for each year for the percentage of counties and the percentage of registered voters using the various methods.
b. Set up side-by-side bar charts by year for the percentage of counties and the percentage of registered voters using the various methods.
c. Which type of graphical display is more helpful in depicting the data? Explain.
d. What differences are there in the results for the counties and the registered voters?

80 In summer 2000, a growing number of warranty claims on Firestone tires sold on Ford SUVs prompted Firestone and Ford to issue a major recall. An analysis of warranty-claims data helped identify which models to recall. A breakdown of 2,504 warranty claims based on tire size is given in the following table.

Tire Size	Warranty Claims
23575R15	2,030
311050R15	137
30950R15	82
23570R16	81
331250R15	58
25570R16	54
Others	62

Source: Extracted from Robert L. Simison, "Ford Steps Up Recall without Firestone," Wall Street Journal, *August 14, 2000, A3.*

The 2,030 warranty claims for the 23575R15 tires can be categorized into ATX models and Wilderness models. The type of incident leading to a warranty claim, by model type, is summarized in the following table.

Incident	ATX Model Warranty Claims	Wilderness Warranty Claims
Tread Separation	1,365	59
Blow out	77	41
Other/Unknown	422	66
Total	1,864	166

Source: Extracted from Robert L. Simison, "Ford Steps Up Recall without Firestone," Wall Street Journal, *August 14, 2000, A3.*

a. Construct a Pareto diagram for number of warranty claims by tire size. What tire size accounts for most of the claims?
b. Construct a pie chart to display the percentage of the total number of warranty claims for the 23575R15 tires that come from the ATX model and Wilderness model. Interpret the chart.
c. Construct a Pareto diagram for the type of incident causing the warranty claim for the ATX model. Does a certain type of incident account for most of the claims?
d. Construct a Pareto diagram for the type of incident causing the warranty claim for the Wilderness model. Does a certain type of incident account for most of the claims?
e. Write a short summary of your analysis.

81 (**Class Project**) Let each student in the class respond to the question "Which type of carbonated soft drink do you most prefer?" so that the results can be tallied into a summary table.
a. Convert the data to percentages and construct a Pareto diagram.
b. Analyze the findings.

82 (**Class Project**) Let each student in the class be cross-classified on the basis of gender (male, female) and current employment status (yes, no) so that the results can be tallied.
a. Construct a table with either row or column percentages, depending on which you think is more informative.
b. What would you conclude from this study?
c. What other variables would you want to know regarding employment in order to enhance your findings?

Report Writing Exercises

83 Referring to the results you obtained in problem 65 concerning the weight of "Boston" and "Vermont" shingles, write a report that evaluates whether the weight of the pallets of the two types of shingles are what the company expects. Be sure to incorporate tables and charts you obtained into the report (see the appendix on Preparing Data for Reports and Presentations Using Microsoft Office).

84 Referring to the results you obtained in problem 80 concerning the warranty claims on Firestone tires, write a report that evaluates warranty claims on Firestone tires sold on Ford SUVs. Be sure to incorporate tables and charts you obtained into the report (see the appendix on Preparing Data for Reports and Presentations Using Microsoft Office).

Internet Exercises

85 Go to the Web site for this text

www.prenhall.com/levine

Select Chapter 2 and then click on Internet exercises.

TEAM PROJECT

TP1 The data file **MUTUAL FUNDS.xls** contains information regarding 13 variables from a sample of 259 mutual funds. The variables are:

Fund—The name of the mutual fund.
Type—Type of stocks comprising the mutual fund—small cap, mid cap, large cap
Objective—Objective of stocks comprising the mutual fund—growth or value
Assets—In millions of dollars
Fees—Sales charges (no or yes)
Expense ratio in percentage
2001 Return—Twelve-month return in 2001
Three-year return—Annualized return 1999–2001
Five-year return—Annualized return 1997–2001
Turnover—Level of trading activity by the mutual fund classified as very low, low, average, high, or very high
Risk—Risk-of-loss factor of the mutual fund classified as very low, low, average, high, or very high
Best quarter—Best quarterly performance 1997–2001
Worst quarter—Worst quarterly performance 1997–2001

a. Construct an ordered array and a stem-and-leaf display of the expense ratio for the 259 mutual funds.
b. Consider only the funds in the data set that have no fee. Construct an ordered array and a stem-and-leaf display of the expense ratio for the funds with no fee.
c. Consider the mutual funds that have fees. Construct an ordered array and a stem-and-leaf display of the expense ratio for the funds that have fees.
d. Discuss the distribution of the expense ratio. Are the distributions similar for mutual funds with and without fees?

For the variable containing 2001 returns:
e. Construct an ordered array and a stem-and-leaf display for the 259 mutual funds.
f. What percentage of the funds in (e) experienced a positive return? A return greater than 10%?
g. Construct an ordered array and a stem-and-leaf display for the funds that have no fee.
h. What percentage of the funds in (g) experienced a positive return? A return greater than 10%?
i. Construct an ordered array and a stem-and-leaf display for the funds that have a fee.
j. What percentage of the funds in (i) experienced a positive return? A return greater than 10%?
k. Discuss the 2001 annual return of mutual funds. Are the returns similar for funds with and without fees?
l. Repeat (e) through (k) for the variable containing the three-year returns.

TP2 The data file **MUTUAL FUNDS.xls** contains information regarding 13 variables from a sample of 259 mutual funds.

a. Construct a percentage histogram for the 2001 annual return variable using the 46 mutual funds specializing in midsize companies.
b. What percentage of the funds in (a) experienced a positive return? A return greater than 10%?
c. Construct a percentage histogram for the 2001 annual return variable using the 42 mutual funds specializing in small companies.
d. What percentage of the funds in (c) experienced a positive return? A return greater than 10%?
e. Compare the results of the mutual funds specializing in midsize companies to those specializing in small companies.
f. Repeat (a) through (e) for the variable containing the three-year returns.

TP3 The data file **MUTUAL FUNDS.xls** is a sample of 259 mutual funds each of which has one of five levels of turnover (very low, low, average, high, and very high).

a. Construct a bar chart indicating the level of turnover for the mutual funds.
b. Construct a pie chart indicating the level of turnover for the mutual funds.
c. Which type of chart do you prefer here and why?
d. Use the mutual funds data contained in the data set **MUTUAL FUNDS.xls** to complete the following contingency table.

	Fund Type			
Level of Turnover	**Small Cap**	**Mid Cap**	**Large Cap**	**Total**
Very low				
Low				
Average				
Very high				
High				
Total				

e. Does there seem to be an underrepresentation of certain types in the high-turnover mutual funds? If so, explain why this might occur.
f. Construct a side-by-side bar chart for these data.

RUNNING CASE MANAGING THE *SPRINGVILLE HERALD*

Advertising fees are an important source of revenue for any newspaper. In an attempt to boost these revenues and to minimize costly errors, the management of the *Herald* has established a task force charged with improving customer service in the advertising department. Review the task force's data collection (open **Ad_Errors.htm** in the HeraldCase folder on the CD-ROM that accompanies this text or link to **www.prenhall.com/HeraldCase/Ad_Errors.htm**) and identify the data that are important in describing the customer service problems. For each set of data you identify, construct the graphical presentation you think is most appropriate for the data and explain your choice. Also, suggest what other information concerning the different types of errors would be useful to examine. Offer possible courses of action for either the task force or management to take that would support the goal of improving customer service.

WEB CASE

In the Using Statistics scenario, you were asked to gather information that would help you make wise investment choices. Sources for such information include brokerage firms and investment counselors. Apply your knowledge about the proper use of tables and charts in this Web Case about the claims of foresight and excellence by a Springville investment service.

Visit the StockTout Investing Service Web site (**www.prenhall.com/Springville/StockTout.htm**). Review their investment claims and supporting data and then answer the following.

1. How does the presentation of the general information about StockTout on its home page affect your perception of their business?
2. Is their claim about having more winners than losers a fair and accurate reflection about the quality of their investment service? If you do not think that the claim is a fair and accurate one, provide an alternate presentation that you think is fair and accurate.
3. StockTout's "Big Eight" mutual funds are part of the sample found in the **MUTUAL FUNDS2002.xls** file. Is there any other relevant data from that file that could have been included in the Big Eight table? How would that new data alter your perception of StockTout's claims?
4. StockTout is proud that all "Big Eight" funds have gained in value over the past five years. Do you agree that they should be proud of their selections? Why or why not?

REFERENCES

1. Cleveland, W. S., "Graphs in Scientific Publications," *The American Statistician* 38 (November 1984), 261–269.
2. Cleveland, W. S., "Graphical Methods for Data Presentation: Full Scale Breaks, Dot Charts, and Multibased Logging," *The American Statistician* 38 (November 1984), 270–280.
3. Cleveland, W. S., and R. McGill, "Graphical Perception: Theory, Experimentation, and Application to the Development of Graphical Methods," *Journal of the American Statistical Association* 79 (September 1984), 531–554.
4. Huff, D., *How to Lie with Statistics* (New York: Norton, 1954).
5. Microsoft Excel 2002 (Redmond, WA: Microsoft Corporation, 2001).
6. Tufte, E. R., *The Visual Display of Quantitative Information*, 2nd ed. (Cheshire, CT: Graphics Press, 2002).
7. Tufte, E. R., *Envisioning Information* (Cheshire, CT: Graphics Press, 1990).
8. Tufte, E. R., *Visual Explanations* (Cheshire, CT: Graphics Press, 1997).
9. Tukey, J., *Exploratory Data Analysis* (Reading, MA: Addison-Wesley, 1977).
10. Velleman, P. F., and D. C. Hoaglin, *Applications, Basics, and Computing of Exploratory Data Analysis* (Boston, MA: Duxbury Press, 1981).
11. Wainer, H., "How to Display Data Badly," *The American Statistician* 38 (May 1984), 137–147.
12. Wainer, H., *Visual Revelations: Graphical Tales of Fate and Deception from Napoleon Bonaparte to Ross Perot* (New York: Copernicus/Springer-Verlag, 1997).

Answers to Selected Even-Numbered Problems

For more detailed solutions including explanations, interpretations, and Excel output, see the *Student Solutions Manual.*

4 50 74 74 76 81 89 92

6 (a) 5, 6, 10, 11, 11, 12, 13, 14, 14, 14, 15, 15, 15, 15, 16, 16, 16, 16, 17, 17, 17, 19, 19, 20, 22, 23, 25, 28, 30, 34. **(c)** The stem-and-leaf display provides more information because it not only orders observations from the smallest to the largest into stems and leaves, it also conveys information on how the values distribute and cluster over the range of the observations in the data set. **(d)** No, there do not seem to be more undervalued stocks than overvalued stocks because there are two stocks with a P/E ratio below 10 and two stocks with P/E ratios above 30.

8 (a) 0 0 5 5 5 5 5 5 6 6 6 7 7 7 7 8 8 9 9 9 10 10 10 10 10 12 12. **(c)** The stem-and-leaf display provides more information because it not only orders observations from the smallest to the largest into stems and leaves, it also conveys information on how the values distribute and cluster over the range of the observations in the data set. **(d)** The monthly service fees seem to be concentrated around 7 dollars since 22 banks have service fees between 5 and 10 dollars.

10 (a) The class boundaries of the nine classes can be "10 to less than 20," "20 to less than 30," "30 to less than 40," "40 to less than 50," "50 to less than 60," "60 to less than 70," "70 to less than 80," "80 to less than 90," and "90 to less than 100." **(b)** 10 **(c)** The nine class midpoints are: 15, 25, 35, 45, 55, 65, 75, 85, and 95.

12 (i) Monthly electricity costs are most concentrated between \$140 and \$160 a month, with better than one-fourth of the costs falling in that interval. **(j)** The percentage histogram displayed in part (d) clearly shows the upper and lower bounds of the seven intervals as well as the percentage of the 50 electricity bills sampled that fall in each interval. In comparison, the percentage polygon displayed in part (e) more clearly shows the typical value for each interval (the midpoint), but, because the individual points are not labeled on this graph, only approximates the percentage of the 50 electricity bills sampled that fall in each interval. Both graphs visually depict the distribution of monthly electricity bills clearly. The ogive displayed in part (h) enables us to focus on the cumulative distribution, but, because it accrues the numbers of bills up to and including each interval, it is not as clear in depicting the distribution of individual monthly electricity bills.

14 (f) Most gasoline purchases seem to be concentrated between 11 and 11.9 gallons.

16 (e) Yes, the steel mill is doing a good job at meeting the requirement as there is only one steel part out of a sample of 100 that is as much as 0.005 inches longer than the specified requirement.

18 (b) Yes, there appears to be a positive relationship between X and Y.

20 (b) There does not appear to be a positive relationship between price and energy cost. **(c)** The data does not seem to indicate that high-priced refrigerators have greater energy efficiency.

22 (b) There does not appear to be any relationship between the battery capacity and the digital-mode talk time. **(c)** No, the data does not support the expectation that higher battery capacity is associated with higher talk time.

24 (b) There seems to be a general downward trend for the S&P 500 Index from January of 2002 to July 2002. It lost about 20% of its value between January 7, 2002 and July 8, 2002. It fluctuated around 900 points between July 8, 2002 and December 30, 2002. **(d)** The prices were rather stable from January 7, 2002 to May 6, 2002. They increased slightly after that until May 28, 2003 and then followed a downward trend from May 28, 2002 to December 30, 2002. **(f)** The stock prices of Target Corporation appeared to be on an upward trend from January 7, 2002 to February 19, 2002. There seemed to be a general downward trend afterward. **(h)** The stock price of Sara Lee was rather stable between January 7, 2002 to July 1, 2002. It then lost about 16% of its value in two weeks before starting a general upward trend till December 30, 2002. **(i)** In general, the S&P 500 index followed a slight downward trend from January 7, 2002 to July 8, 2002 while the stock prices for Target followed similar pattern. The stock prices of both Sears and Sara Lee were rather stable from January 7, 2002 to July 1, 2002. The stock price of Sears then followed a downward trend while the stock price of Sara Lee had an upward trend.

26 (b) There is a downward trend in the amount of soft drink filled. **(c)** The amount of soft drink in the next bottle will probably be around 1.87. **(d)** The prediction in (c), which utilizes the downward pattern, is most likely to be more accurate.

30 (d) The Pareto diagram is better than the pie chart or the bar chart because it not only sorts the frequencies in descending order, it also provides the cumulative polygon on the same scale. From the Pareto diagram, it is obvious that more than 90% of the transactions were carried out in Visa, MasterCard, and American Express.

32 (d) The bar chart is most suitable if the purpose is to compare the categories. The pie chart is most suitable if the main objective is to investigate the portion of the whole that is in a particular category.

34 (d) The Pareto diagram is better than the pie chart to portray these data because it not only sorts the frequencies in descending order, it also provides the cumulative polygon on the same scale. From the Pareto diagram, it is obvious that "little or no knowledge of company" has constituted 44% of the most common mistakes candidates make during job interviews.

36 (b) To reduce the overall number of complaints, the hospital management should focus on improving food service, which accounted for 30.5% of all complaints, followed by timely response to patient buzzers and rudeness of staff, each of which accounted for 18.5% and 16.1% of complaints, respectively. Together, the three areas accounted for more than 65% of all complaints registered on the patient-satisfaction survey.

40 (c) In general, retail sales for the apparel industry has seen a modest growth between April 2001 and April 2002 with the exception of Talbots, whose sales have declined slightly, and Gap, whose sales have declined by almost 200 million dollars.

42 (d) The row percentages allow us to block the effect of disproportionate group size and show us that the pattern for day and evening tests among the nonconforming group is very different from the pattern for day and evening tests among the conforming group. Where 40% of the nonconforming group was tested during the day, 68% of the conforming group was tested during the day. **(e)** The director of the lab may be able to cut the number of nonconforming tests by reducing the number of tests run in the evening, when there is a higher percent of tests run improperly.

48 (a) The size of the policeman for Washington is not only taller but also bigger in overall size. This has a tendency to distort the actual difference in the size of the police forces. A simple bar chart will do a much better job.

62 (f) Yes, there is a great deal of variation in the amount of time it takes to resolve complaints. The number of days ranges from 1 to 165. Although 72% are resolved within 50 days, the remaining 28% take up to another 115 days to finally be resolved. **(g)** You should tell the president of the company that over half of the complaints are resolved within a month, but point out that some complaints take as long as three or four months to settle.

64 (d) 97.50% of the batches are within company specifications.

66 (a) Majority of the games have attendance ranges from 9,000 to 17,000. The distribution is right-skewed with only seven games having attendance over 29,000. **(b)** Majority of the games have attendance ranges from 9,000 to 17,000. The distribution is right-skewed with only seven games having attendance over 29,000. **(c)** When comparing two or more sets of data, a percentage polygon is better than a histogram. Since there is only one set of data being displayed, the percentage histogram in (a) is as good as the percentage polygon in (b). **(d)** The majority of the games with a promotion have attendance ranges from 9000 to 25000 while the majority of the games without any promotion have attendance ranges from 9000 to 17000. Having a promotion does increase attendance.

68 (k) Based on the results of (i) and (j), the percentage of front-wheel drive cars that use regular gasoline appears to be higher than that for rear-wheel drive cars.

70 (g) The percentage histogram and the percentage polygon present essentially the same information. The percentage polygon has the advantage that several polygons can be plotted on the same graph. If cumulative percentage less than a particular value is needed, the cumulative percentage polygon should be used. It is also useful in comparing more than one group. **(i)** There appears to be a positive linear relationship between number of wins and player compensation and benefits.

72 (e) The only variable that appears to be useful in predicting printer price is text cost. There appears to be a negative relationship between price and text cost. The higher the text cost, the lower is the printer cost.

74 (g) The Pareto diagram is most appropriate because it not only sorts the frequencies in descending order, it also provides the cumulative polygon on the same scale. **(h)** The Middle East, with a share of more than 60%, obviously has the largest proven conventional reserves. Among the set of countries, Saudi Arabia has the largest share of proven conventional reserves followed by Iraq, United Arab Emirates, and Kuwait. These four countries account for more than half of the reserves among the set of countries.

76 (c) Visually, the two graphs are almost identical except for the scale on the *X* axis. If the main interest is on the absolute number of unique users so that a company can justify having a higher advertising rate, the bar chart for the number of unique users will serve the purpose well. However, if the main concern is the market share of a company, then the bar chart for the percentage of total Web audience reached will be more appropriate.

78 (c) When performing comparison between two data sets, the side-by-side bar chart is more helpful. **(d)** AT&T has the largest revenue market share followed by MCI, Sprint, Verizon, and VarTec. AT&T also has the largest household market share followed by MCI, Verizon, Sprint, and VarTec.

80 (a) 23575R15 accounts for over 80% of the warranty claims. **(b)** Tread separation accounts for the majority (70%) of the warranty claims. **(c)** Tread separation accounts for more than 70% of the warranty claims among the ATX model. **(d)** The number of claims is quite evenly distributed among the three incidents with other/unknown incidents accounting for almost 40% of the claims, tread separation accounting for about 35% of the claims, and blow out accounts for about 25% of the claims. **(e)** The tire size 23575R15 accounts for more than 80% of the warranty claims. For this tire size, tread separation is the major incident responsible for claims among the ATX model while there is not any particular incident that accounts for the majority of the claims among the Wilderness model. Tread separation among the ATX model accounts for 1365/2504 = 54.5% of the warranty claims.

Excel Handbook for Tables and Charts

EH1 CORRECTING FREQUENCY DISTRIBUTIONS GENERATED BY THE DATA ANALYSIS HISTOGRAM PROCEDURE

When you use the Data Analysis Histogram procedure directly to generate frequency distributions for numerical data without PHStat2, the resulting frequency distribution improperly includes an additional class labeled "More". For example, if you follow the Using Excel instructions, the frequency distribution that you initially produce for the growth funds data will be similar to the one shown in Figure EH1.

	A	B	C
1	*Bins*	*Frequency*	*umulative %*
2	-10.01	0	.00%
3	-5.01	1	.63%
4	-0.01	3	2.53%
5	4.99	14	11.39%
6	9.99	58	48.10%
7	14.99	61	86.71%
8	19.99	17	97.47%
9	24.99	3	99.37%
10	29.99	1	100.00%
11	More	0	100.00%

FIGURE EH1 Frequency distribution generated by Histogram procedure

To eliminate this class, first manually add the More frequency count to the count of the preceding class and set the cumulative percentage of the preceding class to 100%. (For the example shown, this step would not change the row 10 entries because the More class happens to have a frequency of zero.) Then, select the More row (the cell range A11:C11 in Figure EH1), select **Edit | Delete**, and in the Delete dialog box, select the **Shift cells up** option button and click **OK**.

To improve the formatting of this worksheet, select a cell in **row 1** and then select **Insert | Rows** to insert a row at the top for a title and adjust the column widths for proper column headings display. To add a column of frequency percentages, select **column C** and then select **Insert | Columns**. In the new column C, enter the formula **=B3/SUM(B:B)** in cell C3 and copy the formula down the column. Format this column for percentage display. Enter the column heading **Percentage** in cell C2 to complete the column. In column E, enter the midpoint values and heading as shown in Table EH1 in the next section.

EH2 GENERATING FREQUENCY DISTRIBUTIONS USING THE FREQUENCY ARRAY FUNCTION

You can implement a worksheet that uses the **FREQUENCY** array function in formulas to create a frequency distribution as an alternative to using the Data Analysis Histogram procedure. Such a worksheet will dynamically change the frequency counts as the underlying raw data change.

For example, Table EH1 shows the design of a **Frequencies** worksheet that can be added to the **Growth Funds Sample.xls** workbook. This new worksheet uses the data of the 5YrData worksheet to produce a frequency distribution. The FREQUENCY function is entered as **FREQUENCY(*data range*, *class maximum range*)**, where *data range* is the cell range of the data to be analyzed and *class maximum range* is the cell range that contains the ordered list of class maximum values being used to approximate class intervals.

Because the FREQUENCY function is an array function, use the following special procedure when entering the formulas in the cell range B3:B11:

Select the cell range **B3:B11**.

Type **=FREQUENCY('5YrData'!B1:B158, A3:A11)** but do *not* press the Enter or Tab keys. While holding down the **Control** and **Shift** keys, press the **Enter** key.

Table EH1
Frequencies worksheet design

	A	B	C	D	E
1	Frequency Distribution of 5-Year Returns				
2	*Bins*	*Frequency*	*Pctage*	*Cum. Pctage*	*Midpts.*
3	–10.01	=FREQUENCY('5YrData'!B1:B158, A3:A11)	=B3/B$13	=C3	—
4	–5.01	=FREQUENCY('5YrData'!B1:B158, A3:A11)	=B4/B$13	=D3 + C4	–7.5
5	–0.01	=FREQUENCY('5YrData'!B1:B158, A3:A11)	=B5/B$13	=D4 + C5	–2.5
6	4.99	=FREQUENCY('5YrData'!B1:B158, A3:A11)	=B6/B$13	=D5 + C6	2.5
7	9.99	=FREQUENCY('5YrData'!B1:B158, A3:A11)	=B7/B$13	=D6 + C7	7.5
8	14.99	=FREQUENCY('5YrData'!B1:B158, A3:A11)	=B8/B$13	=D7 + C8	12.5
9	19.99	=FREQUENCY('5YrData'!B1:B158, A3:A11)	=B9/B$13	=D8 + C9	17.5
10	24.99	=FREQUENCY('5YrData'!B1:B158, A3:A11)	=B10/B$13	=D9 + C10	22.5
11	29.99	=FREQUENCY('5YrData'!B1:B158, A3:A11)	=B11/B$13	=D10 + C11	27.5
12					
13	Total:	=SUM(B4:B12)			

EH3 CORRECTING DATA ANALYSIS HISTOGRAMS

To correct histograms generated by the Data Analysis Histogram procedure, first follow the instructions of section EH1 to modify the frequency distributions generated by the Histogram procedure. At this point, your revised histogram will contain these errors: There are gaps between the bars that correspond to the class intervals in the histogram; the "bins" are labeled with their maximum values and not with their midpoint values; the secondary *Y* axis scale exceeds 100%; the title and *X* axis have generic labels; and an unwanted cumulative percentage polygon plot is superimposed over the histogram (see Figure EH2).

FIGURE EH2
Histogram with errors

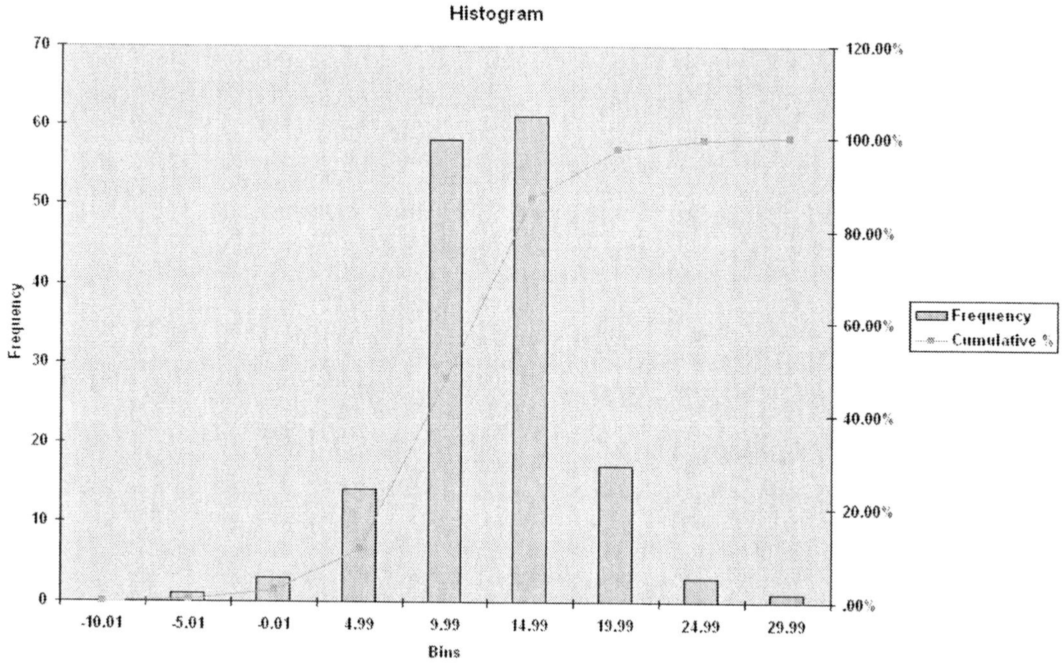

To correct these errors, use the following procedures:

To eliminate the gaps between bars. Right-click on one of the histogram bars. (The tool tip that begins with the phrase "Series 'Frequency'" appears when the mouse pointer is properly positioned over a bar.) Select **Format Data Series** from the shortcut menu. In the Format Data Series dialog box, select the **Options** tab and change the value in the **Gap width** edit box to **0**. Click **OK**.

*or the first empty column of the worksheet if column E contains table data

To change the labels for the bins. Enter midpoint values in **column E***. Right-click the tinted background of the chart. (The tool tip "Plot Area" appears when the mouse pointer is properly positioned.) Select **Source Data** from the shortcut menu. In the Source Data dialog box, select the **Series** tab and enter a *formula* that specifies the cell range of the midpoints, using *Sheetname!CellRange* notation, in the **Category (X) axis labels** edit box. For example, for midpoints entered into cell range E3:E11 of a worksheet named Frequencies, enter **=Frequencies!E3:E11** in that edit box. Delete the entry for the **Second category (X) axis labels** and click **OK**.

To rescale the secondary Y axis. Right-click on the secondary (right) *Y* axis. (The tool tip "Secondary Value Axis" appears when the mouse pointer is properly positioned.) Select **Format Axis** from the shortcut menu. In the **Scale** tab of the Format Axis dialog box, change the value in the **Maximum** edit box to 1 and click **OK**.

To change the generic labels. Click the generic label (a halo appears around the label). In the formula bar, enter the new label value and press the **Enter** key.

To delete the cumulative percentage polygon plot. Right-click the cumulative percentage plot. (The tool tip that begins with "Series 'Cumulative %'" appears when the mouse pointer is properly positioned.) Select **Clear** from the shortcut menu.

EH4 GENERATING HISTOGRAMS FROM PRE-EXISTING TABLES

To generate a histogram from a pre-existing frequency distribution table, use the Chart Wizard. For example, to produce a histogram from the frequency distribution table shown in the Frequencies worksheet design of Table EH1, open to your implemented version of that worksheet (or the **Frequencies** worksheet of the **Chapter 2.xls** workbook), select **Insert | Chart** and make these entries in the Chart Wizard dialog boxes:

Step 1 dialog box. (shown at right) Select the **Standard Types** tab and then select **Column** from the **Chart type** list box. Select the first **Chart sub-type** choice, labeled as **Clustered Column** when selected, and click the **Next** button.

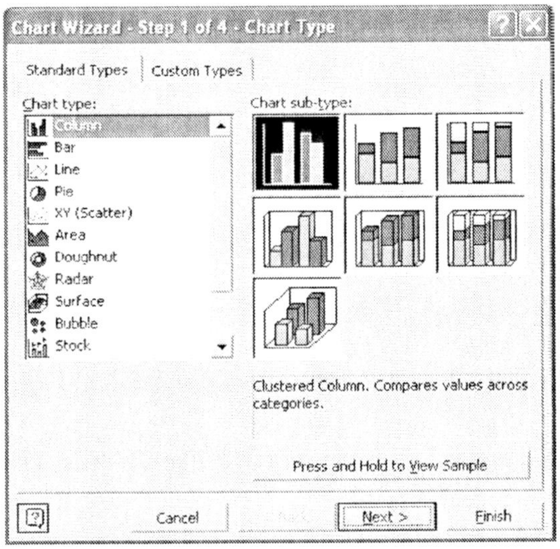

Step 2 dialog box. Select the **Data Range** tab. Enter **B3:B11** in the **Data range** edit box and select the **Columns** option button in the **Series in** group. Select the **Series** tab. Enter the *formula* that specifies the cell range of the frequencies, using the *Sheetname!CellRange* notation, in the **Category (X) axis labels** edit box (if you are using the **Frequencies** worksheet, enter **=Frequencies!E3:E11**) and click **Next**.

Step 3 dialog box. Select the **Titles** tab. Enter **Histogram** as the **Chart title, Midpoints** in the **Category (X) axis** edit box, and **Frequency** in the **Value (Y) axis** edit box. Select, in turn, the **Axes, Gridlines, Legend, Data Labels,** and **Data table** tabs and adjust settings as discussed in Exhibit EP6 of the Excel Primer—consult your instructor if you require this item. Click **Next**.

Step 4 dialog box. Select the **As new sheet** option button, enter a descriptive chart sheet name, and click the **Finish** button to generate the chart.

To eliminate the gaps between the histogram bars, right-click one of the histogram bars. (The tool tip that begins with the phrase "Series 1" appears when the mouse pointer is properly positioned.) Select **Format Data Series** from the shortcut menu. In the Format Data Series dialog box, click the **Options** tab, change the value in the **Gap width** edit box to **0**, and click **OK**.

EH5 GENERATING POLYGONS USING THE CHART WIZARD

To generate polygons from the frequency distribution worksheets created by the instructions of either section EH1 or EH2, use the Chart Wizard. Begin by opening to your frequency distribution worksheet and selecting any cell in **row 3**. Select **Insert | Rows** and enter **0** in the new cells **B3**, **C3**, and **D3**. Also enter **0** in cells **B13** and **C13**. Adjust formatting as necessary. At this point, rows 3 through 13 of your frequency distribution should look similar to those shown in Figure EH3 (a modified frequency distribution for the **5YrData** of the **Growth Funds Sample.xls** workbook).

FIGURE EH3
Modified frequency distribution table example

	A	B	C	D	E
1	**Frequency Distribution For Growth Funds**				
2	*Bins*	*Frequency*	*Percentage*	*Cumulative %*	*Midpts*
3		0	0	0	
4	-10.01	0	0.00%	.00%	---
5	-5.01	1	0.63%	.63%	-7.5
6	-0.01	3	1.90%	2.53%	-2.5
7	4.99	14	8.86%	11.39%	2.5
8	9.99	58	36.71%	48.10%	7.5
9	14.99	61	38.61%	86.71%	12.5
10	19.99	17	10.76%	97.47%	17.5
11	24.99	3	1.90%	99.37%	22.5
12	29.99	1	0.63%	100.00%	27.5
13		0	0		

With your modified frequency distribution worksheet still open, use the Chart Wizard to generate a polygon on a separate chart sheet. For example, to generate a polygon from worksheet named **Frequencies** that contains the table shown in Figure EH3, select **Insert | Chart** and make these entries in the Chart Wizard dialog boxes:

Step 1 dialog box. Select the **Standard Types** tab and then select **Line** from the **Chart-type** list box. Select the first choice in the second row of **Chart sub-type** choices, labeled as **Line with markers displayed at each data value** when selected, and click the **Next** button.

Step 2 dialog box. Select the **Data Range** tab. In the **Data range** edit box, enter **B3:B13**, for a frequency polygon, **or C3:C13**, for a percentage polygon, **or D3:D12**, for a cumulative percentage polygon. Select the **Columns** option button in the **Series in** group. Select the **Series** tab. In the **Category (X) axis labels** edit box, enter the *formula* that specifies the cell range of the frequencies, using the *Sheetname!CellRange* notation, in the **Category (X) axis labels** edit box. If you are using the **Frequencies** worksheet, enter **=Frequencies!E3:E13**, for either a frequency or percentage polygon, or **=Frequencies!E3:E12**, for a cumulative percentage polygon. Click **Next**.

Step 3 dialog box. Select the **Titles** tab. Enter values for the **Chart title**, the **Category (X) axis**, and **Value (Y) axis** edit boxes. Select, in turn, the **Axes**, **Gridlines**, **Data Labels**, and **Data Table** tabs and adjust settings as discussed in Exhibit EP6 of the Excel Primer. Select the **Legend** tab, select the **Show legend** check box, and click **Next**.

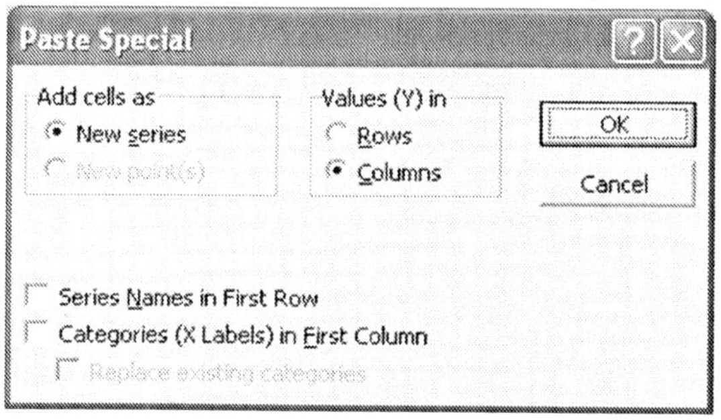

Step 4 dialog box. Select the **As new sheet** option button, enter a descriptive and unique sheet name, and click the **Finish** button to generate the chart.

Additional data series can be added to the polygon to produce charts similar to those shown in Figures 3 and 4. To add a data series, open to your chart sheet and select **Chart | Add Data**. In the Add Data dialog box, enter the cell range of the new data series using the *Sheetname!CellRange* notation and click **OK**. Should the Paste Special dialog box appear, select the **New series** and **Columns** option buttons and click **OK**.

EH6 RELOCATING CHART AXES

When the Chart Wizard generates a scatter diagram from data that contains negative values, the diagram will have its *X* axis and *Y* axis superimposed over the data points and not on the edges of the graph. To relocate the axes, open to the chart and:

To change the position of the X *axis*. Select the *X* **axis**. (The tool tip "Value (X) axis" appears when the mouse pointer is properly positioned as is shown at right.) Right-click the axis and select **Format Axis**. In the Format Axis dialog box, select the **Scale** tab and enter the value found in the Minimum edit box in the **Value (Y) axis Crosses at** edit box. (After entry, the **Auto** check box for this entry will be cleared.) Click the **OK** button.

To change the position of the Y *axis*. Select the *Y* **axis**. (The tool tip "Value (Y) axis" appears when the mouse pointer is properly positioned.) Right-click the axis and select **Format Axis**. In the Format Axis dialog box, select the **Scale** tab and enter the value found in the Minimum edit box in the **Value (X) axis Crosses at** edit box. (After entry, the **Auto** check box for this entry will be cleared.) Click the **OK** button.

EH7 GENERATING SUMMARY TABLES FOR CATEGORICAL DATA

To generate a summary table for categorical data, use the PivotTable Wizard. For example, to generate a summary table similar to Table 7, open the **Mutual Funds.xls** workbook to the **Data** worksheet and select **Data | PivotTable and PivotChart Report*** and make these entries in the PivotTable Wizard dialog boxes:

*Select **Data | PivotChart Report** if you are using Microsoft Excel 97.

**The PivotTable option button does not appear in the Microsoft Excel 97 Step 1 dialog box.

Step 1 dialog box. Select the **Microsoft Excel list or database** and the **PivotTable** option buttons** and click the **Next** button.

Step 2 dialog box. Enter **K1:K260** in the **Range** edit box and click **Next**.

Step 3 dialog box. Select the **New worksheet** option button and click the **Layout** button. In the Layout dialog box, select the **Risk** variable name label to make a copy of the label. Drag this copy to the **ROW** area. Select the **Risk** label a second time to make another copy and drag this second copy to the **DATA** area. Note when you release this second copy, the label changes to **Count of Risk**. Click the **OK** button of the Layout dialog box to return to the Step 3 dialog box.

Continue in the Step 3 dialog box by clicking the **Options** button. In the PivotTable Options dialog box, enter a self-descriptive name for the table in the **Name** edit box, select the **For empty cells, show** check box, and enter **0** in its edit box. Click **OK** to return to the Step 3 dialog box. Click the **Finish** button in the Step 3 dialog box to produce the summary PivotTable.

Rename the new worksheet with a self-descriptive name. (If any floating toolbars or windows appear over the PivotTable, you can close them to better view your table.)

To add a percentage column to make the PivotTable more like Table 7, enter the heading **Percentage** in cell **C4** of the new worksheet and enter the formula **=B5/B$10** in cell **C5**. Copy the formula down column C through cell C9. Adjust the width and formatting of column C, including formatting the cell range **C5:C9** for percentage display. Your completed table will be similar to the one shown at the right in Figure EH4.

	A	B	C
1	Mutual Funds Risk Level		
2			
3	Count of Risk		
4	Risk ▾	Total	Percentage
5	average	82	32%
6	high	80	31%
7	low	76	29%
8	very high	15	6%
9	very low	6	2%
10	Grand Total	259	

FIGURE EH4 Completed summary table

EH8 GENERATING BAR AND PIE CHARTS FOR CATEGORICAL DATA

To generate bar and pie charts from summary tables, use the Chart Wizard. For example, to generate a bar or pie chart from the summary table generated in the previous section (see Figure EH4), open to the worksheet containing that table (or the Table 2.7 worksheet of the **Chapter 2.xls** workbook) and select a cell that is *outside* your table, such as cell D1. Then select **Insert | Chart** and make these entries in the Chart Wizard dialog boxes:

Step 1 dialog box. Select the **Standard Types** tab.

For a bar chart, select **Bar** from the **Chart type** list box and then select the first **Chart sub-type** choice, labeled as **Clustered Bar** when selected, and click the **Next** button.

For a pie chart, select **Pie** from the **Chart type** list box and then select the first **Chart sub-type** choice, labeled as **Pie** when selected, and click **Next.**

Step 2 dialog box. Select the **Data Range** tab and enter the **A3:B9** in the **Data range** edit box, Select the **Columns** option if it is visible, and click **Next.**

Step 3 dialog box. Select the **Titles** tab. Enter a title in the **Chart title** edit box and enter appropriate values in the **Category (X) axis** and **Value (Y) axis** edit boxes, if you are generating a bar chart.

For a bar chart, select, in turn, the **Axes**, **Gridlines**, **Legend**, **Data Labels**, and **Data Table** tabs and adjust settings as discussed in Exhibit EP6 of the Excel Primer and click **Next**. (Consult your instructor if you require the Excel Primer.)

For a pie chart, select the **Legend** tab and clear the **Show legend** check box. Select the **Data Labels** tab. Select the **Show label and percent** option button, if you are using Microsoft Excel 97 or 2000, or select the **Category name** and **Percentage** check boxes, if you are using Microsoft Excel 2002 or later and click **Next**.

Step 4 dialog box. Select the **As new sheet** option button, enter a descriptive chart sheet name, and click the **Finish** button to generate the chart.

On the new chart sheet, right-click the **Risk** drop-down list and select **Hide PivotChart Field Buttons** for the shortcut menu to eliminate some clutter. (Skip this step if you are using Microsoft Excel 97.)

EH9 GENERATING PARETO DIAGRAMS FOR CATEGORICAL DATA

To generate a Pareto diagram, use a two-step process in which you first add a cumulative percentage column to your summary table and then use the Chart Wizard with that expanded table. For example, to generate a Pareto diagram from the summary table generated by the instructions of section EH7, open to the worksheet containing that table (or the Figure EH4 worksheet of the **Chapter 2.xls** workbook). If your summary table does not already contain a percentage column, first apply the instructions of the last paragraph of section EH7 to add such a column. Then enter the heading **Cumulative Pctage.** in cell **D4**. Enter the formula **=C5** in cell **D5**. Enter the formula **=D5+C6** in cell **D6**. Copy the formula down column D through cell D9. Adjust the width and formatting of column D, including formatting the cell range **D5:D9** for percentage display. Then reorder the rows of the PivotTable by using this procedure:

Right-click cell A4 and select **Field Settings** from the shortcut menu. (**Field**, if using Microsoft Excel 97.)

In the PivotTable Field dialog box, click the **Advanced** button. In the PivotTable Field Advanced Options dialog box (see Figure EH5), select the **Descending** option button and **Count of Risk** from the **Using field** drop-down list box. Click the **OK** button to return to the PivotTable Field dialog box and then click **OK** in that dialog box to have the data in the table reordered in descending order.

Because the reordering can affect other graphs based on the PivotTable summary table, you may want to make a copy of your worksheet using the instructions of section EP5.3 of the Excel Primer and then apply the procedure above to the table in the copied worksheet.

FIGURE EH5
PivotTable Field and Field Advanced Options dialog boxes

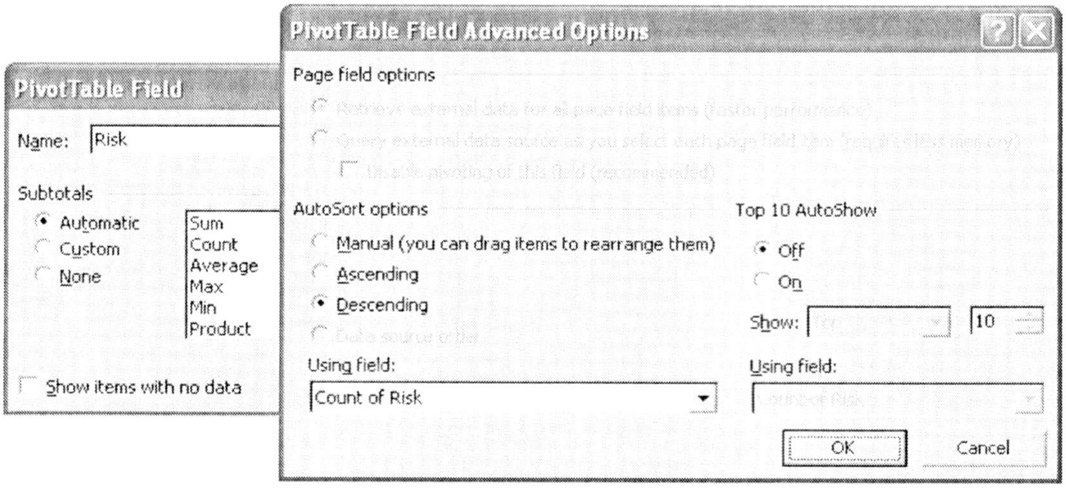

With your modified summary table still onscreen, use the Chart Wizard to generate a Pareto diagram. For example, to generate a Pareto diagram from the summary table just reordered, open to the worksheet containing that reordered table (or the **NewRiskOrder** worksheet of the **Chapter 2.xls** workbook), and select a cell that is outside your table, such as cell **D1**. Then select **Insert | Chart** and make these entries in the Chart Wizard dialog boxes:

Step 1 dialog box. Select the **Custom Types** tab. Select the **Built-in** option button, then select **Line-Column on 2 Axes** from the **Chart type** list box and click the **Next** button.

Step 2 dialog box. Select the **Data Range** tab. Enter **C4:D9** in the **Data range** edit box and select the **Columns** option button in the **Series in** group. Select the **Series** tab. Enter the *formula* **=NewRiskOrder!A5:A9** in the **Category (X) axis labels** edit box. (Adjust the worksheet name to reflect your worksheet's name if it is not NewRiskOrder.) If it appears, leave the **Second category (X) axis labels** edit box blank. Click **Next**.

Step 3 dialog box. Select the **Titles** tab. Enter **Pareto Diagram for Risk** as the **Chart title**, **Risk** in the **Category (X) axis** edit box, and **Percentage** in the **Value (Y) axis** edit box. Leave the other two edit boxes blank. Select, in turn, the **Gridlines**, **Legend**, **Data Labels**, and **Data Table** tabs and adjust settings as discussed in Exhibit EP6 of the Excel Primer. Click **Next**.

Step 4 dialog box. Select the **As new sheet** option button, enter a descriptive chart sheet name, and click the **Finish** button to generate the chart.

Rescale the *Y* axis by applying the instructions "To rescale the secondary *Y* axis" in section EH3 to generate a Pareto diagram similar to Figure 8.

EH10 GENERATING CONTINGENCY TABLES FOR BIVARIATE CATEGORICAL DATA

To generate a contingency table for bivariate categorical data, use the PivotTable Wizard. For example, to generate the summary table similar to Table 10, open the **Mutual Funds Sample.xls** workbook to the **Data** worksheet and select **Data | PivotTable and PivotChart Report*** and make these entries in the PivotTable Wizard dialog boxes:

Select **Data | PivotTable Report if you are using Microsoft Excel 97.*

***The PivotTable option button does not appear in the Microsoft Excel 97 Step 1 dialog box.*

Step 1 dialog box. Select the **Microsoft Excel list or database** and the **PivotTable** option buttons** and click the **Next** button.

Step 2 dialog box. Enter **A1:K260** in the **Range** edit box and click **Next**.

Step 3 dialog box. Select the **New worksheet** option button and click the **Layout** button. In the Layout dialog box, select the **Risk** variable name label to make a copy of the label. Drag this copy to the **ROW** area. Select the **Fees** label and drag its copy to the **COLUMN** area. Select the

Fund label and drag its copy to the **DATA** area. Note when you release this copy, the label changes to **Count of Fund**. Click the **OK** button of the Layout dialog box to return to the Step 3 dialog box.

Continue in the Step 3 dialog box by clicking the **Options** button. In the PivotTable Options dialog box, enter a self-descriptive name of the table in the **Name** edit box, select the **For empty cells, show** check box and enter **0** in its edit box. Click **OK** to return to the Step 3 dialog box. Click the **Finish** button in the Step 3 dialog box to produce the summary PivotTable.

If any floating toolbars or windows appear over the PivotTable, you can close them to better view your table. Add a title in row 1 of the worksheet generated and rename the worksheet with a self-descriptive name. The contingency table generated will be similar to the one in Figure EH6.

FIGURE EH6
Completed PivotTable Contingency Table for Risk and Fees

	A	B	C	D
1	Contingency Table for Risk and Fees			
2				
3	Count of Fund	Fees ▾		
4	Risk ▾	No	Yes	Grand Total
5	average	59	23	82
6	high	45	35	80
7	low	45	31	76
8	very high	11	4	15
9	very low	4	2	6
10	Grand Total	164	95	259

Numerical Descriptive Measures

USING STATISTICS: Evaluating the Performance of Mutual Funds

LEARNING OBJECTIVES

- To describe the properties of central tendency, variation, and shape in numerical data
- To construct and interpret a box-and-whisker plot
- To calculate descriptive summary measures from a population
- To calculate and interpret the coefficient of correlation

USING STATISTICS

Evaluating the Performance of Mutual Funds

As a financial advisor, you are responsible for helping clients decide which types of mutual funds to invest in. You may have learned how to *present* data in tables and charts. However, when dealing with numerical data, like the 5-year annualized return on investments in mutual funds, effective data analysis involves not only *presenting* the data and *observing* what the data are trying to convey but also *computing* and *summarizing* the key features and *analyzing* the findings. What is the central tendency for returns of the various funds? For example, what is the average 5-year annualized return for the very-low-risk, low-risk, average-risk, high-risk, and very-high-risk mutual funds? How much variability is present in the returns? Are the returns for high-risk funds more variable than for average-risk funds or low-risk funds? How can you use this information when advising your clients?

INTRODUCTION

Although presenting data is an essential component of descriptive statistics, it does not tell the whole story. In this chapter numerical data and their properties are explored. First, measures of central tendency, variation, and shape are discussed. You will learn how to calculate and interpret descriptive summary measures from a sample and a population. Then exploratory data analysis methods are developed. Correlation is then introduced as a measure of association between two numerical variables. Finally, the pitfalls of using descriptive summary measures are discussed as are pertinent ethical issues.

1 EXPLORING NUMERICAL DATA AND THEIR PROPERTIES

In determining an investment strategy, a place to start is to examine the stock market returns during the volatile 5-year period ending December 31, 2001. The 5-year annualized return of the different mutual funds could be compared based on their perceived risk. First, the 15 funds rated as very-high-risk will be studied. One would expect that the very-high-risk mutual funds might be more variable, but possibly perform better, than the other funds. The 5-year annualized returns for the very-high-risk funds are listed in Figure 1.

What can be learned from these data that will assist you in an evaluation for future investments? The following is an ordered array of the 5-year annualized returns for these 15 very-high-risk mutual funds.

$$-6.1 \quad -2.8 \quad -1.2 \quad -0.7 \quad 4.3 \quad 5.5 \quad 5.9 \quad 6.5 \quad 7.6 \quad 8.3 \quad 9.6 \quad 9.8 \quad 12.9 \quad 13.1 \quad 18.5$$

On the basis of this sample, the following statements can be made:

1. All mutual funds experienced different returns.
2. The spread of the 5-year annualized returns for the very-high-risk funds ranges from −6.1 to 18.5.
3. There appears to be one very high 5-year annualized return—the 18.5 obtained by RS Emerging Growth A.

FIGURE 1
5-year annualized returns for very-high-risk mutual funds

MUTUAL FUNDS.xls

Very High Risk Fund	5-Yr Return
Amer. Century GiftTrust Inv.	-2.8
AXP Stategy Aggressive A	5.5
Berger Small Company Growth Inv	8.3
Consulting Group Small Cap Growth	4.3
Fidelity Aggressive Growth	5.9
Invesco Growth Inv	-0.7
Janus Enterprise	6.5
Janus Venture	9.8
John Hancock Small Cap Growth A	7.6
MS Mid Cap Equity Tr. B	9.6
PBHG Growth	-1.2
Putnam OTC Emerging Growth A	-6.1
RS Emerging Growth A	18.5
Rydex OTC Inv	13.1
Van Kampen Aggressive Growth A	12.9

In this case the 18.5 might be considered an **outlier**, or extreme value. As a financial advisor, you would want to explore the reasons the return for this mutual fund is different from those achieved by the other very-high-risk funds. A comparison of the prospectuses for this fund against those with other more typical performance records might provide some useful insight for future investment purposes. In presenting a short summary of the findings, statements similar to the three given on the previous page are all that could be made without more knowledge of the subject of statistics. You can add to your understanding of the past performance of these funds by examining the three major properties that describe a set of numerical data: *central tendency*, *variation*, and *shape*.

2 MEASURES OF CENTRAL TENDENCY, VARIATION, AND SHAPE

Most sets of data show a distinct tendency to group or cluster around a central point. Thus, for any particular set of data, a single typical value can be used to describe the entire data set. Such a value is referred to as a measure of **central tendency**, or **location**. Three measures of central tendency discussed in this section are the arithmetic mean, the median, and the mode.

The Arithmetic Mean

The **arithmetic mean** (also called the **mean**) is the most commonly used measure of central tendency. The arithmetic mean is calculated by summing the observed numerical values of a variable in a set of data and then dividing the total by the number of observations involved.

For a sample containing a set of n observations $X_1, X_2, \ldots, X_n$, the arithmetic mean of a sample (given by the symbol $\overline{X}$, called *X bar*) is written as

$$\overline{X} = \frac{X_1 + X_2 + \cdots + X_n}{n}$$

To simplify the notation,[1] the term

$$\sum_{i=1}^{n} X_i$$

(meaning the summation of all the X_i values) is used whenever a series of observations is added together, as in the following:

$$\sum_{i=1}^{n} X_i = X_1 + X_2 + \cdots + X_n$$

[1] *See the appendix for a discussion of summation notation.*

Using this summation notation, the arithmetic mean of the sample can be expressed as shown in Equation (1).

ARITHMETIC MEAN

The arithmetic mean is the sum of the values divided by the number of values.

$$\bar{X} = \frac{\sum_{i=1}^{n} X_i}{n} \tag{1}$$

where

$\bar{X}$ = arithmetic mean
n = number of observations or sample size
X_i = ith observation of the variable X
$\sum_{i=1}^{n} X_i$ = summation of all X_i values in the sample

Using the example of the 5-year annualized return of the 15 very-high-risk mutual funds, to compute the arithmetic mean, X_i values are assigned to each of the 15 mutual funds.

$X_1 = -2.8$ for Amer. Century Gift Trust Inv.
$X_2 = 5.5$ for AXP Strategy Aggressive A
$X_3 = 8.3$ for Berger Small Company Growth Inv.
$X_4 = 4.3$ for Consulting Group Small Cap Growth
$X_5 = 5.9$ for Fidelity Aggressive Growth
$X_6 = -0.7$ for Invesco Growth Inv.
$X_7 = 6.5$ for Janus Enterprise
$X_8 = 9.8$ for Janus Venture
$X_9 = 7.6$ for John Hancock Small Cap Growth A
$X_{10} = 9.6$ for MS Mid Cap Equity Tr. B
$X_{11} = -1.2$ for PBHG Growth
$X_{12} = -6.1$ for Putnam OTC Emerging Growth A
$X_{13} = 18.5$ for RS Emerging Growth A
$X_{14} = 13.1$ for Rydex OTC Inv.
$X_{15} = 12.9$ for Van Kampen Aggressive Growth A

The arithmetic mean for this sample is then calculated as follows:

$$\bar{X} = \frac{\sum_{i=1}^{n} X_i}{n} = \frac{-2.8 + 5.5 + 8.3 + \cdots + 12.9}{15}$$

$$\bar{X} = \frac{91.2}{15} = 6.08$$

Observe that the mean 5-year annualized return for the very-high-risk mutual funds is computed as 6.08, even though not one particular fund in the sample actually had that value. This is a good return, especially when compared to the 3% or 4% annualized return investors would have received from cash deposits at a bank or credit union during that period of time. In addition, from the **dot scale** in Figure 2, you can see that eight observations are larger than the mean and seven are smaller. The mean acts as a *balancing point* so that smaller observations balance out larger ones. Note that the calculation of the mean is based on all the observations ($X_1, X_2, X_3, \ldots, X_{15}$) in the set of data. No other commonly used measure of central tendency has this characteristic.

FIGURE 2

Dot scale obtained from Microsoft Excel of the 5-year annualized returns for the 15 very-high-risk mutual funds

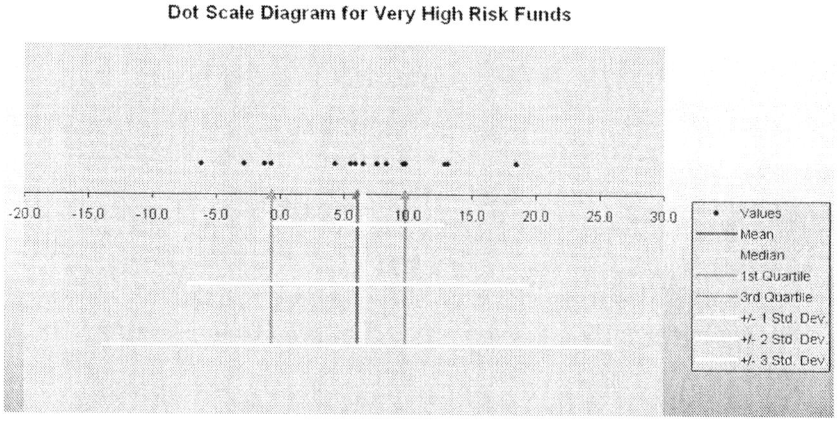

WHEN TO USE THE ARITHMETIC MEAN

Because its computation is based on every observation, the arithmetic mean is greatly affected by any extreme value or values. In such instances, only reporting the arithmetic mean may present a distorted representation of what the data are conveying. Therefore, when describing or summarizing a set of data that has extreme values, you should report the median or report both the median and the mean.

To demonstrate the effect that extreme values have when summarizing and describing the property of central tendency,[2] suppose the extreme value of 18.5 observed for RS Emerging Growth A is removed. Example 1 illustrates how the arithmetic mean of the 5-year annualized returns changes.

[2]*To explore the effect of a change in a value on the arithmetic mean and median, open the Visual Explorations in Statistics Excel workbook that is included on the CD. Select Descriptive Statistics from the Visual Explorations menu.*

EXAMPLE 1

COMPUTE THE ARITHMETIC MEAN OF THE 5-YEAR ANNUALIZED RETURNS AFTER REMOVING RS EMERGING GROWTH A

SOLUTION

The arithmetic mean for this sample of 14 funds is calculated as follows:

$$\bar{X} = \frac{\sum_{i=1}^{n} X_i}{n} = \frac{-2.8 + 5.5 + 8.3 + \cdots + 12.9}{14}$$

$$\bar{X} = \frac{72.7}{14} = 5.19$$

Removing RS Emerging Growth A caused the arithmetic mean to decrease from 6.08 to 5.19. The revised dot scale is presented in Figure 3.

FIGURE 3
Dot scale obtained from Microsoft Excel of the 5-year annualized returns for the 14 very-high-risk mutual funds

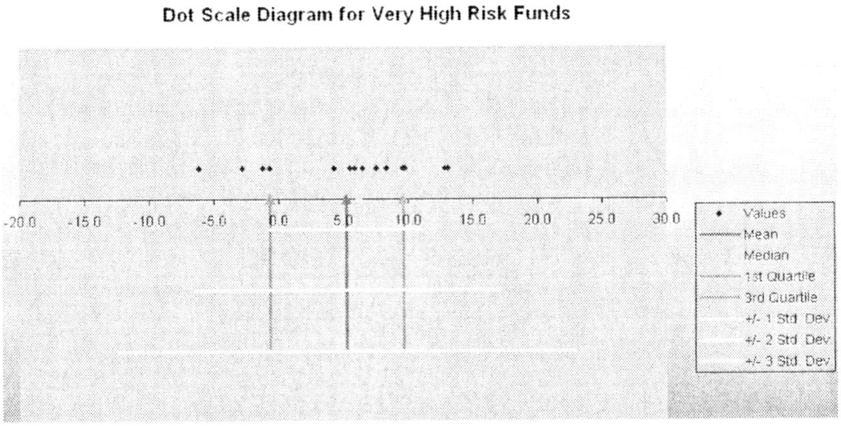

Excel Strategies Generating Dot Scale Diagrams ▼

CHAPTER 3.xls

*Retrieve the Figure 3.2 worksheet of the **Chapter 3.xls** workbook to view a dot scale diagram similar to Figure 2.*

You generate a dot scale diagram by using either a special PHStat2 procedure or by manually adapting a worksheet included in the **Chapter 3.xls** workbook. (Microsoft Excel does not have a built-in capacity to generate a dot scale diagram.) For example, to generate the dot scale diagram similar to one in Figure 2, open the **Chapter 3.xls** workbook and use one of these strategies:

Using Excel with PHStat2

Use the PHStat2 Dot Scale Diagram procedure to generate a dot scale diagram as a chart on a new worksheet that contains a copy of the source data. Open to the **VHRiskFunds** worksheet of the Chapter 3 workbook and:

Select **PHStat | Descriptive Statistics | Dot Scale Diagram**.

In the Dot Scale Diagram dialog box (shown at right):

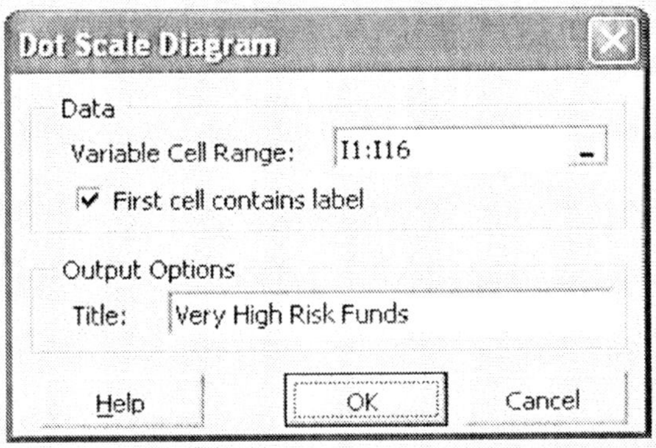

Enter **I1:I16** in the **Variable Cell Range** edit box.

Select the **First cell contains label** check box.

Enter a title in the **Title** edit box.

Click the **OK** button.

In the new worksheet generated, you can interact with the dot scale diagram by changing the data in column A and seeing how those changes affect the diagram.

Using Excel

Open to the **DotScale** worksheet of the Chapter 3 workbook and follow the instructions of section EH1 (at the end of this chapter) to adapt this worksheet to your data.

The Median

The **median** is the middle value in an ordered array of data. If there are no ties, half the observations will be smaller than the median and half will be larger. The median is unaffected by any extreme observations in a set of data. Whenever an extreme observation is present, the median can be used rather than the mean to describe a set of data.

To calculate the median from a set of data, first organize the data into an ordered array. Then the median is obtained using Equation (2).

MEDIAN

The median is the value for which 50% of the observations are smaller and 50% of the observations are larger.

$$\text{Median} = \frac{n+1}{2} \text{ ordered observation} \tag{2}$$

Equation (2) is used to find the place in the ordered array that corresponds to the median value by following one of two rules:

Rule 1 If there are an *odd* number of observations in the data set, the median is represented by the numerical value corresponding to the positioning point, the $(n + 1)/2$ ordered observation.
Rule 2 If there are an *even* number of observations in the data set, then the positioning point lies between the two observations in the middle of the data set. The median is then the *average* of the numerical values corresponding to these two middle observations.

To compute the median for the sample of 15 very-high-risk mutual funds, the raw data are placed in the following ordered array:

	−6.1	−2.8	−1.2	−0.7	4.3	5.5	5.9	6.5	7.6	8.3	9.6	9.8	12.9	13.1	18.5
								↑ Median = 6.5 ↓							
Ordered observation:	1	2	3	4	5	6	7	8	9	10	11	12	13	14	15

Using rule 1 for an odd-sized sample, the positioning point is $(n + 1)/2 = (15 + 1)/2 = 8$. Therefore, the median is 6.5. This means that half of the very-high-risk funds have an annualized return less than or equal to 6.5 and half have returns greater than or equal to 6.5. Note that this median of 6.5 is slightly larger than the arithmetic mean of 6.08.

EXAMPLE 2

COMPUTING THE MEDIAN FROM AN EVEN-SIZED SAMPLE

There are six very-low-risk mutual funds in the sample of mutual funds. Compute the median for these six mutual funds.

SOLUTION

The ordered array becomes

	11	12	12.1	12.3	15.1	18.2
Ordered observation:	1	2	3 ↑	4	5	6
			Median = 12.2			

Using rule 2 for even-sized samples, the positioning point is $(n + 1)/2 = (6 + 1)/2 = 3.5$. Therefore the median is obtained by averaging the third and fourth observations. Therefore the median is equal to 12.2.

The Mode

The **mode** is the value in a set of data that appears most frequently. Unlike the arithmetic mean, the mode is not affected by the occurrence of any extreme values. The mode is used only for descriptive purposes because it is more variable from sample to sample than other measures of central tendency.

For continuous variables such as the 5-year annualized returns from mutual funds, a mode often does not exist. Because there are so many possible values for the variable, it is likely that no single value occurs more than once. Example 3 illustrates the computation of the mode.

EXAMPLE 3

OBTAINING THE MODE

A systems manager in charge of a company's network keeps track of the number of server failures that occur in a day. The following data represent the number of server failures in a day for the past two weeks.

1 3 0 3 26 2 7 4 0 2 3 3 6 3

Obtain the mode for these data.

SOLUTION

The ordered array for these data is

0 0 1 2 2 3 3 3 3 3 4 6 7 26

The most typical value, or mode, is 3. Thus, the systems manager can say that the most common occurrence is to have three server failures in a day. Note that for this data set the median is equal to 3 and the arithmetic mean is equal to 4.5. The value 26 is an outlier; thus, the median and/or the mode is a better description of central tendency than the mean.

A set of data may have no mode if none of the values is "most typical." This is illustrated in Example 4.

EXAMPLE 4

DATA WITH NO MODE

Obtain the mode for the 5-year annualized returns attained by the 15 very-high-risk mutual funds.

SOLUTION

The ordered array is

−6.1 −2.8 −1.2 −0.7 4.3 5.5 5.9 6.5 7.6 8.3 9.6 9.8 12.9 13.1 18.5

Here there is no mode. None of the values is most typical because no values are repeated.

Quartiles

Quartiles are the most widely used measures of noncentral location and are used to describe properties of large sets of numerical data. While the median is the value that splits the ordered array in half (50.0% of the observations are smaller and 50.0% of the observations are larger), the quartiles are descriptive measures that split the ordered data into four quarters.

The quartiles[3] are defined in Equations (3) and (4).

FIRST QUARTILE Q_1

The **first quartile, Q_1,** is a value for which 25.0% of the observations are smaller and 75.0% are larger.

$$Q_1 = \frac{n+1}{4} \text{ ordered observation} \tag{3}$$

*[3]The Q_1, median, and Q_3 are also the 25th, 50th, and 75th percentile, respectively. Equations (2), (3), and (4) can be expressed generally in terms of finding percentiles: (p * 100)th percentile = p * (n + 1) ordered observation.*

THIRD QUARTILE Q_3

The **third quartile, Q_3**, is a value for which 75.0% of the observations are smaller and 25.0% are larger.

$$Q_3 = \frac{3(n+1)}{4} \text{ ordered observation} \tag{4}$$

The following rules are used for obtaining the quartile values:

1. If the resulting positioning point is an integer, the particular numerical observation corresponding to that positioning point is chosen for the quartile.
2. If the resulting positioning point is halfway between two integers, the average of their corresponding observations is selected.
3. If the resulting positioning point is neither an integer nor a value halfway between two integers, a simple rule is to round off to the nearest integer and select the numerical value of the corresponding observation.

Using the ordered array for the 5-year annualized returns for the 15 very-high-risk funds, the quartiles are computed as follows. The ordered array is

−6.1 −2.8 −1.2 −0.7 4.3 5.5 5.9 6.5 7.6 8.3 9.6 9.8 12.9 13.1 18.5

For these data

$$Q_1 = (n+1)/4 \text{ ordered observation}$$
$$= \frac{15+1}{4} = 4\text{th ordered observation}$$

Therefore, using rule 1, Q_1 is the fourth ordered observation.

$$Q_1 = -0.7$$

This means that 25% of the very-high-risk funds have an annualized return less than or equal to −0.7. In addition,

$$Q_3 = 3(n+1)/4 \text{ ordered observation}$$
$$= \frac{3(15+1)}{4} = 12\text{th ordered observation}$$

Therefore, using rule 1, Q_3 is the 12th ordered observation.

$$Q_3 = 9.8$$

This means that 75% of the very-high-risk funds have an annualized return less than or equal to 9.8.

The Geometric Mean

Not to be confused with the arithmetic mean, the geometric mean and the geometric rate of return measure the status of an investment over time. The **geometric mean** is a useful measure of the rate of change of a variable over time. The geometric mean is defined in Equation (5).

GEOMETRIC MEAN

The geometric mean is the *n*th root of the product of *n* values.

$$\bar{X}_G = (X_1 \times X_2 \times \cdots \times X_n)^{1/n} \quad \textbf{(5)}$$

The geometric mean rate of return is defined in Equation (6).

GEOMETRIC MEAN RATE OF RETURN

$$\bar{R}_G = [(1 + R_1) \times (1 + R_2) \times \cdots \times (1 + R_n)]^{1/n} - 1 \quad \textbf{(6)}$$

where

R_i is the rate of return in time period i

To illustrate these measures, consider an investment of \$100,000 that declined to a value of \$50,000 at the end of year 1 and then rebounded back to its original \$100,000 value at the end of year 2. The rate of return for this investment for the two-year period is 0, because the starting and ending value of the investment is unchanged. However, the arithmetic mean of the yearly rates of return is

$$\bar{X} = \frac{(-0.50) + (1.00)}{2} = 0.25 \text{ or } 25\%$$

since the rate of return for year 1 is

$$R_1 = \left(\frac{50{,}000 - 100{,}000}{100{,}000}\right) = -0.50 \text{ or } -50\%$$

and the rate of return for year 2 is

$$R_2 = \left(\frac{100{,}000 - 50{,}000}{50{,}000}\right) = 1.00 \text{ or } 100\%$$

However, the geometric mean rate of return for the two years, using Equation (6), is

$$\begin{aligned}
\bar{R}_G &= [(1 + R_1) \times (1 + R_2)]^{1/n} - 1 \\
&= [(1 + (-0.50)) \times (1 + (1.0))]^{1/2} - 1 \\
&= [(0.50) \times (2.0)]^{1/2} - 1 \\
&= [1.0]^{1/2} - 1 \\
&= 1 - 1 = 0
\end{aligned}$$

Thus, the geometric mean more accurately reflects the (zero) change in the value of the investment for the two-year period than does the arithmetic mean.

A second important property that describes a set of numerical data is variation. **Variation** is the amount of **dispersion**, or "spread," in the data. Two sets of data may differ in both central tendency and variation; or, as shown in the polygons of Figure 4, two sets of data may have the same measures of variation but different central tendencies or, as depicted in the polygons of Figure 5, two sets of data may have the same measures of central tendency but greatly different variation. The data set depicted in polygon C of Figure 5 is much less variable than that depicted in polygon A.

FIGURE 4
Two symmetrical bell-shaped distributions differing only in central tendency

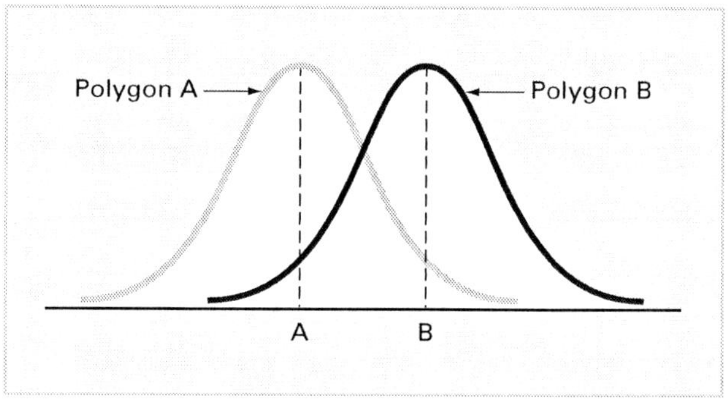

FIGURE 5
Two symmetrical bell-shaped distributions differing only in variation

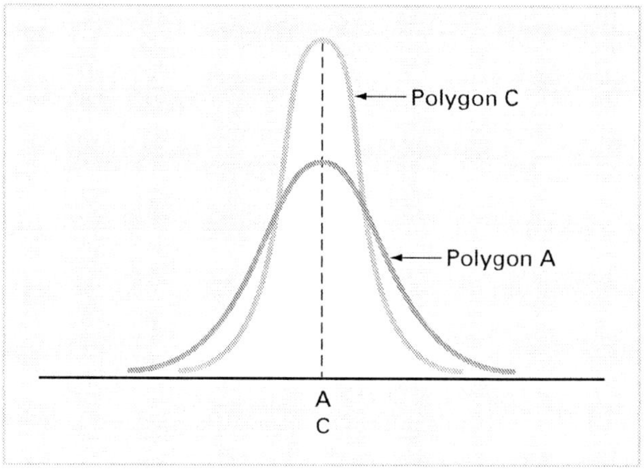

Five measures of variation include the *range*, the *interquartile range*, the *variance*, the *standard deviation*, and the *coefficient of variation*.

The Range

The **range** is the difference between the *largest* and *smallest* observations in a set of data.

RANGE

The range is equal to the largest value minus the smallest value.

$$\text{Range} = X_{\text{largest}} - X_{\text{smallest}} \qquad \textbf{(7)}$$

The ordered array for the 5-year annualized returns achieved by the very-high-risk mutual funds is as follows:

−6.1 −2.8 −1.2 −0.7 4.3 5.5 5.9 6.5 7.6 8.3 9.6 9.8 12.9 13.1 18.5

Using Equation (7), the range is 18.5 − (−6.1) = 24.6. This means that the largest difference in the annualized return of any two very-high-risk mutual funds is 24.6.

The range measures the *total spread* in the set of data. Although the range is a simple measure of total variation in the data, its weakness is that it does not take into account *how* the data are distributed between the smallest and largest values. For example, in Figure 6, dot scale diagrams are displayed for three sets of data all having a range of 6, but with different dispersion characteristics.

As evidenced in scale C, using the range as a measure of variation when at least one value is an extreme observation is misleading.

FIGURE 6

Comparing three data sets with the same range

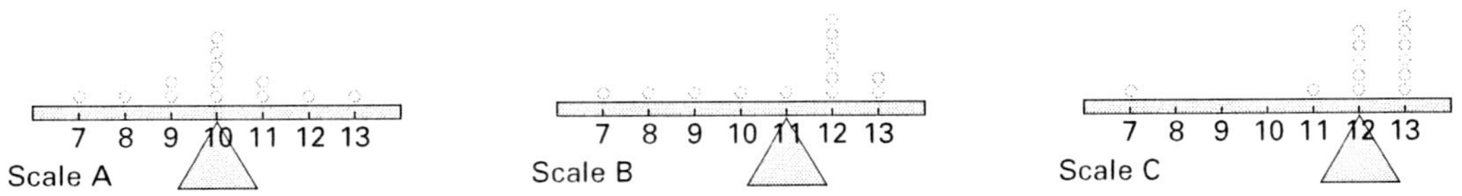

The Interquartile Range

The **interquartile range** (also called **midspread**) is the difference between the *third* and *first quartiles* in a set of data.

INTERQUARTILE RANGE

The interquartile range is obtained by subtracting the first quartile from the third quartile.

$$\text{Interquartile range} = Q_3 - Q_1 \qquad \textbf{(8)}$$

This measure considers the spread in the middle 50% of the data; therefore, it is not influenced by extreme values. Using the ordered array for the 5-year annualized returns achieved by the very-high-risk mutual funds, the interquartile range is computed as follows: The ordered array is

$$-6.1 \quad -2.8 \quad -1.2 \quad -0.7 \quad 4.3 \quad 5.5 \quad 5.9 \quad 6.5 \quad 7.6 \quad 8.3 \quad 9.6 \quad 9.8 \quad 12.9 \quad 13.1 \quad 18.5$$

For these data, from the earlier results, $Q_1 = -0.7$ and $Q_3 = 9.8$. Using Equation (8),

$$\text{Interquartile range} = 9.8 - (-0.7) = 10.5$$

Therefore, 10.5 is the interquartile range in 5-year annualized returns achieved by the middle 50% of the very-high-risk mutual funds. The interval 9.8 to −0.7 is often referred to as the *middle fifty*. This means that the largest difference in the annualized return in the middle fifty funds is 10.5.

It is important to note that Q_1 and Q_3, and, therefore, the interquartile range, cannot be affected by potential outliers, because no observation smaller than Q_1 or larger than Q_3 is considered. Summary measures such as the median, Q_1, Q_3, and the interquartile range, which cannot be influenced by outliers, are called **resistant measures**.

The Variance and the Standard Deviation

Although the range is a measure of the total spread and the interquartile range is a measure of the middle spread, neither of these measures of variation takes into consideration how all the observations distribute or cluster. Two commonly used measures of variation that do take into account how all the values in the data are distributed are the *variance* and the *standard deviation*. These measures evaluate how the values fluctuate about the mean. The sample variance is *roughly* (or *almost*) the average of the squared differences between each of the observations in a set of data and the mean.

For a sample containing n observations, $X_1, X_2, X_3, \ldots, X_n$, the sample variance (given by the symbol S^2) is

$$S^2 = \frac{(X_1 - \bar{X})^2 + (X_2 - \bar{X})^2 + \cdots + (X_n - \bar{X})^2}{n - 1}$$

Using summation notation, this formula is expressed as shown in Equation (9).

SAMPLE VARIANCE

The **sample variance** is the sum of the squared differences around the arithmetic mean divided by the sample size minus one.

$$S^2 = \frac{\sum_{i=1}^{n}(X_i - \bar{X})^2}{n-1} \qquad \textbf{(9)}$$

where

$\bar{X}$ = arithmetic mean
n = sample size
X_i = ith value of the variable X
$\sum_{i=1}^{n}(X_i - \bar{X})^2$ = summation of all the squared differences between the X_i values and $\bar{X}$

If the denominator were n instead of $n - 1$, the average of the squared differences around the mean would have been obtained. However, $n - 1$ is used here because of certain desirable mathematical properties possessed by the statistic S^2 that make it appropriate for statistical inference. As the sample size increases, the difference between dividing by n or $n - 1$ becomes smaller and smaller.

The most practical and most commonly used measure of variation is the **sample standard deviation**, which is represented by the symbol S. This measure is the square root of the sample variance and is defined in Equation (10).

SAMPLE STANDARD DEVIATION

The sample standard deviation is the square root of the sum of the squared differences around the arithmetic mean divided by the sample size minus one.

$$S = \sqrt{S^2} = \sqrt{\frac{\sum_{i=1}^{n}(X_i - \bar{X})^2}{n-1}} \qquad \textbf{(10)}$$

The steps for computing both the sample variance and the sample standard deviation are presented in Exhibit 1.

EXHIBIT 1 COMPUTING S^2 AND S

To compute S^2, the sample variance, do the following:

1. Obtain the difference between each observation and the mean.
2. Square each difference.
3. Add the squared differences.
4. Divide this total by $n - 1$.

To compute S, the sample standard deviation, take the square root of the sample variance.

To compute the sample variance and sample standard deviation for the very-high-risk mutual funds, the four-step approach of Exhibit 1 is used as illustrated in Figure 7. (Note that in the first example the arithmetic mean of the very-high-risk mutual funds was computed as 6.08.)

FIGURE 7

Computing the sample variance and sample standard deviation of the 5-year annualized return for the very-high-risk mutual funds

	A	B	C	D	E
			$\bar{X}$	$(X_i - \bar{X})$	$(X_i - \bar{X})^2$
1	Very High Risk Fund	X_i (5-Yr Return)	XBar	$(X_i$ - XBar)	$(X_i$ - XBar$)^2$
2	Amer. Century GiftTrust Inv.	-2.8	6.08	-8.88	78.854
3	AXP Stategy Aggressive A	5.5	6.08	-0.58	0.336
4	Berger Small Company Growth Inv	8.3	6.08	2.22	4.928
5	Consulting Group Small Cap Growth	4.3	6.08	-1.78	3.168
6	Fidelity Aggressive Growth	5.9	6.08	-0.18	0.032
7	Invesco Growth Inv	-0.7	6.08	-6.78	45.968
8	Janus Enterprise	6.5	6.08	0.42	0.176
9	Janus Venture	9.8	6.08	3.72	13.838
10	John Hancock Small Cap Growth A	7.6	6.08	1.52	2.310
11	MS Mid Cap Equity Tr. B	9.6	6.08	3.52	12.390
12	PBHG Growth	-1.2	6.08	-7.28	52.998
13	Putnam OTC Emerging Growth A	-6.1	6.08	-12.18	148.352
14	RS Emerging Growth A	18.5	6.08	12.42	154.256
15	Rydex OTC Inv	13.1	6.08	7.02	49.280
16	Van Kampen Aggressive Growth A	12.9	6.08	6.82	46.512
17			*Sums:*	0.00	613.404
				$\sum_{i=1}^{n}(X_i - \bar{X})$	$\sum_{i=1}^{n}(X_i - \bar{X})^2$

From Equation (9), the sample variance is

$$
\begin{aligned}
S^2 &= \frac{\sum_{i=1}^{n}\left(X_i - \bar{X}\right)^2}{n-1} \\
&= \frac{(-2.8-6.08)^2 + (5.5-6.08)^2 + \cdots + (12.9-6.08)^2}{15-1} \\
&= \frac{613.404}{14} \\
&= 43.8146
\end{aligned}
$$

Using Equation (10), the sample standard deviation S is

$$
S = \sqrt{S^2} = \sqrt{\frac{\sum_{i=1}^{n}(X_i - \bar{X})^2}{n-1}} = \sqrt{43.8146} = 6.62
$$

In making these computations the differences between each of the observations and the mean are squared. Therefore, *neither the variance nor the standard deviation can ever be negative*. The only time S^2 and S can be zero is when there is no variation at all in the data—when each observation in the sample is exactly the same and therefore equal to the sample mean. In such an unusual case, the range and interquartile range are also zero.

Numerical data are inherently variable—not constant. Any variable of interest usually takes on a variety of values. For example, different mutual funds achieve different 5-year annualized rates of return. Because numerical data inherently vary, it is important to study not only measures of central tendency that summarize the data but also measures of variation that reflect how the numerical data are dispersed.

INTERPRETING THE VARIANCE AND THE STANDARD DEVIATION

The variance and the standard deviation measure the "average" scatter around the mean—how larger observations fluctuate above it and how smaller observations distribute below it. The variance possesses certain useful mathematical properties. However, its computation results in squared units—squared percentages, squared dollars, squared inches, and so on. Thus, the primary measure of variation is the standard deviation, whose value is in the original units of the data—percentage of return, dollars, or inches.

The standard deviation helps you to know how a set of data clusters or distributes around its mean. For almost all sets of data, the majority of the observed values lie within an interval of plus and minus one standard deviation above and below the arithmetic mean. Therefore, knowledge of the arithmetic mean and the standard deviation usually helps define where at least the majority of the data values are clustering.

WHAT THE STANDARD DEVIATION INDICATES

In the example of the 15 very-high-risk mutual funds, the standard deviation in 5-year annualized returns is 6.62. This indicates that the 5-year annualized returns from the majority of the mutual funds in this sample are clustering within 6.62 around the mean of 6.08 (i.e., clustering between $\overline{X} - 1S = -0.54$ and $\overline{X} + 1S = 12.70$). In fact, 53.3% (8 out of 15) of the 5-year annualized returns lie within this interval.

Note that a series of "squared" values is summed as follows when you are computing the variance and standard deviation:

$$\sum_{i=1}^{n}(X_i - \overline{X})^2$$

In the squaring process, observations that are farther from the mean get more weight than do observations that are closer to the mean. The squared deviations for the 15 very-high-risk mutual funds are displayed in the last column of Figure 7. Note that the 13th observation $X_{13} = 18.5$, obtained by RS Emerging Growth A, is the farthest away from the mean of 6.08. In the squaring process, this observation contributes substantially more to the calculation of S^2 and S than do the other observations in the sample, which are much closer to the mean. In addition, observe that in the fourth column of Figure 7, the sum of the deviations around the arithmetic mean sum to zero. This property

$$\sum_{i=1}^{n}(X_i - \overline{X}) = 0$$

is one of the important reasons that the arithmetic mean is used as the most common measure of central tendency.

Exhibit 2 summarizes the characteristics of the range, interquartile range, variance, and standard deviation.

EXHIBIT 2 UNDERSTANDING VARIATION IN DATA

1. The more spread out, or dispersed, the data are, the larger will be the range, the interquartile range, the variance, and the standard deviation.
2. The more concentrated, or homogeneous, the data are, the smaller will be the range, the interquartile range, the variance, and the standard deviation.
3. If the observations are all the same (so that there is no variation in the data), the range, interquartile range, variance, and standard deviation will all be zero.
4. None of the measures of variation (the range, interquartile range, standard deviation, and variance) can *ever* be negative.

Example 5 illustrates the comparison of several standard deviations.

EXAMPLE 5

COMPARING TWO OR MORE STANDARD DEVIATIONS

Compare the variability of very-low-risk, low-risk, average-risk, high-risk, and very-high-risk mutual funds by computing the standard deviations of 5-year annualized returns for all five of the risk categories.

SOLUTION

The standard deviations are as follows:

Very-low-risk	$S = 2.700$
Low-risk	$S = 3.583$
Average-risk	$S = 4.179$
High-risk	$S = 4.543$
Very-high-risk	$S = 6.620$

The variability for the very-high-risk and the high-risk mutual funds is greater than for the average-risk funds, and that for the average-risk funds is greater than the variability for low-risk and very-low-risk funds. The 5-year annualized returns for mutual funds with lower perceived risk tend to cluster more closely around their respective arithmetic means than do the high-risk funds. In other words, investors in high-risk funds have a greater possibility of obtaining a return that is much less than its respective mean value. On the other hand, those investors also have a greater possibility of obtaining a much larger return on their investment.

The Coefficient of Variation

Unlike the previous measures of variation presented, the **coefficient of variation** is a *relative measure* of variation. It is always expressed as a percentage rather than in terms of the units of the particular data. The coefficient of variation, denoted by the symbol *CV*, measures the scatter in the data relative to the mean.

COEFFICIENT OF VARIATION

The coefficient of variation is equal to the standard deviation divided by the arithmetic mean, multiplied by 100%.

$$CV = \left(\frac{S}{\overline{X}}\right) 100\% \qquad \textbf{(11)}$$

where

S = standard deviation of a sample
$\overline{X}$ = arithmetic mean of a sample

VISUAL EXPLORATIONS Exploring Descriptive Statistics

Use the Visual Explorations Descriptive Statistics procedure to observe the effect of changing data values on measures of location and dispersion. This procedure uses the dot scale diagram for the 5-year returns for the 15 very-high-risk mutual funds of Figure 1 as its example.

Open the **Visual Explorations.xla** macro workbook.

Select **VisualExplorations | Descriptive Statistics** from the Microsoft Excel menu bar.

Review the instructions and click the **OK** button in the pop-up dialog box (shown below).

Alter the values in the tinted cell range **A2:A16** and note how the various statistics are affected.

For example, change the largest value, 18.5, to 85 and examine how increasing this value changes the mean and median.

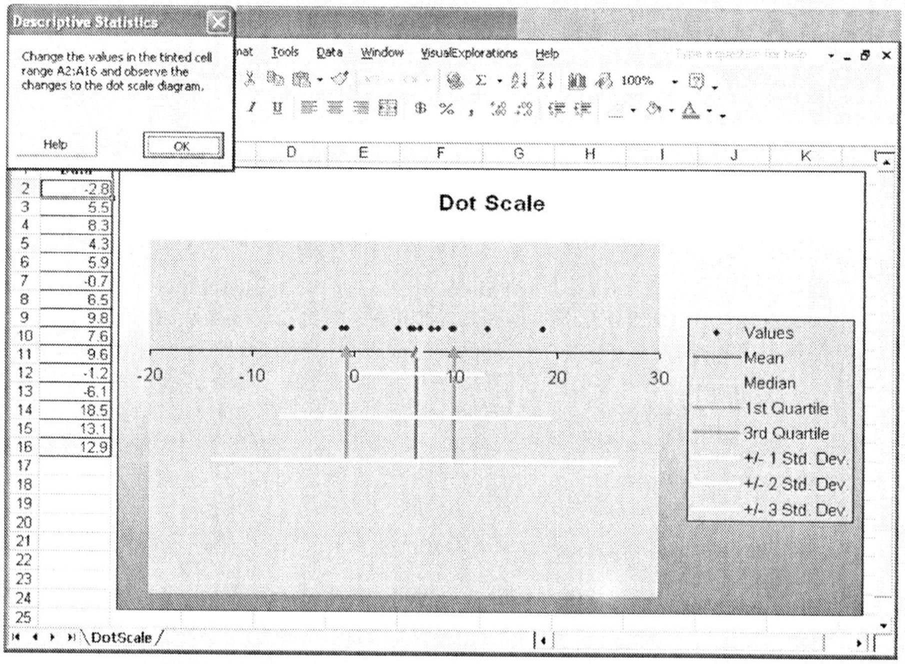

From the sample of 5-year annualized returns for very-low-risk, low-risk, average-risk, high-risk, and very-high-risk mutual funds, the coefficients of variation are computed as follows. The arithmetic means and standard deviations of the five risk categories are:

Very-low-risk:	$\bar{X} = 13.45$	$S = 2.70$
Low-risk:	$\bar{X} = 12.234$	$S = 3.583$
Average-risk:	$\bar{X} = 11.209$	$S = 4.179$
High-risk:	$\bar{X} = 9.547$	$S = 4.543$
Very-high-risk:	$\bar{X} = 6.08$	$S = 6.62$

Using Equation (11) the coefficients of variation are

$$\text{Very-low-risk:} \quad CV = \left(\frac{S}{\overline{\overline{X}}}\right)100\% = \left(\frac{2.70}{13.45}\right)100\% = 20.07\%$$

$$\text{Low-risk:} \quad CV = \left(\frac{S}{\overline{\overline{X}}}\right)100\% = \left(\frac{3.583}{12.234}\right)100\% = 29.29\%$$

$$\text{Average-risk:} \quad CV = \left(\frac{S}{\overline{\overline{X}}}\right)100\% = \left(\frac{4.179}{11.209}\right)100\% = 37.28\%$$

$$\text{High-risk:} \quad CV = \left(\frac{S}{\overline{\overline{X}}}\right)100\% = \left(\frac{4.543}{9.547}\right)100\% = 47.58\%$$

$$\text{Very-high-risk:} \quad CV = \left(\frac{S}{\overline{\overline{X}}}\right)100\% = \left(\frac{6.62}{6.08}\right)100\% = 108.88\%$$

In these data, the higher the risk category, the larger the relative size of the average spread around the mean is to the mean. Note that the low-risk and average-risk mutual funds have a larger mean return and a lower coefficient of variation than do the high-risk funds, which indicates that their performance was more favorable than that of the high-risk funds.

The coefficient of variation is also very useful when comparing two or more sets of data that are measured in different units. This is illustrated in Example 6.

EXAMPLE 6

COMPARING TWO COEFFICIENTS OF VARIATION WHEN TWO VARIABLES HAVE DIFFERENT UNITS OF MEASUREMENT

The operations manager of a package delivery service is contemplating purchasing a new fleet of trucks. When packages are stored in the trucks in preparation for delivery, two major constraints have to be considered—the weight (in pounds) and the volume (in cubic feet) for each item.

Suppose that in a sample of 200 packages, the average weight is 26.0 pounds, with a standard deviation of 3.9 pounds, and the average volume for each of these packages is 8.8 cubic feet, with a standard deviation of 2.2 cubic feet. How can the variation of the weight and the volume be compared?

SOLUTION

Because the units of measure differ for the weight and volume constraints, the operations manager should compare the relative variability in the two types of measurements. For weight, the coefficient of variation is $CV_W = (3.9/26.0)100\% = 15.0\%$; for volume, the coefficient of variation is $CV_V = (2.2/8.8)100\% = 25.0\%$. Thus, relative to the mean, the package volume is much more variable than the package weight.

Shape

A third important property of a set of data is its **shape**—the manner in which the data are distributed. Either the distribution of the data is **symmetrical** or it is not. If the distribution of data is not symmetrical, it is called **asymmetrical**, or skewed.

To describe the shape, one can compare the mean and the median. If these two measures are equal, the distribution is considered to be symmetrical (or zero-skewed). If the mean is greater than the median, the distribution is described as *positive*, or **right-skewed**. If the mean is less than the median, the distribution is called *negative*, or **left-skewed**. That is,

mean < median: negative, or left-skewness

mean = median: symmetry, or zero-skewness

mean > median: positive, or right-skewness

Positive skewness arises when the mean is increased by some unusually high values. Negative skewness occurs when the mean is reduced by some extremely low values. Distributions are symmetrical when there are no really extreme values in a particular direction so that low and high values balance each other out.

Figure 8 depicts the shapes of three data sets. The data in panel A are negative, or left-skewed. In this panel there is a long tail and distortion to the left that is caused by extremely small values. These extremely small values pull the mean downward so that the mean is less than the median.

FIGURE 8
A comparison of three data sets differing in shape

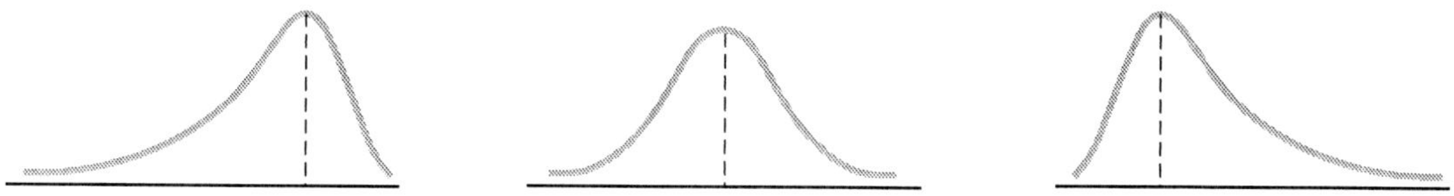

Panel A — Negative, or left-skewed | Panel B — Symmetrical | Panel C — Positive, or right-skewed

The data in panel B are symmetrical; each half of the curve is a mirror image of the other half of the curve. The low and high values on the scale balance, and the mean equals the median. The data in panel C are positive, or right-skewed. In this panel there is a long tail on the right of the distribution and a distortion to the right that is caused by extremely large values. These extremely large values pull the mean upward so that the mean is greater than the median.

For the sample containing the 15 very-high-risk mutual funds, the data are displayed along the dot scale in Figure 2. What can be said about the shape of this data set? In the first example, the mean was computed to be 6.08 and further on the median was computed as 6.50. Therefore, because the mean is less than the median, this data set can be described as negative, or left-skewed.

Microsoft Excel Descriptive Statistics Output

The descriptive statistics output obtained from Microsoft Excel of the 5-year annualized return of the various funds based on risk level is illustrated in Figure 9.

FIGURE 9
Descriptive statistics obtained from Microsoft Excel of the 5-year annualized return of the very-high-risk, high-risk, average-risk, low-risk, and very-low-risk mutual funds

	A	B	C	D	E	F
1	*Descriptive Statistics By Risk Category*					
2		Very Low	Low	Average	High	Very High
3	Mean	13.45	12.23421	11.20854	9.5475	6.08
4	Standard Error	1.103555	0.411009	0.46148	0.5079	1.709085
5	Median	12.2	11.75	10.55	9.4	6.5
6	Mode	#N/A	9.4	10.5	9.9	#N/A
7	Standard Deviation	2.703146	3.583092	4.178877	4.542792	6.6192576
8	Sample Variance	7.307	12.83855	17.46301	20.63696	43.814571
9	Kurtosis	1.118103	1.411879	1.478965	0.352353	-0.22474
10	Skewness	1.365864	1.017377	0.965596	0.501692	-0.148298
11	Range	7.2	18.4	23.5	22.4	24.6
12	Minimum	11	6.6	2.8	0.5	-6.1
13	Maximum	18.2	25	26.3	22.9	18.5
14	Sum	80.7	929.8	919.1	763.8	91.2
15	Count	6	76	82	80	15
16	Largest(1)	18.2	25	26.3	22.9	18.5
17	Smallest(1)	11	6.6	2.8	0.5	-6.1

Note that Excel has provided the (arithmetic) mean, median, mode, standard deviation, variance, range, minimum, maximum, and count (sample size), all of which have been discussed in this section. In addition, Excel has computed the standard error, along with statistics for kurtosis and skewness. The *standard error* is the standard deviation divided by the square root of the sample size. *Skewness* is a measure of lack of symmetry in the data and is based on a statistic that is a function of the *cubed* differences around the arithmetic mean. *Kurtosis* is a measure of the relative concentration of values in the center of the distribution as compared with the tails and is based on the differences around the arithmetic mean raised to the fourth power. This measure is not discussed in this text (see reference 2).

From Figure 9 there appear to be clear differences in the descriptive statistics for the various risk levels. The highest annualized 5-year returns were achieved by the mutual funds with the lowest risk, while the lowest returns were achieved by the mutual funds with the highest risk. The very-low-risk mutual funds had an arithmetic mean annualized 5-year return of 13.45 and a median of 12.2. The low-risk mutual funds had an arithmetic mean annualized 5-year return of 12.234 and a median of 11.75. The average-risk mutual funds had an arithmetic mean annualized 5-year return of 11.209 and a median of 10.55. The high-risk mutual funds had an arithmetic mean annualized 5-year return of 9.547 and a median of 9.40. The very-high-risk mutual funds had an arithmetic mean annualized 5-year return of 6.08 and a median of 6.5.

The same pattern was evident with the medians. For example, 50% of the low-risk mutual funds had an annualized 5-year return below 11.75, 50% of the average-risk mutual funds had an annualized 5-year return below 10.55, while 50% of the high-risk mutual funds had an annualized 5-year return below 9.4. In summary, you can conclude that for this group of mutual funds for the time period of 1997–2001, risk did not pay off in higher returns. In addition, the lower the risk of the mutual funds, the smaller the variation in returns among the funds in that risk group. The standard deviation for the very-low-risk group was 2.7, for the low-risk group it was 3.583, for the average-risk group it was 4.179, for the high-risk group it was 4.543, and for the very-high-risk group it was 6.62.

Excel Strategies Generating Descriptive Statistics

You use the Data Analysis Descriptive Statistics procedure to generate a table of descriptive statistics or Excel statistical functions to calculate individual statistics for a set of data. (PHStat2 does not have a special descriptive statistics procedure, although many PHStat2 procedures, such as Stem-and-Leaf Display and Dot Scale Diagram, also produce tables of descriptive statistics.)

CHAPTER 3.xls

*Retrieve the Figure 3.9 worksheet of the **Chapter 3.xls** workbook to view a table similar to the one in Figure 9.*

To generate descriptive statistics for the 5-year returns for the sample of 15 very-high-risk funds, open the **Chapter 3.xls** workbook to the **VHRiskFunds** worksheet and do either of these tasks:

Generate Table of Descriptive Statistics Task. Use the Data Analysis Descriptive Statistics procedure to generate a table of descriptive statistics.

Select **Tools | Data Analysis** and then select **Descriptive Statistics** from the **Analysis Tools** list and click the **OK** button.

In the Descriptive Statistics dialog box (shown at right):

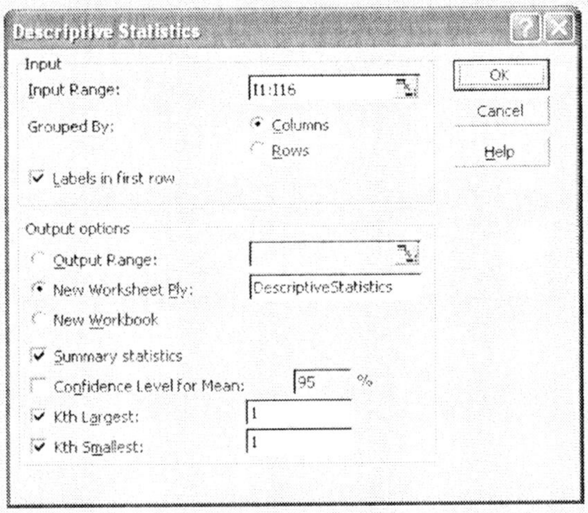

Enter **I1:I16** in the **Input Range** edit box.

Select the **Columns** option button and the **Labels in first row** check box.

Select the **New Worksheet Ply** option button and enter a self-descriptive name for the new worksheet.

Select the **Summary statistics** check box. Select the **Kth Largest** and the **Kth Smallest** check boxes, leaving their default values (1) unchanged.

Clear, if checked, the **Confidence Level for Mean** check box.

Click the **OK** button.

Besides statistics discussed in this chapter, this procedure also reports the standard error; the skewness, a measure related to the concept of shape as discussed in this chapter; and the kurtosis, a measure of the relative concentration of values in the center of the distribution as compared to the tails, a statistic which is not discussed in this text. (See reference 2 for further information.)

Calculate Individual Statistics Task. To calculate measures of location, variation, and shape for data values in a given cell range, use the following worksheet functions, all entered in the form **FUNCTION(*cell range of values*)**, in simple formulas:

AVERAGE (arithmetic mean)	MIN	MAX
COUNT (sample size)	MEDIAN	MODE
STDEV (standard deviation)	VAR (variance)	SKEW

For example, to calculate the arithmetic mean for the 5-year returns for the sample of 15 very-high-risk funds, enter the formula **=AVERAGE(VHRiskFunds!I2:I16)** in any empty cell of any worksheet in the **Chapter 3.xls** workbook. If you want to calculate quartiles, follow the instructions of section EH2 at the end of this chapter, and avoid using the Excel QUARTILE function, which produces incorrect results for first and third quartiles for some sets of data.

Use the related functions **STDEVP** and **VARP** to calculate the population standard deviation and variance, respectively (see section 3).

PROBLEMS FOR SECTION 2

Learning the Basics

1 The following is a set of data from a sample of size $n = 5$:

7 4 9 8 2

a. Compute the mean, median, and mode.
b. Compute the range, interquartile range, variance, standard deviation, and coefficient of variation.
c. Describe the shape of the data set.

2 The following is a set of data from a sample of size $n = 6$:

7 4 9 7 3 12

a. Compute the mean, median, and mode.
b. Compute the range, interquartile range, variance, standard deviation, and coefficient of variation.
c. Describe the shape of the data set.

3 The following set of data is from a sample of size $n = 7$:

12 7 4 9 0 7 3

a. Compute the mean, median, and mode.
b. Compute the range, interquartile range, variance, standard deviation, and coefficient of variation.
c. Describe the shape of the data set.

4 The following is a set of data from a sample of size $n = 5$:

7 −5 −8 7 9

a. Compute the mean, median, and mode.
b. Compute the range, interquartile range, variance, standard deviation, and coefficient of variation.
c. Describe the shape of the data set.

5 The following are two sets of data—each with a sample of size $n = 7$:

Set 1:	10	2	3	2	4	2	5
Set 2:	20	12	13	12	14	12	15

a. For each set, compute the mean, median, and mode.
b. Compare your results and summarize your findings.
c. Compare the first sampled item in each set, compare the second sampled item in each set, and so on. Briefly describe your findings here in light of your summary in (b).
d. For each set, compute the range, interquartile range, variance, standard deviation, and coefficient of variation.
e. Describe the shape of each set.
f. Compare your results in (d) and (e) and discuss your findings.
g. On the basis of your answers to (a)–(f), what can you generalize about the properties of central tendency, variation, and shape?

6 Suppose that the rate of return for a particular stock during the past two years was 10% and 30%. Compute the geometric mean rate of return. (*Note:* A rate of return of 10% is recorded as 0.10 and a rate of return of 30% is recorded as 0.30.)

Applying the Concepts

Problem 7–19 can be solved manually or by using Microsoft Excel.

7 The operations manager of a plant that manufactures tires wants to compare the actual inner diameter of two grades of tires, each of which is expected to be 575 millimeters. A sample of five tires of each grade was selected, and the results representing the inner diameters of the tires, ordered from smallest to largest, were as follows:

Grade X					Grade Y				
568	570	575	578	584	573	574	575	577	578

a. For each of the two grades of tires, compute the arithmetic mean, median, and standard deviation.
b. Which grade of tire is providing better quality? Explain.
c. What would be the effect on your answers in (a) and (b) if the last value for grade Y were 588 instead of 578? Explain.

8 The following data represent the total fat for burgers and chicken items from a sample of fast-food chains. **FASTFOOD.xls**

Burgers

19 31 34 35 39 39 43

Chicken

7 9 15 16 16 18 22 25 27 33 39

Source: "Quick Bites." Copyright © 2001 by Consumers Union of U.S., Inc. Adapted from Consumer Reports, *March 2001, 46, by permission of Consumers Union U.S., Inc., Yonkers, NY 10703–1057.*

For the burgers and chicken items separately:
a. Compute the arithmetic mean, median, first quartile, and third quartile.
b. Compute the variance, standard deviation, range, interquartile range, and coefficient of variation.
c. Are the data skewed? If so, how?
d. Based on the results of (a)–(c), what conclusions can you reach concerning the differences in total fat of burgers and chicken items?

9 The median price of a U.S. home in 2001 rose to $147,500, an increase of over 6% from 2000. This rise in the median home price exceeded the increase in the median family income, thus making the dream of owning a home out of reach for many families (Barbara Hagenbaugh, "Homes Too Expensive for Many," **www.usatoday.com**, May 5, 2002).
a. Why do you think the article reports the median home price and not the mean home price?
b. Describe the shape of the distribution of family incomes. Be sure to discuss the relationship between the mean and the median.

10 The data file **PE.xls** contains a random sample of 30 stocks traded on the New York Stock Exchange. For each of the stocks, the ticker symbol and price-to-earnings ratio as reported in the *Wall Street Journal* on January 2, 2003, is given. The price-to-earnings ratio, or more simply, the P/E ratio, is determined by dividing the closing market price by the company's diluted per-share earnings for the past four quarters. Stocks with extremely high P/E ratios are typically called overvalued stocks, while stocks with unusually low P/E ratios are often called undervalued stocks.
a. Calculate the arithmetic mean, median, mode, range, variance, and standard deviation for the P/E ratios.
b. Interpret the measures of central tendency and variability in (a).
c. Using a current listing of stocks in the *Wall Street Journal, USA Today*, or some other source, collect your own random sample of size 30 and compare your results to the sample taken on January 2, 2003.
d. Using a current listing of stocks in the *Wall Street Journal, USA Today*, or some other source, collect a random sample of size 30 from the NASDAQ listings and compare your results to the sample you took from the New York Stock Exchange.

11 In the 2002–2003 academic year, many public universities in the United States raised tuition and fees due to a decrease in state subsidies (Mary Beth Marklein, "Public Universities Raise Tuition, Fees—and Ire," *USA Today*, August 8, 2002, 1A–2A). The change in the cost of tuition, a shared dormitory room, and the most popular meal plan from the 2001–2002 academic year for a sample of 10 public universities were as follows. **COLLEGECOST.xls**

University	Change in Cost ($)
University of California, Berkeley	1,589
University of Georgia, Athens	593
University of Illinois, Urbana–Champaign	1,223
Kansas State University, Manhattan	869
University of Maine, Orono	423
University of Mississippi, Oxford	1,720
University of New Hampshire, Durham	708
Ohio State University, Columbus	1,425
University of South Carolina, Columbia	922
Utah State University, Logan	308

a. Compute the arithmetic mean, median, first quartile, and third quartile.
b. Compute the variance, standard deviation, range, interquartile range, and coefficient of variation.
c. Are the data skewed? If so, how?
d. Based on the results of (a)–(c), what conclusions can you reach concerning the change in costs between the 2001–2002 and 2002–2003 academic years.

12 A software development and consulting firm located in the Phoenix metropolitan area develops software for supply chain management systems using systematic software reuse. That is, instead of starting from scratch when writing and developing new custom software systems, the firm uses a database of reusable components totaling more than 2,000,000 lines of code collected from 10 years of continuous reuse effort. Eight analysts at the firm were asked to estimate the reuse rate when developing a new software system. The following data are given as a percentage of the total code written for a software system that is part of the reuse database. **REUSE.xls**

50 62.5 37.5 75.0 45.0 47.5 15.0 25.0

Source: Rothenberger, M. A., and K. J. Dooley, "A Performance Measure for Software Reuse Projects," Decision Sciences, *Fall 1999, 30(4): 1131–1153.*

a. Compute the mean, median, and mode.
b. Compute the range, variance, and standard deviation.
c. Interpret the summary measures calculated in (a) and (b).

13 A manufacturer of flashlight batteries took a sample of 13 batteries from a day's production and used them continuously until they were drained. The numbers of hours they were used until failure were **BATTERIES.xls**

342 426 317 545 264 451 1,049 631 512 266 492 562 298

a. Compute the mean, median, and mode. Looking at the distribution of times to failure, which measures of location do you think are best and which worst? Why?
b. In what ways would this information be useful to the manufacturer? Discuss.
c. Calculate the range, variance, and standard deviation.
d. For many sets of data, the range is about six times the standard deviation. Is this true here? If not, why do you think it is not?
e. Using the information above, what would you advise if the manufacturer wanted to be able to say in advertisements that these batteries "should last 400 hours"? (*Note*: There is no right answer to this question; the point is to consider how to make such a statement precise.)
f. Suppose that the first value was 1,342 instead of 342. Repeat (a), using this value. Comment on the difference in the results.
g. Perform (c)–(e) with the first value equal to 1,342 instead of 342. Comment on the difference in the results.
h. How would you describe the shape of the data set if the first value were 342?
i. How would you describe the shape of the data set if the first value were 1,342?

14 A bank branch located in a commercial district of a city has developed an improved process for serving customers during the 12:00 P.M. to 1:00 P.M. peak lunch period. The waiting time in minutes (defined as the time the customer enters the line to when he or she is served) of all customers during this hour is recorded over a period of one week. A random sample of 15 customers is selected, and the results are as follows: **BANK1.xls**

4.21 5.55 3.02 5.13 4.77 2.34 3.54 3.20 4.50 6.10 0.38 5.12 6.46 6.19 3.79

a. Compute the arithmetic mean, median, first quartile, and third quartile.
b. Compute the variance, standard deviation, range, interquartile range, and coefficient of variation.
c. Are the data skewed? If so, how?
d. As a customer walks into the branch office during the lunch hour, she asks the branch manager how long she can expect to wait. The branch manager replies, "Almost certainly less than five minutes." On the basis of the results of (a) and (b), evaluate the accuracy of this statement.
e. Suppose that the branch manager would like to guarantee a certain level of service during the peak lunch period. Failure to obtain service within a specified time would result in a small monetary payment or gift to the customer. What waiting time do you think should be used as a cutoff above which this gift would be provided? Explain your answer.

15 Suppose that another branch, located in a residential area, is most concerned with the Friday evening hours from 5:00 P.M. to 7:00 P.M. The waiting time in minutes (defined as the time the customer enters the line to the time he or she is served) of all customers during these hours is recorded over a period of one week. A random sample of 15 customers is selected, and the results are as follows: **BANK2.xls**

9.66 5.90 8.02 5.79 8.73 3.82 8.01 8.35 10.49 6.68 5.64 4.08 6.17 9.91 5.47

a. Compute the arithmetic mean, median, first quartile, and third quartile.
b. Compute the variance, standard deviation, range, interquartile range, and coefficient of variation.
c. Are the data skewed? If so, how?
d. As a customer walks into the branch office during the Friday evening hours, he asks the branch manager how long he can expect to wait. The branch manager replies, "Almost certainly less than five minutes." On the basis of the results of (a) and (b), evaluate the accuracy of this statement.
e. Suppose that the branch manager would like to guarantee a certain level of service during the Friday evening hours. Failure to obtain service within a specified time would result in a small monetary payment or some other gift to the customer. What waiting time do you think should be used as a cutoff above which this small payment or gift would be provided? Explain your answer.
f. What arguments can be raised that would make it inappropriate to compare the waiting times in problem 14 with those in this problem?

16 The stock price for the Microsoft Corporation rose 7.88% in November 2002 and declined by 10.37% in December 2002.
a. Compute the arithmetic mean rate of return.
b. Compute the geometric mean rate of return. Note that for November the value of R_1 is 0.0788.
c. Explain the difference in the results of (a) and (b).

17 The time period from 2000 to 2002 saw a great deal of volatility in the value of stocks. The data in the following table **STOCKRETURN.xls** represents the total rate of return of the Dow Jones Industrial Index, the Standard & Poor's 500, the Russell 2000 Index, and the Wilshire 5000 Index from 2000 to 2002.

Year	DJIA	SP500	Russell2000	Wilshire5000
2002	−15.01	−22.1	−21.58	−20.90
2001	−5.44	−11.9	−1.03	−10.97
2000	−6.20	−9.1	−3.02	−10.89

a. Calculate the geometric rate of return for the Dow Jones Industrial Index.
b. Calculate the geometric rate of return for the Standard & Poor's 500.
c. Calculate the geometric rate of return for the Russell 2000 Index.
d. Calculate the geometric rate of return for the Wilshire 5000 Index.
e. What conclusion can you reach concerning the geometric rates of return of the four stock indexes?
f. Compare the results of (e) to those of problems 18 (d) and 19 (d).

18 The time period from 2000 to 2002 saw a great deal of volatility in the value of investments. The data in the following table **BANKRETURN.xls** represents the total rate of return of the one-year certificate of deposit, the thirty-month certificate of deposit, and the money market deposit from 2000 to 2002.

Year	One Year	Thirty Month	Money Market
2002	1.98	2.74	1.02
2001	3.60	3.97	1.73
2000	5.46	5.64	2.09

a. Calculate the geometric rate of return for the one-year certificate of deposit.
b. Calculate the geometric rate of return for the thirty-month certificate of deposit.
c. Calculate the geometric rate of return for the money market deposit.
d. What conclusions can your reach concerning the geometric rates of return of the three deposits?
e. Compare the results of (d) to those of problems 17 (e) and 19 (d).

19 The time period from 2000 to 2002 saw a great deal of volatility in the value of investments. The data in the following table **METALRETURN.xls** represents the total rate of return for platinum, gold, and silver from 2000 to 2002.

Year	Platinum	Gold	Silver
2002	24.5	24.5	5.5
2001	−21.3	1.2	−3.0
2000	−23.3	1.8	−5.9

a. Calculate the geometric rate of return for platinum.
b. Calculate the geometric rate of return for gold.
c. Calculate the geometric rate of return for silver.
d. What conclusions can you reach concerning the geometric rates of return of the three metals?
e. Compare the results of (d) to those of problems 17 (e) and 18 (d).

3 OBTAINING DESCRIPTIVE SUMMARY MEASURES FROM A POPULATION

In section 2 various *statistics* that described the properties of central tendency, variation, and shape from a *sample* were discussed. However, if the data set includes numerical measurements for an entire *population*, the *parameters* of the *population* can be computed and interpreted. In this section, parameters including the population mean, population variance, and population standard deviation are discussed.

Table 1 provides the name of the five largest bond funds and their average annual 5-year percentage returns for the period ending December 31, 2002. These data represent a population of interest, namely, the five largest bond funds.

LARGEST BONDS.xls

TABLE 1

The 5-year average annual percentage return ending December 31, 2002, for the population consisting of the five largest bond funds

Fund	5-Year Return (%)
Vanguard GNMA	7.3
Vanguard Total Bond Market Index	7.1
Franklin California Tax-Free Income A	5.2
Bond Fund of America A	5.4
Vanguard Short-Term Corporate	6.2

The Population Mean

The **population mean** is represented by the symbol μ, the Greek lowercase letter *mu*. Equation (12) defines the population mean.

POPULATION MEAN

The population mean is the sum of the values in the population divided by the population size N.

$$\mu = \frac{\sum_{i=1}^{N} X_i}{N} \qquad (12)$$

where

μ = population mean

X_i = ith observation of the variable X

$\sum_{i=1}^{N} X_i$ = summation of all X_i values in the population

To compute the mean return for the population of bond funds given in Table 1, use Equation (12),

$$\mu = \frac{\sum_{i=1}^{N} X_i}{N} = \frac{7.3 + 7.1 + 5.2 + 5.4 + 6.2}{5} = \frac{31.2}{5} = 6.24$$

Thus, the mean 5-year return for these bond funds is 6.24%.

The Population Variance and Standard Deviation

The **population variance** is represented by the symbol σ^2, the Greek lowercase letter sigma squared.

POPULATION VARIANCE

The population variance is the sum of the squared differences around the population mean divided by the population size.

$$\sigma^2 = \frac{\sum_{i=1}^{N} (X_i - \mu)^2}{N} \qquad (13)$$

where

μ = population mean

X_i = ith value of the variable X

$\sum_{i=1}^{N} (X_i - \mu)^2$ = summation of all the squared differences between the X_i values and μ

The **population standard deviation** is the square root of the population variance. It is represented by the symbol σ.

POPULATION STANDARD DEVIATION

$$\sigma = \sqrt{\frac{\sum_{i=1}^{N}(X_i - \mu)^2}{N}} \quad \textbf{(14)}$$

Note that the formulas for the population variance and standard deviation differ from those for the sample variance and standard deviation in that $(n - 1)$ in the denominator of S^2 and S [see Equations (9) and (10)] is replaced by N in the denominator of σ^2 and σ.

To compute the population variance for the data of Table 1, use Equation (13),

$$\begin{aligned}\sigma^2 &= \frac{\sum_{i=1}^{n}(X_i - \mu)^2}{N} \\ &= \frac{(7.3 - 6.24)^2 + (7.1 - 6.24)^2 + (5.2 - 6.24)^2 + (5.4 - 6.24)^2 + (6.2 - 6.24)^2}{5} \\ &= \frac{3.652}{5} = 0.7304\end{aligned}$$

Thus, the variance of the returns is 0.7304 squared percent. Since variances are in squared units, this number is hard to interpret. An easier interpretation of variation can be obtained from the standard deviation. Note from Equation (14) that the population standard deviation is the square root of the population variance.

$$\sigma = \sqrt{\sigma^2} = \sqrt{\frac{\sum_{i=1}^{N}(X_i - \mu)^2}{N}} = \sqrt{0.7304} = 0.8546$$

Thus, the typical 5-year annual return deviates from the mean of 6.24% by approximately 0.8546%. This small amount of variation suggests that these large bond funds produce very similar results and are therefore low-risk investments.

Empirical Rule
In bell-shaped distributions, approximately 68% of the observations are contained within a distance of ±1 standard deviation around the mean, approximately 95% of the observations are contained within a distance of ±2 standard deviations around the mean and approximately 99.7% are contained within a distance of ±3 standard deviations around the mean.

The Empirical Rule

In most data sets, a large portion of the observations tends to cluster somewhat near the median. In right-skewed data sets, this clustering occurs to the left of (i.e., *below*) the mean, and in left-skewed data sets, the observations tend to cluster to the right of (i.e., *above*) the mean. In symmetrical data sets, where the median and mean are the same, the observations often tend to cluster around these measures of central tendency producing a bell-shaped distribution. When extreme skewness is not present and such clustering is observed in a data set, the **empirical rule** can be used to examine the variability and get a better sense of what the standard deviation is measuring.

Thus, the standard deviation, as a measure of average variation around the mean, helps you understand how the observations distribute above and below the mean. This understanding can help you to identify unusual observations (i.e., outliers) when analyzing a set of numerical data. The empirical rule implies that for bell-shaped distributions only about one out of 20 observations will be beyond two standard deviations from the mean. Thus observations not contained in the interval $\mu \pm 2\sigma$ could be considered outliers. The rule also implies that only about three in 1,000 will be beyond three standard deviations from the mean. Therefore, observations not contained in the interval $\mu \pm 3\sigma$ are almost always considered outliers. For heavily skewed data sets, or those not appearing bell-shaped for any other reason, the Bienaymé-Chebyshev rule discussed below should be applied instead of the empirical rule.

EXAMPLE 7

A population of 12-ounce cans of cola is known to have a mean fill-weight of 12.06 ounces and a standard deviation of 0.02. It is also known that the population is bell-shaped. Describe the distribution of fill-weights. Is it very likely that a can will contain less than 12 ounces of cola?

SOLUTION

$$\mu \pm \sigma = 12.06 \pm 0.02 = (12.04, 12.08)$$

$$\mu \pm 2\sigma = 12.06 \pm 2(0.02) = (12.02, 12.10)$$

$$\mu \pm 3\sigma = 12.06 \pm 3(0.02) = (12.00, 12.12)$$

Using the empirical rule, approximately 68% of the cans will contain between 12.04 and 12.08 ounces, approximately 95% will contain between 12.02 and 12.10 ounces, and approximately 99.7% will contain between 12.00 and 12.12 ounces. Therefore, it is highly unlikely that a can will contain less than 12 ounces.

The Bienaymé-Chebyshev Rule

Bienaymé-Chebyshev Rule At least 3/4 or 75% of all observations in any data set are contained within a distance of ±2 standard deviations around the mean, at least 8/9 or 88.89% are contained within a distance of ±3 standard deviations around the mean, and at least 15/16 or 93.75% are contained within a distance of ±4 standard deviations around the mean.

More than a century ago, the mathematicians Bienaymé and Chebyshev (reference 1) independently discovered a useful property regarding the standard deviation. They found that for any data set, regardless of shape, the percentage of observations that are contained within distances of k standard deviations around the mean must be at least

$$(1 - 1/k^2) \times 100\%$$

Consider $k = 2$. The **Bienaymé-Chebyshev rule** states that at least $[1 - (1/2)^2]100\% = 75\%$ of the observations must be contained within ±2 standard deviations of the mean. The rule can be applied to any value of k greater than 1.

The Bienaymé-Chebyshev rule is very general and applies to any type of distribution. The rule indicates *at least* how likely that any particular observation falls within a given distance about the mean. However, if the data set is approximately bell-shaped, the empirical rule will more accurately reflect the greater concentration of data close to the mean. Table 2 summarizes these two rules.

TABLE 2
How Data Vary Around the Mean

	% of Observations Contained in Intervals Around the Mean	
Interval	**Bienaymé-Chebyshev (for any distribution)**	**Empirical Rule (bell-shaped distribution)**
$(\mu - \sigma, \mu + \sigma)$	At least 0%	Approximately 68%
$(\mu - 2\sigma, \mu + 2\sigma)$	At least 75%	Approximately 95%
$(\mu - 3\sigma, \mu + 3\sigma)$	At least 88.89%	Approximately 99.7%

EXAMPLE 8

As in Example 7, a population of 12-ounce cans of cola is known to have a mean fill-weight of 12.06 ounces and a standard deviation of 0.02. However, the shape of the population is unknown and you cannot assume that it is bell-shaped. Describe the distribution of fill-weights. Is it very likely that a can will contain less than 12 ounces of cola?

SOLUTION

$$\mu \pm \sigma = 12.06 \pm 0.02 = (12.04, 12.08)$$
$$\mu \pm 2\sigma = 12.06 \pm 2(0.02) = (12.02, 12.10)$$
$$\mu \pm 3\sigma = 12.06 \pm 3(0.02) = (12.00, 12.12)$$

Because the distribution may be skewed, the empirical rule cannot be used. Using the Bienaymé-Chebyshev rule, nothing useful can be said about the percentage of cans containing between 12.04 and 12.08 ounces. What can be determined is that at least 75% of the cans will contain between 12.02 and 12.10 ounces, and at least 88.89% will contain between 12.00 and 12.12 ounces. Therefore, between 0 and 11.11% of the cans contain less than 12 ounces.

PROBLEMS FOR SECTION 3

Learning the Basics

20 The following is a set of data for a population of size $N = 10$:

7 5 11 8 3 6 2 1 9 8

a. Compute the population mean.
b. Compute the population standard deviation.

21 The following is a set of data for a population of size $N = 10$:

7 5 6 6 6 4 8 6 9 3

a. Compute the population mean.
b. Compute the population standard deviation.

Applying the Concepts

Problems 22–27 can be solved manually or by using Microsoft Excel.

22 The following data represent the quarterly sales tax receipts (in thousands of dollars) submitted to the comptroller of the Village of Fair Lake for the period ending March 2003 by all 50 business establishments in that locale: **TAX.xls**

10.3	11.1	9.6	9.0	14.5
13.0	6.7	11.0	8.4	10.3
13.0	11.2	7.3	5.3	12.5
8.0	11.8	8.7	10.6	9.5
11.1	10.2	11.1	9.9	9.8
11.6	15.1	12.5	6.5	7.5
10.0	12.9	9.2	10.0	12.8
12.5	9.3	10.4	12.7	10.5
9.3	11.5	10.7	11.6	7.8
10.5	7.6	10.1	8.9	8.6

a. Organize the data into an ordered array or a stem-and-leaf display.
b. Compute the arithmetic mean for this population.
c. Compute the variance and standard deviation for this population.

What proportion of these businesses have quarterly sales tax receipts
d. within ±1 standard deviation of the mean?
e. within ±2 standard deviations of the mean?
f. within ±3 standard deviations of the mean?
g. Are you surprised at the results in (d)? (*Hint:* Compare and contrast your findings with what would be expected on the basis of the empirical rule.)

23 Consider a population of 1,024 mutual funds that primarily invested in large companies. It is determined that μ, the mean one-year total percentage return achieved by all the funds, is 8.20 and that σ, the standard deviation, is 2.75. In addition, suppose it is determined that the range in the one-year total returns is from −2.0 to 17.1 and that the quartiles are, respectively, 5.5 (Q_1) and 10.5 (Q_3). According to the empirical rule, what percentage of these funds is expected to be
a. within ±1 standard deviation of the mean?
b. within ±2 standard deviations of the mean?
c. According to the Bienaymé-Chebyshev rule, what percentage of these funds are expected to be within ±1 standard deviation of the mean?
d. According to the Bienaymé-Chebyshev rule, what percentage of these funds are expected to be within ±2 standard deviations of the mean?
e. According to the Bienaymé-Chebyshev rule, what percentage of these funds are expected to be within ±3 standard deviations of the mean?
f. According to the Bienaymé-Chebyshev rule, at least 93.75% of these funds are expected to have one-year total returns between what two amounts?

24 The following table **LARGEST BONDS 1 YR.xls** gives the 52-week return for the five largest bond mutual funds.

Fund	One-Year Return (%)
Pimco Inst TotRet	9.5
Vanguard GNMA	8.6
Vanguard TotBroad	8.1
Pimco Admin TotRet	9.3
Frank Temp CA	5.7

Source: Extracted from Wall Street Journal, *February 27, 2003.*

a. Compute the arithmetic mean for this population of the five largest bond mutual funds. Interpret this parameter.
b. Compute the variance and standard deviation for this population. Interpret these parameters.
c. Is there a lot of variability in the returns of the bond mutual funds?

25 The data in the file **ENERGY.xls** contains the per capita energy consumption in kilowatt hours for each of the 50 states and the District of Columbia during a recent year.

a. Organize the data into a stem-and-leaf display, a histogram, or a percentage polygon.
b. Compute the arithmetic mean for the population.
c. Compute the variance and standard deviation for the population.
d. What proportion of these states has average per capita energy consumption within ±1 standard deviation of the mean, within ±2 standard deviations of the mean, and within ±3 standard deviations of the mean?
e. Are you surprised at the results in (d)? (*Hint:* Compare and contrast your findings versus what would be expected based on the empirical rule.)
f. Do (a)–(e) with the District of Columbia removed. How have the results changed?

26 The following table **BIGSTOCKFUNDS.xls** gives the 52-week return ending February 26, 2003, for the 10 largest stock mutual funds.

Fund	Return
Vanguard 500	–24.1
Fidelity Magellan	–24.3
American ICAA	–17.6
American WshA	–19.8
American GrwthA	–21.6
Fidelity Contrafd	–13.9
Fidelity GwthInc	–20.9
American EupacA	–17.1
American PerA	–20.0
American Funds CI A: Income Fund of America	–6.6

Source: Extracted from the Wall Street Journal, *February 27, 2003.*

a. Compute the arithmetic mean for the population containing the 10 largest mutual funds. Interpret this number.
b. Compute the variance and standard deviation for the population containing the 10 largest stock funds. Interpret the standard deviation.
c. Use the empirical rule or the Bienaymé-Chebyshev rule, whichever is appropriate, to further explain the variation in this data set.
d. Using the results in (c), are there any outliers? Explain.
e. Compare your results in (a) and (b) to the population of the five largest bond funds given in Table 1. Which population experienced the highest average return on investment? Which population experienced the largest variability in return on investment?

27 How big are the companies that comprise the Dow Jones Industrial Average? Is there much variation in the size of these companies? One way to measure the size of a company is to calculate its market capitalization value. This value is equal to the total market value of all the stock for the company (i.e., the total number of shares multiplied by the current market price of a share). The data in the file **DOW CAPITAL.xls** gives the market capitalization for the 30 companies in the Dow Jones Industrials as reported by **www.money.cnn.com** on February 27, 2003.

a. Compute the arithmetic mean for this population. Interpret this number.
b. Compute the variance and standard deviation for this population. Interpret the standard deviation.
c. Use the empirical rule or the Bienaymé-Chebyshev rule, whichever is appropriate, to further explain the variation in this data set.
d. Using the results in (c), are there any outliers? Explain.

4 EXPLORATORY DATA ANALYSIS

Now that the three major properties of numerical data (central tendency, variation, and shape) have been discussed, the major features of the data can be summarized and further explored by developing a *five-number summary* and constructing a *box-and-whisker plot* (references 3 and 4).

The Five-Number Summary

A **five-number summary** that consists of

$$X_{\text{smallest}} \quad Q_1 \quad \text{Median} \quad Q_3 \quad X_{\text{largest}}$$

provides a way to determine the shape of the distribution.

If the data are perfectly symmetrical, the relationship among the various measures in the five-number summary is expressed as in Exhibit 3.

EXHIBIT 3 USING THE FIVE-NUMBER SUMMARY TO RECOGNIZE SYMMETRY IN DATA

1. The distance from $X_{smallest}$ to the median equals the distance from the median to $X_{largest}$.
2. The distance from $X_{smallest}$ to Q_1 equals the distance from Q_3 to $X_{largest}$.
3. The distance from Q_1 to the median equals the distance from the median to Q_3.

For skewed distributions, the relationship among the various measures of location is expressed as in Exhibit 4.

EXHIBIT 4 USING THE FIVE-NUMBER SUMMARY TO RECOGNIZE ASYMMETRY IN DATA

1. In right-skewed distributions, the distance from the median to $X_{largest}$ is greater than the distance from $X_{smallest}$ to the median.
2. In right-skewed distributions, the distance from Q_3 to $X_{largest}$ is greater than the distance from $X_{smallest}$ to Q_1.
3. In left-skewed distributions, the distance from $X_{smallest}$ to the median is greater than the distance from the median to $X_{largest}$.
4. In left-skewed distributions, the distance from $X_{smallest}$ to Q_1 is greater than the distance from Q_3 to $X_{largest}$.

The five-number summary for the 5-year annualized returns for the 15 very-high-risk mutual funds is obtained from previous computations of the median = 6.5, the first quartile = −0.7, and the third quartile = 9.8. In addition, the smallest value in the data set is −6.1 and the largest value is 18.5. Therefore, the five-number summary is

$$-6.1 \quad -0.7 \quad 6.5 \quad 9.8 \quad 18.5$$

The distance from the median to $X_{largest}$ ($18.5 - 6.5 = 12$) is approximately the same as the distance from $X_{smallest}$ to the median ($6.5 - (-6.1) = 12.6$). However, the distance from Q_3 to $X_{largest}$ ($18.5 - 9.8 = 8.7$) exceeds the distance from $X_{smallest}$ to Q_1 ($-0.7 - (-6.1) = 5.4$). Therefore, the 5-year annualized returns are slightly right-skewed.

The Box-and-Whisker Plot

A **box-and-whisker plot** provides a graphical representation of the data based on the five-number summary. In Figure 10, the box-and-whisker plot is depicted for the 5-year annualized returns achieved by the sample of 15 very-high-risk mutual funds.

The vertical line drawn within the box represents the median. The vertical line at the left side of the box represents the location of Q_1 and the vertical line at the right side of the box represents the location of Q_3. Thus, the box contains the middle 50% of the observations in the distribution. The lower 25% of the data are represented by a line (i.e., a *whisker*) connecting the left side of the box to the location of the smallest value, $X_{smallest}$. Similarly, the upper 25% of the data are represented by a whisker connecting the right side of the box to $X_{largest}$.

INTERPRETING THE BOX-AND-WHISKER PLOT

The visual representation of the 5-year annualized returns depicted in Figure 10 indicates approximate symmetry since the distance between the median and the highest value is approximately the same as the distance between the lowest value and the median. The other results, however, are not consistent with a symmetric distribution. The right whisker is longer than the left whisker due to the outlier value of 18.5, and the median is closer to the right side of the box than the left side of the box.

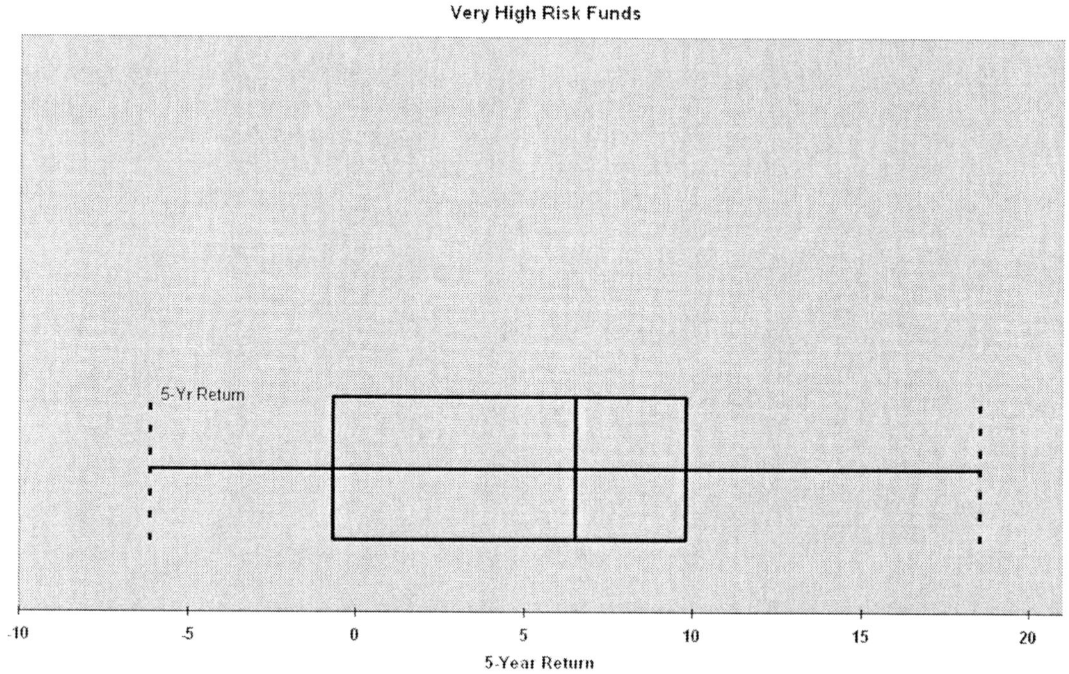

FIGURE 10
Box-and-whisker plot of the 5-year annualized returns achieved by the sample of 15 very-high-risk mutual funds

To summarize what has been learned from a graphical representation of the data, Figure 11 demonstrates the relationship between the box-and-whisker plot and polygon for four different distributions. When a data set is perfectly symmetrical, as is the case in Figure 11(a) and (d), the mean and median are the same. In addition, the length of the left whisker will equal the length of the right whisker, and the median line will divide the box in half.

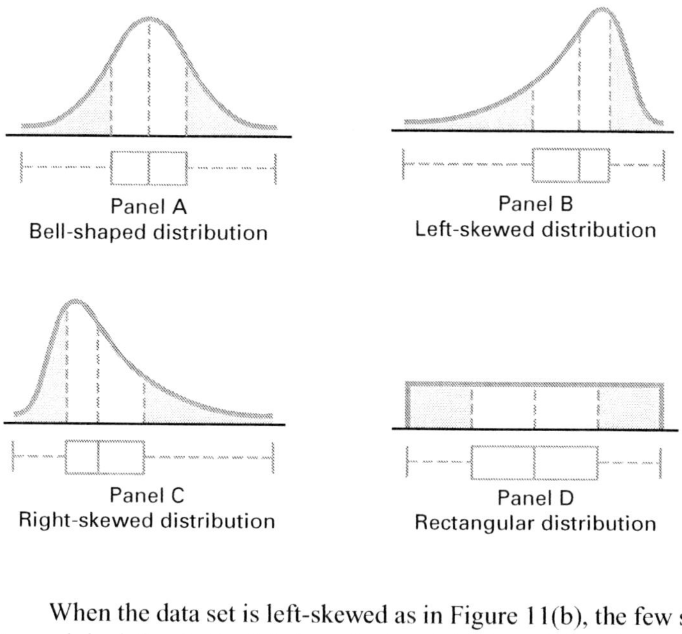

FIGURE 11
Four hypothetical distributions examined through their box-and-whisker plots and corresponding polygons *(Note: Area under each polygon is split into quartiles corresponding to the five-number summary for the respective box-and-whisker plot)*

When the data set is left-skewed as in Figure 11(b), the few small observations distort the mean toward the left tail. For this hypothetical left-skewed distribution, observe that the skewed nature of the data set indicates that there is a heavy clustering of observations at the high end of the scale (i.e., the right side); 75% of all data values are found between the left edge of the box (Q_1) and the end of the right whisker ($X_{largest}$). Therefore, the long left whisker contains the distribution of only the smallest 25% of the observations, demonstrating the distortion from symmetry in this data set.

For the right-skewed data set in Figure 11(c) the concentration of data points is on the low end of the scale (i.e., the left side of the box-and-whisker plot). Here, 75% of all data values are found between the beginning of the left whisker ($X_{smallest}$) and the right edge of the box (Q_3), and the remaining 25% of the observations are dispersed along the long right whisker at the upper end of the scale.

Microsoft Excel also provides the capability to display multiple (side-by-side) box-and-whisker plots. In Figure 12, box-and-whisker plots for the 5-year annualized returns for very- low-risk, low-risk, average-risk, high-risk, and very-high-risk mutual funds obtained from Excel are presented.

FIGURE 12

Box-and-whisker plots obtained from Microsoft Excel of the 5-year annualized returns achieved by the very-low-risk, low-risk, average-risk, high-risk, and very-high-risk mutual funds

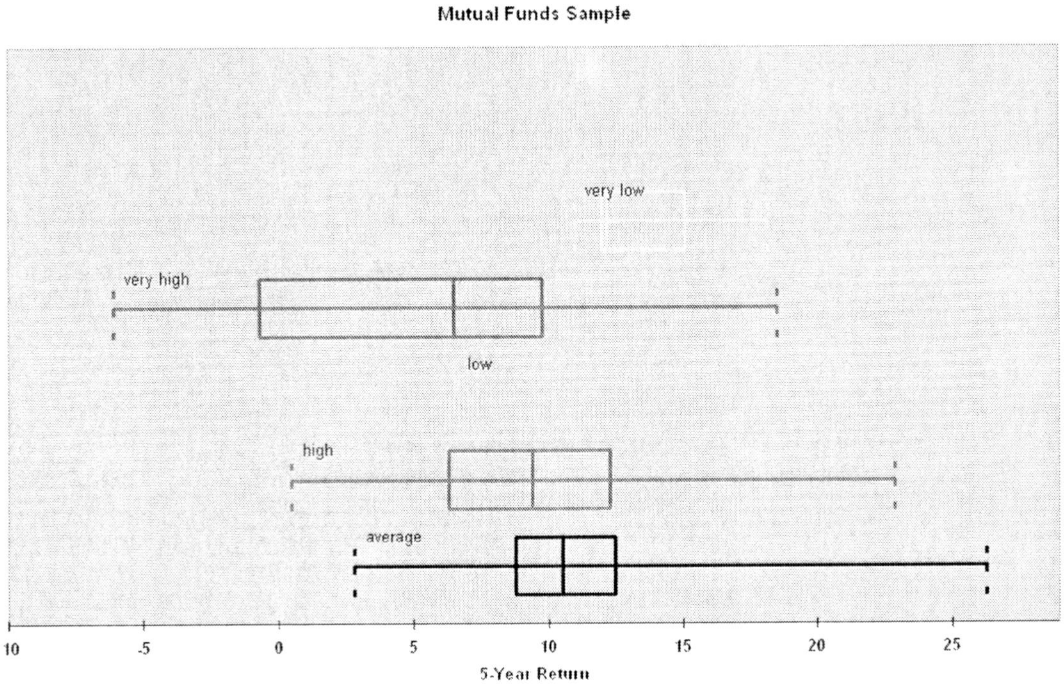

The side-by-side display is especially valuable when comparing the returns for the five risk groups. All the risk groups except for the very-high-risk funds produced 5-year annualized returns that are right-skewed. As expected, the very-high-risk funds exhibited the most variability as indicated by the largest box and the longest whiskers. The very-low-risk and the low-risk funds have the least variability. The median and the quartiles are highest for those funds that have the least risk (very-low, low, and average), and is lowest for those funds that have the most risk (high and very-high). Thus, the funds with the least risk actually performed better during the 1997–2001 time period studied.

Excel Strategies Generating Box-and-Whisker Plots

You generate a box-and-whisker plot in one of two ways, depending on whether you have computed the five-number summary for your set of data. If you have the raw data, you generate a box-and-whisker plot from raw data using a special PHStat2 procedure. If you have computed the five-number summary, you can fill in those statistics in the **BoxWhiskerPlot** worksheet included in the **Chapter 3.xls** workbook and generate a plot.

CHAPTER 3.xls

Retrieve the Figure 3.10 and Figure 3.12 sheets of the ***Chapter 3.xls*** *workbook to view box-and-whisker plots similar to Figures 10 and 12.*

Microsoft Excel does not have a built-in capacity to generate a box-and-whisker plot from raw data. Both PHStat2 and the BoxWhiskerPlot worksheet use obscure features of Microsoft Excel charting to create a box-and-whisker plot in ways unintended by Excel's developers.

To generate the box-and-whisker plot similar to one in Figure 10, open the **Chapter 3.xls** workbook and use one of these strategies:

Using Excel with PHStat2

Use the PHStat2 **Box-and-Whisker Plot** procedure to generate a box-and-whisker plot on a new chart sheet and, optionally, a five-number summary table on a new worksheet. Open to the **VHRiskFunds** worksheet of the Chapter 3 workbook and:

Select **PHStat | Descriptive Statistics | Box-and-Whisker Plot**.

In the Box-and-Whisker dialog box (shown at right):

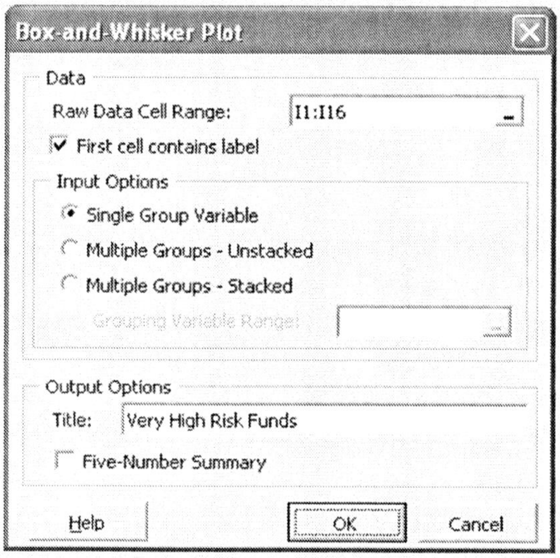

Enter **I1:I16** in the **Raw Data Cell Range** edit box.

Select the **Single Group Variable** option button.

Enter a title in the **Title** edit box.

Click the **OK** button.

This procedure can also generate plots on the same chart for data that contains multiple groups. For example, to generate a plot similar to Figure 12, open to the **Data** worksheet of the Chapter 3 workbook and select **PHStat | Descriptive Statistics | Box-and-Whisker Plot**. In the Box-and-Whisker dialog box enter **I1:I260** in the **Raw Data Cell Range** edit box and select the **Multiple Groups-Stacked** option button. In the enabled **Grouping Variable Range** edit box enter **K1:K260**, enter a title in the **Title** edit box, and click the **OK** button.

Using Excel

With your five-number summary at hand, open to the **BoxWhiskerPlot** worksheet of the Chapter 3 workbook. This worksheet contains demonstration data (the five-number summary for the 5-year return data for very-high-risk mutual funds) that generates a demonstration box-and-whisker plot. Enter your five-number summary in the tinted cell range **B2:B6** to generate a box-and-whisker plot for your data.

If you would like to have the box-and-whisker plot appear on its own chart sheet, right-click the background of the plot and select **Location** from the shortcut menu. In the Chart location dialog box, select the **As new sheet** option button, enter a self-descriptive name, and click the **OK** button.

PROBLEMS FOR SECTION 4

Learning the Basics

28 The following is a set of data from a sample of size $n = 5$:

7 4 9 8 2

a. List the five-number summary.
b. Form the box-and-whisker plot and describe the shape.
c. Compare your answer in (b) with that from problem 1(c). Discuss.

29 The following is a set of data from a sample of size $n = 6$:

7 4 9 7 3 12

a. List the five-number summary.
b. Form the box-and-whisker plot and describe the shape.
c. Compare your answer in (b) with that from problem 2(c). Discuss.

30 The following is a set of data from a sample of size $n = 7$:

12 7 4 9 0 7 3

a. List the five-number summary.
b. Form the box-and-whisker plot and describe the shape.
c. Compare your answer in (b) with that from problem 3(c). Discuss.

31 The following is a set of data from a sample of size $n = 5$:

7 −5 −8 7 9

a. List the five-number summary.
b. Form the box-and-whisker plot and describe the shape.
c. Compare your answer in (b) with that from problem 4(c). Discuss.

Applying the Concepts

Problems 32–38 can be solved manually or by using Microsoft Excel.

32 A manufacturer of flashlight batteries took a sample of 13 batteries from a day's production and used them continuously until they were drained. The numbers of hours they were used until failure were **BATTERIES.xls**

342 426 317 545 264 451 1,049 631 512 266 492 562 298

a. List the five-number summary.
b. Form the box-and-whisker plot, and describe the shape.
c. Compare your answer in (b) with that from problem 13(h). Discuss.

33 The data file **PE.xls** contains a random sample of 30 stocks traded on the New York Stock Exchange. For each of the stocks, the stock's ticker symbol and price-to-earnings ratio as reported in the *Wall Street Journal* on January 2, 2003, is given. The price-to-earnings ratio, or more simply, the P/E ratio, is determined by dividing the closing market price by the company's diluted per-share earnings for the past four quarters. Stocks with extremely high P/E ratios are typically called overvalued stocks, and stocks with unusually low P/E ratios are often called undervalued stocks.
a. List the five-number summary.
b. Form the box-and-whisker plot and describe its shape.

34 The following data represent the bounced check fee (in dollars) for a sample of 23 banks for direct-deposit customers who maintain a \$100 balance and the monthly service fee (in dollars) for direct-deposit customers if their accounts fall below the minimum required balance of \$1,500 for a sample of 26 banks. **BANKCOST1.xls** **BANKCOST2.xls**

Bounced Check Fee

26 28 20 20 21 22 25 25 18 25 15 20 18 20 25 25 22 30 30 30 15 20 29

Monthly Service Fee

12 8 5 5 6 6 10 10 9 7 10 7 7 5 0 10 6 9 12 0 5 10 8 5 5 9

Source: "The New Face of Banking." Copyright © 2000 by Consumers Union of U.S., Inc. Adapted from Consumer Reports, *June 2000, by permission of Consumers Union U.S., Inc., Yonkers, NY 10703–1057.*

a. List the five-number summary of the bounced check fee.
b. Form the box-and-whisker plot, and describe the shape of the distribution of the bounced check fee.
c. List the five-number summary of the monthly service fee.
d. Form the box-and-whisker plot, and describe the shape of the distribution of the monthly service fee.
e. Compare the results of (a) and (b) to those of (c) and (d). What similarities and differences are there in the distributions for the bounced check fee and the monthly service fee?

35 The following data represent the total fat for burgers and chicken items from a sample of fast-food chains. **FASTFOOD.xls**

Burgers

19 31 34 35 39 39 43

Chicken

7 9 15 16 16 18 22 25 27 33 39

Source: "Quick Bites." Copyright © 2001 by Consumers Union of U.S., Inc. Adapted from Consumer Reports, *March 2001, 46, by permission of Consumer's Union U.S., Inc., Yonkers, NY 10703–1057.*

a. List the five-number summary for the burgers.
b. Form the box-and-whisker plot, and describe the shape of the distribution for the burgers.
c. List the five-number summary for the chicken items.
d. Form the box-and-whisker plot and describe the shape of the distribution for the chicken items.
e. Compare the results of (a) and (b) to those of (c) and (d). What similarities and differences are there in the distributions for the burgers and the chicken items?

36 In the 2002–2003 academic year, many public universities in the United States raised tuition and fees due to a decrease in state subsidies (Mary Beth Marklein, "Public Universities Raise Tuition, Fees—and Ire," *USA Today*, August 8, 2002, 1A–2A). The change in the cost of tuition, a shared dormitory room, and the most popular meal plan from the 2001–2002 academic year for a sample of 10 public universities were as follows. **COLLEGECOST.xls**

University	Change in Cost ($)
University of California, Berkeley	1,589
University of Georgia, Athens	593
University of Illinois, Urbana–Champaign	1,223
Kansas State University, Manhattan	869
University of Maine, Orono	423
University of Mississippi, Oxford	1,720
University of New Hampshire, Durham	708
Ohio State University, Columbus	1,425
University of South Carolina, Columbia	922
Utah State University, Logan	308

a. List the five-number summary.
b. Form the box-and-whisker plot, and describe the shape.

37 A software development and consulting firm located in the Phoenix metropolitan area develops software for supply chain management systems using systematic software reuse. That is, instead of starting from scratch when writing and developing new custom software systems, the firm uses a database of reusable components totaling more than 2,000,000 lines of code collected from 10 years of continuous reuse effort. Eight analysts at the firm were asked to estimate the reuse rate when developing a new software system. The following data are given as a percentage of the total code written for a software system that is part of the reuse database. **REUSE.xls**

50 62.5 37.5 75.0 45.0 47.5 15.0 25.0

Source: Rothenberger, M. A., and K. J. Dooley, "A Performance Measure for Software Reuse Projects," Decision Sciences, *Fall 1999, 30(4): 1131–1153.*

a. List the five-number summary.
b. Form the box-and-whisker plot, and describe the shape of the data.

38 A bank branch located in a commercial district of a city has developed an improved process for serving customers during the 12:00 P.M. to 1:00 P.M. peak period. The waiting time in minutes (defined as the time the customer enters the line to the time he or she is served) of all customers during this hour is recorded over a period of one week. A random sample of 15 customers is selected, and the results are as follows: **BANK1.xls**

4.21 5.55 3.02 5.13 4.77 2.34 3.54 3.20
4.50 6.10 0.38 5.12 6.46 6.19 3.79

Another branch, located in a residential area, is most concerned with the Friday evening hours from 5:00 P.M. to 7:00 P.M. The waiting time in minutes (defined as the time the customer enters the line until he or she is served) of all customers during these hours is recorded over a period of one week. A random sample of 15 customers is selected, and the results are as follows: **BANK2.xls**

9.66 5.90 8.02 5.79 8.73 3.82 8.01 8.35
10.49 6.68 5.64 4.08 6.17 9.91 5.47

a. List the five-number summary of the waiting time at the bank branch located in a commercial district of a city.
b. Form the box-and-whisker plot and describe the shape of the distribution of the bank branch located in a commercial district of a city.
c. List the five-number summary of the waiting time at the bank branch located in a residential area.
d. Form the box-and-whisker plot and describe the shape of the distribution of the waiting time at the bank branch located in a residential area.
e. Compare the results of (a) and (b) to those of (c) and (d). What similarities and differences are there in the distribution of the waiting time at the two bank branches?

5 THE COVARIANCE AND COEFFICIENT OF CORRELATION

Scatter diagrams are used to graphically display bivariate numerical data. In this section, two numerical descriptive measures for measuring the strength of the linear relationship between two variables are developed. These two measures are the covariance and the coefficient of correlation. The covariance measures the strength of the linear relationship between two numerical variables (X and Y). The sample covariance is defined in Equation (15).

THE SAMPLE COVARIANCE

$$\text{cov}(X, Y) = \frac{\sum_{i=1}^{n}(X_i - \bar{X})(Y_i - \bar{Y})}{n - 1} \qquad \textbf{(15)}$$

The computation of the covariance is illustrated in Example 9.

EXAMPLE 9

COMPUTING THE SAMPLE COVARIANCE

Consider the 5-year annualized return and the expense ratio of the very-low-risk mutual funds in Table 3. Compute the sample covariance.

TABLE 3
The 5-Year annualized return and the expense ratio of the very-low-risk mutual funds

5-Yr-Return	Expense ratio
11.0	0.59
18.2	1.09
15.1	1.00
12.3	0.81
12.0	0.80
12.1	0.78

In Figure 13, Microsoft Excel is used to perform the computations needed to obtain the sample covariance.

FIGURE 13
Summary computations obtained from Microsoft Excel for the covariance. between 5-year annualized return and the expense ratio

	A	B	C	D	E	F
1	5-Yr Return	Expense ratio	(X-XBar)(Y-YBar)			
2	11.0	0.59	0.62475			
3	18.2	1.09	1.16375		Summary	
4	15.1	1.00	0.25575		XBar	13.45
5	12.3	0.81	0.04025		YBar	0.845
6	12.0	0.80	0.06525		Cov	0.4475
7	12.1	0.78	0.08775			
8		Sum:	2.23750			

From Figure 13 and Equation (15),

$$\text{cov}(X, Y) = \frac{2.2375}{6 - 1} = 0.4475$$

As a measure of the linear relationship between two numerical variables, the covariance has a major flaw. Using the covariance, you are unable to determine the relative strength of the relationship. To better determine the relative strength of the relationship, you need to study the coefficient of correlation.

The relative strength of a linear relationship, or the association, between two variables is typically measured by the **coefficient of correlation**, whose values range from −1 for a perfect negative correlation up to +1 for a perfect positive correlation. When dealing with bivariate numerical data representing a population, the coefficient of correlation is denoted by the Greek letter (ρ). *Perfect* means that if all the points were plotted in a scatter diagram, all the points could be connected with a straight line. Figure 14 illustrates three different types of association between two variables.

FIGURE 14
Types of association between variables

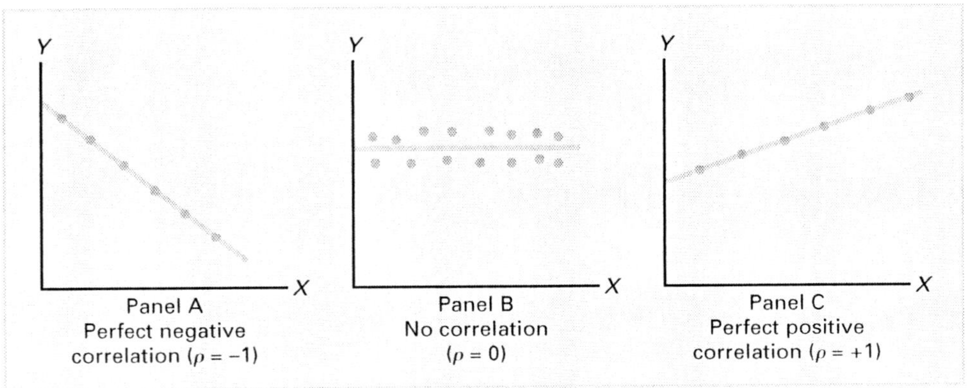

In panel A of Figure 14 there is a perfect negative linear relationship between *X* and *Y*. Thus, the coefficient of correlation ρ equals −1, and when *X* increases in the sample, *Y* decreases in a perfectly predictable manner. Panel B shows a situation in which there is no relationship between *X* and *Y*. In this case, the coefficient of correlation ρ equals 0, and as *X* increases there is no tendency for *Y* to increase or decrease. Panel C illustrates a perfect positive relationship where ρ equals +1. In this case, *Y* increases in a perfectly predictable manner when *X* increases.

When dealing with a sample of bivariate numerical data, the sample coefficient of correlation *r*, is calculated. It is highly unlikely to ever get a sample coefficient of exactly +1, 0, or −1. Figure 15 below presents scatter diagrams along with their respective sample coefficients of correlation *r* for six data sets, each of which contains 100 values of *X* and *Y*.

In panel A, the coefficient of correlation *r* is −0.9, and you can see that for small values of *X* there is a very strong tendency for *Y* to be large. Likewise, the large values of *X* tend to be paired with small values of *Y*. The data do not all fall on a straight line, however, so the association between

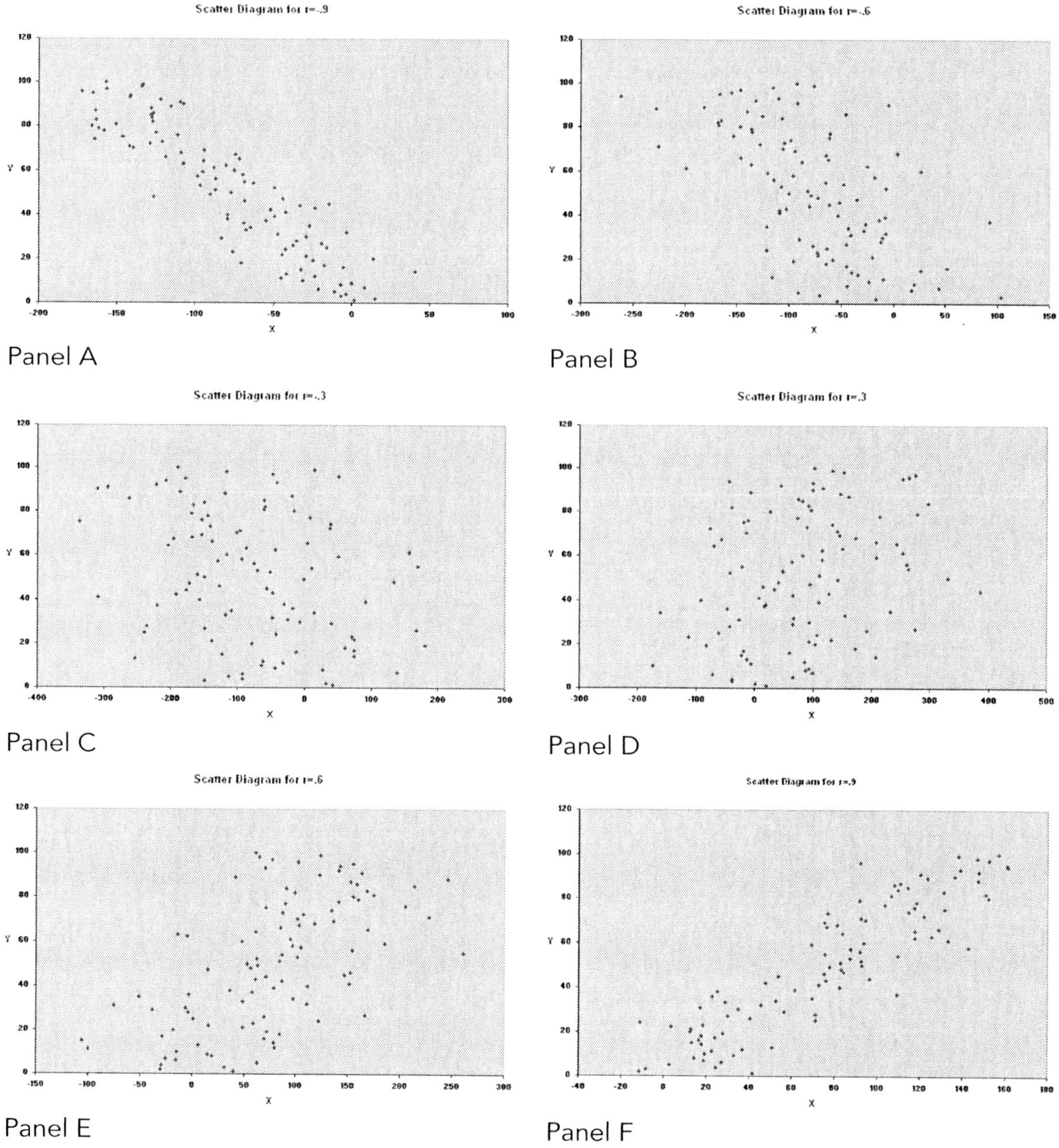

FIGURE 15

Six scatter diagrams obtained from Microsoft Excel and their sample coefficients of correlation *r*

X and Y cannot be described as *perfect*. The data in panel B have a coefficient of correlation equal to –0.6, and the small values of X tend to be paired with large values of Y. Note that the linear relationship between X and Y in panel B is not as strong as in panel A and, thus, the coefficient of correlation in panel B is not as negative as in panel A. In panel C the linear relationship between X and Y is very weak, $r = -0.3$, and there is only a slight tendency for the small values of X to be paired with the larger values of Y. Panels D–F depict data sets that have positive coefficients of correlation because small values of X tend to be paired with small values of Y, and the large values of X tend to be associated with large values of Y.

In the discussion of Figure 15, the relationships were described as *tendencies* and not as *cause-and-effect*. This wording was used on purpose. Correlation alone cannot prove that there is a causation effect, i.e., that the change in the value of one variable *caused* the change in the other variable. A strong correlation can be produced simply by chance, by the effect of a third variable not considered in the calculation of the correlation, or by a cause-and-effect relationship. Additional analysis is required to determine which of these three situations actually produced the correlation. Thus, one can say that causation implies correlation, but correlation alone does not imply causation.

The sample coefficient of correlation r is calculated using Equation (16a) or (16b).

THE SAMPLE COEFFICIENT OF CORRELATION r

$$r = \frac{\sum_{i=1}^{n}(X_i - \bar{X})(Y_i - \bar{Y})}{\sqrt{\sum_{i=1}^{n}(X_i - \bar{X})^2}\sqrt{\sum_{i=1}^{n}(Y_i - \bar{Y})^2}} \quad \textbf{(16a)}$$

$$r = \frac{\text{cov}(X,Y)}{S_X S_Y} \quad \textbf{(16b)}$$

where

$$\text{cov}(X,Y) = \frac{\sum_{i=1}^{n}(X_i - \bar{X})(Y_i - \bar{Y})}{n-1}$$

$$S_X = \sqrt{\frac{\sum_{i=1}^{n}(X_i - \bar{X})^2}{n-1}}$$

$$S_Y = \sqrt{\frac{\sum_{i=1}^{n}(Y_i - \bar{Y})^2}{n-1}}$$

In the Using Statistics scenario, several numeric variables for all the mutual funds were collected. For the 15 very-high-risk mutual funds, Figure 16 indicates the percentage returns for 2001 and the annualized 5-year return.

In Figure 17, Microsoft Excel is used to obtain r.

From Figure 17 and Equation (16a),

$$r = \frac{361.43}{\sqrt{1998.2}\sqrt{613.404}}$$
$$= 0.326461$$

FIGURE 16
Percentage returns for 2001 and the 5-year annualized returns for very-high-risk funds

Very High Risk Fund	Return 2001 (X)	5-Yr Return (Y)
Amer. Century GiftTrust Inv.	-35.4	-2.8
AXP Stategy Aggressive A	-32.9	5.5
Berger Small Company Growth Inv	-33.8	8.3
Consulting Group Small Cap Growth	-13.3	4.3
Fidelity Aggressive Growth	-47.3	5.9
Invesco Growth Inv	-49.1	-0.7
Janus Enterprise	-39.9	6.5
Janus Venture	-11.9	9.8
John Hancock Small Cap Growth A	-14.2	7.6
MS Mid Cap Equity Tr. B	-39.4	9.6
PBHG Growth	-34.5	-1.2
Putnam OTC Emerging Growth A	-46.1	-6.1
RS Emerging Growth A	-27.3	18.5
Rydex OTC Inv	-34.7	13.1
Van Kampen Aggressive Growth A	-39.7	12.9

FIGURE 17
Summary computations obtained from Microsoft Excel for the correlation of 2001 percentage returns and 5-year annualized returns for very-high-risk funds

	A	B	C	D	E	F	G	H
1	X_i (Return 2001)	Y_i (5-Yr Return)	$(X_i$ – XBar$)^2$	$(Y_i$ – YBar$)^2$	$(X_i$ – XBar) $(Y_i$ – YBar)			
2	-35.4	-2.8	4.41	78.85	18.65		Summary	
3	-32.9	5.5	0.16	0.34	-0.23		XBar	-33.30
4	-33.8	8.3	0.25	4.93	-1.11		YBar	6.08
5	-13.3	4.3	400.00	3.17	-35.60		r	0.3265
6	-47.3	5.9	196.00	0.03	2.52			
7	-49.1	-0.7	249.64	45.97	107.12			
8	-39.9	6.5	43.56	0.18	-2.77			
9	-11.9	9.8	457.96	13.84	79.61			
10	-14.2	7.6	364.81	2.31	29.03			
11	-39.4	9.6	37.21	12.39	-21.47			
12	-34.5	-1.2	1.44	53.00	8.74			
13	-46.1	-6.1	163.84	148.35	155.90			
14	-27.3	18.5	36.00	154.26	74.52			
15	-34.7	13.1	1.96	49.28	-9.83			
16	-39.7	12.9	40.96	46.51	-43.65			
17		*Sums:*	1998.2	613.40	361.43			
18		*Square roots:*	44.70	24.77				

Annotations: XBar → $\bar{X}$; YBar → $\bar{Y}$; 1998.2 → $\sum_{i=1}^{n}(X_i-\bar{X})^2$; 613.40 → $\sum_{i=1}^{n}(Y_i-\bar{Y})^2$; 361.43 → $\sum_{i=1}^{n}(X_i-\bar{X})(Y_i-\bar{Y})$

Or using Equation (16b)

$$r = \frac{\text{cov}(X,Y)}{S_X S_Y}$$

$$\text{cov}(X,Y) = \frac{361.43}{15-1}$$

$$= 25.816428$$

$$S_X = \sqrt{\frac{1998.2}{15-1}}$$

$$= 11.946906$$

$$S_Y = \sqrt{\frac{613.404}{15-1}}$$

$$= 6.6192575$$

Thus,

$$r = \frac{25.816428}{(11.946906)(6.6192575)}$$

$$= 0.326461$$

The 2001 returns and the 5-year returns for the 15 very-high-risk funds are positively correlated. The mutual funds with the larger returns in 2001 tend to be associated with larger 5-year returns, and the lower returns in 2001 tend to be associated with lower 5-year returns. This relationship is rather weak, as indicated by a coefficient of correlation $r = 0.326$ that is closer to 0, than it is to 1.0. Moreover, you cannot assume that having a large 5-year return caused the large return in 2001. Rather, you can only say that this is what tended to happen in the sample. As with all investments, past performance does not guarantee future performance.

In summary, the coefficient of correlation indicates the linear relationship, or association, between two numerical variables. When the coefficient of correlation gets closer to +1 or −1, the stronger is the linear relationship between the two variables. When the coefficient of correlation is near 0, little or no linear relationship exists. The sign of the coefficient of correlation indicates whether the data are positively correlated (i.e., the larger values of X are typically paired with the larger values of Y) or negatively correlated (i.e., the larger values of X are typically paired with the smaller values of Y). The existence of a strong correlation does not imply a causation effect. It only indicates the tendencies present in the data.

Excel Strategy Calculating the Correlation Coefficient

Use the Microsoft Excel worksheet function **CORREL** to calculate the coefficient of correlation. Enter this function in the form **CORREL(*X values cell range*, *Y values cell range*)**. To see an application of this function open the **Chapter 3.xls** workbook to the **Figure 17** worksheet. The worksheet uses the formula **=CORREL(A2:A16, B2:B16)** in cell G5 to compute *r*.

PROBLEMS FOR SECTION 5

Learning the Basics

39 The following is a set of data from a sample of $n = 11$ items,

X	7	5	8	3	6	10	12	4	9	15	18
Y	21	15	24	9	18	30	36	12	27	45	54

a. Compute the coefficient of correlation r.
b. How strong is the relationship between X and Y? Explain.

Applying the Concepts

Problems 42–45 can be solved manually or by using Microsoft Excel.

40 From 1990 to 1999, the NASDAQ posted impressive gains. According to business researchers George Anders and Scott Thurm, these gains were fueled by substantial increases in the investments of U.S. businesses in computers and other technologies. In fact, information technology outlays by U.S. businesses now accounts for more than one-quarter of all U.S. business investment ("The Rocket under the Tech Boom: Big Spending by Basic Industries," *Wall Street Journal*, March 30, 1999).
a. According to the article, were the NASDAQ and U.S. investment in information technology during the 1990s independent of one another, negatively correlated, or positively correlated? Explain.
b. Draw a scatter diagram that might describe the relationship between annualized return for 20 companies in the NASDAQ and information-technology investment during the 1990s.

41 Baltimore Gas & Electric Company indicated that the unusually cold weather during the first three months of 1999 boosted its first-quarter net income to \$86.2 million as compared to \$80.2 million for first-quarter 1998 ("Cold Weather Helps Boost Earnings 7.5% in 1st Period," *Wall Street Journal*, April 19, 1999).
a. Are quarterly net earnings for Baltimore Gas & Electric correlated with the average temperature for the period? Explain.
b. How might investors use this information to their advantage?
c. Does your answer to (b) apply to all natural resource stocks, to a subset of natural resource stocks, or just to the Baltimore Gas & Electric Company?

42 The data in the file **REFRIGERATOR.xls** represent the approximate retail price and the energy cost per year of 15 refrigerators.

Source: "Refrigerators." Copyright © 2002 by Consumers Union of U.S., Inc. Adapted from Consumer Reports, *August 2002, 26, by permission of Consumers Union U.S., Inc., Yonkers, NY 10703–1057.*

a. Compute the coefficient of correlation r.
b. How strong is the relationship between the price and the energy cost of refrigerators? Explain.

43 The following data **SECURITY.xls** represent the turnover rate of pre-boarding screeners at airports in 1998–1999 and the security violations detected per million passengers.

City	Turnover	Violations
St. Louis	416	11.9
Atlanta	375	7.3
Houston	237	10.6
Boston	207	22.9
Chicago	200	6.5
Denver	193	15.2
Dallas	156	18.2
Baltimore	155	21.7
Seattle/Tacoma	140	31.5
San Francisco	110	20.7
Orlando	100	9.9
Washington-Dulles	90	14.8
Los Angeles	88	25.1
Detroit	79	13.5
San Juan	70	10.3
Miami	64	13.1
New York-JFK	53	30.1
Washington-Reagan	47	31.8
Honolulu	37	14.9

Source: Alan B. Krueger, "A Small Dose of Common Sense Would Help Congress Break the Gridlock over Airport Security," The New York Times, *November 15, 2001, C2.*

a. Compute the coefficient of correlation r.
b. What conclusions can you reach about the relationship between the turnover rate of pre-boarding screeners and the security violations detected?

44 The following data **CELLPHONE.xls** represent the digital-mode talk time in hours and the battery capacity in milliampere-hours of cellphones.

Talk Time	Battery Capacity	Talk Time	Battery Capacity
4.50	800	1.50	450
4.00	1500	2.25	900
3.00	1300	2.25	900
2.00	1550	3.25	900
2.75	900	2.25	700
1.75	875	2.25	800
1.75	750	2.50	800
2.25	1100	2.25	900
1.75	850	2.00	900

Source: "Service Shortcomings." Copyright © 2002 by Consumers Union of U.S., Inc. Adapted from Consumer Reports, *February 2002, 25, by permission of Consumers Union U.S., Inc., Yonkers, NY 10703–1057.*

a. Compute the coefficient of correlation r.
b. What conclusions can you reach about the relationship between the battery capacity and the digital-mode talk time?
c. You would expect the cellphones with higher battery capacity to have a higher talk time. Is this borne out by the data?

45 The data in the file **BATTERIES2.xls** represent the price and cold-cranking amps (which denotes the starting current the battery can deliver) of automobile batteries.

Source: "Leading the Charge." Copyright © 2001 by Consumers Union of U.S., Inc. Adapted from Consumer Reports, *October 2001, 25, by permission of Consumers Union U.S., Inc., Yonkers, NY 10703–1057.*

a. Compute the coefficient of correlation r.
b. What conclusions can you reach about the relationship between the cold-cranking amps and the price?
c. You would expect the batteries with higher cold-cranking amps to have a higher price. Is this borne out by the data?

6 PITFALLS IN NUMERICAL DESCRIPTIVE MEASURES AND ETHICAL ISSUES

In this chapter you have studied how a set of numerical data can be characterized by various statistics that measure the properties of central tendency, variation, and shape. The next step is analysis and interpretation of the calculated statistics; the analysis is *objective*, the interpretation is *subjective*. You must avoid errors that may arise either in the objectivity of your analysis or in the subjectivity of your interpretation.

The analysis of the 15 very-high-risk mutual funds is *objective* and reveals several impartial findings. All the mutual funds have different returns; the *spread* in the returns range from −6.1 to 18.5; and the mean is 6.08. Objectivity in data analysis means reporting the most appropriate summary measures for a given data set. Having now read the chapter and thus gained a knowledge about various descriptive summary measures and their strengths and weaknesses, how should you proceed with the objective analysis? Because the data distribute in a slightly asymmetrical manner, shouldn't you report the median in addition to the mean? Doesn't the standard deviation provide more information about the property of variation than the range? Shouldn't you describe the data set as right-skewed?

On the other hand, data interpretation is *subjective*; different people form different conclusions when interpreting the analytical findings. Everyone sees the world from different perspectives. Some look at the summary measures for the 5-year annualized returns for the 15 very-high-risk mutual funds and are satisfied with the performances achieved. Others might look at the same data and conclude that the performance has been too low. Thus, because data interpretation is subjective, it must be done in a fair, neutral, and clear manner.

Ethical Issues

Ethical issues are vitally important to all data analysis. As a daily consumer of information, you need to question what you read in newspapers and magazines, what you hear on the radio or television, and what you see on the World Wide Web. Over time, much skepticism has been expressed about the purpose, the focus, and the objectivity of published studies. Perhaps no comment on this topic is more telling than a quip often attributed to the famous 19th-century British statesman Benjamin Disraeli: "There are three kinds of lies: lies, damned lies, and statistics."

Again, as mentioned in section 1.12, ethical considerations arise when one is deciding what results to include in a report. Both good and bad results should be documented. In addition, when making oral presentations and presenting written reports, results need to be given in a fair, objective, and neutral manner. You must try to distinguish between poor presentation of results and unethical presentation. Once more, as noted in earlier discussions on ethical considerations, the key is intent. When pertinent information is omitted, often it is done out of ignorance. However, unethical behavior occurs when you willfully choose an inappropriate summary measure (e.g., the mean for a very skewed set of data) to distort the facts in order to support a particular position. In addition, unethical behavior occurs when you selectively fail to report pertinent findings because it would be detrimental to the support of a particular position.

7 OBTAINING DESCRIPTIVE SUMMARY MEASURES FROM A FREQUENCY DISTRIBUTION (CD-ROM TOPIC)

section 3.7.pdf

It is sometimes the case that raw data are not available and the only source of data is a frequency distribution. To study how to compute the arithmetic mean and standard deviation from a frequency distribution, go to the **section 3.7.pdf** file located on the CD-ROM that accompanies this text.

SUMMARY

This chapter was about numerical descriptive measures. You have studied the subject matter of descriptive statistics: how data are collected, presented in tabular or chart format, and then summarized, described, analyzed, and interpreted. Also, you have learned how a financial analyst can help clients with future investments in mutual funds by analyzing past performance. When dealing with the mutual fund data, a very large data set, you were able to present useful information through the use of pie charts, histograms, and other graphical methods. Characteristics of past performance such as central tendency, variability, and shape were explored using various numerical summary measures such as the mean, median, quartiles, range, standard deviation, and coefficient of correlation. Detailed analyses of the five different risk classifications allowed you to determine that the very-low-risk mutual funds displayed the least amount of variation in the return and, in that sense, were indeed the least risky. The median return on investments was the largest for the mutual funds classified as very-low-risk, followed by low-risk, then average-risk, and smallest for the high-risk and very-high-risk. Thus it is reasonable to conclude that the funds with the least risk performed best.

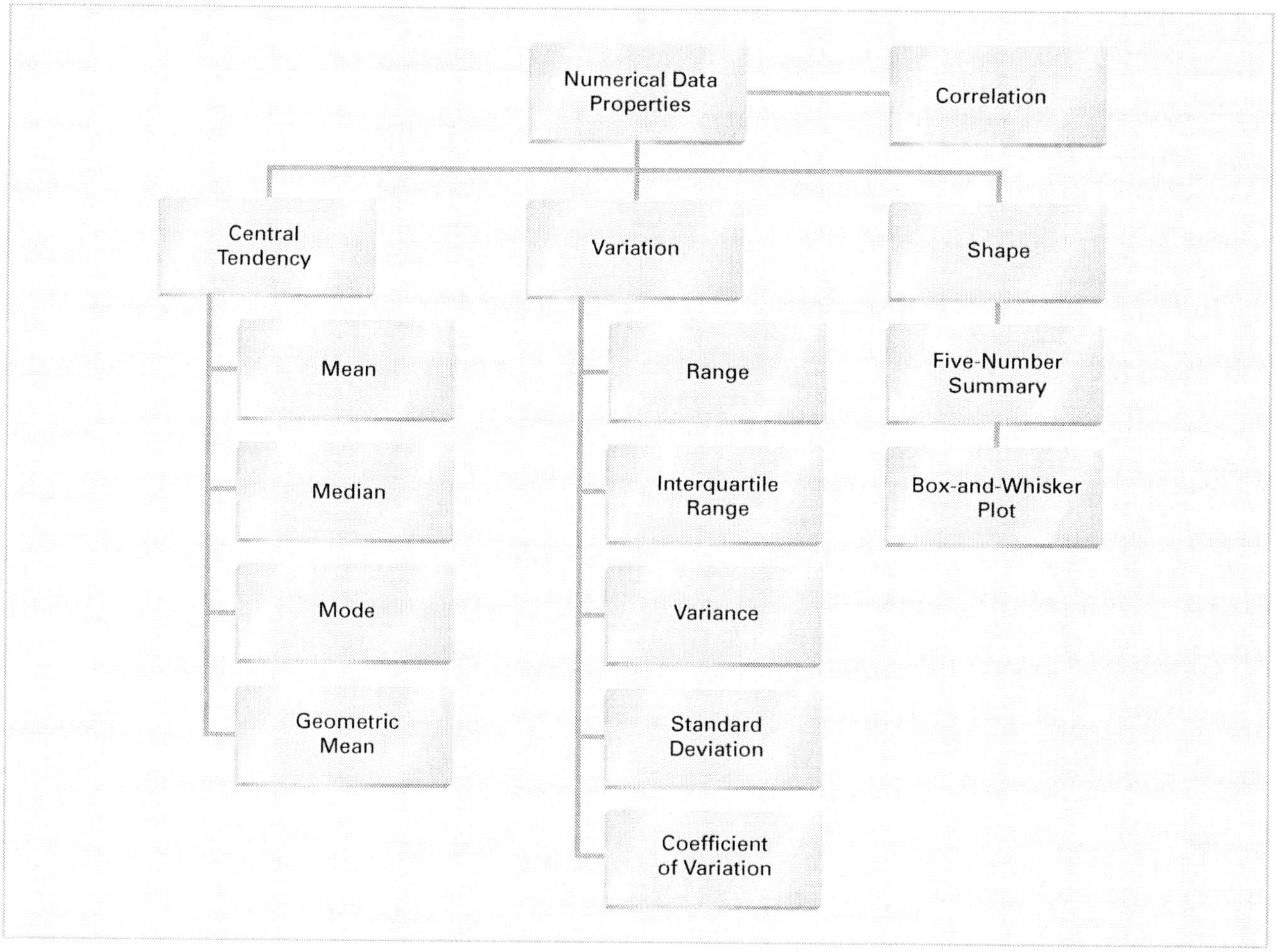

Chapter summary structure chart

KEY TERMS

arithmetic mean
asymmetrical
Bienaymé-Chebyshev rule
box-and-whisker plot
central tendency
coefficient of correlation
coefficient of variation
covariance
dispersion
dot scale
empirical rule
five-number summary
geometric mean
interquartile range
left-skewed
location
mean
median
midspread
mode
outlier
population mean
population standard deviation
population variance
Q_1: first quartile
Q_3: third quartile
quartiles
range
resistant measures
right-skewed
sample standard deviation
sample variance
shape
symmetrical
variation

CHAPTER REVIEW PROBLEMS

Checking Your Understanding

46 What are the properties of a set of numerical data?

47 What is meant by the property of location or central tendency?

48 What are the differences among the mean, median, and mode, and what are the advantages and disadvantages of each?

49 What is the difference between measures of central tendency and measures of noncentral tendency?

50 What is meant by the property of variation?

51 What are the differences among the various measures of variation such as the range, interquartile range, variance, standard deviation, and coefficient of variation, and what are the advantages and disadvantages of each?

52 How does the empirical rule help explain the ways in which the observations in a set of numerical data cluster and distribute?

53 What is meant by the property of shape?

54 Why are such exploratory data analysis techniques as the five-number summary and the box-and-whisker plot so useful?

Applying the Concepts

Problems 55–63 can be solved manually or by using Microsoft Excel. We recommend that Problems 64–71 and 74 be solved using Microsoft Excel.

55 A quality characteristic of interest for a tea-bag-filling process is the weight of the tea in the individual bags. If the bags are underfilled, two problems arise. First, customers may not be able to brew the tea to be as strong as they wish. Second, the company may be in violation of the truth-in-labeling laws. In this example, the label weight on the package indicates that, on average, there are 5.5 grams of tea in a bag. If the average amount of tea in a bag exceeds the label weight, the company is giving away product. Getting an exact amount of tea in a bag is problematic because of variation in the temperature and humidity inside the factory, differences in the density of the tea, and the extremely fast filling operation of the machine (approximately 170 bags a minute). The following table provides the weight in grams of a sample of 50 tea bags produced in one hour by a single machine. **TEABAGS.xls**

5.65	5.44	5.42	5.40	5.53	5.34	5.54	5.45	5.52	5.41
5.57	5.40	5.53	5.54	5.55	5.62	5.56	5.46	5.44	5.51
5.47	5.40	5.47	5.61	5.53	5.32	5.67	5.29	5.49	5.55
5.77	5.57	5.42	5.58	5.58	5.50	5.32	5.50	5.53	5.58
5.61	5.45	5.44	5.25	5.56	5.63	5.50	5.57	5.67	5.36

a. Compute the arithmetic mean and median.
b. Compute the first quartile and third quartile.
c. Compute the range, interquartile range, variance, standard deviation, and coefficient of variation.
d. Interpret the measures of central tendency within the context of this problem. Why should the company producing the tea bags be concerned about the central tendency?
e. Interpret the measures of variation within the context of this problem. Why should the company producing the tea bags be concerned about variation?
f. Construct a box-and-whisker plot.
g. Are the data skewed? If so, how?
h. Is the company meeting the requirement set forth on the label that, on average, there are 5.5 grams of tea in a bag?
i. If you were in charge of this process, what changes, if any, would you try to make concerning the distribution of weights in the individual bags?

56 In New York State, savings banks are permitted to sell a form of life insurance called Savings Bank Life Insurance (SBLI). The approval process consists of underwriting, which includes a review of the application, a medical information bureau check, possible requests for additional medical information and medical exams, and a policy compilation stage during which the policy pages are generated and sent to the bank for delivery. The ability to deliver approved policies to customers in a timely manner is critical to the profitability of this service to the bank. During a period of one month, a random sample of 27 approved policies was selected and the following total processing time in days was recorded: **INSURANCE.xls**

73	19	16	64	28	28	31	90	60	56	31	56	22	18
45	48	17	17	17	91	92	63	50	51	69	16	17	

a. Compute the arithmetic mean and median.
b. Compute the first quartile and third quartile.
c. Compute the range, interquartile range, variance, standard deviation, and coefficient of variation.
d. Construct a box-and-whisker plot.
e. Are the data skewed? If so, how?
f. What would you tell a customer who enters the bank to purchase this type of insurance policy and asks how long the approval process takes?

57 One of the major measures of the quality of service provided by any organization is the speed with which it responds to customer complaints. A large family-held department store selling furniture and flooring, including carpet, had undergone a major expansion in the past several years. In particular, the flooring department had expanded from 2 installation crews to an installation supervisor, a measurer, and 15 installation crews. A sample of 50 complaints concerning carpet installation was selected during a recent year. The following data represent the number of days between the receipt of the complaint and the resolution of the complaint. **FURNITURE.xls**

54	5	35	137	31	27	152	2	123	81	74	27
11	19	126	110	110	29	61	35	94	31	26	5
12	4	165	32	29	28	29	26	25	1	14	13
13	10	5	27	4	52	30	22	36	26	20	23
33	68										

a. Compute the arithmetic mean and median.
b. Compute the first quartile and third quartile.
c. Compute the range, interquartile range, variance, standard deviation, and coefficient of variation.
d. Construct a box-and-whisker plot.
e. Are the data skewed? If so, how?
f. On the basis of the results of (a)–(e), if you had to tell the president of the company how long a customer should expect to wait to have a complaint resolved, what would you say? Explain.

58 Do marketing promotions, such as bobble-head giveaways, increase attendance at Major League Baseball games? An article in *Sport Marketing Quarterly* reported on the effectiveness of marketing promotions (Boyd, T. C., and T. C. Krehbiel, "Promotion Timing in Major League Baseball and the Stacking Effects of Factors that Increase Game Attractiveness," March 12, 2003). The data file **ROYALS.xls** includes the following variables for the Kansas City Royals during the 2002 baseball season:

GAME = Home games in the order they were played
ATTENDANCE = Paid attendance for the game
PROMOTION – Y = a promotion was held; N = no promotion was held

a. Calculate the mean and standard deviation of attendance for the 43 games where promotions were held and for the 37 games without promotions.
b. Construct a five-number summary for the 43 games where promotions were held and for the 37 games without promotions.
c. Construct a graphical display containing two box-and-whisker plots—one for the 43 games where promotions were held and for the 37 games without promotions.
d. Discuss the results of (a)–(c) and comment on the effectiveness of promotions at Royals' games during the 2002 season.

59 A manufacturing company produces steel housings for electrical equipment. The main component part of the housing is a steel trough that is made out of a 14-gauge steel coil. It is produced using a 250-ton progressive punch press with a wipe-down operation putting two 90-degree forms in the flat steel to make the trough. The distance from one side of the form to the other is critical because of weatherproofing in outdoor applications. The company requires that the width of the trough be between 8.31 inches and 8.61 inches. The following are the widths of the troughs in inches for a sample of $n = 49$. **TROUGH.xls**

8.312	8.343	8.317	8.383	8.348	8.410	8.351	8.373	8.481	8.422
8.476	8.382	8.484	8.403	8.414	8.419	8.385	8.465	8.498	8.447
8.436	8.413	8.489	8.414	8.481	8.415	8.479	8.429	8.458	8.462
8.460	8.444	8.429	8.460	8.412	8.420	8.410	8.405	8.323	8.420
8.396	8.447	8.405	8.439	8.411	8.427	8.420	8.498	8.409	

a. Calculate the mean, median, range, and standard deviation for the width. Interpret these measures of central tendency and variability.
b. List the five-number summary.
c. Form a box-and-whisker plot and describe the shape.
d. What can you conclude about the number of troughs that will meet the company's requirements of troughs being between 8.31 and 8.61 inches wide?

60 The manufacturing company in problem 59 also produces electric insulators. If the insulators break when in use, a short-circuit is likely to occur. To test the strength of the insulators, destructive testing in high-powered labs is carried out to determine how much *force* is required to break the insulators. Force is measured by observing how many pounds must be applied to the insulator before it breaks. The data from 30 observations from this experiment are as follows. **FORCE.xls**

1,870	1,728	1,656	1,610	1,634	1,784	1,522	1,696	1,592	1,662
1,866	1,764	1,734	1,662	1,734	1,774	1,550	1,756	1,762	1,866
1,820	1,744	1,788	1,688	1,810	1,752	1,680	1,810	1,652	1,736

a. Calculate the mean, median, range, and standard deviation for the force variable.
b. Interpret the measures of central tendency and variability in (a).
c. List the five-number summary.
d. Form a box-and-whisker plot and describe the shape.
e. What can you conclude about the strength of the insulators if the company requires a force measurement of at least 1,500?

61 Problems with a telephone line that prevent a customer from receiving or making calls are disconcerting to both the customer and the telephone company. These problems can be of two types: those that are located inside a central office and those located on lines between the central office and the customer's equipment. The following data represent samples of 20 problems reported to two different offices of a telephone company and the time to clear these problems (in minutes) from the customers' lines: **PHONE.xls**

Central Office I Time to Clear Problems (Minutes)

1.48	1.75	0.78	2.85	0.52	1.60	4.15	3.97	1.48	3.10
1.02	0.53	0.93	1.60	0.80	1.05	6.32	3.93	5.45	0.97

Central Office II Time to Clear Problems (Minutes)

7.55	3.75	0.10	1.10	0.60	0.52	3.30	2.10	0.58	4.02
3.75	0.65	1.92	0.60	1.53	4.23	0.08	1.48	1.65	0.72

For each of the two central office locations:

a. Compute the arithmetic mean and median.
b. Compute the first quartile and third quartile.
c. Compute the range, interquartile range, variance, standard deviation, and coefficient of variation.
d. Construct a side-by-side box-and-whisker plot.
e. Are the data skewed? If so, how?
f. On the basis of the results of (a)–(e), are there any differences between the two central offices? Explain.
g. What would be the effect on your results and your conclusions if the first value for Central Office II was incorrectly recorded as 27.55 instead of 7.55?

62 In many manufacturing processes the term "work-in-process" (often abbreviated WIP) is used. In a book manufacturing plant the WIP represents the time it takes for sheets from a press to be folded, gathered, sewn, tipped on end sheets, and bound. The following data represent samples of 20 books at each of two production plants and the processing time (defined as the time in days from when the books came off the press to when they were packed in cartons) for these jobs. **WIP.xls**

Plant A

5.62	5.29	16.25	10.92	11.46	21.62	8.45	8.58	5.41	11.42
11.62	7.29	7.50	7.96	4.42	10.50	7.58	9.29	7.54	8.92

Plant B

9.54	11.46	16.62	12.62	25.75	15.41	14.29	13.13	13.71	10.04
5.75	12.46	9.17	13.21	6.00	2.33	14.25	5.37	6.25	9.71

For each of the two plants:

a. Compute the arithmetic mean and median.
b. Compute the first quartile and third quartile.
c. Compute the range, interquartile range, variance, standard deviation, and coefficient of variation.
d. Construct a side-by-side box-and-whisker plot.
e. Are the data skewed? If so, how?
f. On the basis of the results of (a)–(e), are there any differences between the two plants? Explain.

63 The data contained in the file **CEREALS.xls** consists of the cost in dollars per ounce, calories, fiber in grams, and sugar in grams for 33 breakfast cereals.

Source: Copyright © 1999 by Consumers Union of U.S., Inc. Adapted from Consumer Reports, *October 1999, 33–34, by permission of Consumers Union U.S., Inc., Yonkers, NY 10703–1057.*

For each variable:

a. Compute the arithmetic mean and median.
b. Compute the first quartile and third quartile.
c. Compute the range, interquartile range, variance, standard deviation, and coefficient of variation.
d. Construct a box-and-whisker plot.
e. Are the data skewed? If so, how?
f. What conclusions can you reach concerning the cost per ounce in cents, calories, fiber in grams, and the sugar in grams for the 33 breakfast cereals?

64 The data contained in the file **PETFOOD2.xls** consists of the cost per serving, cups per can, protein in grams, and fat in grams for 97 varieties of dry and canned dog and cat food.

Source: Copyright © 1998 by Consumers Union of U.S., Inc. Adapted from Consumer Reports, *February 1998, 18–19, by permission of Consumers Union U.S., Inc., Yonkers, NY 10703–1057.*

For each type of food (dry and canned), for each type of animal (dog and cat), for the variables of cost per serving, protein in grams, and fat in grams:

a. Compute the arithmetic mean and median.
b. Compute the first quartile and third quartile.
c. Compute the range, interquartile range, variance, standard deviation, and coefficient of variation.
d. Construct a side-by-side box-and-whisker plot for the four types (dry dog food, canned dog food, dry cat food, and canned cat food).
e. Are the data for any of the types of food skewed? If so, how?
f. What conclusions can you reach concerning any differences among the four types (dry dog food, canned dog food, dry cat food, and canned cat food)?

65 The manufacturer of Boston and Vermont asphalt shingles provide their customers with a 20-year warranty on most of their products. To determine whether a shingle will last as long as the warranty period, accelerated-life testing is conducted at the manufacturing plant. Accelerated-life testing exposes the shingle to the stresses it would be subject to in a lifetime of normal use in a laboratory setting via an experiment that takes only a few minutes to conduct. In this test, a shingle is repeatedly scraped with a brush for a short period of time and the amount of shingle granules that are removed by the brushing is weighed (in grams). Shingles that experience low amounts of granule loss are expected to last longer in normal use than shingles that experience high amounts of granule loss. In this situation, a shingle should experience no more than 0.8 grams of granule loss if it is expected to last the length of the warranty period. The data file **GRANULE.xls** contains a sample of 170 measurements made on the company's Boston shingles, and 140 measurements made on Vermont shingles.

a. List the five-number summary for the Boston shingles.
b. List the five-number summary for the Vermont shingles.
c. Form side-by-side box-and-whisker plots for the two brands of shingles and describe the shapes of the distributions.
d. Comment on the shingles' ability to achieve a granule loss of 0.8 grams or less.

66 The data in the file **STATES.xls** represent the results of the American Community Survey, a sampling of 700,000 households taken in each state during the 2000 U.S. Census. For each of the variables of average travel-to-work time in minutes, percentage of homes with eight or more rooms, median household income, and percentage of mortgage-paying homeowners whose housing costs exceed 30% of income:

a. Compute the arithmetic mean and median.
b. Compute the first quartile and third quartile.
c. Compute the range, interquartile range, variance, standard deviation, and coefficient of variation.
d. Construct a box-and-whisker plot.
e. Are the data skewed? If so, how?
f. What conclusions can you reach concerning the average travel-to-work time in minutes, percentage of homes with eight or more rooms, median household income, and percentage of mortgage-paying homeowners whose housing costs exceed 30% of income?

67 The economics of baseball has caused a great deal of controversy with owners arguing that they are losing money, players arguing that owners are making money, and fans complaining about how expensive it is to attend a game and watch games on cable television. In addition to data related to team statistics for the 2001 season, the file **BB2001.xls** contains team-by-team statistics on ticket prices; the fan cost index; regular season gate receipts; local television, radio, and cable receipts; all other operating revenue, player compensation and benefits; national and other local expenses; and income from baseball operations. For each of these variables,

a. Compute the arithmetic mean and median.
b. Compute the first quartile and third quartile.
c. Compute the range, interquartile range, variance, standard deviation, and coefficient of variation.
d. Construct a box-and-whisker plot.
e. Are the data skewed? If so, how?
f. Compute the correlation between the number of wins and player compensation and benefits. How strong is the relationship between these two variables?
g. What conclusions can you reach concerning the regular season gate receipts; local television, radio, and cable receipts; all other operating revenue; player compensation and benefits; national and other local expenses; and income from baseball operations.

68 The data in the file **AIRCLEANERS.xls** represent the price, yearly energy cost, and yearly cost of room air cleaners.

a. Compute the coefficient of correlation between price and energy cost.
b. Compute the coefficient of correlation between price and filter cost.
c. What conclusions about the relationship of energy cost and filter cost to the price of the air cleaners can you make?

Source: "Portable Room Air Cleaners." Copyright © 2002 by Consumers Union of U.S., Inc. Adapted from Consumer Reports, *February 2002, 47, by permission of Consumers Union U.S., Inc., Yonkers, NY 10703–1057.*

69 The data in the file **PRINTERS.xls** represent the price, text speed, text cost, color photo time, and color photo cost of computer printers.

a. Compute the coefficient of correlation between price and text speed.
b. Compute the coefficient of correlation between price and text cost.
c. Compute the coefficient of correlation between price and color photo time.
d. Compute the coefficient of correlation between price and color photo cost.
e. Based on the results of (a)–(d), do you think that any of the other variables might be useful in predicting printer price? Explain.

Source: "Printers." Copyright © 2002 by Consumers Union of U.S., Inc. Adapted from Consumer Reports, *March 2002, 51, by permission of Consumers Union U.S., Inc., Yonkers, NY 10703–1057.*

70 Suppose that you want to study characteristics of the model year 2002 automobiles in terms of the following variables: miles per gallon, length, width, turning circle requirement, weight, and luggage capacity. **AUTO2002.xls**

Source: "The 2002 Cars." Copyright © 2002 by Consumers Union of U.S. Adapted from Consumer Reports, *April 2002, by permission of Consumers Union of U.S., Inc., Yonkers, NY 10703–1057.*

For each of these variables:

a. Compute the arithmetic mean and median.
b. Compute the first quartile and third quartile.
c. Compute the range, interquartile range, variance, standard deviation, and coefficient of variation.
d. Construct a box-and-whisker plot.
e. Are the data skewed? If so, how?
f. What conclusions can you draw concerning the 2002 automobiles?
g. Compare sports utility vehicles (SUVs) with non-sports utility vehicles. Complete (a)–(f) for each of these groups. What conclusions can you reach concerning differences between SUVs with non SUVs?

71 Zagat's publishes restaurant ratings for various locations in the United States. The data file **RESTRATE.xls** contains the Zagat rating for food, decor, service, and the price per person for a sample of 50 restaurants located in New York City, and 50 restaurants located on Long Island.

Source: Extracted from Zagat Survey 2002 New York City Restaurants and Zagat Survey 2002 Long Island Restaurants.

For New York City and Long Island restaurants, for the variables of food rating, decor rating, service rating, and price per person:

a. Compute the arithmetic mean and median.
b. Compute the first quartile and third quartile.
c. Compute the range, interquartile range, variance, standard deviation, and coefficient of variation.
d. Construct a side-by-side box-and-whisker plot for the New York City and Long Island restaurants.
e. Are the data for any of the variables skewed? If so, how?
f. What conclusions can you reach concerning differences between New York City and Long Island restaurants?

72 As an illustration of the misuse of statistics, an article by Glenn Kramon ("Coaxing the Stanford Elephant to Dance," *The New York Times* Sunday Business Section, November 11, 1990) implied that costs at Stanford Medical Center had been driven up higher than at competing institutions because the former was more likely than other organizations to treat indigent, Medicare, Medicaid, sicker, and more complex patients. To illustrate this, the chart below was provided to compare the average 1989 to 1990 hospital charges for three medical procedures (coronary bypass, simple birth, and hip replacement) at three competing institutions (El Camino, Sequoia, and Stanford).

Suppose you were working in a medical center. Your CEO knows you are currently taking a course in statistics and calls you in to discuss this. She tells you that the article was presented in a discussion group setting as part of a meeting of regional area medical center CEOs last night and that one of them mentioned that this chart was totally meaningless and asked her opinion. She now requests that you prepare her response. You smile, take a deep breath, and reply . . .

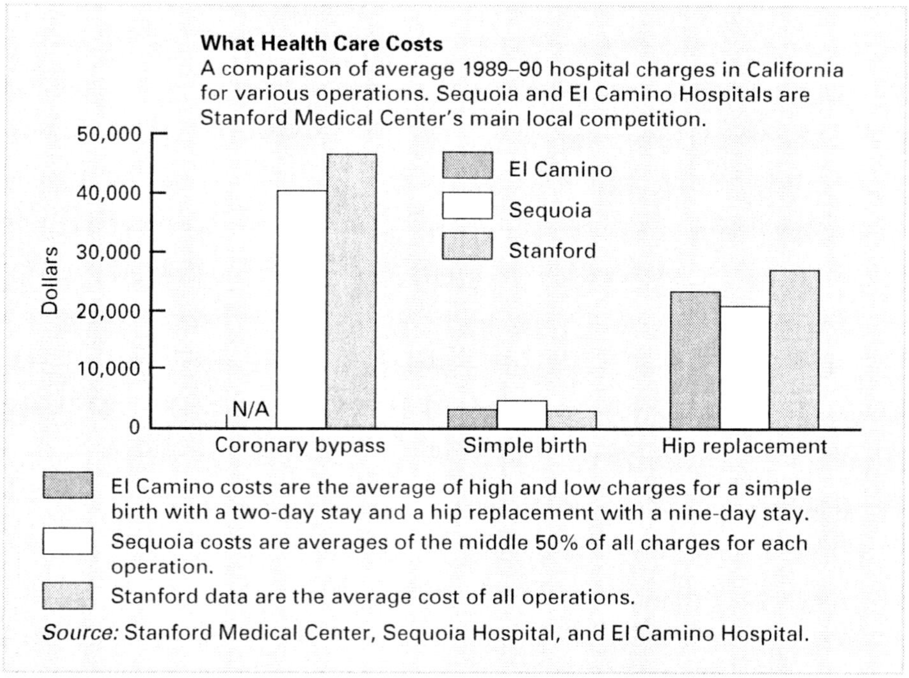

73 You are planning to study for your statistics examination with a group of classmates, one of whom you particularly want to impress. This individual has volunteered to use Microsoft Excel to get the needed summary information, tables, and charts for a data set containing several numerical and categorical variables assigned by the instructor for study purposes. This person comes over to you with the printout and exclaims, "I've got it all—the means, the medians, the standard deviations, the stem-and-leaf display, the box-and-whisker plots, the pie charts—for all our variables. The problem is, some of the output looks weird—like the stem-and-leaf displays and the box-and-whisker plots for gender and for major and the pie charts for grade point index and for height. Also, I can't understand why Professor Krehbiel said we can't get the descriptive stats for some of the variables—I got it for everything! See, the mean for height is 68.23, the mean for grade point index is 2.76, the mean for gender is 1.50, the mean for major is 4.33." What is your reply?

Report Writing Exercises

74 The data found in the data file **BEER.xls** represent the price of a six-pack of 12-ounce bottles, the calories per 12 fluid ounces, the percent of alcohol content per 12 fluid ounces, the type of beer (craft lagers, craft ales, imported lagers, regular and ice beers, and light and nonalcoholic beers), and the country of origin (U.S. versus imported) for each of the 69 beers that were sampled.

Your task is to write a report based on a complete descriptive evaluation of each of the numerical variables—price, calories, and alcoholic content—regardless of type of product or origin. Then perform a similar evaluation comparing each of these numerical variables based on type of product—craft lagers, craft ales, imported lagers, regular and ice beers, and light or nonalcoholic beers. In addition, perform a similar evaluation comparing and contrasting each of these numerical variables based on the origins of the beers—those brewed in the United States versus those that were imported. Appended to your report should be all appropriate tables, charts, and descriptive statistical information obtained from the survey results. Be sure to incorporate tables and charts you may have obtained using Microsoft Excel into the report using Microsoft Office as discussed in the appendix on Preparing Data for Reports and Presentations Using Microsoft Office.

Source: "Beers." Copyright © 1996 by Consumers Union of U.S., Inc. Adapted with permission from Consumer Reports, *June 1996, by permission of Consumers Union of U.S., Inc., Yonkers, NY 10703–1057.*

Internet Exercises

75 Go to the Web site for this text

www.prenhall.com/levine

Select Chapter 3 and then click on Internet exercises.

TEAM PROJECT

TP1 The data file **MUTUAL FUNDS.xls** contains information regarding 13 variables from a sample of 259 mutual funds. The variables are:

Fund—The name of the mutual fund
Type—Type of stocks comprising the mutual fund: small cap, mid cap, large cap
Objective—Objective of stocks comprising the mutual fund: growth or value
Assets—In millions of dollars
Fees—Sales charges (no or yes)
Expense ratio—In percentage of average net assets
2001 Return—Twelve-month return in 2001
Three-year return—Annualized return 1999–2001
Five-year return—Annualized return 1997–2001
Turnover—Level of trading activity by the mutual fund classified as very low, low, average, high, or very high
Risk—Risk-of-loss factor of the mutual fund classified as very low, low, average, high, or very high
Best quarter—Best quarterly performance 1997–2001
Worst quarter—Worst quarterly performance 1997–2001

Consider the variable measuring the expense ratio of the mutual funds. Calculate and interpret the following statistics.

a. Mean
b. Median
c. Range
d. Variance
e. Standard deviation
f. Coefficient of variation
g. Q_1
h. Q_3
i. Interquartile range

TP2 Consider the mutual funds data of problem TP1. In the data set **MUTUAL FUNDS.xls** there are funds without any fee and funds with a fee.

a. Construct a table that includes the arithmetic mean, median, range, and standard deviation for the funds without a fee using the 2001 return variable.
b. List the five-number summary and construct a box-and-whisker plot for the funds without a fee using the 2001 return variable.
c. Construct a table that includes the arithmetic mean, median, range, and standard deviation for the funds with a fee using the 2001 return variable.
d. List the five-number summary and construct a box-and-whisker plot for the funds with a fee using the 2001 return variable.
e. Repeat (a)–(d) using the variable containing the 3-year annualized returns.
f. Write a short summary of your findings.

TP3 Consider the mutual funds data of problem TP1. How did the growth and value mutual funds perform during 2001? **MUTUAL FUNDS.xls**

a. For the two objectives (growth and value), construct a table that includes the arithmetic mean, median, range, and standard deviation for the growth and value funds using the 2001 return variable.
b. Construct side-by-side box-and-whisker plots for the two different objectives using the 2001 return variable.
c. Repeat (a)–(b) using the 3-year annualized return.
d. Write a short summary of your findings.

TP4 Consider the mutual funds data of Team Project 1. Using the variable containing the 2001 returns, do the following for each of the three categories of small cap, mid cap and large cap. **MUTUAL FUNDS.xls**

a. Calculate and interpret the mean and median.
b. Calculate and interpret the range, variance, and standard deviation.
c. Calculate and interpret the five-number summary.
d. Calculate and interpret the coefficient of variation.
e. Construct and interpret a box-and-whisker plot.
f. Repeat (a)–(e) using the variable containing the 3-year annualized returns.
g. Write a short summary of your conclusions.

RUNNING CASE MANAGING THE *SPRINGVILLE HERALD*

For what variable in the Managing the Springville Herald Case would various descriptive measures be needed? For the variable you identify:

1. Compute the appropriate descriptive measures, and generate a stem-and-leaf display and a box-and-whisker plot.
2. Identify another graphical display that might be useful and construct it. What conclusions can you form from that plot that cannot be made from the stem-and-leaf display and the box-and-whisker plot?

Summarize your findings in a report that can be included with the task force's study.

WEB CASE

Apply your knowledge about the proper use of numerical descriptive measures in this continuing Web Case.

Visit the StockTout Investing Service Web site (**www.prenhall.com/Springville/StockTout.htm**) a second time and reexamine their supporting data and then answer the following:

1. Reexamine the data you inspected when working on the Web Case. Can descriptive measures be computed for any variables? How would such summary statistics support StockTout's claims? How would those summary statistics affect your perception of StockTout's record?
2. Evaluate the methods StockTout used to summarize the results of its customer survey (**www.prenhall.com/Springville/ST_Survey.htm**). Is there anything you would do differently to summarize these results?
3. Note that the last question of the survey has fewer responses. What factors may have limited the number of responses to that question?

REFERENCES

1. Kendall, M. G., and A. Stuart, *The Advanced Theory of Statistics*, vol. 1 (London: Charles W. Griffin, 1958).
2. *Microsoft Excel 2002* (Redmond, WA: Microsoft Corporation, 2001).
3. Tukey, J., *Exploratory Data Analysis* (Reading, MA: Addison-Wesley, 1977).
4. Velleman, P. F., and D. C. Hoaglin, *Applications, Basics and Computing of Exploratory Data Analysis* (Boston, MA: Duxbury Press, 1981).

Answers to Selected Even-Numbered Problems

For more detailed solutions including explanations, interpretations, and Excel output, see the *Student Solutions Manual*.

2 (a) Mean = 7, median = 7, mode = 7. **(b)** Range = 9, variance = 10.8, interquartile range = 5, standard deviation = 3.286, coefficient of variation = (3.286/7) · 100% = 46.94%. **(c)** Since the mean equals the median, the distribution is symmetrical.

4 (a) Mean = 2, median = 7, mode = 7. **(b)** Range = 17, variance = 62, interquartile range = 14.5, standard deviation = 7.874, coefficient of variation = (7.874/2) · 100% = 393.7%. **(c)** Since the mean is less than the median, the distribution is left-skewed.

6 19.58%.

8 (a) Burger: mean = 34.29, median = 35, Q_1 = 31, Q_3 = 39. Chicken: mean = 20.64, median = 18, Q_1 = 15, Q_3 = 27. **(b)** Burger: S^2 = 60.905, S = 7.804, range = 24, IQR = 8, CV = 22.76%. Chicken: S^2 = 95.455, S = 9.770, range = 32, IQR = 12, CV = 47.34%. **(c)** The data for chicken items are skewed to the right and the data for burgers are skewed to the left. **(d)** In general, burgers have more total fat than chicken items. The least total fat among burgers is still higher than 50% of the total fat among chicken items. About 25% of the burgers have higher total fat than the highest total fat among the chicken items.

10 (a) Mean = 16.83, median = 16, mode = 15, range = 29, variance = 41.18, standard deviation = 6.42. **(b)** The average P/E ratio for the 30 stocks traded on the New York Stock Exchange is 16.83. The P/E ratio that occurs most is 15 while the middle ranked P/E ratio is 16. The average of the squared differences between all the P/E ratios in the sample and the sample average P/E ratio is 41.18.

12 (a) $\overline{X}$ = 44.69, median = 46.25. There is no mode. **(b)** Range = 60, S^2 = 370.4241, S = 19.2464. **(c)** The average percentage of the total code written for a software system that is part of the reuse database is 44.69%. The middle ranked percentage of reuse is 46.25. There is no particular reuse rate that occurs more than once. The average of the squared differences between all the reuse rates in the sample and the sample mean is 370.4241. According to the empirical rule, roughly two out of three reuse rates in the population will scatter within 19.25% of 44.69%.

14 (a) Mean = 4.287, median = 4.5, Q_1 = 3.20, Q_3 = 5.55. **(b)** variance = 2.683, standard deviation = 1.638, range = 6.08, interquartile range = 2.35, coefficient of variation = 38.21%. **(c)** Since the mean is less than the median, the distribution is left-skewed. **(d)** The mean and median are both under 5 minutes and the distribution is left-skewed, meaning that there are more unusually low observations than there are high observations. But six of the 15 bank customers sampled (or 40%) had wait times in excess of 5 minutes. So, although the customer is more likely to be served in less than 5 minutes, the manager may have been overconfident in responding that the customer would "almost certainly" not wait longer than 5 minutes for service. **(e)** According to the empirical rule, between 90% to 95% of the observations will fall within two standard deviations around the mean. Hence, using a cutoff of 4.287 + 2(1.638) = 7.563 minutes will result in roughly a 5% chance of having to pay this small payment of a gift.

16 (a) –1.245%. **(b)** –1.667%. **(c)** The geometric mean rate of return is a better measure for stock price changes that are expressed as rate of change over time.

18 (a) 3.67%. **(b)** 4.11%. **(c)** 1.61%. **(d)** The thirty-month certificate of deposit has the higher rate of return over the 3-year period followed by the 1-year certificate of deposit and finally the money market deposit has the lowest rate of return. **(e)** Over the time period from 2000 to 2002, the certificates of deposit and money market have the best rate of return followed by the three precious metals. The stocks have the worst rate of return.

20 (a) Population mean = 6. **(b)** Population variance = 9.4, population standard deviation = 3.066.

22 (b) Mean = 10.28. **(c)** σ^2 = 4.1820, σ = 2.045. **(d)** 64%. **(e)** 94%. **(f)** 100%. **(g)** These percentages are lower than the empirical rule would suggest.

24 (a) Population mean = 8.24. The average 52-week return of the five largest bond mutual funds is 8.24%. **(b)** Population variance = 1.86, population standard deviation = 1.36. The average squared distances between all 52-week returns and the population mean is 1.86. The majority of the 52-week returns are within 1.36% around 8.24%. **(c)** Since the population standard deviation is less than 1/7 the value of the population mean, there is not much variability in the 52-week returns of the five largest bond mutual funds as majority of the 52-week returns are within 1.36% around 8.24%.

26 (a) Mean = –18.59. On average, the 52-week return of the 10 largest stock funds experienced a loss of 18.59%. **(b)** Variance = 24.98, standard deviation = 5.00. The average squared distances between all 52-week returns and the population average return is 24.98. If the distribution is approximately symmetrical, about 68% of the 52-week returns will be within 5% around –18.59%. **(c)** The five-number summary are –24.3, –21.6, –19.9, –17.1, and –6.6. Since the distribution does not appear to be symmetrical, the Bienaymé-Chebyshev rule is more appropriate for explaining the variation in this data set. According to the Bienaymé-Chebyshev rule, at least 75% of the observations will fall within two standard deviations from the mean, that is, between –28.58 and –8.59, and at least 88.89% of the observations will fall within three standard deviations from the mean, that is, between –33.58 and –3.60. In this data set, 90% of the observations fall between –28.58 and –8.59 and all the observations fall between –33.58 and –3.60. **(d)** Since 90% of the observations falls within two standard deviations from the mean and all the observations falls within three standard deviations from the mean, there is no outlier in this data set. **(e)** The five largest bond funds given in Table 3.1 experienced the highest average return on investment. The 10 largest stock funds experienced the largest variability in return on investment.

28 (a) Five-number summary: 2 3 7 8.5 9. **(b)** The distribution is left-skewed. **(c)** There is a longer distance from Q_1 to the median than from the median to Q_3, confirming our conclusion that the data are left-skewed.

30 (a) Five-number summary: 0 3 7 9 12. **(b)** The distribution is left-skewed. **(c)** The box-and-whisker plot shows a longer left box from Q_1 to the median than from the median to Q_3, visually confirming our conclusion that the data are left-skewed.

32 (a) Five-number summary: 264 307.5 451 553.5 1,049. **(b)** The distribution is right-skewed. **(c)** Because the data set is small, one very large value (1,049) skews the distribution to the right.

34 (a) Five-number summary: 15 20 22 26 30. **(b)** The distribution of bounced-check fee is skewed slightly to the right. **(c)** Five-number summary: 0 5 7 10 12. **(d)** The distribution of monthly service charge is skewed to the left. **(e)** The central tendency of the bounced-check fee is substantially higher than that of the monthly service fee. While the distribution of the bounced-check fee is quite symmetrical, the distribution of the monthly service fee is skewed more to the left with a few banks charging a very low or no monthly service fee.

36 (a) Minimum = 308, 1st quartile = 593, median = 895.5, 3rd quartile = 1425 and maximum = 1720. **(b)** The distribution is skewed to the right.

38 (a) Five-number summary: 0.38 3.2 4.5 5.55 6.46. **(b)** The distribution is skewed to the left. **(c)** Five-number summary: 3.82 5.64 6.68 8.73 10.49. **(d)** The distribution is skewed slightly to the right. **(e)** The central tendency of the waiting times for the bank branch located in the commercial district of a city is lower than that of the branch located in the residential area. There are a few longer than normal waiting times for the branch located in the residential area, whereas there are a few exceptionally short waiting times for the branch located in the commercial area.

40 (a) According to the article, the NASDAQ and U.S. investment in information technology during the nineties were positively correlated. The NASDAQ is a weighted average of mostly technology stocks and, hence, the rapid increase in investments of U.S. businesses in computers and information technology will only help boost the performance of stocks of businesses involved in information technology.

42 (a) $r = -0.2810$. **(b)** The coefficient of correlation between price and energy cost indicates that there is a very weak negative linear relationship between the two.

44 (a) $r = 0.3409$. **(b)** The coefficient of correlation between talk time and battery capacity indicates that there is a rather weak positive linear relationship between the two. **(c)** The expectation that cellphones with higher battery capacity will have a higher talk time is not borne out by the data.

56 (a) Mean = 43.89, Median = 45. **(b)** 1st quartile = 18, 3rd quartile = 63. **(c)** Range = 76 interquartile range = 45, variance = 639.2564, standard deviation = 25.28, coefficient of variation = 57.61%. **(e)** The distribution is skewed to the right because there are a few policies that require an exceptionally long period to be approved. **(f)** The average approval process takes 43.89 days with 50% of the policies being approved in less than 45 days. Then 50% of the applications are approved between 18 and 63 days. About 67% of the applications are approved between 18.6 to 69.2 days.

58 (a) With promotion: mean = 20,748.93, standard deviation = 8,109.50. Without promotion: mean = 13,935.70, standard deviation = 4,437.92. **(b)** With promotion: minimum = 10,470, 1st quartile = 14,905, median = 19,775, 3rd quartile = 24,456, maximum = 40,605. Without promotion: minimum = 9,555, 1st quartile = 11,779, median = 12,952, 3rd quartile = 14,367, maximum = 28,834. **(d)** The average attendance is 6,813 more when there is a promotion than when there is not and the variation of attendance when there is a promotion is larger than that when there is not a promotion. There are many factors that can cause variation in the paid attendance. Some of them are weather condition, time and day of the game, which is the visiting team, etc.

60 (a) Mean = 1,723.4, median = 1,735, range = 348, standard deviation = 89.55. **(b)** The average force required to break the insulators in the sample is 1,723.4 pounds. The middle ranked breaking force is 1,735 pounds. The differences between the smallest and largest breaking force is 348 pounds. Roughly about 68% of the insulators will have breaking force that falls within 89.55 pounds of 1723.4 pounds. **(c)** Five-number summary: 1,522 1,662 1,735 1,784 1,870. **(d)** The distribution is skewed to the left. **(e)** All the observations in the sample have breaking force that is greater than 1,500 pounds and, hence, will fulfill the company's requirement.

62 Plant A: **(a)** mean = 9.382, median = 8.515. **(b)** First quartile = 7.29, third quartile = 11.42. **(c)** Range = 17.2, interquartile range = 4.13, variance = 15.981, standard deviation = 3.998, coefficient of variation = 42.61%. **(e)** The distribution of processing times for Plant A is right-skewed. Plant B: **(a)** mean = 11.354, median = 11.96. **(b)** First quartile = 6.25, third quartile = 14.25. **(c)** Range = 23.42, interquartile range = 8, variance = 26.277, standard deviation = 5.126, coefficient of variation = 45.15%. **(e)** The distribution of processing times for Plant B is left-skewed. **(f)** Processing times for Plants A and B are quite different. Plant B has a greater range of processing times, much more dispersion among data values, a higher median, a higher value for the third quartile, and a greater extreme value than Plant A.

64 Cost per serving (dry dog food): **(a)** mean = 0.549, median = 0.54 **(b)** first quartile = 0.49, third quartile = 0.65 **(c)** range = 0.69, interquartile range = 0.16, variance = 0.0226, standard deviation = 0.150, coefficient of variation = 27.41%. Cost per serving (canned dog food): **(a)** mean = 1.990, median = 1.555 **(b)** first quartile = 1.39, third quartile = 1.96 **(c)** range = 7.41, interquartile range = 0.57, variance = 2.108, standard deviation = 1.452, coefficient of variation = 72.98%. Cost per serving (dry cat food): **(a)** mean = 0.27, median = 0.26 **(b)** first quartile = 0.2, third quartile = 0.29 **(c)** range = 0.46, interquartile range = 0.09, variance = 0.0106, standard deviation = 0.103 coefficient of variation = 38.15%. Cost per serving (canned cat food): **(a)** mean = 1.095, median = 0.84 **(b)** first quartile = 0.68, third quartile = 1.39 **(c)** range = 2.09, interquartile range = 0.71, variance = 0.354, standard deviation = 0.595, coefficient of variation = 54.32%. Protein (dry dog food): **(a)** mean = 65.393, median = 65.5 **(b)** first quartile = 59, third quartile = 69 **(c)** range = 30, interquartile range = 10, variance = 61.136, standard deviation = 7.819, coefficient of variation = 11.96%. Protein (canned dog food): **(a)** mean = 92.042, median = 92 **(b)** first quartile = 81, third quartile = 103 **(c)** range = 86, interquartile range = 22, variance = 400.563, standard deviation = 20.014, coefficient of variation = 21.74%. Protein (dry cat food): **(a)** mean = 35.846, median = 36.5 **(b)** first quartile = 35, third quartile = 38 **(c)** range = 14, interquartile range = 3, variance = 8.935, standard deviation = 2.989, coefficient of variation = 8.34%. Protein (canned cat food): **(a)** mean = 45.421, median = 45 **(b)** first quartile = 38, third quartile = 51 **(c)** range = 29, interquartile range = 13, variance = 75.924, standard deviation = 8.713, coefficient of variation = 19.18%. Fat (dry dog food): **(a)** mean = 34.607, median = 32.5 **(b)** first quartile = 29, third quartile = 41 **(c)** range = 24, interquartile range = 12, variance = 43.062, standard deviation = 6.562, coefficient of variation = 18.96%. Fat (canned dog food): **(a)** mean = 53.125, median = 52, **(b)** first quartile = 42, third quartile = 67 **(c)** range = 57, interquartile range = 25, variance = 245.245, standard deviation = 15.660, coefficient of variation = 29.48%. Fat (dry cat food): **(a)** mean = 14.731, median = 14 **(b)** first quartile = 12, third quartile = 16 **(c)** range = 13, interquartile range = 4, variance = 13.085, standard deviation = 3.6, coefficient of variation = 24.56%. Fat (canned cat food): **(a)** mean = 23.947, median = 26 **(b)** first quartile = 19, third quartile = 27 **(c)** range = 20, interquartile range = 8, variance = 27.608, standard deviation = 5.254, coefficient of variation = 21.94%. **(e)** For cost per serving, all but dry dog food are skewed to the right. The skewness is particularly severe for canned dog food. Canned cat food is also skewed significantly to the right. For protein in grams, canned cat food and dry dog food are slightly skewed to the right while dry cat food is skewed to the left. For fat in grams, canned cat food is slightly skewed to the left while dry cat food and dry dog food are skewed to the right. **(f)** On average, canned dog food is more expensive than dry dog food. Canned cat food is also more expensive than dry cat food on average. Canned dog food has more protein than dry dog food and canned cat food also has more protein than dry cat food on average. On average, canned dog food has more fat than dry dog food and canned cat food has more fat than dry cat food. The range of cost per serving for canned dog food and canned cat food is wider than the range of cost per serving for dry dog food and dry cat food. The range of protein in grams for canned dog food and canned cat food is wider than the range of protein in grams for dry dog food and dry cat food. Similarly, the range of fat in grams for canned dog food and canned cat food is also wider than the range of fat in grams for dry dog food and dry cat food.

66 Commuting: **(a)** mean = 22.428, median = 22.50 **(b)** first quartile = 20.10, third quartile = 24.30 **(c)** range = 15.80, interquartile range = 4.20, variance = 12.536, standard deviation = 3.541, coefficient of variation = 15.79%. Homes 8 Room: **(a)** mean = 15.835, median = 15.50 **(b)** first quartile = 12.0, third quartile = 19.50 **(c)** range = 20.70, interquartile range = 7.50, variance = 26.312, standard deviation = 5.130, coefficient of variation = 32.39%. Housing More Than 30% Income: **(a)** mean = 25.128, median = 24.80 **(b)** first quartile = 21.40, third quartile = 27.10 **(c)** range = 23.50, interquartile range = 5.70, variance = 24.381, standard deviation = 4.938, coefficient of variation = 19.65%. Median Income: **(a)** mean = 40794.255, median = 39480.00 **(b)** first quartile = 36385.00, third quartile = 45654.00 **(c)** range = 25657.00, interquartile range = 9269.00, variance = 41471014.794, standard deviation = 6439.799, coefficient of variation = 15.79%. **(e)** All the variables are slightly skewed to the right.

68 **(a)** $r = 0.0210$. **(b)** $r = -0.2255$ **(c)** There is no relationship between price and energy cost and a slight negative relationship between price and filter cost.

70 MPG: **(a)** mean = 20.703, median = 21 **(b)** first quartile = 18, third quartile = 22 **(c)** range = 31, interquartile range = 4, variance = 21.894, standard deviation = 4.679, coefficient of variation = 22.60%. Length: **(a)** mean = 187.190, median = 187 **(b)** first quartile = 177.5, third quartile = 194.5 **(c)** range = 72, interquartile range = 17, variance = 173.939, standard deviation = 13.188, coefficient of variation = 7.05%. Width: **(a)** mean = 71.339, median = 71 **(b)** first quartile = 69, third quartile = 73 **(c)** range = 15, interquartile range = 4, variance = 10.426, standard deviation = 3.229, coefficient of variation = 4.53%. Cargo Volume: **(a)** mean = 27.508, median = 18 **(b)** first quartile = 14, third quartile = 37 **(c)** range = 79, interquartile range = 23, variance = 362.633, standard deviation = 19.043, coefficient of variation = 69.23%. Turning Circle: **(a)** mean = 39.926, median = 40 **(b)** first quartile = 38, third quartile = 41 **(c)** range = 19, interquartile range = 3, variance = 7.669, standard deviation = 2.769, coefficient of variation = 6.94%. Weight: **(a)** mean = 3616.074, median = 3530 **(b)** first quartile = 3162.5, third quartile = 3990 **(c)** range = 5120, interquartile range = 827.5, variance = 515343.003, standard deviation = 717.874, coefficient of variation = 19.85%. **(e)** Width, luggage capacity, and weight are skewed to the right; miles per gallon, and turning circle requirement are slightly skewed to the right; length is symmetrical. **(g)** For not SUV: MPG: **(a)** mean = 22.156, median = 21 **(b)** first quartile = 19, third quartile = 23 **(c)** range = 24, interquartile range = 4, variance = 8.740, standard deviation = 4.329, coefficient of variation = 19.54%. Length: **(a)** mean = 187.978, median = 189 **(b)** first quartile = 178, third quartile = 198 **(c)** range = 60, interquartile range = 20, variance = 161.438, standard deviation = 12.706, coefficient of variation = 6.76%. Width: **(a)** mean = 71.00, median = 71 **(b)** first quartile = 68, third quartile = 73 **(c)** range = 14, interquartile range = 5, variance = 9.865, standard deviation = 3.141, coefficient of variation = 4.42%. Cargo Volume: **(a)** mean = 22.394, median = 15 **(b)** first quartile = 13, third quartile = 19 **(c)** range = 70.5, interquartile range = 6, variance = 323.784, standard deviation = 17.994, coefficient of variation = 80.35%. Turning Circle: **(a)** mean = 39.700, median = 40 **(b)** first quartile = 38, third quartile = 41 **(c)** range = 12, interquartile range = 3, variance = 6.325, standard deviation = 2.515, coefficient of variation = 6.33%. Weight: **(a)** mean = 3,391.722, median = 3,427.5 **(b)** first quartile = 3,095, third quartile = 3,750 **(c)** range = 2165, interquartile range = 655, variance = 232,210.765, standard deviation = 481.883, coefficient of variation = 14.21%. **(g) (e)** Miles per gallon, and luggage capacity are skewed to the right; length and weight are skewed to the left; width is slightly skewed to the right and turning circle requirement is quite symmetrical. For SUV MPG: **(a)** mean = 16.484, median = 16 **(b)** first quartile = 15, third quartile = 18 **(c)** range = 12, interquartile range = 3, variance = 7.258, standard deviation = 2.694, coefficient of variation = 16.34%. Length: **(a)** mean = 184.903, median = 183 **(b)** first quartile = 175, third quartile = 190 **(c)** range = 64, interquartile range = 15, variance = 209.557, standard deviation = 14.476, coefficient of variation = 7.83%. Width: **(a)** mean = 72.323, median = 72 **(b)** first quartile = 70, third quartile = 74 **(c)** range = 13, interquartile range = 4, variance = 11.093, standard deviation = 3.331, coefficient of variation = 4.61%. Cargo Volume: **(a)** mean = 42.355, median = 37.5 **(b)** first quartile = 34.5, third quartile = 45.5 **(c)** range = 56, interquartile range = 11, variance = 183.753, standard deviation = 13.556, coefficient of variation = 32.00%. Turning Circle: **(a)** mean = 40.581, median = 40 **(b)** first quartile = 39, third quartile = 41 **(c)** range = 15, interquartile range = 2, variance = 11.318, standard deviation = 3.364, coefficient of variation = 8.29%. Weight: **(a)** mean = 4267.419, median = 4135 **(b)** first quartile = 3590, third quartile = 4715 **(c)** range = 4215, interquartile range = 1125, variance = 783086.452, standard deviation = 884.922, coefficient of variation = 20.74%. **(e)** All variables are skewed to the right except miles per gallon is only slightly skewed to the right.

76 (a) mean = 25 **(b)** standard deviation = 11.01.

78 (a) March: mean = 4,720, April: mean = 4,400. **(b)** March: standard deviation = 2,250.0794, April: standard deviation = 2,657.2965. **(c)** The arithmetic mean has declined by $320 while the standard deviation has increased by $407.2171.

80 (a) Division *A*: mean = 40.4348. Division *B*: mean = 36.8310. **(b)** Division *A*: standard deviation = 11.0969. Division *B*: standard deviation = 8.3341. **(c)** Division *A* has a higher average and standard deviation in age than division *B*.

Excel Handbook for Numerical Descriptive Measures

EH1 GENERATING DOT SCALE DIAGRAMS MANUALLY

You generate dot scale diagrams manually by adapting the **Dot Scale** worksheet of the **Chapter 3.xls** workbook to your data. The worksheet (shown in Figure EH1) contains several sets of formulas that have been already implemented (some of which are discussed in the next section) as well as a preformatted chart object in which the *Y* axis is hidden and eight data series named values, Mean, Median, 1st Quartile, 3rd Quartile, +/– 1 Std. Dev., +/– 2 Std. Dev., and +/– 3 Std. Dev. have been defined. By copying your data to column A of this worksheet, making changes to the formulas in column B, and revising the cell ranges associated with the Values data series of the chart, you can adapt this worksheet to any set of data.

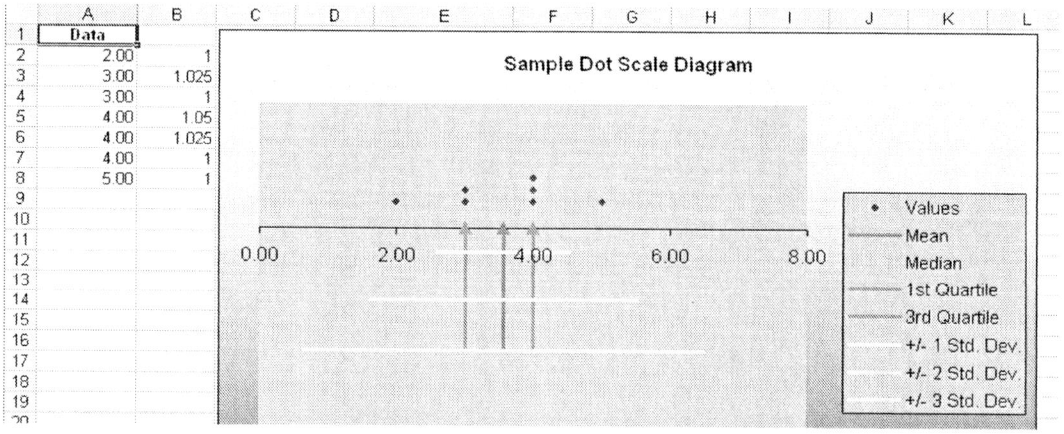

FIGURE EH1 Dot Scale worksheet (partial view)

Open to the **Dot Scale** worksheet. This worksheet contains seven data values in column A that are used to demonstrate the sheet. Review the formulas in column B that are used to calculate the *Y*-axis coordinate for each of these points. The column B formulas use the **COUNTIF** function to count the number of times that the column A value in a particular row appears in the entire cell range to be plotted. This value, less 1, is then used as a multiplier in calculating the *Y*-axis coordinate value. (The coordinate will be 1 if the data value is unique.) If there are duplicated data values in the cell range to plot, the coordinate of the first duplicated value will be 1 plus (the number of preceding similar values minus 1) times 0.025. For example, since there are three 4.00 values the coordinate for the first 4.00 value is 1.05 that is (1 + (3 – 1) * 0.025).

The formula in cell B2 that calculates the coordinate value for the first data value in cell A2 is a unique case and appears in the form **=(COUNTIF(*column A cell range*, $A2) – 1) * 0.025+1**. The second and subsequent formulas in column B use a second COUNTIF function to ensure that each duplicated data value will have a unique *Y* axis coordinate. These formulas appear in the form **=(COUNTIF(*column A cell range, this row's column A cell*) – 1) * 0.025 + 1 – (COUNTIF(*column A cell range above this row, this row's column A cell*) * 0.025)**.

To adapt this worksheet, first copy your data to column A. Then use the following procedures:

To modify the Column B formulas. As the first step, update the cell range to plot by selecting column B and then selecting **Edit | Replace**. In the Replace dialog box, enter the cell range of the original demonstration data **$A$2:$A$8** in the **Find** edit box, enter the cell range, using absolute references, of your copied data in the **Replace** edit box, and click the **Replace All** button. For example, if you copied the 15 data values from one of the columns of the

VHRiskFunds worksheet of the Chapter 3 workbook, enter the range **$A$2:$A$16** in the Replace edit box (shown at right). If a Microsoft Excel dialog box reporting changes appears, click **OK** and then in the Find and Replace dialog box, click close.

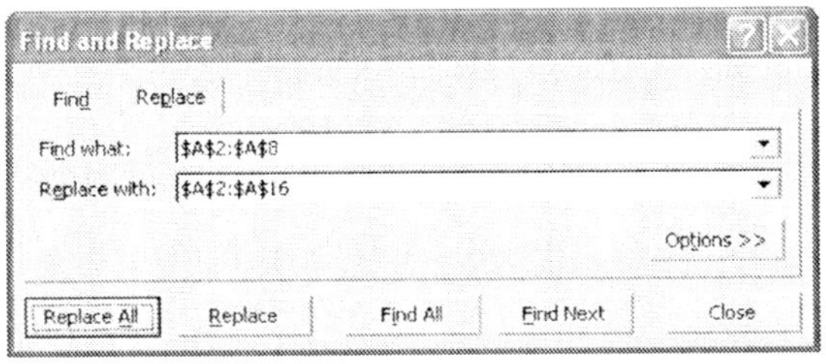

Reselect cell B3 and copy its revised formula down column B through the last row of your data range.

To revise the cell ranges associated with the Values data series. Right-click the background of the dot scale diagram and select **Source Data** from the shortcut menu. In the Source data dialog box, select the **Series** tab and select **Values** from the Series list box (shown at right). Edit the formulas in the **X Values** and **Y Values** edit boxes to match the range of your copied data, being careful to preserve the worksheet name, and click the **OK** button to finish. For example, if you copied one of the columns from the VHRiskFunds sheet, change the X values formula to **='Dot Scale'!A2:A16** and change the Y values formula to **='Dot Scale'!B2:B16**.

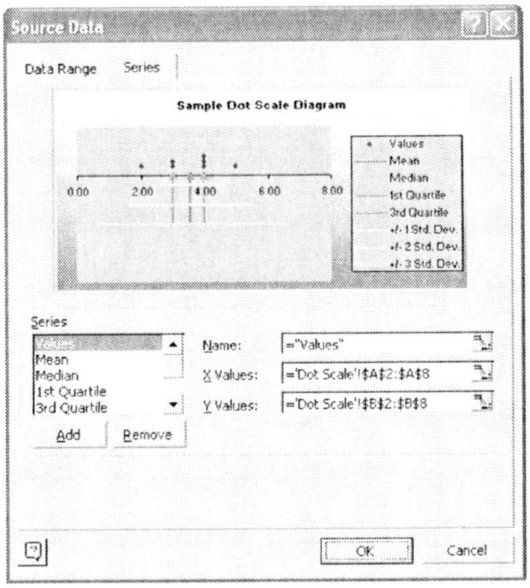

EH2 GENERATING QUARTILES

Although Microsoft Excel includes a QUARTILE function to calculate quartiles, you should avoid using the function because it can produce incorrect results for first and third quartiles for some sets of data. To replace this function, implement the worksheet design of Table EH1.

To implement, first change all six occurrences of ***Range*** to the cell range of your data, entered in *Sheetname!CellRange* notation. Enter all formulas as one continuous line (some formulas in the table have been typeset as two or more lines). Phases such as "Rule 2 applies" and "average the ranks" that appear inside formulas should be entered with a pair of double quotation marks. Note that the formulas for cells B3, B4, B7, B8, and B9 contain consecutive right parentheses and that the formulas for cells C4, C5, C9, and C10 contain consecutive double quotation marks.

If you prefer not to implement this design, you can examine an equivalent design in the **Dot Scale** worksheet of the **Chapter 3.xls** workbook. Open to that worksheet and then select and move the chart until you can see the cell range F2:I12. (Cell G2 in that sheet corresponds to cell A1 in Table EH1.)

	A	B	C
1	Quartile Calculations		
2	Initial first quartile rank	=(COUNT(***Range***) + 1)/4	
3		=IF(B2 = INT(B2), "Rule 1 applies", IF (B2 = CEILING(B2, 0.5), "Rule 2 applies", "Rule 3 applies"))	
4	=IF(B3="Rule 2 applies", "average the ranks:", "use rank:")	=IF(B3 = "Rule 2 applies", FLOOR(B2,1), ROUND(B2, 0))	=IF(B3 = "Rule 2 applies", CEILING(B2, 1),"")
5	=IF(B3 ="Rule 2 applies", average the values:", "value of rank:")	=SMALL(***Range***, B4)	=IF(B3 = "Rule 2 applies", SMALL(***Range***, C4),"")
6	first quartile:	=IF(B3 = "Rule 2 applies",(B5 + C5)/2,B5)	
7	initial third quartile rank	=(3*(COUNT(***Range***) + 1))/4	
8		=IF(B7 = INT(B7), "Rule 1 applies", IF (B7 = CEILING(B7, 0.5), "Rule 2 applies", "Rule 3 applies"))	
9	=IF(B8="Rule 2 applies", "average the ranks:", "use rank:")	=IF(B8 = "Rule 2 applies", FLOOR(B7,1), ROUND(B7, 0))	=IF(B8 = "Rule 2 applies", CEILING(B7, 1),"")
10	=IF(B8 ="Rule 2 applies", average the values:", "value of rank:")	=SMALL(***Range***, B9)	=IF(B8 = "Rule 2 applies", SMALL(***Range***, C9),"")
11	third quartile:	=IF(B8 = "Rule 2 applies", (B10 + C10) / 2, B10)	

Table EH1
Quartile calculation worksheet design

Basic Probability

USING STATISTICS: The Consumer Electronics Company

LEARNING OBJECTIVES

- To understand basic probability concepts
- To understand conditional probability
- To use Bayes' theorem to revise probabilities

USING STATISTICS

The Consumer Electronics Company

You are the marketing manager for a consumer electronics company interested in studying the intention of 1,000 households to purchase a big-screen television set (defined as 31 inches or larger) in the next 12 months. Investigations of this type are known as intent to purchase studies. As a follow-up, you will survey the same households 12 months later to see whether they actually purchased the television set. In addition, for those who did purchase a big-screen television set, you are interested in whether they purchased a high-definition television (HDTV) set, whether they also purchased a DVD player in the last 12 months, and whether they were satisfied with their purchase of the big-screen television set. On the basis of the survey, some of the questions you would like to answer include the following:

- What is the probability that a household is planning to purchase a big-screen television set in the next year?
- What is the probability that the household will actually purchase a big-screen television set?
- What is the probability that a household is planning to purchase a big-screen television set and actually purchases the television set?
- Given that the household is planning to purchase a big-screen television set, what is the probability that the purchase is made?
- Does knowledge of whether the household plans to purchase the television set change the likelihood of predicting whether the household will purchase the television set?
- What is the probability that a household that purchases a big-screen television set will purchase an HDTV?
- What is the probability that a household that purchases a big-screen television set will also purchase a DVD player?
- What is the probability that a household that purchases a big-screen television set will be satisfied with their purchase?

Answers to these questions and others can help you develop future sales and marketing strategies. For example, should marketing campaigns for big-screen television sets target those customers indicating intent to purchase? Are those individuals purchasing big-screen television sets easily persuaded to buy a higher-priced HDTV and/or a DVD player?

INTRODUCTION

In this chapter you will learn about probability, the topic that serves as the link between describing and presenting information obtained from samples and being able to make inferences to larger populations. Three different approaches to determining the probability of occurrence of different phenomena are discussed: *a priori* classical probability, empirical classical probability, and subjective probability. A variety of types of probabilities are developed and probabilities are revised in light of new information. These topics are the foundations for the probability distribution; the concept of mathematical expectation; and the binomial, hypergeometric, and Poisson distributions.

1 BASIC PROBABILITY CONCEPTS

What is meant by the word probability? **Probability** is the likelihood or chance that a particular event will occur. Probability could refer to the chance of picking a black card from a deck of cards, the chance that an individual prefers one product over another, or the chance that a new consumer product on the market will be successful. Note that an event that has no chance of occurring (i.e., the **impossible event**) has a probability of 0, while an event that is sure to occur (i.e., the **certain event**) has a probability of 1. Thus, every probability must be between 0 and 1, inclusively.

There are three approaches to the subject of probability. The first is the ***a priori* classical probability** approach. The probability of success is based on prior knowledge of the process involved. In the simplest case, where each outcome is equally likely, this chance of occurrence of the event is defined in Equation (1).

PROBABILITY OF OCCURRENCE

$$\text{Probability of occurrence} = \frac{X}{T} \tag{1}$$

where

X = number of ways in which the event occurs
T = total number of elementary outcomes

Consider a standard deck of cards that has 26 red cards and 26 black cards. The probability of selecting a black card is 26/52 = 0.50 since there are $X = 26$ black cards and $T = 52$ total cards. What does this probability mean? If each card is replaced after it is drawn, does it mean that one out of the next two cards selected will be black? No, because you cannot say for certain what will happen on the next several selections. However, you can say that in the long run, if this selection process is continually repeated, the proportion of black cards selected will approach 0.50.

In the above example, which uses the *a priori* classical probability approach, the number of successes and the number of outcomes are known from the composition of the deck of cards. However, in the second approach to probability, called the **empirical classical probability** approach, although the probability is still defined as the ratio of the number of favorable outcomes to the total number of outcomes, the outcomes are based on observed data, not on prior knowledge of a process. This type of probability could refer to the proportion of individuals in a survey who actually purchase a television, who prefer a certain political candidate, or who have a part-time job while attending school. For example, if a poll is taken and 60% of the respondents indicate that they prefer the Republican candidate, then there is a 0.60 probability that an individual respondent randomly selected prefers the Republican candidate.

The third approach to probability is called the **subjective probability** approach. While the probability of a favorable event with the previous two approaches was computed objectively, either from prior knowledge or from actual data, subjective probability refers to the chance of occurrence assigned to an event by a particular individual. This chance will likely be different from the subjective probability assigned by another individual. For example, the development team of a new product may assign a probability of 0.6 to the chance of success for the product while the president of the company is less optimistic and assigns a probability of 0.3. The assignment of subjective probabilities to various events is usually based on a combination of an individual's past experience, personal opinion, and analysis of a particular situation. Subjective probability is especially useful in making decisions in situations in which the probability of various events cannot be determined empirically.

Event
Each possible type of occurrence is referred to as an event.

Simple Event
A simple event can be described by a single characteristic.

Sample Space
The collection of all the possible events is called the sample space.

Sample Spaces and Events

The basic elements of probability theory are the outcomes of the process or variable under study. A better understanding of events, simple events, and sample spaces (defined on the left) can be achieved by referring to the Using Statistics scenario concerning the Consumer Electronics Company. Table 1 presents the results of the sample of 1,000 households in terms of purchase behavior for big-screen television sets.

TABLE 1
Purchase behavior for big-screen television sets

PLANNED TO PURCHASE	ACTUALLY PURCHASED Yes	No	Total
Yes	200	50	250
No	100	650	750
Total	300	700	1,000

The sample space consists of the entire set of 1,000 respondents. The events within the sample space depend on how the different outcomes are classified. For example, if one is interested in purchase plans, the events are "planned to purchase" and "did not plan to purchase." If one is interested in actual purchases, the events are "purchase" and "did not purchase." Thus, the manner in which the sample space is subdivided depends on the types of probabilities that are to be determined.

Complement
The complement of event *A* includes all events that are not part of event *A*. The complement of *A* is given by the symbol *A′*.

Joint Event
A joint event is an event that has two or more characteristics.

Two useful definitions are shown on the left. In Table 1, the complement of the event "planned to purchase" is "did not plan to purchase." In Table 1, the event "planned to purchase and actually purchased" is a joint event because the respondent must plan to purchase the television *and* actually purchase it.

Contingency Tables

There are several ways in which a particular sample space can be viewed. The method used in this text involves assigning the appropriate events to a **table of cross-classifications** such as the one displayed in Table 1. This table is also called a **contingency table**. The values in the cells of the table were obtained by subdividing the sample space of 1,000 households according to whether someone planned to purchase and actually purchased the big-screen television set. Thus, for example, 200 of the respondents planned to purchase a big-screen television set and subsequently did purchase the big-screen television set.

Simple (Marginal) Probability

Thus far, the focus of this chapter has been on the meaning of probability and defining and illustrating sample spaces. Now some of the questions posed in the Using Statistics scenario can be answered by developing rules for obtaining different types of probability. Since the results will be based on data collected in a survey (see Table 1 above), the empirical classical probability approach will be used.

The most fundamental rule for probabilities is that they range in value from 0 to 1. An impossible event has a probability of occurrence of 0, and an event that is certain to occur has a probability of 1. **Simple probability** refers to the probability of occurrence of a simple event, $P(A)$, such as the probability of planning to purchase a big-screen television.

How can the probability of selecting a household that planned to purchase a big-screen television set be determined? Using Equation (1):

$$P(\text{planned to purchase}) = \frac{\text{number who planned to purchase}}{\text{total number of households}}$$

$$= \frac{250}{1{,}000} = 0.25$$

Thus, there is a 0.25 (or 25%) chance that a household planned to purchase a big-screen television set.

Simple probability is also called **marginal probability**, because the total number of successes (those who planned to purchase) can be obtained from the appropriate margin of the contingency table (see Table 1 above). Example 1 illustrates another application of simple probability.

EXAMPLE 1

COMPUTING THE PROBABILITY THAT THE BIG-SCREEN TELEVISION SET PURCHASED WILL BE AN HDTV

In the Using Statistics follow-up survey, additional questions were asked of the 300 households that actually purchased a big-screen television set. Table 2 indicates the consumers' responses to whether the television set purchased was an HDTV and whether they also purchased a DVD player in the last 12 months.

TABLE 2
Purchase behavior regarding HDTVs and DVD players

	PURCHASED DVD		
PURCHASED HDTV	**Yes**	**No**	**Total**
HDTV	38	42	80
Not HDTV	70	150	220
Total	108	192	300

Find the probability that if a household that purchased a big-screen television set is randomly selected, the television set purchased is an HDTV.

SOLUTION

Using the following definitions:

A = purchased an HDTV B = purchased a DVD player
A' = did not purchase an HDTV B' = did not purchase a DVD player

$$P(\text{HDTV}) = \frac{\text{number of HDTV television sets purchased}}{\text{total number of television sets purchased}}$$

$$= \frac{80}{300} = 0.267$$

There is a 26.7% chance that a randomly selected big-screen television set purchase is an HDTV.

Joint Probability

Marginal probability refers to the occurrence of simple events. **Joint probability** refers to situations involving two or more events, such as the probability of planned to purchase *and* actually purchased a big-screen television set.

Recall that a joint event A and B means that both event A *and* event B must occur simultaneously. With reference to Table 1, those individuals who planned to purchase and actually purchased a big-screen television set consist only of the outcomes in the single cell "yes—planned to purchase *and* yes—actually purchased." Because this group consists of 200 households, the probability of picking a household that planned to purchase *and* actually purchased a big-screen television set is

$$P(\text{planned to purchase } \textit{and} \text{ actually purchased}) = \frac{\text{planned to purchase } \textit{and} \text{ actually purchased}}{\text{total number of respondents}}$$

$$= \frac{200}{1{,}000} = 0.20$$

Example 2 also demonstrates how to determine joint probability.

EXAMPLE 2

DETERMINING THE JOINT PROBABILITY THAT A BIG-SCREEN TELEVISION SET CUSTOMER PURCHASED AN HDTV AND A DVD PLAYER

In Table 2 above, the purchases are cross-classified as HDTV or otherwise and whether the household purchased a DVD player. Find the probability that a randomly selected household that purchased a big-screen television set also purchased an HDTV and a DVD player.

SOLUTION

Using Equation (1),

$$P(\text{HDTV } \textit{and} \text{ DVD player}) = \frac{\text{number that purchased an HDTV } \textit{and} \text{ a DVD player}}{\text{total number of big-screen television set purchasers}}$$

$$= \frac{38}{300} = 0.127$$

Therefore, there is a 12.7% chance that a randomly selected household that purchased a big-screen television set purchased an HDTV and a DVD player.

Now that the concept of joint probability has been discussed, the marginal probability of a particular event can be viewed in an alternative manner. In fact, the marginal probability of an event consists of a set of joint probabilities. For example, if B consists of two events, B_1 and B_2, then $P(A)$, the probability of event A, consists of the joint probability of event A occurring with event B_1 and the joint probability of event A occurring with event B_2. Marginal probabilities are computed using Equation (2).

COMPUTING MARGINAL PROBABILITY

$$P(A) = P(A \textit{ and } B_1) + P(A \textit{ and } B_2) + \cdots + P(A \textit{ and } B_k) \qquad \textbf{(2)}$$

where $B_1, B_2, \ldots, B_k$ are k mutually exclusive and collectively exhaustive events

Mutually Exclusive
Two events are mutually exclusive if both the events cannot occur at the same time.

Collectively Exhaustive
A set of mutually exclusive events is collectively exhaustive if one of the events must occur.

Mutually exclusive events and collectively exhaustive events are defined on the left.

Being male and being female are mutually exclusive and collectively exhaustive events. No one is both (they are mutually exclusive), and everyone is one or the other (they are collectively exhaustive).

Equation (2) can be used to compute the marginal probability planned to purchase a big-screen television set.

$$P(\text{planned to purchase}) = P(\text{planned to purchase } \textit{and} \text{ purchased}) + P(\text{planned to purchase } \textit{and} \text{ did not purchase})$$

$$= \frac{200}{1{,}000} + \frac{50}{1{,}000}$$

$$= \frac{250}{1{,}000} = 0.25$$

This is the same result obtained if you add the number of outcomes that make up the simple event "planned to purchase."

General Addition Rule

Having found the probability of event A and the probability of event "A *and* B," a rule for finding the probability of event "A *or* B" can be developed. This rule considers the occurrence of either event A or event B or both A and B.

How can the probability that a household planned to purchase *or* actually purchased a big-screen television set be determined? The event "planned to purchase *or* actually purchased" includes all households who had planned to purchase and all households who had actually purchased the big-screen television set. Each cell of the contingency table (Table 1) can be examined to determine whether it is part of the event in question. To study the event "planned to purchase *or* actually purchased" from Table 1, the cell "planned to purchase *and* did not actually purchase" is part of the event, because it includes respondents who planned to purchase. The cell "did not plan to purchase *and* actually purchased" is included because it contains respondents who actually purchased. Finally, the cell "planned to purchase *and* actually purchased" has both characteristics of interest. Therefore, the probability of planned to purchase *or* actually purchased can be obtained as follows:

$$\begin{aligned} P(\text{planned to purchase } or \text{ actually purchased}) &= P(\text{planned to purchase } and \text{ did not actually purchase}) + P(\text{did not plan to purchase } and \text{ actually purchased}) + P(\text{planned to purchase } and \text{ actually purchased}) \\ &= \frac{50}{1{,}000} + \frac{100}{1{,}000} + \frac{200}{1{,}000} = \frac{350}{1{,}000} = 0.35 \end{aligned}$$

It is often easier to determine $P(A \text{ or } B)$, the probability of the event A *or* B, by using the **general addition rule** given in Equation (3).

GENERAL ADDITION RULE

The probability of A or B is equal to the probability of A plus the probability of B minus the probability of A and B.

$$P(A \text{ or } B) = P(A) + P(B) - P(A \text{ and } B) \tag{3}$$

Applying the general addition rule to the previous example, the following result is obtained:

$$\begin{aligned} P(\text{planned to purchase } or \text{ actually purchased}) &= P(\text{planned to purchase}) + P(\text{actually purchased}) - P(\text{planned to purchase } and \text{ actually purchased}) \\ &= \frac{250}{1{,}000} + \frac{300}{1{,}000} - \frac{200}{1{,}000} \\ &= \frac{350}{1{,}000} = 0.35 \end{aligned}$$

The general addition rule consists of taking the probability of A and adding it to the probability of B; and then subtracting the joint event of A *and* B from this total because it has already been included twice in computing the probability of A and the probability of B. Referring to Table 1, if the outcomes of the event "planned to purchase" are added to those of the event "actually purchased," then the joint event "planned to purchase *and* actually purchased" has been included in each of these simple events. Therefore, because this joint event has been double-counted, it must be subtracted to provide the correct result. Example 3 illustrates another application of the general addition rule.

EXAMPLE 3

USING THE ADDITION RULE FOR THE HOUSEHOLDS THAT PURCHASED BIG-SCREEN TELEVISION SETS

In Example 1, the purchases were cross-classified as an HDTV or otherwise and whether the household purchased a DVD player. Find the probability that a randomly selected household that purchased a big-screen television set purchased an HDTV or a DVD player.

SOLUTION

Using Equation (3),

$$P(\text{HDTV } \textit{or} \text{ DVD player}) = P(\text{HDTV}) + P(\text{DVD player}) - P(\text{HDTV } \textit{and} \text{ DVD player})$$
$$= \frac{80}{300} + \frac{108}{300} - \frac{38}{300}$$
$$= \frac{150}{300} = 0.50$$

There is a 50.0% chance that a randomly selected household that purchased a big-screen television set purchased an HDTV or a DVD player.

Addition Rule for Mutually Exclusive Events

In certain circumstances, the joint probability does not need to be subtracted because it is equal to zero as illustrated in Example 4.

EXAMPLE 4

USING THE ADDITION RULE FOR MUTUALLY EXCLUSIVE EVENTS

Consider the 300 households surveyed in the consumer electronics company example that actually purchased a big-screen television set. These respondents were asked to identify how the purchase was transacted. These results are summarized in Table 3.

TABLE 3
Summary table of purchase transactions

Type of Purchase	Number of Respondents
In store	183
Internet	87
Mail order	30

What is the probability that a randomly selected household that purchased a big-screen television set purchased the television set via the Internet or via mail order?

SOLUTION

Thus,

$$P(\text{Internet } \textit{or} \text{ mail order}) = P(\text{Internet}) + P(\text{mail order}) - P(\text{Internet } \textit{and} \text{ mail order})$$
$$= \frac{87}{300} + \frac{30}{300} - \frac{0}{300}$$
$$= \frac{117}{300} = 0.39$$

There is a 39.0% chance that a randomly selected household that purchased a big-screen television set purchased the television set via the Internet or by mail order.

You must understand that the probability that a customer could transact the purchase via the Internet and by mail order simultaneously is zero. The actual transaction must occur in only one medium, or the customer would end up paying twice! The joint occurrence in this case is nonexistent because it contains no outcomes. As mentioned previously, whenever the joint event cannot occur, the events are considered to be mutually exclusive. This refers to the fact that the occurrence of one event (Internet order) means that the other event (mail order) cannot occur. Thus, the **addition rule for mutually exclusive events** reduces to Equation (4).

ADDITION RULE FOR MUTUALLY EXCLUSIVE EVENTS

The probability of A or B is equal to the probability of A plus the probability of B.

$$P(A \text{ or } B) = P(A) + P(B) \quad \textbf{(4)}$$

Addition Rule for Collectively Exhaustive Events

Example 5 considers the **addition rule for collectively exhaustive events**.

EXAMPLE 5

USING THE ADDITION RULE FOR COLLECTIVELY EXHAUSTIVE EVENTS

In Table 2, the purchases were cross-classified as HDTV or otherwise and whether the household purchased a DVD player. Find the probability that a randomly selected household that purchased a big-screen television set purchased a DVD player or did not purchase a DVD player.

SOLUTION

Thus, using Equation (4) above

$$P(\text{purchased a DVD player } \textit{or} \text{ did not purchase a DVD player}) = P(\text{purchased a DVD player}) + P(\text{did not purchase a DVD player})$$

$$= \frac{108}{300} + \frac{192}{300} = \frac{300}{300} = 1.0$$

The probability of purchasing a DVD player or not purchasing a DVD player is 1.0 because these two categories are collectively exhaustive.

Excel Strategy Calculating Basic Probabilities

You calculate basic probabilities by filling in the sample space table of the **Basic Probabilities** worksheet of the **Chapter 4.xls** workbook, which uses using simple arithmetic formulas to calculate simple and joint probabilities. PHStat2 can generate a copy of this worksheet, which you then also fill in.

CHAPTER 4.xls

To calculate basic probabilities for the purchase behavior data of Table 2, open to the **Basic Probabilities** worksheet of the **Chapter 4.xls** workbook, or select **PHStat | Probability & Prob. Distributions | Simple & Joint Probabilities,** if you want to use PHStat2. In the Basic Probabilities worksheet, make these entries:

Sample Space Table Label Entries. Enter **HDTV Purchase** as the event A label in cell **A5**. Enter **HDTV Yes** (the event A_1 label) in cell **B5**. Enter **HDTV No** (the event A_2 label) in cell **B6**. Enter **DVD Purchase** as the event B caption in cell **C3**. Enter **DVD Yes** (the event B_1 label) in cell **C4**. Enter **DVD No** (the event B_2 label) in cell **D4**.
In the same worksheet:

Sample Space Table Data Entries. Enter **38** in cell **C5** (the event HDTV Yes and DVD Yes). Enter **70** in cell **C6** (the event HDTV No and DVD Yes). Enter **42** in cell **D5** (the event HDTV Yes and DVD No). Enter **150** in cell **D6** (the event HDTV No and DVD No.)

Section EH1 discusses how the concatenation operator is used in several formulas of the Basic Probabilities worksheet to generate probability labels that incorporate sample space labels.

PROBLEMS FOR SECTION 1

Learning the Basics

1 Two coins are tossed.

a. Give an example of a simple event.
b. Give an example of a joint event.
c. What is the complement of a head on the first toss?

2 An urn contains 12 red balls and 8 white balls. One ball is to be selected from the urn.

a. Give an example of a simple event.
b. What is the complement of a red ball?

3 Given the following contingency table:

	B	*B′*
A	10	20
A′	20	40

What is the probability of

a. event *A*?
b. event *B*?
c. event *A′*?
d. event *A and B*?
e. event *A and B′*?
f. event *A′ and B′*?
g. event *A or B*?
h. event *A or B′*?
i. event *A′ or B′*?

4 Given the following contingency table:

	B	*B′*
A	10	30
A′	25	35

What is the probability of

a. event *A*?
b. event *B*?
c. event *A′*?
d. event *A and B*?
e. event *A and B′*?
f. event *A′ and B′*?
g. event *A or B*?
h. event *A or B′*?
i. event *A′ or B′*?

Applying the Concepts

5 For each of the following, indicate whether the type of probability involved is an example of *a priori* classical probability, empirical classical probability, or subjective probability.

a. The next toss of a fair coin will land on heads.
b. Italy will win soccer's World Cup the next time the competition is held.
c. The sum of the faces of two dice will be 7.
d. The train taking a commuter to work will be more than 10 minutes late.
e. A Republican will win the next presidential election in the United States.

6 For each of the following, state whether the events created are mutually exclusive and/or collectively exhaustive. If they are not mutually exclusive and/or collectively exhaustive, either reword the categories to make them mutually exclusive and/or collectively exhaustive or explain why this would not be useful.

a. Registered voters in the U.S. were asked whether they registered as Republicans or Democrats.
b. Respondents were classified by country of manufacture of car owned into the categories American, European, Japanese, or other.
c. People were asked, "Do you currently live in (i) an apartment or (ii) a house?"
d. A product was classified as defective or not defective.
e. People were asked, "Do you intend to purchase a new car in the next 6 months?" and answered (i) yes (ii) no.

7 The probability of each of the following events is zero. For each, state why. Tell what common characteristic of these events makes their probability zero.

a. A voter in the U.S. who is registered as a Republican and a Democrat
b. A product that is defective and not defective
c. An automobile that is a Ford and a Toyota

8 The results of a study made as part of a yield improvement effort at a semiconductor manufacturing facility provided defect data for a sample of 450 wafers. The following table presents a summary of the responses to two questions: "Was a particle found on the die that produced the wafer?" and "Is the wafer good or bad?"

	CONDITION OF DIE		
QUALITY OF WAFER	**No Particles**	**Particles**	**Totals**
Good	320	14	334
Bad	80	36	116
Totals	400	50	450

Source: *S. W. Hall, Analysis of Defectivity of Semiconductor Wafers by Contingency Table.* Proceedings Institute of Environmental Sciences, *Vol. 1, (1994), 177–183.*

a. Give an example of a simple event.
b. Give an example of a joint event.
c. What is the complement of a good wafer?
d. Why is a "good wafer" and a die "with particles" a joint event?

If a wafer is selected at random, what is the probability that

e. it was produced from a die with no particles?
f. the wafer is bad?
g. it is a bad wafer *and* was produced from a die with no particles?
h. it is a good wafer *and* was produced from a die with no particles?

i. it is a good wafer *or* was produced from a die with no particles?
j. it is a bad wafer *or* was produced from a die with particles?
k. Explain the difference in the results in (h) and (i).

9 A U.S. Census American Housing Survey studied how U.S. homeowners get to work ("How People Get to Work," *USA Today* Snapshots, February 25, 2003, 1A). Suppose that the survey consisted of a sample of 1,000 homeowners and 1,000 renters. A contingency table revealed the following results.

DRIVES TO WORK	Homeowner	Renter	Total
Yes	824	681	1,505
No	176	319	495
Total	1,000	1,000	2,000

a. Give an example of a simple event.
b. Give an example of a joint event.
c. What is the complement of "drives to work"?
d. Why is "drives to work" and "is a homeowner" a joint event?

If a respondent is selected at random, what is the probability that he or she
e. drives to work?
f. is a homeowner?
g. drives to work *and* is a homeowner?
h. does not drive to work *and* is a renter?
i. drives to work *or* is a homeowner?
j. does not drive to work *or* is a renter?
k. Explain the difference in the results in (g) and (i).

10 Are large companies less likely to offer board members stock options than small- to mid-sized companies? A survey conducted by the Segal Company of New York found that in a sample of 189 large companies, 40 offered stock options to their board members as part of their non-cash compensation packages. For small- to mid-sized companies, 43 of the 180 surveyed indicated that they offer stock options as part of their non-cash compensation packages to their board members (Kemba J. Dunham, "The Jungle: Focus on Recruitment, Pay and Getting Ahead," *Wall Street Journal*, August 21, 2001, B6).
a. Set up a 2×2 contingency table to evaluate the probabilities.
b. Give an example of a simple event.
c. Give an example of a joint event.
d. What is the complement of offered stock options to their board members?
e. Why is "large company" and "offered stock options to their board members" a joint event?

If a company is selected at random, what is the probability that the company
f. is large?
g. offered stock options to their board members?
h. is large *and* offered stock options to their board members?
i. is small- to mid-sized *and* did not offer stock options to their board members?
j. is large *or* offered stock options to their board members?
k. is small- to mid-sized *or* offered stock options to their board members?
l. Explain the difference in the results in (h) and (j).

11 Are whites more likely to claim bias? A survey conducted by Barry Goldman ("White Fight: A Researcher Finds Whites Are More Likely to Claim Bias," *Wall Street Journal*, Work Week, April 10, 2001, *A*1) found that of 56 white workers terminated, 29 claimed bias. Of 407 black workers terminated, 126 claimed bias.
a. Set up a 2×2 contingency table to evaluate the probabilities.
b. Give an example of a simple event.
c. Give an example of a joint event.
d. What is the complement of a worker who claimed bias?
e. Why is "a white worker" and "claiming bias" a joint event?

If a worker is selected at random, what is the probability that he or she
f. is white?
g. claimed bias?
h. is white *and* claimed bias?
i. is black *and* did not claim bias?
j. is white *or* claimed bias?
k. is black *or* claimed bias?
l. Explain the difference in the results in (h) and (j).

12 A sample of 500 respondents was selected in a large metropolitan area to determine various information concerning consumer behavior. Among the questions asked was "Do you enjoy shopping for clothing?" Of 240 males, 136 answered yes. Of 260 females, 224 answered yes.
a. Set up a 2×2 contingency table to evaluate the probabilities.
b. Give an example of a simple event.
c. Give an example of a joint event.
d. What is the complement of "enjoy shopping for clothing"?

What is the probability that a respondent chosen at random
e. is a male?
f. enjoys shopping for clothing?
g. is a female *and* enjoys shopping for clothing?
h. is a male *and* does not enjoy shopping for clothing?
i. is a female *or* enjoys shopping for clothing?
j. is a male *or* does not enjoy shopping for clothing?
k. is a male *or* a female?

13 Each year, ratings are compiled concerning the performance of new cars during the first 90 days of use. Suppose that the cars have been categorized according to two attributes: whether the car needs warranty-related repair (yes or no) and the country in which the company manufacturing the car is based (United States or not United States). Based on the data collected, the probability that the new car needs a warranty repair is 0.04, the probability that the car is manufactured by a U.S.-based company is 0.60, and the probability that the new car needs a warranty repair *and* was manufactured by a U.S.-based company is 0.025.

a. Set up a 2 × 2 contingency table to evaluate the probabilities of a warranty-related repair.
b. Give an example of a simple event.
c. Give an example of a joint event.
d. What is the complement of "manufactured by a U.S.-based company"?

What is the probability that a new car selected at random

e. needs a warranty-related repair?
f. is not manufactured by a U.S.-based company?
g. needs a warranty repair *and* is manufactured by a company based in the United States?
h. does not need a warranty repair *and* is not manufactured by a company based in the United States?
i. needs a warranty repair *or* was manufactured by a U.S.-based company?
j. needs a warranty repair *or* was not manufactured by a U.S.-based company?
k. needs a warranty repair *or* does not need a warranty repair?

2 CONDITIONAL PROBABILITY

Computing Conditional Probabilities

Each situation examined thus far in this chapter has involved the probability of a particular event when sampling from the entire sample space. However, how would various probabilities be determined if certain information about the events involved were already known?

When computing the probability of a particular event A, given information about the occurrence of another event B, this probability is referred to as **conditional probability**, $P(A \mid B)$. The conditional probability $P(A \mid B)$ is defined in Equation (5).

CONDITIONAL PROBABILITY

The probability of A given B is equal to the probability of A *and* B divided by the probability of B

$$P(A \mid B) = \frac{P(A \text{ and } B)}{P(B)} \quad \textbf{(5a)}$$

The probability of B given A is equal to the probability of A *and* B divided by the probability of A

$$P(B \mid A) = \frac{P(A \text{ and } B)}{P(A)} \quad \textbf{(5b)}$$

where

$P(A \text{ and } B)$ = joint probability of A *and* B
$P(A)$ = marginal probability of A
$P(B)$ = marginal probability of B

As an alternative to using Equation (5a) or (5b) to find a conditional probability, the contingency table could be used. Referring to the Using Statistics scenario being discussed in this chapter, suppose you were told that a household planned to purchase a big-screen television set. What would be the probability that the household actually purchased the television set? In this case, the objective is to find P(actual purchase | planned to purchase). Here the information is given that the household planned to purchase the big-screen television set. Therefore, the sample space does not consist of all 1,000 households in the survey. It consists of only those households that planned to purchase the big-screen television set. Of 250 such households, 200 actually purchased the big-screen television set. Therefore, the probability that a household actually purchased the big-screen television set (see Table 1) given that he or she planned to purchase is

$$P(\text{actually purchased} \mid \text{planned to purchase}) = \frac{\text{planned to purchase } \textit{and} \text{ actually purchased}}{\text{planned to purchase}}$$

$$= \frac{200}{250} = 0.80$$

This result can also be obtained by using Equation (5b):

$$P(B \mid A) = \frac{P(A \text{ and } B)}{P(A)}$$

where

event A = planned to purchase
event B = actually purchased

Then

$$P(\text{actually purchased} \mid \text{planned to purchase}) = \frac{200/1{,}000}{250/1{,}000}$$

$$= \frac{200}{250} = 0.80$$

Example 6 further illustrates conditional probability.

EXAMPLE 6

FINDING A CONDITIONAL PROBABILITY CONCERNING THE HOUSEHOLDS THAT ACTUALLY PURCHASED A BIG-SCREEN TELEVISION SET

In Example 1, a contingency table was developed for the purchase of an HDTV or otherwise and whether the household purchased a DVD player. Of the households that purchased an HDTV, what is the probability that they also purchased a DVD player?

SOLUTION

Because it is known that the household purchased an HDTV, the sample space has been reduced to 80 households. Of these 80 households, observe that 38 also purchased a DVD player. Therefore, the probability that a household purchased a DVD player, given that it purchased an HDTV, is obtained as follows:

$$P(\text{purchased DVD player} \mid \text{purchased HDTV}) = \frac{\text{number of households purchasing HDTV } \textit{and} \text{ DVD player}}{\text{number of households purchasing HDTV}}$$

$$= \frac{38}{80} = 0.475$$

If Equation (5a) is used and:

A = purchased DVD player $\quad$ B = purchased HDTV

then

$$P(A \mid B) = \frac{P(A \text{ and } B)}{P(B)} = \frac{38/300}{80/300} = 0.475$$

Therefore, given that the household purchased an HDTV, there is a 47.5% chance that the household also purchased a DVD player. Note that the marginal probability of purchasing a DVD player is 108/300 = 0.36, or 36%. Thus, households purchasing an HDTV are more likely to have purchased a DVD player than are households that purchased a big-screen television set that is not an HDTV.

Decision Trees

In Table 1 households are classified according to whether they planned to purchase and whether they actually purchased a big-screen television set. An alternative way to view the breakdown of the possibilities into four cells is through the use of a **decision tree**. Figure 1 represents the decision tree for this example.

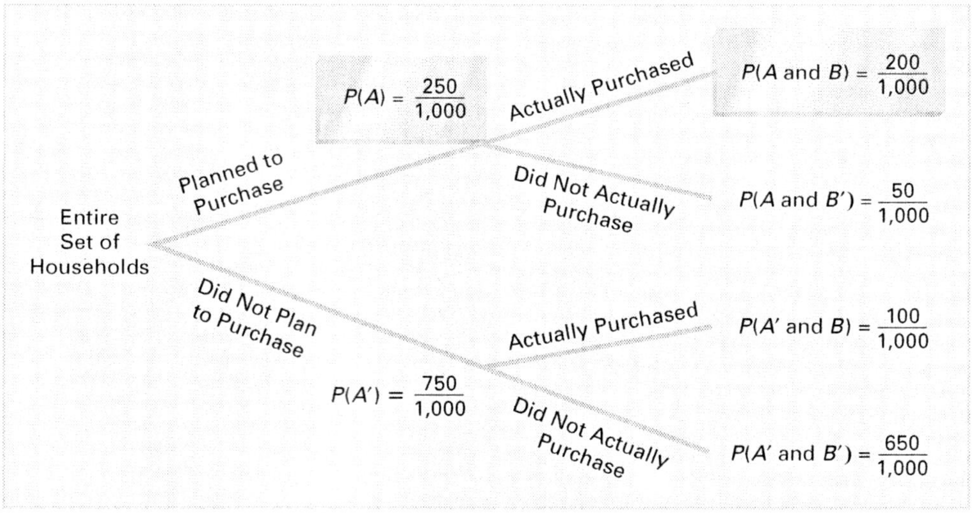

FIGURE 1
Decision tree for the consumer electronics example

In Figure 1, beginning at the left with the entire set of households, there are two "branches" for whether or not the household planned to purchase a big-screen television set. Each of these branches has two subbranches, corresponding to whether the household actually purchased or did not actually purchase the big-screen television set. The probabilities at the end of the initial branches represent the marginal probabilities of A and A'. The probabilities at the end of each of the four subbranches represent the joint probability for each combination of events A and B. The conditional probability is obtained by dividing the joint probability by the appropriate marginal probability.

For example, to obtain the probability that the household actually purchased given that they planned to purchase the big-screen television set, take P(planned to purchase *and* actually purchased) and divide by P(planned to purchase). From Figure 1

$$P(\text{actually purchased} \mid \text{planned to purchase}) = \frac{200/1{,}000}{250/1{,}000} = \frac{200}{250} = 0.80$$

Example 7 illustrates how to form a decision tree.

EXAMPLE 7

FORMING THE DECISION TREE FOR THE HOUSEHOLDS THAT PURCHASED BIG-SCREEN TELEVISION SETS

Using the cross-classified data in Table 2, form the decision tree. Use the decision tree to find the probability that a household purchased a DVD player, given that the household purchased an HDTV.

SOLUTION

The decision tree for purchased a DVD player and an HDTV is displayed in Figure 2. Using Equation (5b) and the following definitions:

$$A = \text{purchased HDTV} \quad B = \text{purchased DVD player}$$

$$P(B \mid A) = \frac{P(A \text{ and } B)}{P(A)} = \frac{38/300}{80/300} = 0.475$$

FIGURE 2
Decision tree for purchased a DVD player and an HDTV

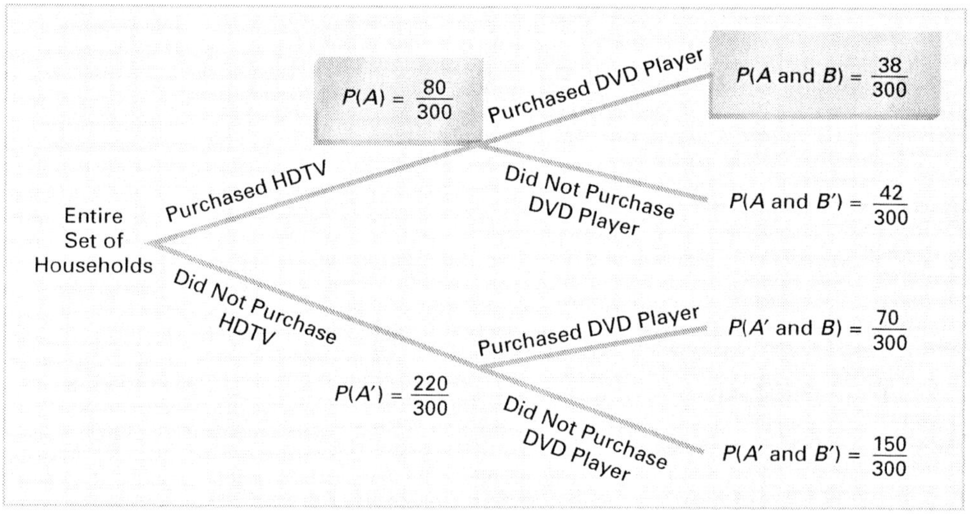

Statistical Independence

In the example concerning the purchase of big-screen television sets, the probability that the household selected actually purchased the big-screen television set, given that the household planned to purchase, is 200/250 = 0.80. Remember that the probability of selecting a household that actually purchased is 300/1,000, which reduces to 0.30. This result reveals some important information. The prior knowledge that the household planned to purchase affected the probability that the household actually purchased the television set. The outcome is conditional on prior information. In other words, the outcome of one event is *dependent* on the outcome of a second event.

When the outcome of one event does not affect the probability of occurrence of another event, the events are said to be statistically independent. **Statistical independence** can be determined by using Equation (6).

STATISTICAL INDEPENDENCE

Two events A and B are statistically independent if and only if

$$P(A \mid B) = P(A) \quad (6)$$

where

$P(A \mid B)$ = conditional probability of A given B
$P(A)$ = marginal probability of A

Example 8 demonstrates the use of Equation (6).

EXAMPLE 8

DETERMINING STATISTICAL INDEPENDENCE

In the follow-up survey of the 300 households that actually purchased big-screen television sets, the households were asked if they were satisfied with their purchase. Table 4 cross-classifies the responses to the satisfaction question with their responses to whether the television set was an HDTV.

TABLE 4
Satisfaction with purchase of big-screen television sets

TYPE OF TELEVISION	SATISFIED WITH PURCHASE? Yes	No	Total
HDTV	64	16	80
Not HDTV	176	44	220
Total	240	60	300

Determine whether being satisfied with the purchase and type of television set purchased are statistically independent.

SOLUTION

For these data,

$$P(\text{satisfied} \mid \text{HDTV}) = \frac{64/300}{80/300} = \frac{64}{80} = 0.80$$

which is equal to

$$P(\text{satisfied}) = \frac{240}{300} = 0.80$$

Thus, being satisfied with the purchase and type of television set purchased are statistically independent. Knowledge of one event does not affect the probability of the other event.

Multiplication Rule

The formula for conditional probability can be manipulated algebraically so that the joint probability $P(A \text{ and } B)$ is determined from the conditional probability of an event. Using Equation (5a),

$$P(A \mid B) = \frac{P(A \text{ and } B)}{P(B)}$$

and solving for the joint probability $P(A \text{ and } B)$, the **general multiplication rule** is obtained.

GENERAL MULTIPLICATION RULE

The probability of A and B is equal to the probability of A given B times the probability of B.

$$P(A \text{ and } B) = P(A \mid B)P(B) \qquad \textbf{(7)}$$

Examples 9 and 10 demonstrate the use of the general multiplication rule.

EXAMPLE 9

USING THE MULTIPLICATION RULE

Consider the 80 households that purchased an HDTV. In Table 4 above observe that 64 households were satisfied with their purchase and 16 households were dissatisfied. Suppose two households are randomly selected from the 80 customers. Find the probability that both households are satisfied with their purchase.

SOLUTION

Here the multiplication rule can be used in the following way. If:

A = second household selected is satisfied
B = first household selected is satisfied

then,

$$P(A \text{ and } B) = P(A \mid B)P(B)$$

The probability that the first household is satisfied with the purchase is 64/80. However, the probability that the second household is also satisfied with the purchase depends on the result of the first selection. If the first household is not returned to the sample after the satisfaction level is determined (sampling without replacement), then the number of households remaining will be 79. If the first household is satisfied, the probability that the second is also satisfied is 63/79, because 63 satisfied households remain in the sample. Therefore, using Equation (7)

$$P(A \text{ and } B) = \left(\frac{63}{79}\right)\left(\frac{64}{80}\right) = 0.6380$$

There is a 63.80% chance that both of the households sampled will be satisfied with their purchase.

EXAMPLE 10

USING THE MULTIPLICATION RULE WHEN SAMPLING WITH REPLACEMENT

What if the first household is returned to the sample after the satisfaction level is determined? Find the probability that both of the households sampled will be satisfied with their purchase.

SOLUTION

In this example, the probability of picking a satisfied household on the second selection is the same as on the first selection when sampling with replacement, because there are 64 satisfied customers out of 80 in the sample. Therefore,

$$\begin{aligned} P(A \text{ and } B) &= P(A \mid B)P(B) \\ &= \left(\frac{64}{80}\right)\left(\frac{64}{80}\right) = 0.64 \end{aligned}$$

There is a 64% chance that both households sampled will be satisfied with their purchases.

Example 10 illustrates that the second selection is independent of the first because the second probability was not influenced by the first selection. Therefore, by substituting $P(A)$ for $P(A \mid B)$ in Equation (7), the **multiplication rule for independent events** can be expressed in Equation (8).

MULTIPLICATION RULE FOR INDEPENDENT EVENTS

If A and B are statistically independent, the probability of A *and* B is equal to the probability of A times the probability of B.

$$P(A \text{ and } B) = P(A)P(B) \qquad \textbf{(8)}$$

If this rule holds for two events, A and B, then A and B are statistically independent. Therefore, there are two ways to determine statistical independence.

1. Events A and B are statistically independent if and only if $P(A \mid B) = P(A)$.
2. Events A and B are statistically independent if and only if $P(A \text{ and } B) = P(A)P(B)$.

Now that the multiplication rule has been discussed, the formula for marginal probability [Equation (2)] can be changed. If

$$P(A) = P(A \text{ and } B_1) + P(A \text{ and } B_2) + \cdots + P(A \text{ and } B_k)$$

then, using the multiplication rule, you can define the marginal probability using Equation (9).

MARGINAL PROBABILITY

$$P(A) = P(A \mid B_1)P(B_1) + P(A \mid B_2)P(B_2) + \cdots + P(A \mid B_k)P(B_k) \quad \textbf{(9)}$$

where $B_1, B_2, \ldots, B_k$ are the k mutually exclusive and collectively exhaustive events.

The use of this equation is illustrated by referring to Table 1. Using Equation (9), the probability of planning to purchase is computed as follows:

$$P(A) = P(A \mid B_1)P(B_1) + P(A \mid B_2)P(B_2)$$

where

$$P(A) = \text{probability of planned to purchase}$$
$$P(B_1) = \text{probability of actually purchased}$$
$$P(B_2) = \text{probability of did not actually purchase}$$
$$P(A) = \left(\frac{200}{300}\right)\left(\frac{300}{1{,}000}\right) + \left(\frac{50}{700}\right)\left(\frac{700}{1{,}000}\right)$$
$$= \frac{200}{1{,}000} + \frac{50}{1{,}000} = \frac{250}{1{,}000} = 0.25$$

PROBLEMS FOR SECTION 2

Learning the Basics

14 Given the following contingency table:

	B	B′
A	10	20
A′	20	40

What is the probability of

a. $A \mid B$?
b. $A \mid B'$?
c. $A' \mid B'$?
d. Are events A and B statistically independent?

15 Given the following contingency table:

	B	B′
A	10	30
A′	25	35

What is the probability of

a. $A \mid B$?
b. $A \mid B'$?
c. $A' \mid B'$?
d. Are A and B statistically independent?

16 If $P(A \text{ and } B) = 0.4$ and $P(B) = 0.8$, find $P(A \mid B)$.

17 If $P(A) = 0.7$ and $P(B) = 0.6$, and if A *and* B are statistically independent, find $P(A \text{ and } B)$.

18 If $P(A) = 0.3$ and $P(B) = 0.4$, and if $P(A \text{ and } B) = 0.2$, are A *and* B statistically independent?

Applying the Concepts

19 The results of a study made as part of a yield improvement effort at a semiconductor manufacturing facility provided defect data for a sample of 450 wafers. The following table presents a summary of the responses to two questions: "Was a particle found on the die that produced the wafer?" and "Is the wafer good or bad?"

	CONDITION OF DIE		
QUALITY OF WAFER	**No Particles**	**Particles**	**Totals**
Good	320	14	334
Bad	80	36	116
Totals	400	50	450

Source: S. W. Hall, Analysis of Defectivity of Semiconductor Wafers by Contingency Table. Proceedings Institute of Environmental Sciences, *Vol. 1, (1994), 177–183.*

a. Suppose you know that a wafer is bad. What then is the probability that it was produced from a die that had particles?
b. Suppose you know that a wafer is good. What then is the probability that it was produced from a die that had particles?
c. Are the two events, a good wafer and a die with no particle, statistically independent? Explain.

20 A U.S. Census American Housing Survey studied how U.S. homeowners get to work ("How People Get to Work," *USA Today* Snapshots, February 25, 2003, 1A). Suppose that the survey consisted of a sample of 1,000 homeowners and 1,000 renters. A contingency table revealed the following results.

DRIVES TO WORK	Homeowner	Renter	Total
Yes	824	681	1,505
No	176	319	495
Total	1,000	1,000	2,000

a. Given that the respondent drives to work, what then is the probability that he or she is homeowner?
b. Given that the respondent is a homeowner, what then is the probability that he or she drives to work?
c. Explain the difference in the results in (a) and (b).
d. Are the two events, driving to work and whether the respondent is a homeowner or a renter statistically independent?

21 Are large companies less likely to offer board members stock options than small- to mid-sized companies? A survey conducted by the Segal Company of New York found that in a sample of 189 large companies, 40 offered stock options to their board members as part of their non-cash compensation packages. For small- to mid-sized companies, 43 of the 180 surveyed indicated that they offer stock options as part of their non-cash compensation packages to their board members (Kemba J. Dunham, "The Jungle: Focus on Recruitment, Pay and Getting Ahead," *Wall Street Journal*, August 21, 2001, B6).
a. Given that a company is large, what then is the probability that the company offered stock options to their board members?
b. Given that a company is small- to mid-sized, what then is the probability that the company offered stock options to their board members?
c. Is the size of the company statistically independent of whether stock options are offered to their board members? Explain.

22 Are whites more likely to claim bias? A survey conducted by Barry Goldman ("White Fight: A Researcher Finds Whites Are More Likely to Claim Bias," *Wall Street Journal*, Work Week, April 10, 2001, A1) found that of 56 white workers terminated, 29 claimed bias. Of 407 black workers terminated, 126 claimed bias.
a. Given that a worker is white, what then is the probability that the worker has claimed bias?
b. Given that a worker has claimed bias, what then is the probability that the worker is white?
c. Explain the difference in the results in (a) and (b).
d. Are the two events, being white and claiming bias, statistically independent? Explain.

23 A sample of 500 respondents was selected in a large metropolitan area to determine various information concerning consumer behavior. The following contingency table was obtained:

	GENDER		
ENJOYS SHOPPING FOR CLOTHING	Male	Female	Total
Yes	136	224	360
No	104	36	140
Total	240	260	500

a. Suppose the respondent chosen is a female. What, then, is the probability that she does not enjoy shopping for clothing?
b. Suppose the respondent chosen enjoys shopping for clothing. What, then, is the probability that the individual is a male?
c. Are enjoying shopping for clothing and the gender of the individual statistically independent? Explain.

24 Each year, ratings are compiled concerning the performance of new cars during the first 90 days of use. Suppose that the cars have been categorized according to two attributes, whether or not the car needs warranty-related repair (yes or no) and the country in which the company manufacturing the car is based (United States or not United States). Based on the data collected, the probability that the new car needs a warranty repair is 0.04, the probability that the car is manufactured by a U.S.-based company is 0.60, and the probability that the new car needs a warranty repair *and* was manufactured by a U.S.-based company is 0.025.
a. Suppose you know that a company based in the United States manufactured the car. What, then, is the probability that the car needs a warranty repair?
b. Suppose you know that a company based in the United States did not manufacture the car. What, then, is the probability that the car needs a warranty repair?
c. Are need for a warranty repair and location of the company manufacturing the car statistically independent?

25 Suppose you believe the probability that you will get an A in Statistics is 0.6 and the probability that you will get an A in Organizational Behavior is 0.8. If these events are independent, what is the probability that you will get an A in both Statistics *and* Organizational Behavior? Give some plausible reasons why these events may not be independent, even though the teachers of these two subjects may not communicate about your work.

26 A standard deck of cards is being used to play a game. There are four suits (hearts, diamonds, clubs, and spades), each having 13 faces (ace, 2, 3, 4, 5, 6, 7, 8, 9, 10, jack, queen, and king), making a total of 52 cards. This complete deck is thoroughly mixed, and you will receive the first two cards from the deck without replacement.

a. What is the probability that both cards are queens?
b. What is the probability that the first card is a 10 *and* the second card is a 5 or 6?
c. If you were sampling *with* replacement, what would be the answer in (a)?
d. In the game of blackjack, the picture cards (jack, queen, king) count as 10 points and the ace counts as either 1 or 11 points. All other cards are counted at their face value. Blackjack is achieved if your two cards total 21 points. What is the probability of getting blackjack in this problem?

27 A box of nine golf gloves contains two left-handed gloves and seven right-handed gloves.

a. If two gloves are randomly selected from the box *without* replacement, what is the probability that both gloves selected will be right-handed?
b. If two gloves are randomly selected from the box *without* replacement, what is the probability there will be one right-handed glove *and* one left-handed glove selected?
c. If three gloves are selected with replacement, what is the probability that all three will be left-handed?
d. If we were sampling *with* replacement, what would be the answers to (a) and (b)?

3 BAYES' THEOREM

Conditional probability takes into account information about the occurrence of one event to find the probability of another event. This concept can be extended to revise probabilities based on new information and to determine the probability that a particular effect was due to a specific cause. The procedure for revising these probabilities is known as **Bayes' theorem**, having been originally developed by the Rev. Thomas Bayes in the 18th century (see reference 1).

Bayes' theorem can be applied to the following situation in the Using Statistics scenario at the beginning of the chapter. The company is considering marketing a new model of television. In the past, 40% of the televisions introduced by the company have been successful and 60% have been unsuccessful. Before introducing the television to the marketplace, the marketing research department conducts an extensive study and releases a report, either favorable or unfavorable. In the past, 80% of the successful televisions had received a favorable market research report and 30% of the unsuccessful televisions had received a favorable report. For the new model of television under consideration, the marketing research department has issued a favorable report. What is the probability that the television will be successful?

Bayes' theorem can be developed from the definition of conditional probability [see Equations (5a), (5b), and (9)]. To find $P(B|A)$, Equation (5b) is used to obtain

$$P(B \mid A) = \frac{P(A \mid B)P(B)}{P(A)}$$

Equation (9) is substituted for $P(A)$, and Bayes' theorem is obtained. Bayes' theorem defines the probability of event B_i occurring given event A has occurred as the ratio of the probability of both A and B_i occurring divided by the sum of the probabilities of both A and B_1, both A and B_2, . . . , and both A and B_k.

BAYES' THEOREM

$$P(B_i \mid A) = \frac{P(A \mid B_i)P(B_i)}{P(A \mid B_1)P(B_1) + P(A \mid B_2)P(B_2) + \cdots + P(A \mid B_k)P(B_k)} \quad \textbf{(10)}$$

where B_i is the ith event out of k mutually exclusive and collectively exhaustive events.

To use Equation (10), let

$$\text{event } S = \text{successful television} \qquad \text{event } F = \text{favorable report}$$
$$\text{event } S' = \text{unsuccessful television} \qquad \text{event } F' = \text{unfavorable report}$$

and

$$P(S) = 0.40 \quad P(F|S) = 0.80$$
$$P(S') = 0.60 \quad P(F|S') = 0.30$$

Then, using Equation (10),

$$\begin{aligned} P(S \mid F) &= \frac{P(F \mid S)P(S)}{P(F \mid S)P(S) + P(F \mid S')P(S')} \\ &= \frac{(0.80)(0.40)}{(0.80)(0.40) + (0.30)(0.60)} \\ &= \frac{0.32}{0.32 + 0.18} = \frac{0.32}{0.50} \\ &= 0.64 \end{aligned}$$

The probability of a successful television, given that a favorable report was received, is 0.64. Thus, the probability of an unsuccessful television, given that a favorable report was received, is $1 - 0.64 = 0.36$. The computation of the probabilities is summarized in tabular form in Table 5 and displayed in the form of a decision tree in Figure 3.

TABLE 5

Bayes' theorem calculations for the television-marketing problem

EVENT S_i	Prior Probability $P(S_i)$	Conditional Probability $P(F \mid S_i)$	Joint Probability $P(F \mid S_i)P(S_i)$	Revised Probability $P(S_i \mid F)$
S = successful television	0.40	0.80	0.32	$0.32/0.50 = 0.64 = P(S \mid F)$
S' = unsuccessful television	0.60	0.30	0.18	$0.18/0.50 = 0.36 = P(S' \mid F)$
			0.50	

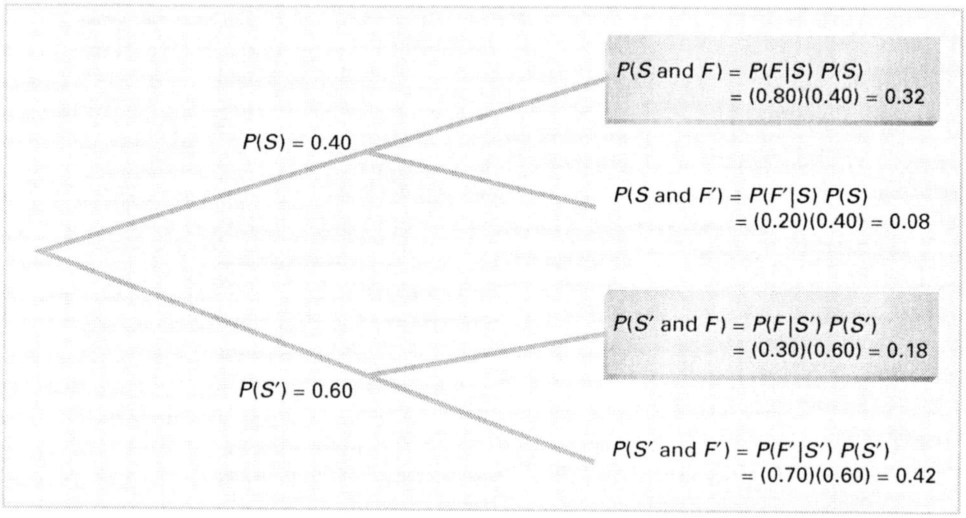

FIGURE 3

Decision tree for marketing a new television

Bayes' theorem is applied to a medical diagnosis problem in Example 11.

EXAMPLE 11

USING BAYES' THEOREM IN A MEDICAL DIAGNOSIS PROBLEM

The probability that a person has a certain disease is 0.03. Medical diagnostic tests are available to determine whether the person actually has the disease. If the disease is actually present, the probability that the medical diagnostic test will give a positive result (indicating that the disease is present) is 0.90. If the disease is not actually present, the probability of a positive test result (indicating that the disease is present) is 0.02. Suppose that the medical diagnostic test has given a positive result (indicating that the disease is present). What is the probability that the disease is actually present? What is the probability of a positive test result?

SOLUTION

Let event D = has disease, event D' = does not have disease, event T = test is positive, event T' = test is negative

and $P(D) = 0.03$, $P(D') = 0.97$, $P(T \mid D) = 0.90$, $P(T \mid D') = 0.02$

Using Equation (10),

$$P(D \mid T) = \frac{P(T \mid D)P(D)}{P(T \mid D)P(D) + P(T \mid D')P(D')}$$
$$= \frac{(0.90)(0.03)}{(0.90)(0.03) + (0.02)(0.97)}$$
$$= \frac{0.0270}{0.0270 + 0.0194} = \frac{0.0270}{0.0464}$$
$$= 0.582$$

The probability that the disease is actually present given a positive result has occurred (indicating that the disease is present) is 0.582. The computation of the probabilities is summarized in Table 6 and also displayed in the form of a decision tree in Figure 4.

TABLE 6
Bayes' theorem calculations for the medical diagnosis problem

EVENT D_i	Prior Probability $P(D_i)$	Conditional Probability $P(T \mid D_i)$	Joint Probability $P(T \mid D_i)P(D_i)$	Revised Probability $P(D_i \mid T)$
D = has disease	0.03	0.90	0.0270	$0.0270/0.0464 = 0.582 = P(D \mid T)$
D' = does not have disease	0.97	0.02	0.0194	$0.0194/0.0464 = 0.418 = P(D' \mid T)$
			0.0464	

FIGURE 4
Decision tree for the medical diagnosis problem

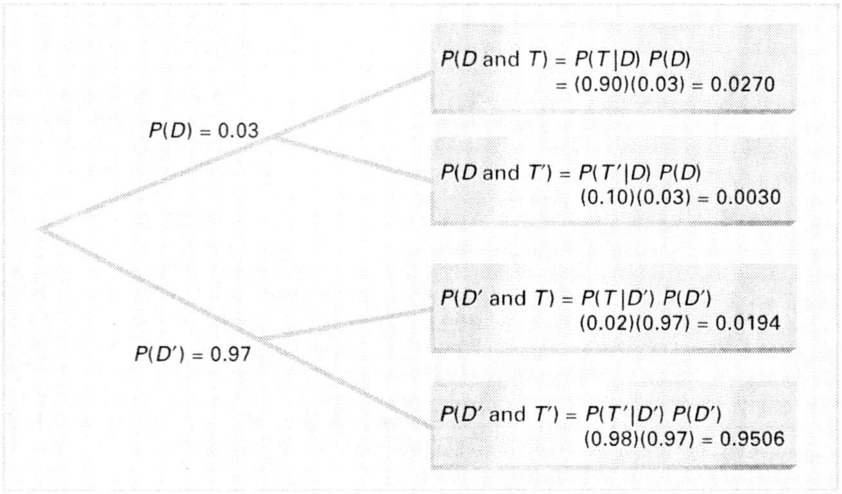

To determine the proportion of medical diagnostic tests that are positive, note that the denominator in Bayes' theorem represents $P(T)$, the probability of a positive test result, which in this case is 0.0464. Therefore, the probability of a positive test result is 4.64%.

CHAPTER 4.xls

Excel Strategy Applying Bayes' Theorem

Fill in probability values in the **Bayes** worksheet of the **Chapter 4.xls** workbook to perform the calculations associated with the application of Bayes' theorem. The design of this worksheet is shown below.

	A	B	C	D	E
1	Bayes' Theorem Calculations				
2					
3		Probabilities			
4	Event	Prior	Conditional	Joint	Revised
5	S			=B5*C5	=D5/$D$7
6	S′			=B6*C6	=D6/$D$7
7			Total:	=D5 + D6	

Open to the Bayes worksheet and enter probabilities to replace the demonstration data in the tinted cell range B5:C6. To generate a table similar to Table 5, enter **0.4** in cell **B5**, **0.6** in cell **B6**, **0.8** in cell **C5**, and **0.3** in cell **C6**.

PROBLEMS FOR SECTION 3

Learning the Basics

28 If $P(B) = 0.05$, $P(A \mid B) = 0.80$, $P(B') = 0.95$, and $P(A \mid B') = 0.40$, find $P(B \mid A)$.

29 If $P(B) = 0.30$, $P(A \mid B) = 0.60$, $P(B') = 0.70$, and $P(A \mid B') = 0.50$, find $P(B \mid A)$.

Applying the Concepts

30 In Example 11, suppose that the probability that a medical diagnostic test will give a positive result if the disease is not present is reduced from 0.02 to 0.01. Given this information,

a. If the medical diagnostic test has given a positive result (indicating the disease is present), what is the probability that the disease is actually present?

b. If the medical diagnostic test has given a negative result (indicating that the disease is not present), what is the probability that the disease is not present?

31 An advertising executive is studying television viewing habits of married men and women during prime time hours. On the basis of past viewing records, the executive has determined that during prime time, husbands are watching television 60% of the time. It has also been determined that when the husband is watching television, 40% of the time the wife is also watching. When the husband is not watching television, 30% of the time the wife is watching television. Find the probability that

a. if the wife is watching television, the husband is also watching television.

b. the wife is watching television in prime time.

32 Olive Construction Company is determining whether it should submit a bid for a new shopping center. In the past, Olive's main competitor, Base Construction Company, has submitted bids 70% of the time. If Base Construction Company does not bid on a job, the probability that Olive Construction Company will get the job is 0.50. If Base Construction Company does bid on a job, the probability that Olive Construction Company will get the job is 0.25.

a. If Olive Construction Company gets the job, what is the probability that Base Construction Company did not bid?

b. What is the probability that Olive Construction Company will get the job?

33 Laid-off workers who become entrepreneurs because they cannot find meaningful employment with another company are known as *entrepreneurs by necessity*. The *Wall Street Journal* reports that these entrepreneurs by necessity are less likely to grow into large businesses than are *entrepreneurs by choice* (Jeff Bailey, "Desire—More Than Need—Builds a Business," *Wall Street Journal*, May 21, 2001, B4). This article states that 89% of the entrepreneurs in the United States are entrepreneurs by choice and 11% are entrepreneurs by necessity. Only 2% of entrepreneurs by necessity expect their new business to employ 20 or more people within five years, while 14% of entrepreneurs by choice expect to employ at least 20 people within five years.

a. If an entrepreneur is selected at random and that individual expects that their new business will employ 20 or more people within five years, what then is the probability that this individual is an entrepreneur by choice?

b. Discuss several possible reasons why entrepreneurs by choice are more likely to believe that they will grow their business?

34 The editor of a major textbook publishing company is trying to decide whether to publish a proposed business statistics textbook. Information on previous textbooks published indicates that 10% are huge successes, 20% are modest successes, 40% break even, and 30% are losers. However, before a publishing decision is made, the book will be reviewed. In the past, 99% of the huge successes received favorable reviews, 70% of the moderate successes received favorable reviews, 40% of the break-even books received favorable reviews, and 20% of the losers received favorable reviews.

a. If the proposed text receives a favorable review, how should the editor revise the probabilities of the various outcomes to take this information into account?

b. What proportion of textbooks receives favorable reviews?

35 A municipal bond service has three rating categories (A, B, and C). Suppose that in the past year, of the municipal bonds issued throughout the United States, 70% were rated A, 20% were rated B, and 10% were rated C. Of the municipal bonds rated A, 50% were issued by cities, 40% by suburbs, and 10% by rural areas. Of the municipal bonds rated B, 60% were issued by cities, 20% by suburbs, and 20% by rural areas. Of the municipal bonds rated C, 90% were issued by cities, 5% by suburbs, and 5% by rural areas.

a. If a new municipal bond is to be issued by a city, what is the probability that it will receive an A rating?

b. What proportion of municipal bonds is issued by cities?

c. What proportion of municipal bonds is issued by suburbs?

4 ETHICAL ISSUES AND PROBABILITY

Ethical issues can arise when any statements relating to probability are being presented for public consumption, particularly when these statements are part of an advertising campaign for a product or service. Unfortunately, a substantial portion of the population is not very comfortable with any type of numerical concept (see reference 3) and misinterprets the meaning of the probability. In some instances, the misinterpretation is not intended, but in other cases, advertisements may unethically try to mislead potential customers.

One example of a potentially unethical application of probability relates to the sales of tickets to a state lottery in which the customer typically selects a set of numbers (such as 6) from a larger list of numbers (such as 54). Although virtually all participants know that they are unlikely to win the lottery, they also have very little idea of how unlikely it is for them to select all 6 winning numbers out of the list of 54 numbers. In addition, they have even less of an idea of how likely it is that they can win a consolation prize by selecting either 4 or 5 winning numbers.

Given this background, it appears that a recent advertising campaign in which a commercial for a state lottery said, "We won't stop until we have made everyone a millionaire," is at the very least deceptive and at the worst unethical. Actually, given the fact that the lottery brings millions of dollars in revenue into the state treasury, the state is never going to stop running it, although in our lifetime no one of us can be sure of becoming a millionaire by winning the lottery.

Another example of a potentially unethical application of probability relates to an investment newsletter promising a 90% probability of a 20% annual return on investment. In such a situation, it seems imperative that the investment service needs to (a) explain the basis on which this probability estimate rests, (b) provide the probability statement in another format such as 9 chances in 10, and (c) explain what happens to the investment in the 10% of the cases in which a 20% return is not achieved (e.g., Is the entire investment lost?).

PROBLEMS FOR SECTION 4

Applying the Concepts

36 Write an advertisement for the state lottery that describes in an ethical fashion the probability of winning.

37 Write an advertisement for the investment newsletter that states in an ethical fashion the probability of a 20% return.

5 COUNTING RULES (CD-ROM TOPIC)

section4.5.pdf

In many situations, because of the large number of possible outcomes, it is impractical to list each of the possible outcomes. In such situations, rules for counting the number of outcomes have been developed. To study these rules, go to the **section4.5.pdf** file located on the CD-ROM that accompanies this text.

SUMMARY

As shown in the chapter summary flowchart, this chapter developed concepts concerning basic probability, conditional probability, and Bayes' theorem. From here, important discrete probability distributions such as the binomial, hypergeometric, and Poisson distributions can be developed.

Chapter summary flowchart

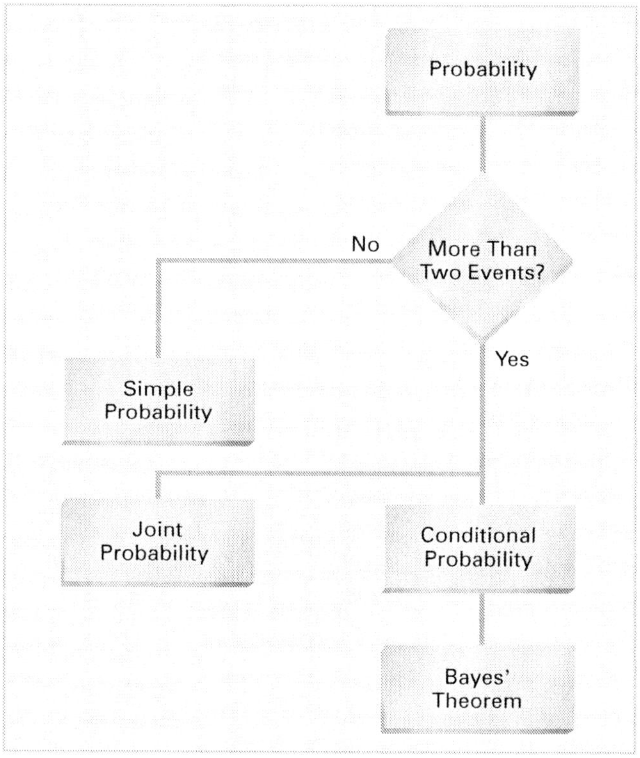

KEY TERMS

addition rule for collectively exhaustive events
addition rule for mutually exclusive events
a priori classical probability
Bayes' theorem
certain event
collectively exhaustive
complement
conditional probability
contingency table
decision tree
empirical classical probability
event
general addition rule
general multiplication rule
impossible event
joint event
joint probability
marginal probability
multiplication rule for independent events
mutually exclusive
probability
sample space
simple event
simple probability
statistical independence
subjective probability
table of cross-classifications

CHAPTER REVIEW PROBLEMS

Checking Your Understanding

38 What are the differences between *a priori* classical probability, empirical classical probability, and subjective probability?

39 What is the difference between a simple event and a joint event?

40 How can the addition rule be used to find the probability of occurrence of event *A or B*?

41 What is the difference between mutually exclusive events and collectively exhaustive events?

42 How does conditional probability relate to the concept of statistical independence?

43 How does the multiplication rule differ for events that are and are not independent?

44 How can Bayes' theorem be used to revise probabilities in light of new information?

Applying the Concepts

45 A soft-drink bottling company maintains records concerning the number of unacceptable bottles of soft drink obtained from the filling and capping machines. Based on past data, the probability that a bottle came from machine I and was nonconforming is 0.01 and the probability that a bottle came from machine II and was nonconforming is 0.025. Half the bottles are filled on machine I and the other half are filled on machine II.

a. Give an example of a simple event.
b. Give an example of a joint event.

If a filled bottle of soft drink is selected at random, what is the probability that

c. it is a nonconforming bottle?
d. it was filled on machine II?
e. it was filled on machine I *and* is a conforming bottle?
f. it was filled on machine II *and* is a conforming bottle?
g. it was filled on machine I *or* is a conforming bottle?
h. Suppose you know that the bottle was produced on machine I. What is the probability that it is nonconforming?
i. Suppose you know that the bottle is nonconforming. What is the probability that it was produced on machine I?
j. Explain the difference in the answers to (h) and (i).

(*Hint:* Set up a 2×2 contingency table to evaluate the probabilities.)

46 A recent survey ("Snapshot" *USA Today*, May 15, 2000) explored things that workers say are "extremely important" aspects of a job. Suppose the survey was based on the responses of 500 men and 500 women. The percentage of men and women who think the following aspects are extremely important:

ASPECT OF JOB	Men	Women
Good relationship with boss	63%	77%
Up-to-date equipment	59	69
Resources to do the job	55	74
Easy commute	48	60
Flexible hours at work	40	53
Able to work at home	21	34

(*Hint:* Set up a 2×2 contingency table for the responses concerning each aspect of the job.)

Suppose that a respondent is chosen at random. What is the probability that

a. he or she feels that a good relationship with the boss is an important aspect of the job?
b. he or she feels that an easy commute is an important aspect of the job?
c. the person is a male who feels that a good relationship with the boss is an important aspect of the job?
d. the person is a female and feels that having flexible hours is an important aspect of the job?
e. Given that the person feels that having a good relationship with the boss is an important aspect of the job, what is the probability that the person is a male?
f. Are any of the things that workers say are extremely important aspects of a job, statistically independent of the gender of the respondent? Explain.

47 A recent survey ("Snapshot," *USA Today*, October 22, 2001) explored technology's positive impact. Suppose the survey was based on 500 respondents in 1998 and 500 respondents in 2001. The percentages who appreciate the following benefits were as follows:

BENEFIT	1998	2001
Expands job-related knowledge	54%	87%
Increases productivity during normal work hours	66	80
Increases communication with clients and customers	42	80
Relieves job stress	26	54

(*Hint:* Set up a 2×2 contingency table for the responses concerning each benefit.)

Suppose that a respondent is chosen at random. What is the probability that he or she

a. feels that technology expands job-related knowledge?
b. feels that technology increases communication with clients and customers?
c. feels that technology increases communication with clients and customers and responded in 2001?
d. feels that technology relieves job stress and responded in 1998?
e. Are any of the benefits of technology statistically independent of the year of response? Explain.

48 The owner of a restaurant serving Continental-style entrées was interested in studying ordering patterns of patrons for the Friday to Sunday weekend time period. Records were maintained that indicated the demand for dessert during the same time period. The owner decided that two other variables were to be studied along with whether a dessert was ordered: the gender of the individual and whether a beef entrée was ordered. The results are as follows:

	GENDER		
DESSERT ORDERED	**Male**	**Female**	**Total**
Yes	96	40	136
No	224	240	464
Total	320	280	600

	BEEF ENTRÉE		
DESSERT ORDERED	**Yes**	**No**	**Total**
Yes	71	65	136
No	116	348	464
Total	187	413	600

A waiter approaches a table to take an order. What is the probability that the first customer to order at the table

a. orders a dessert?
b. does not order a beef entrée?
c. orders a dessert *or* a beef entrée?
d. is a female *and* does not order a dessert?
e. orders a dessert *and* a beef entrée?
f. is a female *or* does not order a dessert?
g. Suppose the first person that the waiter takes the dessert order from is a female. What is the probability that she does not order dessert?
h. Suppose the first person that the waiter takes the dessert order from ordered a beef entrée. What is the probability that this person orders dessert?
i. Are gender and ordering dessert statistically independent?
j. Is ordering a beef entrée statistically independent of whether the person orders dessert?

49 Unsolicited commercial e-mail messages containing product advertisements, commonly referred to as spam, are routinely deleted before being read by more than 80% of all e-mail users. Furthermore, a small percentage of those reading the spam actually follow through and purchase items. Yet, many companies use these unsolicited e-mail advertisements because of the extremely low cost involved. Movies Unlimited, a mail-order video and DVD business in Philadelphia, is one of the more successful companies in terms of generating sales through this form of e-marketing. Ed Weiss, general manager of Movies Unlimited, estimates that somewhere from 15% to 20% of their e-mail recipients read the advertisements. Moreover, approximately 15% of those who read the advertisements place an order (Stacy Forster, "E-Marketers Look to Polish Spam's Rusty Image," *Wall Street Journal*, May 22, 2002, D2).

a. Using Mr. Weiss's lower estimate that the probability a recipient will read the advertisement is 0.15, what is the probability that a recipient will read the advertisement and place an order?
b. Movies Unlimited uses a 175,000-customer database to send e-mail advertisements. If an e-mail advertisement is sent to everyone in its customer database, how many customers do you expect will read the advertisement and place an order?
c. If the probability a recipient will read the advertisement is 0.20, what is the probability that a recipient will read the advertisement and place an order?
d. What is your answer to (b) assuming the probability that a recipient will read the advertisement is 0.20?

50 In February of 2002, the Argentine peso lost 70% of its value compared to the United States dollar. This devaluation drastically raised the price of imported products. According to a survey conducted by AC Nielsen in April 2002, 68% of the consumers in Argentina were buying fewer products than before the devaluation, 24% were buying the same number of products, and 8% were buying more products. Furthermore, in a trend toward purchasing less-expensive brands, 88% indicated that they had changed the brands they purchased (Michelle Wallin, "Argentines Hone Art of Shopping in a Crisis," *Wall Street Journal*, May 28, 2002, A15). Suppose the following complete set of results were reported.

	NUMBER OF PRODUCTS PURCHASED			
BRANDS PURCHASED	**Fewer**	**Same**	**More**	**Total**
Same	10	14	24	48
Changed	262	82	8	352
Total	272	96	32	400

What is the probability that a consumer selected at random:

a. purchased fewer products than before?
b. purchased the same number of products as before?
c. purchased the same number or more products than before?
d. purchased fewer products and changed brands?
e. purchased the same number of products and the same brands?

Given that a consumer changed the brands they purchased, what then is the probability that the consumer:

f. purchased fewer products than before?
g. purchased the same number of products as before?
h. purchased the same number or more products than before?
i. Compare the results from (a)–(c) with (f)–(h).

51 Sport utility vehicles (SUVs), vans, and pickups are generally considered to be more prone to rollover than cars. In 1997, 24.0% of all highway fatalities involved a rollover; 15.8% of all fatalities in 1997 involved SUVs, vans, and pickups, given that the fatality involved a rollover. Given that a rollover was not involved, 5.6% of all fatalities involved SUVs, vans, and pickups. (Anna Wilde Mathews, "Ford Ranger, Chevy Tracker Tilt in Test," *Wall Street Journal*, July 14, 1999, A2). Consider the following definitions:

A = fatality involved an SUV, van, or pickup

B = fatality involved a rollover

a. Use Bayes' theorem to find the probability that the fatality involved a rollover, given that the fatality involved an SUV, van, or pickup.

b. Compare the result in (a) to the probability that the fatality involved a rollover, and comment on whether SUVs, vans, and pickups are generally more prone to rollover accidents.

52 Enzyme-linked immunosorbent assays (ELISA) is the most common type of screening test for detecting the HIV virus. A positive result from an ELISA indicates that the HIV virus is present. For most populations, ELISA has a high degree of *sensitivity* (to detect infection) and *specificity* (to detect noninfection). (See HIVInsite, at **HIVInsite.ucsf.edu/**.) Suppose that the probability a person is infected with the HIV virus for a certain population is 0.015. If the HIV virus is actually present, the probability that the ELISA test will give a positive result is 0.995. If the HIV virus is not actually present, the probability of a positive result from an ELISA is 0.01. If the ELISA has given a positive result, use Bayes' theorem to find the probability that the HIV virus is actually present.

Internet Exercises

53 Go to the Web site for this text

www.prenhall.com/levine

Select Chapter 4 and then click on Internet exercises.

WEB CASE

Apply your knowledge about contingency tables and the proper application of simple and joint probabilities in this continuing Web Case.

Visit the StockTout Guaranteed Investment Package Web page (**www.prenhall.com/Springville/ST_Guaranteed.htm**), read the claims and examine the supporting data. Then answer the following:

1. How accurate is the claim of the probability of success for StockTout's Guaranteed Investment Package? In what ways is the claim misleading? How would you calculate and state the probability of having an annual rate of return not less than 15%?

2. What mistake was made in reporting the 7% probability claim? Using the table found on the "Winning Probabilities" Web page (**ST_Guaranteed3.htm**), compute the proper probabilities for the group of investors.

3. Are there any probability calculations that would be appropriate for rating an investment service? Why, or why not?

REFERENCES

1. Kirk, R. L., ed., *Statistical Issues: A Reader for the Behavioral Sciences* (Belmont, CA: Wadsworth, 1972).
2. *Microsoft Excel 2002* (Redmond, WA: Microsoft Corp., 2001).
3. Paulos, J. A., *Innumeracy* (New York: Hill and Wang, 1988).

Answers to Selected Even-Numbered Problems

For more detailed solutions including explanations, interpretations, and Excel output, see the *Student Solutions Manual*.

2 (a) Simple events include selecting a red ball. **(b)** Selecting a white ball

4 (a) 0.4 **(b)** 0.35 **(c)** 0.6 **(d)** 0.1 **(e)** 0.3 **(f)** 0.35 **(g)** 0.65 **(h)** 0.75 **(i)** 0.90.

6 (a) Mutually exclusive, not collectively exhaustive. **(b)** Not mutually exclusive, not collectively exhaustive. **(c)** Mutually exclusive, not collectively exhaustive. **(d)** Mutually exclusive, collectively exhaustive. **(e)** Mutually exclusive, collectively exhaustive.

8 (a) "A wafer is good." **(b)** "A wafer is good and no particle was found on the die." **(c)** "bad wafer." **(d)** A wafer can be a "good wafer" and was produced by a die "with particles." **(e)** 0.8889 **(f)** 0.2578 **(g)** 0.1778 **(h)** 0.7111 **(i)** 0.92 **(j)** 0.2889 **(k)** The probability of "good or no particles" includes the probability of "good and no particles," the probability of "good and particles" and the probability of "bad and no particles."

10 (b) "A large company." **(c)** "A large company that offers stock options to their board members as part of their non-cash compensation." **(d)** "Did not offer stock options to their board members." **(e)** A company can be "large" and at the same time "offer stock options to their board members." **(f)** 0.5122 **(g)** 0.2249 **(h)** 0.1084 **(i)** 0.3713 **(j)** 0.6287 **(k)** 0.5962 **(l)** The probability of "large or offered stock options" includes the probability of "large and offered stock options," the probability of "large but did not offer stock options," and the probability of "small-to-midsized and offered stock options."

12 (b) Since simple events have only one criterion specified, an example could be any one of the following: (1) Being a male, (2) Being a female, (3) Enjoying clothes shopping, (4) Not enjoying clothes shopping. **(c)** Since joint events specify two criteria simultaneously, an example could be any one of the following: (1) Being a male and enjoying clothes shopping, (2) Being a male and not enjoying clothes shopping, (3) Being a female and enjoying clothes shopping, (4) Being a female and not enjoying clothes shopping. **(d)** "Not enjoying clothes shopping" is the complement of "enjoying shopping for clothes," since it involves all events other than enjoying clothes shopping. **(e)** 0.48 **(f)** 0.72 **(g)** 0.448 **(h)** 0.208 **(i)** 0.792 **(j)** 0.552 **(k)** 1.00.

14 (a) 0.33 **(b)** 0.33 **(c)** 0.67 **(d)** Events *A* and *B* are statistically independent.

16 0.5.

18 Events *A* and *B* are not statistically independent.

20 (a) 0.5475 **(b)** 0.8240 **(c)** The conditional events are reversed. **(d)** Driving oneself to work and whether the respondent is a homeowner or a renter are not statistically independent.

22 (a) 0.5179 **(b)** 0.1871 **(c)** The conditional events are reversed. **(d)** Being white and claiming bias are not statistically independent.

24 (a) 0.0417 **(b)** 0.0375 **(c)** The two events are not statistically independent.

26 (a) 0.0045 **(b)** 0.012 **(c)** 0.0059 **(d)** 0.0483.

28 0.095.

30 (a) 0.736 **(b)** 0.997.

32 (a) 0.4615 **(b)** 0.325.

34 (a) *P*(huge success | favorable review) = 0.2157. *P*(moderate success | favorable review) = 0.3050. *P*(break even | favorable review) = 0.3486. *P*(loser | favorable review) = 0.1307. **(b)** *P*(favorable review) = 0.459.

38 With *a priori* probability, the probability of success is based on prior knowledge of the process involved. With empirical probability, outcomes are based on observed data. Subjective probability refers to the chance of occurrence assigned to an event by a particular individual.

46 (a) 0.7 **(b)** 0.54 **(c)** 0.315 **(d)** 0.265 **(e)** 0.45 **(f)** Easy commute is important is not statistically independent of male. Similarly, none of the probability of any of the things workers say are extremely important aspects of a job is equal to the corresponding probability conditioned on gender, none of the things workers say are extremely important aspects of a job are statistically independent of gender.

48 (a) 0.227 **(b)** 0.688 **(c)** 0.42 **(d)** 0.4 **(e)** 0.118 **(f)** 0.84 **(g)** 0.8571 **(h)** 0.3797 **(i)** Not statistically independent **(j)** Not statistically independent.

50 (a) 0.68 **(b)** 0.24 **(c)** 0.32 **(d)** 0.655 **(e)** 0.035 **(f)** 0.7443 **(g)** 0.233 **(h)** 0.2557 **(i)** The results from (a)–(c) involve all consumers while the results from (f)–(g) are limited only to those consumers who have changed the brands they have purchased.

52 0.6024.

54 59049.

56 (a) 128 **(b)** 279936 **(c)** There are two mutually exclusive and collective exhaustive outcomes in **(a)** and six in **(b)**.

58 24.

60 120.

62 1,320.

64 35.

66 1,140.

Excel Handbook for Basic Probability

EH1 USING THE CONCATENATION OPERATOR

The **Basic Probabilities** worksheet of the **Chapter 4.xls** workbook contains formulas that use the Excel concatenation operator (&) to generate probability labels that incorporate sample space event labels. Some of these formulas are shown in the partial worksheet design of Table EH1.

Table EH1
Partial Basic Probabilities worksheet design

	A
9	**Simple Probabilities**
10	="P(" & B5 & ")"
11	="P(" & B6 & ")"
12	="P(" & C4 & ")"
13	="P(" & D4 & ")"
14	
15	**Joint Probabilities**
16	="P(" & B5 & "and" & C4 & ")"
17	="P(" & B5 & "and" & D4 & ")"
18	="P(" & B6 & "and" & C4 & ")"
19	="P(" & B6 & "and" & D4 & ")"

In the formulas in cell range A10:A13, two concatenation operators are used to join the two ends of a probability label "P(" and ")" with an event label from the sample space table (not shown in Table EH1) to form a new label. For example, if cell B5 contained the label **HDTV YES**, then the cell A10 formula would display **P(HDTV YES)**. Formulas in the cell range C16:C19 (and C22:C25, not shown) use two *sets* of concatenation operators to form a new label from label values of two other cells. For example, if C4 contained the label **DVD YES**, then the cell A16 formula would display **P(HDTV YES and DVD YES)**.

Table EH1 illustrates that while formulas are often associated with mathematical calculations, formulas have other applications as well in Microsoft Excel.

Some Important Discrete Probability Distributions

LEARNING OBJECTIVES

- To understand the properties of a probability distribution
- To compute the expected value and variance of a probability distribution
- To calculate the covariance and understand its use in finance
- To understand how to compute and be able to use the probabilities from binomial, hypergeometric, and Poisson distributions to solve business problems

USING STATISTICS

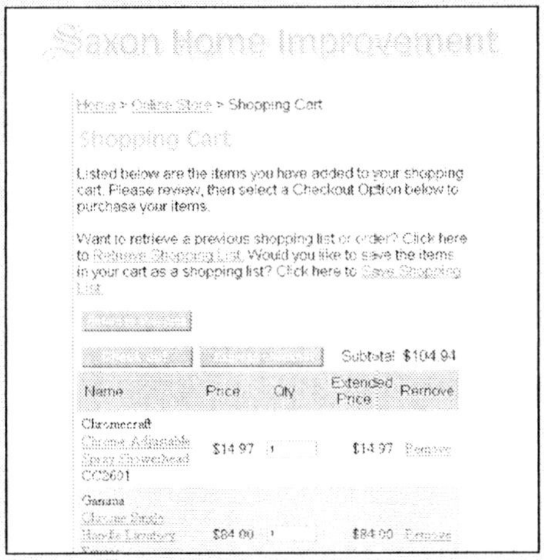

The Accounting Information System of the Saxon Home Improvement Company

An information system is a set of interrelated systems that work together to collect, process, store, transform, and distribute information for planning, decision making, and control. An accounting information system (AIS) is the subsystem of the system that typically focuses on communicating financially oriented information to a company's external and internal parties (see reference 5). A computerized AIS allows for continuous auditing of accounting information. For example, when customers of the Saxon Home Improvement Company place an order, they can complete an online order form and submit it to the company. These order forms are then checked by the AIS for errors or incomplete or improbable information. Any questionable invoices are *tagged* and included in a daily *exceptions report*. Recent data collected by the company indicate that the likelihood is 0.10 that an order form will be tagged. The company is interested in determining the likelihood of obtaining a certain number of tagged order forms for a given sample of orders. For example, if four order forms are completed, what is the likelihood that none of the order forms will be tagged? How can such probabilities be determined?

1 THE PROBABILITY DISTRIBUTION FOR A DISCRETE RANDOM VARIABLE

Probability Distribution for a Discrete Random Variable A probability distribution for a discrete random variable is a mutually exclusive listing of all possible numerical outcomes for that random variable such that a particular probability of occurrence is associated with each outcome.

A *numerical variable* is one in which the responses or outcomes are expressed numerically. Numerical variables are classified as *discrete* or *continuous*—the former arising from a counting process and the latter from a measuring process. This chapter deals with several probability distributions that represent discrete random variables.

For example, the distribution of the number of mortgages approved per week at the local branch office of a bank is given in Table 1. Because all possible outcomes are included in Table 1, the listing is collectively exhaustive, and thus the probabilities must sum to 1. A graphical representation of Table 1 is illustrated in Figure 1.

TABLE 1 Probability distribution of home mortgages approved per week

Home Mortgages Approved per Week	Probability
0	0.10
1	0.10
2	0.20
3	0.30
4	0.15
5	0.10
6	0.05

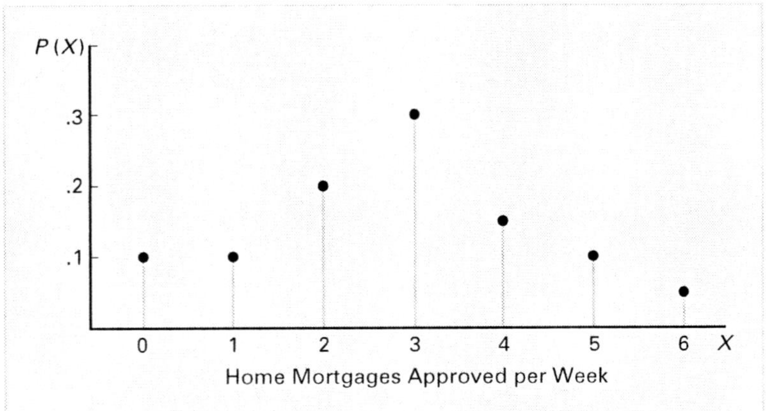

FIGURE 1 Probability distribution of the number of home mortgages approved per week

Expected Value of a Discrete Random Variable

The mean μ of a probability distribution is the *expected value* of its random variable. To calculate the expected value, multiply each possible outcome X by its corresponding probability $P(X)$ and then sum these products.

Expected Value μ of a Discrete Random Variable The expected value μ of a discrete random variable is a *weighted* average over all possible outcomes—the weights being the probability associated with each of the outcomes.

EXPECTED VALUE μ OF A DISCRETE RANDOM VARIABLE

$$\mu = E(X) = \sum_{i=1}^{N} X_i P(X_i) \tag{1}$$

where

X_i = the ith outcome of X, the discrete variable of interest
$P(X_i)$ = probability of occurrence of the ith outcome of X

For the probability distribution of the number of home mortgages approved per week (Table 1), the expected value is computed using Equation (1).

$$\begin{aligned}\mu = E(X) &= \sum_{i=1}^{N} X_i P(X_i)\\ &= (0)(0.1) + (1)(0.1) + (2)(0.2) + (3)(0.3) + (4)(0.15) + (5)(0.1) + (6)(0.05)\\ &= 0 + 0.1 + 0.4 + 0.9 + 0.6 + 0.5 + 0.3\\ &= 2.8\end{aligned}$$

Notice that the expected value of the number of mortgages approved, 2.8, is not "literally meaningful" because the actual number of mortgages approved in a given week must be an integer value. The expected value represents the *mean* or *average* number of mortgages approved per week.

Variance and Standard Deviation of a Discrete Random Variable

The variance is a summary measure obtained by multiplying each possible squared difference $[X_i - E(X)]^2$ by its corresponding probability $P(X_i)$ and then summing the resulting products. Equation (2) defines the variance of a discrete random variable.

Variance σ^2 of a Discrete Random Variable The variance σ^2 of a discrete random variable is defined as the *weighted* average of the squared differences between each possible outcome and its mean—the weights being the probabilities of each of the respective outcomes.

VARIANCE OF A DISCRETE RANDOM VARIABLE

$$\sigma^2 = \sum_{i=1}^{N} [X_i - E(X)]^2 P(X_i) \tag{2}$$

where

X_i = the ith outcome of X, the discrete variable of interest
$P(X_i)$ = probability of occurrence of the ith outcome of X

The **standard deviation σ of a discrete random variable** is given in Equation (3).

STANDARD DEVIATION OF A DISCRETE RANDOM VARIABLE

$$\sigma = \sqrt{\sigma^2} = \sqrt{\sum_{i=1}^{N} [X_i - E(X)]^2 P(X_i)} \tag{3}$$

The variance and the standard deviation of the number of home mortgages approved per week are computed using Equations (2) and (3):

$$\begin{aligned}\sigma^2 &= \sum_{i=1}^{N}[X_i - E(X)]^2 P(X_i)\\ &= (0-2.8)^2(0.10) + (1-2.8)^2(0.10) + (2-2.8)^2(0.20) + (3-2.8)^2(0.30)\\ &\quad + (4-2.8)^2(0.15) + (5-2.8)^2(0.10) + (6-2.8)^2(0.05)\\ &= 0.784 + 0.324 + 0.128 + 0.012 + 0.216 + 0.484 + 0.512\\ &= 2.46\end{aligned}$$

and

$$\sigma = \sqrt{\sigma^2} = \sqrt{2.46} = 1.57$$

Thus, the mean for the distribution of the number of mortgages approved per week is 2.8, the variance is 2.46, and the standard deviation is 1.57.

Excel Strategy Calculating the Expected Value of a Discrete Random Variable

To calculate the expected value, variance, and standard deviation of a discrete random variable, implement a version of the worksheet design presented below. This design uses Table 1 as its demonstration data to illustrate the application of the worksheet to the home mortgage approval problem of section 1. For problems with fewer or greater than seven outcomes, adjust the design by deleting rows or copying the formulas in cell range C10:E10 down as many rows as is necessary.

CHAPTER 5.xls

*Retrieve the Discrete worksheet of the **Chapter 5.xls** workbook to view the calculations for the Table 1 data.*

To use this design, open to an empty worksheet in any workbook and enter the values, labels, and formulas shown in the design or retrieve the **Discrete** worksheet of the **Chapter 5.xls** workbook, adjusting it as necessary. Note that the formulas in cells H4 and H5 use the SUM function to calculate the expected value and variance and that the formula in cell H6 uses the SQRT (square root) function to calculate the standard deviation.

Discrete Random Variable Probability Distribution Worksheet Design

	A	B	C	D	E	F	G	H
1	Discrete Random Variable Probability Distribution							
2								
3	X	P(X)	X * P(X)	[X – E(X)]^2	[X – E(X)]^2 * P(X)		Statistics	
4	0	0.1	=A4 * B4	=(A4 – $H$4)^2	=D4 * B4		Expected Value	=SUM(C:C)
5	1	0.1	=A5 * B5	=(A5 – $H$4)^2	=D5 * B5		Variance	=SUM(E:E)
6	2	0.2	=A6 * B6	=(A6 – $H$4)^2	=D6 * B6		Standard deviation	=SQRT(H5)
7	3	0.3	=A7 * B7	=(A7 – $H$4)^2	=D7 * B7			
8	4	0.15	=A8 * B8	=(A8 – $H$4)^2	=D8 * B8			
9	5	0.1	=A9 * B9	=(A9 – $H$4)^2	=D9 * B9			
10	6	0.05	=A10 * B10	=(A10 – $H$4)^2	=D10 * B10			

PROBLEMS FOR SECTION 1

Learning the Basics

1 Given the following probability distributions:

Distribution A		Distribution B	
X	*P(X)*	*X*	*P(X)*
0	0.50	0	0.05
1	0.20	1	0.10
2	0.15	2	0.15
3	0.10	3	0.20
4	0.05	4	0.50

a. Compute the expected value for each distribution.
b. Compute the standard deviation for each distribution.
c. Compare and contrast the results of distributions A and B.

2 Given the following probability distributions:

Distribution C		Distribution D	
X	*P(X)*	*X*	*P(X)*
0	0.20	0	0.10
1	0.20	1	0.20
2	0.20	2	0.40
3	0.20	3	0.20
4	0.20	4	0.10

a. Compute the expected value for each distribution.
b. Compute the standard deviation for each distribution.
c. Compare and contrast the results of distributions C and D.

Applying the Concepts

3 Using the company records for the past 500 working days, the manager of Konig Motors, a suburban automobile dealership, has summarized the number of cars sold per day into the following table:

Number of Cars Sold per Day	Frequency of Occurrence
0	40
1	100
2	142
3	66
4	36
5	30
6	26
7	20
8	16
9	14
10	8
11	2
Total	500

a. Form the probability distribution for the number of cars sold per day.
b. Compute the mean or expected number of cars sold per day.
c. Compute the standard deviation.

What is the probability that on any given day
d. fewer than four cars will be sold?
e. at most four cars will be sold?
f. at least four cars will be sold?
g. exactly four cars will be sold?
h. more than four cars will be sold?

4 The following table contains the probability distribution for the number of traffic accidents daily in a small city.

Number of Accidents Daily (*X*)	*P(X)*
0	0.10
1	0.20
2	0.45
3	0.15
4	0.05
5	0.05

a. Compute the mean or expected number of accidents per day.
b. Compute the standard deviation.

5 The manager of a large computer network has developed the following probability distribution of the number of interruptions per day:

Interruptions (*X*)	*P(X)*
0	0.32
1	0.35
2	0.18
3	0.08
4	0.04
5	0.02
6	0.01

a. Compute the mean or expected number of interruptions per day.
b. Compute the standard deviation.

6 In the carnival game Under-or-Over-Seven, a pair of fair dice is rolled once, and the resulting sum determines whether the player wins or loses his or her bet. For example, the player can bet \$1.00 that the sum will be under 7—that is, 2, 3, 4, 5, or 6. For such a bet the player will lose \$1.00 if the outcome equals or exceeds 7 or will win \$1.00 if the result is under 7. Similarly, the player can bet \$1.00 that the sum will be over 7—that is, 8, 9, 10, 11, or 12. Here the player wins \$1.00 if the result is over 7 but loses \$1.00 if the result is 7 or under. A third method of play is to bet \$1.00 on the outcome 7. For this bet the player will win \$4.00 if the result of the roll is 7 and lose \$1.00 otherwise.

a. Form the probability distribution function representing the different outcomes that are possible for a \$1.00 bet on being under 7.

b. Form the probability distribution function representing the different outcomes that are possible for a \$1.00 bet on being over 7.

c. Form the probability distribution function representing the different outcomes that are possible for a \$1.00 bet on 7.

d. Show that the expected long-run profit (or loss) to the player is the same, no matter which method of play is used.

2 COVARIANCE AND ITS APPLICATION IN FINANCE

In section 1 the expected value, variance, and standard deviation of a discrete random variable of a probability distribution were discussed. In this section the concept of the covariance between two variables is introduced and applied to portfolio management, a topic of great interest to financial analysts.

The Covariance

The **covariance** σ_{XY} between two discrete random variables X and Y is defined in Equation (4).

COVARIANCE

$$\sigma_{XY} = \sum_{i=1}^{N} [X_i - E(X)][Y_i - E(Y)]P(X_iY_i) \quad \textbf{(4)}$$

where

X = discrete variable X
X_i = ith outcome of X
Y = discrete variable Y
Y_i = ith outcome of Y
$P(X_iY_i)$ = probability of occurrence of the condition affecting the ith outcome of X and the ith outcome of Y
$i = 1, 2, \ldots, N$

To illustrate the covariance, suppose that you are deciding between two alternative investments for the coming year. The first investment is a mutual fund whose portfolio consists of a combination of stocks that make up the Dow Jones Industrial Average. The second investment consists of shares of a mutual fund that is expected to perform best when economic conditions are weak. Your estimate of the returns (per \$1,000 investment) for each investment under three economic conditions, each with a given probability of occurrence, is summarized in Table 2.

TABLE 2

Estimated returns for each investment under three economic conditions

		Investment	
$P(X_iY_i)$	Economic Condition	Dow Jones Fund	Weak-Economy Fund
0.2	Recession	−\$100	+\$200
0.5	Stable economy	+100	+50
0.3	Expanding economy	+250	−100

The expected value and standard deviation for each investment and the covariance of the two investments is computed as follows:

If X = Dow Jones fund and Y = weak-economy fund

$$E(X) = \mu_X = (-100)(0.2) + (100)(0.5) + (250)(0.3) = \$105$$

$$E(Y) = \mu_Y = (+200)(0.2) + (50)(0.5) + (-100)(0.3) = \$35$$

$$Var(X) = \sigma_X^2 = (-100 - 105)^2(0.2) + (100 - 105)^2(0.5) + (250 - 105)^2(0.3)$$
$$= 14{,}725$$

$$\sigma_X = \$121.35$$

$$Var(Y) = \sigma_Y^2 = (200 - 35)^2(0.2) + (50 - 35)^2(0.5) + (-100 - 35)^2(0.3)$$
$$= 11{,}025$$

$$\sigma_Y = \$105.00$$

$$\sigma_{XY} = (-100 - 105)(200 - 35)(0.2) + (100 - 105)(50 - 35)(0.5) + (250 - 105)(-100 - 35)(0.3)$$
$$= -6{,}765 - 37.5 - 5{,}872.5$$
$$= -12{,}675$$

Thus, the Dow Jones fund has a higher expected value or return than the weak-economy fund but has a higher standard deviation (i.e., more risk). The covariance of −12,675 between the two investments indicates a negative relationship in which the two investments are varying in the *opposite* direction. Therefore, when the return on one investment is increasing, the return on the other is typically decreasing.

The Expected Value, Variance, and Standard Deviation of the Sum of Two Random Variables

Having computed the covariance between two variables X and Y, the **expected value, variance**, and **standard deviation of the sum of two random variables** can now be defined.

EXPECTED VALUE OF THE SUM OF TWO RANDOM VARIABLES

The expected value of the sum of two random variables is equal to the sum of the expected values.

$$E(X + Y) = E(X) + E(Y) \tag{5}$$

VARIANCE OF THE SUM OF TWO RANDOM VARIABLES

The variance of the sum of two random variables is equal to the sum of the variances plus twice the covariance.

$$Var(X + Y) = \sigma_{X+Y}^2 = \sigma_X^2 + \sigma_Y^2 + 2\sigma_{XY} \tag{6}$$

STANDARD DEVIATION OF THE SUM OF TWO RANDOM VARIABLES

The standard deviation is the square root of the variance.

$$\sigma_{X+Y} = \sqrt{\sigma_{X+Y}^2} \tag{7}$$

To illustrate the expected value, variance, and standard deviation of the sum of two random variables, consider the two investments previously discussed. If X = Dow Jones fund and Y = weak-economy fund, using Equations (5), (6), and (7),

$$\begin{aligned} E(X+Y) &= E(X)+E(Y) = 105+35 = \$140 \\ \sigma^2_{X+Y} &= \sigma^2_X + \sigma^2_Y + 2\sigma_{XY} \\ &= 14{,}725 + 11{,}025 + (2)(-12{,}675) \\ &= 400 \\ \sigma_{X+Y} &= \$20 \end{aligned}$$

The expected return of the sum of the Dow Jones fund and the weak-economy fund is \$140 with a standard deviation of \$20. Observe that the standard deviation of the sum of the two investments is much less than the standard deviation of either single investment. This is due to the fact that there is a large negative covariance between the investments.

Portfolio Expected Return and Portfolio Risk

Now that the covariance and the expected return and standard deviation of the sum of two random variables have been defined, these concepts can be applied to the study of a group of assets referred to as a **portfolio**. By diversifying their investments, investors combine securities into portfolios to reduce their risk (see references 1 and 2). Often the objective is to maximize the return while minimizing the risk. For such portfolios, rather than studying the sum of two random variables, each investment is weighted by the proportion of assets assigned to that investment. This enables the **portfolio expected return** and the **portfolio risk** to be computed as defined in Equations (8) and (9).

PORTFOLIO EXPECTED RETURN

The portfolio expected return for a two-asset investment is equal to the weight assigned to asset X multiplied by the expected return of asset X plus the weight assigned to asset Y multiplied by the expected return of asset Y.

$$E(P) = wE(X) + (1-w)E(Y) \qquad \textbf{(8)}$$

where

$E(P)$ = portfolio expected return
w = portion of the portfolio value assigned to asset X
$(1-w)$ = portion of the portfolio assigned to asset Y
$E(X)$ = expected return of asset X
$E(Y)$ = expected return of asset Y

PORTFOLIO RISK

$$\sigma_p = \sqrt{w^2\sigma^2_X + (1-w)^2\sigma^2_Y + 2w(1-w)\sigma_{XY}} \qquad \textbf{(9)}$$

In the previous example, the expected return of two different investments, a Dow Jones fund and a weak-economy fund, was evaluated, and the standard deviation of the return of each investment and the covariance of the two investments was computed. Now suppose that you wish to form a portfolio of these two investments that consists of an equal investment of \$500 (because $w = 0.5$) in each of these two funds. To compute the portfolio expected return and the portfolio risk, using Equations (8) and (9), with $w = 0.50$, $E(X) = \$105$, $E(Y) = \$35$, $\sigma_X^2 = 14{,}725$, $\sigma_Y^2 = 11{,}025$, and $\sigma_{XY} = -12{,}675$

$$E(P) = (0.5)(105) + (1 - 0.5)(35) = \$70$$

$$\sigma_p = \sqrt{(0.5)^2(14{,}725) + (1 - 0.5)^2(11{,}025) + 2(0.5)(1 - 0.5)(-12{,}675)}$$

$$\sigma_p = \sqrt{100} = \$10$$

Thus, the portfolio has an expected return of \$70 for each \$1,000 invested (a return of 7%) and has a portfolio risk of \$10. Note here that the portfolio risk is small because there is a large negative covariance between the two investments. The fact that each investment performs best under different circumstances has reduced the overall risk of the portfolio.

CHAPTER 5.xls

*Retrieve the Portfolio worksheet of the **Chapter 5.xls** workbook to view an analysis based on the Table 2 data.*

Excel Strategies Calculating Portfolio Expected Return and Portfolio Risk

You implement a worksheet that features the **SUMPRODUCT** function to calculate the portfolio expected return and portfolio risk. PHStat2 can construct this worksheet for you in a single step.

For example, to generate an analysis based on the data of Table 2, use one of these strategies:

Using Excel with PHStat2

Use the PHStat2 **Decision-Making | Covariance and Portfolio Analysis** procedure to generate a new worksheet in which you fill in probability, outcome, and weight data.

Select **PHStat | Decision-Making | Covariance and Portfolio Analysis**.

In the Covariance and Portfolio Management dialog box (shown at right):

Enter **3** in the **Number of Outcomes** edit box.

Enter a title in the **Title** edit box.

Select the **Portfolio Management Analysis** check box.

Click the **OK** button.

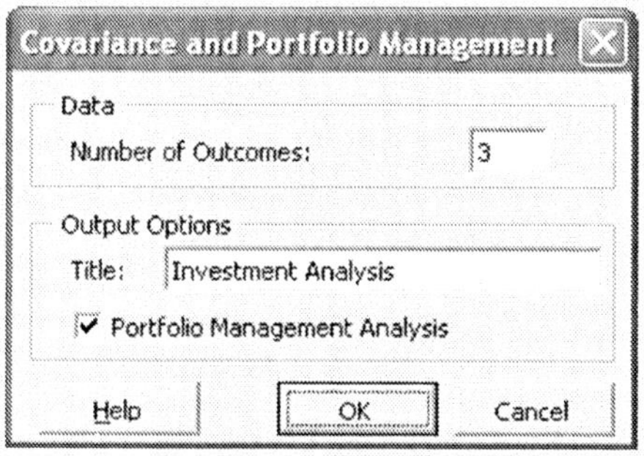

In the worksheet created by PHStat2, enter the values for the probabilities and outcomes from Table 2 in the cell range B4:D6. Enter **0.2**, **0.5**, and **0.3** in cells **B4**, **B5**, and **B6**, respectively. Enter –**100**, **100**, and **250** in cells **C4**, **C5**, and **C6**, respectively. Enter **200**, **50**, and –**100** in cells **D4**, **D5**, and **D6**. Also, enter .5, the weight assigned to investment, in cell **B8**.

Using Excel

Follow the instructions of section EH1 at the end of this chapter to manually implement a worksheet to calculate the portfolio expected return and portfolio risk.

PROBLEMS FOR SECTION 2

Learning the Basics

7 Given the following for variables X and Y:

$P(X_iY_i)$	X	Y
0.4	100	200
0.6	200	100

Compute

a. $E(X)$
b. $E(Y)$
c. σ_X
d. σ_Y
e. σ_{XY}
f. $E(X+Y)$
g. σ_{X+Y}

8 Given the following for variables X and Y:

$P(X_iY_i)$	X	Y
0.2	−100	50
0.4	50	30
0.3	200	20
0.1	300	20

Compute

a. $E(X)$
b. $E(Y)$
c. σ_X
d. σ_Y
e. σ_{XY}
f. $E(X+Y)$
g. σ_{X+Y}

9 Two investments X and Y have the following characteristics:

$$E(X) = \$50,\ E(Y) = \$100,\ \sigma_X^2 = 9{,}000,$$
$$\sigma_Y^2 = 15{,}000,\ \text{and}\ \sigma_{XY} = 7{,}500$$

If the weight assigned to investment X of portfolio assets is 0.4, compute the

a. portfolio expected return.
b. portfolio risk.

Applying the Concepts

10 In the example on the previous couple of pages, half the portfolio assets are invested in the Dow Jones fund and half in a weak-economy fund. Recalculate the portfolio expected return and the portfolio risk if

a. 30% are invested in the Dow Jones fund and 70% in a weak-economy fund.
b. 70% are invested in the Dow Jones fund and 30% in a weak-economy fund.
c. Which of the three investment strategies (30%, 50%, or 70% in the Dow Jones fund) would you recommend? Why?

11 You are trying to develop a strategy for investing in two different stocks. The anticipated annual return for a \$1,000 investment in each stock has the following probability distribution:

	Returns	
Probability	**Stock X**	**Stock Y**
0.1	−\$100	\$50
0.3	0	150
0.3	80	−20
0.3	150	−100

Compute the

a. expected return for stock X.
b. expected return for stock Y.
c. standard deviation for stock X.
d. standard deviation for stock Y.
e. covariance of stock X and stock Y.
f. Do you think you will invest in stock X or stock Y? Explain.

Suppose you wanted to create a portfolio that consists of stock X and stock Y. Compute the portfolio expected return and portfolio risk for each of the following proportions invested in stock X:

g. 0.10
h. 0.30
i. 0.50
j. 0.70
k. 0.90
l. On the basis of the results of (g)–(k), which portfolio would you recommend? Explain.

12 You are trying to develop a strategy for investing in two different stocks. The anticipated annual return for a \$1,000 investment in each stock has the following probability distribution:

	Returns	
Probability	**Stock X**	**Stock Y**
0.1	−\$50	−\$100
0.3	20	50
0.4	100	130
0.2	150	200

Compute the

a. expected return for stock X.
b. expected return for stock Y.
c. standard deviation for stock X.
d. standard deviation for stock Y.
e. covariance of stock X and stock Y.
f. Do you think you will invest in stock X or stock Y? Explain.

Suppose you wanted to create a portfolio that consists of stock X and stock Y. Compute the portfolio expected return and portfolio risk for each of the following proportions invested in stock X.

g. 0.10
h. 0.30
i. 0.50
j. 0.70
k. 0.90
l. On the basis of the results of (g)–(k), which portfolio would you recommend? Explain.

13 You are trying to set up a portfolio that consists of a corporate bond fund and a common stock fund. The following information about the annual return (per $1,000) of each of these investments under different economic conditions is available along with the probability that each of these economic conditions will occur.

Probability	State of the Economy	Corporate Bonds	Common Stocks
0.10	Recession	–$30	–$150
0.15	Stagnation	50	–20
0.35	Slow growth	90	120
0.30	Moderate growth	100	160
0.10	High growth	110	250

Compute the
a. expected return for the corporate bond fund.
b. expected return for the common stock fund.
c. standard deviation for the corporate bond fund.
d. standard deviation for the common stock fund.
e. covariance of the corporate bond fund and the common stock fund.
f. Do you think you will invest in the corporate bond fund or the common stock fund? Explain.

Suppose you wanted to create a portfolio that consists of corporate bonds and common stocks. Compute the portfolio expected return and portfolio risk for each of the following proportions invested in corporate bonds.
g. 0.10
h. 0.30
i. 0.50
j. 0.70
k. 0.90
l. On the basis of the results of (g)–(k), which portfolio would you recommend? Explain.

3 BINOMIAL DISTRIBUTION

Mathematical Model
A mathematical model is a mathematical expression representing a variable of interest. For a discrete random variable, this mathematical expression is known as a **probability distribution**.

The next three sections focus on the outcomes of a mathematical model representing a variable of interest. When a mathematical expression is available, the exact probability of occurrence of any particular outcome of the random variable can be computed. In such cases, the entire probability distribution can be obtained and listed. Many mathematical models have been developed to represent various discrete variables that occur in business, in the social and natural sciences, and in medical research. One of the most useful of these represents variables that can be characterized by the binomial probability distribution. The **binomial distribution** is a discrete probability distribution with many everyday applications. The binomial distribution has four essential properties, as shown in Exhibit 1 below.

EXHIBIT 1 THE BINOMIAL DISTRIBUTION

The binomial distribution is used to model situations that have the following properties:

1. The sample consists of a fixed number of observations, n.
2. Each observation is classified into one of two mutually exclusive and collectively exhaustive categories, usually called *success* and *failure*.
3. The probability of an observation being classified as success, p, is constant from observation to observation. Thus, the probability of an observation being classified as failure, $1 - p$, is constant over all observations.
4. The outcome (i.e., success or failure) of any observation is independent of the outcome of any other observation. To ensure independence, the observations can be obtained by using two different sampling methods. Each observation is randomly selected either from an *infinite population without replacement* or from a *finite population with replacement*.

The binomial distribution is used when the discrete random variable of interest is the number of successes obtained in a sample of n observations. Returning to the Using Statistics scenario concerning the accounting information system, suppose *success* is defined as a tagged order form and *failure* as any other outcome. Of interest is the number of tagged order forms in a given sample of orders.

What results can occur? If, for example, a sample of four invoices is considered, there could be none, one, two, three, or four tagged order forms. Can the binomial random variable, the number of tagged order forms, take on any other value? That is impossible because the number of tagged order forms cannot be more than the sample size n and cannot be less than zero. Thus, the range of a binomial random variable is from 0 to n.

Suppose that the following result is observed in a sample of four orders:

First Order	Second Order	Third Order	Fourth Order
Tagged	Tagged	Not Tagged	Tagged

What is the probability of obtaining three successes (tagged order forms) in a sample of four orders in this particular sequence? Because the assumption can be made that selecting an order is a stable process with a historical probability of 0.10 of occurring, the probability that each order occurs as noted is

First Order	Second Order	Third Order	Fourth Order
$p = 0.10$	$p = 0.10$	$1 - p = 0.90$	$p = 0.10$

Each outcome is independent of the others because the order forms are being selected from an extremely large or practically infinite population without replacement. Therefore, the probability of obtaining this particular sequence is

$$pp(1-p)p = p^3(1-p)^1 = (0.10)^3(0.90)^1 = 0.0009$$

However, this indicates only the probability of obtaining three tagged order forms (successes) out of a sample of four order forms in a *specific sequence*. To find the number of ways of selecting X objects out of n objects *irrespective of sequence*, use the **rule of combinations** given in Equation (10).

COMBINATIONS

The number of combinations of selecting X objects out of n objects is given by

$$\frac{n!}{X!(n-X)!} \qquad \textbf{(10)}$$

where

$n! = (n)(n-1)\ldots(1)$ is called n factorial, $0! = 1$, and $1! = 1$

The expression in Equation (10) often is denoted by the symbol $\binom{n}{X}$. Therefore, with $n = 4$ and $X = 3$, there are

$$\binom{n}{X} = \frac{n!}{X!(n-X)!} = \frac{4!}{3!(4-3)!} = \frac{4 \times 3 \times 2 \times 1}{(3 \times 2 \times 1)(1)} = 4$$

such sequences. These four possible sequences are:

Sequence 1 = *tagged*, *tagged*, *tagged*, not *tagged* with probability
$ppp(1-p) = p^3(1-p)^1 = 0.0009$

Sequence 2 = *tagged*, *tagged*, *not tagged*, *tagged* with probability
$pp(1-p)p = p^3(1-p)^1 = 0.0009$

Sequence 3 = *tagged, not tagged, tagged, tagged* with probability
$p(1-p)pp = p^3(1-p)^1 = 0.0009$

Sequence 4 = *not tagged, tagged, tagged, tagged* with probability
$(1-p)ppp = p^3(1-p)^1 = 0.0009$

Therefore, the probability of obtaining exactly three tagged order forms is equal to

$$\begin{aligned}&(\text{number of possible sequences}) \times (\text{probability of a particular sequence})\\&= (4) \times (0.0009) = 0.0036\end{aligned}$$

A similar, intuitive derivation can be obtained for the other possible outcomes of the random variable—zero, one, two, and four tagged order forms. However, as n, the number of observations, gets large, this type of intuitive approach becomes laborious, and a mathematical model is more appropriate. The mathematical model given in Equation (11) represents the binomial probability distribution for obtaining a number of successes (X), given a knowledge of this distribution's parameters n and p.

BINOMIAL DISTRIBUTION

$$P(X) = \frac{n!}{X!(n-X)!}p^X(1-p)^{n-X} \qquad \textbf{(11)}$$

where

$P(X)$ = probability of X successes given the parameters n and p
n = sample size
p = probability of success
$1-p$ = probability of failure
X = number of successes in the sample ($X = 0, 1, 2, \ldots, n$)

Note that the generalized form shown in Equation (11) is a restatement of what had been intuitively derived. The binomial random variable X can have any integer value X from 0 through n. In Equation (11) the product

$$p^X(1-p)^{n-X}$$

indicates the probability of obtaining exactly X successes out of n observations in a *particular sequence*; the term

$$\frac{n!}{X!(n-X)!}$$

indicates *how many combinations* of the X successes out of n observations are possible. Hence, given the number of observations n and the probability of success p, the probability of X successes is:

$$\begin{aligned}P(X) &= (\text{number of possible sequences}) \times (\text{probability of a particular sequence})\\&= \frac{n!}{X!(n-X)!}p^X(1-p)^{n-X}\end{aligned}$$

In Example 1 the use of Equation (11) is illustrated.

EXAMPLE 1

DETERMINING $P(X = 3)$, GIVEN $n = 4$ AND $p = 0.1$

If the likelihood of a tagged order form is 0.1, what is the probability that three tagged order forms are found in the sample of four order forms?

SOLUTION

Using Equation (11), the probability of obtaining exactly three tagged order forms from a sample of four order forms is

$$\begin{aligned} P(X = 3) &= \frac{4!}{3!(4-3)!}(0.1)^3(1-0.1)^{4-3} \\ &= \frac{4!}{3!(4-3)!}(0.1)^3(0.9)^1 \\ &= 4(0.1)(0.1)(0.1)(0.9) = 0.0036 \end{aligned}$$

Other computations concerning different values of X can also be obtained, as in Examples 2 and 3.

EXAMPLE 2

DETERMINING $P(X \geq 3)$, GIVEN $n = 4$ AND $p = 0.1$

If the likelihood of a tagged order form is 0.1, what is the probability that three or more (i.e., at least three) tagged order forms are selected out of the sample of four order forms?

SOLUTION

As shown in Example 1, the probability of obtaining exactly three tagged order forms from a sample of four orders is 0.0036. To obtain the probability of at least three tagged order forms, you need to add the probability of three tagged order forms to the probability of four tagged order forms. The probability of four tagged order forms is

$$\begin{aligned} P(X = 4) &= \frac{4!}{4!(4-4)!}(0.1)^4(1-0.1)^{4-4} \\ &= \frac{4!}{4!(0)!}(0.1)^4(0.9)^0 \\ &= 1(0.1)(0.1)(0.1)(0.1) = 0.0001 \end{aligned}$$

Thus the probability of at least three tagged order forms is

$$\begin{aligned} P(X \geq 3) &= P(X = 3) + P(X = 4) \\ &= 0.0036 + 0.0001 \\ &= 0.0037 \end{aligned}$$

There is a 0.37% chance that there will be at least three tagged order forms in a sample of four orders.

EXAMPLE 3

DETERMINING $P(X < 3)$, GIVEN $n = 4$ AND $p = 0.1$

If the likelihood of a tagged order form is 0.1, what is the probability that there are fewer than three tagged order forms in the sample of four orders that are selected?

SOLUTION

The probability that fewer than three tagged order forms are selected is

$$P(X < 3) = P(X = 0) + P(X = 1) + P(X = 2)$$

Using Equation (11) these probabilities are,

$$P(X=0)=\frac{4!}{0!(4-0)!}(0.1)^0(1-0.1)^{4-0}=0.6561$$

$$P(X=1)=\frac{4!}{1!(4-1)!}(0.1)^1(1-0.1)^{4-1}=0.2916$$

$$P(X=2)=\frac{4!}{2!(4-2)!}(0.1)^2(1-0.1)^{4-2}=0.0486$$

Therefore, $P(X<3)=0.6561+0.2916+0.0486=0.9963$.

Rather than using Equation (11), note that $P(X<3)$ can be obtained from its complement, $P(X \geq 3)$ as follows:

$$\begin{aligned} P(X<3) &= 1-P(X\geq 3) \\ &= 1-0.0037=0.9963 \end{aligned}$$

Computations such as those in Example 3 can become tedious, especially as n gets large. To avoid computational drudgery, many binomial probabilities can be obtained directly from the Table of Binomial Probabilities, a portion of which is reproduced in Table 3. This table provides the probabilities that the binomial random variable takes on values of $X = 0, 1, 2, \ldots, n$, for various selected combinations of the parameters n and p. For example, to obtain the probability of exactly two successes in a sample of four when the probability of success is 0.1, the probability corresponding to the row $X = 2$ and column $p = 0.10$ is obtained. The result is 0.0486, as demonstrated in Table 3.

TABLE 3
Obtaining a binomial probability for $n = 4$, $X = 2$, and $p = 0.1$

		p			
n	*X*	0.01	0.02	...	0.10
4	0	0.9606	0.9224	...	0.6561
	1	0.0388	0.0753	...	0.2916
	2	0.0006	0.0023	...	0.0486
	3	0.0000	0.0000	...	0.0036
	4	0.0000	0.0000	...	0.0001

Source: Table of Binomial Probabilities.

The binomial probabilities given in the Table of Binomial Probabilities can also be obtained by using Microsoft Excel. Figure 2 presents Microsoft Excel output.

FIGURE 2
Binomial distribution calculations for $n = 4$ and $p = 0.1$ obtained from Microsoft Excel

	A	B	C	D	E	F	G
1	**Binomial Probabilities**						
2							
3	**Data**						
4	**Sample size**	4					
5	**Probability of success**	0.1					
6							
7	**Statistics**						
8	**Mean**	0.4					
9	**Variance**	0.36					
10	**Standard deviation**	0.6					
11							
12	**Binomial Probabilities Table**						
13		X	P(X)	P(<=X)	P(<X)	P(>X)	P(>=X)
14		0	0.6561	0.6561	0	0.3439	1
15		1	0.2916	0.9477	0.6561	0.0523	0.3439
16		2	0.0486	0.9963	0.9477	0.0037	0.0523
17		3	0.0036	0.9999	0.9963	1E-04	0.0037
18		4	0.0001	1	0.9999	0	1E-04

CHAPTER 5.xls

Retrieve the Figure 5.2 and Figure 5.3 worksheets of the ***Chapter 5.xls*** *workbook to view a table and histogram of binomial probabilities.*

Excel Strategies Calculating Binomial Probabilities

You implement a worksheet that features the **BINOMDIST** function to calculate binomial probabilities. PHStat2 can construct this worksheet for you in a single step.

For example, to calculate the binomial probabilities shown in Figure 2, use one of these strategies:

Using Excel with PHStat2

Use the PHStat2 Binomial procedure to calculate binomial probabilities on a new worksheet.

Select **PHStat | Probability & Prob. Distributions | Binomial**.

In the Binomial Probability Distribution dialog box (shown at right):

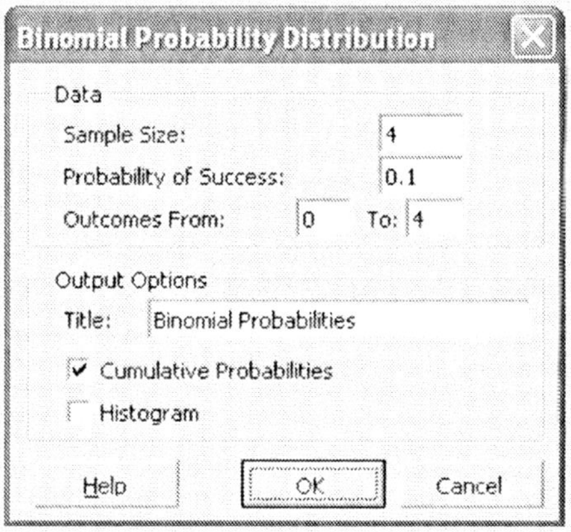

Enter **4** in the **Sample Size** edit box.

Enter **0.1** in the **Probability of Success** edit box.

Enter **0** in the **Outcomes From** edit box.

Enter **4** in the **Outcomes To** edit box.

Enter a title in the **Title** edit box.

Select the **Cumulative Probabilities** check box.

Click the **OK** button.

Using Excel

Follow the instructions of section EH2 (at the end of this chapter) to manually implement a worksheet to calculate binomial probabilities. To produce a histogram based on the worksheet, follow the instructions of section EH5.

Characteristics of the Binomial Distribution

Each time a set of parameters (n and p) is specified, a particular binomial probability distribution can be generated.

Shape Note that a binomial distribution can be symmetrical or skewed. Whenever $p = .5$, the binomial distribution will be symmetrical, regardless of how large or small the value of n. However, when $p \neq 0.5$, the distribution will be skewed. The closer p is to 0.5 and the larger the number of observations n, the less skewed the distribution will be. Thus, the distribution of the number of tagged order forms is skewed to the right because $p = 0.1$. This can be observed in Figure 3, which is a plot of the distribution for $n = 4$ and $p = 0.1$.

The Mean The mean of the binomial distribution is obtained as the product of its two parameters, n and p. Rather than use Equation (1), which holds for all discrete probability distributions, Equation (12) is used to compute the mean for variables that follow the binomial distribution.

FIGURE 3
Binomial probability distribution for $n = 4$ and $p = 0.1$ obtained from Microsoft Excel

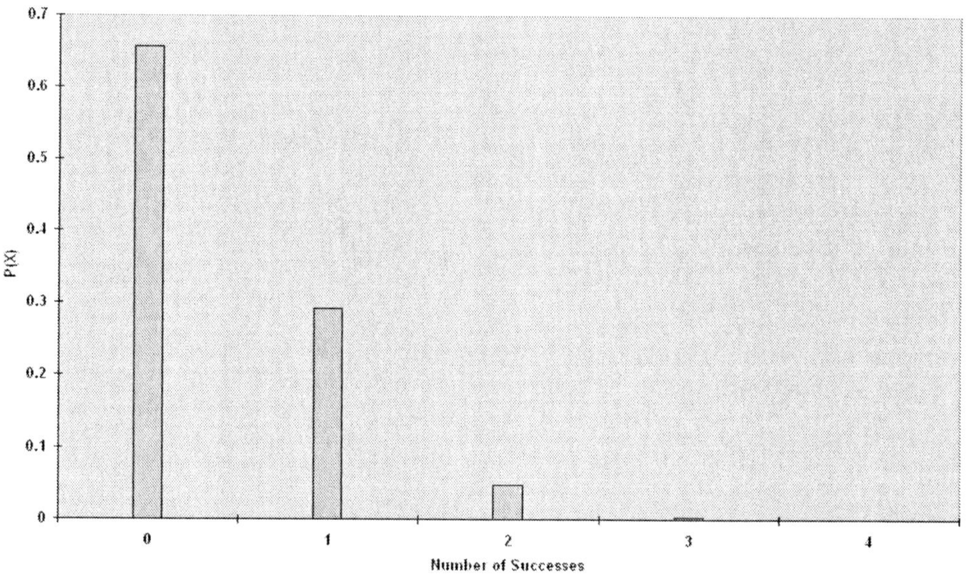

THE MEAN OF THE BINOMIAL DISTRIBUTION

The mean μ of the binomial distribution is equal to the sample size n multiplied by the probability of success p.

$$\mu = E(X) = np \tag{12}$$

On the average, over the long run, one would theoretically expect $\mu = E(X) = np = (4)(0.1) = 0.4$ tagged order form in a sample of four orders.

The Standard Deviation The standard deviation of the binomial distribution is calculated using Equation (13).

THE STANDARD DEVIATION OF THE BINOMIAL DISTRIBUTION

$$\sigma = \sqrt{\sigma^2} = \sqrt{Var(X)} = \sqrt{np(1-p)} \tag{13}$$

Referring to the accounting information systems example, the standard deviation is computed as

$$\sigma = \sqrt{4(0.1)(0.9)} = 0.60$$

This is the same result that would be obtained from the more general expression shown in Equation (3).

In this section the binomial model has been developed as a useful discrete probability distribution, and its characteristics have been demonstrated through an application involving an accounting information system. However, the binomial distribution plays an even more important role when it is used in statistical inference problems regarding the estimation or testing of hypotheses about proportions.

PROBLEMS FOR SECTION 3

Learning the Basics

14 Determine the following:

a. If $n = 4$ and $p = 0.12$, then what is $P(X = 0)$?
b. If $n = 10$ and $p = 0.40$, then what is $P(X = 9)$?
c. If $n = 10$ and $p = 0.50$, then what is $P(X = 8)$?
d. If $n = 6$ and $p = 0.83$, then what is $P(X = 5)$?
e. If $n = 10$ and $p = 0.90$, then what is $P(X = 9)$?

15 Determine the mean and standard deviation of the random variable X in each of the following binomial distributions:

a. If $n = 4$ and $p = 0.10$
b. If $n = 4$ and $p = 0.40$
c. If $n = 5$ and $p = 0.80$
d. If $n = 3$ and $p = 0.50$

Applying the Concepts

16 The increase or decrease in the price of a stock between the beginning and the end of a trading day is assumed to be an equally likely random event. What is the probability that a stock will show an increase in its closing price on five consecutive days?

17 The commission rate commercial airlines pay travel agents has been declining for several years. In an attempt by travel agencies to raise revenue, many agencies are now charging their customers a ticket fee, typically between \$10 and \$15. According to the American Society of Ticket Agents, about 90% of travel agents charge customers fees when purchasing an airline ticket (Kortney Stringer, "American Air Fees for Travel Agents to be Cut Again," *Wall Street Journal*, August 20, 2001, B2).

a. Is the 90% figure quoted by the American Society of Ticket Agents best classified as *a priori* classical probability, empirical classical probability, or subjective probability?
b. Suppose that a random sample of 10 travel agencies is selected. Assume that the number of the 10 travel agencies charging a ticket fee is distributed as a binomial random variable. What are the mean and standard deviation of this distribution?
c. What assumptions are necessary in (b)?

Compute the probability that of the 10 travel agencies:

d. zero charges ticket fees?
e. exactly one charges ticket fees?
f. exactly two charge ticket fees?
g. two or fewer charge ticket fees?
h. three or more charge ticket fees?

18 The broadcast networks introduce new television shows each fall. In an attempt to get viewers interested in the new shows, television commercials are aired during the summer as part of a promotional campaign conducted prior to the fall debuts. The networks then conduct surveys to see what percentage of the viewing public is *aware* of the shows. According to network sources, in the fall of 2001, 68% of viewers aged 18–49 were aware of the new series *Criminal Intent*, whereas only 24% of viewers aged 18–49 were aware of *Inside Schwartz* (Joe Flint, "Viewers Awareness of New Shows Rises," *Wall Street Journal*, August 20, 2001, B7).

a. Give a definition of *aware*.
b. Are the 68% and 24% figures quoted by networks best classified as *a priori* classical probability, empirical classical probability, or subjective probability?

Use Microsoft Excel to answer the following questions assuming that a random sample of 20 viewers aged 18–49 is selected. What is the probability that:

c. fewer than 5 of the viewers are aware of *Criminal Intent*?
d. 10 or more are aware of *Criminal Intent*?
e. 15 or more are aware of *Criminal Intent*?
f. all 20 are aware of *Criminal Intent*?
g. What is the expected number of viewers in the sample of 20 that will be aware of *Criminal Intent*?
h. Consider another sample of 20 viewers aged 18–49. Answer (c)–(g) for the new show *Inside Schwartz*.

19 An important part of the customer service responsibilities of a telephone company relates to the speed with which troubles in residential service can be repaired. Suppose past data indicate that the likelihood is 0.70 that troubles in residential service can be repaired on the same day. For the first five troubles reported on a given day, what is the probability that

a. all five will be repaired on the same day?
b. at least three will be repaired on the same day?
c. fewer than two will be repaired on the same day?
d. What assumptions are necessary in (a)–(c)?
e. What are the mean and the standard deviation of the probability distribution?
f. What would be your answers in (a)–(c) and (e) if the probability is 0.80 that troubles in residential service can be repaired on the same day?
g. Compare the results of (a)–(c) and (f).

20 A student is taking a multiple-choice exam in which each question has four choices. Assuming that she has no knowledge of the correct answers to any of the questions, she has decided on a strategy in which she will place four balls (marked A, B, C, and D) into a box. She randomly selects one ball for each question and replaces the ball in the box. The marking on the ball will determine her answer to the question. There are five multiple-choice questions on the exam. What is the probability that she will get

a. five questions correct?
b. at least four questions correct?
c. no questions correct?
d. no more than two questions correct?
e. What assumptions are necessary in (a)–(d)?
f. What are the mean and the standard deviation of the number of questions that she will get correct?
g. Suppose that the exam has 50 multiple-choice questions and 30 or more correct answers is a passing score. What is

the probability that the student will pass the exam by following her strategy? (Use Microsoft Excel to compute this probability.)

21 When a customer places an order with Rudy's On-Line Office Supplies, a computerized accounting information system (AIS) automatically checks to see if the customer has exceeded his or her credit limit. Past records indicate that the probability of customers exceeding their credit limit is 0.05. Suppose that, on a given day, 20 customers place orders. Assume that the number of customers that the AIS detects as having exceeded their credit limit is distributed as a binomial random variable.

a. What are the mean and standard deviation of the number of customers exceeding their credit limits?

b. What is the probability that zero customers will exceed their limit?

c. What is the probability that one customer will exceed his or her limits?

d. What is the probability that two or more customers will exceed their limits?

4 HYPERGEOMETRIC DISTRIBUTION

The binomial distribution and the **hypergeometric distribution** are concerned with the same thing, the number of successes in a sample containing n observations. What differentiates these two discrete probability distributions is the manner in which the data are obtained. For the binomial distribution, the sample data are drawn *with* replacement from a *finite* population or *without* replacement from an *infinite* population. On the other hand, for the hypergeometric distribution, the sample data are drawn *without* replacement from a *finite* population. Thus, although the probability of success p is constant over all observations of a binomial distribution, and the outcome of any particular observation is independent of any other, the same is not true for a hypergeometric distribution. In the case of the hypergeometric distribution, the outcome of one observation is affected by the outcomes of the previous observations.

In general, a mathematical expression of the hypergeometric distribution for obtaining X successes, given a knowledge of the parameters n, N, and A, is shown in Equation (14).

HYPERGEOMETRIC DISTRIBUTION

$$P(X) = \frac{\binom{A}{X}\binom{N-A}{n-X}}{\binom{N}{n}} \tag{14}$$

where

$P(X)$ = the probability of X successes, given knowledge of n, N, and A
n = sample size
N = population size
A = number of successes in the population
$N - A$ = number of failures in the population
X = number of successes in the sample
$N - X$ = number of failures in the sample

The number of successes in the sample X cannot be greater than the number of successes in the population A or the sample size n. Thus, the range of the hypergeometric random variable is limited to the sample size (as is the range for the binomial random variable) or to the number of successes in the population—whichever is smaller.

The mean of the hypergeometric distribution is computed from Equation (15).

THE MEAN OF THE HYPERGEOMETRIC DISTRIBUTION

$$\mu = E(X) = \frac{nA}{N} \tag{15}$$

The standard deviation of the hypergeometric distribution is obtained by using Equation (16).

THE STANDARD DEVIATION OF THE HYPERGEOMETRIC DISTRIBUTION

$$\sigma = \sqrt{\frac{nA(N - A)}{N^2}} \cdot \sqrt{\frac{N - n}{N - 1}} \quad \textbf{(16)}$$

In Equation (16), the expression $\sqrt{\frac{N - n}{N - 1}}$ is a **finite population correction factor** that results from sampling without replacement from a finite population.

To illustrate the hypergeometric distribution, suppose that an organization is trying to create a team of 8 people from different departments who have knowledge of a particular process. A total of 30 people within the organization have knowledge of the process, and 10 of these people are from the design department. If members of the team are to be selected at random, what is the probability that the team will contain 2 members from the design department? Here the population of $N = 30$ people within the organization who have knowledge of the process is finite. In addition, $A = 10$ are from the design department. A team of $n = 8$ members is to be selected.

Using Equation (14),

$$P(X = 2) = \frac{\binom{10}{2}\binom{20}{6}}{\binom{30}{8}}$$

$$= \frac{\frac{10!}{2!(8)!} \times \frac{(20)!}{(6)!(14)!}}{\frac{30!}{8!(22)!}}$$

$$= 0.298$$

Thus, the probability that the team will contain two members from the design department is 0.298, or 29.8%.

Such computations can become tedious, especially as N gets large. However, the probabilities can be obtained by using Microsoft Excel. Figure 4 represents output from Microsoft Excel for the hypergeometric distribution example.

FIGURE 4

Hypergeometric distribution probabilities for $N = 30$, $A = 10$, and $n = 8$ obtained from Microsoft Excel

	A	B	C
1	**Hypergeometic Probabilities**		
2			
3	**Data**		
4	**Sample size**	8	
5	**No. of successes in population**	10	
6	**Population size**	30	
7			
8	**Hypergeometric Probabilities Table**		
9		X	P(X)
10		0	0.021523
11		1	0.132447
12		2	0.298005
13		3	0.317872
14		4	0.173836
15		5	0.049083
16		6	0.006817
17		7	0.00041
18		8	7.69E-06

CHAPTER 5.xls

*Retrieve the Figure 5.4 worksheet of the **Chapter 5.xls** workbook to view hypergeometric probabilities.*

Excel Strategies Calculating Hypergeometric Probabilities

You implement a worksheet that features the **HYPGEOMDIST** function to calculate hypergeometric probabilities. PHStat2 can construct this worksheet for you in a single step.

For example, to calculate the hypergeometric probabilities shown in Figure 4, use one of these strategies:

Using Excel with PHStat2

Use the PHStat2 Hypergeometric procedure to calculate hypergeometric probabilities on a new worksheet.

Select **PHStat | Probability & Prob. Distributions | Hypergeometric.**

In the Hypergeometric Probability Distribution dialog box (shown at right):

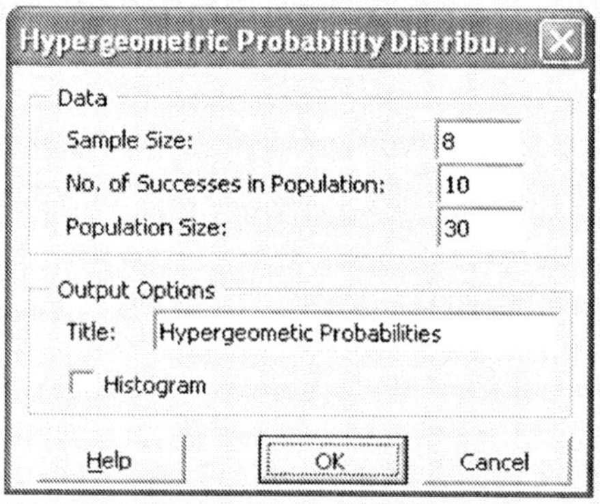

Enter **8** in the **Sample Size** edit box.

Enter **10** in the **No. of Successes in Population** edit box.

Enter **30** in the **Population Size** edit box.

Enter a title in the **Title** edit box.

Click the **OK** button.

Using Excel

Follow the instructions of section EH3 (see the end of this chapter) to manually implement a worksheet to calculate hypergeometric probabilities. To produce a histogram based on the worksheet, follow the instructions of section EH5.

PROBLEMS FOR SECTION 4

Learning the Basics

22 Determine the following:

a. If $n = 4$, $N = 10$, and $A = 5$, then find $P(X = 3)$.
b. If $n = 4$, $N = 6$, and $A = 3$, then find $P(X = 1)$.
c. If $n = 5$, $N = 12$, and $A = 3$, then find $P(X = 0)$.
d. If $n = 3$, $N = 10$, and $A = 3$, then find $P(X = 3)$.

23 Referring to problem 22, compute the mean and standard deviation for the hypergeometric distributions described in (a)–(d).

Applying the Concepts

24 An auditor for the Internal Revenue Service is selecting a sample of 6 tax returns from persons in a particular profession for possible audit. If 2 or more of these indicate "improper" deductions, the entire group (population) of 100 tax returns will be audited. What is the probability that the entire group will be audited if the true number of improper returns in the population is

a. 25?
b. 30?
c. 5?
d. 10?
e. Discuss the differences in your results depending on the true number of improper returns in the population.

25 The dean of a business school wishes to form an executive committee of 5 from among the 40 tenured faculty members at the school. The selection is to be random, and at the school there are 8 tenured faculty members in accounting. What is the probability that the committee will contain

a. none of them?
b. at least 1 of them?
c. not more than 1 of them?
d. What would be your answer to (a) if the committee consisted of 7 members?

26 From an inventory of 48 cars being shipped to local automobile dealers, 12 have had defective radios installed.

What is the probability that one particular dealership receiving 8 cars

a. obtains all with defective radios?
b. obtains none with defective radios?
c. obtains at least 1 with a defective radio?
d. What would be your answers to (a)–(c) if 6 cars have had defective radios installed?

27 A state lottery is conducted in which 6 winning numbers are selected from a total of 54 numbers. What is the probability that if 6 numbers are randomly selected,

a. all 6 numbers will be winning numbers?
b. 5 numbers will be winning numbers?
c. 4 numbers will be winning numbers?
d. 3 numbers will be winning numbers?
e. none of the numbers will be winning numbers?
f. What would be your answers to (a)–(e) if the 6 winning numbers were selected from a total of 40 numbers?

28 In a shipment of 15 hard disks, 5 are defective. If 4 of the disks are inspected, what is the probability that

a. exactly 1 is defective?
b. at least 1 is defective?
c. no more than 2 are defective?
d. What is the average number of defective hard disks that you would expect to find in the sample of 4 hard disks?

5 POISSON DISTRIBUTION

The **Poisson distribution** is a useful discrete probability distribution when you are interested in the number of times a certain event will occur in a given unit of area or time. This type of situation occurs frequently in business. For example, a quality assurance manager is interested in the number of noticeable surface defects on a new refrigerator; an accountant is interested in the number of numerical errors occurring per 100 invoices; a network manager is interested in the number of network failures in a day; or a plant manager is interested in the number of industrial accidents per month. Exhibit 2 describes the properties that must be true about a specific situation in order to use the Poisson distribution.

EXHIBIT 2 THE POISSON DISTRIBUTION

The Poisson distribution is used to model situations that have the following properties:

1. You are interested in counting the number of times a particular event occurs in a given area of opportunity. The *area of opportunity* is defined by time, length, surface area, and so forth.
2. The probability that an event occurs in a given area of opportunity is the same for all of the areas of opportunity.
3. The number of events that occur in one area of opportunity is independent of the number of events that occur in other areas of opportunity.
4. The probability that two or more events will occur in an area of opportunity approaches zero as the area of opportunity becomes smaller.

Consider the number of customers arriving during the lunch hour at a bank located in the central business district in a large city. Of interest to you is the number of customers that arrive each minute. Does this situation match the four properties of the Poisson distribution given in Exhibit 2? First, the *event* of interest is a customer arriving and the *given area of opportunity* is defined as a 1-minute interval. Will zero customers arrive, one customer arrive, two customers arrive, and so on? Second, it is reasonable to assume that the probability that a customer arrives during a 1-minute interval is the same as the probability for all the other 1-minute intervals. Third, the arrival of one customer in any 1-minute interval has no effect on (i.e., is statistically independent of) the arrival of any other customer in any other 1-minute interval. Finally, note that the probability that two or more customers will arrive in a given time period approaches zero as the time interval becomes small. For example, there is virtually no probability that two customers will arrive in a time interval with a width of 1/100th of a second. Thus, the Poisson distribution is applicable to the number of customers arriving at the bank in a 1-minute time interval during the lunch hour.

The Poisson distribution has one parameter, called λ (the Greek lowercase letter *lambda*), which is the average or expected number of events per unit. The variance of a Poisson distribution is also equal to λ, and the standard deviation is equal to $\sqrt{\lambda}$. The number of events X of the Poisson random variable ranges from 0 to infinity.

The mathematical expression for the Poisson distribution for obtaining X events, given that λ events are expected, is shown in Equation (17).

POISSON DISTRIBUTION

$$P(X) = \frac{e^{-\lambda}\lambda^X}{X!} \quad \textbf{(17)}$$

where

$P(X)$ = the probability of X successes given a knowledge of λ
λ = expected number of successes
e = mathematical constant approximated by 2.71828
X = number of successes per unit

To demonstrate the Poisson distribution, recall the example of bank customer arrivals. Suppose that, on average, three customers arrive per minute at the bank during the noon to 1 P.M. hour. What is the probability that in a given minute exactly two customers will arrive? And what is the probability that more than two customers will arrive in a given minute?

Using Equation (17) and $\lambda = 3$, the probability that in a given minute exactly two customers will arrive is

$$P(X = 2) = \frac{e^{-3.0}(3.0)^2}{2!} = \frac{9}{(2.71828)^3(2)} = 0.2240$$

To determine the probability that in any given minute more than two customers will arrive

$$P(X > 2) = P(X = 3) + P(X = 4) + \cdots + P(X = \infty)$$

Because all the probabilities in a probability distribution must sum to 1, the terms on the right side of the equation $P(X > 2)$ also represent the complement of the probability that X is less than or equal to 2 [i.e., $1 - P(X \leq 2)$]. Thus,

$$P(X > 2) = 1 - P(X \leq 2) = 1 - [P(X = 0) + P(X = 1) + P(X = 2)]$$

Now, using Equation (17),

$$\begin{aligned} P(X > 2) &= 1 - \left[\frac{e^{-3.0}(3.0)^0}{0!} + \frac{e^{-3.0}(3.0)^1}{1!} + \frac{e^{-3.0}(3.0)^2}{2!}\right] \\ &= 1 - [0.0498 + 0.1494 + 0.2240] \\ &= 1 - 0.4232 = 0.5768 \end{aligned}$$

Thus, there is roughly a 42.3% chance that two or fewer customers will arrive at the bank per minute. Therefore, a 57.7% chance exists that three or more customers will arrive in the same minute.

Such computations can become tedious. To avoid computational drudgery, many Poisson probabilities can be obtained directly from the Table of Poisson Probabilities, a portion of which is reproduced in Table 4. The Table of Poisson Probabilities provides the probabilities that the Poisson random variable takes on values of $X = 0, 1, 2, \ldots$, for various selected values of the parameter λ. To obtain the probability that exactly two customers will arrive in a given minute when, on average, three customers arrive per minute, the probability corresponding to the row $X = 2$ and column $\lambda = 3.0$ is read from the table. The result is 0.2240, as demonstrated in Table 4.

TABLE 4
Obtaining a Poisson probability for λ = 3

	λ			
X	2.1	2.2	...	3.0
0	.1225	.1108	...	.0498
1	.2572	.2438	...	.1494
2	.2700	.2681	...	.2240
3	.1890	.1966	...	.2240
4	.0992	.1082	...	.1680
5	.0417	.0476	...	.1008
6	.0146	.0174	...	.0504
7	.0044	.0055	...	.0216
8	.0011	.0015	...	.0081
9	.0003	.0004	...	.0027
10	.0001	.0001	...	.0008
11	.0000	.0000	...	.0002
12	.0000	.0000	...	.0001

Source: The Table of Poisson Probabilities.

Poisson probabilities given in the Table of Poisson Probabilities can also be obtained by using Microsoft Excel. Figure 5 presents output from Microsoft Excel.

FIGURE 5
Poisson distribution calculations for λ = 3 obtained from Microsoft Excel

	A	B	C	D	E	F	G
1	Poisson Probabilities						
2							
3			Data				
4	Average/Expected number of successes:				3		
5							
6	Poisson Probabilities Table						
7		X	P(X)	P(<=X)	P(<X)	P(>X)	P(>=X)
8		0	0.049787	0.049787	0.000000	0.950213	1.000000
9		1	0.149361	0.199148	0.049787	0.800852	0.950213
10		2	0.224042	0.423190	0.199148	0.576810	0.800852
11		3	0.224042	0.647232	0.423190	0.352768	0.576810
12		4	0.168031	0.815263	0.647232	0.184737	0.352768
13		5	0.100819	0.916082	0.815263	0.083918	0.184737
14		6	0.050409	0.966491	0.916082	0.033509	0.083918
15		7	0.021604	0.988095	0.966491	0.011905	0.033509
16		8	0.008102	0.996197	0.988095	0.003803	0.011905
17		9	0.002701	0.998898	0.996197	0.001102	0.003803
18		10	0.000810	0.999708	0.998898	0.000292	0.001102
19		11	0.000221	0.999929	0.999708	0.000071	0.000292
20		12	0.000055	0.999984	0.999929	0.000016	0.000071
21		13	0.000013	0.999997	0.999984	0.000003	0.000016
22		14	0.000003	0.999999	0.999997	0.000001	0.000003
23		15	0.000001	1.000000	0.999999	0.000000	0.000001
24		16	0.000000	1.000000	1.000000	0.000000	0.000000
25		17	0.000000	1.000000	1.000000	0.000000	0.000000
26		18	0.000000	1.000000	1.000000	0.000000	0.000000
27		19	0.000000	1.000000	1.000000	0.000000	0.000000
28		20	0.000000	1.000000	1.000000	0.000000	0.000000

Excel Strategies Calculating Poisson Probabilities

CHAPTER 5.xls

*Retrieve the Figure 5.5 worksheet of the **Chapter 5.xls** workbook to view Poisson probabilities.*

You implement a worksheet that features the **POISSON** function to calculate Poisson probabilities. PHStat2 can construct this worksheet for you in a single step.

For example, to calculate the Poisson probabilities shown in Figure 5 above, use one of these strategies:

Using Excel with PHStat2
Use the PHStat2 Poisson procedure to calculate Poisson probabilities on a new worksheet.

Select **PHStat | Probability & Prob. Distributions | Poisson**.

In the Poisson Probability Distribution dialog box (shown at right):

Enter **3** in the **Average/Expected No. of Successes** edit box.

Enter a title in the **Title** edit box.

Select the **Cumulative Probabilities** check box.

Click the **OK** button.

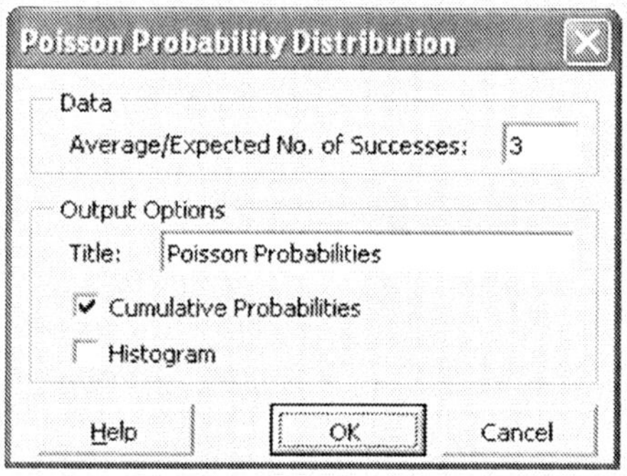

Using Excel
Follow the instructions of section EH4 (at the end of this chapter) to manually implement a worksheet to calculate Poisson probabilities. To produce a histogram based on the worksheet, follow the instructions of section EH5.

PROBLEMS FOR SECTION 5

Learning the Basics

29 Assume a Poisson distribution.

a. If $\lambda = 2.5$, then what is $P(X = 2)$?
b. If $\lambda = 8.0$, then what is $P(X = 8)$?
c. If $\lambda = 0.5$, then what is $P(X = 1)$?
d. If $\lambda = 3.7$, then what is $P(X = 0)$?
e. If $\lambda = 4.4$, then what is $P(X = 7)$?

30 Assume a Poisson distribution.

a. If $\lambda = 2.0$, then what is $P(X \geq 2)$?
b. If $\lambda = 8.0$, then what is $P(X \geq 3)$?
c. If $\lambda = 0.5$, then what is $P(X \leq 1)$?
d. If $\lambda = 4.0$, then what is $P(X \geq 1)$?
e. If $\lambda = 5.0$, then what is $P(X \leq 3)$?

Applying the Concepts

31 J. D. Power & Associates calculates and publishes various statistics concerning car quality. The Initial Quality score measures the number of problems per new car sold. For 2002 model cars, the Lexus was the top brand with 0.85 problems per car. Korea's Kia came in last with 2.67 problems per car (Gregory L. White and Northiko Shirouzu, "What's in a Car-Quality Score?" *Wall Street Journal*, May 30, 2002, D6). Let the random variable X be equal to the number of problems with a newly purchased Lexus.

a. What assumptions must be made in order for X to be distributed as a Poisson random variable? Are these assumptions reasonable?

If you purchase a 2002 Lexus, what is the probability that the new car will have:

b. zero problems?
c. exactly one problem?
d. exactly two problems?
e. two or fewer problems?
f. three or more problems?
g. Give a definition for "problem." Why is the definition important in interpreting the Initial Quality score?
h. Repeat (b)–(f) for a 2002 Kia. Compare your answers to a Lexus.

32 A toll-free phone number is available from 9 A.M. to 9 P.M. to your customers wanting to register a complaint with a product purchased from your company. Past history indicates that an average 0.4 calls are received per hour.

a. What properties must be true about the situation described above in order to use the Poisson distribution to calculate probabilities concerning the number of phone calls received in a 1-hour period?

Assuming that this situation matches the properties you discussed in (a), what then is the probability that during a 1-hour period:

b. zero phone calls will be received?
c. one phone call will be received?
d. two phone calls will be received?
e. three or more phone calls will be received?
f. What is the maximum number of phone calls that will be received in a 1-hour period 99.99% of the time?

33 Assume that the number of network errors experienced in a day on a local area network (LAN) is distributed as a Poisson random variable. The average number of network errors experienced in a day is 2.4. What is the probability that in any given day

a. zero network errors will occur?
b. exactly one network error will occur?
c. two or more network errors will occur?
d. fewer than three network errors will occur?

34 The quality control manager of Marilyn's Cookies is inspecting a batch of chocolate-chip cookies that has just been baked. If the production process is in control, the average number of chip parts per cookie is 6.0. What is the probability that in any particular cookie being inspected

a. fewer than five chip parts will be found?
b. exactly five chip parts will be found?
c. five or more chip parts will be found?
d. four or five chip parts will be found?
e. What would be your answers to (a)–(d) if the average number of chip parts per cookie were 5.0?

35 Refer to problem 34. How many cookies in a batch of 100 being sampled should the manager expect to discard if company policy requires that all chocolate-chip cookies sold must have at least four chocolate-chip parts?

36 The number of claims for missing baggage in a small city for a well-known airline averages nine per day. What is the probability that, on a given day, there will be

a. fewer than three claims?
b. exactly three claims?
c. three or more claims?
d. more than three claims?

37 Based on past experience, it is assumed that the number of flaws per foot in rolls of grade 2 paper follows a Poisson distribution with an average of 1 flaw per 5 feet of paper (0.2 flaw per foot). What is the probability that in a

a. 1-foot roll there will be at least 2 flaws?
b. 12-foot roll there will be at least 1 flaw?
c. 50-foot roll there will be between 5 and 15 (inclusive) flaws?

6 USING THE POISSON DISTRIBUTION TO APPROXIMATE THE BINOMIAL DISTRIBUTION (CD-ROM TOPIC)

section5.6.pdf

Under certain circumstances the Poisson distribution can be used to approximate the binomial distribution. To study this topic, go to the **section5.6.pdf** file located on the CD-ROM that accompanies this text.

SUMMARY

As shown in the chapter summary flowchart, this chapter was about mathematical expectation, the covariance and the development and application of some important discrete probability distributions—the binomial, hypergeometric, and Poisson distributions. In the Using Statistics scenario, you learned how to calculate probabilities from the binomial distribution concerning the observation of tagged invoices in the accounting information system used by the Saxon Home Improvement Company.

KEY TERMS

binomial distribution
covariance σ_{XY}
expected value: μ of a discrete random variable
expected value of the sum of two random variables
finite population correction factor
hypergeometric distribution
mathematical model
Poisson distribution
portfolio
portfolio expected return
portfolio risk
probability distribution for a discrete random variable
probability distribution function
rule of combinations
standard deviation σ of a discrete variable
standard deviation of the sum of two random variables
variance σ^2 of a discrete random variable
variance of the sum of two random variables

Chapter summary flowchart

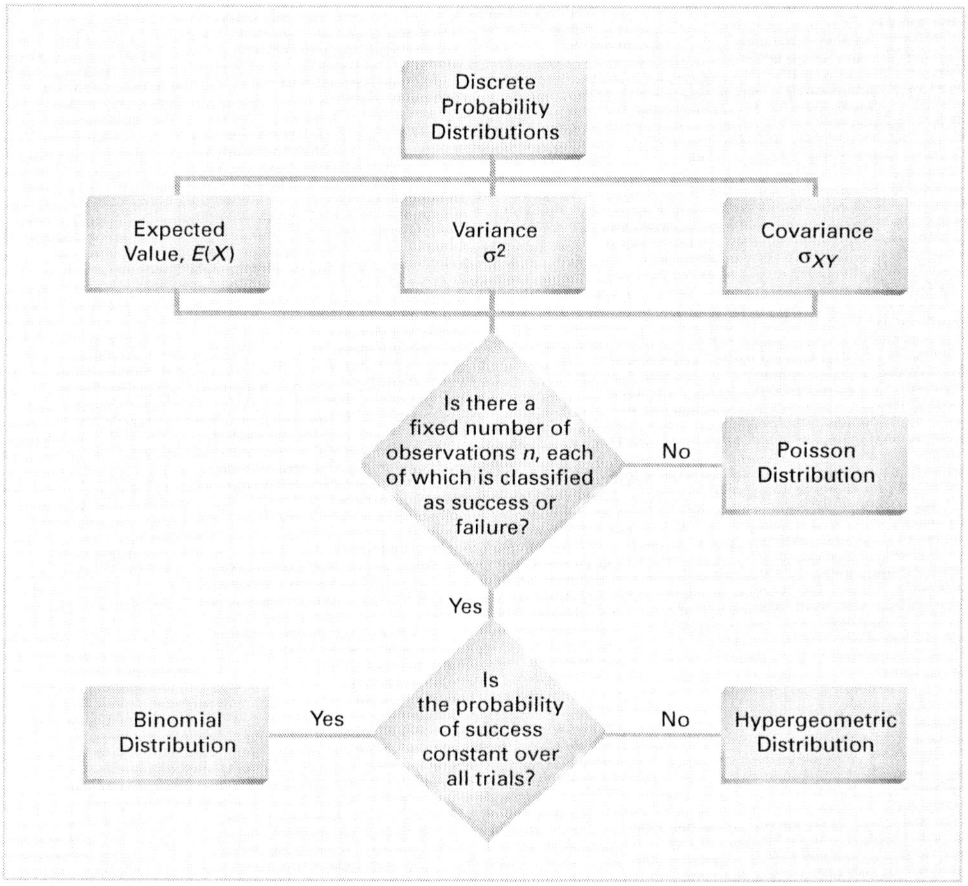

CHAPTER REVIEW PROBLEMS

Checking Your Understanding

38 What is the meaning of the expected value of a probability distribution?

39 What are the assumptions of the binomial distribution?

40 What are the assumptions of the Poisson distribution, and how do they differ from those of the binomial distribution?

41 When should the hypergeometric distribution be used instead of the binomial distribution?

42 Why is it important to know the covariance when determining the portfolio risk?

Applying the Concepts

43 Event insurance allows promoters of sporting and entertainment events to protect themselves from financial losses due to uncontrollable circumstances such as rain-outs. For example, each spring Cincinnati's Downtown Council puts on the Taste of Cincinnati. This is a rainy time of year in Cincinnati, and the chance of receiving an inch or more of rain during a spring weekend is about one out of four. An article in the *Cincinnati Enquirer*, by Jim Knippenberg ("Chicken Pox Means 3 Dog Night Remedy," *Cincinnati Enquirer*, May 28, 1997, E1), gave the details for an insurance policy purchased by the Downtown Council. The policy would pay $100,000 if it rained more than an inch during the weekend festival. The cost of the policy was reported to be $6,500.

a. Determine whether or not you believe that these dollar amounts are correct. (*Hint:* Calculate the expected value of the profit to be made by the insurance company.)

b. Assume that the dollar amounts are correct. Is this policy a good deal for Cincinnati's Downtown Council?

44 A phone call handled by an automated customer-service system costs a company an average of $0.45. A phone call passed on to a "live" operator costs a company an average of $5.50. However, as more and more companies have implemented automated service systems, customer annoyance with such systems has grown. Furthermore, more customers are quick to leave the automated system when given an option such as "Press zero to talk to a customer-service representative." According to the Center for Client Retention, 40% of all callers to automated customer-service systems will automatically opt to go to a live operator when given the chance (Jane Spencer, "In Search of the Operator," *Wall Street Journal*, May 8, 2002, D1).

If 10 independent callers contact an automated customer-service system, what is the probability

a. zero will automatically opt to talk to a live operator?
b. exactly one will automatically opt to talk to a live operator?
c. exactly two will automatically opt to talk to a live operator?
d. two or fewer will automatically opt to talk to a live operator?
e. all ten will automatically opt to talk to a live operator?
f. If all ten automatically opt to talk to a live operator, do you think that the 40% figure given in the article applies to this particular system? Explain.

45 Credit card companies are increasing their revenues by raising the late fees charged to their customers. According to a study by **CardWeb.com**, late fees represent the third largest revenue source for card companies after interest charges and payments from the merchants who accept their cards. Moreover, in the last year, 58% of all credit card customers had to pay a late fee (Ron Lieber, "Credit-Card Firms Collect Record Levels of Late Fees," *Wall Street Journal*, May 21, 2002, D1).

If a random sample of 20 credit card holders is selected, what is the probability that

a. zero had to pay a late fee?
b. no more than 5 had to pay a late fee?
c. no more than 10 had to pay a late fee?
d. more than 10 had to pay a late fee?
e. What assumptions did you have to make to answer (a)–(d)?

46 Priority Mail is the United States Postal Service's alternative to commercial express mail companies like Federal Express. An article in the *Wall Street Journal* presents some interesting conclusions comparing Priority Mail shipments with the much cheaper first-class shipments (Rick Brooks, "New Data Reveal 'Priority Mail' Is Slower Than a Stamp," *Wall Street Journal*, May 29, 2002, D1). When comparing shipments intended for delivery in 3 days, first-class deliveries failed to deliver on-time 19% of the time, while Priority Mail failed 33% of the time. Note that at the time of the article, first-class deliveries started as low as $0.34 and Priority Mail started at $3.50.

If 10 items are to be shipped first-class to 10 different destinations claimed to be in a 3-day delivery location, what is the probability that

a. zero items will take more than 3 days?
b. exactly one will take more than 3 days?
c. two or more will take more than 3 days?
d. What are the mean and the standard deviation of the probability distribution?
e. Repeat (a)–(d) if the shipments are made using Priority Mail.

47 Cinema advertising is increasing. Normally 60 to 90 seconds long, these advertisements are longer and more extravagant, and tend to have more captive audiences than television advertisements. Thus, it is not surprising that the recall rates for viewers of cinema advertisements are higher than for television advertisements. According to survey research conducted by the ComQUEST division of BBM Bureau of Measurement in Toronto, the probability a viewer will remember a cinema advertisement is 0.74, whereas the probability a viewer will remember a 30-second television advertisement is 0.37 (Nate Hendley, "Cinema Advertising Comes of Age," *Marketing Magazine*, May 6, 2002, 16).

a. Is the 0.74 probability reported by the BBM Bureau of Measurement best classified as *a priori* classical probability, empirical classical probability, or subjective probability?
b. Suppose that 10 viewers of a cinema advertisement are randomly sampled. Consider the random variable defined by the number of viewers that recall the advertisement. What assumptions must be made in order to assume that this random variable is distributed as a binomial random variable?
c. Assuming that the number of viewers that recall the cinema advertisement is a binomial random variable, what are the mean and standard deviation of this distribution?
d. Based on your answer to (c), if none of the viewers can recall the ad, what can be inferred about the 0.74 probability given in the article?

Compute the probability that of the 10 viewers:

e. exactly zero can recall the advertisement.
f. exactly one can recall the advertisement.
g. exactly two can recall the advertisement.
h. all 10 can recall the advertisement.
i. more than half can recall the advertisement.
j. eight or more can recall the advertisement.
k. Repeat c, (e)–(j) for a television advertisement using the given probability of recall, 0.37.

48 In a survey conducted by the Council for Marketing and Opinion Research (CMOR), a national nonprofit research industry trade group based in Cincinnati, 1,628 of 3,700 adults contacted in the United States refuse to participate in phone surveys (Steve Jarvis, "CMOR Finds Survey Refusal Rate Still Rising," *Marketing News*, February 4, 2002, 4). Suppose that you are to randomly call 10 adults in the United States and ask them to participate in a phone survey. Using the results of the CMOR study, what is the probability:

a. all 10 will refuse?
b. exactly 5 will refuse?
c. at least 5 will refuse?
d. fewer than 5 will refuse?
e. fewer than 5 will agree to be surveyed?
f. What is the expected number of people that will refuse to participate? Explain the practical meaning of this number.

49 For e-commerce merchants, getting a customer to visit a Web site isn't enough. Merchants must also persuade online shoppers to spend money by completing a purchase. Experts at Andersen Consulting estimated that 88% of Web shoppers abandon their virtual shopping carts before completing their transaction (Rebecca Quick, "The Lessons Learned," *Wall Street Journal*, April 17, 2000, R6). Consider a sample of 20 customers who visit an e-commerce Web site and assume that the probability a customer will leave the site before completing their transaction is 0.88. Use the binomial model to answer the following questions:

a. What is the expected value, or mean, of the binomial distribution?
b. What is the standard deviation of the binomial distribution?
c. What is the probability that all 20 of the customers will leave the site without completing a transaction?
d. What is the probability that 18 or more of the customers will leave the site without completing a transaction?
e. What is the probability that 15 or more of the customers will leave the site without completing a transaction?
f. If the Web site is enhanced so that only 70% of the customers will leave the site without completing their transaction, how does that change your answers to (a)–(e)?

50 To measure radio listenership, Arbitron mails surveys to randomly selected households in 283 markets in the United States. The respondents are given diaries to record the radio stations they listen to. When the diaries are complete, the respondents return them to Arbitron and they receive a cash award for their participation (currently $10 in most markets). According to an article, responses to the diary surveys hit a 20-year low in 2002, with only 32.6% being returned (K. Bachman, "Consumers: Respond, S.V.P.," *Mediaweek*, January 6, 2003, 5). Suppose that in a particular market, 100 surveys are sent.

a. What assumptions do you need to make in order to use the binomial distribution to model the number of surveys returned?
b. What is the expected value, or mean, of the binomial distribution?
c. What is the standard deviation of the binomial distribution?
d. What is the probability that 30 or fewer surveys will be returned?
e. What is the probability that 25 or fewer surveys will be returned?
f. What is the probability that more than 40 surveys will be returned?
g. What is the probability that at least 30 but no more than 35 surveys will be returned?
h. If Arbitron increases the cash incentive so that the response rate is 40%, what are the answers to (a)–(f)?

Note: Use Microsoft Excel to solve (d)–(h).

51 Are people who sample music on the Internet via digital downloading and other services likely to follow up by purchasing compact discs in stores or online? A survey by the market research firm Yankelovich Partners indicates that 66% of all consumers that listen to a song online have at least once been prompted later to buy a CD or cassette featuring the song (Anna Wilde Mathew, "Music Samplers on Web Buy CDs in Stores," *Wall Street Journal*, June 15, 2000, A3). Consider a random sample of 20 Internet users who have listened to songs online. Assume the number of Internet users who have been prompted later to buy a CD or cassette featuring the song is distributed as a binomial random variable.

a. What is the mean, or expected value, of the number of Internet users in the sample who have at least once been prompted later to buy a CD or cassette?
b. What is the standard deviation of the number of Internet users in the sample who have at least once been prompted later to buy a CD or cassette?
c. What is the probability that 15 or more have at least once been prompted later to buy a CD or cassette?
d. What is the probability that 10 or more have at least once been prompted later to buy a CD or cassette?

52 From 1872 to 2000, stock prices have risen in 74% of the years (Mark Hulbert, "The Stock Market Must Rise in 2002? Think Again," *The New York Times*, December 6, 2001, Business, 6). Based on this information, and assuming a binomial distribution, what do you think the probability is that the stock market will rise

a. next year?
b. the year after next?
c. in four of the next five years?
d. in none of the next five years?
e. For this situation, what assumption of the binomial distribution might not be valid?

53 Spurious correlation refers to the apparent relationship between variables that either have no true relationship or are related to other variables that have not been measured. One widely publicized stock market indicator in the United States that is an example of spurious correlation is the relationship between the winner of the National Football League Superbowl and the performance of the Dow Jones Industrial Average in that year. The indicator states that when a team representing the National Football Conference wins the Superbowl, the Dow Jones Industrial Average will increase in that year. When a team representing the American Football Conference wins the Superbowl, the Dow Jones Industrial Average will decline in that year. During the time period 1967 to 2002, a 36-year period, the indicator has been correct 30 out of 36 times. Assuming that this indicator is a random event with no predictive value, you would expect that the indicator would be correct 50% of the time.

a. Using Microsoft Excel, what is the probability that the indicator would be correct 30 or more times in 36 years?
b. What does this tell you about the usefulness of this indicator?

54 Mega Millions is one of the most popular lottery games in the United States. Participating states in Mega Millions are Georgia, Illinois, Maryland, Massachusetts, Michigan, New Jersey, New York, Ohio, and Virginia. Rules for playing and the list of prizes are given on the following page ("Win Megamoney Playing Ohio's Biggest Jackpot Game," Ohio Lottery Headquarters, 2002):

Rules:

- Select five numbers from a pool of 1 to 52 and one Mega Ball number from a second pool of numbers from 1 to 52.
- Each wager cost $1.

Prizes:

- Match all five numbers + Mega Ball—win jackpot (minimum of $10,000,000)
- Match all five numbers—win $175,000
- Match four numbers + Mega Ball—win $5,000
- Match four numbers—win $150
- Match three numbers + Mega Ball—win $150
- Match two numbers + Mega Ball—win $10
- Match three numbers—win $7
- Match one number + Mega Ball—win $3
- Mega Ball—win $2

Find the probability of winning

a. the jackpot.
b. the $175,000 prize. Note that this requires matching all five numbers but not matching the Mega Ball.
c. $5,000.
d. $150.
e. $10.
f. $7.
g. $3.
h. $2.
i. nothing.
j. All stores selling Mega Millions tickets are required to have a brochure that gives complete game rules and probabilities of winning each prize (the probability of having a losing ticket is not given). The slogan for all lottery games in the state of Ohio is "Play Responsibly. Odds Are, You'll Have Fun." Do you think Ohio's slogan and the requirement of making available complete game rules and probabilities of winning is an ethical approach to running the lottery system?

55 In 2000 worldwide golf ball sales totaled an estimated 988 million golf balls worth $1.3 billion. One reason for such a large number of golf ball purchases is that golfers lose them at a rate of 4.5 per 18-hole round (James P. Sterba, "Does Your Golf Ball Beep, Tick, Perform Some Special Trick?" *Wall Street Journal*, June 15, 2000, A1). Assume that the number of golf balls lost in an 18-hole round is distributed as a Poisson random variable.

a. What assumptions need to be made so that the number of golf balls lost in an 18-hole round is distributed as a Poisson random variable?

What is the probability that

b. 0 balls will be lost in an 18-hole round?
c. exactly 1 ball will be lost in an 18-hole round?
d. exactly 2 balls will be lost in an 18-hole round?
e. exactly 3 balls will be lost in an 18-hole round?
f. exactly 4 balls will be lost in an 18-hole round?
g. exactly 5 balls will be lost in an 18-hole round?
h. 5 or fewer balls will be lost in an 18-hole round?
i. 6 or more balls will be lost in an 18-hole round?

56 A study of the homepages for Fortune 500 companies reports that the average number of bad links per homepage is 0.4 and the average number of spelling errors per homepage is 0.16 (Nabil Tamimi, Murii Rajan, and Rose Sebastianella, "Benchmarking the Home Pages of 'Fortune' 500 Companies," *Quality Progress*, July 2000). Use the Poisson distribution to find the probability that a randomly selected homepage will contain

a. exactly 0 bad links.
b. exactly 1 bad link.
c. 2 or more bad links.
d. 5 or more bad links.
e. exactly 0 spelling errors.
f. exactly 1 spelling error.
g. 2 or more spelling errors.
h. 10 or more spelling errors.

Internet Exercises

57 Go to the Web site for this text

www.prenhall.com/levine

Select Chapter 5 and then click on Internet exercises.

RUNNING CASE MANAGING THE SPRINGVILLE HERALD

The *Herald* marketing department has been seeking to increase home-delivery sales through an aggressive direct-marketing campaign that has included mailings, discount coupons, and telephone solicitations. Feedback from these efforts has indicated that getting their newspapers delivered early in the morning is a very important factor for both prospective as well as existing subscribers.

After several brainstorming sessions, a team consisting of members from the marketing and circulation departments decided that guaranteeing newspaper delivery by a specific time could be an important selling point in retaining and getting new subscribers. The team concluded that the *Herald* should offer a guarantee that customers will receive their newspapers by a certain time or else that day's issue is free.

To assist the team in setting a guaranteed delivery time, Al Leslie, the research director, noted that the circulation department had the data that would show the percentage of newspapers yet undelivered every quarter-hour from 6 A.M. to 8 A.M. Jan Shapiro remembered that customers were asked on their subscription forms at what time would they be looking for their copy of the *Herald* to be delivered. These data were subsequently combined and posted on an internal *Herald* Web page (see **Circulation_Data.htm** in the HeraldCase folder on the CD-ROM that accompanies this text or link to **www.prenhall.com/HeraldCase/Circulation_Data.htm**).

EXERCISE

Review the internal data and propose a reasonable time (to the nearest quarter-hour) to guarantee delivery. To help explore the effects of your choice, calculate the following probabilities:

SH1 If a sample of 50 customers is drawn on a given day, what is the probability, given your selected delivery time, that:

a. fewer than 3 customers would receive a free newspaper?
b. 2, 3, or 4 customers would receive a free newspaper?
c. more than 5 customers would receive a free newspaper?

SH2 Consider the effects of improving the newspaper delivery process so that the percentage of newspapers that go undelivered by your guaranteed delivery time decreases by 2%. If a sample of 50 customers is drawn on a given day, what is the probability, given your selected delivery time (and the delivery improvement), that:

a. fewer than 3 customers would receive a free newspaper?
b. 2, 3, or 4 customers would receive a free newspaper?
c. more than 5 customers would receive a free newspaper?

WEB CASE

Apply your knowledge about the covariance and its application in finance in this continuing Web Case.

Visit the StockTout Bulls and Bears Web page (**www.prenhall.com/Springville/ST_BullsandBears.htm**), read the claims and examine the supporting data. Then, answer the following:

1. Are there any "catches" about the rate of return claims the Web site makes for the Happy Bull and Worried Bear Funds?
2. What subjective data influence the rate of return analyses of these funds? Could StockTout be accused of making false and misleading statements? Why, or why not?
3. The expected return analysis seems to show that the Worried Bear Fund has a greater expected return than the Happy Bull Fund. Should a rational investor then never invest in the Happy Bull Fund? Why, or why not?
4. If you wanted to minimize your risk in these plans, how should you invest your money? Explain.

REFERENCES

1. Bernstein, P. L., *Against the Gods: The Remarkable Story of Risk* (New York: Wiley, 1996).
2. Emery, D. R., J. D. Finnerty, and J. D. Stowe, *Corporate Financial Management*, 3rd ed. (Upper Saddle River, NJ: Prentice Hall, 2004).
3. Kirk, R. L., ed., *Statistical Issues: A Reader for the Behavioral Sciences* (Belmont, CA: Wadsworth, 1972).
4. Levine, D. M., P. Ramsey, and R. Smidt, *Applied Statistics for Engineers and Scientists Using Microsoft Excel and Minitab* (Upper Saddle River, NJ: Prentice Hall, 2001).
5. Mescove, S. A., M. G. Simkin, and A. Barganoff, *Core Concepts of Accounting Information Systems*, 7th ed. (New York: John Wiley, 2001).
6. *Microsoft Excel 2002* (Redmond, WA: Microsoft Corp., 2001).

Answers to Selected Even-Numbered Problems

For more detailed solutions including explanations, interpretations, and Excel output, see the *Student Solutions Manual.*

2 (a) Distribution C: $\mu = 2.00$. Distribution D: $\mu = 2.00$. **(b)** Distribution C: $\sigma = 1.414$. Distribution D: $\sigma = 1.095$. **(c)** Distribution C is uniform and symmetric; D is unimodal and symmetric. Means are the same but variances are different.

4 (a) 2.00 **(b)** 1.18321596.

6 (d) \$–0.167 for each method of play.

8 (a) \$90 **(b)** \$30 **(c)** 126.10 **(d)** 10.95 **(e)** –1300 **(f)** \$120 **(g)** 115.84.

10 (a) $E(P) = \$56$ $\sigma_P = \$37.47$ $CV = 66.91\%$ **(b)** $E(P) = \$84$ $CV = 63.93\%$ **(c)** $CV = 14.29\%$.

12 (a) \$71 **(b)** \$97 **(c)** 61.88 **(d)** 84.27 **(e)** 5113 **(f)** Stock *Y* gives the investor a higher expected return than stock *X*, but also has a higher standard deviation. A risk-averse investor should invest in stock *X*, but an investor willing to sustain a higher risk can expect a higher return from stock *Y*. **(g)** $E(P) = \$94.40$ $\sigma_P = 81.92$ **(h)** $E(P) = \$89.20$ $\sigma_P = 77.28$ **(i)** $E(P) = \$84.00$ $\sigma_P = 72.73$ **(j)** $E(P) = \$78.80$ $\sigma_P = 68.2$ **(k)** $E(P) = \$73.60$ $\sigma_P = 63.98$ **(l)** Based on the results of (g)–(k), you should recommend a portfolio with 10% stock *X* and 90% stock *Y* if you make the decision solely on the expected return but recognize that as your expected return increases, so does the portfolio risk.

14 (a) 0.5997 **(b)** 0.0016 **(c)** 0.0439 **(d)** 0.4018 **(e)** 0.3874.

16 0.0312.

18 (a) An operational definition of *aware* can be "remembering having seen the commercials on TV." **(b)** Since the 68% and 24% figures are obtained from the survey results conducted by the networks, they are best classified as empirical classical probability. **(c)** 0.000014 **(d)** 0.9721 **(e)** 0.3426 **(f)** 0.000447 **(g)** 13.6 **(h) (c)** 0.4561 **(d)** 0.0103 **(e)** 0.0000022 **(f)** 0.00000 **(g)** 4.8

20 (a) 0.0010 **(b)** 0.0156 **(c)** 0.2373 **(d)** 0.8965 **(e)** Two assumptions: (1) Independence of her answers, (2) Only two outcomes—answer correct or answer incorrect. **(f)** Mean = 1.25, standard deviation = 0.968 **(g)** 0.00000016 or 1.6423×10^{-7}.

22 (a) 0.2381 **(b)** 0.2 **(c)** 0.1591 **(d)** 0.0083.

24 (a) 0.4691 **(b)** 0.5854 **(c)** 0.0279 **(d)** 0.1090 **(e)** The probability that the entire group will be audited is very sensitive to the true number of improper returns in the population. If the true number is very low ($A = 5$), the probability is very low (0.0279). When the true number is increased by a factor of six ($A = 30$), the probability the group will be audited increases by a factor of almost 21 (0.5854).

26 (a) 1.31E-06 **(b)** 0.080192 **(c)** 0.9198 **(d)** 2.28E-06; 0.3128; 0.6872.

28 (a) 0.4396 **(b)** 0.8462 **(c)** 0.9231 **(d)** 1.33.

30 (a) 0.5940 **(b)** 0.9863 **(c)** 0.9098 **(d)** 0.9817 **(e)** 0.2650.

32 (a) For the number of phone calls received in a 1-hour period to be distributed as a Poisson random variable, we need to assume that (i) the probability that a phone call is received in a given 1-hour period is the same for all the other 1-hour periods, (ii) the number of phone calls received in a given 1-hour period is independent of the number of phone calls received in any other 1-hour period, (iii) the probability that two or more phone calls received in a time period approaches zero as the duration of the time period becomes smaller. **(b)** 0.6703 **(c)** 0.2681 **(d)** 0.0536 **(e)** 0.0079 **(f)** 0.99994. A maximum of four phone calls will be received in a 1-hour period 99.99% of the time.

34 (a) 0.285057 **(b)** 0.160623 **(c)** 0.714943 **(d)** 0.294476 **(e) (a)** 0.440493 **(b)** 0.17546 **(c)** 0.559507 **(d)** 0.350935.

36 (a) 0.00623 **(b)** 0.01499 **(c)** 0.99377 **(d)** 0.97877.

44 (a) 0.006047 **(b)** 0.040311 **(c)** 0.120932 **(d)** 0.16729 **(e)** 0.000105 **(f)** The probability is essentially zero that all 10 automatically opt to talk to a live operator if the probability that a randomly selected caller will automatically opt to go to a live operator is 40%. Hence, the 40% figure given in the article does not appear to apply to this particular system.

46 (a) 0.121577 **(b)** 0.28518 **(c)** 0.593244 **(d)** 1.9, 1.240564 **(e) (a)** 0.018228 **(b)** 0.089782 **(c)** 0.89199 **(d)** 3.3, 1.486943.

48 (a) 0.000272 **(b)** 0.228878 **(c)** 0.469581 **(d)** 0.530419 **(e)** 0.240703 **(f)** 4.4.

50 (a) The assumptions needed to model the number of surveys returned by the binomial distribution are (i) the probability of each returned response is the same and (ii) the result of one returned response does not affect the result of the other. **(b)** 32.6 **(c)** 4.6875 **(d)** 0.3308 **(e)** 0.0626 **(f)** 0.0478 **(g)** 0.4778 **(h) (a)** The assumptions needed to model the number of surveys returned by the binomial distribution are (i) the probability of each returned response is the same and (ii) the result of one returned response does not affect the result of the other. **(b)** 40 **(c)** 4.8990 **(d)** 0.0248 **(e)** 0.0012 **(f)** 0.4567 **(g)** 0.1647.

52 (a) 0.74 **(b)** 0.74 **(c)** 0.3898 **(d)** 0.0012 **(e)** Stock prices tend to rise in the years when the economy is expanding and fall in the years of recession or contraction. Hence, the probability that the price will rise in one year is not likely to be independent from year to year.

54 (a) $7.39941 \cdot 10^{-9}$ **(b)** 3.84769E-7 **(c)** 1.73886E-6 **(d)** 0.0001704084 **(e)** 0.001199814 **(f)** 0.004159356 **(g)** 0.006598978 **(h)** 0.019230769 **(i)** 0.968638543

56 (a) 0.67032 **(b)** 0.26813 **(c)** 0.06155 **(d)** 0.00006 **(e)** 0.85214 **(f)** 0.13634 **(g)** 0.01151 **(h)** 0.00000

Excel Handbook for Some Important Discrete Probability Distributions

EH1 CALCULATING PORTFOLIO EXPECTED RETURN AND PORTFOLIO RISK

To calculate the portfolio expected return and the portfolio risk of two investments, implement a worksheet that features the **SUMPRODUCT** function. This function is entered as **SUMPRODUCT(*multiplier cell range, multiplicand cell range*)**, where *multiplier cell range* is the cell range containing the probabilities, and *multiplicand cell range* is the cell range containing the outcomes for one of the discrete random variables.

Tables EH1 and Table EH2 contain the design for a Portfolio worksheet that generates an analysis based on the data of Table 2. When implementing this design, enter the formula for cell B25, which has been typeset in the table as two lines as one continuous line, and leave rows 1 through 9 in columns E through I blank.

Table EH1
Portfolio sheet design for columns A through D

	A	B	C	D
1	Investment Decision Analysis			
2				
3	Probabilities & Outcomes:	P	X	Y
4		0.2	−100	200
5		0.5	100	50
6		0.3	250	−100
7				
8	Weight Assigned to X	0.5		
9				
10	Statistics			
11	E(X)	=SUMPRODUCT(B4:B6, C4:C6)		
12	E(Y)	=SUMPRODUCT(B4:B6, D4:D6)		
13	Variance(X)	=SUMPRODUCT(B4:B6, G13:G15)		
14	Standard Deviation(X)	=SQRT(B13)		
15	Variance(Y)	=SUMPRODUCT(B4:B6, H13:H15)		
16	Standard Deviation(Y)	=SQRT(B15)		
17	Covariance(XY)	=SUMPRODUCT(B4:B6, I13:I15)		
18	Variance(X + Y)	=B13 + B15 + 2 * B17		
19	Standard Deviation(X + Y)	=SQRT(B18)		
20				
21	Portfolio Management			
22	Weight Assigned to X	=B8		
23	Weight Assigned to Y	=1 – B22		
24	Portfolio Expected Return	=B22 * B11 + B23 * B12		
25	Portfolio Risk	=SQRT(B22 ^2 * B13 + B23 ^2 * B15 + 2 * B22 * B23 * B17)		

Table EH2
Portfolio sheet design for cell range E10:I15 (other cells in columns E through I are blank)

	E	F	G	H	I
10	Calculations Area				
11	For variance and standard deviation:				For covariance:
12	X – mu	Y – mu	(X – mu)^2	(Y – mu)^2	(X – mu)(Y – mu)
13	=C4 – $B$11	=D4 – $B$12	=E13 ^2	=F13 ^2	=E13 * F13
14	=C5 – $B$11	=D5 – $B$12	=E14 ^2	=F14 ^2	=E14 * F14
15	=C6 – $B$11	=D6 – $B$12	=E15 ^2	=F15 ^2	=E15 * F15

The worksheet design can be adjusted for problems that have either two or more than three conditions. When implementing the worksheet design, make the appropriate adjustments given below.

For two conditions. Select cell range **E15:I15** and then select **Edit | Delete**. Select row **5** (click on the legend 5 on the left edge of the worksheet). Select **Edit | Delete**.

For more than three conditions. Select row **5**. Select **Insert | Rows**. Repeat **Insert | Rows** for as many additional times as is needed. Select the cell range **E15:I15** and copy the range down to as many additional rows as there are additional possibilities. (For example, for two additional possibilities, copy the range down 2 rows to rows 16 and 17.)

EH2 CALCULATING BINOMIAL PROBABILITIES

To calculate binomial probabilities, implement a worksheet that features the **BINOMDIST** function. This function is entered as **BINOMDIST(*X, n, p, cumulative*)**, where X is the number of successes, n is the sample size, p is the probability of success, and *cumulative* is a True or False value in which True causes the function to calculate the probability of X or fewer successes and False, the probability of exactly X successes.

Tables EH3 and EH4 contain the design for a **Binomial** worksheet in which $n = 4$ and $p = 0.1$, similar to one shown in Figure 2. When implementing this design, enter the labels for cells A5 and A10 and the formulas for cell range C14:D18 as single continuous lines. (These entries have been typeset in Table EH4 as two lines each.) To enter the formulas in the probabilities table, enter the formulas for cell range C14:G14 first and then copy this set of five formulas down to row 18. (Cell ranges that are not shown in the tables, such as C1:G11, should be left empty.)

The worksheet design can be adjusted to calculate binomial probabilities for different sample sizes. Copy row 18 entries down additional rows to expand the probabilities table for larger sample sizes, or delete table rows, starting with row 18, for smaller sample sizes.

Table EH3
Binomial sheet design for cell range A1:B10

	A	B
1	Binomial Probabilities	
2		
3	Data	
4	Sample size	4
5	Probability of success	0.1
6		
7	Statistics	
8	Mean	=B4 * B5
9	Variance	=B8 * (1 – B5)
10	Standard deviation	=SQRT(B9)

	A	B	C	D	E	F	G
12	Binomial Probabilities Table						
13		X	P(X)	P(<= X)	P(<X)	P(>X)	P(>= X)
14		0	=BINOMDIST(B14, $B$4, $B$5, FALSE)	=BINOMDIST(B14, $B$4, $B$5, True)	=D14 – C14	=1 – D14	=1 – E14
15		1	=BINOMDIST(B15, $B$4, $B$5, FALSE)	=BINOMDIST(B15, $B$4, $B$5, True)	=D15 – C15	=1 – D15	=1 – E15
16		2	=BINOMDIST(B16, $B$4, $B$5, FALSE)	=BINOMDIST(B16, $B$4, $B$5, True)	=D16 – C16	=1 – D16	=1 – E16
17		3	=BINOMDIST(B17, $B$4, $B$5, FALSE)	=BINOMDIST(B17, $B$4, $B$5, True)	=D17 – C17	=1 – D17	=1 – E17
18		4	=BINOMDIST(B18, $B$4, $B$5, FALSE)	=BINOMDIST(B18, $B$4, $B$5, True)	=D18 – C18	=1 – D18	=1 – E18

Table EH4
Binomial sheet design for cell range A12:B10

EH3 CALCULATING HYPERGEOMETRIC PROBABILITIES

To calculate hypergeometric probabilities, implement a worksheet that features the **HYPGEOMDIST** function, This function is entered as **HYPGEOMDIST(*X, n, A, N*)**, where *X* is the number of successes, *n* is the sample size, *A* is the number of successes in the population, and *N* is the population size.

Table EH5 contains the partial design for a **Hypergeometric** worksheet for the management team organization problem discussed earlier. When implementing the probabilities table portion of this design, enter the formula in the cell C10 first and then copy it down to row 18 (rows 12 through 16 are not shown in Table EH5).

This design can be adjusted for other values of the number of successes by either expanding or contracting the probabilities table. Copy row 18 entries down additional rows to expand the probabilities table, or delete table rows, starting with row 18, to contract the table.

Table EH5
Hypergeometric sheet design

	A	B	C
1	Hypergeometric Probabilities		
2			
3	Data		
4	Sample size	8	
5	No. of successes in population	10	
6	Population size	30	
7			
8	Hypergeometric Probabilities Table		
9		X	P(X)
10		0	=HYPGEOMDIST(B10, $B$4, $B$5, $B$6)
11		1	=HYPGEOMDIST(B11, $B$4, $B$5, $B$6)
⋮	⋮	⋮	⋮
17		7	=HYPGEOMDIST(B17, $B$4, $B$5, $B$6)
18		8	=HYPGEOMDIST(B18, $B$4, $B$5, $B$6)

EH4 CALCULATING POISSON PROBABILITIES

To calculate Poisson probabilities, implement a worksheet that features the **POISSON** function. This function is entered as **POISSON(*X, lambda, cumulative*)**, where *X* is the number of successes, *lambda* is the average or expected number of successes, and *cumulative* is a True or False value in which True causes the function to calculate the probability of *X* or fewer successes and False, the probability of exactly *X* successes.

Table EH6 contains the partial design for a **Poisson** worksheet for the bank customer arrivals problem of section 5. When implementing this design, enter the formulas for columns C and D as one continuous line using the mix of relative and absolute addresses as shown in the design table. (These formulas in the table have been typeset as two lines.) To enter the formulas in the probabilities table, enter the formulas for cell range C8:G8 first and then copy the set of five formulas down to row 23 (rows 10 through 21 are not shown in Table EH6).

To enhance the readability of the table of numbers, adjust the formatting of the table numbers, as necessary.

This design arbitrarily limits the number of successes to 15, a reasonable value when the average or expected number of successes is 3. The worksheet design can be modified for other values for the number of successes by either expanding or contracting the probabilities table. Copy row 23 entries down additional rows to expand the probabilities table, or delete table rows, starting with row 23, to contract the table.

Table EH6
Poisson sheet design

	A	B	C	D	E	F	G
1	Poisson Probabilities						
2							
3	Data						
4	Average/Expected number of successes:				3		
5							
6	Poisson Probabilities Table						
7		X	P(X)	P(<= X)	P(<X)	P(>X)	P(>= X)
8		0	=POISSON(B8, $E$4, FALSE)	=POISSON(B8, $E$4, True)	=D8 – C8	=1 – D8	=1 – E8
9		1	=POISSON(B9, $E$4, FALSE)	=POISSON(B9, $E$4, True)	=D9 – C9	=1 – D9	=1 – E9
⋮	⋮	⋮	⋮	⋮	⋮	⋮	⋮
22		14	=POISSON(B22, $E$4, FALSE)	=POISSON(B22, $E$4, True)	=D22 – C22	=1 – D22	=1 – E22
23		3	=POISSON(B23, $E$4, FALSE)	=POISSON(B23, $E$4, True)	=D23 – C23	=1 – D23	=1 – E23

EH5 GENERATING HISTOGRAMS FOR DISCRETE PROBABILITY DISTRIBUTIONS

To generate a histogram for a discrete probability distribution, use the Chart Wizard with one of the three worksheets (Binomial, Hypergeometric, or Poisson) discussed in the previous three sections. To produce histograms for the example used in those sections, open to the worksheet you want to use, select **Insert | Chart** and make these entries in the Chart Wizard dialog boxes, using Table EH7 for the Step 2 dialog box entries:

Step 1 dialog box. Select the **Standard Types** tab and then select **Column** from the **Chart type** list box. Select the first **Chart sub-type** choice, labeled as **Clustered Column** when selected, and click the **Next** button.

Step 2 dialog box. Select the **Data Range** tab. Enter the appropriate cell range from Table EH7 in the **Data range** edit box and select the **Columns** option button in the **Series in** group. Select the **Series** tab. Enter the appropriate *formula* from Table EH7 in the **Category (X) axis labels** edit box using the *Sheetname!CellRange* format shown in Table EH7 and click **Next**.

Step 3 dialog box. Select the **Titles** tab. Enter a title in the **Chart title** edit box, enter **Number of Successes (X)** in **Category (X) axis** edit box, and enter **P(X)** in the **Value (Y) axis** edit box. Select, in turn, the **Axes**, **Gridlines**, **Legend**, **Data Labels**, and **Data Table** tabs and adjust settings as discussed in Exhibit EP6 in the Excel Primer, and click **Next**. (Consult your instructor if you require the Excel Primer.)

Step 4 dialog box. Select the **As new sheet** option button, enter a descriptive and unique sheet name, and click the **Finish** button to generate the chart.

Because this distribution is for a discrete random variable, the bars on the histograms should be drawn as spikes. This can be approximated in the new histogram by doing the following:

Right-click one of the histogram bars. (The mouse pointer is over a bar when a tool tip that includes the word "Series" is displayed.)

Select **Format Data Series** from the shortcut menu.

In the Format Data Series dialog box, click the **Options** tab and change the value in the **Gap width** edit box to **500** and click the **OK** button.

Table EH7
Step 2 dialog box entries when using the Binomial, Hypergeometric, or Poisson worksheets

Worksheet Used	Data Range Edit Box	Category (X) Axis Labels Edit Box
Binomial	C14:C18	=Binomial!B14:B18
Hypergeometric	C10:C18	=Hypergeometric!B10:B18
Poisson	C8:C23	=Poisson!B8:B23

The Normal Distribution and Other Continuous Distributions

LEARNING OBJECTIVES

- To compute probabilities from the normal distribution
- To use the normal probability plot to determine whether a set of data is approximately normally distributed
- To compute probabilities from the uniform distribution
- To compute probabilities from the exponential distribution
- To understand the concept of the sampling distribution
- To compute probabilities related to the sample mean and the sample proportion
- To understand the importance of the central limit theorem

USING STATISTICS

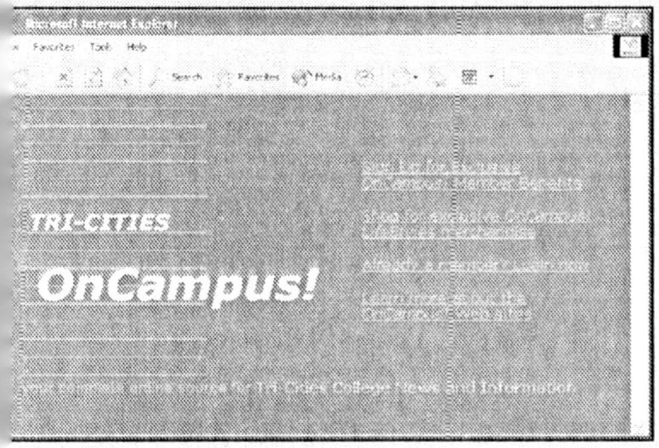

Download Time for a Web Site Home Page

You are the Web site designer for On Campus!, an electronic portal membership Web site aimed at current college students. To attract and retain users, it is also imperative that the home page of this site downloads quickly. Depending on the design of the home page and the load on the company's Web server, the download time will vary. To check how fast the home page loads, you open a Web browser on a PC at the headquarters of On Campus! and measure the download time, that is, the time it takes for the home page to be fully displayed in the browser. Past data indicate that the mean download time is 7 seconds and the standard deviation is 2 seconds. Approximately two-thirds of the download times are between 5 and 9 seconds, and about 95% of the download times are between 3 and 11 seconds. In other words, the length of time it takes to download the home page is distributed as a bell-shaped curve with a clustering around the mean of 7 seconds. How can you use this information to answer questions about the current home page, such as what proportion of the home page downloads take more than 10 seconds? How many seconds elapse before 10% of the downloads are complete? Before 99% are complete? If the home page is redesigned to download faster, how does this change the answers to these questions?

INTRODUCTION

Numerical random variables are classified as either discrete or continuous. You may have already discussed discrete random variables (i.e., those arising from a counting process), and in this chapter, continuous random variables are discussed. **Continuous random variables** arise from a measuring process where the response can take on any value within a continuum or interval. Examples include the weight of a product, time to download a Web page, advertising expenditures, sales revenues, customer servicing times, and the time between customers arriving at a bank.

The mathematical expression that defines the distribution of the values for a continuous random variable is called a **continuous probability density function**. Figure 1 graphically displays the three continuous probability density functions introduced in this chapter. Panel A depicts a normal distribution. The normal distribution is symmetric and bell-shaped, implying that most values tend to cluster around the mean, which, due to its symmetric shape, is equal to the median. Although the values in a normal distribution can range from negative infinity to positive infinity, the shape of the distribution makes it very unlikely that extremely large or extremely small values will occur. Panel B depicts a uniform distribution where the probability of occurrence of a value is equally likely to occur anywhere in the range between the smallest value a and the largest value b. Sometimes referred to as the rectangular distribution, the uniform distribution is symmetric and therefore the mean equals the median. An exponential distribution is illustrated in panel C. This distribution is skewed to the right, making the mean larger than the median. The range for an exponential distribution is zero to positive infinity but note that its shape makes the occurrence of extremely large values unlikely.

1 THE NORMAL DISTRIBUTION

The most common continuous distribution used in statistics is the **normal distribution**. Sometimes referred to as the *Gaussian* distribution, the normal distribution is represented by the classic bell-shape depicted in panel A of Figure 1. The probability that various values occur within certain ranges or intervals of the normal distribution can be calculated. However, the *exact* probability of a *particular value* from a continuous distribution is zero. This is what distinguishes continuous vari-

FIGURE 1
Three Continuous Distributions

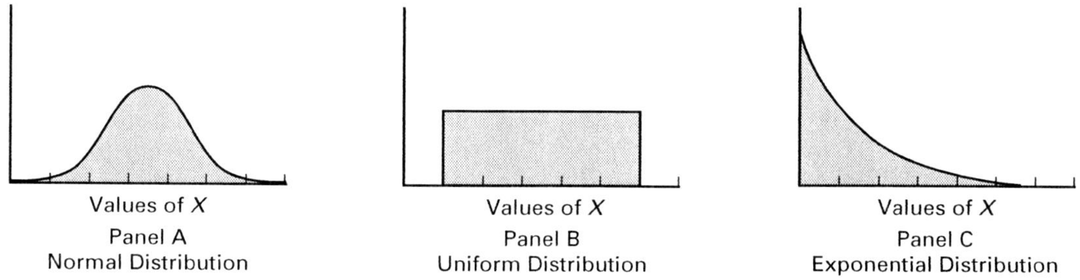

ables, which are measured, from discrete variables, which are counted. As an example, time (in seconds) is measured, not counted. Thus, the probability that the download time for a home page on a Web browser is between 7 and 10 seconds can be computed. Narrowing this interval, the probability that the download time is between 8 and 9 seconds can be computed. The probability that the download time is between 7.99 and 8.01 seconds can also be computed. However, the probability that the download time is *exactly* 8 seconds is zero.

Obtaining probabilities or computing expected values and standard deviations for continuous variables involves mathematical expressions that require a knowledge of integral calculus and are beyond the scope of this book. Nevertheless, the normal distribution is considered so important for applications that special probability tables have been devised to eliminate the need for what would otherwise require laborious mathematical computations. The normal distribution is vitally important in statistics for three main reasons:

1. Numerous continuous variables common in the business world have distributions that closely resemble the normal distribution.
2. The normal distribution can be used to approximate various discrete probability distributions (see section 6.8 on the CD-ROM).
3. The normal distribution provides the basis for *classical statistical inference* because of its relationship to the *central limit theorem* (which is discussed in section 6).

The normal distribution has several important theoretical properties, as illustrated in Exhibit 1.

EXHIBIT 1 PROPERTIES OF THE NORMAL DISTRIBUTION

There are four key properties associated with the normal distribution:

1. It is bell-shaped (and thus symmetrical) in its appearance.
2. Its measures of central tendency (mean, median, and mode) are all identical.
3. Its "middle spread" is equal to 1.33 standard deviations. This means that the interquartile range is contained within an interval of two-thirds of a standard deviation below the mean to two-thirds of a standard deviation above the mean.
4. Its associated random variable has an infinite range ($-\infty < X < \infty$).

In practice, many variables have distributions that only approximate the theoretical properties of the normal distribution given in Exhibit 1. As a case in point, refer to Table 1.

The data in Table 1 represent the thickness (in inches) of 10,000 brass washers manufactured by a large company. The continuous variable of interest, thickness, can be approximated by the normal distribution. The measurements of the thickness of the 10,000 brass washers cluster in the interval 0.0190 to 0.0192 inch and distribute symmetrically around that grouping, forming a "bell-shaped" pattern. As demonstrated in this table, if the nonoverlapping (*mutually exclusive*) listing contains all possible class intervals (is *collectively exhaustive*), the probabilities will sum to 1. Such a probability distribution can be considered as a relative frequency distribution, where, except for the two open-ended classes, the midpoint of every other class interval represents the data in that interval.

TABLE 1
Thickness of 10,000 brass washers

Thickness (inches)	Relative Frequency
Under 0.0180	48/10,000 = 0.0048
0.0180 < 0.0182	122/10,000 = 0.0122
0.0182 < 0.0184	325/10,000 = 0.0325
0.0184 < 0.0186	695/10,000 = 0.0695
0.0186 < 0.0188	1,198/10,000 = 0.1198
0.0188 < 0.0190	1,664/10,000 = 0.1664
0.0190 < 0.0192	1,896/10,000 = 0.1896
0.0192 < 0.0194	1,664/10,000 = 0.1664
0.0194 < 0.0196	1,198/10,000 = 0.1198
0.0196 < 0.0198	695/10,000 = 0.0695
0.0198 < 0.0200	325/10,000 = 0.0325
0.0200 < 0.0202	122/10,000 = 0.0122
0.0202 or above	48/10,000 = 0.0048
Total	1.0000

Figure 2 depicts the relative frequency histogram and polygon for the distribution of the thickness of 10,000 brass washers. For these data, the first three theoretical properties of the normal distribution seem to be satisfied; however, the fourth does not hold. The random variable of interest, thickness, cannot possibly take on values of zero or below, and a washer cannot be so thick that it becomes unusable. From Table 1 above note that only 48 out of every 10,000 brass washers manufactured are expected to have a thickness of 0.0202 inch or more, whereas an equal number are expected to have a thickness under 0.0180 inch. Thus, the chance of randomly obtaining a washer so thin or so thick is 0.0048 + 0.0048 = 0.0096—or less than 1 in 100.

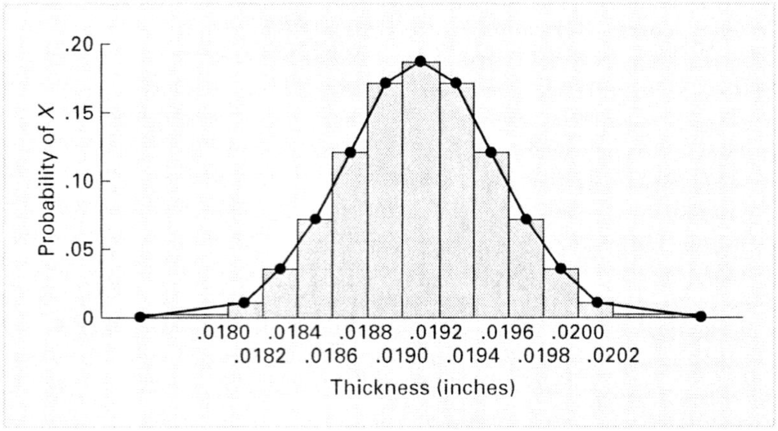

FIGURE 2
Relative frequency histogram and polygon of the thickness of 10,000 brass washers
Source: Data are taken from Table 1 above.

The mathematical model or expression representing a probability density function is denoted by the symbol $f(X)$. For the normal distribution, the **normal probability density function** is given in Equation (1).

THE NORMAL PROBABILITY DENSITY FUNCTION

$$f(X) = \frac{1}{\sqrt{2\pi}\sigma} e^{-(1/2)[(X-\mu)/\sigma]^2} \quad (1)$$

where

e is the mathematical constant approximated by 2.71828
π is the mathematical constant approximated by 3.14159
μ is the population mean
σ is the population standard deviation
X is any value of the continuous variable, where $(-\infty < X < \infty)$

Note that because e and π are mathematical constants, the probabilities of the random variable X are dependent only on the two parameters of the normal distribution—the population mean μ and the population standard deviation σ. Every time a *particular combination* of μ and σ is specified, a *different* normal probability distribution is generated. Figure 3 illustrates three different normal distributions. Distributions A and B have the same mean (μ) but have different standard deviations. On the other hand, distributions A and C have the same standard deviation (σ) but have different means. Furthermore, distributions B and C depict two normal probability density functions that differ with respect to both μ and σ.

FIGURE 3
Three normal distributions having different parameters μ and σ

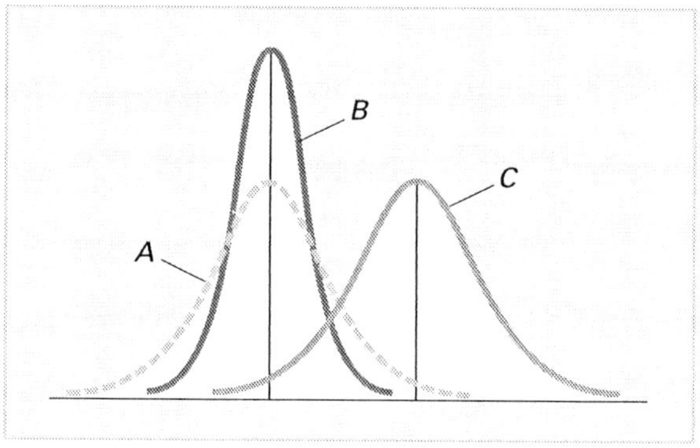

Unfortunately, the mathematical expression in Equation (1) is computationally tedious. To avoid such computations, a set of tables that provide the desired probabilities would be useful. However, because an infinite number of combinations of the parameters μ and σ exist, an infinite number of such tables would be required. By *standardizing* the data, only one table is needed. By the use of the **transformation formula** given in Equation (2), any normal random variable X can be converted to a standardized normal random variable Z.

THE TRANSFORMATION FORMULA

The Z value is equal to the difference between X and the population mean μ, divided by the standard deviation σ.

$$Z = \frac{X - \mu}{\sigma} \tag{2}$$

Although the original data for the random variable X had mean μ and standard deviation σ, the standardized random variable Z will always have mean $\mu = 0$ and standard deviation $\sigma = 1$.

By substituting $\mu = 0$ and $\sigma = 1$ in Equation (1), the probability density function of a standardized normal variable Z is given in Equation (3).

THE STANDARDIZED NORMAL PROBABILITY DENSITY FUNCTION

$$f(Z) = \frac{1}{\sqrt{2\pi}} e^{-(1/2)Z^2} \tag{3}$$

Standardized Normal Distribution
A standardized normal distribution is one whose random variable Z always has a mean $\mu = 0$ and a standard deviation $\sigma = 1$.

Any set of normally distributed data can be converted to its standardized form, and then any desired probabilities can be determined from a table of the **cumulative standardized normal distribution**.

To see how the transformation formula is applied and the results used to find probabilities from the Cumulative Standardized Normal table,[1] the Using Statistics scenario can be examined. Recall that past data indicate that the time to download the Web page is normally distributed with a mean $\mu = 7$ seconds and a standard deviation $\sigma = 2$ seconds.

[1] *This text uses the Cumulative Standardized Normal table. To use the Standardized Normal table see section 6.1a, Using the Standardized Normal Distribution table, on the CD-ROM.*

From Figure 4, observe that every measurement X has a corresponding standardized measurement Z obtained from the transformation formula [Equation (2)]. Therefore, a download time of 9 seconds is equivalent to 1 standardized unit (i.e., 1 standard deviation above the mean) because

$$Z = \frac{9 - 7}{2} = +1$$

and that a download time of 1 second is equivalent to 3 standardized units (i.e. 3 standard deviations) below the mean because

$$Z = \frac{1 - 7}{2} = -3$$

Thus, the standard deviation is the unit of measurement. In other words, a time of 9 seconds is 2 seconds (i.e., 1 standard deviation) higher, or *slower*, than the average time of 7 seconds, and a time of 1 second is 6 seconds (i.e., 3 standard deviations) lower, or *faster*, than the average time.

FIGURE 4
Transformation of scales

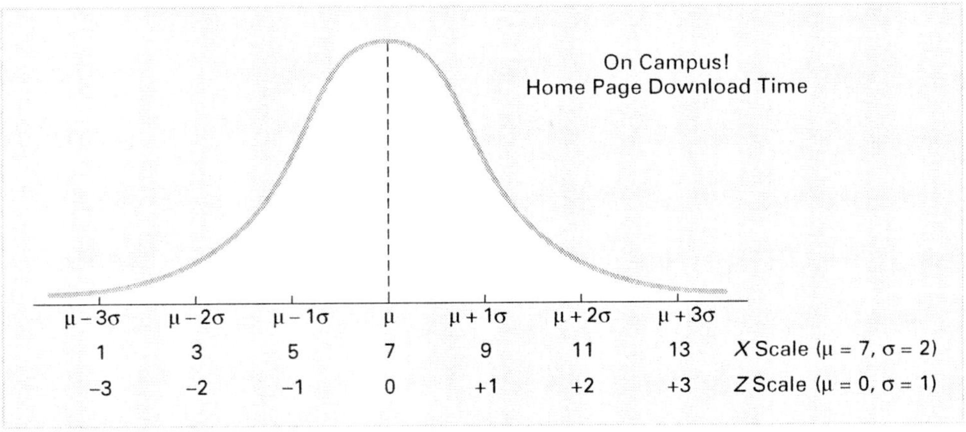

In order to further illustrate the transformation formula, suppose that the home page of another Web site had a download time that was normally distributed with a mean μ of 4 seconds and a standard deviation σ of 1 second. This distribution is depicted in Figure 5.

Comparing these results with those of the On Campus! Web site, observe that a download time of 5 seconds is 1 standard deviation above the average download time because

$$Z = \frac{5 - 4}{1} = +1$$

and a time of 1 second is also 3 standard deviations below the average download time because

$$Z = \frac{1 - 4}{1} = -3$$

The two bell-shaped curves in Figures 4 and 5 depict the relative frequency polygons of the normal distributions representing the download time (in seconds) for the two Web sites. Because the download times represent the entire population, the *probabilities* or proportion of area under the entire curve must add to 1.

FIGURE 5
A different transformation of scales

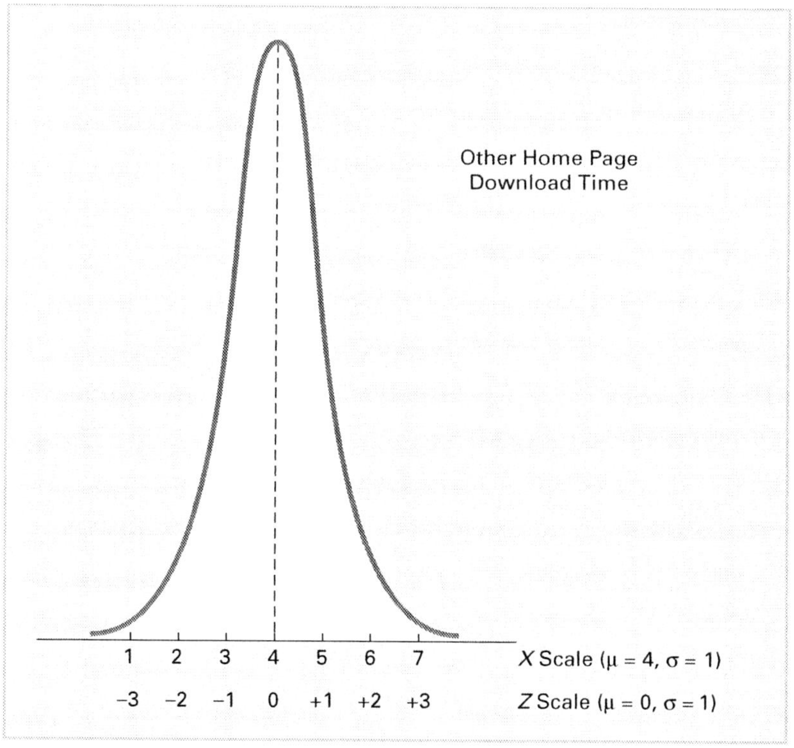

Suppose you wanted to find the probability that the download time for the On Campus! site is less than 9 seconds. Because 9 seconds is one standard deviation above the mean, you need to find the probability that the download time is below +1 standard deviation. The Cumulative Standardized Normal table represents the cumulative probabilities or areas under the normal curve calculated less than (i.e., to the left of) the particular values of interest X. Using Equation (2), this corresponds to the probabilities or areas under the standardized normal curve less than the transformed values of interest Z. To use the Cumulative Standardized Normal table, note that Z values need to be recorded to two decimal places. Thus, the particular Z value of interest is recorded as +1.00. To read the probability or area under the curve less than $Z = +1.00$, scan down the Z column from the Cumulative Standardized Normal table until you locate the Z value of interest (in 10ths) in the Z row for 1.0. Next read across this row until you intersect the column that contains the 100ths place of the Z value. Therefore, in the body of the table, the tabulated probability for $Z = 1.00$ corresponds to the intersection of the row $Z = 1.0$ with the column $Z = .00$ as shown in Table 2 below, which is extracted from the Cumulative Standardized Normal table. This probability is 0.8413. As illustrated in Figure 6, there is an 84.13% chance that the download time will be less than 9 seconds.

TABLE 2
Obtaining a cumulative area under the normal curve

Z	.00	.01	.02	.03	.04	.05	.06	.07	.08	.09
0.0	.5000	.5040	.5080	.5120	.5160	.5199	.5239	.5279	.5319	.5359
0.1	.5398	.5438	.5478	.5517	.5557	.5596	.5636	.5675	.5714	.5753
0.2	.5793	.5832	.5871	.5910	.5948	.5987	.6026	.6064	.6103	.6141
0.3	.6179	.6217	.6255	.6293	.6331	.6368	.6406	.6443	.6480	.6517
0.4	.6554	.6591	.6628	.6664	.6700	.6736	.6772	.6808	.6844	.6879
0.5	.6915	.6950	.6985	.7019	.7054	.7088	.7123	.7157	.7190	.7224
0.6	.7257	.7291	.7324	.7357	.7389	.7422	.7454	.7486	.7518	.7549
0.7	.7580	.7612	.7642	.7673	.7704	.7734	.7764	.7794	.7823	.7852
0.8	.7881	.7910	.7939	.7967	.7995	.8023	.8051	.8078	.8106	.8133
0.9	.8159	.8186	.8212	.8238	.8264	.8289	.8315	.8340	.8365	.8389
1.0 →	.8413	.8438	.8461	.8485	.8508	.8531	.8554	.8577	.8599	.8621

Source: Extracted from the Cumulative Standardized Normal table.

FIGURE 6

Determining the area up to Z from a cumulative standardized normal distribution

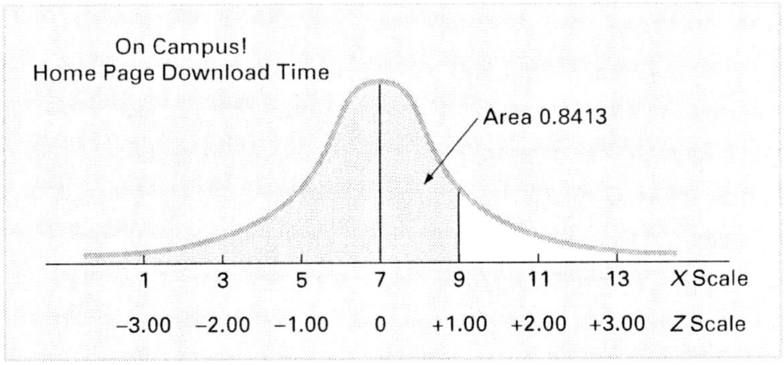

On the other hand, observe from Figure 5 that for the other home page, a time of 5 seconds is 1 standardized unit above the mean time of 4 seconds. Thus, the likelihood that the download time will be less than 5 seconds is also 0.8413. Figure 7 shows that regardless of the value of the mean μ and standard deviation σ of a normally distributed variable, a transformation to a standardized scale can always be made from Equation (2) and, by using the Cumulative Standardized Normal table, any probability or portion of area under the curve can be obtained. From Figure 7 observe that the probability or area under the curve less than 5 seconds for the second home page is identical to the probability or area under the curve less than 9 seconds for the On Campus! home page.

FIGURE 7

Demonstrating a transformation of scales for corresponding portions under two cumulative normal curves

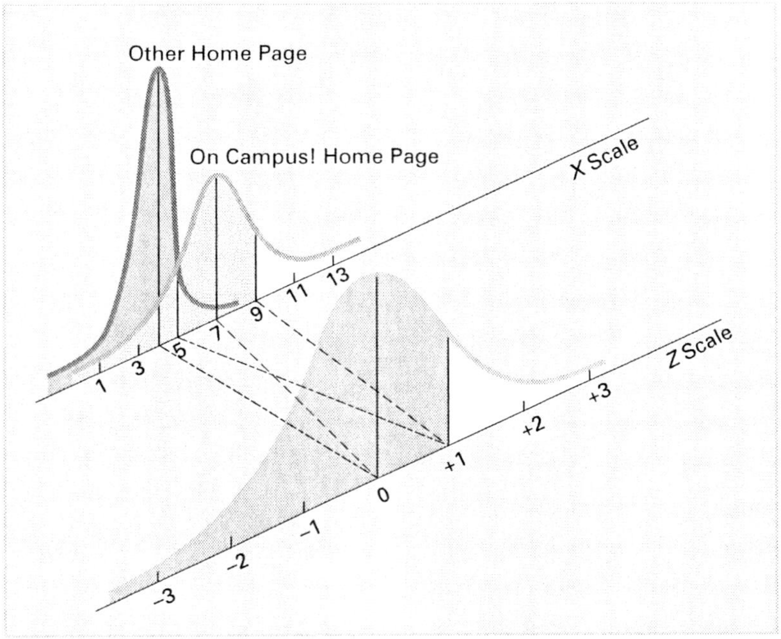

Now that you have learned to use the Cumulative Standardized Normal table in conjunction with Equation (2), many different types of probability questions pertaining to the normal distribution can be answered. Examples 1–7 illustrate this for the On Campus! home page.

EXAMPLE 1

FINDING $P(X > 9)$

What is the probability that the download time will be more than 9 seconds?

SOLUTION

Because the probability that the download time will be less than 9 seconds was already determined from Figure 6 above, the desired probability must be its *complement*, $1 - 0.8413 = 0.1587$. This is depicted in Figure 8.

FIGURE 8
Finding $P(X > 9)$

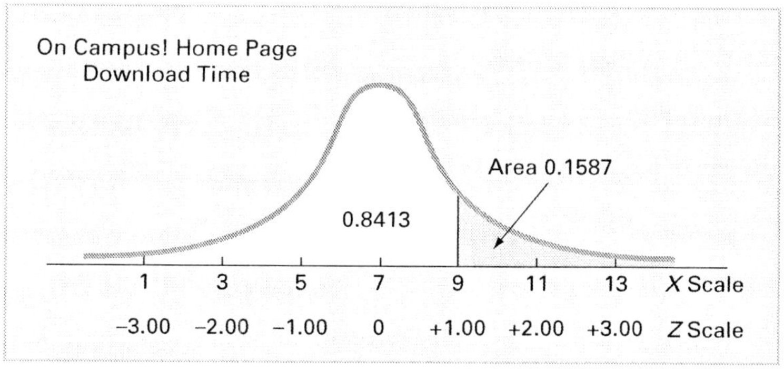

EXAMPLE 2

FINDING $P(7 < X < 9)$

What is the probability that the download time will be between 7 and 9 seconds?

SOLUTION

From Figure 6 you already determined that the probability that a download time will be less than 9 seconds is 0.8413. To obtain the desired results you now must determine the probability that the download time will be under 7 seconds and subtract this from the probability that the download time is under 9 seconds. This is depicted in Figure 9.

FIGURE 9
Finding $P(7 < X < 9)$

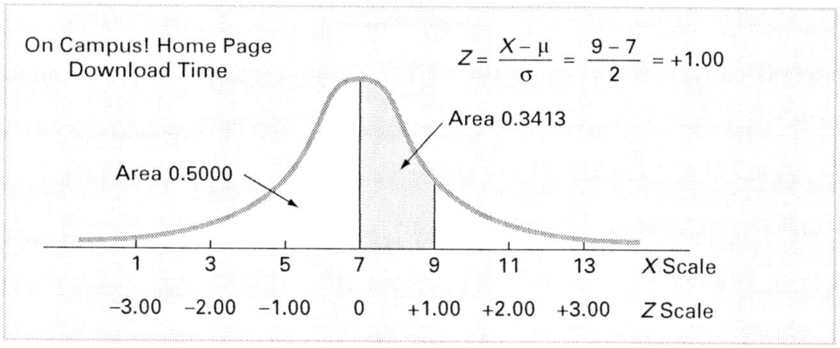

Because the mean and median are theoretically the same for a normally distributed variable, 50% of the download times will be under 7 seconds. To show this, using Equation (2).

$$Z = \frac{7 - 7}{2} = 0.00$$

Using the Cumulative Standardized Normal table, observe the area under the normal curve less than the mean of $Z = 0.00$ is 0.5000. Hence, the area under the curve between $Z = 0.00$ and $Z = 1.00$ must be $0.8413 - 0.5000 = 0.3413$.

EXAMPLE 3

FINDING $P(X < 7 \text{ OR } X > 9)$

What is the probability that the download time is under 7 seconds or over 9 seconds?

SOLUTION

Because the probability is 0.3413 that the download time between 7 and 9 seconds has already been determined, from Figure 9, observe that the probability must be its *complement*, $1 - 0.3413 = 0.6587$.

Another way to view this problem, however, is to separately obtain both the probability of a download time of under 7 seconds and the probability of a download time of over 9 seconds and to then add these two probabilities together to obtain the desired result. This result is depicted in Figure 10. Because the mean and median are theoretically the same for normally distributed data, it follows that 50% of download times are under 7 seconds. From Example 1, the probability of a download time of over 9 seconds is 0.1587. Hence, the probability that a download time is under 7 or over 9 seconds, $P(X < 7 \text{ or } X > 9)$, is $0.5000 + 0.1587 = 0.6587$.

FIGURE 10
Finding $P(X < 7 \text{ or } X > 9)$

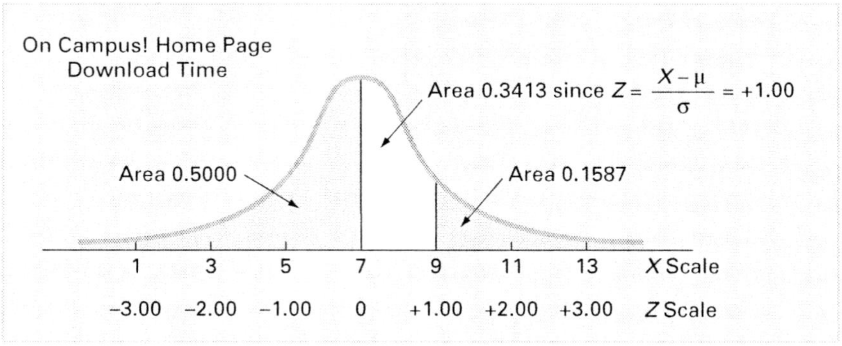

EXAMPLE 4

FINDING $P(5 < X < 9)$

What is the probability that the download time will be between 5 and 9 seconds, that is, $P(5 < X < 9)$?

SOLUTION

Note from Figure 11 that one of the values of interest is above the mean download time of 7 seconds and the other value is below the mean. Because the Cumulative Standardized Normal table permits you only to find probabilities less than a particular value of interest, the desired probability can be found in three steps:

1. Determine the probability of less than 9 seconds.
2. Determine the probability of less than 5 seconds.
3. Subtract the smaller result from the larger.

For this example, you have already completed step 1; the area under the normal curve less than 9 seconds is 0.8413. To find the area under the normal curve less than 5 seconds (step 2),

$$Z = \frac{5-7}{2} = -1.00$$

Using the Cumulative Standardized Normal table, look up the value $Z = -1.00$ and find the probability to be 0.1587. Hence, from step 3, the probability that the download time will be between 5 and 9 seconds is $0.8413 - 0.1587 = 0.6826$, as displayed in Figure 11.

FIGURE 11
Finding $P(5 < X < 9)$

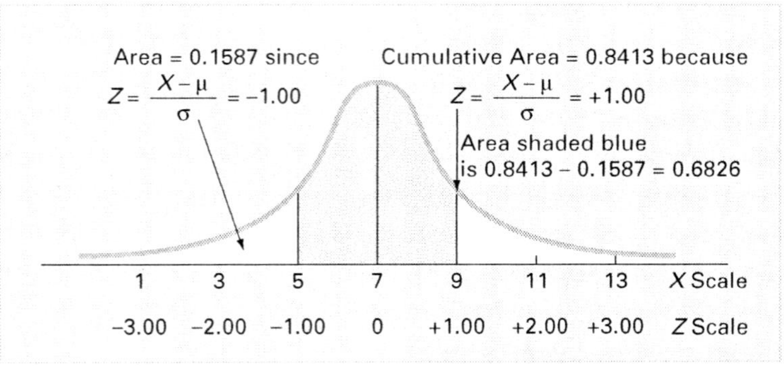

The result of Example 4 is rather important and allows you to generalize the findings.[2] For any normal distribution there is a 0.6826 chance that a randomly selected item will fall within ±1 standard deviation of the mean. From Figure 12, observe that slightly more than 95% of the items will fall within ±2 standard deviations of the mean. Thus, 95.44% of the download times can be expected to be between 3 and 11 seconds. From Figure 13, observe that 99.73% of the items will fall within ±3 standard deviations above or below the mean. Thus, 99.73% of the download times can be expected to be between 1 and 13 seconds. Therefore, it is unlikely (0.0027, or only 27 in 10,000) that a download time will be so fast or so slow that it will take under 1 second or more than 13 seconds. This is why 6σ (i.e., 3 standard deviations above the mean to 3 standard deviations below the mean) is often used as a *practical approximation of the range* for normally distributed data.

[2] *The empirical rule is based on the normal distribution. The closer a data set follows the normal distribution, the more accurate the empirical rule is. If a data set radically differs from a normal distribution, the percentages given by the empirical rule will be grossly inaccurate.*

FIGURE 12
Finding $P(3 < X < 11)$

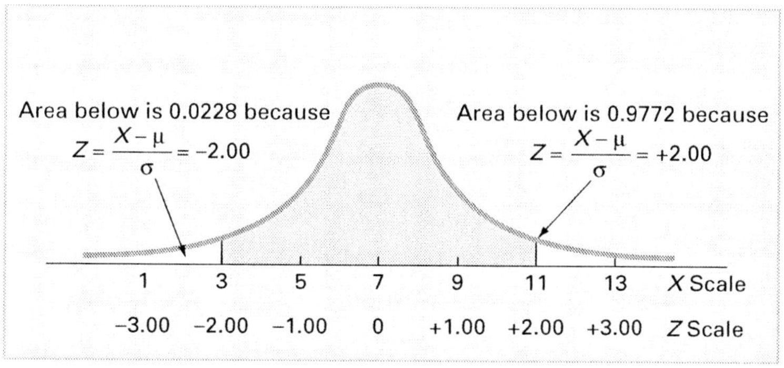

FIGURE 13
Finding $P(1 < X < 13)$

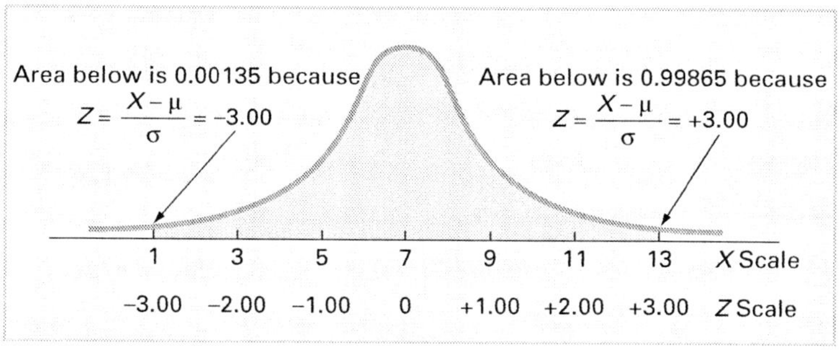

EXAMPLE 5

FINDING $P(X < 3.5)$

What is the probability that a download time will be under 3.5 seconds?

SOLUTION

To obtain the probability that a download time will be under 3.5 seconds, you need to examine the shaded lower left-tail region of Figure 14.

FIGURE 14
Finding $P(X < 3.5)$

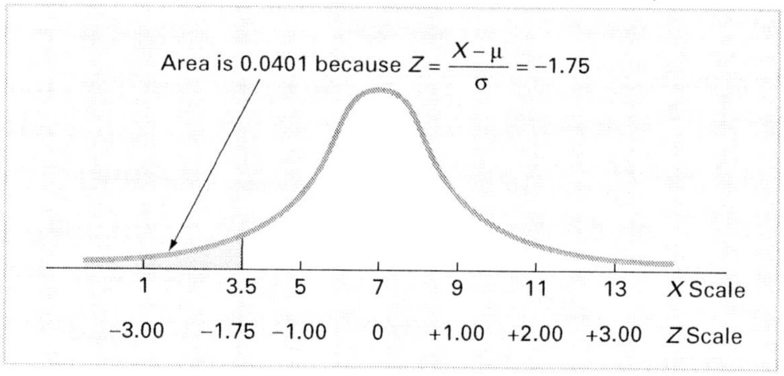

To determine the area under the curve below 3.5 seconds, first calculate

$$Z = \frac{X - \mu}{\sigma} = \frac{3.5 - 7}{2} = -1.75$$

Look up the Z value of -1.75 in the Cumulative Standardized Normal table by matching the appropriate Z row (-1.7) with the appropriate Z column (.05) as shown in Table 3 (which is extracted from the Cumulative Standardized Normal table). The resulting probability or area under the curve less than -1.75 standard deviations below the mean is 0.0401.

TABLE 3

Obtaining a cumulative area under the normal curve

Z	.00	.01	.02	.03	.04	.05	.06	.07	.08	.09
.	.	.	.	.	.		.	.	.	.
.	.	.	.	.	.		.	.	.	.
.	.	.	.	.	.		.	.	.	.
−1.7	.0446	.0436	.0427	.0418	.0409	.0401	.0392	.0384	.0375	.0367
−1.6	.0548	.0537	.0526	.0516	.0505	.0495	.0485	.0475	.0465	.0455

Source: Extracted from the Cumulative Standardized Normal table.

VISUAL EXPLORATIONS: Exploring the Normal Distribution

Use the Visual Explorations Normal Distribution procedure to observe the effects of changes in the arithmetic mean and standard deviation on the area under the curve. Open the **Visual Explorations.xla** macro workbook and select **VisualExplorations | Normal Distribution** from the Microsoft Excel menu bar. The procedure produces a normal curve for the Using Statistics home page download example and a floating control panel that allows you to adjust the shape of the curve and the shaded area under the curve (see illustrations).

Use the spinner buttons in the control panel to change the values for arithmetic mean, standard deviation, and X value, and note their effects on the probability of $X <=$ value and the corresponding shaded area under the curve (see illustration below). Optionally, you can select the **Z Values** option button to see the normal curve labeled with Z Values.

Click the **Reset** button to reset the values of this control panel or click **Help** for more information about the problem. Click **Finish** when you are finished.

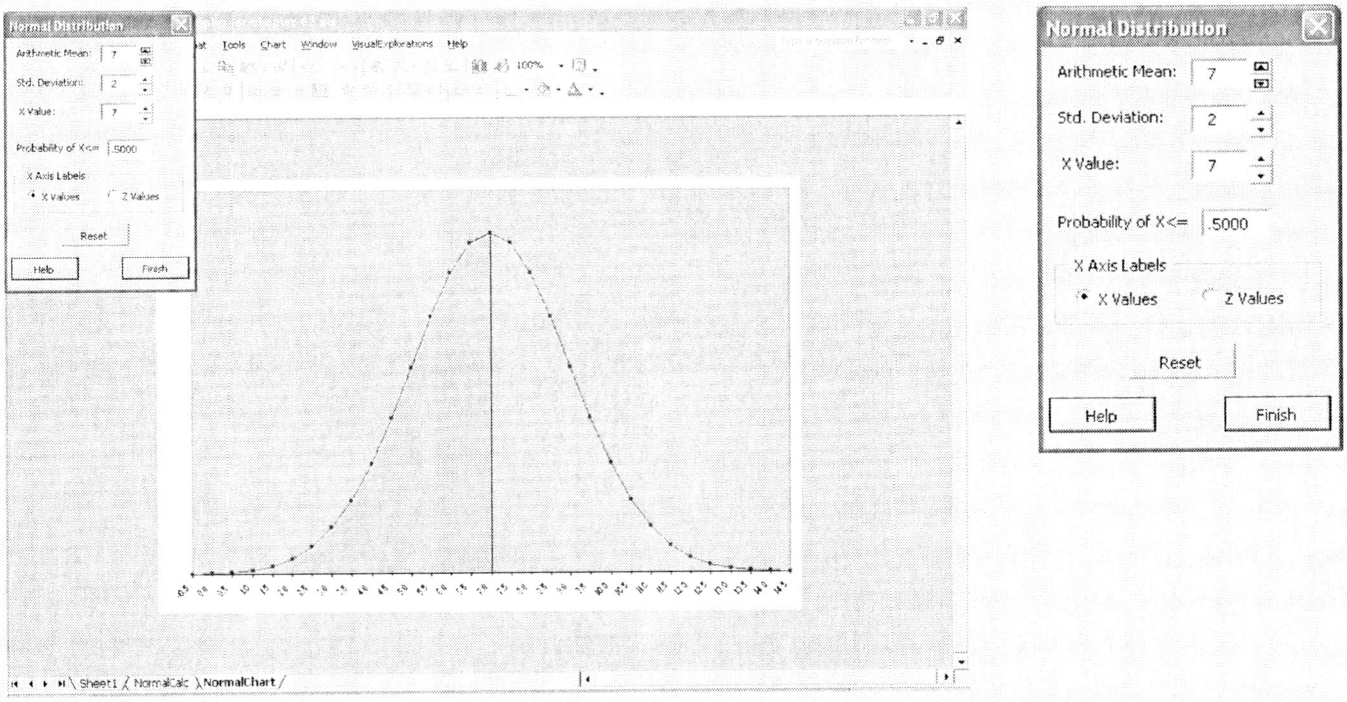

In Examples 1–5 the probabilities associated with various measured values were computed. Examples 6 and 7 illustrate how to determine particular numerical values of the variable of interest that correspond to known probabilities.

EXAMPLE 6

FINDING THE X VALUE FOR A CUMULATIVE PROBABILITY OF 0.10

How much time (in seconds) will elapse before 10% of the downloads are complete?

SOLUTION

Because 10% of the home pages are expected to download in under X seconds, the area under the normal curve less than this Z value must be 0.1000. Using the body of the Cumulative Standardized Normal table, you search for the area or probability of 0.1000. The closest result is 0.1003, as shown in Table 4 (which is extracted from the Cumulative Standardized Normal table).

TABLE 4
Obtaining a Z value corresponding to a particular cumulative area (0.10) under the normal curve

Z	.00	.01	.02	.03	.04	.05	.06	.07	.08	.09
.	.	.	.	.	.	.	.	.	.	.
.	.	.	.	.	.	.	.	.	.	.
.	.	.	.	.	.	.	.	.	.	.
−1.5	.0668	.0655	.0643	.0630	.0618	.0606	.0594	.0582	.0571	.0559
−1.4	.0808	.0793	.0778	.0764	.0749	.0735	.0721	.0708	.0694	.0681
−1.3	.0968	.0951	.0934	.0918	.0901	.0885	.0869	.0853	.0838	.0823
−1.2	.1151	.1131	.1112	.1093	.1075	.0156	.0138	.1020	.1003	.0985

Source: Extracted from the Cumulative Standardized Normal table.

Working from this area to the margins of the table, observe that the Z value corresponding to the particular Z row (−1.2) and Z column (.08) is −1.28 (see Figure 15).

FIGURE 15
Finding Z to determine X

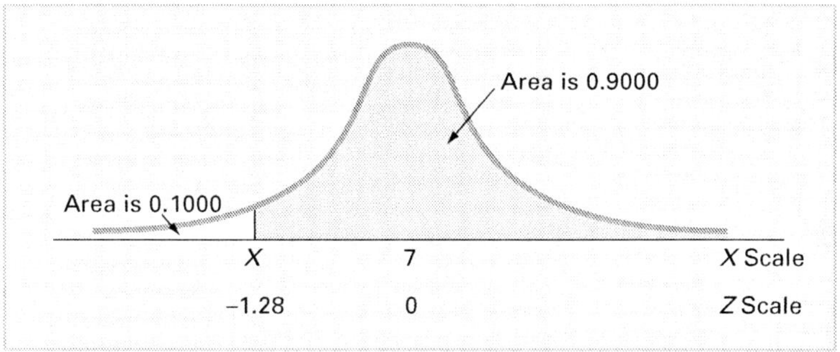

Once Z is obtained, the transformation formula Equation (2) is used to determine the value of interest, X. Let

$$Z = \frac{X - \mu}{\sigma}$$

then

$$Z\sigma = X - \mu$$

and

$$\mu + Z\sigma = X$$

or

$$X = \mu + Z\sigma$$

Substituting $\mu = 7$, $\sigma = 2$, and $Z = -1.28$,

$$X = 7 + (-1.28)(2) = 4.44 \text{ seconds}$$

Thus, you can expect that 10% of the download times will be 4.44 seconds or less.

From Example 6, the X value is defined in Equation (4),

FINDING AN X VALUE ASSOCIATED WITH KNOWN PROBABILITY

The X value is equal to the population mean μ plus the product of the Z value and the standard deviation σ.

$$X = \mu + Z\sigma \qquad \textbf{(4)}$$

To find a *particular* value associated with a known probability, follow the steps as displayed in Exhibit 2.

EXHIBIT 2 FINDING A PARTICULAR VALUE ASSOCIATED WITH A KNOWN PROBABILITY

To find a particular value associated with a known probability:

1. Sketch the normal curve, and then place the values for the means on the respective X and Z scales.
2. Find the cumulative area less than the desired X.
3. Shade the area of interest.
4. Using the Cumulative Standardized Normal table, determine the appropriate Z value corresponding to the area under the normal curve less than the desired X.
5. Using Equation (4), solve for X:

$$X = \mu + Z\sigma$$

EXAMPLE 7

FINDING THE X VALUES THAT INCLUDE 95% OF THE DOWNLOAD TIMES

What are the lower and upper values of X, located symmetrically around the mean, that will include 95% of the download times?

SOLUTION

First, you need to find the lower value of X (called X_L). Then you can find the upper value of X (called X_U). Since 95% of the values will be between X_L and X_U, and X_L and X_U are equal distance from the mean, 2.5% of the values will be below X_L (see Figure 16).

FIGURE 16
Finding Z to determine X_L

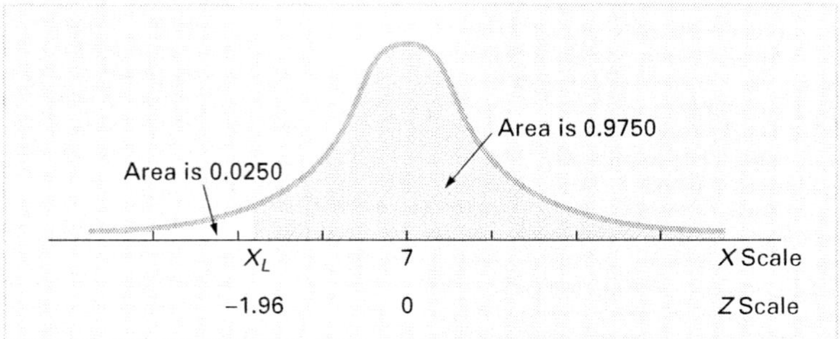

Although X_L is not known, the corresponding standardized value Z can be obtained because the area under the normal curve less than this Z is 0.0250. Using the body of Table 5, search for the probability 0.0250.

TABLE 5
Obtaining a Z value corresponding to a cumulative area of 0.025 under the normal curve

Z	.00	.01	.02	.03	.04	.05	.06	.07	.08	.09
⋮	⋮	⋮	⋮	⋮	⋮	⋮	↑	⋮	⋮	⋮
−2.0	.0228	.0222	.0217	.0212	.0207	.0202	.0197	.0192	.0188	.0183
−1.9	.0287	.0281	.0274	.0268	.0262	.0256	.0250	.0244	.0239	.0233
−1.8	.0359	.0351	.0344	.0336	.0329	.0232	.0314	.0307	.0301	.0294

Source: Extracted from the Cumulative Standardized Normal table.

Working from the body of the table to the margins of the table, observe that the Z value corresponding to the particular Z row (−1.9) and Z column (.06) is −1.96.

Once Z is obtained, the final step is to use Equation (4) as follows,

$$\begin{aligned} X &= \mu + Z\sigma \\ &= 7 + (-1.96)(2) \\ &= 7 - 3.92 \\ &= 3.08 \text{ seconds} \end{aligned}$$

To find X_U, note that only 2.5% of the Web page downloads take longer than X_U seconds, and 97.5% of the Web page download takes less than X_U seconds.

From the symmetry of the normal distribution, the desired Z value as shown in Figure 17 is +1.96 (because Z lies to the right of the standardized mean of 0). However, this Z value can also be extracted from Table 6, since 0.975 of the area under the normal curve is less than the standardized Z value of +1.96.

FIGURE 17
Finding Z to determine X_U

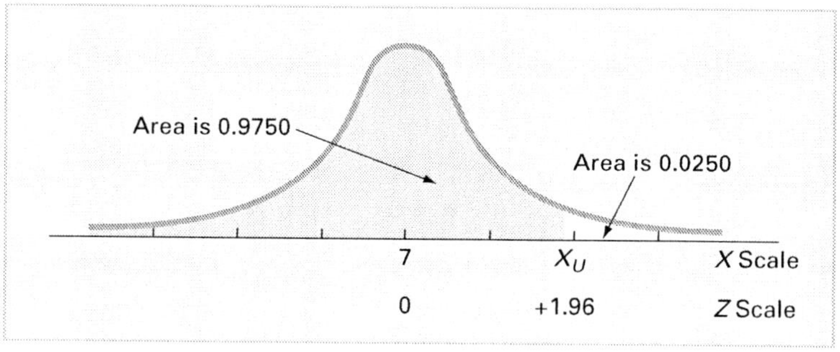

TABLE 6
Obtaining a Z value corresponding to a cumulative area of 0.975 under the normal curve

Z	.00	.01	.02	.03	.04	.05	.06	.07	.08	.09
⋮	⋮	⋮	⋮	⋮	⋮	⋮	↑	⋮	⋮	⋮
+1.8	.9641	.9649	.9656	.9664	.9671	.9678	.9686	.9693	.9699	.9706
+1.9	.9713	.9719	.9726	.9732	.9738	.9744	.9750	.9756	.9761	.9767
+2.0	.9772	.9778	.9783	.9788	.9793	.9798	.9803	.9808	.9812	.9817

Source: Extracted from the Cumulative Standardized Normal table.

Therefore, using Equation (4),

$$\begin{aligned} X &= \mu + Z\sigma \\ &= 7 + (+1.96)(2) \\ &= 7 + 3.92 \\ &= 10.92 \text{ seconds} \end{aligned}$$

Therefore, 95% of the download times will be between 3.08 and 10.92 seconds.

Normal probabilities can also be obtained from Microsoft Excel. Figure 18 illustrates how Microsoft Excel can be used for Examples 1, 2, 3, 5, and 6.

FIGURE 18
Obtaining normal probabilities using Microsoft Excel

	A	B	C	D	E
1	Normal Probabilities				
2					
3	Common Data				
4	Mean	7			
5	Standard Deviation	2			
6				Probability for a Range	
7	Probability for X <=			From X Value	7
8	X Value	3.5		To X Value	9
9	Z Value	-1.75		Z Value for 7	0
10	P(X<=3.5)	0.0400591		Z Value for 9	1
11				P(X<=7)	0.5000
12	Probability for X >			P(X<=9)	0.8413
13	X Value	9		P(7<=X<=9)	0.3413
14	Z Value	1			
15	P(X>9)	0.1587		Find X and Z Given Cum. Pctage.	
16				Cumulative Percentage	10.00%
17	Probability for X<3.5 or X >9			Z Value	-1.281552
18	P(X<3.5 or X >9)	0.1987		X Value	4.436896

CHAPTER 6.xls

Retrieve the Figure 6.18 worksheet of the ***Chapter 6.xls*** *workbook to view a normal probabilities worksheet similar to the one above.*

Excel Strategies Calculating Normal Probabilities

You implement a worksheet that features the **STANDARDIZE**, **NORMDIST**, **NORMSINV**, and **NORMINV** functions to calculate normal probabilities. PHStat2 can construct this worksheet for you in a single step.

For example, to calculate the normal probabilities shown in Figure 18 above, use one of these strategies:

Using Excel with PHStat2

Use the PHStat2 Normal procedure to generate normal probabilities on a new worksheet.

Select **PHStat | Probability & Prob. Distributions | Normal**.

In the Normal Probability Distribution dialog box (shown at right):

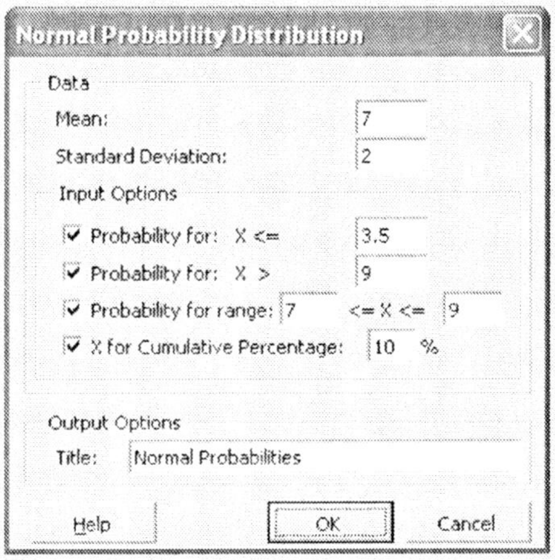

Enter **7** in the **Mean** edit box.

Enter **2** in the **Standard Deviation** edit box.

Select the **Probability for: X <=** check box and enter **3.5** in its edit box (for Example 5).

Select the **Probability for: X >** check box and enter **9** in its edit box (for Examples 1 and 3).

Select the **Probability for range** check box and enter **7** in the "from" and **9** in the "to" edit boxes (for Example 2).

Select the **X for Cumulative Percentage** check box and enter **10** in its edit box (for Example 6).

Enter a title in the **Title** edit box.

Click the **OK** button.

Using Excel

Follow the instructions of section EH1 at the end of this chapter to manually implement a worksheet that uses the STANDARDIZE, NORMDIST, NORMSINV, and NORMINV functions to calculate normal probabilities.

PROBLEMS FOR SECTION 1

Learning the Basics

1 Given a standardized normal distribution (with a mean of 0 and a standard deviation of 1, as in the Cumulative Standardized Normal table), what is the probability that

a. Z is less than 1.57?
b. Z is greater than 1.84?
c. Z is between 1.57 and 1.84?
d. Z is less than 1.57 or greater than 1.84?
e. Z is between −1.57 and 1.84?
f. Z is less than −1.57 or greater than 1.84?
g. What is the value of Z if 50.0% of all possible Z values are larger?
h. What is the value of Z if only 2.5% of all possible Z values are larger?
i. Between what two values of Z (symmetrically distributed around the mean) will 68.26% of all possible Z values be contained?

2 Given a standardized normal distribution (with a mean of 0 and a standard deviation of 1 as in the Cumulative Standardized Normal table), determine the following probabilities:

a. $P(Z > +1.34)$
b. $P(Z < +1.17)$
c. $P(0 < Z < +1.17)$
d. $P(Z < -1.17)$
e. $P(-1.17 < Z < +1.34)$
f. $P(-1.17 < Z < -0.50)$

3 Given a standardized normal distribution (with a mean of 0 and a standard deviation of 1 as in the Cumulative Standardized Normal table), what is the probability that

a. Z is less than +1.08?
b. Z is greater than −0.21?
c. Z is between the mean and +1.08?
d. Z is less than the mean or greater than +1.08?
e. Z is between −0.21 and the mean?
f. Z is less than −0.21 or greater than the mean?
g. Z is between −0.21 and +1.08?
h. Z is less than −0.21 or greater than +1.08?

4 Given a standardized normal distribution (with a mean of 0 and a standard deviation of 1 as in the Cumulative Standardized Normal table), determine the following probabilities:

a. $P(Z > +1.08)$
b. $P(Z < -0.21)$
c. $P(-1.96 < Z < -0.21)$
d. $P(-1.96 < Z < +1.08)$
e. $P(+1.08 < Z < +1.96)$
f. What is the value of Z if 50.0% of all possible Z values are smaller?
g. What is the value of Z if only 15.87% of all possible Z values are smaller?
h. What is the value of Z if only 15.87% of all possible Z values are larger?

5 Given a normal distribution with $\mu = 100$ and $\sigma = 10$, what is the probability that

a. $X > 75$?
b. $X < 70$?
c. $X > 112$?
d. $75 < X < 85$?
e. $X < 80$ or $X > 110$?
f. 10% of the values are less than what X value?
g. 80% of the values are between what two X values (symmetrically distributed around the mean)?
h. 70% of the values will be above what X value?

6 Given a normal distribution with $\mu = 50$ and $\sigma = 4$, what is the probability that

a. $X > 43$?
b. $X < 42$?
c. $X > 57.5$?
d. $42 < X < 48$?
e. $X < 40$ or $X > 55$?
f. 5% of the values are less than what X value?
g. 60% of the values are between what two X values (symmetrically distributed around the mean)?
h. 85% of the values will be above what X value?

Applying the Concepts

7 During 2001, 61.3% of U.S. households purchased ground coffee. These households spent an average of $36.16 on ground coffee during the year ("Annual Product Preference Study," *Progressive Grocer*, May 1, 2002, 31). Consider the annual ground coffee expenditures for households purchasing ground coffee, assuming that these expenditures are approximately distributed as a normal random variable with a mean of $36.16 and a standard deviation of $10.00.

a. Find the probability that a household spent less than $25.00.

b. Find the probability that a household spent more than \$50.00.
c. Find the probability that a household spent more than \$75.00.
d. What proportion of the households spent between \$30.00 and \$40.00?
e. 99% of the households spent less than what amount?
f. 80% of the households spent more than what amount?
g. Do you think that the assumption that the distribution of these expenditures is approximated by a normal distribution is valid? Explain.

8 Toby's Trucking Company determined that on an annual basis the distance traveled per truck is normally distributed with a mean of 50.0 thousand miles and a standard deviation of 12.0 thousand miles.
a. What proportion of trucks can be expected to travel between 34.0 and 50.0 thousand miles in the year?
b. What is the probability that a randomly selected truck travels between 34.0 and 38.0 thousand miles in the year?
c. What percentage of trucks can be expected to travel either below 30.0 or above 60.0 thousand miles in the year?
d. How many of the 1,000 trucks in the fleet are expected to travel between 30.0 and 60.0 thousand miles in the year?
e. How many miles will be traveled by at least 80% of the trucks?
f. What will your answers be to (a)–(e) if the standard deviation is 10.0 thousand miles?

9 Plastic bags used for packaging produce are manufactured so that the breaking strength of the bag is normally distributed with a mean of 5 pounds per square inch and a standard deviation of 1.5 pounds per square inch. What proportion of the bags produced have a breaking strength of
a. less than 3.17 pounds per square inch?
b. at least 3.6 pounds per square inch?
c. between 5 and 5.5 pounds per square inch?
d. between 3.2 and 4.2 pounds per square inch?
e. Between what two values symmetrically distributed around the mean will 95% of the breaking strengths fall?
f. What will your answers be to (a)–(e) if the standard deviation is 1.0 pound per square inch?

10 A set of final examination grades in an introductory statistics course was found to be normally distributed with a mean of 73 and a standard deviation of 8.
a. What is the probability of getting a grade of 91 or less on this exam?
b. What percentage of students scored between 65 and 89?
c. What percentage of students scored between 81 and 89?
d. Only 5% of the students taking the test scored higher than what grade?
e. If the professor grades on a curve (gives A's to the top 10% of the class regardless of the score), are you better off with a grade of 81 on this exam or a grade of 68 on a different exam where the mean is 62 and the standard deviation is 3? Show your answer statistically and explain.

11 A statistical analysis of 1,000 long-distance telephone calls made from the headquarters of the Bricks and Clicks Computer Corporation indicates that the length of these calls is normally distributed with $\mu = 240$ seconds and $\sigma = 40$ seconds.
a. What percentage of these calls lasted less than 180 seconds?
b. What is the probability that a particular call lasted between 180 and 300 seconds?
c. How many calls lasted less than 180 seconds or more than 300 seconds?
d. What percentage of the calls lasted between 110 and 180 seconds?
e. What is the length of a particular call if only 1% of all calls are shorter?

12 **Unisys.com** is one of the most frequented business-to-business Web sites. According to an article in the *Wall Street Journal*, business partners accessing **Unisys.com** spend an average of 65.7 minutes, possibly the longest average time per visit of any business-to-business Web site ("Reality Bytes," February 28, 2000, B6). Assume that the length of a visit on the Unisys Web site is distributed as a normal random variable with a mean of 65.7 minutes and a standard deviation of 15 minutes.
a. What is the probability that a randomly selected visit will last more than 90 minutes?
b. What is the probability that a randomly selected visit to **Unisys.com** will last between 60 and 90 minutes?
c. Only 20% of the visits will last less than how many minutes?
d. Between what two values (in minutes) symmetrically distributed around the population mean will 90% of the visits last?
e. Do you think that the normality assumption is valid for these data? Explain.

13 Many manufacturing problems involve the accurate matching of machine parts such as shafts that fit into a valve hole. A particular design requires a shaft with a diameter of 22.000 mm., but shafts with diameters between 21.900 and 22.010 are acceptable. Suppose that the manufacturing process yields shafts with diameters normally distributed with a mean of 22.002 mm. and a standard deviation of 0.005 mm. For this process, what is
a. the proportion of shafts with a diameter between 21.90 and 22.00?
b. the probability of an acceptable shaft?
c. the diameter that will be exceeded by only 2% of the shafts?
d. What would be your answers in (a)–(c) if the standard deviation of the shaft diameters were 0.004?

2 EVALUATING THE NORMALITY ASSUMPTION

In section 1 the normal distribution and its properties were discussed. Now a very practical question must be considered: How can one evaluate the likelihood that a particular data set comes from an underlying normal distribution?

You must be cautioned here that *not all continuous random variables are normally distributed*! Often the continuous variables that you are interested in studying will neither follow the normal distribution nor be adequately approximated by it.

Thus, for a descriptive analysis of any particular set of data, the practical question remains: How can you determine whether the data are approximately normally distributed so that the methodology of section 1 can be used? Two descriptive *exploratory* approaches will be taken here to evaluate whether a data set seems to be approximated by the normal distribution:

1. A comparison of the data set's characteristics with the properties of an underlying normal distribution
2. The construction of a normal probability plot

Evaluating the Properties

The normal distribution is symmetrical and bell-shaped (thus, all measures of central tendency are equal), has an interquartile range equal to 1.33 standard deviations, is continuous, and has an infinite range.

In actual practice, some continuous variables may have characteristics that approximate these theoretical properties, either because the underlying population distribution is only approximately normal or because the sample data may deviate from the theoretically expected characteristics. In such circumstances, the data may not be perfectly bell-shaped and symmetrical in appearance. The measures of central tendency may differ slightly, and the interquartile range may not be exactly equal to 1.33 standard deviations. In addition, in practice, the range of the data will not be infinite—it will be approximately equal to 6 standard deviations.

Many continuous variables are neither normally distributed nor approximately normally distributed. For such variables, the descriptive characteristics of the respective data sets do not match well with these four properties of a normal distribution.

One approach to check for normality is by comparing the actual data characteristics with the corresponding properties from an underlying normal distribution, as illustrated in Exhibit 3.

EXHIBIT 3 CHECKING FOR NORMALITY

1. Construct charts and observe their appearance. For small- or moderate-sized data sets, construct a stem-and-leaf display and box-and-whisker plot. For large data sets, construct the frequency distribution and plot the histogram or polygon.
2. Compute descriptive summary measures and compare the characteristics of the data with the theoretical and practical properties of the normal distribution. Obtain the mean and median, and note the similarity or difference between these measures of central tendency. Obtain the interquartile range and standard deviation. Note how well the interquartile range can be approximated by 1.33 times the standard deviation. Obtain the range and note how well it can be approximated by 6 times the standard deviation.
3. Evaluate how the observations in the data set distribute themselves. Determine whether approximately two-thirds of the observations lie between the mean ± 1 standard deviation. Determine whether approximately four-fifths of the observations lie between the mean ± 1.28 standard deviations. Determine whether approximately 19 out of every 20 observations lie between the mean ± 2 standard deviations.

Constructing the Normal Probability Plot

Normal Probability Plot
A normal probability plot is a two-dimensional plot of the observed data values on the *vertical* axis, with their corresponding quantile values from a standardized normal distribution on the *horizontal* axis.

Standardized Normal Quantile

- The first standardized normal quantile, O_1, is the Z value on a standardized normal distribution below which the proportion $1/(n + 1)$ of the area under the curve is contained.
- The second standardized normal quantile, O_2, is the Z value on a standardized normal distribution below which the proportion $2/(n + 1)$ of the area under the curve is contained.
- The ith standardized normal quantile, O_i, is the Z value on a standardized normal distribution below which the proportion $i/(n + 1)$ of the area under the curve is contained.
- The nth (and largest) standardized normal quantile, O_n, is the Z value on a standardized normal distribution below which the proportion $n/(n + 1)$ of the area under the curve is contained.

A second approach to evaluating the assumption of normality in data is through the construction of a *normal probability plot*. Quartiles were defined as measures of "noncentral" location. In addition, other measures of noncentral location, such as the deciles (which split the ordered observations in 10ths) and the percentiles (which split the ordered observations in 100ths), can be calculated.

If the plotted points in a normal probability plot lie either on or close to an imaginary straight line rising from the lower-left corner of the graph to the upper-right corner, then the data are (at least approximately) normally distributed. On the other hand, if the plotted points deviate from this imaginary straight line in some patterned fashion, then the data are not normally distributed.

To construct and use a normal probability plot, follow the steps presented in Exhibit 4.

EXHIBIT 4 STEPS USED IN CONSTRUCTING A NORMAL PROBABILITY PLOT

To construct a normal probability plot:

1. Place the values in the data set into an ordered array.
2. Find the corresponding standardized normal quantile values.
3. Plot the corresponding pairs of points using the observed data values on the vertical axis and their associated standardized normal quantile values on the horizontal axis.
4. Evaluate the likelihood that the variable of interest is (at least approximately) normally distributed by inspecting the plot for evidence of linearity (i.e., a straight line).

These steps in Exhibit 4 will now be described in detail.

Obtaining the Ordered Array Because the original data set is likely to be obtained in raw form, the observations must be rearranged into an ordered array from smallest to largest so that the corresponding standardized normal quantile values can be obtained.

Finding the Standardized Normal Quantile Values A standardized normal distribution is characterized by a mean of 0 and standard deviation of 1. Because of the symmetry of the normal distribution, the median from a standardized normal distribution must also be 0. Therefore, in dealing with a standardized normal distribution, the quantile values below the median are negative, and the quantile values above the median are positive. The quantile values are obtained from this distribution by using an **inverse normal scores transformation**.

The inverse normal scores transformation is carried out from a data set containing n observations from a standardized normal distribution by first defining the symbol O_1 as the first (and smallest) ordered or quantile value, the symbol O_2 as the second smallest ordered value, the symbol O_i as the ith smallest ordered value, and the symbol O_n as the largest ordered value. Because of symmetry, the standardized normal quantiles O_1 and O_n will have the same numerical value—except for their sign: O_1 will be negative and O_n will be positive.

Making the Inverse Normal Scores Transformation As in section 1, once the probability or area under the curve is known, the Cumulative Standardized Normal table is used to locate the appropriate area and then its corresponding standardized normal ordered value in the margins of this table. Thus, in general, to find the ith standardized normal ordered value from a data set containing n observations, the standardized normal distribution is sketched and the value O_i is located such that the proportion $i/(n + 1)$ of the area under the curve is contained below that value. The resulting area is located in the body of the Cumulative Standardized Normal table. Working to the margins of that table, the corresponding standardized normal ordered value is obtained.

Example 8 illustrates how to obtain standardized normal ordered values.

EXAMPLE 8

OBTAINING STANDARDIZED NORMAL ORDERED VALUES

Obtain the 1st, 2nd, and 10th standardized normal ordered values in a sample of 19 observations.

SOLUTION

The first standardized normal ordered value, O_1, is the value below which the proportion $\frac{1}{n+1} = \frac{1}{19+1} = 0.05$ of the area under the normal curve is contained. From Figure 19, observe that the area less than O_1 is 0.05. Then, from the body of Table 7 note that O_1 falls halfway between -1.65 and -1.64. Because the standardized normal ordered values are usually reported with two decimal places, the value -1.65 is used here.

FIGURE 19
Finding the first standardized normal ordered value from a data set with 19 observations

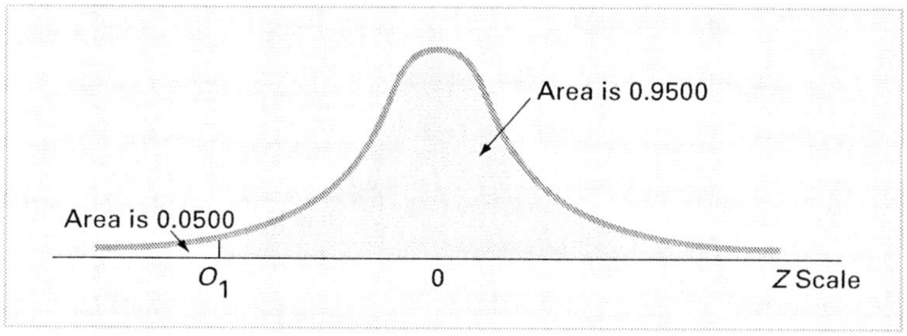

TABLE 7
Obtaining a standardized normal ordered value corresponding to a particular cumulative area (0.05) under the normal curve

Z	.00	.01	.02	.03	.04	.05	.06	.07	.08	.09
.	.	.	.	.	.	.	.	.	.	.
.	.	.	.	.	.	.	.	.	.	.
.	.	.	.	.	.	.	.	.	.	.
−1.9	.0287	.0281	.0274	.0268	.0262	.0256	.0250	.0244	.0239	.0233
−1.8	.0359	.0351	.0344	.0336	.0329	.0322	.0314	.0307	.0301	.0294
−1.7	.0446	.0436	.0427	.0418	.0409	.0401	.0392	.0384	.0375	.0367
−1.6	.0548	.0537	.0526	.0516	.0505	.0495	.0485	.0475	.0465	.0455

Source: Extracted from the Cumulative Standardized Normal table.

The second standardized normal ordered value, O_2, is the value below which the proportion $\frac{2}{n+1} = \frac{2}{19+1} = 0.10$ of the area under the normal curve is obtained. From the Cumulative Standardized Normal table, O_2 falls between -1.29 and -1.28 but closer to the latter. Hence, -1.28 is selected here.

Similarly, the 10th standardized normal ordered value, O_{10}, is the value below which the proportion $\frac{10}{n+1} = \frac{10}{19+1} = 0.50$ of the area under the normal curve is contained. Because this value is the median, the standardized normal ordered value is 0.00.

Table 8 presents ordered arrays of midterm test scores from 19 students in each of four sections (sections I–IV) of a course in introductory finance. Also shown in Table 8 are the corresponding standardized normal ordered values obtained from the previously described inverse normal scores transformation. The normal probability plots for the four class sections are depicted in panels A–D of Figure 20.

In panel A of Figure 20, observe that the points appear to approximately follow a straight line, so you can conclude that the data set from class section I is approximately normally distributed. [Note that the corresponding polygon and box-and-whisker plot are displayed in Figure X (panel A).]

On the other hand, in panel B of Figure 20 observe that there is a nonlinear pattern to the plot. The points seem to rise somewhat more steeply at first and then increase at a decreasing rate. This pattern is an example of a left-skewed data set. The steepness of the left side of the plot is indicative of the elongated left tail of the distribution of test scores from class section II. [Note that the corresponding polygon and box-and-whisker plot are displayed in Figure X (panel B).]

TABLE 8

Ordered arrays of midterm test scores obtained from 19 students in each of four sections (I–IV) of a course in introductory finance and corresponding standardized normal ordered values

(I) Bell-Shaped Normal Distribution	(II) Left-Skewed Distribution	(III) Right-Skewed Distribution	(IV) Rectangular-Shaped Distribution	O_i
48	47	47	38	−1.65
52	54	48	41	−1.28
55	58	50	44	−1.04
57	61	51	47	−0.84
58	64	52	50	−0.67
60	66	53	53	−0.52
61	68	53	56	−0.39
62	71	54	59	−0.25
64	73	55	62	−0.13
65	74	56	65	0.00
66	75	57	68	0.13
68	76	59	71	0.25
69	77	62	74	0.39
70	77	64	77	0.52
72	78	66	80	0.67
73	79	69	83	0.84
75	80	72	86	1.04
78	82	76	89	1.28
82	83	83	92	1.65

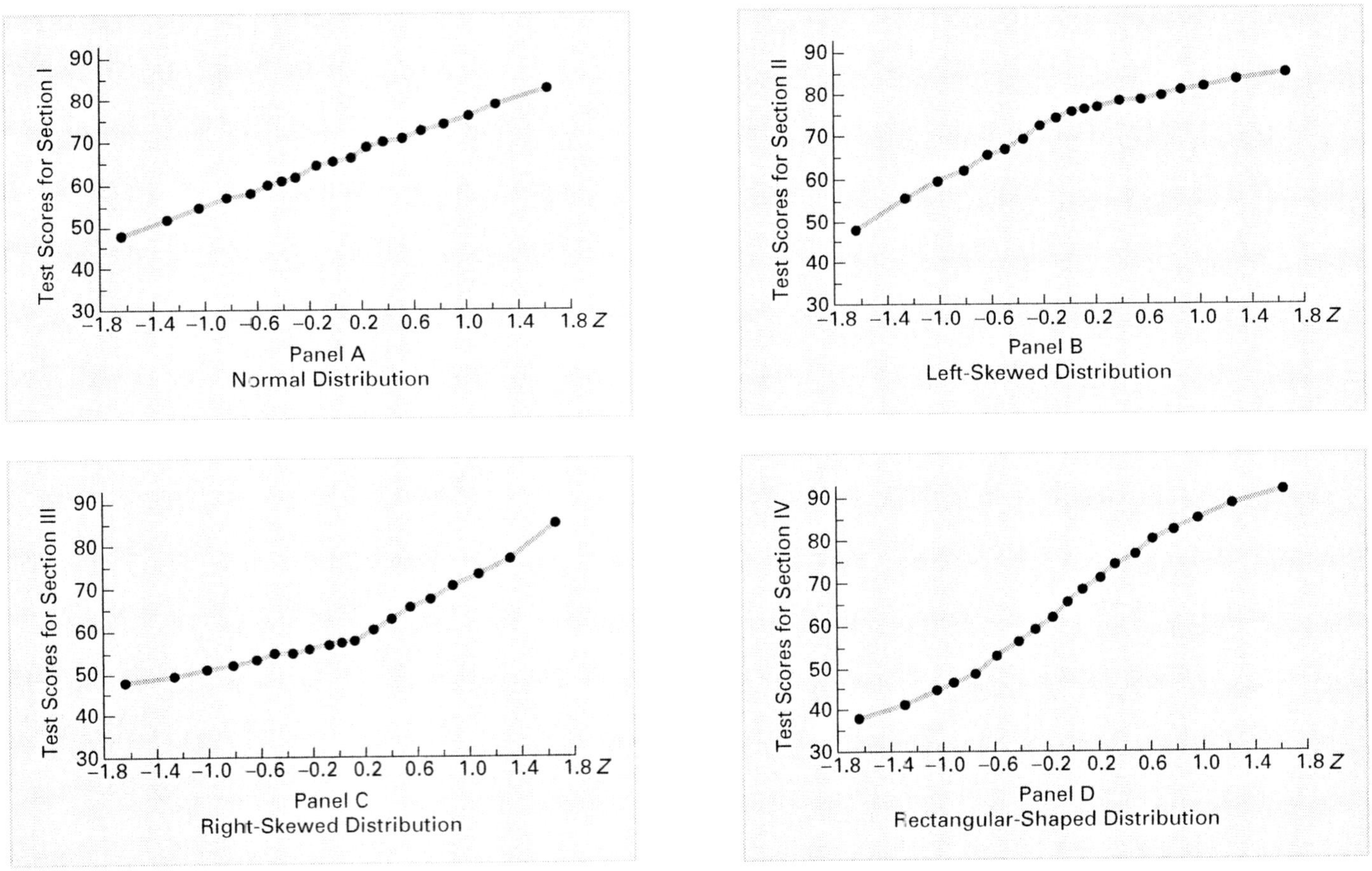

FIGURE 20

Normal probability plots for four data sets

In panel C of Figure 20 the opposite nonlinear pattern is observed. The points here seem to rise more slowly at first and then seem to increase at an increasing rate. This pattern is an example of a right-skewed data set. The steepness of the right side of the plot is indicative of the elongated right tail of the distribution of test scores from class section III. [Note that the corresponding polygon and box-and-whisker plot are displayed in Figure X (panel C).]

In panel D of Figure 20, observe a symmetrical plot with a pattern that is linear over a large middle portion of the plot. However, on each side of the plot the curve seems to flatten out. This flattening out shows the opposite effect to what was observed in panels B and C as a result of skewness. Here there are no elongated tails. In fact, there are really no tails—the test scores in class section IV are distributed as a uniform (or rectangular) distribution (see section 3). [Note the corresponding polygon and box-and-whisker plot from Figure X (panel D).]

FIGURE X

Four hypothetical distributions examined through their box-and-whisker plots and corresponding polygons *(Note: Area under each polygon is split into quartiles corresponding to the five-number summary for the respective box-and-whisker plot)*

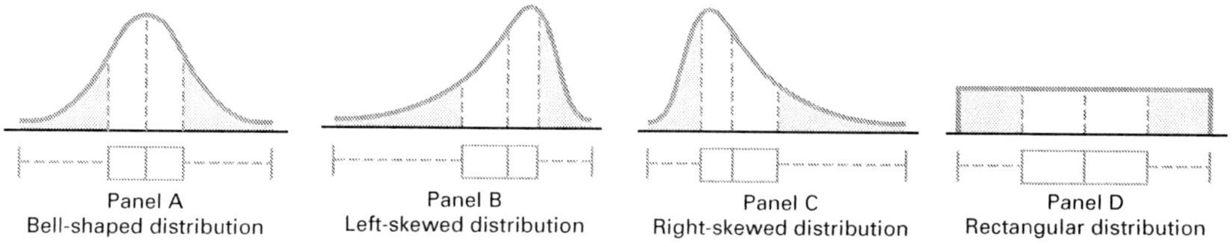

Now that the normality assumption has been evaluated with the set of exam scores, the 5-year annualized returns of the mutual funds (that you may have seen earlier) can be evaluated to determine whether they are normally distributed. Figure 21 depicts the descriptive summary statistics and the box-and-whisker plot obtained from Microsoft Excel of the 5-year annualized returns of 259 mutual funds. Figure 22 depicts the normal probability plot obtained from Microsoft Excel.

FIGURE 21

Descriptive summary measures (panel A) and box-and-whisker plot (panel B) obtained from Microsoft Excel for the 5-year annualized return of 259 mutual funds

	A	B	C	D
1	Box-and-Whisker Plot for 5-Year Returns			
2				
3	Five-number Summary			
4	Minimum	-6.1		
5	First Quartile	8.2		
6	Median	10.5		
7	Third Quartile	13		
8	Maximum	26.3		

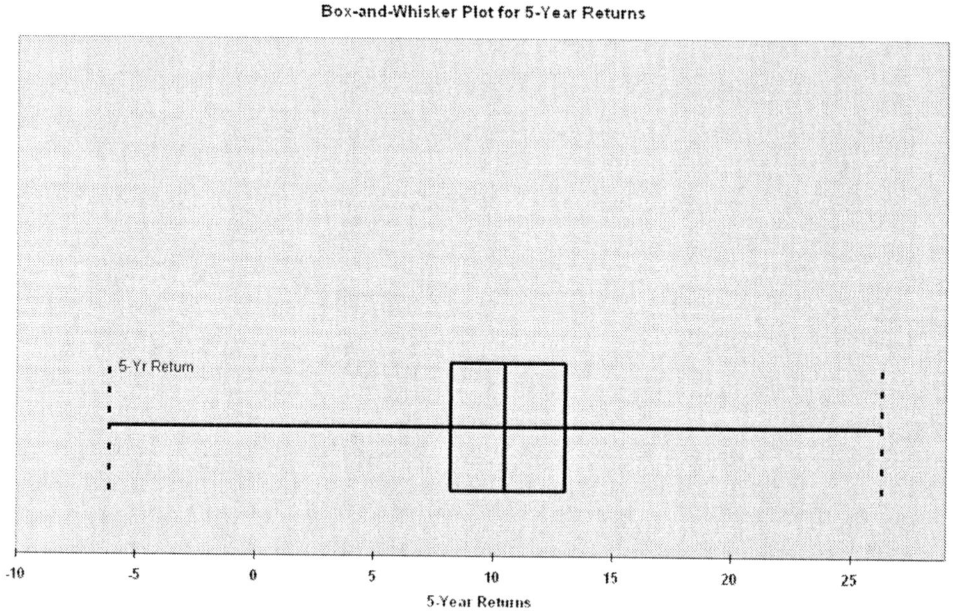

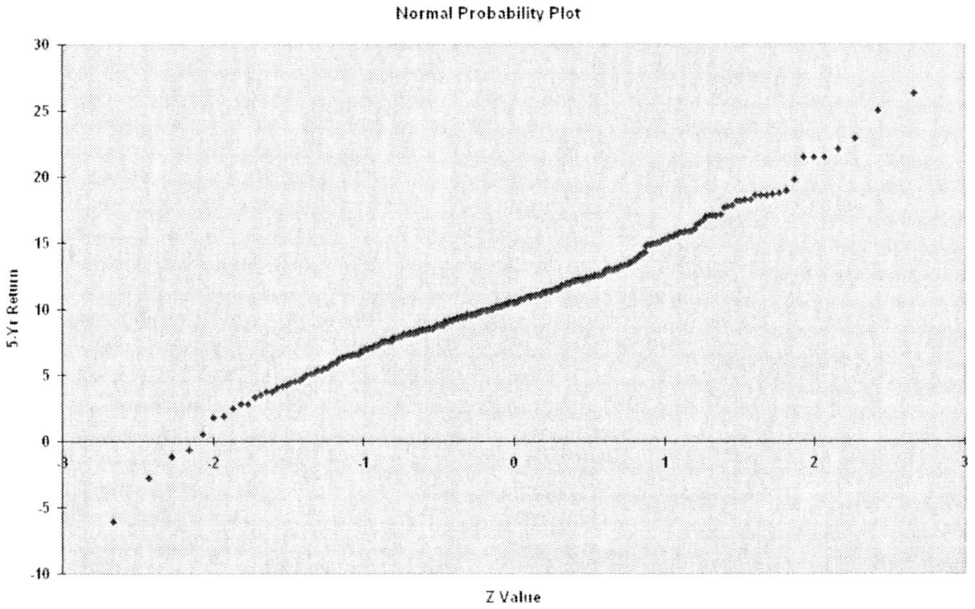

FIGURE 22

Normal probability plot obtained from Microsoft Excel for the 5-year annualized return of 259 mutual funds

In Figure 21, observe that the difference between the median and the maximum value is approximately equal to the difference between the median and the lowest value, and that the box-and-whisker plot indicates an equal tail in the lower portion as in the upper portion of the distribution. This result is consistent with the normal probability plot of Figure 22, which shows the 5-year annualized returns approximate a straight-line increase. You can conclude that the data are approximately normally distributed.

Excel Strategies Generating Normal Probability Plots

CHAPTER 6.xls

Retrieve the Figure 6.22 chart sheet of the ***Chapter 6.xls*** *workbook to view a plot similar to the one above.*

You implement a worksheet that features the **NORMSINV** function and then use the Chart Wizard to generate a normal probability plot. PHStat2 can execute these tasks for you in a single step.

For example, to generate a normal probability plot for the 5-year returns for the sample of 259 mutual funds, similar to Figure 22 above, open the **Mutual Funds.xls** workbook to the **Data** worksheet and use one of these strategies:

Using Excel with PHStat2

Use the PHStat2 Normal Probability Plot procedure to generate a normal probability plot.

Select **PHStat | Probability & Prob. Distributions | Normal Probability Plot**.

In the Normal Probability Plot dialog box (shown at right):

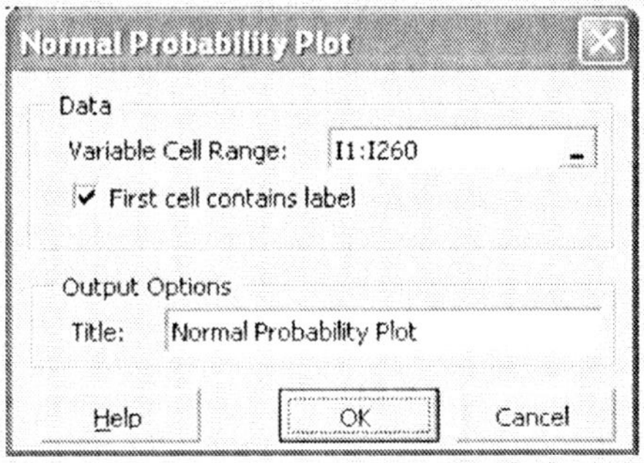

Enter **I1:I260** in the **Variable Cell Range** edit box.

Select the **First cell contains label** check box.

Enter a title in the **Title** edit box.

Click the **OK** button.

PHStat2 first generates a Plot worksheet containing a table of ranks, cumulative proportions, Z values, and the original rates of return data which it then uses to generate the normal probability plot.

Using Excel

Follow the instructions of section EH2 (at the end of this chapter) to implement a worksheet that calculates data for a normal probability plot and to generate a plot using the Chart Wizard from that data.

PROBLEMS FOR SECTION 2

Learning the Basics

14 Show that for a sample of 19 observations, the 18th smallest (i.e., 2nd-largest) standardized normal ordered value obtained from the inverse normal scores transformation is +1.28 and the 19th smallest (i.e., largest) standardized normal ordered value is +1.65.

15 Show that for a sample of 39 observations, the smallest and largest standardized normal ordered values obtained from the inverse normal scores transformation are, respectively, −1.96 and +1.96 and the middle (i.e., 20th) standardized normal ordered value is 0.00.

16 Using the inverse normal scores transformation on a sample of 6 observations, list the 6 expected probabilities or areas under the standardized normal curve along with their corresponding standardized normal ordered values.

Applying the Concepts

Problems 17–19 can be solved with or without using Microsoft Excel. Problems 20–23 are particularly appropriate for solution using Microsoft Excel.

17 A sample of 24 two-bedroom, unfurnished apartments in Cincinnati, Ohio, was selected from the classified ads' section of the *Cincinnati Enquirer*. The following table **APARTMENT.xls** contains the monthly rent quoted for these 24 apartments.

Monthly Rent for a Sample of 24 Two-Bedroom Apartments

735	499	490	475	800	675
550	475	575	575	530	790
510	500	800	485	975	690
475	535	599	700	670	625

Source: Extracted from the Cincinnati Enquirer, *June 23, 2002.*

Decide whether or not the data appear to be approximately normally distributed by:

a. evaluating the actual versus theoretical properties.
b. constructing a normal probability plot.

18 A problem with a telephone line that prevents a customer from receiving or making calls is disconcerting to both the customer and the telephone company. These problems can be of two types: those located inside a central office and those located on lines between the central office and the customer's equipment. The following data represent samples of 20 problems reported to two different offices of a telephone company and the time to clear these problems (in minutes) from the customers' lines: **PHONE.xls**

Central Office I Time to Clear Problems (minutes)

1.48	1.75	0.78	2.85	0.52	1.60	4.15	3.97	1.48	3.10
1.02	0.53	0.93	1.60	0.80	1.05	6.32	3.93	5.45	0.97

Central Office II Time to Clear Problems (minutes)

7.55	3.75	0.10	1.10	0.60	0.52	3.30	2.10	0.58	4.02
3.75	0.65	1.92	0.60	1.53	4.23	0.08	1.48	1.65	0.72

For each of the two central office locations, decide whether the data appear to be approximately normally distributed by

a. evaluating the actual versus theoretical properties.
b. constructing a normal probability plot.

19 Many manufacturing processes use the term work-in-process (often abbreviated as WIP). In a book manufacturing plant, the WIP represents the time it takes for sheets from a press to be folded, gathered, sewn, tipped on end sheets, and bound. The following data represent samples of 20 books at each of two production plants and the processing time (defined as the time in days from when the books came off the press to when they were packed in cartons) for these jobs: **WIP.xls**.

Plant A

15.62	5.29	16.25	10.92	11.46	21.62	8.45	8.58	5.41	11.42
11.62	7.29	17.50	17.96	14.42	10.50	7.58	9.29	7.54	18.92

Plant B

9.54	11.46	16.62	12.62	25.75	15.41	14.29	13.13	13.71	10.04
5.75	12.46	19.17	13.21	16.00	12.33	14.25	15.37	16.25	19.71

For each of the two plants, decide whether or not the data appear to be approximately normally distributed by

a. evaluating the actual versus theoretical properties.
b. constructing a normal probability plot.

20 The NASDAQ composite index closed down approximately 1% on March 4, 2003. The net change for the day (in dollars) for a sample of 50 stocks traded on the NASDAQ are given in the file **NET-CHG.xls**.

Decide whether or not the data appear to be approximately normally distributed by:

a. evaluating the actual versus theoretical properties.
b. constructing a normal probability plot.

21 One operation of a mill is to cut pieces of steel into parts that will later be used as the frame for front seats in an automotive plant. The steel is cut with a diamond saw and requires the resulting parts to be within plus or minus 0.005 inch of the length specified by the automobile company. The data come from a sample of 100 steel parts **STEEL.xls**. The measurement reported is the difference in inches between the actual length of the steel part, as measured by a laser measurement device, and the specified length of the steel part.

Decide whether or not the data appear to be approximately normally distributed by:

a. evaluating the actual versus theoretical properties.
b. constructing a normal probability plot.

22 In a rubber-edge manufacturing factory, the raw rubber is compounded through a kneading machine and then cut into thin ribbon strips. The strips are loaded onto mold machines and thermocast into the desired shapes of rubber edges. The weights (in grams) of a sample of rubber edges are in the file **RUBBER.xls**

Source: W. L. Pearn and K. S. Chen, "A Practical Implementation of the Process Capability Index Cpk," Quality Engineering, *1997, 9, 721–737.*

Decide whether or not the data appear to be approximately normally distributed by:

a. evaluating the actual versus theoretical properties.
b. constructing a normal probability plot.

23 The following data represent the electricity cost in dollars during the month of July 2002 for a random sample of 50 two-bedroom apartments in a large city: **UTILITY.xls**

96	171	202	178	147	102	153	197	127	82
157	185	90	116	172	111	148	213	130	165
141	149	206	175	123	128	144	168	109	167
95	163	150	154	130	143	187	166	139	149
108	119	183	151	114	135	191	137	129	158

Decide whether the data appear to be approximately normally distributed by

a. evaluating the actual versus theoretical properties.
b. constructing a normal probability plot.

3 THE UNIFORM DISTRIBUTION

The **uniform distribution** is one in which the probability of occurrence of a value is equally likely to occur anywhere in the range between the smallest value a, and the largest value b. Because of its shape, it is sometimes called the **rectangular distribution** (see panel B of Figure 1). Equation (5) defines the continuous probability density function for the uniform distribution.

$$f(X) = \frac{1}{b - a} \text{ if } a \le X \le b \text{ and } 0 \text{ elsewhere} \quad (5)$$

where

a = the minimum value of X
b = the maximum value of X

Equation (6) defines the expected value or mean of the uniform distribution.

$$\mu = \frac{a + b}{2} \quad (6)$$

Equation (7) defines the variance and standard deviation of the uniform distribution.

$$\sigma^2 = \frac{(b-a)^2}{12} \quad \textbf{(7a)}$$

$$\sigma = \sqrt{\frac{(b-a)^2}{12}} \quad \textbf{(7b)}$$

One of the most common uses of the uniform distribution is in the selection of random numbers. When simple random sampling is conducted, each value is assumed to come from a distribution that is uniformly distributed between a minimum value of 0, and a maximum value of 1. What would be the probability of obtaining a random number between 0.10 and 0.30?

The uniform distribution in which $a = 0$, and $b = 1$ is plotted in Figure 23. The total area under the rectangle is its base (1.0) times its height, so that the resulting area of 1.0 satisfies the requirement that the area under any probability density function equals 1.0. Thus the area between 0.10 and 0.30, depicted in Figure 24, is equal to the base (which is 0.30 – 0.10 = 0.20) times the height (1.0). Therefore,

$$P(0.10 < X < 0.30) = (\text{Base})(\text{Height}) = (0.20)(1.0) = 0.20$$

FIGURE 23
Probability density function for a uniform distribution with $a = 0$, and $b = 1$

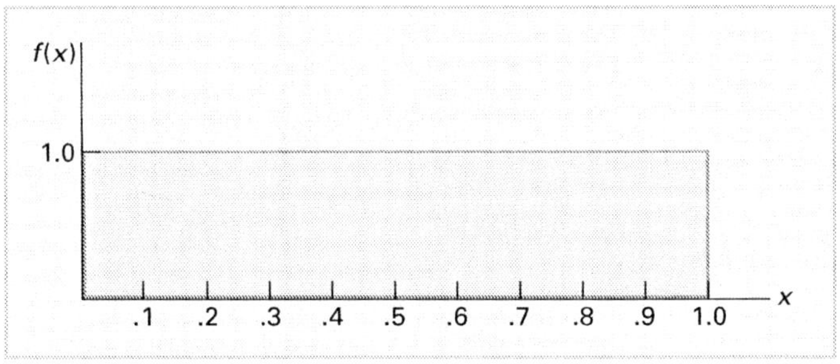

FIGURE 24
Finding $P(0.10 < X < 0.30)$ for a uniform distribution with $a = 0$, and $b = 1$

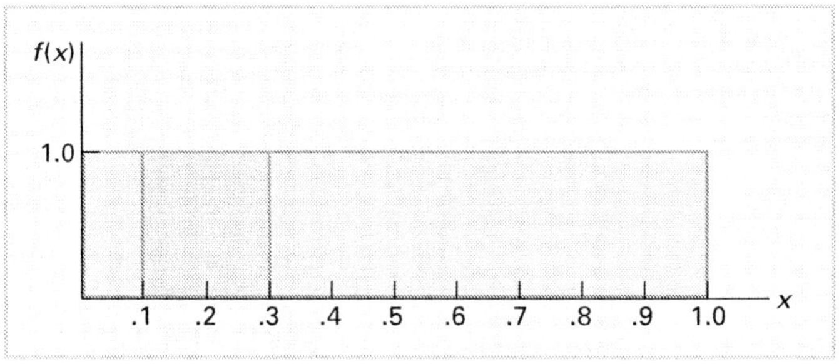

From Equations (6) and (7), the expected value and standard deviation of the distribution for $a = 0$ and $b = 1$ are computed as follows:

$$\mu = \frac{a+b}{2} = \frac{0+1}{2} = 0.5$$

and

$$\sigma^2 = \frac{(b-a)^2}{12} = \frac{(1-0)^2}{12} = \frac{1}{12} = 0.0833$$
$$\sigma = \sqrt{0.0833} = 0.2887$$

Thus the expected value is 0.5 and the standard deviation is 0.2887.

PROBLEMS FOR SECTION 3

Learning the Basics

24 Suppose you sample from a uniform distribution with $a = 0$ and $b = 10$. What is the probability of obtaining a value:

a. between 5 and 7?
b. between 2 and 3?
c. What is the expected value?
d. What is the standard deviation?

Applying the Concepts

25 The time between arrivals of customers at a bank during the noon to 1 P.M. hour has a uniform distribution over an interval from 0 to 120 seconds. What is the probability that the time between the arrival of two customers will be

a. less than 20 seconds?
b. between 10 and 30 seconds?
c. more than 35 seconds?
d. What is the expected value of the time between arrivals?
e. What is the standard deviation of the time between arrivals?

26 At an ocean-side nuclear power plant, seawater is used as part of the cooling system. This raises the temperature of the water that is discharged back into the ocean. The amount that the water temperature is raised has a uniform distribution over the interval from 10 to 25° C.

a. What is the probability that the temperature increase will be less than 20° C?
b. What is the probability that the temperature increase will be between 20 and 22° C?
c. Suppose that a temperature increase of more than 18° C is considered to be potentially dangerous to the aquatic environment. What is the probability that at any point of time, the temperature increase is potentially dangerous?
d. What is the expected value of the temperature increase?
e. What is the standard deviation of the temperature increase?

27 The time of failure for a continuous operation monitoring device of air quality has a uniform distribution over a 24-hour day.

a. If, based on the time of year, daylight is between 5:55 A.M. and 7:38 P.M., what is the probability that failure will occur during daylight hours?
b. If the device is in secondary mode from 10 P.M. to 5 A.M., what is the probability that failure will occur during secondary mode?
c. If the device has a self-checking computer chip that determines if the device is operational every hour on the hour, what is the probability that failure will be detected within ten minutes of its occurrence?
d. If the device has a self-checking computer chip that determines if the device is operational every hour on the hour, what is the probability that it will take at least 40 minutes to detect that a failure has occurred?

28 A token ring local area network provides an inter-token time having a uniform distribution between 0 and 2 seconds. What is the probability that the time will be

a. less than 0.6 seconds?
b. between 0.4 and 1.6 seconds?
c. greater than 1.8 seconds?
d. greater than 2 seconds?
e. What is the expected value of the inter-token time?
f. What is the standard deviation of the inter-token time?

4 THE EXPONENTIAL DISTRIBUTION

In this section the **exponential distribution** is introduced. This continuous distribution is right-skewed and ranges from zero to positive infinity (see panel C of Figure 1). The exponential distribution is useful in a variety of circumstances in business, particularly in evaluating manufacturing and service processes. The exponential distribution has been widely used in waiting line (or queuing) theory to model the length of time between arrivals in processes such as customers at a bank's ATM, clients in a fast-food restaurant, patients entering a hospital emergency room, and hits on a Web site.

The exponential distribution is defined by a single parameter, its mean λ, the average number of arrivals per unit of time. The value $1/\lambda$ is equal to the average time between arrivals. For example, if the average number of arrivals in a minute is $\lambda = 4$, then the average time between arrivals is $1/\lambda = 0.25$ minutes or 15 seconds. The probability that the length of time before the next arrival is less than X, is defined in Equation (8).

EXPONENTIAL DISTRIBUTION

$$P(\text{arrival time} < X) = 1 - e^{-\lambda X} \quad \textbf{(8)}$$

where

e = the mathematical constant approximated by 2.71828
λ = the population mean number of arrivals per unit
X = any value of the continuous variable where $0 < X < \infty$

To illustrate the exponential distribution, suppose that customers arrive at a bank's ATM at the rate of 20 per hour. If a customer has just arrived, what is the probability that the next customer will arrive within 6 minutes (that is, 0.1 hour)?

For this example, $\lambda = 20$ and $X = 0.1$. Using Equation (8),

$$\begin{aligned} P(\text{arrival time} < 0.1) &= 1 - e^{-20(0.1)} \\ &= 1 - e^{-2} \\ &= 1 - 0.1353 = 0.8647 \end{aligned}$$

Thus, the probability that a customer will arrive within 6 minutes is 0.8647, or 86.47%.

Microsoft Excel can also be used to obtain this probability. Figure 25 illustrates output obtained from Microsoft Excel.

FIGURE 25
Obtaining exponential probabilities from Microsoft Excel

	A	B
1	**Exponential Probability**	
2		
3	**Data**	
4	Mean	20
5	X Value	0.1
6		
7	**Results**	
8	P(<=X)	0.8647

CHAPTER 6.xls

*Retrieve the Figure 6.25 chart sheet of the **Chapter 6.xls** workbook to view the exponential probability similar to the one above.*

Excel Strategies Calculating Exponential Probabilities

You implement a worksheet that features the **EXPONDIST** function to calculate an exponential probability. PHStat2 can construct this worksheet for you in a single step.

For example, to calculate the exponential probability shown in Figure 25 above, use one of these strategies:

Using Excel with PHStat2

Use the PHStat2 Exponential procedure to calculate an exponential probability on a new worksheet.

Select **PHStat | Probability & Prob. Distributions | Exponential**.

In the Exponential Probability Distribution dialog box (shown at right):

Enter **20** in the **Mean per unit (Lambda)** edit box.

Enter **0.1** in the **X Value** edit box.

Enter a title in the **Title** edit box.

Click the **OK** button.

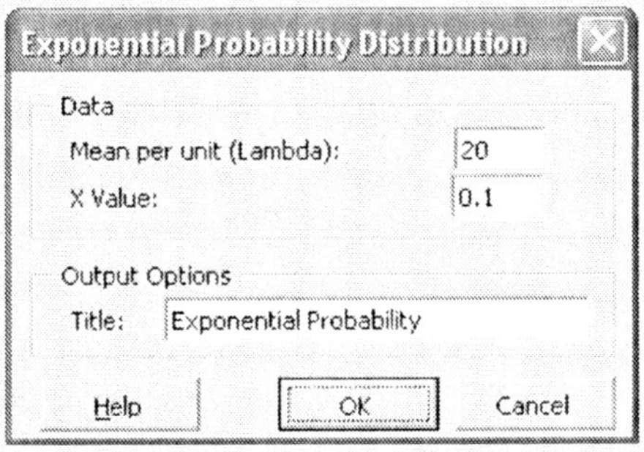

Using Excel

Follow the instructions of section EH3 at the end of this chapter to implement a worksheet that calculates exponential probabilities.

PROBLEMS FOR SECTION 4

Learning the Basics

29 Given an exponential distribution with a mean of $\lambda = 10$, what is the probability that the

a. arrival time is less than $X = 0.1$?
b. arrival time is greater than $X = 0.1$?
c. arrival time is between $X = 0.1$ and $X = 0.2$?
d. arrival time is less than $X = 0.1$ or greater than $X = 0.2$?

30 Given an exponential distribution with a mean of $\lambda = 30$, what is the probability that the

a. arrival time is less than $X = 0.1$?
b. arrival time is greater than $X = 0.1$?
c. arrival time is between $X = 0.1$ and $X = 0.2$?
d. arrival time is less than $X = 0.1$ or greater than $X = 0.2$?

31 Given an exponential distribution with a mean of $\lambda = 20$, what is the probability that the

a. arrival time is less than $X = 4$?
b. arrival time is greater than $X = 0.4$?
c. arrival time is between $X = 0.4$ and $X = 0.5$?
d. arrival time is less than $X = 0.4$ or greater than $X = 0.5$?

Applying the Concepts

32 Autos arrive at a tollbooth located at the entrance to a bridge at the rate of 50 per minute during the 5:00–6:00 P.M. hour. If an auto has just arrived,

a. what is the probability that the next auto arrives within 3 seconds (0.05 minute)?
b. what is the probability that the next auto arrives within 1 second (0.0167 minute)?
c. What would be your answers to (a) and (b) if the rate of arrival of autos were 60 per minute?
d. What would be your answers to (a) and (b) if the rate of arrival of autos were 30 per minute?

33 Customers arrive at the drive-up window of a fast-food restaurant at the rate of 2 per minute during the lunch hour.

a. What is the probability that the next customer will arrive within 1 minute?
b. What is the probability that the next customer will arrive within 5 minutes?
c. During the dinner time period, the arrival rate is 1 per minute. What would be your answers to (a) and (b) for this period?

34 Telephone calls arrive at the information desk of a large computer software company at the rate of 15 per hour.

a. What is the probability that the next call will arrive within 3 minutes (0.05 hour)?
b. What is the probability that the next call will arrive within 15 minutes (0.25 hour)?
c. Suppose the company has just introduced an updated version of one of its software programs and telephone calls are now arriving at the rate of 25 per hour. Given this information, what would be your answers to (a) and (b)?

35 An on-the-job injury occurs once every 10 days on average at an automobile plant. What is the probability that the next on-the-job injury will occur within

a. 10 days?
b. 5 days?
c. 1 day?

36 The time between unplanned shutdowns of a power plant has an exponential distribution with a mean of 20 days. Find the probability that the time between two unplanned shutdowns is

a. less than 14 days.
b. more than 21 days.
c. less than 7 days.

37 Golfers arrive at the starter's booth of a public golf course at the rate of 8 per hour during the Monday-to-Friday midweek period. If a golfer has just arrived,

a. what is the probability that the next golfer arrives within 15 minutes (0.25 hour)?
b. what is the probability that the next golfer arrives within 3 minutes (0.05 hour)?
c. Suppose the actual arrival rate on Fridays is 15 per hour. What would be your answers to (a) and (b) on Fridays?

USING STATISTICS

Cereal-Fill Packaging Process

At Oxford Cereal Company plants, thousands of boxes of cereal are filled during each eight-hour shift. As the operations manager of the plant, you are in charge of monitoring the amount of cereal contained in the boxes. Boxes are supposed to contain, on average, 368 grams of cereal as indicated on the package label. Because of the nature of the process, there is variation in the cereal weight from box to box causing some boxes to be underfilled and some overfilled. Moreover, if the process is not working properly, the average weight in the boxes could deviate too far from the label weight of 368 grams to be acceptable. Because it is too time-consuming, costly, and inefficient to weigh every single box, you must take a sample of boxes and make a decision regarding the likelihood that the cereal-filling process is working properly. Each time a sample of boxes is selected and the individual boxes are weighed, a sample mean $\overline{X}$ is calculated. You need to decide the likelihood that such an $\overline{X}$ could have been randomly drawn from a population whose true mean μ is 368 grams. Based on this assessment, you will have to decide whether to maintain, alter, or shut down the process.

5 INTRODUCTION TO SAMPLING DISTRIBUTIONS

A major goal of data analysis is to make statistical inferences, i.e., to use statistics calculated from samples to estimate the values of population parameters. In the next two sections you will learn about the sample mean, a statistic used to estimate a population mean (a parameter) and the sample proportion, a statistic used to estimate the population proportion (a parameter). Note that the main concern when making a statistical inference is drawing conclusions about a population, *not* about a sample. For example, a political pollster is interested in the sample results only as a way of estimating the actual proportion of the votes that each candidate will receive from the population of voters. Likewise, as the operations manager for the Oxford Cereal Company, you are only interested in using the sample mean calculated from a sample of cereal boxes for estimating the mean weight contained in a population of boxes. The actual value of a sample mean calculated from a small sample is of little interest in and of itself.

In practice, a single sample of a predetermined size is selected at random from the population. The items that are to be included in the sample are determined through the use of a random number generator, such as a table of random numbers, or by using Microsoft Excel.

Hypothetically, to use the sample statistic to estimate the population parameter, one should examine *every* possible sample that could occur. If this selection of all possible samples were actually done, the distribution of the results would be referred to as a **sampling distribution**.

6 SAMPLING DISTRIBUTION OF THE MEAN

Undoubtedly, the most widely used measure of central tendency is the arithmetic mean. The arithmetic mean is also the best measure if the population can be assumed to be normally distributed.

The Unbiased Property of the Arithmetic Mean

The arithmetic mean is said to be **unbiased** because the average of all the possible sample means (of a given sample size n) will be equal to the population mean μ. This property can be demonstrated empirically with an example. Suppose that each of the four typists making up a population of secretarial support service in a company is asked to type the same page of a manuscript. The number of errors made by each typist is presented in Table 9.

TABLE 9
Number of errors made by each of four typists

Typist	Number of Errors
Ann	$X_1 = 3$
Bob	$X_2 = 2$
Carla	$X_3 = 1$
Dave	$X_4 = 4$

This population distribution is shown in Figure 26.

FIGURE 26
Number of errors made by a population of four typists

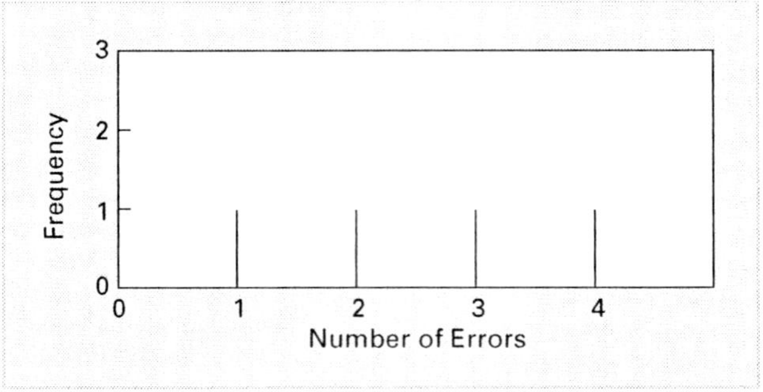

When the data from a population are available, the mean is computed using Equation (9):

POPULATION MEAN

The population mean is the sum of the values in the population divided by the population size N.

$$\mu = \frac{\sum_{i=1}^{N} X_i}{N} \tag{9}$$

Recall also the standard deviation σ is computed using Equation (10):

POPULATION STANDARD DEVIATION

$$\sigma = \sqrt{\frac{\sum_{i=1}^{N} (X_i - \mu)^2}{N}} \tag{10}$$

Thus, for the data of Table 9,

$$\mu = \frac{3 + 2 + 1 + 4}{4} = 2.5 \text{ errors}$$

and

$$\sigma = \sqrt{\frac{(3 - 2.5)^2 + (2 - 2.5)^2 + (1 - 2.5)^2 + (4 - 2.5)^2}{4}} = 1.12 \text{ errors}$$

If samples of two typists are selected *with* replacement from this population, 16 possible samples can be selected ($N^n = 4^2 = 16$). These possible sample outcomes are shown in Table 10. If all 16 of these sample means are averaged, the mean of these values, $\mu_{\bar{X}}$, is equal to 2.5, which is also the mean of the population μ.

TABLE 10

All 16 samples of $n = 2$ typists from a population of $N = 4$ typists when sampling with replacement

Sample	Typists	Sample Outcomes	Sample Mean
1	Ann, Ann	3, 3	$\bar{X}_1 = 3$
2	Ann, Bob	3, 2	$\bar{X}_2 = 2.5$
3	Ann, Carla	3, 1	$\bar{X}_3 = 2$
4	Ann, Dave	3, 4	$\bar{X}_4 = 3.5$
5	Bob, Ann	2, 3	$\bar{X}_5 = 2.5$
6	Bob, Bob	2, 2	$\bar{X}_6 = 2$
7	Bob, Carla	2, 1	$\bar{X}_7 = 1.5$
8	Bob, Dave	2, 4	$\bar{X}_8 = 3$
9	Carla, Ann	1, 3	$\bar{X}_9 = 2$
10	Carla, Bob	1, 2	$\bar{X}_{10} = 1.5$
11	Carla, Carla	1, 1	$\bar{X}_{11} = 1$
12	Carla, Dave	1, 4	$\bar{X}_{12} = 2.5$
13	Dave, Ann	4, 3	$\bar{X}_{13} = 3.5$
14	Dave, Bob	4, 2	$\bar{X}_{14} = 3$
15	Dave, Carla	4, 1	$\bar{X}_{15} = 2.5$
16	Dave, Dave	4, 4	$\bar{X}_{16} = 4$
			$\mu_{\bar{X}} = 2.5$

Thus, the sample arithmetic mean is an unbiased estimator of the population mean. Therefore, although you do not know how close the average of any particular sample selected comes to the population mean, you are at least assured that the average of all the possible sample means that could have been selected will be equal to the population mean.

Standard Error of the Mean

The variation in the average number of typing errors obtained from all 16 possible samples when sampling *with* replacement is illustrated in Figure 27. Although there is a good deal of variation in the sample means, depending on which typists were selected in the various samples, there is not nearly as much variation as in the actual population itself. The fact that the sample means are less variable than the population data follows directly from the fact that a particular sample mean averages together all

FIGURE 27

Sampling distribution of the average number of errors based on all possible samples containing two typists

Source: Data are from Table 10.

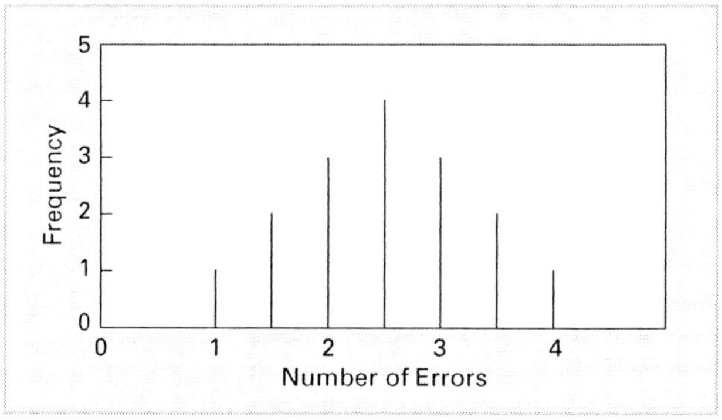

the values in the sample. A population consists of individual outcomes that can take on a wide range of values from extremely small to extremely large. However, if an extreme value falls into the sample, although this value will have an effect on the mean, the effect will be reduced because it is being averaged in with all the other values in the sample. As the sample size increases, the effect of a single extreme value gets even smaller because it is being averaged with more observations.

How the arithmetic mean varies from sample to sample is expressed statistically by the value of the standard deviation of all possible sample means. This measure of variability in the mean from sample to sample is referred to as the **standard error of the mean**, $\sigma_{\overline{X}}$. When sampling *with* replacement, or when sampling *without* replacement from infinite populations, the standard error of the mean is defined by Equation (11):

STANDARD ERROR OF THE MEAN

The standard error of the mean $\sigma_{\overline{X}}$ is equal to the standard deviation in the population σ divided by the square root of the sample size n.

$$\sigma_{\overline{X}} = \frac{\sigma}{\sqrt{n}} \qquad \textbf{(11)}$$

Therefore, as the sample size increases, the standard error of the mean decreases by a factor equal to the square root of the sample size. This relationship between the standard error of the mean and the sample size may be further examined, when the issue of sample size determination is discussed.

Equation (11) can also be used as an approximation to the standard error of the mean when the sample is selected without replacement if the sample contains less than 5% of the entire population. The standard error of the mean is computed in Example 9. (See the section 6.9.pdf file on the CD-ROM that accompanies this text for the case in which more than 5% of the population is contained in a sample obtained without replacement.)

EXAMPLE 9

COMPUTING THE STANDARD ERROR OF THE MEAN

Return to the cereal-filling process described in the Using Statistics scenario. If a sample of 25 boxes is randomly selected without replacement from the thousands of boxes filled during a shift, the sample contains far less than 5% of the population. Given that the standard deviation of the cereal-filling process is 15 grams, compute the standard error of the mean.

SOLUTION

Using Equation (11) above with $n = 25$ and $\sigma = 15$, the standard error of the mean is computed as

$$\sigma_{\overline{X}} = \frac{\sigma}{\sqrt{n}} = \frac{15}{\sqrt{25}} = \frac{15}{5} = 3$$

Note how much smaller the variation is in means based on samples of size 25 compared with the variation in the individual boxes of cereal (i.e., $\sigma_{\overline{X}} = 3$ while $\sigma = 15$).

Sampling from Normally Distributed Populations

Now that the idea of a sampling distribution has been introduced and the standard error of the mean has been defined, what distribution will the sample mean $\overline{X}$ follow? It can be shown that if sampling is done from a population that is normally distributed with mean μ and standard deviation σ, the **sampling distribution of the mean** will also be normally distributed for *any size n* with mean $\mu_{\overline{X}} = \mu$ and standard error of the mean $\sigma_{\overline{X}}$.

In the most elementary case, if samples of size $n = 1$ are taken, each possible sample mean is a single observation from the population because

$$\bar{X} = \frac{\sum_{i=1}^{n} X_i}{n} = \frac{X_i}{1} = X_i$$

Therefore, if the population is normally distributed with mean μ and standard deviation σ, then the sampling distribution of $\bar{X}$ for samples of $n = 1$ must also follow the normal distribution with mean $\mu_{\bar{X}} = \mu$ and standard error of the mean $\sigma_{\bar{X}} = \sigma/\sqrt{1} = \sigma$. In addition, note that, as the sample size increases, the sampling distribution of the mean still follows a normal distribution with mean $\mu_{\bar{X}} = \mu$. However, as the sample size increases, the standard error of the mean decreases, so that a larger proportion of sample means are closer to the population mean. This reduction in variability is illustrated in Figure 28 where 500 samples of sizes 1, 2, 4, 8, 16, and 32 were randomly selected from a normally distributed population. Observe from the polygons in Figure 28 that, although the sampling distribution of the mean is approximately[3] normal for each sample size, the sample means are distributed more tightly around the population mean as the sample size is increased.

[3]*Remember that "only" 500 samples out of an infinite number of samples have been selected, so that the sampling distributions shown are only approximations of the true distributions.*

FIGURE 28
Sampling distribution of the mean from 500 samples of sizes $n = 1$, 2, 4, 8, 16, and 32 selected from a normal population

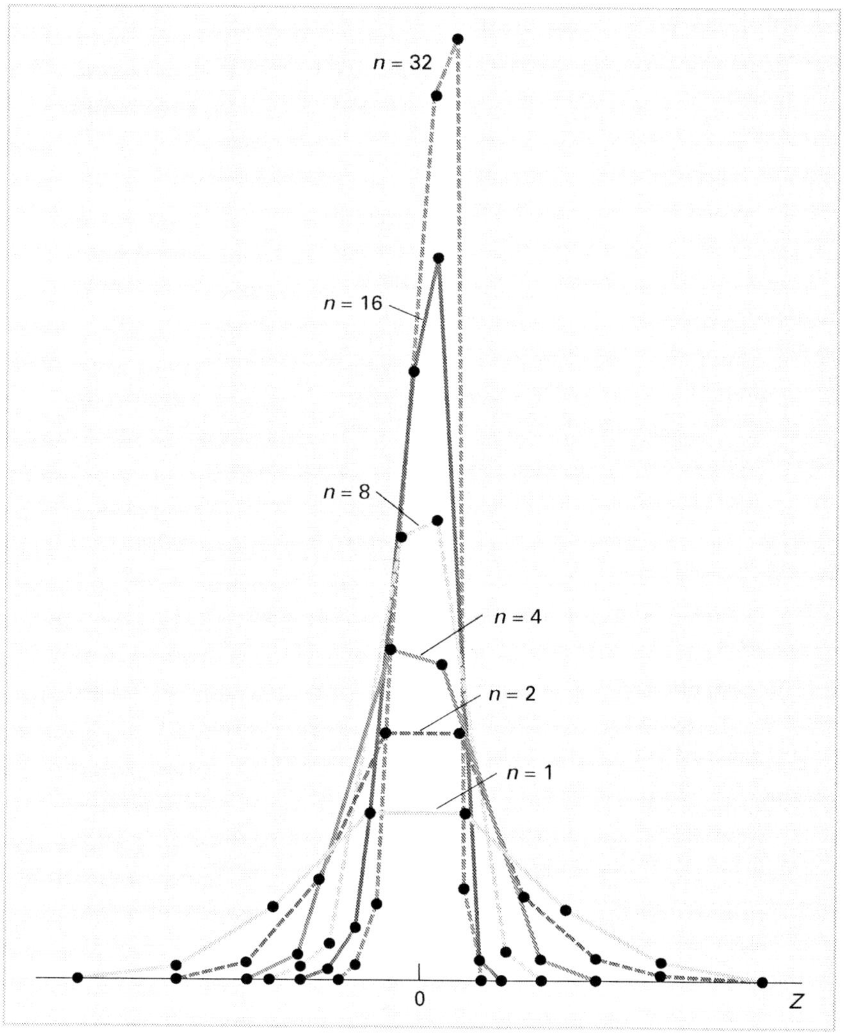

For a deeper insight into the concept of the sampling distribution of the mean, again consider the Using Statistics scenario. Suppose the packaging equipment that is filling 368-gram boxes of cereal is set so that the amount of cereal in a box is normally distributed with a mean of 368

grams. From past experience, the population standard deviation for this filling process is known to be 15 grams.

If a sample of 25 boxes is randomly selected from the many thousands that are filled in a day and the average weight is computed for this sample, what type of result could be expected? For example, do you think that the sample mean could be 368 grams? 200 grams? 365 grams?

The sample acts as a miniature representation of the population, so if the values in the population are normally distributed, the values in the sample should be approximately normally distributed. Thus, if the population mean is 368 grams, the sample mean has a good chance of being close to 368 grams.

How can you determine the probability that the sample of 25 boxes will have a mean below 365 grams? From the normal distribution (section 1) you know that the area below any value X can be found by converting to standardized Z units and finding the appropriate value in the Cumulative Standardized Normal table.

$$Z = \frac{X - \mu}{\sigma}$$

In the examples in section 1, you studied how any single value X deviates from the mean. Now, in the cereal-fill example, the value involved is a sample mean $\bar{X}$ and you wish to determine the likelihood of obtaining a sample mean below 365. Thus, by substituting $\bar{X}$ for X, $\mu_{\bar{X}}$ for μ, and $\sigma_{\bar{X}}$ for σ, the appropriate Z value is defined in Equation (12):

FINDING Z FOR THE SAMPLING DISTRIBUTION OF THE MEAN

The Z value is equal to the difference between the sample mean $\bar{X}$ and the population mean μ, divided by the standard error of the mean $\sigma_{\bar{X}}$.

$$Z = \frac{\bar{X} - \mu_{\bar{X}}}{\sigma_{\bar{X}}} = \frac{\bar{X} - \mu}{\frac{\sigma}{\sqrt{n}}} \quad \textbf{(12)}$$

Note that, based on the property of *unbiasedness*, it is always true that $\mu_{\bar{X}} = \mu$. To find the area below 365 grams, from Equation (12),

$$Z = \frac{\bar{X} - \mu_{\bar{X}}}{\sigma_{\bar{X}}} = \frac{365 - 368}{\frac{15}{\sqrt{25}}} = \frac{-3}{3} = -1.00$$

The area corresponding to $Z = -1.00$ in the Cumulative Standardized Normal table is 0.1587. Therefore, 15.87% of all the possible samples of size 25 have a sample mean below 365 grams.

This is not the same as saying that a certain percentage of *individual* boxes will have less than 365 grams of cereal. That percentage can be computed as follows:

$$Z = \frac{X - \mu}{\sigma} = \frac{365 - 368}{15} = \frac{-3}{15} = -0.20$$

The area corresponding to $Z = -0.20$ in the Cumulative Standardized Normal table is 0.4207. Therefore, 42.07% of the *individual* boxes are expected to contain less than 365 grams. Comparing these results, observe that many more *individual boxes* than *sample means* will be below 365 grams. This result can be explained by the fact that each sample consists of 25 different boxes, some lighter and some heavier. The averaging process dilutes the importance of any individual box, particularly when the sample size is large. Thus, the chance that the mean of a sample of 25 will be far away from the population mean is less than the chance that a *single individual* box will be.

The results can also be affected by using a different sample size, as observed in Examples 10 and 11.

EXAMPLE 10

THE EFFECT OF SAMPLE SIZE *n* ON THE COMPUTATION OF $\sigma_{\bar{X}}$

How is the standard error of the mean affected by increasing the sample size, from 25 to 100 boxes?

SOLUTION

If $n = 100$ boxes, then using Equation (11):

$$\sigma_{\bar{X}} = \frac{\sigma}{\sqrt{n}} = \frac{15}{\sqrt{100}} = \frac{15}{10} = 1.5$$

Observe that a fourfold increase in the sample size from 25 to 100 results in reducing the standard error of the mean by half—from 3 grams to 1.5 grams. This demonstrates that taking a larger sample results in less variability in the possible sample means from sample to sample.

EXAMPLE 11

THE EFFECT OF SAMPLE SIZE *n* ON THE CLUSTERING OF MEANS IN THE SAMPLING DISTRIBUTION

In the cereal-fill example, if a sample of 100 boxes is selected, what is the likelihood of obtaining a sample mean below 365 grams?

SOLUTION

Using Equation (12),

$$Z = \frac{\bar{X} - \mu_{\bar{X}}}{\sigma_{\bar{X}}} = \frac{365 - 368}{\frac{15}{\sqrt{100}}} = \frac{-3}{1.5} = -2.00$$

From the Cumulative Standardized Normal table, the area less than $Z = -2.00$ is 0.0228. Therefore, 2.28% of the samples of size 100 would be expected to have means below 365 grams, as compared with 15.87% for samples of size 25.

Sometimes you need to find the interval within which a fixed proportion of the samples (means) fall. Similar to Equation (4), a distance below and above the population mean containing a specific area of the normal curve needs to be determined. From Equation (12),

$$Z = \frac{\bar{X} - \mu}{\frac{\sigma}{\sqrt{n}}}$$

Therefore, $\bar{X}$ is defined by Equation (13).

FINDING THE VALUE OF $\bar{X}$

$$\bar{X} = \mu + Z\frac{\sigma}{\sqrt{n}} \tag{13}$$

The use of Equation (13) is illustrated in Example 12.

EXAMPLE 12

DETERMINING THE INTERVAL THAT INCLUDES A FIXED PROPORTION OF THE MEANS

In the cereal-fill example, find an interval around the population mean that will include 95% of the sample means based on samples of 25 boxes.

SOLUTION

The 95% is divided into two equal parts, half below the mean and half above the mean. The value of Z corresponding to an area of 0.0250 in the lower tail of the normal curve in the Cumulative Standardized Normal table is -1.96, and the value of Z corresponding to a cumulative area of 0.975 (that is, 0.025 in the upper tail of the normal curve) in the table is $+1.96$. The lower value of $\overline{X}$ (called $\overline{X}_L$) and the upper value of $\overline{X}$ (called $\overline{X}_U$) are found by using Equation (13):

$$\overline{X}_L = 368 + (-1.96)\frac{15}{\sqrt{25}} = 368 - 5.88 = 362.12$$

$$\overline{X}_U = 368 + (1.96)\frac{15}{\sqrt{25}} = 368 + 5.88 = 373.88$$

Therefore, 95% of all sample means based on samples of 25 boxes will fall between 362.12 and 373.88 grams.

Sampling from Nonnormally Distributed Populations

The Central Limit Theorem
The Central Limit Theorem states that as the sample size (i.e., the number of observations in each sample) gets *large enough*, the sampling distribution of the mean can be approximated by the normal distribution. This is true regardless of the shape of the distribution of the individual values in the population.

So far in this section, the sampling distribution of the mean for a normally distributed population has been discussed. However, in many instances, either it is known that the population is not normally distributed or it is unrealistic to assume a normal distribution. An important theorem in statistics, the central limit theorem given in the definition box on the left, deals with this situation.

What sample size is large enough? A great deal of statistical research has gone into this issue. As a general rule, statisticians have found that for many population distributions, when the sample size is at least 30, the sampling distribution of the mean will be approximately normal. However, you may be able to apply the central limit theorem for even smaller sample sizes if the distribution is known to be approximately bell-shaped. In the uncommon case where the distribution is extremely skewed or has more than one mode, sample sizes larger than 30 may be needed to ensure normality in the sampling distribution of the mean.

The application of the central limit theorem to different populations is illustrated in Figure 29. The sampling distributions from three different continuous distributions (normal, uniform, and exponential) for varying sample sizes ($n = 2, 5, 30$) are displayed. The effects that the sample size has on the shape and the amount of variability are illustrated.

The first panel of Figure 29 illustrates the sampling distribution of the mean selected from a normal population. As mentioned earlier, when the population is normally distributed, the sampling distribution of the mean will be normally distributed regardless of the sample size. As the sample size increases, the variability as described by the standard error of the mean (Equation 11) decreases. Because of the unbiasedness property, the mean of any sampling distribution is always equal to the mean of the population.

The second panel of Figure 29 depicts the sampling distribution from a population with a uniform (or rectangular) distribution (see section 3). When samples of size $n = 2$ are selected, there is a peaking or *central limiting* effect already working. For $n = 5$, the sampling distribution is bell-shaped and approximately normal. When $n = 30$, the sampling distribution appears to be very similar to a normal distribution. In general, the larger the sample size the more closely the sampling distribution will follow a normal distribution. As with all cases, the mean of each sampling distribution is equal to the mean of the population, and the variability decreases as the sample size increases.

The third panel of Figure 29 presents an exponential distribution (see section 4). This population is heavily skewed to the right. When $n = 2$ the sampling distribution is still highly skewed to the right but less so than the distribution of the population. For $n = 5$, the sampling distribution is more

FIGURE 29
Sampling distribution of the mean for different populations for samples of $n = 2, 5$, and 30

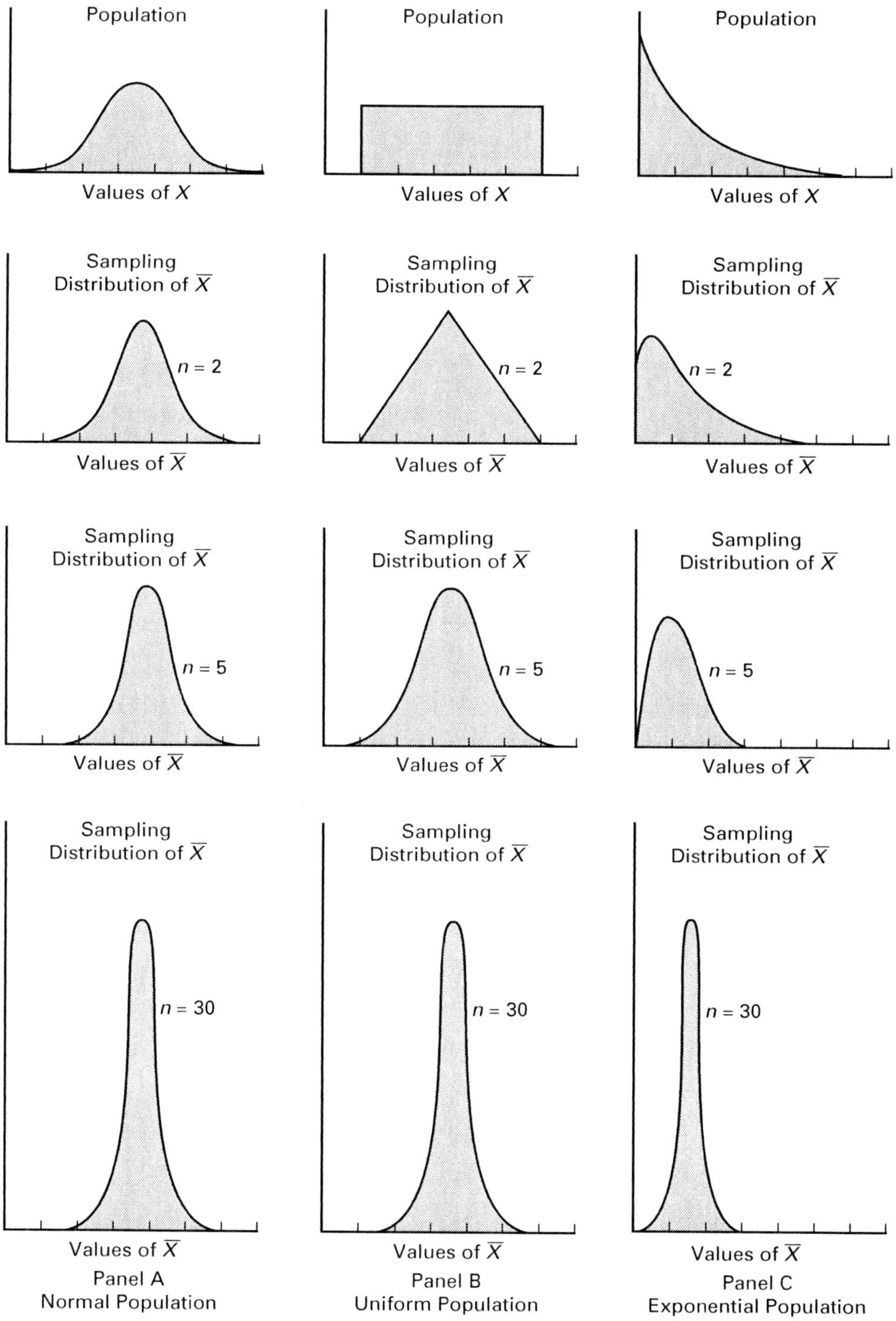

symmetric with only a slight skew to the right. When $n = 30$, the sampling distribution appears to be approximately normal. Again, the mean of each sampling distribution is equal to the mean of the population, and the variability decreases as the sample size increases. Using the results obtained from these well-known statistical distributions (normal, uniform, and exponential), some conclusions regarding the central limit theorem are presented in Exhibit 5.

EXHIBIT 5 NORMALITY AND THE SAMPLING DISTRIBUTION OF THE MEAN

1. For most population distributions, regardless of shape, the sampling distribution of the mean is approximately normally distributed if samples of at least 30 observations are selected.
2. If the population distribution is fairly symmetrical, the sampling distribution of the mean is approximately normal if samples of at least 15 observations are selected.
3. If the population is normally distributed, the sampling distribution of the mean is normally distributed regardless of the sample size.

The central limit theorem is of crucial importance in using statistical inference to draw conclusions about a population. It allows you to make inferences about the population mean without having to know the specific shape of the population distribution.

VISUAL EXPLORATIONS: Exploring Sampling Distributions

Use the Visual Explorations Two Dice Probability procedure to observe the effects of simulated throws on the frequency distribution of the sum of the two dice. Open the **Visual Explorations.xla** macro workbook and select **VisualExplorations | Two Dice Probability** from the Microsoft Excel menu bar. The procedure produces a worksheet that contains an empty frequency distribution table and histogram and a floating control panel (see illustrations on this page).

Click the Tally button to tally a set of throws in the frequency distribution table and histogram.

Optionally, use the spinner buttons to adjust the number of throws per tally (round).

Click the **Help** button for more information about this simulation. Click **Finish** when you are finished.

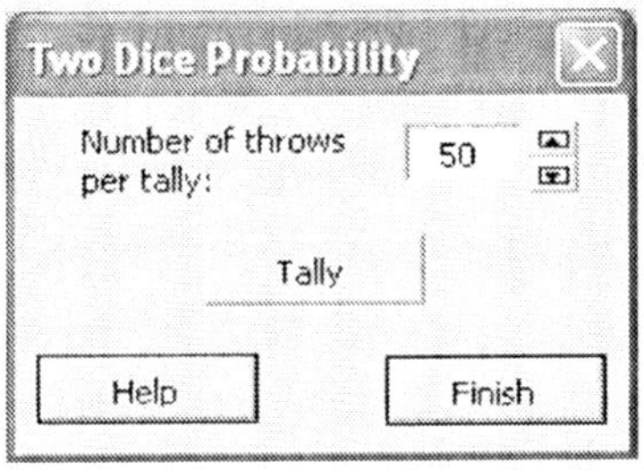

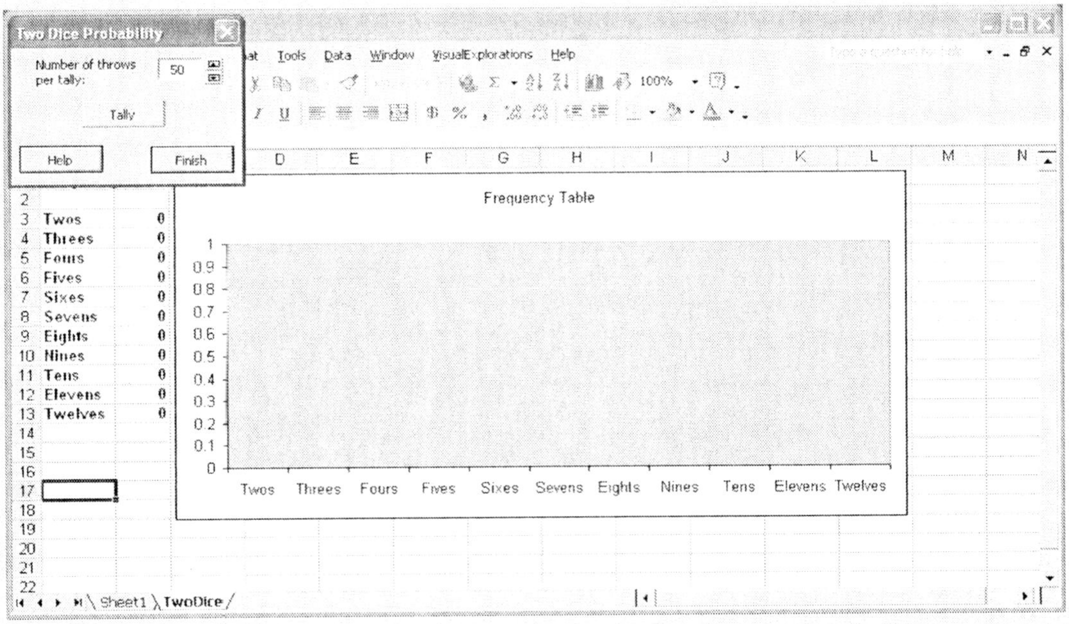

CHAPTER 6.xls

*Retrieve the SDS and SDSHistogram sheets of the **Chapter 6.xls** workbook to view a simulated sampling distribution similar to the one produced by these strategies.*

Excel Strategies Generating Simulated Sampling Distributions

You generate simulated sampling distributions by first using the Data Analysis Random Number Generator procedure to generate a worksheet containing multiple random samples and then by adding formulas to this worksheet to calculate the sample means and other appropriate measures. PHStat2 can do both tasks for you in one step.

For example, to generate a simulated sampling distribution from a uniformly distributed population, using 100 samples of sample size 30, open to an empty worksheet and use one of these strategies:

Using Excel with PHStat2

Use the PHStat2 Sampling Distributions Simulation procedure to generate a simulated sampling distribution.

Select **PHStat | Sampling | Sampling Distributions Simulation**.

In the Sampling Distributions Simulation dialog box (shown at right):

Enter **100** in the **Number of Samples** edit box.

Enter **30** in the **Sample Size** edit box.

Select the **Uniform** option button.

Enter a title in the **Title** edit box.

Select the **Histogram** check box.

Click the **OK** button.

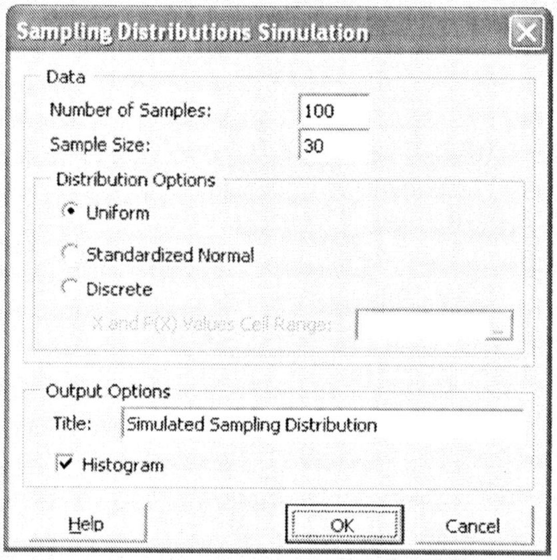

*PHStat2 can also generate a simulation from a standardized normal distribution or a discrete population. To generate a simulation from a discrete population, open to a worksheet that contains a table of X and P(X) values and enter that table range in the **X and P(X) Values Cell Range** edit box after selecting the **Discrete** option button.*

Using Excel

Follow the instructions for the following two tasks to generate a simulated sample distribution.

Generate Multiple Samples Worksheet Task. Follow the instructions of section EH4 at the end of this chapter to use the Data Analysis Random Number Generator procedure to generate multiple random samples in the cell range A1:CV30 on a new worksheet. When you generate this new sheet, modify it to calculate the sample means and overall average. To calculate the sample means, enter the label value **Sample Means:** in cell **A31** and then enter the formula **=AVERAGE(A1:A30)** in cell **A32** and copy it across the 100 columns to cell **CV32**. To calculate the overall average, enter the label value **Overall Average:** in cell **A33** and then enter the formula **=AVERAGE(32:32)** in cell **A34**.

*For problems that require generating multiple samples from either a standardized normal distribution or a discrete distribution, also calculate the standard error of the mean by entering the label **Standard Error of the Mean** in cell **A35** and the formula **=STDEV(32:32)** in cell **A36**.*

Generate Histogram Task. Follow the instructions of section EH5 to generate a histogram from the sample means found in the multiple samples worksheet.

PROBLEMS FOR SECTION 6

Learning the Basics

38 Given a normal distribution with $\mu = 100$ and $\sigma = 10$, if a sample of $n = 25$ is selected, what is the probability that $\bar{X}$ is

a. less than 95?
b. between 95 and 97.5?
c. above 102.2?
d. between 99 and 101?
e. There is a 65% chance that $\bar{X}$ will be above what value?
f. What would be your answers to (a)–(e) if $n = 16$?

39 Given a normal distribution with $\mu = 50$ and $\sigma = 5$, if a sample of $n = 100$ is selected, what is the probability that $\bar{X}$ is

a. less than 47?
b. between 47 and 49.5?
c. above 51.1?
d. between 49 and 51?
e. There is a 35% chance that $\bar{X}$ will be above what value?
f. What would be your answers to (a)–(e) if $n = 25$?

Applying the Concepts

40 For each of the following three populations, indicate what the sampling distribution for samples of 25 would consist of.

a. Travel expense vouchers for a university in an academic year
b. Absentee records (days absent per year) in 2003 for employees of a large manufacturing company
c. Yearly sales (in gallons) of unleaded gasoline at service stations located in a particular county

41 The following data represent the number of days absent per year in a population of six employees of a small company:

1 3 6 7 7 12

a. Assuming that you sample without replacement, select all possible samples of size 2 and set up the sampling distribution of the mean. Compute the mean of all the sample means and also compute the population mean. Are they equal? What is this property called?
b. Do (a) for all possible samples of size 3.
c. Compare the shape of the sampling distribution of the mean obtained in (a) and (b). Which sampling distribution seems to have less variability? Why?
d. Assuming that you sample with replacement, do (a)–(c) and compare the results. Which sampling distributions seem to have the least variability, those in (a) or (b)? Why?

42 The diameter of Ping-Pong balls manufactured at a large factory is expected to be approximately normally distributed with a mean of 1.30 inches and a standard deviation of 0.04 inch. What is the probability that a randomly selected Ping-Pong ball will have a diameter

a. less than 1.28 inches?
b. between 1.31 and 1.33 inches?
c. Between what two values (symmetrically distributed around the mean) will 60% of the Ping-Pong balls fall (in terms of the diameter)?

If many random samples of 16 Ping-Pong balls are selected,

d. what will be the values of the population mean and standard error of the mean?
e. what distribution will the sample means follow?
f. what proportion of the sample means will be less than 1.28 inches?
g. what proportion of the sample means will be between 1.31 and 1.33 inches?
h. between what two values symmetrically distributed around the mean will 60% of the sample means be?
i. Compare the answers of (a) with (f) and (b) with (g). Discuss.
j. Explain the difference in the results of (c) and (h).
k. Which is more likely to occur—an individual ball above 1.34 inches, a sample mean above 1.32 inches in a sample of size 4, or a sample mean above 1.31 inches in a sample of size 16? Explain.

43 The basic materials stock sector, comprised of companies specializing in industrial commodities, had a very poor showing during the first six months of 2000. The average stock price in this sector was down an average of 27% for this period ("Business Bulletin," *Wall Street Journal*, July 20, 2000, A1). Assume that the returns were distributed as a normal random variable with a mean of −27% and a standard deviation of 15%.

If an individual stock were selected from this population, what is the probability that it would have a return

a. between −32% and −22%?
b. between −37% and −17%?
c. between −47% and −7%?
d. return greater than 0.0%, i.e. a profit?

If random samples of 10 stocks were selected from this population, what proportion of the samples would have a mean return

e. between −32% and −22%?
f. between −37% and −17%?
g. between −47% and −7%?
h. greater than 0.0%, i.e. a profit?
i. Compare the results of (a) with (e), (b) with (f), (c) with (g), and (d) with (h). Explain.

44 Time spent using e-mail per session is normally distributed with $\mu = 8$ minutes and $\sigma = 2$ minutes. If random samples of 25 sessions were selected,

a. what proportion of the sample means would be between 7.8 and 8.2 minutes?
b. what proportion of the sample means would be between 7.5 and 8 minutes?
c. If random samples of 100 sessions were selected, what proportion of the sample means would be between 7.8 and 8.2 minutes?
d. Explain the difference in the results of (a) and (c).
e. Which is more likely to occur—a particular session of e-mail for more than 11 minutes, a sample mean above 9 minutes in a sample of 25 sessions, or a sample mean above 8.6 minutes in a sample of 100 sessions? Explain.

45 The amount of time a bank teller spends with each customer has a population mean $\mu = 3.10$ minutes and standard deviation $\sigma = 0.40$ minute. If a random sample of 16 customers is selected,
a. what is the probability that the average time spent per customer will be at least 3 minutes?
b. there is an 85% chance that the sample mean will be below how many minutes?
c. What assumption must be made in order to solve (a) and (b)?
d. If a random sample of 64 customers is selected, there is an 85% chance that the sample mean will be below how many minutes?
e. What assumption, if any, must be made in order to solve (d)?
f. Which is most likely to occur—an individual service time below 2 minutes, a sample mean above 3.4 minutes in a sample of 16 customers, or a sample mean below 2.9 minutes in a sample of 64 customers? Explain.

46 The *New York Times* reported (Laurie J. Flynn, "Tax Surfing," The *New York Times*, March 25, 2002, C10) that the average time to download the homepage from the Internal Revenue Service Web site **www.irs.gov** was 0.8 seconds. Suppose that the download time was normally distributed with a standard deviation of 0.2 seconds. If random samples of 30 download times are selected,
a. what proportion of the sample means will be less than 0.75 second?
b. what proportion of the sample means will be between 0.70 and 0.90 second?
c. 80% of the sample means will be between what two values symmetrically distributed around the population mean?
d. 90% of the sample means will be less than what value?

The same article also reported that the average download time for the H&R Block Web site **www.hrblock.com** was 2.5 seconds. Suppose that the download time for the H&R Block Web site was normally distributed with a standard deviation of 0.5 seconds. If random samples of 30 download times are selected,
e. what proportion of the sample means will be less than 2.75 seconds?
f. what proportion of the sample means will be between 2.70 and 2.90 seconds?
g. 80% of the sample means will be between what two values symmetrically distributed around the population mean?
h. 90% of the sample means will be less than what value?
i. What assumptions, if any, about the probability distributions of the population download times do you have to make to complete (a)–(h)?

47 According to The U.S. Census Bureau, the mean household income in the United States in 2000 was $57,045 and the median household income was $42,148 (U.S. Census Bureau, "Money Income in the United States: 2000," **www.census.gov**, September 2001). The variability of household income is quite large, with the 10th percentile approximately equal to $10,600, the 90th percentile approximately equal to $111,600, and an overall standard deviation of approximately $25,000. Suppose random samples of 225 households were selected.
a. What proportion of the sample means would be below $55,000?
b. What proportion of the sample means would be above $60,000?
c. What proportion of the sample means would be above $111,600?
d. Why is the probability you calculated in (c) so much lower than 0.10, even though 10% of individual households have incomes above $111,600?
e. If random samples of size 20 were selected, can you use the methods discussed in this chapter to calculate the probabilities requested in (a)–(c)? Explain.

48 Although the first quarter of 2002 was quite dismal on Wall Street, mutual funds investing in gold companies rose an average of 35.2% ("Stock Funds Perk Up in the First Quarter," **www.usatoday.com**, April 4, 2002). Assume that the distribution of returns in the first quarter of 2002 for mutual funds specializing in gold companies is fairly symmetrical with a mean of 35.2% and a standard deviation of 20%. If random samples of 16 gold stock funds were selected:
a. Find the probability that the sample mean return is less than 25%.
b. Find the probability that the sample mean return is greater than 40%.
c. Find the probability that the sample mean return is between 25% and 45%.
d. 80% of the sample mean returns are between what two values symmetrically distributed around the mean?
e. 90% of the sample mean returns are between what two values symmetrically distributed around the mean?
f. 95% of the sample mean returns are between what two values symmetrically distributed around the mean?

7 SAMPLING DISTRIBUTION OF THE PROPORTION

When dealing with a categorical variable where each individual or item in the population is classified as either possessing or not possessing a particular characteristic such as male or female, or prefer brand A or do not prefer brand A, the two possible outcomes are assigned scores of 1 or 0 to represent the presence or absence of the characteristic. If only a random sample of n individuals is available, the sample mean for such a categorical variable is found by summing all the 1 and 0 scores and then dividing by n. For example, if, in a sample of five individuals, three preferred brand A and two did not, there are three 1's and two 0's. Summing the three 1's and two 0's and dividing by the sample size of 5 gives a mean of 0.60, which is also the proportion of individuals in the sample who prefer brand A. Reporting the value 0.60 as a proportion is more descriptive of the real-world situation than reporting it as a mean of the assigned 0/1 values. Therefore, when dealing with categorical data, the statistic of interest is the proportion in a *sample* having the characteristic of interest. This statistic is called the sample proportion and is denoted by the symbol p_s [see Equation (14)]. The sample proportion is an estimate of the population parameter, p, the proportion of the *population* having the characteristic of interest.

THE SAMPLE PROPORTION

$$p_s = \frac{X}{n} = \frac{\text{number of items having the characteristic of interest}}{\text{sample size}} \quad \textbf{(14)}$$

The sample proportion p_s has a special property; it takes on values between 0 and 1. If all individuals possess the characteristic, each is assigned a score of 1 and p_s is equal to 1. If half the individuals possess the characteristic, half are assigned a score of 1, the other half are assigned a score of 0, and p_s is equal to 0.5. If none of the individuals possesses the characteristic, each is assigned a score of 0 and p_s is equal to 0.

While the sample mean is an unbiased estimator of the population mean μ, the statistic p_s is an unbiased estimator of the population proportion p. By analogy to the standard error of the mean, the **standard error of the proportion** σ_{p_s} is given in Equation (15).

STANDARD ERROR OF THE PROPORTION

$$\sigma_{p_s} = \sqrt{\frac{p(1-p)}{n}} \quad \textbf{(15)}$$

When sampling with replacement from a finite population or without replacement from an infinite population, the **sampling distribution of the proportion** follows the binomial distribution. However, the normal distribution can be used to approximate the binomial distribution when np and $n(1-p)$ are each at least 5 (see section 8 on the CD). In most cases in which inferences are made about the proportion, the sample size is substantial enough to meet the conditions for using the normal approximation (see reference 1). Therefore, in many instances, the normal distribution can be used to estimate the sampling distribution of the proportion. Thus, substituting p_s for $\bar{X}$, p for μ, and $\sqrt{\frac{p(1-p)}{n}}$ for $\frac{\sigma}{\sqrt{n}}$ in Equation (12), results in Equation (16).

DIFFERENCE BETWEEN THE SAMPLE PROPORTION AND THE POPULATION PROPORTION IN STANDARDIZED NORMAL UNITS

$$Z = \frac{p_S - p}{\sqrt{\frac{p(1-p)}{n}}} \quad \textbf{(16)}$$

To illustrate the sampling distribution of the proportion, suppose that the manager of the local branch of a savings bank determines that 40% of all depositors have multiple accounts at the bank. If you select a random sample of 200 depositors, the probability that the sample proportion of depositors with multiple accounts is no more than 0.30 is calculated as follows.

Because $np = 200(0.40) = 80 \geq 5$ and $n(1-p) = 200(0.60) = 120 \geq 5$, the sample size is large enough to assume that the sampling distribution of the proportion is approximately normally distributed. Using Equation (16),

$$\begin{aligned} Z &= \frac{p_S - p}{\sqrt{\frac{p(1-p)}{n}}} \\ &= \frac{0.30 - 0.40}{\sqrt{\frac{(0.40)(0.60)}{200}}} = \frac{-0.10}{\sqrt{\frac{0.24}{200}}} = \frac{-0.10}{0.0346} \\ &= -2.89 \end{aligned}$$

Using the Cumulative Standardized Normal table, the area under the normal curve less than $Z = -2.89$ is 0.0019. Therefore, the probability of obtaining a sample proportion of no more than 0.30 is 0.0019—a highly unlikely event. This means that if the true proportion of successes in the population were 0.40, then less than one-fifth of 1% of the samples of size 200 are expected to have sample proportions of less than 0.30.

PROBLEMS FOR SECTION 7

Learning the Basics

49 In a random sample of 64 people, 48 were classified as "successful." If the population proportion is 0.70,

a. determine the sample proportion p_s of "successful" people.

b. determine the standard error of the proportion.

50 A random sample of 50 households was selected for a telephone survey. The key question asked was, "Do you or any member of your household own a DVD player?" Of the 50 respondents, 15 said yes and 35 said no. If the population proportion is 0.40,

a. determine the sample proportion p_s of households with DVD players.

b. determine the standard error of the proportion.

51 The following raw data represent the responses (Y for yes and N for no) from a sample of 40 college students to the question, "Do you currently own shares in any stocks?"

N N Y N N Y N Y N Y N N Y N Y Y N N N Y
N Y N N N N Y N N Y Y N N N Y N N Y N N

If the population proportion is 0.30,

a. Determine the sample proportion p_s of college students who own shares of stock.

b. determine the standard error of the proportion.

Applying the Concepts

52 A political pollster is conducting an analysis of sample results in order to make predictions on election night. Assuming a two-candidate election, if a specific candidate receives at least 55% of the vote in the sample, then that candidate will be forecast as the winner of the election. If a random sample of 100 voters is selected, what is the probability that a candidate will be forecast as the winner when

a. the true percentage of her vote is 50.1%?

b. the true percentage of her vote is 60%?

c. the true percentage of her vote is 49% (and she will actually lose the election)?

d. If the sample size is increased to 400, what will be your answers to (a), (b), and (c)? Discuss?

53 A marketing experiment is to be conducted in which students are to taste two different brands of soft drink. Their task is to correctly identify the brand tasted. Random samples of 200 students are selected, and it is assumed that the students have no ability to distinguish between the two brands. (*Hint:* If an individual has no ability to distinguish between the two soft drinks, then each brand is equally likely to be selected.)

a. What proportion of the samples will have between 50% and 60% of the identifications correct?

b. Within what symmetrical limits of the population percentage will 90% of the sample percentages fall?

c. What is the probability of obtaining a sample percentage of correct identifications greater than 65%?

d. Which is more likely to occur—more than 60% correct identifications in the sample of 200 or more than 55% correct identifications in a sample of 1,000? Explain.

54 Approximately 5% of U.S. families have a net worth in excess of $1 million, and thus can be called millionaires. However, 30% of Microsoft's 31,000 employees are millionaires (Suzy Wetlanfer, "Who Want$ to Manage a Millionaire?" *Harvard Business Review*, July–August, 2000, 53–60). If random samples of 100 Microsoft employees are selected, what proportion of the samples will have

a. between 25% and 35% millionaires?

b. between 20% and 40% millionaires?

c. more than 40% millionaires?

d. If samples of size 50 are taken, how does this change your answers to (a)–(c)?

55 According to an article in *MediaWeek*, 58.3% of the 222,900 households in Montgomery County get the Sunday edition of the *Dayton Daily News* (Eileen Davis Hudson, "Market Profile: Dayton, Ohio," July 17, 2000, 16–24). Suppose that random samples of 200 Montgomery County households are selected.

a. In what proportion of the samples will between 55% and 60% of the households get the Sunday edition of the *Dayton Daily News*?

b. In what proportion will this percentage be between 50% and 65%?

c. In what proportion will this percentage be less than 45%?

d. If samples of size 100 are taken, how does this change your answers to (a)–(c)?

56 According to an article in *American Demographics*, 19% of the entire U.S. population listens to Internet radio (Rebecca Gardyn, "High Frequency," July 2000, 32–36). If random samples of size 200 are selected, what proportion will have

a. between 14% and 24% who listen to Internet radio?

b. between 9% and 29% who listen to Internet radio?

c. more than 30% who listen to Internet radio?

d. If random samples of size 100 are selected, how does this change your answers to (a)–(c)?

57 Online customer service is a key element of online retailing. According to the WSJ Market Data Group, 37.5% of **www.priceline.com** customers take advantage of this service ("Reality Bytes," *Wall Street Journal*, June 5, 2000, C2). If random samples of 200 **www.priceline.com** customers are selected,

a. what proportion of samples are likely to have between 35% and 40% who take advantage of online customer service?

b. within what symmetrical limits of the population percentage will 90% of the sample percentages fall?

c. within what symmetrical limits of the population percentage will 95% of the sample percentages fall?

58 According to the National Restaurant Association, 20% of fine-dining restaurants have instituted policies restricting the use of cell phones ("Business Bulletin," *Wall Street Journal*, June 1, 2000, A1). If random samples of 100 fine-dining restaurants are selected,

a. what proportion of samples are likely to have between 15% and 25% that have established policies restricting use?

b. within what symmetrical limits of the population percentage will 90% of the sample percentages fall?

c. within what symmetrical limits of the population percentage will 95% of the sample percentages fall?

59 Researchers at Student Monitor estimate that 13% of U.S. college students purchased items from an online bookseller during the spring semester of 2000 (Ronna Abramson, "Textbook Sellers Get an Education," *The Industry Standard*, July 10–17, 2000, 96). If random samples of 400 U.S. college students are selected,

a. what proportion of samples are likely to have between 10% and 15% who purchased items from an online bookseller?

b. If a current sample of 400 U.S. college students has more than 18% who purchased items from an online bookseller, what can you infer about the population estimate of 13%. Explain.

c. If a current sample of 100 U.S. college students has more than 18% who purchased items from an online bookseller, what can you infer about the population estimate of 13%. Explain.

60 The Internal Revenue Service (IRS) discontinued random audits in 1988. Instead, the IRS conducts audits on returns deemed as questionable by their Discriminant Function System (DFS), a complicated and highly secretive computerized analysis system. In an attempt to reduce the proportion of "no-change" audits (i.e., audits that uncover that no additional taxes are due) the IRS only audits returns the DFS scores as highly questionable. The proportion of "no-change" audits has risen over the years and is currently approximately 0.25 (Tom Herman, "Unhappy Returns: IRS Moves to Bring Back Random Audits," *Wall Street Journal*, June 20, 2002, A1). Suppose that random samples of 100 audits are selected.

a. What proportion of the samples will have between 24% and 26% no-change audits?

b. What proportion of the samples will have between 20% and 30% no-change audits?
c. What proportion of the samples will contain more than 30% no-change audits?

The IRS announced that it plans to resume totally random audits in 2002. Suppose that random samples of 200 totally random audits are selected, and that only 10% of all the returns filed would result in audits requiring additional taxes.

d. What proportion of the samples will have between 89% and 91% no-change audits?
e. What proportion of the samples will have between 85% and 95% no-change audits?
f. What proportion of the samples will have more than 95% no-change audits?

8 THE NORMAL APPROXIMATION TO THE BINOMIAL AND POISSON DISTRIBUTIONS (CD-ROM TOPIC)

section6.8.pdf

In many circumstances, the normal distribution can be used to approximate the binomial and the Poisson distributions. For further discussion, see **section6.8.pdf** located on the CD-ROM that accompanies this text.

9 SAMPLING FROM FINITE POPULATIONS (CD-ROM TOPIC)

section6.9.pdf

In this section, sampling without replacement from finite populations is considered. For further discussion see the **section6.9.pdf** on the CD-ROM that accompanies the text.

SUMMARY

In this chapter the normal distribution was used in the Using Statistics scenario to study the time to download a Web page. As seen in the summary flowchart, in addition to the normal distribution, the uniform distribution, the exponential distribution, and the normal probability plot have been studied.

This chapter also introduced the sampling distribution of the sample mean and the sampling distribution of the sample proportion. You learned that the sample mean is an unbiased estimator of the population mean and the sample proportion is an unbiased estimator of the population proportion. The importance of the normal distribution in statistics has been further emphasized through an examination of the central limit theorem. The concepts concerning sampling distributions are central to the development of statistical inference. The main objective of statistical inference is to take information based only on a sample and use this information to draw conclusions and make decisions about various population values. For example, by observing the mean weight in a sample of cereal boxes filled by the Oxford Cereal Company, you were able to draw conclusions concerning the average weight in the population of cereal boxes. You were then able to decide the likelihood that the average fill-weight of the population of cereal boxes was 368 grams.

KEY TERMS

central limit theorem
continuous probability density function
continuous random variable
cumulative standardized normal distribution
exponential distribution
inverse normal scores transformation
normal distribution
normal probability density function
normal probability plot
rectangular distribution
sampling distribution
sampling distribution of the mean
sampling distribution of the proportion
standard error of the mean
standard error of the proportion
standardized normal quantile
standardized normal distribution
transformation formula
unbiased
uniform distribution

Chapter summary flowchart

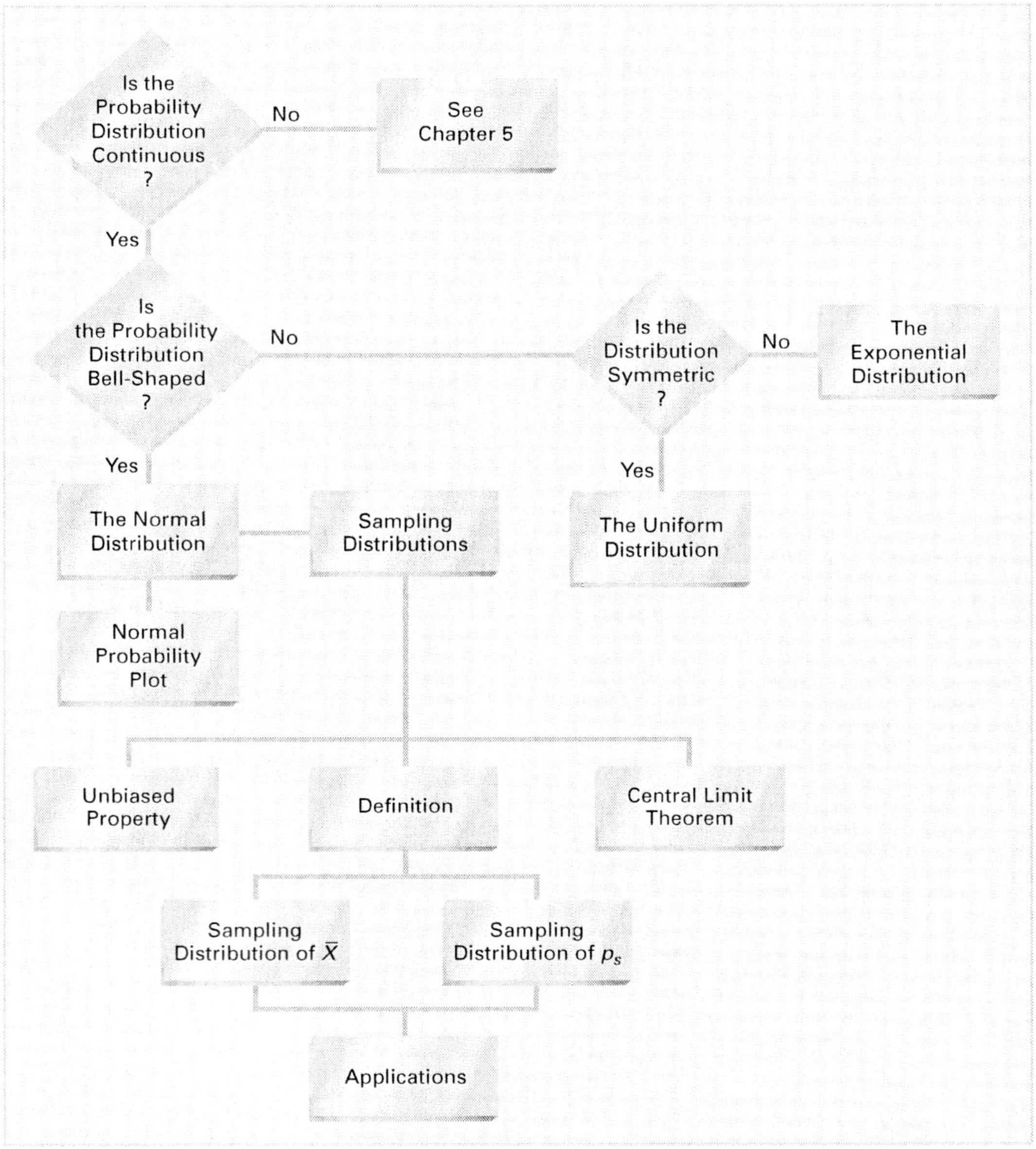

CHAPTER REVIEW PROBLEMS

Checking Your Understanding

61 Why is it that only one table of the normal distribution such as the Cumulative Standardized Normal table is needed to find any probability under the normal curve?

62 How do you find the area between two values under the normal curve?

63 How do you find the X value that corresponds to a given percentile of the normal distribution?

64 Why do the individual observations have to be converted to standardized normal ordered values in order to develop a normal probability plot?

65 What are some of the distinguishing properties of a normal distribution?

66 How does the normal probability plot allow you to evaluate whether a set of data is normally distributed?

67 Under what circumstances can the exponential distribution be used?

68 Why is the sample arithmetic mean an unbiased estimator of the population arithmetic mean?

69 Why does the standard error of the mean decrease as the sample size n increases?

70 Why does the sampling distribution of the mean follow a normal distribution for a large enough sample size even though the population may not be normally distributed?

71 Explain why a manager is interested in drawing conclusions about a population rather than merely describing the results of a sample.

72 What is the difference between a probability distribution and a sampling distribution?

73 Under what circumstances does the sampling distribution of the proportion approximately follow the normal distribution?

Applying the Concepts

74 An industrial sewing machine uses ball bearings that are targeted to have a diameter of 0.75 inch. The lower and upper specification limits under which the ball bearing can operate are 0.74 inch and 0.76 inch, respectively. Past experience has indicated that the actual diameter of the ball bearings is approximately normally distributed with a mean of 0.753 inch and a standard deviation of 0.004 inch. What is the probability that a ball bearing will be

a. between the target and the actual mean?
b. between the lower specification limit and the target?
c. above the upper specification limit?
d. below the lower specification limit?
e. Above which value in diameter will 93% of the ball bearings be?

If a random sample of 25 ball bearings is selected, what is the probability that

f. the sample mean will be between the target and the population mean of 0.753?
g. the sample mean will be between the lower specification limit and the target?
h. the sample mean will be above the upper specification limit?
i. the sample mean will be below the lower specification limit?
j. 93% of the sample mean diameters will be above what value?

75 The fill amount of bottles of soft drink has been found to be normally distributed with a mean of 2.0 liters and a standard deviation of 0.05 liter. Bottles that contain less than 95% of the listed net content (1.90 liters in this case) can make the manufacturer subject to penalty by the state office of consumer affairs, whereas bottles that have a net content above 2.10 liters may cause excess spillage upon opening. What proportion of the bottles will contain

a. between 1.90 and 2.0 liters?
b. between 1.90 and 2.10 liters?
c. below 1.90 liters?
d. below 1.90 liters or above 2.10 liters?
e. above 2.10 liters?
f. between 2.05 and 2.10 liters?
g. 99% of the bottles would be expected to contain at least how much soft drink?
h. 99% of the bottles would be expected to contain an amount that is between which two values (symmetrically distributed)?
i. Explain the difference in the results in (g) and (h).
j. Suppose that in an effort to reduce the number of bottles that contain less than 1.90 liters, the bottler sets the filling machine so that the mean is 2.02 liters. Under these circumstances, what would be your answers in (a)–(h)?

If a random sample of 25 bottles is selected, what is the probability that the sample mean will be

k. between 1.99 and 2.0 liters?
l. between 1.99 and 2.01 liters?
m. below 1.98 liters?
n. below 1.98 liters or above 2.02 liters?
o. above 2.01 liters?
p. between 2.01 and 2.03 liters?
q. 99% of the sample means would be expected to contain at least how much soft drink?
r. 99% of the sample means would be expected to contain an amount that is between which two values (symmetrically distributed around the mean)?
s. Explain the difference in the results in (q) and (r).

76 An orange juice producer buys all his oranges from a large orange grove. The amount of juice squeezed from each of these oranges is approximately normally distributed with a mean of 4.70 ounces and a standard deviation of 0.40 ounce.

a. What is the probability that a randomly selected orange will contain between 4.70 and 5.00 ounces?
b. What is the probability that a randomly selected orange will contain between 5.00 and 5.50 ounces?
c. 77% of the oranges will contain at least how many ounces of juice?
d. Between what two values (in ounces) symmetrically distributed around the population mean will 80% of the oranges fall?

Suppose that a sample of 25 oranges is selected:

e. What is the probability that the sample mean will be at least 4.60 ounces?
f. Between what two values symmetrically distributed around the population mean will 70% of the sample means fall?
g. 77% of the sample means will be above what value?

77 According to *Investment Digest* ("Diversification and the Risk/Reward Relationship," Winter 1994, 1–3), the mean of the annual return for common stocks from 1926 to 1992 was 12.4%, and the standard deviation of the annual return was 20.6%. During the same 67-year time span, the mean of the annual return for long-term government bonds was 5.2%, and the standard deviation was 8.6%. The article claims that the distributions of annual returns for both common stocks and long-term government bonds are approximately bell-shaped and symmetric. Assume that these distributions are distributed as normal random variables with the means and standard deviations given as noted.

a. Find the probability that the return for common stocks will be greater than 0%.
b. Find the probability that the return for common stocks will be less than 0%.
c. Find the probability that the return for common stocks will be greater than 10%.
d. Find the probability that the return for common stocks will be greater than 20%.
e. Find the probability that the return for common stocks will be greater than 30%.
f. Find the probability that the return for common stocks will be less than −10%.
g. Repeat parts (a)–(f) for long-term government bonds.
h. Discuss the differences between these two investment opportunities.

78 During the first half of 2002 the stock market was quite volatile and most major indexes lost ground. By June 14, the S&P 500 Index was down 12.3% and the NASDAQ Composite Index was down 23%. U.S. stock mutual funds fared slightly better and managed to limit losses to 10% (Mara der Hovanesian, "Active Managers Flex Their Muscles," *Business Week*, July 1, 2002, 127–128). Assume that the returns for the stock mutual funds during this time period are approximately normally distributed with a mean of −10.0% and a standard deviation of 8.0%.

a. Find the probability that a stock mutual fund lost 18% or more.
b. Find the probability that a stock mutual fund lost 25% or more.
c. Find the probability that a stock mutual fund gained in value.
d. Find the probability that a stock mutual fund gained at least 10%.
e. The return for 80% of the stock mutual funds was greater than what value?
f. The return for 90% of the stock mutual funds was less than what value?
g. 95% of the stock mutual funds had returns between what two values symmetrically distributed around the mean?

79 The *New York Times* reported (Laurie J. Flynn, "Tax Surfing," The *New York Times*, March 25, 2002, C10) that the average time to download the homepage from the Internal Revenue Service Web site **www.irs.gov** was 0.8 seconds. Suppose that the download time was normally distributed with a standard deviation of 0.2 seconds. What is the probability that a download time will be

a. less than 1 second?
b. between 0.5 and 1.5 seconds?
c. above 0.5 second?
d. 99% of the download times will be above how many seconds?
e. 95% of the download times will be between what two values symmetrically distributed around the mean?

The same article also reported that the average download time for the H&R Block Web site **www.hrblock.com** was 2.5 seconds. Suppose that the download time was normally distributed with a standard deviation of 0.5 seconds. What is the probability that a download time will be

f. less than 1 second?
g. between 0.5 and 1.5 seconds?
h. above 0.5 second?
i. 99% of the download times will be above how many seconds?
j. 95% of the download times will be between what two values symmetrically distributed around the mean?
k. Compare the results for the IRS site obtained in (a)–(e) to those of the H&R Block site in (f)–(j).

80 Mutual funds specializing in telecommunications companies lost an average of 18.4% in the first quarter of 2002 ("Stock Funds Perk Up in the First Quarter," **www.usatoday.com**, April 4, 2002). Assume that the distribution of returns in the first quarter of 2002 for mutual funds specializing in telecommunications companies is fairly symmetrical with a mean of −18.4% and a standard deviation of 20%. If random samples of 25 telecommunications stock funds were selected:

a. Find the probability that a sample mean return is less than −20%.
b. Find the probability that a sample mean return is less than −25%.
c. Find the probability that a sample mean return is above 0.0%.
d. 80% of the sample mean returns are less than what value?
e. 90% of the sample mean returns are less than what value?
f. If random samples of size 4 were selected, can you use the methods discussed in this chapter to answer (a)–(e)? Explain.

81 DiGiorno's frozen pizza has some of the most creative and likeable advertisements on television. *USA Today's* Ad Track claims that 20% of viewers like the ads "a lot" (Theresa Howard, "DiGiorno Campaign Delivers Major Sales," **www.usatoday.com**, April 1, 2002). Suppose that samples of 400 television viewers are shown the advertisements.

a. What proportion of the samples will have between 18% and 22% who like the ads "a lot"?
b. What proportion of the samples will have between 16% and 24% who like the ads "a lot"?
c. What proportion of the samples will have between 14% and 26% who like the ads "a lot"?
d. What proportion of the samples will have between 12% and 28% who like the ads "a lot"?

82 **(Class Project)** According to Burton G. Malkiel, the daily changes in the closing price of stock follow a *random walk*—that is, these daily events are independent of each other and move upward or downward in a random manner—and can be approximated by a normal distribution.

To test this theory, use either a newspaper or the Internet to select one company traded on the New York Stock Exchange, one company traded on the American Stock Exchange, and one company traded "over the counter" (that is, on the NASDAQ national market) and then do the following:

1. Record the daily closing stock price of each of these companies for 6 consecutive weeks (so that you have 30 observations per company).
2. Record the daily changes in the closing stock price of each of these companies for 6 consecutive weeks (so that you have 30 observations per company).

For each of your six data sets, decide whether the data appear to be approximately normally distributed by

a. examining the stem-and-leaf display, histogram or polygon, and box-and-whisker plot.
b. evaluating the actual versus theoretical properties.
c. constructing a normal probability plot.
d. Discuss the results of (a), (b), and (c).

Note: The random-walk theory pertains to the daily changes in the closing stock price, not the daily closing stock price.

e. Based on your conclusions in (d), what can you now say about your three distributions of each type—daily closing prices and daily changes in closing prices? Which, if any, of the data sets appear to be approximately normally distributed?

83 **(Class Project)** The table of random numbers is an example of a uniform distribution because each digit is equally likely to occur. Starting in the row corresponding to the day of the month in which you were born, use the table of random numbers to take one digit at a time.

Select five different samples of sizes $n = 2$, $n = 5$, and $n = 10$. Compute the sample mean of each sample. Develop a frequency distribution of the sample means for the results of the entire class based on samples of sizes $n = 2$, $n = 5$, and $n = 10$.

What can be said about the shape of the sampling distribution for each of these sample sizes?

84 **(Class Project)** A coin having one side heads and the other side tails is to be tossed 10 times and the number of heads obtained is to be recorded. If each student performs this experiment five times, a frequency distribution of the number of heads can be developed from the results of the entire class. Does this distribution seem to approximate the normal distribution?

85 **(Class Project)** The number of cars waiting in line at a car wash is distributed as follows:

Number of Cars	Probability
0	0.25
1	0.40
2	0.20
3	0.10
4	0.04
5	0.01

The table of random numbers can be used to select samples from this distribution by assigning numbers as follows:

1. Start in the row corresponding to the day of the month in which you were born.
2. Select a two-digit random number.
3. If a random number from 00 and 24 is selected, record a length of 0; if from 25 and 64, record a length of 1; if from 65 and 84, record a length of 2; if from 85 and 94, record a length of 3; if from 95 and 98, record a length of 4; if it is 99, record a length of 5.

Select samples of sizes $n = 2$, $n = 5$, and $n = 10$. Compute the mean for each sample. For example, if a sample of size 2 results in random numbers 18 and 46, these would correspond to lengths of 0 and 1, respectively, producing a sample mean of 0.5. If each student selects five different samples for each sample size, a frequency distribution of the sample means (for each sample size) can be developed from the results of the entire class.

What conclusions can you draw about the sampling distribution of the mean as the sample size is increased?

86 **(Class Project)** The table of random numbers can simulate the selection of different colored balls from a bowl as follows:

1. Start in the row corresponding to the day of the month in which you were born.
2. Select one-digit numbers.
3. If a random digit between 0 and 6 is selected, consider the ball white; if a random digit is a 7, 8, or 9, consider the ball red.

Select samples of sizes $n = 10$, $n = 25$, and $n = 50$ digits. In each sample, count the number of white balls and compute the proportion of white balls in the sample. If each student in the class selects five different samples for each sample size, a frequency distribution of the proportion of white balls (for each sample size) can be developed from the results of the entire class.

What conclusions can be drawn about the sampling distribution of the proportion as the sample size is increased?

87 **(Class Project)** Suppose that step 3 of problem 86 uses the following rule: "If a random digit between 0 and 8 is selected, consider the ball to be white; if a random digit of 9 is selected, consider the ball to be red." Compare and contrast the results obtained in this problem and in problem 86.

Internet Exercises

88 Go to the Web site for this text

www.prenhall.com/levine

Select Chapter 6 and then click on Internet exercises.

TEAM PROJECT

TP1 The data file **MUTUAL FUNDS.xls** contains information regarding 13 variables from a sample of 259 mutual funds. The variables are:

Fund—The name of the mutual fund
Type—Type of stocks comprising the mutual fund—small cap, mid cap, large cap
Objective—Objective of stocks comprising the mutual fund—growth or value
Assets—In millions of dollars
Fees—Sales charges (no or yes)
Expense ratio—In percentage of net assets
2001 Return—Twelve-month return in 2001
3-year return—Annualized return 1999–2001
5-year return—Annualized return 1997–2001
Turnover—Level of trading activity by the mutual fund classified as very low, low, average, high, or very high
Risk—Risk-of-loss factor of the mutual fund classified as very low, low, average, high, or very high
Best quarter—Best quarterly performance 1997–2001
Worst quarter—Worst quarterly performance 1997–2001

Consider the variables expense ratio, 2001 return, and 3-year annualized return. For each of these variables decide whether the data appear to be approximately normally distributed by
a. evaluating the actual versus theoretical properties.
b. constructing a normal probability plot.

RUNNING CASE MANAGING THE *SPRINGVILLE HERALD*

The production department of the newspaper has embarked on a quality improvement effort and has chosen as its first project an issue that relates to the blackness of the newspaper print. Each day a determination needs to be made concerning how "black" the newspaper is printed. Blackness is measured on a standard scale in which the target value is 1.0. Data collected over the past year indicate that the blackness is normally distributed with an average of 1.005 and a standard deviation of 0.10.

Each day, one spot on the first newspaper printed is chosen and the blackness of the spot is measured. Suppose the blackness of the newspaper is considered acceptable if the blackness of the spot is between 0.95 and 1.05.

SH1 Assuming that the distribution has not changed from what it was in the past year, what is the probability that the blackness of the spot is:
a. less than 1.0?
b. between 0.95 and 1.0?
c. between 1.0 and 1.05?
d. less than 0.95 or greater than 1.05?

SH2 If the objective of the production team is to reduce the probability that the blackness is below 0.95 or above 1.05, would it be better off focusing on process improvement that lowered the blackness to the target value of 1.0 or on process improvement that reduced the standard deviation to 0.075? Explain.

SH3 Each day, a sample of 25 spots on the first newspaper printed are chosen and the blackness of the spots is measured. Assuming that the distribution has not changed from what it was in the past year, what is the probability that the average blackness of the spots is:
a. less than 1.0?
b. between 0.95 and 1.0?
c. between 1.0 and 1.05?
d. less than 0.95 or greater than 1.05?
e. Suppose that the average blackness of today's sample of 25 spots is 0.952. What conclusion would you draw about the blackness of the newspaper based on this result? Explain.

WEB CASE

Apply your knowledge about the normal distribution in this Web Case that extends the OnCampus! Using Statistics scenario from this chapter.

To satisfy concerns of potential advertisers, the management of *OnCampus!* has undertaken a research project to learn the amount of time viewers linger at their Web sites (known as the "stickiness" of viewers). The marketing department at *OnCampus!* has collected data that it asserts follow a normal distribution and has made some claims based on that distribution. These data and conclusions can be found in a report located on the internal Web page (**www.prenhall.com/Springville/OC_MarketingSurvey.htm**).

Read this marketing report and then answer the following:

1. Show that the collected data can be approximated by the normal distribution.
2. Review and evaluate the conclusions made by the *OnCampus!* marketing department. Which conclusions are correct? Which ones are incorrect?
3. If *OnCampus!* can improve the mean time by five more minutes, how would the probabilities change?

WEB CASE

Apply your knowledge about sampling distributions in this Web Case that reconsiders the Oxford Cereals Using Statistics scenario.

The TriCities Consumers Concerned About Cereal Companies That Cheat organization (TCCACCTC) suspects that cereal companies, including Oxford Cereals, are cheating consumers by packaging cereals at less than labeled weights. Visit the organization's Web site (**www.prenhall.com/Springville/CerealCheaters.htm**), examine their claims and supporting data and then answer the following:

1. Are the data collection procedures used by the TCCACCTC to form its conclusions flawed? What procedures could the group follow to make their analysis more rigorous?

2. Assume that the two samples of five cereal boxes (one sample for each of two cereal varieties) listed on the TCCACCTC Web site were collected randomly by organization members. For each sample, do the following:

a. Calculate the sample mean.

b. Assume the standard deviation of the process is 15 grams. Calculate the percentage of all samples for each process that would have a sample mean less than the value you calculated in step (a).

c. Again, assuming the standard deviation is 15 grams, calculate the percentage of individual boxes of cereal that would have a weight less than the value you calculated in step (a).

3. What, if any, conclusions can you form using your calculations about the filling processes of the two different cereals?

4. A representative from Oxford Cereals has asked that the TCCACCTC take down its page discussing shortages in boxes of Oxford Cereals. Is that request reasonable? Why, or why not?

5. Can the techniques of this chapter be used to prove cheating in the manner alleged by the TCCACCTC? Why, or why not?

REFERENCES

1. Cochran, W. G., *Sampling Techniques*, 3rd ed. (New York: Wiley, 1977).
2. Gunter, B., "Q-Q Plots," *Quality Progress* (February 1994), 81–86.
3. Levine, D. M., P. Ramsey, and R. Smidt, *Applied Statistics for Engineers and Scientists Using Microsoft Excel and Minitab* (Upper Saddle River, NJ: Prentice Hall, 2001).
4. Marascuilo, L. A., and M. McSweeney, *Nonparametric and Distribution-Free Methods for the Social Sciences* (Monterey, CA: Brooks/Cole, 1977).
5. *Microsoft Excel 2002* (Redmond, WA: Microsoft Corp., 2001).
6. Ramsey, P. P., and P. H. Ramsey, "Simple Tests of Normality in Small Samples," *Journal of Quality Technology* 22 (1990): 299–309.
7. Sievers, G. L., "Probability Plotting." In *Encyclopedia of Statistical Sciences*, vol. 7, edited by S. Kotz and N. L. Johnson (New York: Wiley, 1986), 232–237.

Answers to Selected Even-Numbered Problems

For more detailed solutions including explanations, interpretations, and Excel output, see the *Student Solutions Manual*.

2 (a) 0.0901 **(b)** 0.8790 **(c)** 0.3790 **(d)** 0.1210 **(e)** 0.7889 **(f)** 0.1875

4 (a) 0.1401 **(b)** 0.4168 **(c)** 0.3918 **(d)** 0.8349 **(e)** 0.1151 **(f)** Since the *normal* distribution is symmetric about its mean, half of the area will be below $Z = 0$. **(g)** −1.00. **(h)** 1.00.

6 (a) 0.9599 **(b)** 0.0228 **(c)** 0.0301 **(d)** 0.2857 **(e)** $P(X < 40) = 0.0062$, $P(X > 55) = 0.1056$, $P(X < 40) + P(X > 55) = 0.1118$ **(f)** 43.42 **(g)** 46.64 and 53.36 **(h)** 45.84.

8 (a) 0.4082 **(b)** 0.0669 **(c)** 0.2508 **(d)** 749 trucks **(e)** 39.92 thousand miles or 39,920 miles **(f)** The smaller standard deviation makes the Z-values larger. **(a)** 0.4452 **(b)** 0.0603 **(c)** 0.1815 **(d)** 819 trucks **(e)** 41.6 thousand miles or 41,600 miles.

10 (a) 0.9878 **(b)** 0.8185 **(c)** 0.1359 **(d)** 86.16% **(e)** *Option 1:* Since your score of 81% on this exam represents a Z-score of 1.00, which is below the minimum Z-score of 1.28, you will not earn an "A" grade on the exam under this grading option. Since your score of 68% on this exam represents a Z-score of 2.00, which is well above the minimum Z-score of 1.28, you will earn an "A" grade on the exam under this grading option. You should prefer Option 2.

12 (a) 0.0526 **(b)** 0.5954 **(c)** 53.08 **(d)** 41.03 and 90.37 **(e)** It is reasonable to assume that the length of a visit follows a normal distribution.

14 With 19 observations, the 18th largest observation covers an area under the normal curve of .90. The corresponding Z-value is +1.28. The largest observation covers an area under the normal curve of .95. The corresponding Z-value is either +1.645, +1.64, or +1.65, depending on the "rule" used for this selection.

16 Area under normal curve covered: 0.1429 0.2857 0.4286 0.5714 0.7143 0.8571. Standardized normal quantile value: −1.07 −0.57 −0.18 +0.18 +0.57 +1.07.

18 (a) Office I: $\bar{X} = 2.214$, $S = 1.718$, Five-number summary: 0.52 0.93 1.54 3.93 6.32. The distribution is right-skewed. Office II: $\bar{X} = 2.011$, $S = 1.892$, Five-number summary: 0.08 0.60 1.505 3.75 7.55. The distribution is right-skewed.

20 (a) The data do not appear to be approximately normally distributed. **(b)** The data do not appear to be normally distributed.

22 (a) In general, the actual properties of the data appear to be quite close to the theoretical properties of a normal distribution. **(b)** The data appear to be approximately normally distributed.

24 (a) 0.2 **(b)** 0.1 **(c)** 5 **(d)** 2.8868.

26 (a) 0.6667 **(b)** 0.1333 **(c)** 0.4667 **(d)** 17.5 **(e)** 4.3301.

28 (a) 0.3 **(b)** 0.6 **(c)** 0.1 **(d)** 0 **(e)** 1 **(f)** 0.5774.

30 (a) 0.9502 **(b)** 0.0498 **(c)** 0.0473 **(d)** 0.9527.

32 (a) 0.9179 **(b)** 0.5661 **(c)** 0.9502 and 0.6329 **(d)** 0.7769 and 0.3941.

34 (a) 0.5276 **(b)** 0.9765 **(c)** 0.7135 and 0.9981.

36 (a) 0.5034 **(b)** 0.3499 **(c)** 0.2953.

38 (a) 0.0062 **(b)** 0.0994 **(c)** 0.1357 **(d)** 0.3830 **(e)** 99.22 **(f) (a)** 0.0228 **(b)** 0.1359 **(c)** 0.1894 **(d)** 0.3108 **(e)** 99.025.

40 (a) The sampling distribution of sample means is the distribution of means from all possible samples of 25 vouchers that could occur. **(b)** The sampling distribution of sample means is the distribution of means from all possible samples of 25 records that could occur. **(c)** The sampling distribution of sample means is the distribution of means from all possible samples of 25 sales that could occur.

42 (a) 0.3085 **(b)** 0.1747 **(c)** 1.2664 and 1.3336 **(d)** 1.30 and 0.01 **(e)** Approximately normally distributed. **(f)** 0.0228 **(g)** 0.15735 **(h)** 1.2916, 1.3084 **(i)** As n increases, the value of the denominator increases, resulting in a smaller value of the overall fraction. **(j)** The standard error for the distribution of sample means of size 16 is 1/4 of the population standard deviation of individual values and means that the sampling distribution is more concentrated around the population mean. **(k)** They are equally likely to occur (probability = 0.1587) since as n increases, more sample means will be closer to the mean of the distribution and $Z = 1$ in all cases.

44 (a) 0.3830 **(b)** 0.3944 **(c)** 0.6826 **(d)** With the sample size increasing from $n = 25$ to $n = 100$, more sample means will be closer to the population mean. The standard error of the sampling distribution of size 100 is much smaller than that of size 25, so the likelihood that the sample mean will fall within 0.2 minutes of the population mean is much higher for samples of size 100 (probability = 0.6826) than for samples of size 25 (probability = 0. 3830). **(e)** It is more likely to have an individual e-mail session of greater than 11 minutes.

46 (a) 0.0855 **(b)** 0.9938 **(c)** 0.7532 and 0.8468 **(d)** 0.8468 **(e)** 0.9969 **(f)** 0.0142 **(g)** 2.3830 and 2.6170 **(h)** 2.6170 **(i)** Since the sample size is fairly large at 30, we do not need to assume that the probability distribution of the population download times is normally distributed to complete (a)–(h).

48 (a) 0.0207 **(b)** 0.1685 **(c)** 0.9543 **(d)** 28.7922 and 41.6078 **(e)** 26.9757 and 43.4243 **(f)** 25.4002 and 44.9998.

50 (a) 0.30 **(b)** 0.0693.

52 (a) 0.1635 **(b)** 0.8461 **(c)** 0.1151 **(d)** Increasing the sample size by a factor of 4 decreases the standard error by a factor of 2. **(a)** 0.0250 **(b)** 0.9793 **(c)** 0.0082.

54 (a) 0.7242 **(b)** 0.9708 **(c)** 0.0146 **(d) (a)** 0.5588 **(b)** 0.8764 **(c)** 0.0618.

56 (a) 0.9285 **(b)** 0.9997 **(c)** 0.0000 **(d) (a)** 0.7975 **(b)** 0.9897 **(c)** 0.0025.

58 (a) 0.7887 **(b)** 0.1342 and 0.2658 **(c)** 0.1216 and 0.2784.

60 (a) 0.1826 **(b)** 0.7518 **(c)** 0.1241 **(d)** 0.3626 **(e)** 0.9816 **(f)** 0.0092.

74 (a) 0.2734 **(b)** 0.2260 **(c)** 0.0401 **(d)** 0.00058 **(e)** 0.7471 **(f)** 0.4999 **(g)** 0.00009 **(h)** virtually zero **(i)** virtually zero **(j)** 0.7518.

76 (a) 0.2734 **(b)** 0.2038 **(c)** 4.404 ounces **(d)** 4.188 ounces and 5.212 ounces **(e)** 0.8944 **(f)** 4.6168 ounces and 4.7832 ounces **(g)** 4.6408.

78 (a) 0.1587 **(b)** 0.0304 **(c)** 0.1056 **(d)** 0.0062 **(e)** −16.7330 **(f)** 0.2524 **(g)** −25.6797 and 5.6797.

80 (a) 0.3446 **(b)** 0.0495 **(c)** 0.0000 **(d)** −15.0335 **(e)** −13.2738 **(f)** If random samples of size 4 were selected, the methods discussed in this chapter cannot be used to answer (a)–(e) without the additional assumption that the mutual funds data are normally distributed.

90 The normal distribution can be used to approximate the binomial distribution whenever np and $n(1 - p)$ are at least 5.

92 (a) 0.2051 **(b)** 0.8281 **(c)** 0.3770 **(d)** 0.1719 **(e)** 0.6230 **(f)** 0.8281 **(g)** **(a)** 0.2045 **(b)** 0.8286 **(c)** 0.3759 **(d)** 0.1714 **(e)** 0.6241 **(f)** 0.8284 **(h)** The normal distribution provides a good approximation to the binomial distribution in (g).

94 (a) 0.216 **(b)** 0.288 **(c)** 0.352 **(d)** 0.936 **(e)** 0.7864 **(f)** 0.0852 **(g)** 0.1932.

96 (a) 0.0821 **(b)** 0.5438 **(c)** 0.1841 **(d)** 0.6803.

98 (a) 0.0223 **(b)** 0.9927 **(c)** The assumptions made were: (1) the probability that a videocassette tape is returned per day is the same for every day, (2) the number of videocassette tapes returned in a particular day is independent of the number of tapes returned in any other day, (3) the probability that two or more returns will occur in a single time period of a day approaches zero as the time period becomes shorter. **(d)** **(a)** 0.0257 The normal probability provides a very good approximation. **(b)** 0.9812. The normal probability provides a very good approximation.

100 A sample of size 100 selected without replacement from a population of size 400 has a greater effect in reducing the standard error.

102 0.1479.

104 (a) 0.2563 **(b)** 0.0824.

Excel Handbook for the Normal Distribution and Continuous Distributions

EH1 CALCULATING NORMAL PROBABILITIES

To calculate normal probabilities, implement a worksheet that features the **STANDARDIZE**, **NORMDIST**, **NORMSINV**, and **NORMINV** functions. These functions are entered as:

STANDARDIZE(*X*, *mean*, *standard deviation*)

NORMDIST(*X*, *mean*, *standard deviation*, True), where X is the X value of interest, and *mean* and *standard deviation* are the mean and standard deviation for a normal distribution.

NORMSINV(*P* < *X*), where $P < X$ is the area under the curve that is less than X.

NORMINV(*P* < *X*, *mean*, *standard deviation*), where $P < X$, *mean*, and *standard deviation* are as defined for the NORMDIST function.

The STANDARDIZE function returns the Z value for a particular X value, mean, and standard deviation. The NORMDIST function returns the area or probability of less than a given X value. The NORMSINV function returns the Z value corresponding to the probability of less than a given X. The NORMINV function returns the X value for a given probability, mean, and standard deviation.

Tables EH1 and EH2 contain a design for a **Normal** worksheet that calculates normal probabilities for *OnCampus!* Web site Examples 1, 2, 3, 5 and 6. When implementing this design, enter the formulas for cell A18 and D13, typeset in the tables as two lines, as single continuous lines and leave column C blank. Also note the formulas for cells A10, A15, A17, A18, D11, and D12 contain two pairs of double quotation marks and the formula for cell D13 contains three pairs of double quotation marks. This design also uses the ABS (absolute value) worksheet function in cell E13 in order to present the probability for a range as a positive value.

For similar problems, the worksheet design can be adjusted by deleting unwanted ranges. For example, for a problem that does not require a probability for a range, select cell range D6:E13 and then select **Edit** | **Delete**. In Delete dialog box, select the **Shift cells up** option button and click **OK**.

Table EH1
Normal worksheet design for columns A and B

	A	B
1	Normal Probabilities	
2		
3	Common Data	
4	Mean	7
5	Standard Deviation	2
6		
7	Probability for X <=	
8	X Value	3.5
9	Z Value	=STANDARDIZE(B8, B4, B5)
10	="P(X<=" & B8 & ")"	=NORMDIST(B8, B4, B5, True)
11		
12	Probability for X >	
13	X Value	9
14	Z Value	=STANDARDIZE(B13, B4, B5)
15	="P(X> " & B13 & ")"	=1 – NORMDIST(B13, B4, B5,TRUE)
16		
17	="Probability for X<"&B8 &" or X >"&B13	
18	="P(X<" & B8 & " or X>" & B13 &")"	=B10+B15

Table EH2
Normal worksheet design for cell range D6:E18 (cell range D1:E5 is blank)

	D	E
6	Probability for a Range	
7	From X Value	7
8	To X Value	9
9	="Z Value for " &E7	=STANDARDIZE(E7, B4, B5)
10	="Z Value for " &E8	=STANDARDIZE(E8, B4, B5)
11	="P(X<=" & E7 &")"	=NORMDIST(E7, B4, B5, TRUE)
12	="P(X<=" & E8 &")"	=NORMDIST(E8, B4, B5, TRUE)
13	="P(" & E7 & "<=X<=" & E8 & ")"	=ABS(E12 – E11)
14		
15	Find X and Z Given Cumulative Percentage	
16	Cumulative Percentage	0.1
17	Z Value	=NORMSINV(E16)
18	X Value	=NORMINV(E16, B4, B5)

EH2 GENERATING NORMAL PROBABILITY PLOTS

To generate a normal probability plot, first implement a worksheet that features the **NORMSINV** function to serve as the source data for a normal probability plot generated by using the Chart Wizard.

Table EH3 shows a design for a **NormalPlotData** worksheet for the 5-year returns for the sample of 259 mutual funds. To implement this design, first open the **MUTUAL FUNDS.xls** workbook to the **Data** worksheet and copy the 5-year return data in cell range I1:I260 to the worksheet that will contain the implemented worksheet design. Sort this copied data in ascending order using the Excel Sort command. Then, enter the rank values 1 through 259 in column A. Then, enter the formulas for cells B2 and C2 and copy these formulas down through row 260.

To quickly enter the ranks in column A, use the Excel Series command. Enter **1** in cell **A2**, reselect cell **A2** and then select **Edit | Fill | Series**. In the Series dialog box (shown at right), select the **Columns** and **Linear** option buttons, enter **259** into the **Stop Value** edit box, and click **OK**. Excel fills in values from 2 to 259 in the cell range A3:A260.

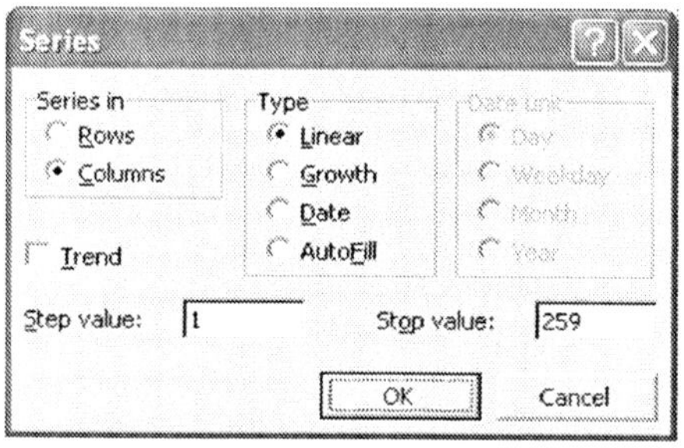

Table EH3
NormalPlotData worksheet design (first and last three rows of data)

	A	B	C	D
1	Rank	Proportion	Z Value	5-Yr Return
2	1	=A2/260	=NORMSINV(B2)	–6.1
3	2	=A3/260	=NORMSINV(B3)	–2.8
4	3	=A4/260	=NORMSINV(B4)	–1.2
⋮	⋮	⋮	⋮	⋮
258	257	=A258/260	=NORMSINV(B258)	22.9
259	258	=A259/260	=NORMSINV(B259)	25.0
260	259	=A260/260	=NORMSINV(B260)	26.3

To generate the normal probability plot, open to an implemented version of the NormalDataPlot worksheet design, select **Insert | Chart** and make these entries in the Chart Wizard dialog boxes:

Step 1 dialog box: Select the **Standard Types** tab and then select **XY (Scatter)** from the **Chart type** list box. Select the first **Chart sub-type** choice, labeled as "**Scatter. Compares pairs of values**" when selected, and click the **Next** button.

Step 2 dialog box: Select the **Data Range** tab. Enter **C1:D260** in the **Data range** edit box and select the **Columns** option button in the **Series in** group.

Step 3 dialog box: Select the **Titles** tab. Enter a title in the **Chart title** edit box, enter **Z Value** in the **Category (X) axis** edit box, and enter **5-Year Returns** in the **Value (Y) axis** edit box. Select, in turn, the **Axes**, **Gridlines**, **Data Labels**, and **Data Table** tabs and adjust settings as discussed in Exhibit EP6 in the Excel Primer. Select the **Legend** tab, select the **Show legend** check box, and click **Next**. (Consult your instructor if you require the Excel Primer.)

Step 4 dialog box: Select the **As new sheet** option button, enter a descriptive and unique sheet name, and click the **Finish** button to generate the chart.

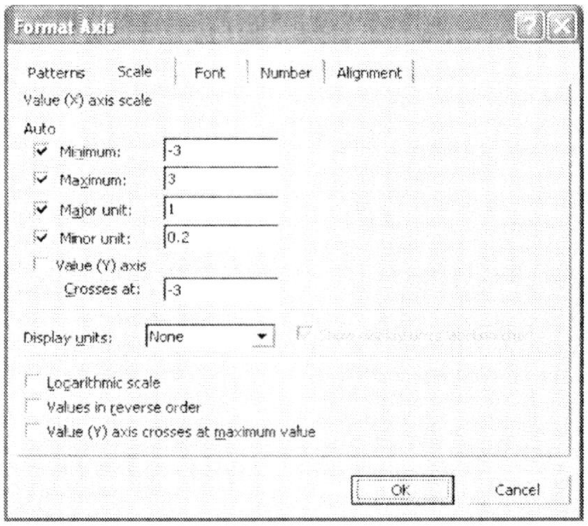

The plot generated by the Chart Wizard improperly places the *Y* axis in the center of the chart. To move the *Y* axis to the left side of the chart, right-click the *X* axis. (The tool tip "Value (X) axis" appears when the mouse pointer is properly positioned over the axis.) Select **Format Axis** from the shortcut menu and in the Format Axis dialog box (shown at right), click the **Scale** tab, enter **–3** in the **Value (Y) axis Crosses at** edit box, and click **OK**. The corrected chart will be similar to the normal probability plot shown in Figure 22.

To generate normal probability plots for other sets of data, adjust the NormalPlotData worksheet design by either adding or deleting rows and adjusting the divisor in the column B formulas. (The divisor will always be 1 more than the sample size.) Also, when moving the *Y* axis, set the **Value (Y) axis crosses at** value to the value found in the Minimum edit box.

EH3 CALCULATING EXPONENTIAL PROBABILITIES

To calculate an exponential probability, implement a worksheet that features the **EXPONDIST** function. This function is entered as **EXPONDIST(*X*, *mean*, True)**, where *X* is the *X* value of interest and *mean* is the population mean λ.

Table EH4 contains a design for an **Exponential** worksheet that includes the data for the bank ATM problem. Use this design for all exponential probability problems, changing the data as is necessary.

Table EH4
Exponential worksheet design

	A	B
1	Exponential Probability	
2		
3	Data	
4	Mean	20
5	X Value	0.1
6		
7	Results	
8	P(<=X)	=EXPONDIST(B5, B4, TRUE)

EH4 GENERATING MULTIPLE RANDOM SAMPLES

To generate a worksheet containing multiple random samples, use the Data Analysis Random Number Generator procedure. For example, to generate samples from a uniformly distributed population between 0 and 1, using 100 samples of sample size 30, open any workbook and:

Select **Tools | Data Analysis,** select **Random Number Generator** from the list in the Data Analysis dialog box and click the **OK** button.

In the Random Number Generator dialog box (shown at right):

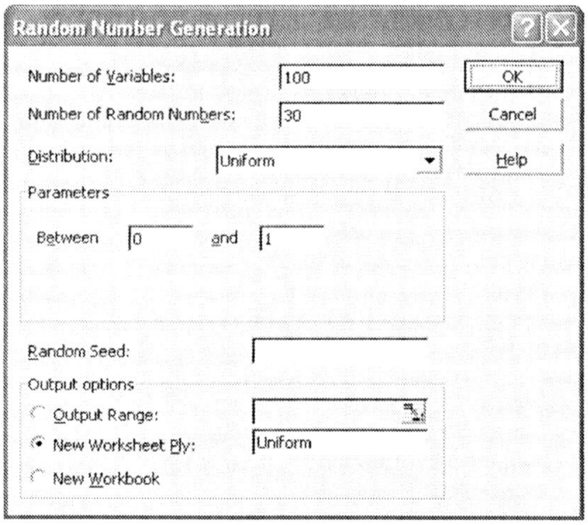

Enter **100** in the **Number of Variables** edit box.

Enter **30** in the **Number of Random Numbers** edit box.

Select **Uniform** from the **Distribution** drop-down list and in the **Parameters** area that appears, enter **0** in the **Between** and **1** in the **and** edit boxes.

Select **New Worksheet Ply** option button and enter a self-descriptive name for the new sheet.

Click the **OK** button.

This procedure can also generate a simulation from a standardized normal or discrete population. To generate a simulation from a standardized normal population, select ***Normal*** *from the* ***Distribution*** *drop-down list and enter* ***0*** *(zero) in the* ***Mean*** *and* ***1*** *in the* ***Standard Deviation*** *edit box in the* ***Parameters*** *section that appears.*

To generate a simulation from a discrete population, open to a worksheet that contains a table of X and P(X) values, such as the ***DiscreteData*** *worksheet of the* ***Chapter 6.xls*** *workbook, and enter that table range in the* ***Value and Probability Input Range*** *edit box (A2:B7 for the DiscreteData worksheet) after selecting* ***Discrete*** *from the Distribution drop-down list.*

EH5 GENERATING HISTOGRAMS FROM CALCULATED SAMPLE MEANS

To generate a histogram from a set of calculated sample means, open to the worksheet that contains those means and use the Data Analysis Histogram procedure. For example, to generate the histogram for the simulated sampling distribution example of the "Excel Strategies" section, first follow the "Generate Multiple Samples Worksheet Task" instructions of that section. Those instructions allow you to implement a worksheet in which a set of calculated sample means appear in the cell range A32:CV32.

With your workbook still open to this new implemented worksheet, select **Tools | Data Analysis**. Select **Histogram** from the list box in the Data Analysis dialog box and click the **OK** button. In the Histogram dialog box (shown at right), enter **A32:CV32** in the **Input Range** edit box and leave the **Bin Range** edit box blank. Select the **New Worksheet Ply** option button and enter a self-descriptive name for the new sheet. Select the **Chart Output** check box and click the **OK** button.

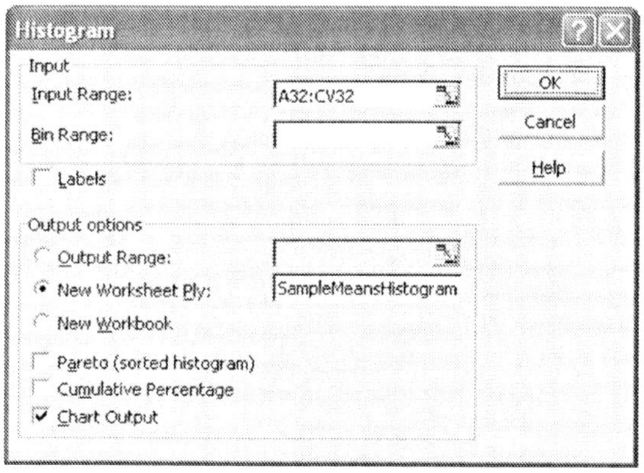

FIGURE EH1
Frequency distribution and histogram for a simulated sampling distribution

	A	B
1	*Bin*	*Frequency*
2	0.017914	1
3	0.115635	12
4	0.213355	11
5	0.311075	10
6	0.408795	6
7	0.506516	15
8	0.604236	10
9	0.701956	8
10	0.799677	7
11	0.897397	20

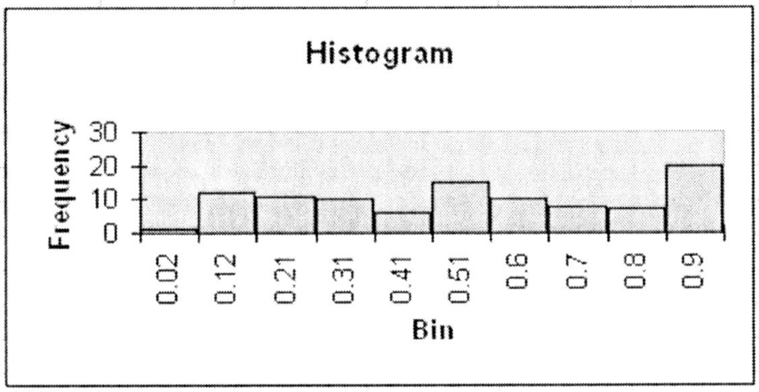

Apply the instructions of sections EH1 and EH3 in the Excel Handbook for Presenting Data in Tables and Charts, to modify the frequency table and histogram produced. After applying these instruction, the new worksheet will be similar to the one shown in Figure EH1 of this chapter. (Consult your instructor if you require the Excel Handbook for Presenting Data in Tables and Charts.)

Confidence Interval Estimation

LEARNING OBJECTIVES

- To develop confidence interval estimates for the mean and the proportion
- To determine the sample size necessary to obtain a confidence interval estimate for the mean or proportion
- To use confidence interval estimates in auditing

USING STATISTICS

Auditing Sales Invoices at the Saxon Home Improvement Company

Saxon Home Improvement Company is a large distributor of wholesale home improvement supplies in a suburban area outside a city in the northeastern United States. As an accountant for the company, you are responsible for the accuracy of the records in the integrated inventory management and sales information system. Reviewing the contents of each and every record would be one way to assess this accuracy, although such an extensive review would be time-consuming and costly. Statistical inference techniques can be used to draw conclusions about the population of all records from a relatively small sample collected during an audit of the system. At the end of each month a sample of the sales invoices is selected to determine the following:

- The average dollar amount listed on the sales invoices for the month.
- The total dollar amount of all sales invoices for the month.
- Any differences between the dollar amounts on the sales invoice and the amounts entered into the sales information system.
- The frequency of occurrence of various types of errors that violate the internal control policy of the warehouse. These errors include making a shipment when there is no authorized warehouse removal slip, failure to include the correct account number, and shipment of the incorrect home improvement item.

How accurate are the results from the samples and how do you use this information? Are the sample sizes large enough to give you the information you need?

INTRODUCTION

Statistical inference is the process of using sample results to draw conclusions about the characteristics of a population. In this chapter, inferential statistical procedures that enable you to *estimate* characteristics such as a population mean or a population proportion are discussed.

There are two types of estimates: point estimates and interval estimates. A **point estimate** consists of a single sample statistic that is used to estimate the true value of a population parameter. For example, the sample mean $\bar{X}$ is a point estimate of the population mean μ and the sample variance S^2 is a point estimate of the population variance σ^2. The sample mean has the highly desirable property of *unbiasedness*. Although in practice only one sample is selected, it can be shown that the average value of all possible sample means is μ, the true population parameter.[1] A sample statistic such as $\bar{X}$ varies from sample to sample because it depends on the items selected in the sample, and this variation must be taken into consideration when providing an estimate of the population characteristic. Therefore, by taking into account the known variability in the sampling distribution of the mean, an **interval estimate** of the true population mean is developed. The interval that is constructed will have a specified confidence of correctly estimating the true value of the population parameter μ. For example, an interval can be constructed for which there will be 95% certainty that the interval includes the average dollar amount of the sales invoices for Saxon Home Improvement Company in a given month. A similar interval estimate is also developed for the population proportion p to determine the proportion of shipments at Saxon Home Improvement Company that were made without the proper authorization.

In this chapter, how to determine the size of the sample that should be selected is also discussed along with some important estimation procedures accountants use when performing audits.

[1] Similarly, the denominator of the sample variance is $n - 1$ instead of n so that S^2 is an unbiased estimator of σ^2. In other words, the average of all possible sample variances is σ^2.

1 CONFIDENCE INTERVAL ESTIMATION OF THE MEAN (σ KNOWN)

The central limit theorem and/or knowledge of the population distribution is used to determine the percentage of sample means that fall within certain distances of the population mean. For instance, in a hypothetical cereal-filling example, 95% of all sample means are between 362.12 and 373.88 grams. This statement is based on *deductive reasoning*. However, it is exactly opposite the *inductive reasoning* that is needed here.

Inductive reasoning is needed because, in statistical inference, the results of a single sample are used to draw conclusions about the population, not vice versa. In practice, the population mean is the unknown quantity that is to be estimated. Suppose that, in the cereal-fill example, the true population mean μ is unknown but the true population standard deviation σ is known to be 15 grams. Thus, rather than take $\mu \pm (1.96)(\sigma/\sqrt{n})$ to find the upper and lower limits around μ, the sample mean $\bar{X}$ is substituted for the unknown μ and $\bar{X} \pm (1.96)(\sigma/\sqrt{n})$ is used as an interval to estimate the unknown μ. Although in practice a single sample of size n is selected and the mean $\bar{X}$ is computed, in order to understand the full meaning of the interval estimate, a hypothetical set of all possible samples, each of size n, should be examined.

Suppose, for example, that a sample of size $n = 25$ boxes has a mean of 362.3 grams. The interval developed to estimate μ is $362.3 \pm (1.96)(15)/(\sqrt{25})$ or 362.3 ± 5.88. The estimate of μ is

$$356.42 \le \mu \le 368.18$$

Because the population mean μ (equal to 368) is included within the interval, this sample has led to a correct statement about μ (see Figure 1 below).

FIGURE 1
Confidence interval estimates for five different samples of $n = 25$ taken from a population where $\mu = 368$ and $\sigma = 15$

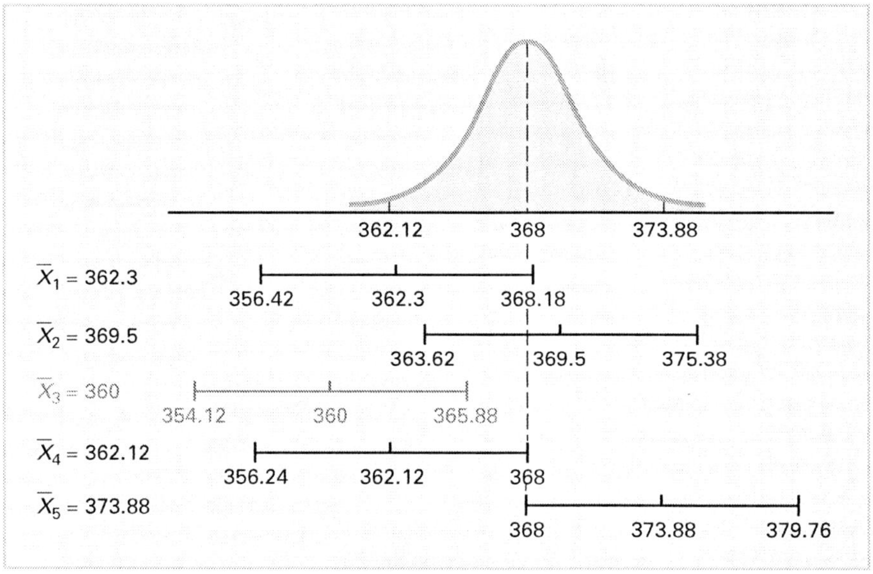

To continue this hypothetical example, suppose that for a different sample of $n = 25$ boxes, the mean is 369.5. The interval developed from this sample is $369.5 \pm (1.96)(15)/(\sqrt{25})$ or 369.5 ± 5.88. The estimate is

$$363.62 \le \mu \le 375.38$$

Because the true population mean μ (equal to 368) is also included within this interval, this statement about μ is correct.

Now, before you begin to think that correct statements about μ will always be made by developing a confidence interval estimate from the sample, suppose a third hypothetical sample of size $n = 25$ boxes is selected and the sample mean is equal to 360 grams. The interval developed here is $360 \pm (1.96)(15)/(\sqrt{25})$ or 360 ± 5.88. In this case, the estimate of μ is

$$354.12 \le \mu \le 365.88$$

Observe that this estimate is *not* a correct statement, because the population mean μ is not included in the interval developed from this sample (see Figure 1). Thus, for some samples the interval estimate of μ will be correct, but for others it will be incorrect. In addition, in practice only one sample is selected, and because the true population mean is unknown, a determination cannot be made whether the interval estimate is correct.

To resolve this dilemma of sometimes having an interval that provides a correct estimate and sometimes having an interval that provides an incorrect estimate, you need to determine the proportion of samples producing intervals that result in correct statements about the population mean μ. To do this, two other hypothetical samples are examined: the case in which $\bar{X} = 362.12$ grams and the case in which $\bar{X} = 373.88$ grams. If $\bar{X} = 362.12$, the interval is $362.12 \pm (1.96)(15)/(\sqrt{25})$ or 362.12 ± 5.88. This leads to the following interval

$$356.24 \le \mu \le 368.00$$

Because the population mean of 368 is at the upper limit of the interval, the statement is a correct one (see Figure 1).

When $\bar{X} = 373.88$, the interval is $373.88 \pm (1.96)(15)/(\sqrt{25})$ or 373.88 ± 5.88. The interval for the sample mean is

$$368.00 \le \mu \le 379.76$$

In this case, because the population mean of 368 is included at the lower limit of the interval, the statement is correct.

Thus, from these examples, observe in Figure 1 that if the sample mean based on a sample of $n = 25$ boxes falls anywhere between 362.12 and 373.88 grams, the population mean is included *somewhere* within the interval. You may recall that 95% of the sample means fall between 362.12 and 373.88 grams. Therefore, 95% of all samples of $n = 25$ boxes have sample means that include the population mean within the interval developed.

Because only one sample is selected in practice and μ is unknown, you never know for sure whether the specific interval obtained includes the population mean. However, there is 95% confidence that a sample has been selected whose interval does include the population mean.

In some situations, a higher degree of assurance (such as 99%) of including the population mean within the interval might be desired. In other cases, less assurance (such as 90%) of correctly estimating the population mean might be acceptable.

In general, the **level of confidence** is symbolized by $(1 - \alpha) \times 100\%$, where α is the proportion in the tails of the distribution that is outside the confidence interval. The proportion in the upper tail of the distribution is $\alpha/2$, and the proportion in the lower tail of the distribution is $\alpha/2$. To obtain the $(1 - \alpha) \times 100\%$ confidence interval estimate of the mean with σ known, use Equation (1).

Confidence Interval Estimate
In general, a 95% confidence interval estimate is interpreted as follows: If all possible samples of the same size *n* are taken and their sample means are computed, 95% of the intervals include the true population mean somewhere within the interval and only 5% of them do not.

CONFIDENCE INTERVAL FOR A MEAN (σ KNOWN)

$$\bar{X} \pm Z\frac{\sigma}{\sqrt{n}}$$

or

$$\bar{X} - Z\frac{\sigma}{\sqrt{n}} \le \mu \le \bar{X} + Z\frac{\sigma}{\sqrt{n}} \quad (1)$$

where Z = the value corresponding to a cumulative area of $1 - \alpha/2$ from the standardized normal distribution, i.e., an upper-tail probability of $\alpha/2$.

The value of Z selected for constructing a confidence interval is called the **critical value** for the distribution. Ninety-five percent confidence corresponds to an α value of 0.05. The critical Z value corresponding to an area of $0.95/2 = 0.4750$ from the center of the standardized normal distribution is 1.96 because there is 0.025 in the upper tail of the distribution and the cumulative area less than $+Z = 1.96$ is 0.975.

There is a different critical value for each level of confidence $1 - \alpha$. A level of confidence of 95% leads to a Z value of ± 1.96 (see Figure 2 below). Ninety-nine percent confidence corresponds to an α value of 0.01. The Z value is approximately 2.58 because the upper-tail area is 0.005 and the cumulative area below $+Z$ is 0.995 (see Figure 3).

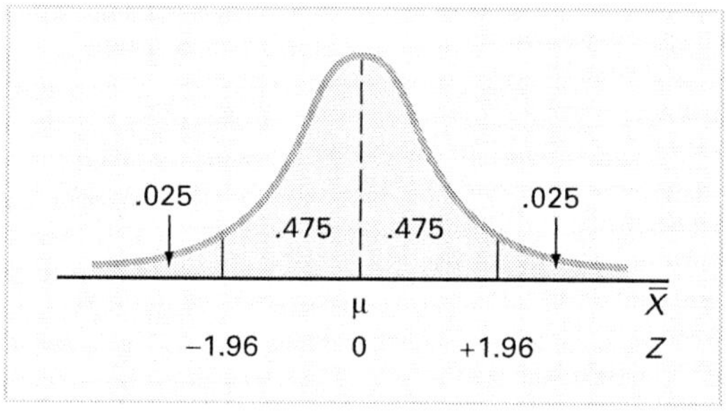

FIGURE 2
Normal curve for determining the Z value needed for 95% confidence

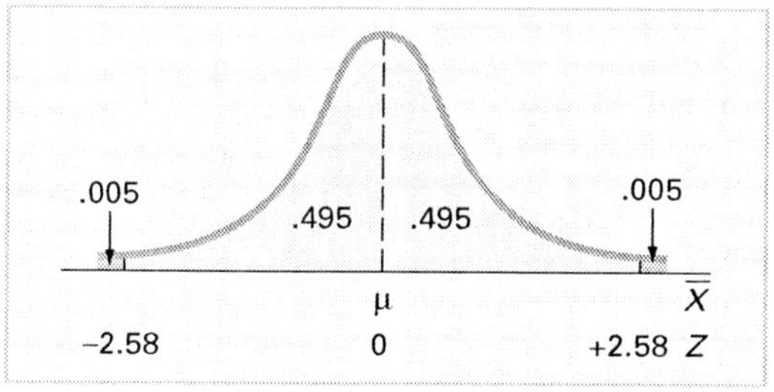

FIGURE 3
Normal curve for determining the Z value needed for 99% confidence

Now that various levels of confidence have been considered, why not make the confidence level as close to 100% as possible? Before doing so, you need to realize that any increase in the level of confidence is achieved only by simultaneously widening (and making less precise) the confidence interval obtained. There is "no free lunch" here. You would have more confidence that the population mean is within a broader range of values. However this might make the interpretation of the confidence interval less useful. The trade-off between the width of the confidence interval and the level of confidence is discussed in greater depth in the context of determining the sample size in section 4.

Example 1 illustrates the application of the confidence interval estimate.

EXAMPLE 1

ESTIMATING THE MEAN PAPER LENGTH WITH 95% CONFIDENCE

A manufacturer of computer paper has a production process that operates continuously throughout an entire production shift. The paper is expected to have a mean length of 11 inches and the standard deviation of the length is known to be 0.02 inch. At periodic intervals, samples are selected to determine whether the mean paper length is still equal to 11 inches or whether something has gone wrong in the production process to change the length of the paper produced. If such a situation has occurred, corrective action is needed. Suppose a random sample of 100 sheets is selected, and the mean paper length is found to be 10.998 inches. Set up a 95% confidence interval estimate of the population mean paper length.

SOLUTION

Using Equation (1), with $Z = 1.96$ for 95% confidence,

$$\bar{X} \pm Z\frac{\sigma}{\sqrt{n}} = 10.998 \pm (1.96)\frac{0.02}{\sqrt{100}}$$

$$= 10.998 \pm 0.00392$$

$$10.99408 \le \mu \le 11.00192$$

Thus, with 95% confidence, the population mean is estimated to be between 10.99408 and 11.00192 inches. Because 11, the value indicating that the production process is working properly, is included within the interval, there is no reason to believe that anything is wrong with the production process.

To observe the effect of using a 99% confidence interval, examine Example 2.

EXAMPLE 2

ESTIMATING THE MEAN PAPER LENGTH WITH 99% CONFIDENCE

Set up a 99% confidence interval estimate of the population mean paper length.

SOLUTION

Using Equation (1), with $Z = 2.58$ for 99% confidence,

$$\bar{X} \pm Z\frac{\sigma}{\sqrt{n}} = 10.998 \pm (2.58)\frac{0.02}{\sqrt{100}}$$
$$= 10.998 \pm 0.00516$$
$$10.99284 \leq \mu \leq 11.00316$$

Once again, because 11 is included within this wider interval, there is no reason to believe that anything is wrong with the production process.

CHAPTER 7.xls

*Retrieve the Example 7.1 worksheet of the **Chapter 7.xls** workbook to view the confidence interval estimate of Example 1.*

Excel Strategies Calculating the Confidence Interval Estimate for the Mean (σ Known)

You implement a worksheet that features the **CONFIDENCE** function to calculate the confidence interval estimate for the mean (σ known). PHStat2 can construct this worksheet for you in a single step.

For example, to calculate the confidence interval estimate for the mean paper length for Example 1, use one of these strategies:

Using Excel with PHStat2

Use the PHStat2 Estimate for the Mean, sigma known, procedure to calculate the confidence interval estimate for the mean (σ known).

Select **PHStat | Confidence Intervals | Estimate for the Mean, sigma known**.

In the Estimate for the Mean, sigma known, dialog box (shown at right):

Enter **0.02** in the **Population Standard Deviation** edit box.

Enter **95** in the **Confidence Level** edit box.

Select the **Sample Statistics Known** option button and enter **100** in the **Sample Size** and **10.998** in the **Sample Mean** edit boxes.

Enter a title in the **Title** edit box.

Click the **OK** button.

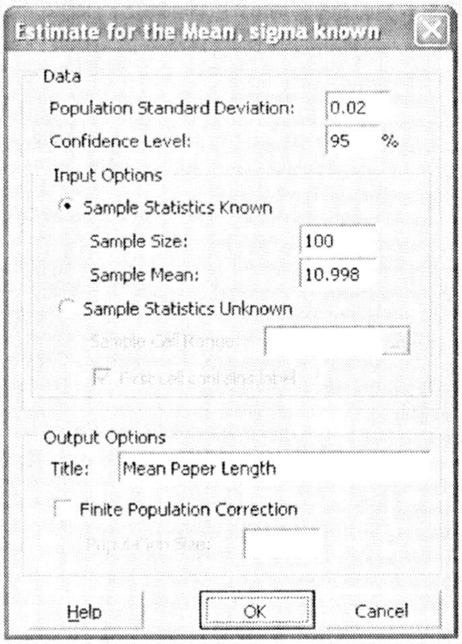

*For problems in which the sample mean is not known and needs to be calculated, select the **Sample Statistics Unknown** option button and enter the cell range of the sample data in the **Sample Cell Range** edit box (dimmed in the illustration).*

Using Excel

Follow the instructions of section EH1 at the end of this chapter to manually implement a worksheet to calculate the confidence interval estimate for the mean (σ known).

PROBLEMS FOR SECTION 1

Learning the Basics

1 If $\bar{X} = 85$, $\sigma = 8$, and $n = 64$, set up a 95% confidence interval estimate of the population mean μ.

2 If $\bar{X} = 125$, $\sigma = 24$, and $n = 36$, set up a 99% confidence interval estimate of the population mean μ.

3 A market researcher states that she has 95% confidence that the true mean monthly sales of a product are between \$170,000 and \$200,000. Explain the meaning of this statement.

4 Why is it not possible for the operations manager in Example 1 to have 100% confidence? Explain.

5 From the results of Example 1 regarding paper production, is it true that 95% of the sample means will fall between 10.99408 and 11.00192 inches? Explain.

6 Is it true in Example 1 that we do not know for sure whether the true population mean is between 10.99408 and 11.00192 inches? Explain.

Applying the Concepts

7 The manager of a paint supply store wants to estimate the actual amount of paint contained in 1-gallon cans purchased from a nationally known manufacturer. It is known from the manufacturer's specifications that the standard deviation of the amount of paint is equal to 0.02 gallon. A random sample of 50 cans is selected, and the sample mean amount of paint per 1-gallon can is 0.995 gallon.

a. Set up a 99% confidence interval estimate of the true population mean amount of paint included in a 1-gallon can.
b. On the basis of your results, do you think that the manager has a right to complain to the manufacturer? Why?
c. Does the population amount of paint per can have to be normally distributed here? Explain.
d. Explain why an observed value of 0.98 gallon for an individual can is not unusual, even though it is outside the confidence interval you calculated.
e. Suppose that you used a 95% confidence interval estimate. What would be your answers to (a) and (b)?

8 The quality control manager at a lightbulb factory needs to estimate the mean life of a large shipment of lightbulbs. The process standard deviation is known to be 100 hours. A random sample of 64 lightbulbs indicated a sample mean life of 350 hours.

a. Set up a 95% confidence interval estimate of the true population mean life of lightbulbs in this shipment.
b. Do you think that the manufacturer has the right to state that the lightbulbs last an average of 400 hours? Explain.
c. Does the population of lightbulb life have to be normally distributed here? Explain.
d. Explain why an observed value of 320 hours for a single lightbulb is not unusual, even though it is outside the confidence interval you calculated.
e. Suppose that the process standard deviation changed to 80 hours. What would be your answers in (a) and (b)?

9 The inspection division of the Lee County Weights and Measures Department is interested in estimating the actual amount of soft drink that is placed in 2-liter bottles at the local bottling plant of a large nationally known soft-drink company. The bottling plant has informed the inspection division that the standard deviation for 2-liter bottles is 0.05 liter. A random sample of 100 2-liter bottles obtained from this bottling plant indicates a sample mean of 1.99 liters.

a. Set up a 95% confidence interval estimate of the true population mean amount of soft drink in each bottle.
b. Does the population of soft-drink fill have to be normally distributed here? Explain.
c. Explain why an observed value of 2.02 liters for a single bottle is not unusual, even though it is outside the confidence interval you calculated.
d. Suppose that the sample mean had been 1.97 liters. What would be your answer to (a)?

2 CONFIDENCE INTERVAL ESTIMATION OF THE MEAN (σ UNKNOWN)

Just as the mean of the population μ is usually not known, the actual standard deviation of the population σ is also usually unknown. Therefore, a confidence interval estimate of μ using only the sample statistics of $\bar{X}$ and S needs to be developed.

Student's t Distribution

At the beginning of the 20th century, a statistician named William S. Gosset, an employee of Guinness Breweries in Ireland (see reference 3), was interested in making inferences about the mean when σ was unknown. Because Guinness employees were not permitted to publish research work under their own names, Gosset adopted the pseudonym "Student." The distribution that he developed has come to be known as **Student's *t* distribution**.

If the random variable X is normally distributed, then the following statistic has a t distribution with $n - 1$ **degrees of freedom**:

$$t = \frac{\overline{X} - \mu}{\frac{S}{\sqrt{n}}}$$

Notice that this expression has the same form as the Z statistic in Equation (Z) below, except that S is used to estimate σ, which is unknown in this case. The concept of *degrees of freedom* is discussed further on the next page.

FINDING Z FOR THE SAMPLING DISTRIBUTION OF THE MEAN

The Z value is equal to the difference between the sample mean $\overline{X}$ and the population mean μ, divided by the standard error of the mean $\sigma_{\overline{X}}$.

$$Z = \frac{\overline{X} - \mu_{\overline{X}}}{\sigma_{\overline{X}}} = \frac{\overline{X} - \mu}{\frac{\sigma}{\sqrt{n}}} \quad \textbf{(Z)}$$

In appearance, the t distribution is very similar to the standardized normal distribution. Both distributions are bell-shaped and symmetrical. However, the t distribution has more area in the tails and less in the center than does the standardized normal distribution (see Figure 4). Because the value of σ is unknown and S is used to estimate it, the values of t that are observed will be more variable than for Z.

FIGURE 4
Standardized normal distribution and *t* distribution for 5 degrees of freedom

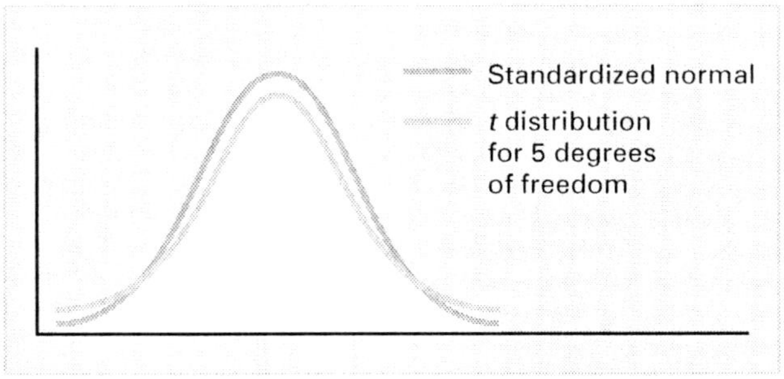

As the number of degrees of freedom increases, the t distribution gradually approaches the standardized normal distribution until the two are virtually identical, since S becomes a better estimate of σ as the sample size gets larger. With a sample size of about 120 or more, S estimates σ precisely enough that there is little difference between the t and Z distributions. For this reason, most statisticians use Z instead of t when the sample size is greater than 120.

CHECKING THE ASSUMPTIONS

Recall that the t distribution assumes that the random variable X being studied is normally distributed. In practice, however, as long as the sample size is large enough and the population is not very skewed, the t distribution can be used to estimate the population mean when σ is unknown. You should be concerned about the validity of the confidence interval primarily when dealing with a small sample size and a skewed population distribution. The assumption of normality in the population can be assessed by evaluating the shape of the sample data by using a histogram, stem-and-leaf display, box-and-whisker plot, or normal probability plot.

The critical values of t for the appropriate degrees of freedom are obtained from the table of the t distribution (see the Critical Values of t table in the appendix). The top of each column of the table indicates the area in the upper tail of the t distribution (because positive entries for t are supplied, the values for t are for the upper tail). Each row represents the particular t value for each specific degree of freedom. For example, with 99 degrees of freedom, if 95% confidence is desired, the appropriate value of t is found as shown in Table 1. The 95% confidence level means that 2.5% of the values (an area of .025) are in each tail of the distribution. Looking in the column for an upper-tail area of .025 and in the row corresponding to 99 degrees of freedom results in a critical value for t of 1.9842. Because t is a symmetrical distribution with a mean of 0, if the upper-tail value is +1.9842, the value for the lower-tail area (lower .025) will be −1.9842. A t value of 1.9842 means that the probability that t exceeds +1.9842 is 0.025, or 2.5% (see Figure 5).

TABLE 1

Determining the critical value from the t table for an area of 0.025 in each tail with 99 degrees of freedom

	Upper-Tail Areas					
Degrees of Freedom	**.25**	**.10**	**.05**	**.025**	**.01**	**.005**
1	1.0000	3.0777	6.3138	12.7062	31.8207	63.6574
2	0.8165	1.8856	2.9200	4.3027	6.9646	9.9248
3	0.7649	1.6377	2.3534	3.1824	4.5407	5.8409
4	0.7407	1.5332	2.1318	2.7764	3.7469	4.6041
5	0.7267	1.4759	2.0150	2.5706	3.3649	4.0322
.	.	.	.	.	.	.
.	.	.	.	.	.	.
.	.	.	.	.	.	.
96	0.6771	1.2904	1.6609	1.9850	2.3658	2.6280
97	0.6770	1.2903	1.6607	1.9847	2.3654	2.6275
98	0.6770	1.2902	1.6606	1.9845	2.3650	2.6269
99	0.6770	1.2902	1.6604	1.9842	2.3646	2.6264
100	0.6770	1.2901	1.6602	1.9840	2.3642	2.6259

Source: Extracted from the Critical Values of t table.

FIGURE 5

t distribution with 99 degrees of freedom

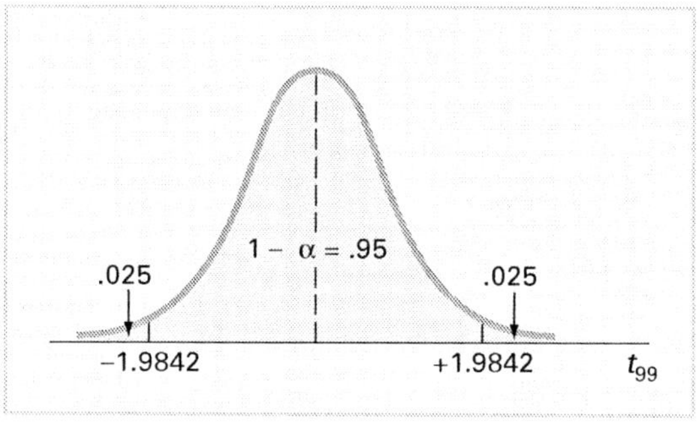

The Concept of Degrees of Freedom

The numerator of the sample variance S^2 requires the computation of

$$\sum_{i=1}^{n}(X_i - \overline{X})^2$$

In order to compute S^2, $\overline{X}$ needs to be known. Therefore, only $n - 1$ of the sample values are free to vary. This means that there are $n - 1$ degrees of freedom. For example, suppose a sample of five values has a mean of 20. How many distinct values need to be known before the remainder can be obtained? The fact that $n = 5$ and $\overline{X} = 20$ also tells you that

$$\sum_{i=1}^{n} X_i = 100$$

because

$$\frac{\sum_{i=1}^{n} X_i}{n} = \overline{X}$$

Thus, when four of the values are known, the fifth one will *not* be free to vary because the sum must add to 100. For example, if four of the values are 18, 24, 19, and 16, the fifth value must be 23 so that the sum equals 100.

The Confidence Interval Statement

The $(1 - \alpha) \times 100\%$ confidence interval estimate for the mean with σ unknown is defined in Equation (2).

CONFIDENCE INTERVAL FOR A MEAN (σ UNKNOWN)

$$\bar{X} \pm t_{n-1} \frac{S}{\sqrt{n}}$$

or

$$\bar{X} - t_{n-1} \frac{S}{\sqrt{n}} \le \mu \le \bar{X} + t_{n-1} \frac{S}{\sqrt{n}} \quad \textbf{(2)}$$

where t_{n-1} is the critical value of the t distribution with $n - 1$ degrees of freedom for an area of $\alpha/2$ in the upper tail.

To illustrate the application of the confidence interval estimate for the mean when the standard deviation σ is unknown, return to the Saxon Home Improvement Company Using Statistics scenario. Suppose that a sample of 100 sales invoices is selected from the population of sales invoices during the month and the sample mean of the 100 sales invoices is \$110.27 with a sample standard deviation of \$28.95. If the company requires 95% confidence, the critical value from the t distribution (as shown in Table 1) is 1.9842. Using Equation (2),

$$\begin{aligned} &\bar{X} \pm t_{n-1} \frac{S}{\sqrt{n}} \\ &= 110.27 \pm (1.9842)\frac{28.95}{\sqrt{100}} \\ &= 110.27 \pm 5.74 \\ &\$104.53 \le \mu \le \$116.01 \end{aligned}$$

Output obtained from Microsoft Excel for these data is presented in Figure 6.

FIGURE 6

Confidence interval estimate obtained from Microsoft Excel for the mean sales invoice amount for the Saxon Home Improvement Company

	A	B
1	**Mean Sales Invoice Amount**	
2		
3	**Data**	
4	**Sample Standard Deviation**	**28.95**
5	**Sample Mean**	**110.27**
6	**Sample Size**	**100**
7	**Confidence Level**	**95%**
8		
9	Intermediate Calculations	
10	Standard Error of the Mean	2.895
11	Degrees of Freedom	99
12	t Value	1.984217306
13	Interval Half Width	5.744309101
14		
15	**Confidence Interval**	
16	**Interval Lower Limit**	**104.53**
17	**Interval Upper Limit**	**116.01**

Thus, with 95% confidence, the conclusion is reached that the mean amount of all the sales invoices is between \$104.53 and \$116.01. This 95% confidence means that if all possible samples of 100 were selected (something that would never be done in practice), 95% of the intervals developed would include the true population mean somewhere within the interval. The validity of this confidence interval estimate depends on the assumption of normality for the distribution of the amount of the sales invoices. With a sample of 100, the normality assumption is not overly restrictive and the use of the t distribution is likely to be appropriate. In practice, the results of this interval on the basis of the actual invoices would be compared with the average invoice as entered into the company's computer system. If there appeared to be large differences, further investigation would be undertaken.

CHAPTER 7.xls

*Retrieve the Figure 7.6 worksheet of the **Chapter 7.xls** workbook to view the confidence interval estimate in Figure 6.*

Excel Strategies: Calculating the Confidence Interval Estimate for the Mean (σ Unknown)

You implement a worksheet that features the **TINV** function to calculate the confidence interval estimate for the mean (σ unknown). PHStat2 can construct this worksheet for you in a single step.

For example, to calculate the confidence interval estimate for the mean sales invoice amount for the Saxon Home Improvement Company problem, use one of these strategies:

Using Excel with PHStat2

Use the PHStat2 Estimate for the Mean, sigma unknown, procedure to calculate the confidence interval estimate for the mean (σ unknown).

Select **PHStat | Confidence Intervals | Estimate for the Mean, sigma unknown**.

In the Estimate for the Mean, sigma unknown, dialog box (shown at right):

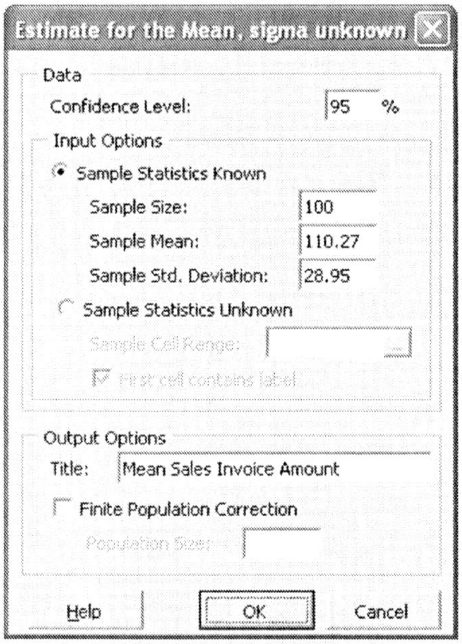

Enter **95** in the **Confidence Level** edit box.

Select the **Sample Statistics Known** option button and enter **100** in the **Sample Size**, **110.27** in the **Sample Mean**, and **28.95** in the **Sample Std. Deviation** edit boxes.

Enter a title in the **Title** edit box.

Click the **OK** button.

*For problems in which the sample mean and the standard deviation are not known and need to be calculated, select the **Sample Statistics Unknown** option button and enter the cell range of the sample data in the **Sample Cell Range** edit box (dimmed in the illustration).*

Using Excel

Follow the instructions of section EH2 at the end of this chapter to manually implement a worksheet to calculate the confidence interval estimate for the mean (σ unknown).

Example 3 further illustrates how the confidence interval for a mean is constructed when the population standard deviation is unknown.

EXAMPLE 3

ESTIMATING THE MEAN FORCE REQUIRED TO BREAK ELECTRIC INSULATORS

A manufacturing company produces electric insulators. If the insulators break when in use, a short circuit is likely to occur. To test the strength of the insulators, destructive testing in high-powered labs is carried out to determine how much *force* is required to break the insulators. Force is measured by observing how many pounds must be applied to the insulator before it breaks. Thirty observations from this experiment are summarized in Table 2. Set up a 95% confidence interval estimate of the population mean force required to break the insulator.

TABLE 2

Force (in the number of pounds) required to break the insulator

1870	1728	1656	1610	1634	1784	1522	1696	1592	1662
1866	1764	1734	1662	1734	1774	1550	1756	1762	1866
1820	1744	1788	1688	1810	1752	1680	1810	1652	1736

SOLUTION

For these data, Figure 7, obtained from Microsoft Excel, shows that the sample mean is $\bar{X} = 1{,}723.4$ pounds and the sample standard deviation is $S = 89.55$ pounds. To obtain the confidence interval using Equation (2), the critical value from the t table for an area of 0.025 in each tail with 29 degrees of freedom needs to be determined. From the Critical Values of t table, observe that $t_{29} = 2.0452$.

FIGURE 7

Confidence interval estimate obtained from Microsoft Excel for the mean amount of force required to break electrical insulators

	A	B
1	**Mean Amount of Force Required**	
2		
3	**Data**	
4	**Sample Standard Deviation**	89.55083319
5	**Sample Mean**	1723.4
6	**Sample Size**	30
7	**Confidence Level**	95%
8		
9	Intermediate Calculations	
10	Standard Error of the Mean	16.34967046
11	Degrees of Freedom	29
12	*t* Value	2.045230758
13	Interval Half Width	33.43884891
14		
15	**Confidence Interval**	
16	**Interval Lower Limit**	1689.96
17	**Interval Upper Limit**	1756.84

Thus, using $\bar{X} = 1{,}723.4$, $S = 89.55$, $n = 30$, and $t_{29} = 2.0452$,

$$\bar{X} \pm t_{n-1}\frac{S}{\sqrt{n}}$$

$$= 1{,}723.4 \pm (2.0452)\frac{89.55}{\sqrt{30}}$$

$$= 1{,}723.4 \pm 33.44$$

$$1{,}689.96 \le \mu \le 1{,}756.84$$

The conclusion is reached with 95% confidence that the mean force required is between 1,689.96 and 1,756.84 pounds. The 95% confidence interval states that you are 95% sure that the sample selected is one in which the population mean μ is located within the interval. The validity of this confidence interval estimate depends on the assumption that the force required is normally distributed. Remember, however, that for large sample sizes this assumption can be slightly relaxed. Thus, with a sample of 30, the use of the t distribution is appropriate even if the data are slightly skewed. From the normal probability plot displayed in Figure 8 or the box-and-whisker plot displayed in Figure 9, the data appear to be only slightly skewed at most. Thus, the t distribution is appropriate for these data.

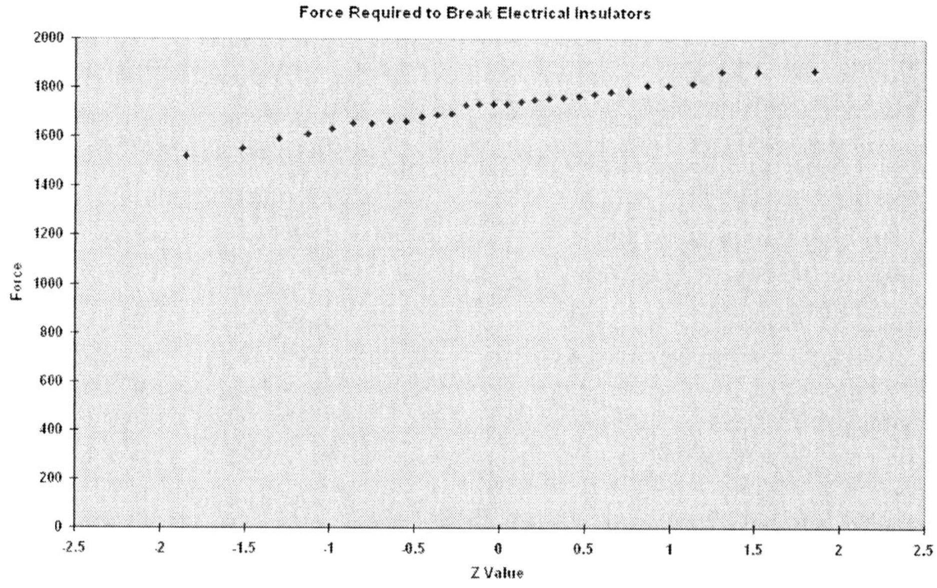

FIGURE 8
Normal probability plot obtained from Microsoft Excel for the amount of force required to break electrical insulators data

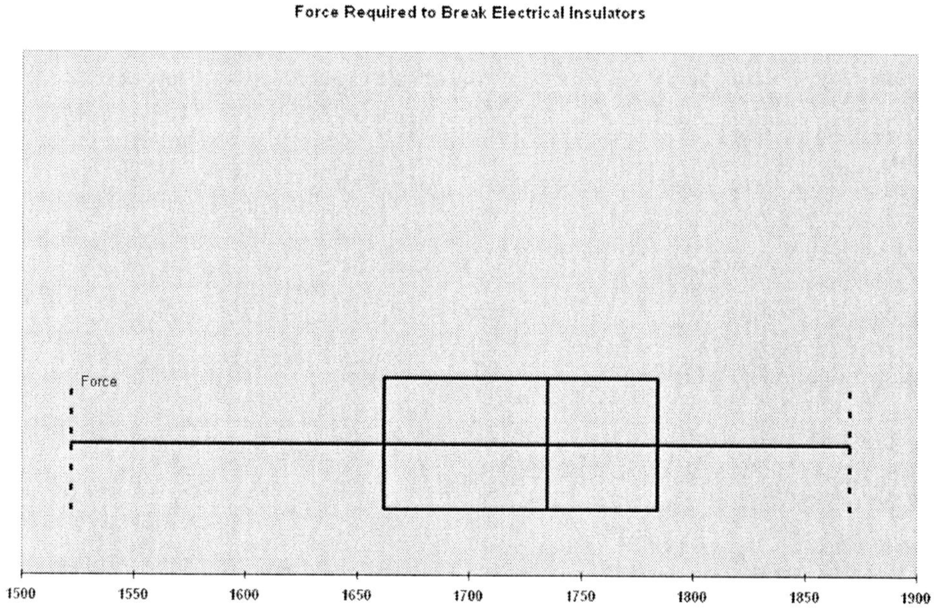

FIGURE 9
Box-and-whisker plot obtained from Microsoft Excel for the force required to break electrical insulators data

PROBLEMS FOR SECTION 2

Learning the Basics

10 Determine the critical value of t in each of the following circumstances:

a. $1 - \alpha = 0.95$, $n = 10$.
b. $1 - \alpha = 0.99$, $n = 10$.
c. $1 - \alpha = 0.95$, $n = 32$.
d. $1 - \alpha = 0.95$, $n = 65$.
e. $1 - \alpha = 0.90$, $n = 16$.

11 If $\overline{X} = 75$, $S = 24$, $n = 36$, and assuming that the population is normally distributed, set up a 95% confidence interval estimate of the population mean μ.

12 If $\overline{X} = 50$, $S = 15$, $n = 16$, and assuming that the population is normally distributed, set up a 99% confidence interval estimate of the population mean μ.

13 Set up a 95% confidence interval estimate for the population mean, based on each of the following sets of data, assuming that the population is normally distributed:

Set 1: 1, 1, 1, 1, 8, 8, 8, 8
Set 2: 1, 2, 3, 4, 5, 6, 7, 8

Explain why these data sets have different confidence intervals even though they have the same mean and range.

14 Compute a 95% confidence interval for the population mean, based on the numbers 1, 2, 3, 4, 5, 6, and 20. Change the number 20 to 7 and recalculate the confidence interval. Using these results, describe the effect of an outlier (i.e., extreme value) on the confidence interval.

Applying the Concepts

Problems 15–19 can be solved with and without Microsoft Excel. Problems 20 and 21 are particularly appropriate for solution with Microsoft Excel.

15 The U.S. Department of Transportation requires tire manufacturers to provide tire performance information on the sidewall of the tire so that a prospective customer can be better informed when making a purchasing decision. One very important measure of tire performance is the tread wear index, which indicates the tire's resistance to tread wear compared with a tire graded with a base of 100. This means that a tire with a grade of 200 should last twice as long, on average, as a tire graded with a base of 100. Suppose that a consumer organization wants to estimate the actual tread wear index of a brand name of tires graded 200 that are produced by a certain manufacturer. A random sample of 18 of these tires indicates a sample mean tread wear index of 195.3 and a sample standard deviation of 21.4.

a. Assuming that the population of tread wear indices is normally distributed, set up a 95% confidence interval estimate of the population mean tread wear index for tires produced by this manufacturer under this brand name.
b. Do you think that the consumer organization should accuse the manufacturer of producing tires that do not meet the performance information provided on the sidewall of the tire? Explain.
c. Tell why an observed tread wear index of 210 for a particular tire is not unusual, even though it is outside the confidence interval developed in (a).

16 A stationery store wants to estimate the mean retail value of greeting cards that it has in its inventory. A random sample of 20 greeting cards indicates an average value of $1.67 and a standard deviation of $0.32.

a. Assuming a normal distribution, set up a 95% confidence interval estimate of the mean value of all greeting cards in the store's inventory.
b. How might the results obtained in (a) be useful in assisting the store owner to estimate the total value of her inventory?

17 One of the major measures of the quality of service provided by any organization is the speed with which it responds to customer complaints. A large family-held department store selling furniture and flooring including carpeting had undergone a major expansion in the past several years. In particular, the flooring department had expanded from 2 installation crews to an installation supervisor, a measurer, and 15 installation crews. During a recent year there were 50 complaints concerning carpeting installation. The following data **FURNITURE.xls** represent the number of days between the receipt of the complaint and the resolution of the complaint.

54 5 35 137 31 27 152 2 123 81 74 27 11 19 126 110 110 29
61 35 94 31 26 5 12 4 165 32 29 28 29 26 25 1 14 13 13 10 5
27 4 52 30 22 36 26 20 23 33 68

a. Set up a 95% confidence interval estimate of the mean number of days between the receipt of the complaint and the resolution of the complaint.
b. What assumption about the population distribution must be made in (a)?
c. Do you think that the assumption made in (b) has been seriously violated? Explain.
d. What effect might your conclusion in (c) have on the validity of the results obtained in (a)?

18 In New York state, savings banks are permitted to sell a form of life insurance called Savings Bank Life Insurance (SBLI). The approval process consists of underwriting, which includes a review of the application, a medical information bureau check, possible requests for additional medical information and medical exams, and a policy compilation stage where the policy pages are generated and sent to the bank for delivery. The ability to deliver approved policies to customers in a timely manner is critical to the profitability of this service to the bank. During a period of 1 month, a random sample of 27 approved policies was selected **INSURANCE.xls** and the total processing time in days was recorded with the following results:

73 19 16 64 28 28 31 90 60 56 31 56 22 18
45 48 17 17 17 91 92 63 50 51 69 16 17

a. Set up a 95% confidence interval estimate of the mean processing time.
b. What assumption about the population distribution must be made in (a)?
c. Do you think that the assumption made in (b) has been seriously violated? Explain.

19 Hotel and car rental rates for business travelers vary from city to city. The rates in 20 cities for June 4 to June 9, 2002, as given by the Dow Jones Travel Index are presented in the following table. **TRAVEL.xls**

City	Hotel	Car Rental	City	Hotel	Car Rental
Seattle	176	45	Detroit	141	53
San Francisco	178	42	Cleveland	145	40
Los Angeles	223	36	New Orleans	142	49
Phoenix	124	38	Pittsburgh	148	49
Denver	139	38	Atlanta	173	46
Minneapolis	167	53	Boston	243	46
Chicago	257	51	New York	273	69
St. Louis	159	53	Washington	262	47
Dallas	167	46	Orlando	133	40
Houston	180	48	Miami	116	39

Source: Extracted from "Travel," Wall Street Journal, *June 7, 2002.*

a. Construct a 95% confidence interval for the population mean hotel rate.
b. Construct a 95% confidence interval for the population mean car rental rate.
c. What assumptions do you need to make about the populations of interest to construct the intervals requested in (a) and (b)?
d. Given the data presented, do you think the assumption needed in (a) and (b) is valid? Explain.

20 One operation of a mill is to cut pieces of steel into parts that will later be used as the frame for front seats in an automotive plant. The steel is cut with a diamond saw and requires the resulting parts to be within plus or minus 0.005 inch of the length specified by the automobile company. The measurement reported **STEEL.xls** is the difference in inches between the actual length of the steel part, as measured by a laser measurement device, and the specified length of the steel part. For example, the first observation, –0.002, represents a steel part that is 0.002 inch shorter than the specified length.
a. Set up a 95% confidence interval estimate of the mean difference between the actual length of the steel part, as measured by a laser measurement device, and the specified length of the steel part.
b. What assumption about the population distribution must be made in (a)?
c. Do you think that the assumption made in (b) has been seriously violated? Explain.

21 In an article in *Quality Engineering*, the viscosity (resistance to flow) of a chemical product produced in batches was examined. The data for 120 batches are in the data file **CHEMICAL.xls**

Source: Holmes and Mergen, "Parabolic Control Limits for the Exponentially Weighted Moving Average Control Charts," (1992) Quality Engineering, *4(4): 487–495.*

a. Set up a 99% confidence interval estimate of the mean viscosity.
b. What assumption about the population distribution must be made in (a)?
c. Do you think that the assumption made in (b) has been seriously violated? Explain.

3 CONFIDENCE INTERVAL ESTIMATION OF THE PROPORTION

In this section the concept of the confidence interval is extended to categorical data to estimate the population proportion p from the sample proportion $p_s = X/n$. When both np and $n(1 - p)$ are at least 5, the binomial distribution can be approximated by the normal distribution. Therefore, a $(1 - \alpha) \times 100\%$ confidence interval estimate for the population proportion p is defined by Equation (3).

CONFIDENCE INTERVAL ESTIMATE FOR THE PROPORTION

$$p_s \pm Z\sqrt{\frac{p_s(1-p_s)}{n}}$$

or

$$p_s - Z\sqrt{\frac{p_s(1-p_s)}{n}} \le p \le p_s + Z\sqrt{\frac{p_s(1-p_s)}{n}} \quad (3)$$

where

p_s = sample proportion = $\frac{X}{n} = \frac{\text{number of successes}}{\text{sample size}}$

p = population proportion
Z = critical value from the standardized normal distribution
n = sample size

To see how this confidence interval estimate of the proportion is developed, return to the Using Statistics scenario concerning the Saxon Home Improvement Company. Recall that the company needs to determine the frequency of occurrence of various types of errors that violate the accounting controls of the company. A 95% confidence interval estimate of the population proportion of sales invoices that contain these errors can be used to help evaluate the frequency of this happening. Suppose that in a sample of 100 sales invoices, 10 contain errors. Thus, for these data $p_s = 10/100 = 0.10$. For 95% confidence $Z = 1.96$ so that using Equation (3),

$$
\begin{aligned}
& p_s \pm Z\sqrt{\frac{p_s(1-p_s)}{n}} \\
&= 0.10 \pm (1.96)\sqrt{\frac{(0.10)(0.90)}{100}} \\
&= 0.10 \pm (1.96)(0.03) \\
&= 0.10 \pm 0.0588 \\
&\quad 0.0412 \le p \le 0.1588
\end{aligned}
$$

Therefore, there is 95% confidence that between 4.12% and 15.88% of the sales invoices have errors that violate company policy. Figure 10 shows Microsoft Excel output for these data.

Excel Strategies: Calculating the Confidence Interval Estimate for the Proportion

CHAPTER 7.xls

Retrieve the Figure 7.10 worksheet of the ***Chapter 7.xls*** *workbook to view the confidence interval estimate shown in Figure 10.*

You implement a worksheet that features the **NORMSINV** function to calculate the confidence interval estimate for the proportion. PHStat2 can construct this worksheet for you in a single step.

For example, to calculate the confidence interval estimate for the proportion of sales invoices that violate the accounting controls of the Saxon Home Improvement Company, shown in Figure 10, use one of these strategies:

Using Excel with PHStat2

Use the PHStat2 Estimate for the Proportion procedure to calculate the confidence interval estimate for the proportion.

Select **PHStat | Confidence Intervals | Estimate for the Proportion**.

In the Estimate for the Proportion dialog box (shown at right):

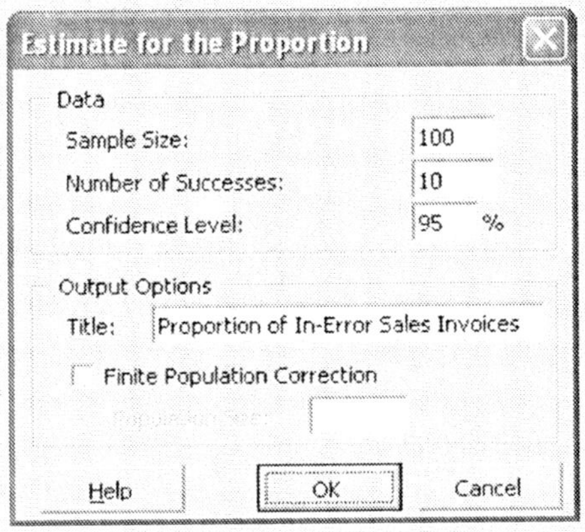

Enter **100** in the **Sample Size** edit box.

Enter **10** in the **Number of Successes** edit box.

Enter **95** in the **Confidence Level** edit box.

Enter a title in the **Title** edit box.

Click the **OK** button.

Using Excel

Follow the instructions of section EH3 at the end of this chapter to implement manually a worksheet to calculate the confidence interval estimate for the proportion.

FIGURE 10

Confidence interval estimate obtained from Microsoft Excel for the proportion of sales invoices that contain errors that violate the accounting controls of the Saxon Home Improvement Company

	A	B
1	**Proportion of In-Error Sales Invoices**	
2		
3	**Data**	
4	**Sample Size**	100
5	**Number of Successes**	10
6	**Confidence Level**	95%
7		
8	Intermediate Calculations	
9	Sample Proportion	0.1
10	Z Value	-1.95996279
11	Standard Error of the Proportion	0.03
12	Interval Half Width	0.058798884
13		
14	**Confidence Interval**	
15	**Interval Lower Limit**	**0.041201116**
16	**Interval Upper Limit**	**0.158798884**

Example 4 illustrates another application of calculating the confidence interval estimate for the proportion.

EXAMPLE 4

ESTIMATING THE PROPORTION OF NONCONFORMING NEWSPAPERS PRINTED

The operations manager for a large newspaper wants to determine the proportion of newspapers printed that have a nonconforming attribute, such as excessive ruboff, improper page setup, missing pages, and duplicate pages. The operations manager determines that a random sample of 200 newspapers should be selected for analysis. Suppose that, of this sample of 200, thirty-five contain some type of nonconformance. If the operations manager wants to have 90% confidence of estimating the true population proportion, set up the confidence interval estimate.

SOLUTION

The confidence interval is computed using Equation (3) as follows:

$$p_s = \frac{35}{200} = 0.175, \text{ and with a 90\% level of confidence } Z = 1.645$$

$$\begin{aligned} & p_s \pm Z\sqrt{\frac{p_s(1-p_s)}{n}} \\ &= 0.175 \pm (1.645)\sqrt{\frac{(0.175)(0.825)}{200}} \\ &= 0.175 \pm (1.645)(0.0269) \\ &= 0.175 \pm 0.0442 \\ & 0.1308 \le p \le 0.2192 \end{aligned}$$

Therefore, the operations manager estimates with 90% confidence that between 13.08% and 21.92% of the newspapers printed on that day have some type of nonconformance.

CHECKING THE ASSUMPTIONS

In Example 4 the number of successes and failures is sufficiently large that the normal distribution provides an excellent approximation for the binomial distribution. However, if the sample size is not large or the percentage of successes is either very low or very high, then the binomial distribution rather than the normal distribution is used (see references 1 and 6). The exact confidence intervals for various sample sizes and proportions of successes have been tabulated by Fisher and Yates (reference 2).

For a given sample size, confidence intervals for proportions often seem to be wider than those for continuous variables. With continuous variables, the measurement on each respondent contributes more information than does a categorical variable. In other words, a categorical variable with only two possible values is a very crude measure compared with a continuous variable, so each observation contributes less information about the parameter being estimated.

PROBLEMS FOR SECTION 3

Learning the Basics

22 If $n = 200$ and $X = 50$, set up a 95% confidence interval estimate of the population proportion.

23 If $n = 400$ and $X = 25$, set up a 99% confidence interval estimate of the population proportion.

Applying the Concepts

24 The telephone company wants to estimate the proportion of households that would purchase an additional telephone line if it were made available at a substantially reduced installation cost. A random sample of 500 households is selected. The results indicate that 135 of the households would purchase the additional telephone line at a reduced installation cost.

a. Set up a 99% confidence interval estimate of the population proportion of households that would purchase the additional telephone line.

b. How would the manager in charge of promotional programs concerning residential customers use the results in (a)?

25 An article in the *Wall Street Journal* suggests that women start new businesses for freedom and flexibility and not money ("Work Week," *Wall Street Journal*, June 8, 1999, A1). In a survey of 763 women who had started their own businesses, 229 said that they launched their business for greater freedom. Only 99 indicated that a desire to make more money drove them to start their business.

a. Set up a 90% confidence interval estimate of the population proportion of women who start new businesses to gain greater freedom.

b. Set up a 90% confidence interval estimate of the population proportion of women who start new businesses to earn more money.

26 In a study conducted by Randstad North America, only 41% of 1,110 U.S. workers surveyed believe that their bosses are loyal to them (Carlos Tejada, "Work Week," *Wall Street Journal*, May 29, 2002, B10).

a. Construct a 95% confidence interval estimate for the population proportion of U.S. workers who believe that their bosses are loyal to them.

b. Construct a 90% confidence interval estimate for the population proportion of U.S. workers who believe that their bosses are loyal to them.

c. Which interval is wider? Explain why this is true.

27 A survey conducted by *Reader's Digest* ("Testing Honesty Around the World," *USA Today*, May 1, 2001, 1A) that studied honesty around the world reported that of 1,100 wallets containing up to $50 in local currency and a name and phone number that were "lost," 484 were not returned. Construct a 95% confidence interval for the proportion of all wallets that would be returned if lost.

28 In an attempt to study the problem of using cell phones while driving ("Drivers Using Cell Phones Have Problems," *USA Today*, May 16, 2001, 1A), a survey of drivers who use cell phones determined that 46% of the respondents reported having to swerve and 10% knew someone who had a crash while talking on a cell phone. Suppose the survey was based on 500 respondents.

a. Construct a 95% confidence interval for the proportion of drivers who reported having to swerve.

b. Construct a 95% confidence interval for the proportion of drivers who knew someone who had a crash while talking on a cell phone.

29 Walker Information, Inc., surveyed 2,800 U.S. workers and asked them if they felt comfortable reporting misconduct by their fellow workers. The results were 1,344 answered yes and 1,456 answered no ("Work Week," *Wall Street Journal*, September 4, 2001, A1).

a. Construct a 95% confidence interval for the proportion of all U.S. workers who feel comfortable reporting misconduct by their fellow workers.

b. Construct a 99% confidence interval for the proportion of all U.S. workers who feel comfortable reporting misconduct by their fellow workers.

c. Based on your answers to (a) and (b), how strongly do you believe that less than half of all U.S. workers feel comfortable about reporting misconduct by their fellow workers?

d. The article also states that in 1999, 34% of all U.S. workers felt comfortable reporting misconduct by their fellow workers. How strongly do you believe that this percentage increased between 1999 and 2001?

30 A survey of working women in North America was conducted by the Clinique unit of Estee Lauder Cosmetics. Of the 1,000 women surveyed, 55% believed that companies should hold positions for those on maternity leave for six months or less, and 45% felt that they should hold those positions for more than six months ("Work Week," *Wall Street Journal*, September 11, 2001, A1).

a. Construct a 95% confidence interval for the proportion of all working women in North America who believe that companies should hold positions for those on maternity leave for more than six months.

b. Interpret the interval constructed in (a).

31 During June and July of 2001, the European Union Executive Commission conducted a study of 6,543 European adults. Of those surveyed, 56% said that the euro single currency would promote economic growth and 73% knew the correct date of the changeover (January 1, 2002). ("Retail Cheating Seen as Likely," *Marketing News*, September 24, 2001, 42.)

a. Construct a 95% confidence interval estimate for the proportion of European adults who believe that the euro would promote economic growth.

b. Construct a 95% confidence interval estimate for the proportion of European adults who knew the correct date of the currency changeover.

4 DETERMINING SAMPLE SIZE

In each example concerning confidence interval estimation, the sample size was selected without regard to the width of the resulting confidence interval. In the business world, determining the proper sample size is a complicated procedure, subject to the constraints of budget, time, and ease of selection. If, in the Saxon Home Improvement Company example, you want to estimate the mean dollar amount of the sales invoices or the proportion of sales invoices that contain errors, you must determine in advance how good the estimate must be. Thus, you need to decide how large a sampling error to allow in estimating each of the parameters. You must also determine in advance how confident you want to be of correctly estimating the true population parameter.

Sample Size Determination for the Mean

To develop a formula for determining the appropriate sample size needed when constructing a confidence interval estimate of the mean, recall Equation (1):

$$\bar{X} \pm Z\frac{\sigma}{\sqrt{n}}$$

The amount added to or subtracted from $\bar{X}$ is equal to half the width of the interval. This quantity represents the amount of imprecision in the estimate that results from sampling error. The **sampling error**[2] e is defined as

$$e = Z\frac{\sigma}{\sqrt{n}}$$

Solving for n gives the sample size needed to construct the appropriate confidence interval estimate for the mean. "Appropriate" means that the resulting interval will have an acceptable amount of sampling error.

[2] *In this context, some statisticians refer to e as the "margin of error."*

SAMPLE SIZE DETERMINATION FOR THE MEAN

The sample size n is equal to the product of the Z value squared and the variance σ^2, divided by the sampling error e squared.

$$n = \frac{Z^2\sigma^2}{e^2} \quad (4)$$

To determine the sample size, you must know three factors:

1. The desired confidence level, which determines the value of Z, the critical value from the standardized normal distribution[3]
2. The acceptable sampling error e
3. The standard deviation σ

[3] *Z is used instead of t because, to determine the critical value of t, the sample size needs to be known, but it is not known yet. For most studies, the sample size needed will be large enough that the standardized normal distribution is a good approximation of the t distribution.*

In some business-to-business relationships requiring estimation of important parameters, acceptable levels of sampling error and the confidence level required are specified in legal contracts. For companies in the food or drug sectors, sampling errors and confidence levels are often specified by government regulations. In general, however, it is usually not easy to specify the two factors needed to determine the sample size. How can you determine the level of confidence and sampling error? Typically, these questions are answered only by the subject matter expert (i.e., the individual most familiar with the variables to be analyzed). Although 95% is the most common confidence level used (in which case $Z = 1.96$), if more confidence is desired, then 99% might be more appropriate. If less confidence is deemed acceptable, then 90% might be used. For the sampling error, you should be thinking not of how much sampling error you would like to have (you really do not want any error) but of how much can be tolerated while still permitting you to draw adequate conclusions from the data.

In addition to specifying the confidence level and the sampling error, an estimate of the standard deviation must be available. Unfortunately, the population standard deviation σ is rarely known. In some instances, the standard deviation can be estimated from past data. In other situations, an educated guess can be made by taking into account the range and distribution of the variable. For example, if a normal distribution is assumed, the range is approximately equal to 6σ (i.e., $\pm 3\sigma$ around the mean) so that σ is estimated as the range/6. If σ cannot be estimated in this manner, a *pilot study* can be conducted and the standard deviation can be estimated from the resulting data.

To explore how to determine the sample size needed for estimating the population mean, consider again the audit to be performed this month at Saxon Home Improvement Company. In section 2, a sample of 100 sales invoices was selected and a 95% confidence interval estimate of the population average sales invoice amount was developed. How was this sample size determined? Should a different sample size have been selected?

Suppose that, after consultation with company officials, it is determined that a sampling error of no more than ±$5 is desired along with 95% confidence. Past data indicate that the standard deviation of the sales amount has been approximately $25 for a substantial period of time. Thus, $e = \$5$, $\sigma = \$25$, and $Z = 1.96$ (for 95% confidence). Using Equation (4),

$$n = \frac{Z^2\sigma^2}{e^2} = \frac{(1.96)^2(25)^2}{(5)^2}$$
$$= 96.04$$

Therefore, $n = 97$ because the general rule is to slightly oversatisfy the criteria by rounding the sample size up to the next whole integer. Thus, the sample size of 100 that was taken is close to what is necessary to satisfy the needs of the company based on the estimated standard deviation, desired confidence level, and sampling error. However, note from the confidence interval that because the sample standard deviation is $28.95, the width of the confidence interval was slightly more than was desired. Figure 11 illustrates the use of Microsoft Excel to determine the sample size.

FIGURE 11
Sample size determination obtained from Microsoft Excel for estimating the mean sales invoice amount for the Saxon Home Improvement Company

	A	B
1	**For Mean Sales Invoice Amount**	
2		
3	**Data**	
4	**Population Standard Deviation**	25
5	**Sampling Error**	5
6	**Confidence Level**	95%
7		
8	Intemediate Calculations	
9	Z Value	-1.95996279
10	Calculated Sample Size	96.0363532
11		
12	Result	
13	**Sample Size Needed**	97

CHAPTER 7.xls

Retrieve the Figure 7.11 worksheet of the ***Chapter 7.xls*** *workbook to view the sample size calculations needed for estimating the mean similar to the one above.*

Excel Strategies: Calculating the Sample Size Needed for Estimating the Mean

You implement a worksheet that features the **NORMSINV** function to calculate the sample size needed for estimating the mean. PHStat2 can construct this worksheet for you in a single step.

For example, to calculate the sample size needed for estimating the mean sales invoice amount for the Saxon Home Improvement Company problem above, use one of these strategies:

Using Excel with PHStat2

Use the PHStat2 Determination for the Mean procedure to calculate the sample size needed for estimating the mean.

Select **PHStat | Sample Size | Determination for the Mean**.

In the **Sample Size Determination for the Mean** dialog box (shown at right):

Enter **25** in the **Population Standard Deviation** edit box.

Enter **5** in the **Sampling Error** edit box.

Enter **95** in the **Confidence Level** edit box.

Enter a title in the **Title** edit box.

Click the **OK** button.

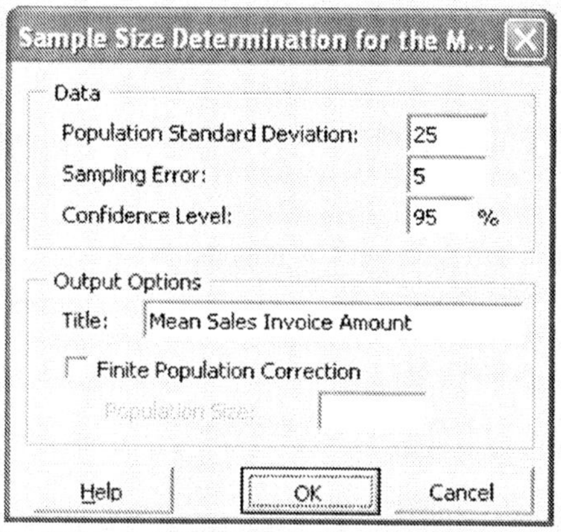

Using Excel

Follow the instructions of section EH4 at the end of this chapter to manually implement a worksheet to calculate the sample size needed for estimating the mean.

Example 5 illustrates another application of determining the sample size needed to develop a confidence interval estimate for the mean.

EXAMPLE 5

DETERMINING THE SAMPLE SIZE FOR THE MEAN

Returning to Example 3, suppose you want to estimate the population mean force required to break the insulator to within ±25 pounds of the true value and you want to be 95% confident of correctly estimating the true mean. On the basis of a study taken the previous year, you believe that the standard deviation is 100 pounds. Find the sample size needed.

SOLUTION

With this information, the sample size is determined in the following manner for $e = 25$, $\sigma = 100$, and 95% confidence ($Z = 1.96$):

$$n = \frac{Z^2\sigma^2}{e^2} = \frac{(1.96)^2(100)^2}{(25)^2}$$
$$= 61.47$$

Therefore, $n = 62$. A sample size of 62 insulators is selected because the general rule for determining sample size is to always round up to the *next integer value* in order to slightly oversatisfy the criteria desired.

Note that if you use these criteria, a sample of 62 insulators will be taken—not a sample of 30 as was used in Example 3. Also, the standard deviation that was used was estimated at 100 based on a previous survey. If the standard deviation obtained in the actual survey is very different from this value, the computed sampling error will be directly affected.

Sample Size Determination for a Proportion

So far in this section, only the determination of the sample size needed for estimating the population mean has been discussed. Now suppose that the sample size necessary for estimating the population proportion of sales invoices that have errors violating the Saxon Home Improvement Company policy needs to be determined. The methods of sample size determination that are used in estimating a population proportion are similar to those employed in estimating a mean.

Recall that in developing the sample size for a confidence interval for the mean, the sampling error was defined by

$$e = Z\frac{\sigma}{\sqrt{n}}$$

When estimating a proportion, σ is replaced by $\sqrt{p(1-p)}$. Thus the sampling error is

$$e = Z\sqrt{\frac{p(1-p)}{n}}$$

Solving for n, the sample size necessary to develop a confidence interval estimate for a proportion is obtained.

SAMPLE SIZE DETERMINATION FOR A PROPORTION

The sample size n is equal to the Z value squared times the true proportion p, times 1 minus the true proportion p, divided by the sampling error e squared.

$$n = \frac{Z^2p(1-p)}{e^2} \quad \textbf{(5)}$$

To determine the sample size for estimating a proportion, three unknowns must be defined:

1. The desired level of confidence that determines the value of Z
2. The acceptable sampling error e
3. The true proportion of "successes" p

In practice, the selection of these quantities requires some planning. Once the desired level of confidence is determined, you can obtain the appropriate Z value from the standardized normal distribution. The sampling error e indicates the amount of error that you are willing to accept or tolerate in estimating the population proportion. The third quantity—the true proportion of success p—is actually the population parameter that you want to find! Thus, how do you state a value for the very thing that you are taking a sample in order to determine?

Here there are two alternatives. First, in many situations, past information or relevant experiences may be available that provide an educated estimate of p. Second, if past information or relevant experiences are not available, you can try to provide a value for p that would never *underestimate* the sample size needed. Referring to Equation (5), observe that the quantity $p(1-p)$ appears in the numerator. Thus, you need to determine the value of p that will make the quantity $p(1-p)$ as large as possible. It can be shown that when $p = 0.5$, the product $p(1-p)$ achieves its maximum result. Several values of p along with the accompanying products of $p(1-p)$ are

$$\text{When } p = 0.9, \text{ then } p(1-p) = (0.9)(0.1) = 0.09$$

$$\text{When } p = 0.7, \text{ then } p(1-p) = (0.7)(0.3) = 0.21$$

$$\text{When } p = 0.5, \text{ then } p(1-p) = (0.5)(0.5) = 0.25$$

$$\text{When } p = 0.3, \text{ then } p(1-p) = (0.3)(0.7) = 0.21$$

$$\text{When } p = 0.1, \text{ then } p(1-p) = (0.1)(0.9) = 0.09$$

Therefore, when there is no prior knowledge or estimate of the true proportion p, you should use $p = 0.5$ as the most conservative way of determining the sample size. This produces the largest possible sample size, but results in the highest possible cost of sampling. Thus, the use of $p = 0.5$ may overestimate the sample size needed because the actual sample proportion is used in developing the confidence interval. If the actual sample proportion is very different from 0.5, the width of the confidence interval may be substantially narrower than originally intended. The increased precision comes at the cost of spending more time and money for an increased sample size.

Returning to the Saxon Home Improvement Company Using Statistics scenario, suppose that the auditing procedures require you to have 95% confidence in estimating the population proportion of sales invoices with errors to within ± 0.07 of the true population proportion. The results from past months indicate that the largest proportion has been no more than 0.15. Thus, $e = 0.07$, $p = 0.15$, and $Z = 1.96$ (for 95% confidence). Using Equation (5),

$$\begin{aligned} n &= \frac{Z^2 p(1-p)}{e^2} \\ &= \frac{(1.96)^2(0.15)(0.85)}{(0.07)^2} \\ &= 99.96 \end{aligned}$$

Therefore, $n = 100$ because the general rule is to round the sample size up to the next whole integer to slightly oversatisfy the criteria. Thus, the sample size of 100 that was taken was exactly what was needed to satisfy the requirements of the company based on the estimated proportion, desired confidence level, and sampling error. However, note from the confidence interval obtained earlier that, because the sample proportion was 0.10, the width of the confidence level is actually narrower than required. Figure 12 shows Microsoft Excel output.

FIGURE 12
Sample size determination obtained from Microsoft Excel for estimating the proportion of sales invoices with errors for the Saxon Home Improvement Company

	A	B
1	For Proportion of In-Error Sales Invoices	
2		
3	Data	
4	Estimate of True Proportion	0.15
5	Sampling Error	0.07
6	Confidence Level	95%
7		
8	Intermediate Calculations	
9	Z Value	-1.95996279
10	Calculated Sample Size	99.95620435
11		
12	Result	
13	Sample Size Needed	100

CHAPTER 7.xls

Retrieve the Figure 7.12 worksheet of the ***Chapter 7.xls*** *workbook to view the sample size calculations needed for estimating the proportion similar to the one above.*

Excel Strategies: Calculating the Sample Size Needed for Estimating the Proportion

You implement a worksheet that features the **NORMSINV** function to calculate the sample size needed for estimating the proportion. PHStat2 can construct this worksheet for you in a single step.

For example, to calculate the sample size needed for estimating the proportion of sales invoices in error that violate the accounting controls of the Saxon Home Improvement Company, shown in Figure 12 above, use one of these strategies:

Using Excel with PHStat2

Use the PHStat2 Determination for the Proportion procedure to calculate the sample size needed for estimating the proportion.

Select **PHStat | Sample Size | Determination for the Proportion**.

In the **Sample Size Determination for the Proportion** dialog box (shown at right):

Enter **0.15** in the **Estimate of True Proportion** edit box.

Enter **0.07** in the **Sampling Error** edit box.

Enter **95** in the **Confidence Level** edit box.

Enter a title in the **Title** edit box.

Click the **OK** button.

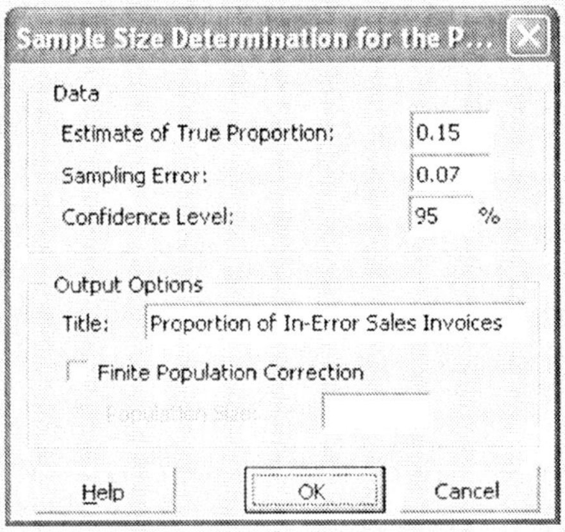

Using Excel

Follow the instructions of section EH5 that begin at the end of this chapter to manually implement a worksheet to calculate the sample size needed for estimating the proportion.

Example 6 provides a second application of determining the sample size for estimating the population proportion.

EXAMPLE 6

DETERMINING THE SAMPLE SIZE FOR THE POPULATION PROPORTION

The operations manager in Example 4 wants to have 90% confidence of estimating the proportion of nonconforming newspapers to within ±0.05 of its true value. In addition, because the publisher of the newspaper has not previously undertaken such a study, no information is available from past data. Determine the sample size needed.

SOLUTION

Because there is no information available from past data, $p = 0.50$. With this and other criteria in mind, the sample size needed can be determined in the following manner when $e = 0.05$, $p = 0.50$, and for 90% confidence, $Z = 1.645$.

$$n = \frac{(1.645)^2(0.50)(0.50)}{(0.05)^2}$$
$$= 270.6$$

Thus, $n = 271$. Therefore, in order to be 90% confident of estimating the proportion to within ±0.05 of its true value, a sample size of 271 newspapers is needed.

PROBLEMS FOR SECTION 4

Learning the Basics

32 If you want to be 95% confident of estimating the population mean to within a sampling error of ±5 and the standard deviation is assumed to be equal to 15, what sample size is required?

33 If you want to be 99% confident of estimating the population mean to within a sampling error of ±20 and the standard deviation is assumed to be equal to 100, what sample size is required?

34 If you want to be 99% confident of estimating the population proportion to within an error of ±0.04, what sample size is needed?

35 If you want to be 95% confident of estimating the population proportion to within an error of ±0.02 and there is historical evidence that the population proportion is approximately 0.40, what sample size is needed?

Applying the Concepts

36 A survey is planned to determine the mean annual family medical expenses of employees of a large company. The management of the company wishes to be 95% confident that the sample mean is correct to within ±\$50 of the true population mean annual family medical expenses. A pilot study indicates that the standard deviation can be estimated as \$400.

a. How large a sample size is necessary?

b. If management wants to be correct to within ±\$25, what sample size is necessary?

37 If the manager of a paint supply store wants to estimate the mean amount of paint in a 1-gallon can to within ±0.004 gallon with 95% confidence and also assumes that the standard deviation is 0.02 gallon, what sample size is needed?

38 If a quality control manager wants to estimate the mean life of lightbulbs to within ±20 hours with 95% confidence and also assumes that the process standard deviation is 100 hours, what sample size is needed?

39 If the inspection division of a county weights and measures department wants to estimate the mean amount of soft-drink fill in 2-liter bottles to within ±0.01 liter with 95% confidence and also assumes that the standard deviation is 0.05 liter, what sample size is needed?

40 A consumer group wants to estimate the mean electric bill for the month of July for single-family homes in a large city. Based on studies conducted in other cities, the standard deviation is assumed to be \$25. The group wants to estimate the mean bill for July to within ±\$5 of the true average with 99% confidence.

a. What sample size is needed?

b. If 95% confidence is desired, what sample size is necessary?

41 An advertising agency that serves a major radio station wants to estimate the mean amount of time that the station's audience spends listening to the radio on a daily basis. From past studies, the standard deviation is estimated as 45 minutes.

a. What sample size is needed if the agency wants to be 90% confident of being correct to within ±5 minutes?

b. If 99% confidence is desired, what sample size is necessary?

42 Suppose that a gas utility company wants to estimate its mean waiting time for installation of service to within ±5 days with 95% confidence. Because it does not have access to previous data, it makes its own independent estimate of the standard deviation, which it believes to be 20 days. What sample size is needed?

43 The data file **NYSE.xls** consists of the number of shares traded on the New York Stock Exchange for a sample of 18 companies on March 4, 2003.

a. Set up a 95% confidence interval estimate of the population mean number of shares traded for a company on the New York Stock Exchange on March 4, 2003.
b. What sample size is needed if you want to be 95% confident of being correct to within ±20,000 shares?
c. If you were to perform this study today, do you think that your answer to (b) would be valid? Explain.

44 A political pollster wants to estimate the proportion of voters who will vote for the Democratic candidate in a presidential campaign. The pollster wants to have 90% confidence that her prediction is correct to within ±0.04 of the population proportion.

a. What sample size is needed?
b. If the pollster wants to have 95% confidence, what sample size is needed?
c. If she wants to have 95% confidence and a sampling error of ±0.03, what sample size is needed?
d. On the basis of your answers to (a)–(c), what general conclusions can be reached about the effects of the confidence level desired and the acceptable sampling error on the sample size needed? Discuss.

45 In 2001 it was estimated that 45% of U.S. households purchased groceries at convenience stores and 29% purchased groceries at wholesale clubs ("68th Annual Report of the Grocery Industry," *Progressive Grocer*, April 2002, 29). Consider a follow-up study focusing on the last calendar year.

a. What sample size is needed to estimate the population proportion of U.S. households purchasing groceries at convenience stores to within ±0.02 with 95% confidence?
b. What sample size is needed to estimate the population proportion of U.S. households purchasing groceries at wholesale clubs to within ±0.02 with 95% confidence?
c. Compare the results of (a) and (b). Explain why these results differ.
d. If you were to design the follow-up study, would you use one sample and ask the respondents both questions, or would you draw two separate samples? Explain the rationale behind your decision.
e. How would you draw your sample(s) for the study in (d)?

46 What proportion of people living in the United States use the Internet when planning their vacation? According to a poll conducted by American Express, 35% use the Internet (A. R. Carey and K. Carter, "Snapshots," *USA Today*, January 14, 2003, 1A).

a. If you were to conduct a follow-up study that would provide 95% confidence that the point estimate is correct to within ±0.04 of the population proportion, how large a sample size would be required?
b. If you were to conduct a follow-up study that would provide 99% confidence that the point estimate is correct to within ±0.04 of the population proportion, how large a sample size would be required?
c. If you were to conduct a follow-up study that would provide 95% confidence that the point estimate is correct to within ±0.02 of the population proportion, how large a sample size would be required?
d. If you were to conduct a follow-up study that would provide 99% confidence that the point estimate is correct to within ±0.02 of the population proportion, how large a sample size would be required?
e. Discuss the effects of changing the desired confidence level and the acceptable sampling error on sample size requirements.

47 Do ringing cell phones disturb business presentations? In a poll of 326 business men and women, 303 answered this question "yes" and only 23 answered "no" ("You Say," *Presentations: Technology and Techniques for Effective Communication*, January 2003, 18).

a. Construct a 95% confidence interval for the population proportion of business men and women who have their presentations disturbed by cell phones.
b. Interpret the interval constructed in (a).
c. If you were to conduct a follow-up study that would provide 95% confidence that the point estimate is correct to within ±0.04 of the population proportion, how large a sample size would be required?
d. If you were to conduct a follow-up study that would provide 99% confidence that the point estimate is correct to within ±0.04 of the population proportion, how large a sample size would be required?
e. If you were to conduct a follow-up study that would provide 95% confidence that the point estimate is correct to within ±0.02 of the population proportion, how large a sample size would be required?
f. If you were to conduct a follow-up study that would provide 99% confidence that the point estimate is correct to within ±0.02 of the population proportion, how large a sample size would be required?
g. Discuss the effects of changing the desired confidence level and the acceptable sampling error on sample size requirements.
h. Discuss the effect of different prior estimates of the true population proportion on sample size requirements by comparing your answers to this problem with problem 46.

48 A study conducted by the Federal Reserve reported that 52% of 4,449 families interviewed in 2001 held stocks, either directly or through mutual funds (Barbara Hagenbaugh, "Nation's Wealth Disparity Widens," *USA Today*, January 22, 2003, 1A).

a. Construct a 95% confidence interval for the proportion of families that held stocks in 2001.
b. Interpret the interval constructed in (a).
c. If you were to conduct a follow-up study to estimate the population proportion of families that currently hold stocks to within ±0.01 with 95% confidence, how many families would you interview?

49 A study conducted by At-A-Glance communications found that 434 office workers out of a sample of 611 responded to e-mail within an hour or two (D. Haralson and S. Ward, "You Have Mail," *USA Today*, May 7, 2002, 1A).

a. Construct a 95% confidence interval for the proportion of workers who responded to e-mail within an hour or two.

b. Interpret the interval constructed in (a).

c. If you were to conduct a follow-up study to estimate the population proportion of workers who responded to e-mail within an hour or two to within ±0.01 with 95% confidence, how many workers would you interview?

5 APPLICATIONS OF CONFIDENCE INTERVAL ESTIMATION IN AUDITING

In the discussion of estimation procedures, the focus has been on estimating either the population mean or the population proportion. One of the areas in business that makes widespread use of statistical sampling for the purposes of estimation is **auditing**.

Exhibit 1 lists six advantages of statistical sampling in auditing.

Auditing
Auditing is the collection and evaluation of evidence about information relating to an economic entity such as a sole business proprietor, a partnership, a corporation, or a government agency in order to determine and report on how well the information obtained corresponds to established criteria.

EXHIBIT 1 ADVANTAGES OF STATISTICAL SAMPLING IN AUDITING

1. The sample result is objective and defensible. Because the sample size is based on demonstrable statistical principles, the audit is defensible before one's superiors and in a court of law.
2. The method provides an objective way of estimating the sample size in advance.
3. The method provides an estimate of the sampling error.
4. This approach can turn out to be more accurate for drawing conclusions about the population because the examination of large populations can be time-consuming and subject to more nonsampling error than a statistical sample.
5. Statistical samples can be combined and evaluated even though accomplished by different auditors. This can be done because there is a scientific basis for the sample. Samples can be treated as if they have been done by a single auditor.
6. Objective evaluation of the results of an audit is possible. The results can be projected with a known sampling error.

Estimating the Population Total Amount

In auditing applications, one is often more interested in obtaining estimates of the population **total amount** than the population mean. Equation (6) shows how to estimate a population total amount.

ESTIMATING THE POPULATION TOTAL AMOUNT

The point estimate for the population total is equal to the population size N times the sample mean.

$$\text{Total} = N\overline{X} \qquad (6)$$

Because the estimated total is $N\overline{X}$, a confidence interval estimate for the population total can be obtained as in Equation (7).

CONFIDENCE INTERVAL ESTIMATE FOR THE TOTAL

$$N\overline{X} \pm N(t_{n-1})\frac{S}{\sqrt{n}}\sqrt{\frac{N-n}{N-1}} \qquad (7)$$

To demonstrate the application of the confidence interval estimate for the population total amount, return to the Saxon Home Improvement Company Using Statistics scenario. Recall that determining the total dollar amount of all sales invoices for the month was one of the auditing tasks. If there were 5,000 invoices for that month, then using Equations (6) and (7), with $N = 5{,}000$, $n = 100$, $\bar{X} = \$110.27$, and $S = \$28.95$, for 95% confidence, $t_{99} = 1.9842$, and

$$N\bar{X} = (5{,}000)(\$110.27) = \$551{,}350$$

so that

$$N\bar{X} \pm N(t_{n-1})\frac{S}{\sqrt{n}}\sqrt{\frac{N-n}{N-1}} = 551{,}350 \pm (5{,}000)(1.9842)\frac{28.95}{\sqrt{100}}\sqrt{\frac{5{,}000-100}{5{,}000-1}}$$

$$= 551{,}350 \pm 28{,}721.295(0.99005)$$

$$\$522{,}914 \le \text{population total} \le \$579{,}786$$

Thus, with 95% confidence the total amount of sales invoices is estimated to be between \$522,914 and \$579,786. Figure 13 below shows Microsoft Excel output.

FIGURE 13
Confidence interval estimate obtained from Microsoft Excel for the total amount of all invoices for the Saxon Home Improvement Company

	A	B
1	**Total Amount of All Sales Invoices**	
2		
3	**Data**	
4	**Population Size**	5000
5	**Sample Mean**	110.27
6	**Sample Size**	100
7	**Sample Standard Deviation**	28.95
8	**Confidence Level**	95%
9		
10	**Intermediate Calculations**	
11	Population Total	551350.00
12	FPC Factor	0.990048503
13	Standard Error of the Total	14330.95209
14	Degrees of Freedom	99
15	*t* Value	1.984217306
16	Interval Half Width	28435.72
17		
18	**Confidence Interval**	
19	**Interval Lower Limit**	522914.28
20	**Interval Upper Limit**	579785.72

Excel Strategies: Calculating the Confidence Interval Estimate for the Population Total

CHAPTER 7.xls

Retrieve the Figure 7.13 worksheet of the ***Chapter 7.xls*** *workbook to view the confidence interval estimate for the population total similar to the one above.*

You implement a worksheet that features the **TINV** function to calculate the confidence interval estimate for the population total. PHStat2 can construct this worksheet for you in a single step.

For example, to generate the confidence interval estimate for the total dollar amount of all Saxon Home Improvement sales invoices for a month, shown in Figure 13 above, use one of these strategies:

Using Excel with PHStat2

Use the PHStat2 Estimate for the Population Total procedure to calculate the confidence interval estimate for the total dollar amount.

Select **PHStat | Confidence Intervals | Estimate for the Population Total**.

In the Estimate for the Population Total dialog box (shown at right):

Enter **5000** in the **Population Size** edit box.

Enter **95** in the **Confidence Level** edit box.

Select the **Sample Statistics Known** option button and enter **100** in the **Sample Size, 110.27** in the **Sample Mean**, and **28.95** in the **Sample Standard Deviation** edit boxes.

Enter a title in the **Title** edit box.

Click the **OK** button.

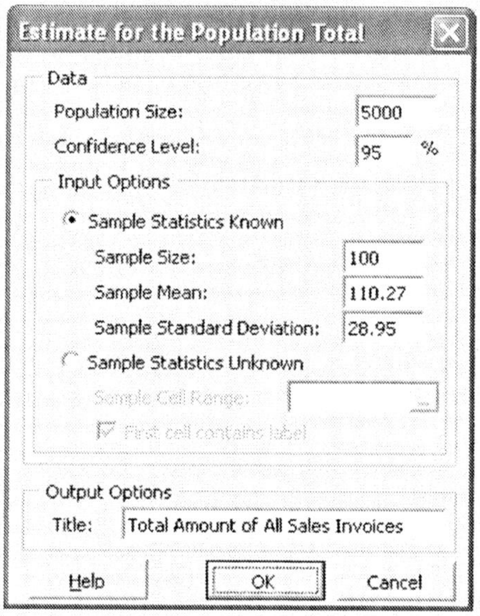

For problems in which the sample mean and sample standard deviation are not known and needs to be calculated, select the ***Sample Statistics Unknown*** *option button and enter the cell range of the sample data in the* ***Sample Cell Range*** *edit box (dimmed in the illustration).*

Using Excel

Follow the instructions of section EH6 that begin at the end of this chapter to manually implement a worksheet to calculate the confidence interval estimate for the population total.

To further illustrate the population total, see Example 7.

EXAMPLE 7

DEVELOPING A CONFIDENCE INTERVAL ESTIMATE FOR THE POPULATION TOTAL

Suppose that an auditor is faced with a population of 1,000 vouchers and wants to estimate the total value of the population of vouchers. A sample of 50 vouchers is selected with the following results:

$$\text{Average voucher amount } (\bar{X}) = \$1{,}076.39$$
$$\text{Standard deviation } (S) = \$273.62$$

Set up a 95% confidence interval estimate of the total amount for the population of vouchers.

SOLUTION

Using Equation (6), the point estimate of the population total is

$$N\bar{X} = (1{,}000)(1{,}076.39) = \$1,076,390$$

From Equation (7), a 95% confidence interval estimate of the population total amount is obtained as follows:

$$(1{,}000)(1{,}076.39) \pm (1{,}000)(2.0096)\frac{273.62}{\sqrt{50}}\sqrt{\frac{1{,}000 - 50}{1{,}000 - 1}}$$
$$= 1{,}076{,}390 \pm 77{,}762.878(0.97517)$$
$$= 1{,}076{,}390 \pm 75{,}832$$
$$\$1{,}000{,}558 \le \text{population total} \le \$1{,}152{,}222$$

Thus, with 95% confidence the total amount of the vouchers is estimated to be between \$1,000,558 and \$1,152,222.

Difference Estimation

Difference estimation is used when an auditor believes that errors exist in a set of items being audited and the auditor wants to estimate the magnitude of the errors based only on a sample. The following steps are used in difference estimation:

1. Determine the sample size required.
2. Calculate the differences between the values obtained during the audit and the original values recorded. Note that the difference in observation i, denoted D_i, is equal to 0 if the auditor finds that the original value is correct, is a positive value when the audited value is larger than the originally recorded value, and is negative when the audited value is smaller than the originally recorded value.
3. Compute the average difference in the sample ($\bar{D}$) by dividing the total difference by the sample size as shown in Equation (8).

AVERAGE DIFFERENCE

$$\bar{D} = \frac{\sum_{i=1}^{n} D_i}{n} \tag{8}$$

where

D_i = audited value – original value

4. Compute the standard deviation of the differences (S_D) as shown in Equation (9). Be sure to remember that any item that is not in error has a difference value of 0.

STANDARD DEVIATION OF THE DIFFERENCE

$$S_D = \sqrt{\frac{\sum_{i=1}^{n} (D_i - \bar{D})^2}{n-1}} \tag{9}$$

5. Set up a confidence interval estimate of the total difference in the population, as shown in Equation (10).

CONFIDENCE INTERVAL ESTIMATE FOR THE TOTAL DIFFERENCE

$$N\bar{D} \pm N(t_{n-1})\frac{S_D}{\sqrt{n}}\sqrt{\frac{N-n}{N-1}} \tag{10}$$

The auditing procedures for Saxon Home Improvement Company require a 95% confidence interval estimate of the difference between the actual dollar amounts on the sales invoice and the amounts entered into the integrated inventory and sales information system. Suppose that in the sample of 100 sales invoices, there are 12 invoices in which the actual amount on the sales invoice and the amount entered into the integrated inventory management and sales information system is different. These 12 differences are:

PLUMBINV.xls

\$9.03 \$7.47 \$17.32 \$8.30 \$5.21 \$10.80 \$6.22 \$5.63 \$4.97 \$7.43 \$2.99 \$4.63

The other 88 invoices are not in error. Their *differences* are each 0. Thus,

$$\bar{D} = \frac{\sum_{i=1}^{n} D_i}{n} = \frac{90}{100} = 0.90$$

and

$$S_D = \sqrt{\frac{\sum_{i=1}^{n}(D_i - \bar{D})^2}{n-1}}$$

$$S_D = \sqrt{\frac{(9.03 - 0.9)^2 + (7.47 - 0.9)^2 + \cdots + (0 - 0.9)^2}{100 - 1}}$$

$$S_D = 2.752$$

To obtain the confidence interval estimate for the total difference in the population of 5,000 sales invoices, using Equation (10),

$$(5{,}000)(0.90) \pm (5{,}000)(1.9842)\frac{2.752}{\sqrt{100}}\sqrt{\frac{5{,}000 - 100}{5{,}000 - 1}}$$

$$= 4{,}500 \pm 2{,}702.91$$

$$\$1{,}797.09 \le \text{total difference} \le \$7{,}202.91$$

Thus, the auditor estimates with 95% confidence that the total difference between the sales invoices as determined during the audit, and the amount originally entered into the accounting system is between \$1,797.09 and \$7,202.91. Figure 14 below shows Microsoft Excel output.

FIGURE 14

Confidence interval estimate obtained from Microsoft Excel for the total difference between the invoice amounts and the amounts entered in the accounting system for the Saxon Home Improvement Company

	A	B	C	D	E
1	**Total Difference In Actual and Entered**				
2					
3	**Data**				
4	**Population Size**	**5000**			
5	**Sample Size**	**100**			
6	**Confidence Level**	**95%**			
7					
8	Intermediate Calculations				
9	Sum of Differences	90		Calculations Area	
10	Average Difference in Sample	0.9		For standard deviation of differences:	
11	Total Difference	4500		Number of Differences Not = 0	12
12	Standard Deviation of Differences	2.751797		Number of Differences = 0	88
13	FPC Factor	0.990049		SS for Differences Not = 0	678.3864
14	Standard Error of the Total Diff.	1362.206		SS for Differences = 0	71.28
15	Degrees of Freedom	99		Sum of Squares	749.6664
16	*t* Value	1.984217		Variance of Differences	7.572388
17	Interval Half Width	2702.913			
18					
19	**Confidence Interval**				
20	**Interval Lower Limit**	**1797.09**			
21	**Interval Upper Limit**	**7202.91**			

CHAPTER 7.xls

Retrieve the Figure 7.14 worksheet of the ***Chapter 7.xls*** *workbook to view the total difference analysis similar to the one above.*

Excel Strategies: Calculating the Confidence Interval Estimate for the Total Difference

You implement a worksheet that contains difference data and implement a worksheet that features the **TINV** function to calculate the confidence interval estimate for the total difference. PHStat2 can implement these worksheets for you in a single step.

For example, to generate the confidence interval estimate for the total difference between the invoice amounts and the amounts entered into the Saxon Home Improvement accounting system, shown in Figure 14, open to the **DifferencesData** worksheet of the **Chapter 7.xls** workbook and use one of these strategies:

Using Excel with PHStat2

Use the PHStat2 Estimate for the Total Difference procedure to calculate the confidence interval estimate for the total difference.

Select **PHStat | Confidence Intervals | Estimate for the Total Difference**.

In the Estimate for the Total Difference dialog box (shown at right):

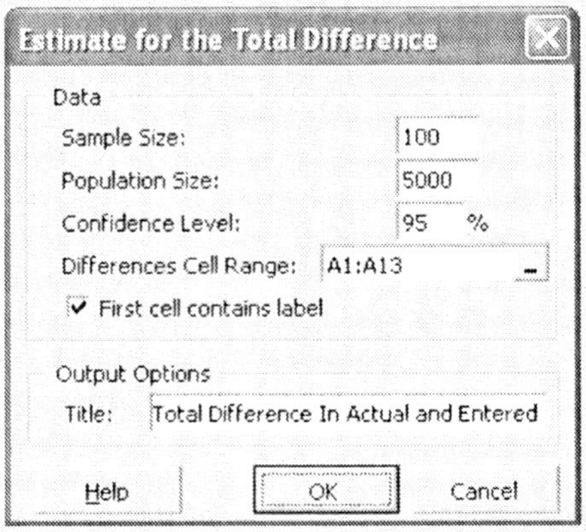

Enter **100** in the **Sample Size** edit box.
Enter **5000** in the **Population Size** edit box.
Enter **95** in the **Confidence Level** edit box.
Enter **A1:A13** in the **Differences Cell Range** edit box.
Select the **First cell contains label** check box.
Enter a title in the **Title** edit box.
Click the **OK** button.

Using Excel

Follow the instructions of section EH7 at the end of this chapter to manually implement a worksheet to calculate the confidence interval estimate for the total difference.

In the previous example, all 12 differences are positive because the actual amount on the sales invoice is more than the amount entered into the accounting system. It is possible that some of the errors could have been negative. To illustrate such an occurrence, see Example 8.

EXAMPLE 8

DIFFERENCE ESTIMATION

DIFFTEST.xls

Returning to Example 7, suppose that in the sample of 50 vouchers there are 14 vouchers that contain errors. Suppose that the values of the 14 errors are as follows, in which two differences are negative.

$75.41 $38.97 $108.54 –$37.18 $62.75 $118.32 –$88.84
$127.74 $55.42 $39.03 $29.41 $47.99 $28.73 $84.05

Set up a 95% confidence interval estimate of the total difference in the population of 1,000 vouchers.

SOLUTION

For these data,

$$\overline{D} = \frac{\sum_{i=1}^{n} D_i}{n} = \frac{690.34}{50} = 13.8068$$

and

$$S_D = \sqrt{\frac{\sum_{i=1}^{n}(D_i - \overline{D})^2}{n-1}}$$

$$S_D = \sqrt{\frac{(75.41 - 13.8068)^2 + (38.97 - 13.8068)^2 + \cdots + (0 - 13.8068)^2}{50 - 1}}$$

$$S_D = 37.427$$

To obtain the confidence interval estimate for the total difference in the population using Equation (10),

$$(1{,}000)(13.8068) \pm (1{,}000)(2.0096)\frac{37.427}{\sqrt{50}}\sqrt{\frac{1{,}000 - 50}{1{,}000 - 1}}$$
$$= 13{,}806.8 \pm 10{,}372.4$$
$$\$3{,}434.40 \le \text{total difference} \le \$24{,}179.20$$

Thus, with 95% confidence the total difference in the population of vouchers is estimated to be between \$3,434.40 and \$24,179.20.

One-Sided Confidence Interval Estimation of the Rate of Noncompliance with Internal Controls

Organizations use internal control mechanisms to ensure that individuals act in accordance with company guidelines. For example, Saxon Home Improvement Company requires that goods not be removed from the warehouse without an authorized warehouse removal slip. During the monthly audit of the company, the auditing team is charged with the task of estimating the proportion of times goods were removed without proper authorization. This is referred to as the rate of noncompliance with the internal control. To estimate the rate of noncompliance, auditors take a random sample of sales invoices and determine how often merchandise was shipped without an authorized warehouse removal slip. The auditors then compare their results with a previously established tolerable exception rate, which is the maximum allowable proportion of items in the population not in compliance. When estimating the rate of noncompliance, it is commonplace to use a **one-sided confidence interval**. That is, the auditors estimate an upper bound on the rate of noncompliance. A one-sided confidence interval for a proportion is determined using Equation (11).

ONE-SIDED CONFIDENCE INTERVAL FOR A PROPORTION

$$\textit{Upper Bound} = p_s + Z\sqrt{\frac{p_s(1-p_s)}{n}}\sqrt{\frac{N-n}{N-1}} \qquad \textbf{(11)}$$

where

Z = the value corresponding to a cumulative area of $(1 - \alpha)$ from the standardized normal distribution, i.e., a right-hand tail probability of α.

If the tolerable exception rate is higher than the upper bound, then the auditor concludes that the company is in compliance with the internal control. If the upper bound is larger than the tolerable exception rate, the auditor concludes that the control noncompliance rate is too high. The auditor may then request that a larger sample be taken.

Suppose that in the monthly audit, you select 400 of the sales invoices from a population of 10,000 invoices. In the sample of 400 sales invoices, 20 are determined to be in violation of the internal control. If the tolerable exception rate for this internal control is 6%, what should you conclude? Use a 95% level of confidence.

The one-sided confidence interval is computed using $p_s = 20/400 = 0.05$ and $Z = 1.645$. Using Equation (11)

$$Upper\ Bound = p_s + Z\sqrt{\frac{p_s(1-p_s)}{n}}\sqrt{\frac{N-n}{N-1}} = 0.05 + 1.645\sqrt{\frac{0.05(1-0.05)}{400}}\sqrt{\frac{10{,}000-400}{10{,}000-1}}$$
$$= 0.05 + 1.645(0.0109)(0.98) = 0.05 + 0.0176 = 0.0676$$

Thus, there is 95% confidence that the rate of noncompliance is less than 6.76%. Because the tolerable exception rate is 6%, the rate of noncompliance may be too high for this internal control. In other words, the noncompliance rate for the population may be higher than the rate deemed tolerable. Therefore, you should request a larger sample.

In some audits, the estimation of the rate of noncompliance allows the auditor to conclude that the company's internal controls are being used an acceptable proportion of the time. Example 9 illustrates such an occurrence.

EXAMPLE 9

ESTIMATING THE RATE OF NONCOMPLIANCE

A large electronics firm writes a million checks a year. An internal control policy for the company is that the authorization to sign each check is granted only after an invoice has been initialed by an accounts payable supervisor. The company's tolerable exception rate for this control is 4%. If control deviations are found in 8 of the 400 invoices sampled, what should the auditor do? Use a 95% level of confidence.

SOLUTION

Set up a 95% one-sided confidence interval for the proportion of invoices found to be in noncompliance and compare this to the tolerable exception rate. For these data $p_s = 8/400 = 0.02$ and with a 95% level of confidence $Z = 1.645$. Using Equation (11),

$$Upper\ Bound = p_s + Z\sqrt{\frac{p_s(1-p_s)}{n}}\sqrt{\frac{N-n}{N-1}} = 0.02 - 1.645\sqrt{\frac{0.02(1-0.02)}{400}}\sqrt{\frac{1{,}000{,}000-400}{1{,}000{,}000-1}}$$
$$= 0.02 + 1.645(0.007)(0.9998) = 0.02 + 0.0115 = 0.0315$$

The auditor concludes with 95% confidence that the rate of noncompliance is less than 3.15%. Since this is less than the tolerable exception rate, the auditor concludes that the internal control compliance is adequate. In other words, the auditor is more than 95% confident that the rate of noncompliance is less than 4%.

PROBLEMS FOR SECTION 5

Learning the Basics

50 A sample of 25 is selected from a population of 500 items. The sample mean is 25.7 and the sample standard deviation is 7.8. Set up a 99% confidence interval estimate of the population total.

51 Suppose that a sample of 200 items is selected from a population of 10,000 items. Ten items are found to have errors of the following amounts:

13.76 42.87 34.65 11.09 14.54 22.87 25.52 9.81 10.03 15.49

Set up a 95% confidence interval estimate of the total difference in the population. **ITEMERR.xls**

52 If $p_s = 0.04$, $n = 300$, and $N = 5{,}000$, calculate the upper bound for a one-sided confidence interval estimate of the population proportion p using a level of confidence of:

a. 90%.

b. 95%.

c. 99%.

Applying the Concepts

53 A stationery store wants to estimate the total retail value of the 300 greeting cards that it has in its inventory. Set up a 95% confidence interval estimate of the population total value of all greeting cards that are in inventory if a random sample of 20 greeting cards indicates an average value of \$1.67 and a standard deviation of \$0.32.

54 The personnel department of a large corporation employing 3,000 workers wants to estimate the family dental expenses of its employees to determine the feasibility of providing a dental insurance plan. A random sample of 10 employees reveals the following family dental expenses (in dollars) for the preceding year: **DENTAL.xls**

110 362 246 85 510 208 173 425 316 179

Set up a 90% confidence interval estimate of the total family dental expenses for all employees in the preceding year.

55 A branch of a chain of large electronics stores is conducting an end-of-month inventory of the merchandise in stock. It was determined that there were 1,546 items in inventory at that time. A sample size of 50 items was randomly selected and an audit was conducted with the following results:

Value of Merchandise	
$\bar{X}$ = \$252.28	S = \$93.67

Set up a 95% confidence interval estimate of the total estimated value of the merchandise in inventory at the end of the month.

56 A customer in the wholesale garment trade is often entitled to a discount for a cash payment for goods. The amount of discount varies by vendor. A sample of 150 items selected from a population of 4,000 invoices at the end of a period of time revealed that in 13 cases the customer failed to take the discount to which he or she was entitled. The amounts (in dollars) of the 13 discounts that were not taken were as follows: **DISCOUNT.xls**

\$6.45 15.32 97.36 230.63 104.18 84.92 132.76
66.12 26.55 129.43 88.32 47.81 89.01

Set up a 99% confidence interval estimate of the population total amount of discounts not taken.

57 Econe Dresses is a small company that manufactures women's dresses for sale to specialty stores. There are 1,200 inventory items and the historical cost is recorded on a first in, first out (FIFO) basis. In the past, approximately 15% of the inventory items were incorrectly priced. However, any misstatements were usually not significant. A sample of 120 items was selected and the historical cost of each item was compared with the audited value. The results indicated that 15 items differed in their historical costs and audited values. These differences were as follows: **FIFO.xls**

Sample Number	Historical Cost (\$)	Audited Value (\$)	Sample Number	Historical Cost (\$)	Audited Value (\$)
5	261	240	60	21	210
9	87	105	73	140	152
17	201	276	86	129	112
18	121	110	95	340	216
28	315	298	96	341	402
35	411	356	107	135	97
43	249	211	119	228	220
51	216	305			

Set up a 95% confidence interval estimate of the total population difference in the historical cost and audited value.

58 Tom and Brent's Alpine Outfitters conduct an annual audit of their financial records. An internal control policy for the company is that a check can be issued only after the accounts payable manager initials the invoice. The tolerable exception rate for this internal control is 0.04. Suppose that during the audit, a sample of 300 invoices is examined from a population of 10,000 invoices and 11 invoices are found to violate the internal control.

a. Calculate the upper bound for a 95% one-sided confidence interval estimate for the rate of noncompliance.

b. Based on (a), what should the auditor conclude?

59 An internal control policy for Rhonda's Online Fashion Accessories requires a quality assurance check before a shipment is made. The tolerable exception rate for this internal control is 0.05. During an audit, 500 shipping records were sampled from a population of 5,000 shipping records and 12 were found that violated the internal control.

a. Calculate the upper bound for a 95% one-sided confidence interval estimate for the rate of noncompliance.

b. Based on (a), what should the auditor conclude?

6 CONFIDENCE INTERVAL ESTIMATION AND ETHICAL ISSUES

Ethical issues relating to the selection of samples and the inferences that accompany them can arise in several ways. The major ethical issue relates to whether or not confidence interval estimates are provided along with the point estimates of the population parameters. To indicate the sample statistic without also including the confidence interval limits (typically set at 95%), the sample size used, and an interpretation of the meaning of the confidence interval in terms that a layperson can understand raises ethical issues because of their omission. Failure to include a confidence interval estimate might mislead the user of the results into thinking that the point estimate obtained from the sample is all that is needed to predict the population characteristic with certainty. Thus, it is important that the interval estimate be indicated in a prominent place in any written communication, along with a simple explanation of the meaning of the confidence interval. In addition, the size of the sample should be highlighted.

One of the most common areas where ethical issues concerning estimation occurs is in the publication of the results of political polls. Often, the results of the polls are highlighted on the front page of the newspaper and the sampling error involved along with the methodology used is printed on the page where the article is typically continued, often in the middle of the newspaper. To ensure an ethical presentation of statistical results, the confidence levels, sample size, and confidence limits should be made available for all surveys and other statistical studies.

7 ESTIMATION AND SAMPLE SIZE DETERMINATION FOR FINITE POPULATIONS (CD-ROM TOPIC)

section7.7.pdf

In this section, confidence intervals are developed and the sample size is determined for situations in which sampling is done without replacement from a finite population. For further discussion, see **section7.7.pdf** on the CD-ROM that accompanies this text.

SUMMARY

As shown in the summary flowchart, in this chapter, confidence intervals for estimating the characteristics of a population have been discussed along with how the necessary sample size can be determined. You learned how an accountant of the Saxon Home Improvement Company can use the data from a sample obtained during an audit to estimate important population parameters such as the average dollar amount of invoices and the proportion of shipments that were made without the proper authorization.

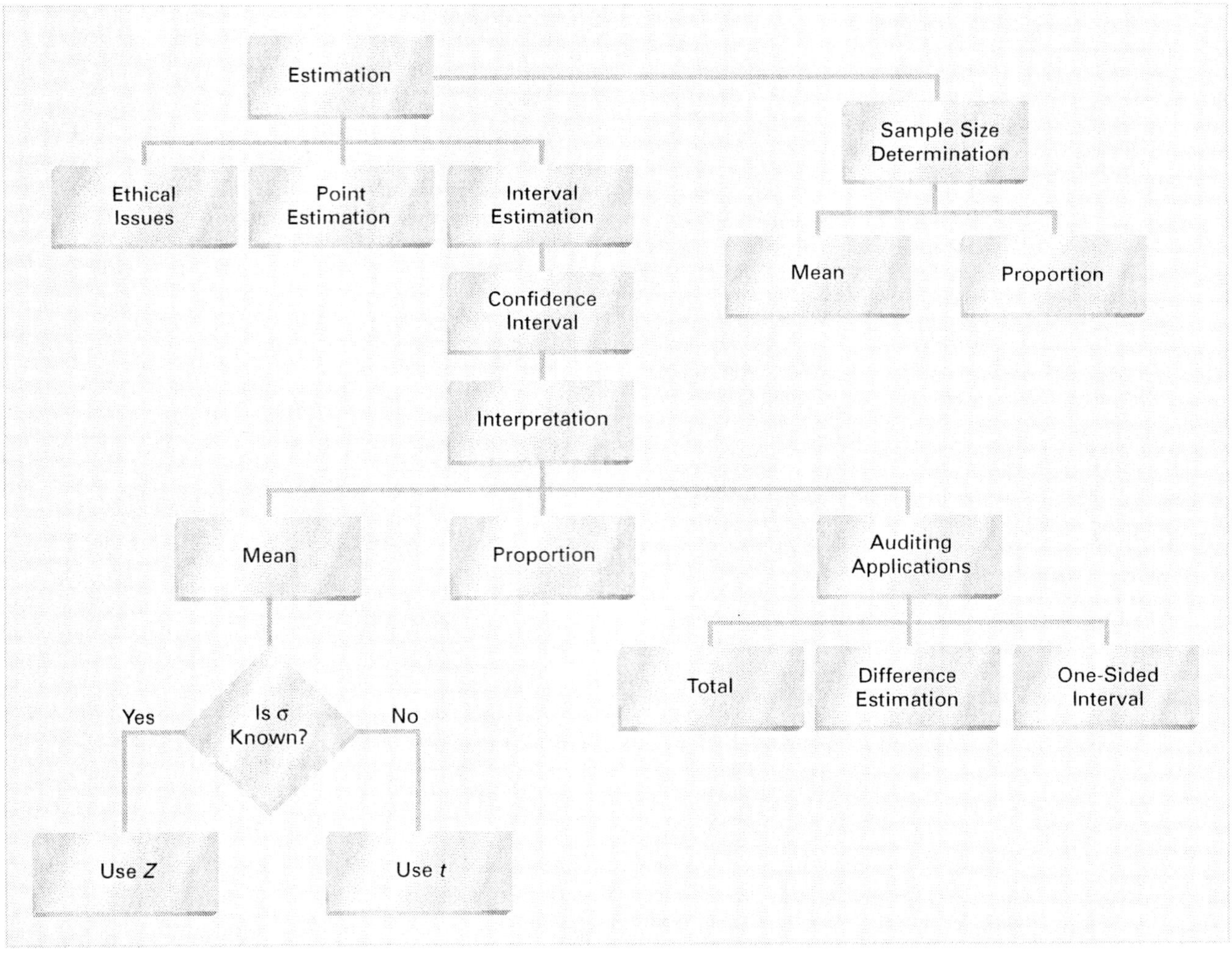

Chapter summary flowchart

KEY TERMS

auditing
confidence interval estimate
critical value
degrees of freedom
difference estimation
interval estimate
level of confidence
one-sided confidence interval
point estimate
sampling error
Student's t distribution
total amount

CHAPTER REVIEW PROBLEMS

Checking Your Understanding

60 Why is it that you can never really have 100% confidence of correctly estimating the population characteristic of interest?

61 When is the t distribution used to develop the confidence interval estimate for the mean?

62 Why is it true that for a given sample size n, an increase in confidence is achieved by widening (and making less precise) the confidence interval obtained?

63 Under what circumstances would a one-sided confidence interval be used instead of a two-sided confidence interval?

64 When would you want to estimate the population total instead of the population mean?

65 How does difference estimation differ from estimating the mean?

Applying the Concepts

Problems 66–80 can be solved with or without Microsoft Excel. We recommended that Microsoft Excel be used to solve problems 81–85.

66 *Redbook* magazine conducted a survey through its Internet Web site (Stacy Kravetz, "Work Week," *Wall Street Journal*, April 13, 1999, A1). People visiting the Web site were given the opportunity to fill out an on-screen survey form. A total of 665 women responded to a question that asked whether they would prefer a four-day workweek or a 20% pay increase. A four-day workweek was the preference for 412 of the respondents.

a. Define the population from which this sample was drawn.
b. Is this a random sample from this population?
c. Is this a statistically valid study?
d. Describe how you would design a statistically valid study to investigate the proportion of *Redbook* subscribers who would prefer a four-day workweek rather than a 20% pay increase. Use the information above to determine the sample size needed to estimate this population proportion to within ±0.02 with 95% confidence.

67 Companies are spending more time screening applicants than in the past. A result of the more in-depth screening process is that companies are finding that many applicants are stretching the truth on their applications. A study conducted by Automatic Data Processing found inaccuracies between the applicant and past employers in 44% of the applications screened. Unfortunately the article did not disclose the sample size used in the study (Stephanie Armour, "Security Checks Worry Workers," *USA Today*, June 19, 2002, B1).

a. Suppose that 500 applications were screened. Construct a 95% confidence interval estimate of the population proportion of applications containing inaccuracies with past employers.
b. Based on (a), is it right to conclude that less than half of all applications contain inaccuracies with past employers?
c. Suppose that the study used a sample size of 200 applications. Construct a 95% confidence interval estimate of the population proportion of applications containing inaccuracies with the past employers.
d. Based on (c), is it right to conclude that less than half of all applications contain inaccuracies with their past employers?
e. Discuss the effect of sample size on your answers to (a)–(d).
f. Discuss the ethical issues involved in reporting the results of a study without disclosing the sample size.

68 A sales and marketing management magazine conducted a survey on salespeople cheating on their expense reports and other unethical conduct (D. Haralson and Q. Tian, "Cheating Hearts," *USA Today*, February 15, 2001, 1A). In the survey, managers have caught salespeople cheating on an expense report 58% of the time, working a second job on company time 50% of the time, listing a "strip bar" as a restaurant on an expense report 22% of the time, and giving a kickback to a customer 19% of the time. Suppose the survey was based on a sample of 200 managers.

a. Construct a 95% confidence interval estimate of the population proportion of managers who have caught salespeople cheating on an expense report.
b. Construct a 95% confidence interval estimate of the population proportion of managers who have caught salespeople working a second job on company time.
c. Construct a 95% confidence interval estimate of the population proportion of managers who have caught salespeople listing a "strip bar" as a restaurant on an expense report.

d. Construct a 95% confidence interval estimate of the population proportion of managers who have caught salespeople giving a kickback to a customer.

e. Use the information given in this problem to determine the sample size needed to estimate the proportion of managers who have caught salespeople working a second job on company time to within ±0.02 with 95% confidence.

f. Is the information given in the problem the same as stating that 58% of all salespeople cheat on an expense report? Explain.

69 Starwood Hotels conducted a survey of 401 top executives who play golf (Del Jones, "Many CEOs Bend the Rules (of Golf)," *USA Today*, June 26, 2002). Among the results were the following:

- 329 cheat at golf
- 329 hate others who cheat at golf
- 289 believe business and golf behavior parallel
- 80 would let a client win to get business
- 40 would call in sick to play golf

Construct 95% confidence interval estimates for each of these questions. What conclusions can you reach about CEO's attitudes toward golf from these results?

70 A market researcher for a consumer electronics company wants to study the television viewing habits of residents of a particular small city. A random sample of 40 respondents is selected, and each respondent is instructed to keep a detailed record of all television viewing in a particular week. The results are as follows:

- Viewing time per week: $\bar{X} = 15.3$ hours, $S = 3.8$ hours.
- 27 respondents watch the evening news on at least 3 weeknights.

a. Set up a 95% confidence interval estimate for the mean amount of television watched per week in this city.

b. Set up a 95% confidence interval estimate for the proportion of respondents who watch the evening news on at least 3 nights per week.

If the market researcher wants to take another survey in a different city, answer these questions:

c. What sample size is required if he wants to be 95% confident of being correct to within ±2 hours and assumes that the population standard deviation is equal to 5 hours?

d. What sample size is needed if he wishes to be 95% confident of being within ±0.035 of the true population proportion who watch the evening news on at least 3 weeknights if no previous estimate is available?

e. Based on (c) and (d), what sample size should the market researcher select if a single survey is being conducted?

71 The real estate assessor for a county government wants to study various characteristics of single-family houses in the county. A random sample of 70 houses reveals the following:

- Heated area of the house (in square feet): $\bar{X} = 1{,}759$, $S = 380$.
- 42 houses have central air-conditioning.

a. Set up a 99% confidence interval estimate of the population mean heated area of the house.

b. Set up a 95% confidence interval estimate of the population proportion of houses that have central air-conditioning.

72 The personnel director of a large corporation wishes to study absenteeism among clerical workers at the corporation's central office during the year. A random sample of 25 clerical workers reveals the following:

- Absenteeism: $\bar{X} = 9.7$ days, $S = 4.0$ days.
- 12 clerical workers were absent more than 10 days.

a. Set up a 95% confidence interval estimate of the mean number of absences for clerical workers last year.

b. Set up a 95% confidence interval estimate of the population proportion of clerical workers absent more than 10 days last year.

If the personnel director also wishes to take a survey in a branch office, answer these questions:

c. What sample size is needed if the director wants to be 95% confident of being correct to within ±1.5 days and the population standard deviation is assumed to be 4.5 days?

d. What sample size is needed if the director wants to be 90% confident of being correct to within ±0.075 of the population proportion of workers who are absent more than 10 days if no previous estimate is available?

e. Based on (c) and (d), what sample size should the personnel director select if a single survey is being conducted?

73 The market research director for Dotty's department store wants to study women's spending per year on cosmetics. A survey is to be sent to a sample of the store's credit cardholders to determine

- the average yearly amount that women spend on cosmetics.
- the population proportion of women who purchase their cosmetics primarily from Dotty's department store.

a. If the market researcher wants to have 99% confidence of estimating the true population average to within ±$5 and the standard deviation is assumed to be $18 (based on previous surveys), what sample size is needed?

b. If the market researcher wishes to have 90% confidence of estimating the population proportion to within ±0.045, what sample size is needed?

c. Based on the results in (a) and (b), how many of the store's credit cardholders should be sampled? Explain.

74 The branch manager of an outlet of a large, nationwide bookstore chain wants to study characteristics of customers of her store, which is located near the campus of a large state university. In particular, she decides to focus on two variables: the amount of money spent by customers and whether the customers would consider purchasing educational videotapes relating to specific courses such as statistics, accounting, or calculus or to graduate preparation exams such as GMAT, GRE, or LSAT. The results from a sample of 70 customers are as follows:

- Amount spent: $\bar{X} = \$28.52$, $S = \$11.39$.
- 28 customers stated that they would consider purchasing educational videotapes.

a. Set up a 95% confidence interval estimate of the population mean amount spent in the bookstore.
b. Set up a 90% confidence interval estimate of the population proportion of customers who would consider purchasing educational videotapes.

Assuming the branch manager of another store from a different bookstore chain wants to conduct a similar survey in his store (which is located near another university), answer these questions:
c. If he wants to have 95% confidence of estimating the true population mean amount spent in his store to within ±$2 and the standard deviation is assumed to be $10, what sample size is needed?
d. If he wants to have 90% confidence of estimating the population proportion who would consider purchasing educational videotapes to within ±0.04, what sample size is needed?
e. Based on your answers to (c) and (d), what size sample should be taken?

75 The branch manager of an outlet (store 1) of a large, nationwide chain of pet supply stores wants to study characteristics of customers of her store. In particular, she decides to focus on two variables: the amount of money spent by customers and whether the customers own only one dog, only one cat, or more than one dog and/or cat. The results from a sample of 70 customers are as follows:

- Amount of money spent: $\bar{X} = \$21.34$, $S = \$9.22$.
- 37 customers own only a dog.
- 26 customers own only a cat.
- 7 customers own more than one dog and/or cat.

a. Set up a 95% confidence interval estimate of the population mean amount spent in the pet supply store.
b. Set up a 90% confidence interval estimate of the population proportion of customers who own only a cat.

If the branch manager of another outlet (store 2) wishes to conduct a similar survey in his store (and does not have any access to the information generated by the manager of store 1), answer these questions:
c. If he wants to have 95% confidence of estimating the true population mean amount spent in his store to within ±$1.50 and the standard deviation is assumed to be $10, what sample size is needed?
d. If he wants to have 90% confidence of estimating the population proportion of customers who own only a cat to within ±0.045, what sample size is needed?
e. Based on your answers to (c) and (d), what size sample should be taken?

76 The owner of a restaurant that serves continental food wants to study characteristics of customers of his restaurant. In particular, he decides to focus on two variables: the amount of money spent by customers and whether customers order dessert. The results from a sample of 60 customers are as follows:

- Amount spent: $\bar{X} = \$38.54$, $S = \$7.26$.
- 18 customers purchased dessert.

a. Set up a 95% confidence interval estimate of the population mean amount spent per customer in the restaurant.
b. Set up a 90% confidence interval estimate of the population proportion of customers who purchase dessert.

If the owner of a competing restaurant wants to conduct a similar survey in her restaurant (and does not have access to the information obtained by the owner of the first restaurant), answer these questions:
c. If she wants to have 95% confidence of estimating the population mean amount spent in her restaurant to within ±$1.50 and the standard deviation is assumed to be $8, what sample size is needed?
d. If she wants to have 90% confidence of estimating the population proportion of customers who purchase dessert to within ±0.04, what sample size is needed?
e. Based on your answers to (c) and (d), what size sample should be taken?

77 A representative for a large chain of hardware stores is interested in testing the claims of a manufacturer of a product called "Ice Melt," which is reported to melt snow and ice at temperatures as low as 0° Fahrenheit. The chain purchases a large shipment of 400 five-pound bags for distribution. The representative wants to know with 95% confidence, within ±0.05, what proportion of bags of Ice Melt perform the job as claimed by the manufacturer.
a. How many bags does the representative need to test? What assumption should be made concerning the true proportion in the population? (This is called *destructive testing*; that is, the product being tested is destroyed by the test and is then unavailable to be sold.)

The representative tests 50 bags, and 42 do the job as claimed.
b. Construct a 95% confidence interval estimate for the population proportion that will do the job as claimed.
c. How can the representative use the results of (b) to determine whether to sell the Ice Melt product?

78 An audit test to establish the percentage of occurrence of failure to follow a specific internal control procedure is to be undertaken. Suppose a sample of 50 from a population of 1,000 items is selected and it is determined that in seven instances the internal control procedure was not followed.
a. Set up a 90% one-sided confidence interval estimate of the population proportion of items in which the internal control procedure was not followed.
b. If the tolerable exception rate is 0.15, what should the auditor conclude?

79 An auditor for a government agency is assigned the task of evaluating reimbursement for office visits to doctors paid by Medicare. The audit is to be conducted for all Medicare payments in a particular geographic zip code during a certain month. A population of 25,056 visits exists in this area for this month. The auditor primarily wants to estimate the total amount paid by Medicare in this area for the month. She wants 95% confidence of estimating the population mean to within ±$5. On the basis of past experience, she estimates the standard deviation to be $30.

a. What sample size should be selected?

Using the sample size selected in (a), an audit is conducted. It is discovered that in 12 of the office visits, an incorrect amount of reimbursement was provided.

Amount of Reimbursement	
$\bar{X}$ = $93.70	S = $34.55

For the 12 office visits in which incorrect reimbursement was provided, the differences between the amount reimbursed and the amount that the auditor determined should have been reimbursed were: **MEDICARE.xls**

$17 $25 $14 −$10 $20 $40 $35 $30 $28 $22 $15 $5

b. Set up a 90% confidence interval estimate of the population proportion of reimbursements that contain errors.

c. Set up a 95% confidence interval estimate of the population mean reimbursement per office visit.

d. Set up a 95% confidence interval estimate of the population total amount of reimbursements for this geographic area in this month.

e. Set up a 95% confidence interval estimate of the total difference between the amount reimbursed and the amount that the auditor determined should have been reimbursed.

80 A large computer store is conducting an end-of-month inventory of the computers in stock. An auditor for the store wants to estimate the mean value of the computers in inventory at that time. She wants to have 99% confidence that her estimate of the average value is correct to within ±$200. On the basis of past experience, she estimates that the standard deviation of the value of a computer is $400.

a. What sample size should be selected?

Using the sample size selected in (a), an audit was conducted with the following results:

Value of Computers	
$\bar{X}$ = $3,054.13	S = $384.62

b. Set up a 99% confidence interval estimate of the total estimated value of the computers in inventory at the end of the month if there were 258 computers in inventory.

81 A quality characteristic of interest for a tea-bag-filling process is the weight of the tea in the individual bags. If the bags are underfilled, two problems arise. First, customers may not be able to brew the tea to be as strong as they wish. Second, the company may be in violation of the truth-in-labeling laws. In this example, the label weight on the package indicates that, on average, there are 5.5 grams of tea in a bag. On the other hand, if the average amount of tea in a bag exceeds the label weight, the company is giving away product. Getting an exact amount of tea in a bag is problematic because of variation in the temperature and humidity inside the factory, differences in the density of the tea, and the extremely fast filling operation of the machine (approximately 170 bags a minute). The following table provides the weight in grams of a sample of 50 tea bags produced in one hour by a single machine. **TEABAGS.xls**

Weight of Tea Bags in Grams

5.65	5.44	5.42	5.40	5.53	5.34	5.54	5.45	5.52	5.41
5.57	5.40	5.53	5.54	5.55	5.62	5.56	5.46	5.44	5.51
5.47	5.40	5.47	5.61	5.53	5.32	5.67	5.29	5.49	5.55
5.77	5.57	5.42	5.58	5.58	5.50	5.32	5.50	5.53	5.58
5.61	5.45	5.44	5.25	5.56	5.63	5.50	5.57	5.67	5.36

a. Construct a 99% confidence interval estimate of the population mean weight of the tea bags.

b. Is the company meeting the requirement set forth on the label that, on average, there are 5.5 grams of tea in a bag?

82 A manufacturing company produces steel housings for electrical equipment. The main component part of the housing is a steel trough that is made out of a 14-gauge steel coil. It is produced using a 250-ton progressive punch press with a wipe-down operation that puts two 90-degree forms in the flat steel to make the trough. The distance from one side of the form to the other is critical because of weatherproofing in outdoor applications. The data from a sample of 49 observations follows: **TROUGH.xls**

Width of Trough (in Inches)

8.312	8.343	8.317	8.383	8.348	8.410	8.351	8.373	8.481	8.422
8.476	8.382	8.484	8.403	8.414	8.419	8.385	8.465	8.498	8.447
8.436	8.413	8.489	8.414	8.481	8.415	8.479	8.429	8.458	8.462
8.460	8.444	8.429	8.460	8.412	8.420	8.410	8.405	8.323	8.420
8.396	8.447	8.405	8.439	8.411	8.427	8.420	8.498	8.409	

a. Construct a 95% confidence interval estimate of the average width of the troughs.

b. Interpret the interval developed in (a).

83 Studies conducted by a manufacturer of "Boston" and "Vermont" asphalt shingles have shown product weight to be a major factor in the customer's perception of quality. The last stage of the assembly line packages the shingles before they are placed on wooden pallets. Once a pallet is full (a pallet for most brands holds 16 squares of shingles), it is weighed and the measurement is recorded. The data file **PALLET.xls** contains the weight (in pounds) from a sample of 368 pallets of Boston shingles and 330 pallets of Vermont shingles.

a. For the Boston shingles, set up a 95% confidence interval estimate of the average weight.
b. For the Vermont shingles, set up a 95% confidence interval estimate of the average weight.
c. Evaluate whether the assumption needed for (a) and (b) have been seriously violated.
d. Based on the results of (a) and (b), what conclusions can you reach concerning the average weight of the Boston and Vermont shingles?

84 The manufacturer of "Boston" and "Vermont" asphalt shingles provide their customers with a 20-year warranty on most of their products. To determine whether a shingle will last as long as the warranty period, accelerated-life testing is conducted at the manufacturing plant. Accelerated-life testing exposes the shingle to the stresses it would be subject to in a lifetime of normal use in a laboratory setting via an experiment that takes only a few minutes to conduct. In this test, a shingle is repeatedly scraped with a brush for a short period of time and the amount of shingle granules that are removed by the brushing is weighed (in grams). Shingles that experience low amounts of granule loss are expected to last longer in normal use than shingles that experience high amounts of granule loss. In this situation, a shingle should experience no more than 0.8 grams of granule loss if it is expected to last the length of the warranty period. The data file **GRANULE.xls** contains a sample of 170 measurements made on the company's Boston shingles, and 140 measurements made on Vermont shingles.

a. For the Boston shingles, set up a 95% confidence interval estimate of the average granule loss.
b. For the Vermont shingles, set up a 95% confidence interval estimate of the average granule loss.
c. Evaluate whether the assumption needed for (a) and (b) have been seriously violated.
d. Based on the results of (a) and (b), what conclusions can you reach concerning the average granule loss of the Boston and Vermont shingles?

85 Zagat's publishes restaurant ratings for various locations in the United States. The data file **RESTRATE.xls** contains the Zagat rating for food, décor, and service, and the price per person for a sample of 50 restaurants located in New York City, and 50 restaurants located on Long Island, a suburb of New York City.

Source: Extracted from Zagat Survey 2002 New York City Restaurants *and* Zagat Survey 2001/2002 Long Island Restaurants.

For New York City and Long Island restaurants separately,

a. Construct 95% confidence interval estimates for the variables of food rating, décor rating, service rating, and price per person.
b. What conclusions can you reach about the New York City and Long Island restaurants from the results obtained in (a)?

Report Writing Exercises

86 Referring to the results you obtained in problem 82 concerning the width of a steel trough, write a report that summarizes your conclusions. Be sure to incorporate the statistical results you obtained from Microsoft Excel into the report by using Microsoft Office as discussed in the appendix on Preparing Data for Reports and Presentations Using Microsoft Office.

Internet Exercises

87 Go to the Web site for this text

www.prenhall.com/levine

Select Chapter 7 and then click on Internet exercises.

TEAM PROJECT

TP1 Refer to TP1 in the chapter on Presenting Data in Tables and Charts. Set up all appropriate interval estimates of population characteristics of very-low-risk, low-risk, average-risk, high-risk, and very-high-risk mutual funds. Include these estimates in written and oral presentation to be made to the vice president for research at the financial investment service. **MUTUAL FUNDS.xls**

RUNNING CASE MANAGING THE SPRINGVILLE HERALD

The marketing department has been considering ways to increase the number of new subscriptions and increase the rate of retention among those customers who agreed to a trial subscription. Following the suggestion of assistant manager Lauren Alfonso, the department staff designed a survey to help determine various characteristics of readers of the newspaper who were not home-delivery subscribers. The survey consists of the following ten questions:

1. Do you or a member of your household ever purchase the *Springville Herald*?
(1) Yes (2) No
[If the respondent answers no, the interview is terminated.]

2. Do you receive the *Springville Herald* via home delivery?
(1) Yes (2) No
[If no, skip to question 4.]

3. Do you receive the *Springville Herald*:
(1) Monday–Saturday (2) Sunday only
(3) Every day
[If every day, skip to question 9.]

4. How often during the Monday–Saturday period do you purchase the *Springville Herald*?
(1) Every day (2) Most days (3) Occasionally

5. How often do you purchase the *Springville Herald* on Sundays?
(1) Every Sunday
(2) 2–3 Sundays per month
(3) No more than once a month

6. Where are you most likely to purchase the *Springville Herald*?
(1) Convenience store
(2) Newsstand/candy store
(3) Vending machine (4) Supermarket (5) Other

7. Would you consider subscribing to the *Springville Herald* for a trial period if a discount was offered?
(1) Yes (2) No
[If no, skip to question 9.]

8. The *Springville Herald* currently costs 50 cents on Monday–Saturday and $1.50 on Sunday for a total of $4.50 per week. How much would you be willing to pay per week to obtain home delivery for a 90-day trial period?

9. Do you read a daily newspaper other than the *Springville Herald*?
(1) Yes (2) No

10. As an incentive for long-term subscribers, the newspaper is considering the possibility of offering all subscribers who pay in advance for six months of home delivery a card that would provide discounts at select restaurants in the Springville area. Would you want to obtain such a card under the terms of this offer?
(1) Yes (2) No

The group agreed to use a random-digit dialing method to poll 500 local households by telephone. Using this approach, the last four digits of a telephone number are randomly selected to go with an access code and telephone exchange (the first 6 digits of a ten-digit telephone number). Only those pairs of access codes and telephone exchanges that were for the Springville city area were used for this survey.

Of the 500 households selected, 94 households either refused to participate, could not be contacted after repeated attempts, or represented telephone numbers that were not in service. The summary results were as follows:

Households that Purchase the *Springville Herald*	Frequency
Yes	352
No	54

Households with Home Delivery	Frequency
Yes	136
No	216

Type of Home Delivery Subscription	Frequency
Monday–Saturday	18
Sunday only	25
7 days a week	93

Purchase Behavior of Nonsubscribers for Monday–Saturday Editions	Frequency
Every day	78
Most days	95
Occasionally	43

Purchase Behavior of Nonsubscribers for Sunday Editions	Frequency
Every Sunday	138
2–3 Sundays a month	54
No more than once a month	24

Nonsubscribers' Purchase Location	Frequency
Convenience store	74
Newsstand/candy store	95
Vending machine	21
Supermarket	13
Other locations	13

Would Consider Trial Subscription if Offered a Discount	Frequency
Yes	46
No	170

Rate Willing to Pay per Week (in Dollars) for a 90-day Home Delivery Trial Subscription SH7.xls

$4.15 3.60 4.10 3.60 3.60 3.60 4.40 3.15 4.00 3.75 4.00 3.25 3.75 3.30 3.75 3.65 4.00 4.10 3.90 3.50 3.75 3.00 3.40 4.00 3.80 3.50 4.10 4.25 3.50 3.90 3.95 4.30 4.20 3.50 3.75 3.30 3.85 3.20 4.40 3.80 3.40 3.50 2.85 3.75 3.80 3.90

Read a Daily Newspaper Other Than the *Springville Herald*	Frequency
Yes	138
No	214

Would Prepay 6 Months to Receive a Restaurant Discount Card	Frequency
Yes	66
No	286

EXERCISES

SH1 Some members of the marketing department were concerned about the random-digit dialing method used to collect survey responses. Prepare a memorandum that examines the following issues:
- The advantages and disadvantages of using the random-digit dialing method.
- Possible alternative approaches for conducting the survey and their advantages and disadvantages.

SH2 Analyze the results of the survey of Springville households. Write a report that discusses the marketing implications of the survey results for the *Springville Herald*.

WEB CASE

Apply your knowledge about confidence interval estimation in this Web Case that extends the OnCampus! *Web Case from.*

Among their other features, the *OnCampus!* Web site allows customers to purchase *OnCampus! LifeStyles* merchandise online. To handle payment processing, the management of *OnCampus!* has contracted with the following firms:

- PayAFriend (PAF): an online payments system in which customers and businesses such as *OnCampus!* register in order to exchange payments in a secure and convenient manner without the need for a credit card.
- Continental Banking Company (Conbanco): a processing services provider that allows *OnCampus!* customers to pay for merchandise using nationally recognized credit cards issued by a financial institution.

To reduce costs, the management is considering eliminating one of these two payment systems. However, Virginia Duffy of the sales department suspects that customers use the two forms of payment in unequal numbers and that customers display different buying behaviors when using the two forms of payment. Therefore, she would like to first obtain the following statistics:

a. The proportion of customers using PAF and the proportion of customers using a credit card to pay for their purchase.

b. The average purchase amount when using PAF and the average purchase amount when using a credit card.

Assist Ms. Duffy by preparing an appropriate analysis based on a random sample of 50 transactions that she has prepared and placed in an internal file on the *OnCampus!* Web site **www.prenhall.com/Springville/OnCampus_PymtSample.htm.** Summarize your findings and determine if Ms. Duffy's conjectures of *OnCampus!* customer purchasing behaviors are correct. If you want the sampling error to be no more than $3, is Ms. Duffy's sample sufficiently large enough to perform a valid analysis?

REFERENCES

1. Cochran, W. G., *Sampling Techniques*, 3rd ed. (New York: Wiley, 1977).
2. Fisher, R. A., and F. Yates, *Statistical Tables for Biological, Agricultural and Medical Research*, 5th ed. (Edinburgh: Oliver & Boyd, 1957).
3. Kirk, R. E., ed., *Statistical Issues: A Reader for the Behavioral Sciences* (Belmont, CA: Wadsworth, 1972).
4. Larsen, R. L., and M. L. Marx, *An Introduction to Mathematical Statistics and Its Applications*, 2nd ed. (Englewood Cliffs, NJ: Prentice Hall, 1986).
5. *Microsoft Excel 2002* (Redmond, WA: Microsoft Corporation, 2001).
6. Snedecor, G. W., and W. G. Cochran, *Statistical Methods*, 7th ed. (Ames, IA: Iowa State University Press, 1980).

Answers to Selected Even-Numbered Problems

For more detailed solutions including explanations, interpretations, and Excel output, see the *Student Solutions Manual*.

2 $114.68 \le \mu \le 135.32$.

4 In order to have every possible interval estimate of the true mean, the entire population would have to be selected.

6 Approximately 5% of the intervals will not include the true population mean somewhere in the interval. Since the true population mean is not known, we do not know for certain whether it is in the one interval we have developed, between 10.99408 and 11.00192 inches.

8 (a) $325.5005 \le \mu \le 374.4995$ **(b)** No. **(c)** No. **(d)** The confidence interval represents bounds on the estimate of the mean of a sample of 64, not an individual value. **(e) (a)** $330.4 \le \mu \le 369.6$ **(b)** No.

10 (a) 2.2622 **(b)** 3.2498 **(c)** 2.0395 **(d)** 1.9977 **(e)** 1.7531.

12 $38.9499 \le \mu \le 61.0501$.

14 Original data: $-0.1229 \le \mu \le 11.8371$. Altered data: $2.0022 \le \mu \le 5.9978$. The presence of an outlier in the original data increases the value of the sample mean and greatly inflates the sample standard deviation.

16 (a) $\$1.52 \le \mu \le \$1.82$ **(b)** The store owner can be 95% confident that the population mean retail value of greeting cards that it has in its inventory is somewhere in between \$1.52 and \$1.82.

18 (a) $33.89 \le \mu \le 53.89$ **(b)** The population distribution needs to be normally distributed. **(c)** Both the normal probability plot and the box-and-whisker show that the population distribution is not normally distributed and is skewed to the right. **(d)** With a sample size of 27 and the population distribution that appears to be skewed, the method used in (a) is not reliable and, hence, any comparison with problem 2.64 is likely to be invalid.

20 (a) $-0.000566 \le \mu \le 0.000106$ **(b)** The population distribution needs to be normally distributed. However, with a sample of 100, the t distribution can still be used as a result of the central limit theorem even if the population distribution is not normal. **(c)** Both the normal probability plot and the box-and-whisker plot suggest that the distribution is skewed to the right. **(d)** Since 0 is contained in the confidence interval, we are 95% confident that the mean between the actual length of the steel part, as measured by a laser measurement device, and the specified length of the steel part are the same.

22 $0.19 \le p \le 0.31$.

24 (a) $0.2189 \le p \le 0.3211$ **(b)** The manager in charge of promotional programs concerning residential customers can infer that the proportion of households that would purchase an additional telephone line if it were made available at a substantially reduced installation cost is somewhere between 0.22 and 0.32 with a 99% level of confidence.

26 (a) $0.3810 < p < 0.4388$ **(b)** $0.3856 < p < 0.4342$ **(c)** The 95% confidence interval is wider because the critical value used in constructing the interval is larger due to the higher level of confidence.

28 (a) $0.4163 < p < 0.5037$ **(b)** $0.0737 < p < 0.1263$.

30 (a) $0.4192 < p < 0.4808$ **(b)** We are 95% confident that the proportion of all working women in North America who believe that companies should hold positions for those on maternity leave for more than six months is somewhere between 0.4192 and 0.4808.

32 35.

34 1,041.

36 (a) 246 **(b)** 984.

38 97.

40 (a) 167 **(b)** 97.

42 62.

44 (a) 423 **(b)** 601 **(c)** 1068 **(d)** In general, a larger sample size is needed if a higher level of confidence is required, holding everything else fixed. If a higher precision is required, which is reflected in lower acceptable sampling error, the sample size will need to be raised to reflect the higher associated cost of holding everything else fixed.

46 (a) 547 **(b)** 944 **(c)** 2,185 **(d)** 3,774 **(e)** Holding everything else constant, the higher the confidence level desired or the lower the acceptable sampling error desired, the larger the sample size needed.

48 (a) $0.5053 < p < 0.5347$ **(b)** We are 95% confident that the proportion of families that held stocks in 2001 is between 0.5053 and 0.5347. **(c)** 9,589.

50 \$10,721.53 ≤ population total ≤ \$14,978.47.

52 (a) $p < 0.0545$ **(b)** $p < 0.0586$ **(c)** $p < 0.0663$.

54 \$543,176.96 ≤ population total ≤ \$1,025,223.04.

56 \$5,125.99 ≤ total difference in the population ≤ \$54,546.57. *Note:* The t-value of 2.6092 for 95% confidence and $df = 149$ were derived on Excel.

58 (a) $p < 0.0542$ **(b)** Since the upper bound is higher than the tolerable exception rate of 0.04, the auditor should request a larger sample.

66 (a) The population from which this sample was drawn was the collection of all subscribers to the *Redbook* magazine who visited the magazine's Web site. **(b)** No. **(c)** No.

68 (a) $0.5116 < p < 0.6484$ **(b)** $0.4307 < p < 0.5693$ **(c)** $0.1626 < p < 0.2774$ **(d)** $0.1356 < p < 0.2444$ **(e)** 2401.

70 (a) $14.085 \le \mu \le 16.515$ **(b)** $0.530 \le p \le 0.820$ **(c)** 25 **(d)** 784 **(e)** The larger of the two sample sizes ($n = 784$) should be used.

72 (a) $8.049 \le \mu \le 11.351$ **(b)** $0.284 \le p \le 0.676$ **(c)** 35 **(d)** 121 **(e)** The larger of the two sample sizes ($n = 121$) should be used.

74 (a) $\$25.80 \le \mu \le \$31.24$ **(b)** $0.3037 \le p \le 0.4963$ **(c)** 97 **(d)** 423 **(e)** The larger of the two sample sizes ($n = 423$) should be used.

76 (a) \$36.66 ≤ μ ≤ \$40.42 **(b)** 0.2027 ≤ p ≤ 0.3973 **(c)** 110 **(d)** 423 **(e)** The larger of the two sample sizes ($n = 423$) should be used.

78 (a) $p \leq 0.2013$ **(b)** Since the upper bound is higher than the tolerable exception rate of 0.15, the auditor should request a larger sample.

80 (a) 27 **(b)** \$737,655.50 ≤ population total ≤ \$838,275.58.

82 (a) $8.41 < \mu < 8.43$ **(b)** With 95% confidence, the population average width of troughs is somewhere between 8.41 and 8.43 inches.

84 (a) $0.2425 < \mu < 0.2856$ **(b)** $0.1975 < \mu < 0.2385$ **(c)** The amount of granule loss for both brands is skewed to the right. **(d)** We can conclude that the average granule loss of Boston shingles is higher than that of Vermont shingles.

88 $67.63 < \mu < 82.37$.

90 (a) $322.6238 < \mu < 377.3762$ **(b)** 92 **(c) (a)** $322.9703 < \mu < 377.0297$ **(b)** 88.

92 (a) $0.2285 < p < 0.3715$ **(b)** 186 **(c) (a)** $0.2265 < p < 0.3735$ **(b)** 205.

94 (a) $1.9804 < \mu < 2.0000$ **(b)** 92 **(c) (a)** $1.9807 < \mu < 1.9993$ **(b)** 88.

Excel Handbook for Confidence Interval Estimation

EH1 CALCULATING THE CONFIDENCE INTERVAL ESTIMATE FOR THE MEAN (σ KNOWN)

To calculate the confidence interval of the mean when σ is known, implement a worksheet that features the **CONFIDENCE** function. This function is entered as **CONFIDENCE(1-*confidence level*, *population standard deviation*, *sample size*)**.

Table EH1 contains the design for a **Confidence Interval Estimate** worksheet that calculates the confidence interval estimate for the paper production problem of Example 1. This design calculates the lower and upper limits of the confidence interval by taking the half width of the confidence interval returned by the CONFIDENCE function and subtracting and adding it to the sample mean. The design also includes separate calculations for the standard error of the mean and the Z value.

When implementing this design, format cell B7 for percentage display so that the decimal value 0.95 appears as 95%. For problems in which the sample mean is not known, replace the cell B5 value with a formula in the form **=AVERAGE(*DataCellRange*)** to calculate the sample mean.

Table EH1
Confidence Interval Estimate worksheet design

	A	B
1	Mean Paper Length	
2		
3	Data	
4	Population Standard Deviation	0.02
5	Sample Mean	10.998
6	Sample Size	100
7	Confidence Level	0.95
8		
9	Intermediate Calculations	
10	Standard Error of the Mean	=B4/SQRT(B6)
11	Z Value	=NORMSINV((1 – B7)/2)
12	Interval Half Width	=CONFIDENCE(1 – B7, B4, B6)
13		
14	Confidence Interval	
15	Interval Lower Limit	=B5 – B12
16	Interval Upper Limit	=B5 + B12

EH2 CALCULATING THE CONFIDENCE INTERVAL ESTIMATE FOR THE MEAN (σ UNKNOWN)

To calculate the confidence interval of the mean when σ is unknown, implement a worksheet that features the **TINV** function. This function is entered as **TINV(1-*confidence level*, *degrees of freedom*)**.

Table EH2 contains the design for a **Confidence Interval Estimate** worksheet that calculates the confidence interval estimate for the mean dollar amount of all Saxon Home Improvement sales invoices for a month, shown in Figure 6. This design calculates the half width of the confidence interval by taking the t value returned by the TINV function and multiplying it by the standard error of the mean. This half width is then subtracted from and added to the sample mean to calculate the lower and upper limits of the confidence interval.

When implementing this design, format cell B7 for percentage display so that the decimal value 0.95 appears as 95%. For problems in which the sample standard deviation and mean are not known, replace the cell B4 value with a formula in the form **=STDEV(*DataCellRange*)** to calculate the sample standard deviation and replace the cell B5 value with a formula in the form **=AVERAGE(*DataCellRange*)** to calculate the sample mean.

Table EH2
Confidence Interval Estimate worksheet design

	A	B
1	Mean Sales Invoice Amount	
2		
3	Data	
4	Sample Standard Deviation	28.95
5	Sample Mean	110.27
6	Sample Size	100
7	Confidence Level	0.95
8		
9	Intermediate Calculations	
10	Standard Error of the Mean	=B4/SQRT(B6)
11	Degrees of Freedom	=B6 – 1
12	*t* Value	=TINV(1 – B7, B11)
13	Interval Half Width	=B12 * B10
14		
15	Confidence Interval	
16	Interval Lower Limit	=B5 – B13
17	Interval Upper Limit	=B5 + B13

EH3 CALCULATING THE CONFIDENCE INTERVAL ESTIMATE FOR THE PROPORTION

To calculate the confidence interval of the proportion, implement a worksheet that features the **NORMSINV** function. This function is entered as **NORMSINV (*P* < *X*)**, where $P < X$ is the area under the curve that is less than X.

Table EH3 contains the design for a **Confidence Interval Estimate** worksheet that calculates the confidence interval estimate for the proportion of sales invoices in error that violate the accounting

Table EH3
Confidence Interval Estimate worksheet design

	A	B
1	Proportion of In-Error Sales Invoices	
2		
3	Data	
4	Sample Size	100
5	Number of Successes	10
6	Confidence Level	0.95
7		
8	Intermediate Calculations	
9	Sample Proportion	=B5/B4
10	Z Value	=NORMSINV((1 – B6)/2)
11	Standard Error of the Proportion	=SQRT(B9*(1 – B9)/B4)
12	Interval Half Width	=ABS(B10 * B11)
13		
14	Confidence Interval	
15	Interval Lower Limit	=B9 – B12
16	Interval Upper Limit	=B9 + B12

controls of the Saxon Home Improvement Company problem. This design calculates the half width of the confidence interval by taking the *Z* value returned by the NORMSINV function and multiplying it by the standard error of the proportion. The design uses the ABS function in cell B12 to ensure that the half width value always will be positive.

When implementing this design, format cell B6 for percentage display so that the decimal value 0.95 appears as 95%.

EH4 CALCULATING THE SAMPLE SIZE NEEDED FOR ESTIMATING THE MEAN

To calculate the sample size needed for estimating the mean, implement a worksheet that features the **NORMSINV** function. This function is entered as **NORMSINV(*P* < *X*)**, where $P < X$ is the area under the curve that is less than *X*.

Table EH4 contains the design for a **Sample Size Needed** worksheet that calculates the sample size needed for estimating the mean sales invoice amount for the Saxon Home Improvement Company problem. This design uses the NORMSINV worksheet function to return the *Z* value needed to determine the sample size and uses the ROUNDUP function to round up the result of the intermediate calculation to the next integer.

When implementing this design, format cell B6 for percentage display so that the decimal value 0.95 appears as 95%.

Table EH4
Sample Size Needed worksheet design

	A	B
1	For Mean Sales Invoice Amount	
2		
3	Data	
4	Population Standard Deviation	25
5	Sampling Error	5
6	Confidence Level	0.95
7		
8	Intermediate Calculations	
9	Z Value	=NORMSINV((1 – B6)/2)
10	Calculated Sample Size	=((B9 * B4)/B5)^2
11		
12	Result	
13	Sample Size Needed	=ROUNDUP(B10, 0)

EH5 CALCULATING THE SAMPLE SIZE NEEDED FOR ESTIMATING THE PROPORTION

To calculate the sample size needed for estimating the proportion, implement a worksheet that features the **NORMSINV** function. This function is entered as **NORMSINV(*P* < *X*)**, where $P < X$ is the area under the curve that is less than *X*.

Table EH5 contains the design for a **Sample Size Needed** worksheet that calculates the sample size needed for estimating the proportion of sales invoices in error that violate the accounting controls of the Saxon Home Improvement Company, shown in Figure 12. This design uses the NORMSINV worksheet function to return the *Z* value needed to determine the sample size and uses the ROUNDUP function to round up the result of the intermediate calculation to the next integer.

When implementing this design, format cell B6 for percentage display so that the decimal value 0.95 appears as 95%.

Table EH5
Sample Size Needed worksheet design

	A	B
1	For Proportion of In-Error Sales Invoices	
2		
3	Data	
4	Estimate of True Proportion	0.15
5	Sampling Error	0.07
6	Confidence Level	0.95
7		
8	Intermediate Calculations	
9	Z Value	=NORMSINV((1 – B6)/2)
10	Calculated Sample Size	=(B9 ^ 2 * B4 * (1 – B4))/B5) ^ 2
11		
12	Result	
13	Sample Size Needed	=ROUNDUP(B10, 0)

EH6 CALCULATING THE CONFIDENCE INTERVAL ESTIMATE FOR THE POPULATION TOTAL

To calculate the confidence interval of the population total, implement a worksheet that features the **TINV** function. This function is entered as **TINV(1-*confidence level*, *degrees of freedom*)**.

Table EH6 contains the design for a **Confidence Interval Estimate** worksheet that calculates the total amount of all Saxon Home Improvement sales invoices for a month, shown in Figure 13. This design takes the t value returned by the TINV function and multiplies it by the standard error of the mean to produce the half width of the confidence interval. This half width is then subtracted from and added to the population total to calculate the lower and upper limits of the confidence interval.

Table EH6
Confidence Interval Estimate worksheet design

	A	B
1	Total Amount of All Sales Invoices	
2		
3	Data	
4	Population Size	5000
5	Sample Mean	110.27
6	Sample Size	100
7	Sample Standard Deviation	28.95
8	Confidence Level	0.95
9		
10	Intermediate Calculations	
11	Population Total	=B4 * B5
12	FPC Factor	=SQRT((B4 – B6)/(B4 – 1))
13	Standard Error of the Total	=(B4 * B7 * B12)/SQRT(B6)
14	Degrees of Freedom	=B6 – 1
15	*t* Value	=TINV(1 – B8, B14)
16	Interval Half Width	=B15 * B13
17		
18	Confidence Interval	
19	Interval Lower Limit	=B11 – B16
20	Interval Upper Limit	=B11 + B16

When implementing this design, format cell B8 for percentage display so that the decimal value 0.95 appears as 95%. For problems in which the sample standard deviation and mean are unknown, replace the cell B5 value with a formula in the form **=AVERAGE(*DataCellRange*)** to calculate the sample mean and replace the cell B7 value with a formula in the form **=STDEV(*DataCellRange*)** to calculate the standard deviation.

EH7 CALCULATING THE CONFIDENCE INTERVAL ESTIMATE FOR THE TOTAL DIFFERENCE

To calculate the confidence interval for the total difference, implement worksheets that feature difference calculations and the **TINV** function, respectively. Tables EH7 through EH9 contain the design for the two worksheets that together calculate the confidence interval estimate for the total difference between the invoice amounts and the amounts entered into the Saxon Home Improvement accounting system, shown in Figure 14.

Table EH7
Modifications to DifferencesData worksheet

	A	B
1	Differences	(D-DBar)^2
2	9.03	=(A2 – CIEstimate!$B$10)^2
3	7.47	=(A3 – CIEstimate!$B$10)^2
4	17.32	=(A4 – CIEstimate!$B$10)^2
11	7.43	=(A11 – CIEstimate!$B$10)^2
12	2.99	=(A12 – CIEstimate!$B$10)^2
13	4.63	=(A13 – CIEstimate!$B$10)^2

Table EH7 shows the formulas to be added to the **DifferencesData** worksheet of the **CHAPTER 7.xls** workbook. These formulas calculate the squares of the differences for those invoices with non-zero errors by squaring the result of subtracting each non-zero difference by the average difference in the sample (itself calculated in cell B10 of the second worksheet). In turn, formulas in cells E11 and E13 of the second, CIEstimate, worksheet (see Table EH8) determine the number of non-zero differences and the sum of the squares calculated, respectively. The rest of the entries shown in Table EH8 help calculate the standard deviation of the differences in cell B12 of the CIEstimate worksheet (see Table EH9).

Table EH8
CIEstimate worksheet design for cell range D9:E16 (rest of the worksheet is shown in Table EH9)

	D	E
9	Calculations Area	
10	For standard deviation of differences:	
11	Number of Differences Not = 0	=COUNT(DifferencesData!A:A)
12	Number of Differences = 0	=B5 – E11
13	SS for Differences Not = 0	=SUM(DifferencesData!B:B)
14	SS for Differences = 0	=E12 * (–B10)^2
15	Sum of Squares	=E13 + E14
16	Variance of Differences	=E15/B15

The design of the second worksheet calculates the half width of the confidence interval in cell B17 by taking the t value returned by the TINV function (entered as **TINV(1-*confidence level*, *degrees of freedom*)**) and multiplying it by the standard error of the mean. This half width is then subtracted from and added to the population total to calculate the lower and upper limits of the confidence interval.

When implementing Table EH7, enter the formula for cell B2 and copy it down through row 13. When implementing Table EH9, format cell B6 for percentage display so that the decimal value 0.95 appears as 95%. For problems involving other sets of differences, modify the first worksheet by entering the differences data in column A. If you have more than 12 differences, copy the B13 formula down as many rows as there are additional differences. If you have fewer than 12 differences, delete table rows, starting with row 13, as many times as is necessary.

Table EH9
CIEstimate worksheet design for columns A and B (column C is blank)

	A	B
1	Total Difference In Actual and Entered	
2		
3	Data	
4	Population Size	5000
5	Sample Size	100
6	Confidence Level	0.95
7		
8	Intermediate Calculations	
9	Sum of Differences	=SUM(DifferencesData!A:A)
10	Average Difference in Sample	=B9/B5
11	Total Difference	=B4 * B10
12	Standard Deviation of Differences	=SQRT(E16)
13	FPC Factor	=SQRT((B4 – B5)/(B4 – 1))
14	Standard Error of the Total Diff.	=(B4 * B12 * B13)/SQRT(B5)
15	Degrees of Freedom	=B5 – 1
16	*t* Value	=TINV(1 – B6, B15)
17	Interval Half Width	=B16 * B14
18		
19	Confidence Interval	
20	Interval Lower Limit	=B11 – B17
21	Interval Upper Limit	=B11 + B17

Fundamentals of Hypothesis Testing: One-Sample Tests

LEARNING OBJECTIVES

- To understand the basic principles of hypothesis testing
- To use hypothesis testing to test a mean or proportion
- To evaluate the assumptions of each hypothesis-testing procedure, and know the consequences if the assumptions are seriously violated
- To avoid the pitfalls involved in hypothesis testing
- To understand the ethical issues that may be involved

USING STATISTICS

The Oxford Cereal Company

Here is a scenario concerning the Oxford Cereal Company. As the operations manager of the plant, you are in charge of monitoring the amount of cereal contained in the boxes. You are concerned with evaluating whether or not the cereal-filling process is working to ensure that, on average, 368 grams of cereal are in each box. A random sample of 25 boxes is selected and the boxes are weighed to determine how close the fill weights are to the company's specifications of a mean of 368 grams. You hope that the process is working properly, but the sampled boxes may contain too little cereal or perhaps too much. As a result, you may need to halt the production process until the reason for the failure to adhere to the specified weight of 368 grams is determined. By analyzing the differences between the weights obtained from the sample and the 368-gram expectation obtained from the company's specifications, you need to decide whether the average fill in the entire process is equal to 368 grams or is not equal to 368 grams. In the first case, no corrective action is needed. In the second case, you will have to take corrective action.

INTRODUCTION

In this chapter the focus is on hypothesis testing, another aspect of statistical inference that, like confidence interval estimation, is based on sample information. A step-by-step methodology is developed that enables you to make inferences about a population parameter by *analyzing differences* between the results observed (the sample statistic) and the results that can be expected if some underlying hypothesis is actually true. For example, is the mean weight of the cereal boxes in the sample taken at Oxford Cereal Company a value that is consistent with what would be expected if the mean of the entire population of cereal boxes is 368 grams? Or, can you infer that the population mean is not equal to 368 grams because the sample mean is significantly different from 368 grams?

1 HYPOTHESIS-TESTING METHODOLOGY

The Null and Alternative Hypotheses

Hypothesis testing typically begins with some theory, claim, or assertion about a particular parameter of a population. For example, for purposes of statistical analysis, your initial hypothesis about the cereal example is that the process is working properly, meaning that the mean fill is 368 grams, and no corrective action is needed.

The hypothesis that the population parameter is equal to the company specification is referred to as the **null hypothesis**. A null hypothesis is always one of status quo, and is identified by the symbol H_0. Here the null hypothesis is that the filling process is working properly, that the mean fill per box is the 368-gram specification. This can be stated as

$$H_0\text{: } \mu = 368$$

Note that even though information is available only from the sample, the null hypothesis is written in terms of the population parameter. This is because the parameter of interest is focused on the entire filling process (the population) of all cereal boxes being filled. The sample statistic will be used to make inferences about the entire filling process. One inference may be that the results observed from the sample data indicate that the null hypothesis is false. If the null hypothesis is considered false, something else must be true.

Whenever a null hypothesis is specified, an alternative hypothesis must also be specified, one that must be true if the null hypothesis is found to be false. The **alternative hypothesis** H_1 is the opposite of the null hypothesis H_0. This is stated in the cereal example as

$$H_1: \mu \neq 368$$

The alternative hypothesis represents the conclusion reached by rejecting the null hypothesis if there is sufficient evidence from the sample information to decide that the null hypothesis is unlikely to be true. In the cereal example, if the weights of the sampled boxes are sufficiently above or below the expected 368-gram mean specified by the company, the null hypothesis is rejected in favor of the alternative hypothesis that the average amount of fill is different from 368 grams. Production is stopped and whatever action is necessary is taken to correct the problem. If the null hypothesis is not rejected, then you should continue to believe in the status quo, that the process is working correctly and therefore no corrective action is necessary. Note that in this second scenario you have not proven that the process is working correctly. Rather, you have failed to prove that it is working incorrectly and therefore you continue your belief (although unproven) in the null hypothesis.

Hypothesis-testing methodology is designed so that the rejection of the null hypothesis is based on evidence from the sample that the alternative hypothesis is far more likely to be true. However, failure to reject the null hypothesis is not proof that it is true. One can never prove that the null hypothesis is correct because the decision is based only on the sample information, not on the entire population. Therefore, if you fail to reject the null hypothesis, you can only conclude that there is insufficient evidence to warrant its rejection. A summary of the null and alternative hypotheses is presented in Exhibit 1.

EXHIBIT 1 THE NULL AND ALTERNATIVE HYPOTHESES

The following key points summarize the null and alternative hypotheses:

1. The null hypothesis H_0 represents the status quo or the current belief in a situation.
2. The alternative hypothesis H_1 is the opposite of the null hypothesis and represents a research claim or specific inference you would like to prove.
3. If you reject the null hypothesis, you have statistical proof that the alternative hypothesis is correct.
4. If you do not reject the null hypothesis, then you have failed to prove the alternative hypothesis. The failure to prove the alternative hypothesis, however, does not mean that you have proven the null hypothesis.
5. The null hypothesis H_0 always refers to a specified value of the population parameter (such as μ), not a sample statistic (such as $\overline{X}$).
6. The statement of the null hypothesis always contains an equal sign regarding the specified value of the population parameter (e.g., H_0: $\mu = 368$ grams).
7. The statement of the alternative hypothesis never contains an equal sign regarding the specified value of the population parameter (e.g., H_1: $\mu \neq 368$ grams).

The Critical Value of the Test Statistic

The logic behind the hypothesis-testing methodology can be developed by thinking about how sample information can be used to determine the plausibility of the null hypothesis.

In the Oxford Cereal Company scenario, the null hypothesis is that the mean amount of cereal per box in the entire filling process is 368 grams (i.e., the population parameter specified by the company). A sample of boxes is obtained from the filling process, each box is weighed, and the sample mean is computed. This statistic is an estimate of the corresponding parameter from the population from which the sample is drawn. Even if the null hypothesis is in fact true, this statistic is likely to differ from the value of the parameter because of variation due to sampling. However, you expect the sample statistic to be close to the population parameter if the null hypothesis is true. In such a situation there is insufficient evidence to reject the null hypothesis. If, for example, the sample mean is

367.9, the instinct is to conclude that the population mean has not changed (i.e., $\mu = 368$), because a sample mean of 367.9 is very close to the hypothesized value of 368. Intuitively, you might think that it is likely that you could obtain a sample mean of 367.9 from a population whose mean is 368.

On the other hand, if there is a large discrepancy between the value of the statistic and its corresponding hypothesized parameter, the instinct is to conclude that the null hypothesis is unlikely to be true. For example, if the sample mean is 320, you would be inclined to conclude that the population mean is not 368 (i.e., $\mu \neq 368$), because the sample mean is very far from the hypothesized value of 368. In such a case it is very unlikely that the sample mean of 320 can be obtained if the population mean is really 368 and, therefore, more logical to conclude that the population mean is not equal to 368. Here you reject the null hypothesis. In either case your decision is reached because of your belief that randomly selected samples are truly representative of the underlying populations from which they are drawn.

Unfortunately, the decision-making process is not always so clear-cut and it cannot be left to an individual's subjective judgment to determine the meaning of "very close" or "very different." Determining what is very close and what is very different is arbitrary without clear definitions. Hypothesis-testing methodology provides clear definitions for evaluating such differences and enables you to quantify the decision-making process so that the probability of obtaining a given sample result can be found if the null hypothesis is true. This is achieved by first determining the sampling distribution for the sample statistic of interest (e.g., the sample mean) and then computing the particular **test statistic** based on the given sample result. Because the sampling distribution for the test statistic often follows a well-known statistical distribution, such as the standardized normal distribution or *t* distribution, these distributions can be used to help determine the likelihood that the null hypothesis is true.

Regions of Rejection and Nonrejection

The sampling distribution of the test statistic is divided into two regions, a **region of rejection** (sometimes called the **critical region**) and a **region of nonrejection** (see Figure 1).

FIGURE 1
Regions of rejection and nonrejection in hypothesis testing

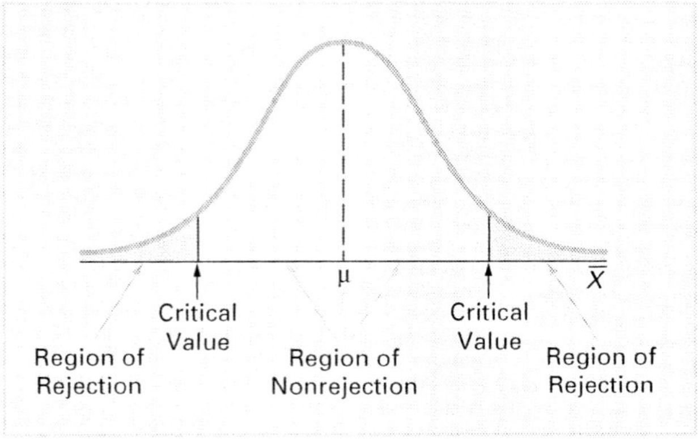

If the test statistic falls into the region of nonrejection, the null hypothesis cannot be rejected. In the cereal example, the conclusion is reached that there is insufficient evidence that the average fill amount is different from 368. If the test statistic falls into the rejection region, the null hypothesis is rejected. In this case, the conclusion is that the population mean is not 368.

The region of rejection consists of the values of the test statistic that are unlikely to occur if the null hypothesis is true. These values are more likely to occur if the null hypothesis is false. Therefore, if a value of the test statistic falls into this *rejection region*, the null hypothesis is rejected because that value is unlikely if the null hypothesis is true.

To make a decision concerning the null hypothesis, you first determine the **critical value** of the test statistic. The critical value divides the nonrejection region from the rejection region. The determination of this critical value depends on the size of the rejection region. The size of the rejection region is directly related to the risks involved in using only sample evidence to make decisions about a population parameter.

Risks in Decision Making Using Hypothesis-Testing Methodology

When using a sample statistic to make decisions about a population parameter, there is a risk that an incorrect conclusion will be reached. Two different types of errors can occur when applying hypothesis-testing methodology, **Type I errors** and **Type II errors**. (See definitions on the left.)

A Type I Error
A Type I error occurs if the null hypothesis H_0 is rejected when in fact it is true and should not be rejected. The probability of a Type I error occurring is α.

Type II Error
A Type II error occurs if the null hypothesis H_0 is not rejected when in fact it is false and should be rejected. The probability of a Type II error occurring is β.

In the cereal-filling-process example, a Type I error occurs if the conclusion is reached (based on sample information) that the average population amount filled is *not* 368 when in fact it *is* 368. On the other hand, the Type II error occurs if the conclusion (based on sample information) is that the average population fill amount *is* 368 when in fact it is *not* 368.

The Level of Significance (α) The probability of committing a Type I error, denoted by α (the lowercase Greek letter alpha), is referred to as the **level of significance** of the statistical test. Traditionally, you control the Type I error rate by deciding the risk level α that can be tolerated in rejecting the null hypothesis when it is in fact true. Because the level of significance is specified before the hypothesis test is performed, the risk of committing a Type I error, α, is directly under the control of the individual performing the test. Traditionally, levels of 0.01, 0.05, or 0.10 are selected. The choice of a particular risk level for making a Type I error is dependent on the cost of making a Type I error. After the value for α is specified, the size of the rejection region is known because α is the probability of rejection under the null hypothesis. From this fact, the critical value or values that divide the rejection and nonrejection regions are determined.

Confidence Coefficient
The confidence coefficient, denoted by $1 - \alpha$, is the probability that the null hypothesis H_0 is not rejected when in fact it is true and should not be rejected. The confidence level of a hypothesis test is $(1 - \alpha)$ 100%.

The Confidence Coefficient The complement $(1 - \alpha)$ of the probability of a Type I error is called the **confidence coefficient**, which, when multiplied by 100%, yields the **confidence level** that was studied when constructing confidence intervals.

In terms of hypothesis-testing methodology, the confidence coefficient represents the probability of concluding that the specified value of the parameter being tested under the null hypothesis is plausible when, in fact, it is true. In the cereal-filling-process example, the confidence coefficient measures the probability of concluding that the average fill per box is 368 grams when it actually is 368 grams.

The β Risk The probability of committing a Type II error is denoted by β (the lowercase Greek letter beta). Unlike the Type I error, which is controlled by the selection of α, the probability of making a Type II error is dependent on the difference between the hypothesized and actual value of the population parameter. Because large differences are easier to find than small ones, if the difference between the hypothesized and actual value of the population parameter is large, β, the probability of committing a Type II error, is small. For example, if the true population mean is 320 grams, there is a small chance (β) of concluding that the mean has not changed from 368. On the other hand, if the difference between the hypothesized and actual value of the parameter is small, the probability of committing a Type II error is large. Thus, if the population mean is really 367 grams, there is a high probability of concluding that the population mean fill amount has not changed from the specified 368 grams (and you would be making a Type II error).

Power of a Statistical Test
The power of a statistical test, $1 - \beta$, is the probability of rejecting the null hypothesis when in fact it is false and should be rejected.

The Power of a Test The complement of the probability of a Type II error $(1 - \beta)$ is called the **power of a statistical test**. In the cereal-filling-process example, the power of the test is the probability of concluding that the mean fill amount is not 368 grams when in fact it actually is not 368 grams. For a detailed discussion of the power of the test, see section 7 on the CD-ROM.

Risks in Decision Making: A Delicate Balance Table 1 illustrates the results of the two possible decisions (do not reject H_0 or reject H_0) that can occur in any hypothesis test. Depending on the specific decision, one of two types of errors may occur[1] or one of two types of correct conclusions may be reached.

TABLE 1

Hypothesis testing and decision making

Statistical Decision	Actual Situation: H_0 True	Actual Situation: H_0 False
Do not reject H_0	Correct decision Confidence = $1 - \alpha$	Type II error P(Type II error) = β
Reject H_0	Type I error P(Type I error) = α	Correct decision Power = $1 - \beta$

[1]An easy way to remember which probability goes with which type of error is to note that α is the first letter of the Greek alphabet and is used to represent the probability of a Type I error. The letter β is the second letter of the Greek alphabet and is used to represent the probability of a Type II error. (If you have trouble remembering the Greek alphabet, note that the word alphabet tells you its first two letters.)

One way in which the probability of making a Type II error in a study can be controlled and reduced is by increasing the size of the sample. Larger sample sizes generally permit you to detect even very small differences between the hypothesized values and the population parameters. For a given level of α, increasing the sample size will decrease β and therefore will increase the power of the test to detect that the null hypothesis H_0 is false. However, there is always a limit to your resources, and this will affect the decision as to how large a sample can be taken. Thus, for a given sample size you must consider the trade-offs between the two possible types of errors. Because you can directly control the risk of Type I error, this risk can be reduced by selecting a smaller value for α. For example, if the negative consequences associated with making a Type I error are substantial, you could select $\alpha = 0.01$ instead of 0.05. However, when α is decreased, β will be increased, so a reduction in risk of Type I error will result in an increased risk of Type II error. If, on the other hand, you wish to reduce β, you could select a larger value for α. Therefore, if it is important to try to avoid a Type II error, you can select α of 0.05 or 0.10 instead of 0.01.

In the cereal-filling-process example, the risk of a Type I error involves concluding that the mean fill per box has changed from the hypothesized 368 grams when in fact it has not changed. The risk of a Type II error involves concluding that the mean fill per box has not changed from the hypothesized 368 grams when in truth it has changed. The choice of reasonable values for α and β depends on the costs inherent in each type of error. For example, if it were very costly to change the cereal-filling process, then you would want to be very sure that a change would be beneficial, so the risk of a Type I error might be most important and would be kept very low. On the other hand, if you wanted to be very certain of detecting changes from a mean of 368 grams, the risk of a Type II error would be most important, and you might choose a higher level of α.

PROBLEMS FOR SECTION 1

Learning the Basics

1 The symbol H_0 is used to denote which hypothesis?

2 The symbol H_1 is used to denote which hypothesis?

3 The level of significance or chance of committing a Type I error is denoted by what symbol?

4 The chance of committing a Type II error is denoted by what symbol?

5 What does $1 - \beta$ represent?

6 What is the relationship of α to the Type I error?

7 What is the relationship of β to the Type II error?

8 How is power related to the probability of making a Type II error?

9 Why is it possible for the null hypothesis to be rejected when in fact it is true?

10 Why is it possible that the null hypothesis will not always be rejected when it is false?

11 For a given sample size, if α is reduced from 0.05 to 0.01, what will happen to β?

12 For H_0: $\mu = 100$, H_1: $\mu \neq 100$, and for a sample of size n, β will be larger if the actual value of μ is 90 than if the actual value of μ is 75. Why?

Applying the Concepts

13 In the U.S. legal system, a defendant is presumed innocent until proven guilty. Consider a null hypothesis H_0, that the defendant is innocent, and an alternative hypothesis H_1, that the defendant is guilty. A jury has two possible decisions: Convict the defendant (i.e., reject the null hypothesis) or do not convict the defendant (i.e., do not reject the null hypothesis). Explain the meaning of the risks of committing either a Type I or Type II error in this example.

14 Suppose the defendant in problem 13 is presumed guilty until proven innocent as in some other judicial systems. How do the null and alternative hypotheses differ from those in problem 13? What are the meanings of the risks of committing either a Type I or Type II error here?

15 The U.S. Food and Drug Administration (FDA) is responsible for approving new drugs. Many consumer groups feel that the approval process is too easy, and, therefore, too many drugs are approved that are later found to be unsafe. On the other hand, there are a number of industry lobbyists who are pushing for a more lenient approval process so that pharmaceutical companies can get new drugs approved more easily and quickly (Rochelle Sharpe, "FDA Tries to Find Right Balance on Drug Approvals," *Wall Street Journal*, April 20, 1999, A24). Consider a null hypothesis that a new, unapproved drug is unsafe and an alternative hypothesis that a new, unapproved drug is safe.

a. Explain the risks of committing a Type I or Type II error.

b. Which type of error are the consumer groups trying to avoid? Explain.

c. Which type of error are the industry lobbyists trying to avoid? Explain.

d. How would it be possible to lower the chance of both Type I and Type II errors?

16 As a result of complaints from both students and faculty about lateness, the registrar at a large university wants to adjust the scheduled class times to allow for adequate travel time between classes and is ready to undertake a study. Until now, the registrar has believed that 20 minutes between scheduled classes should be sufficient. State the null hypothesis H_0 and the alternative hypothesis H_1.

17 The manager of a local branch of a bank believes that over the past few years the bank has begun to cater to a different clientele and that the average amount withdrawn from its ATMs is no longer \$140. State the null hypothesis H_0 and the alternative hypothesis H_1.

2 Z TEST OF HYPOTHESIS FOR THE MEAN (σ KNOWN)

Now that the hypothesis-testing methodology has been introduced, recall that in the Using Statistics scenario, the Oxford Cereal Company wants to determine whether the cereal-filling process is working properly (that is, whether the mean fill per box throughout the entire packaging process remains at the specified 368 grams and no corrective action is needed). To evaluate the 368-gram requirement, a random sample of 25 boxes is taken, each is weighed, and then the difference between the sample statistic and the hypothesized population parameter is evaluated by comparing the mean weight (in grams) from the sample to the expected mean of 368 grams specified by the company. For this filling process, the null and alternative hypotheses are

$$H_0: \mu = 368$$
$$H_1: \mu \neq 368$$

If the standard deviation σ is known, for large enough samples, the sampling distribution of the mean follows the normal distribution, resulting in the ***Z*-test statistic** shown in Equation (1).

Z TEST OF HYPOTHESIS FOR THE MEAN (σ KNOWN)

$$Z = \frac{\bar{X} - \mu}{\frac{\sigma}{\sqrt{n}}} \quad \textbf{(1)}$$

In Equation (1) the numerator measures the distance between the observed sample mean and the hypothesized mean μ. The denominator is the standard error of the mean, so Z represents the difference between $\bar{X}$ and μ in standardized units.

The Critical Value Approach to Hypothesis Testing

If a level of significance of 0.05 is used, the size of the rejection region is 0.05, and the critical values of the normal distribution can be determined. These critical values can be expressed as standardized Z values (i.e., in standard-deviation units). Because the rejection region is divided into the two tails of the distribution (this is called a **two-tail test**), the 0.05 is divided into two equal parts of 0.025 each. A rejection region of 0.025 in each tail of the normal distribution results in a cumulative area of 0.025 below the lower critical value and a cumulative area of 0.975 below the upper critical value. According to the standardized normal distribution table, the critical values that divide the rejection and nonrejection regions are (in standard-deviation units) −1.96 and +1.96. Figure 2 illustrates this case; it shows that if the mean is actually 368 grams, as H_0 claims, then the values of the test statistic Z have a standardized normal distribution centered at 0 (which corresponds to an $\bar{X}$ value of 368 grams). Observed values of Z greater than +1.96 or less than −1.96 indicate that $\bar{X}$ is so far from the hypothesized $\mu = 368$ that it is unlikely that such a value would occur if H_0 were true.

FIGURE 2
Testing a hypothesis about the mean (σ known) at the 0.05 level of significance

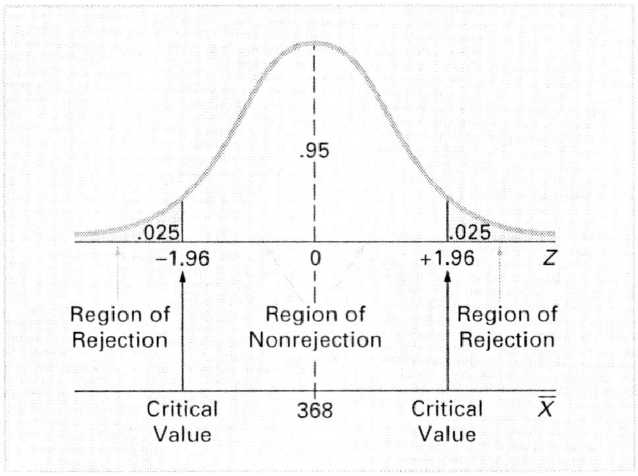

Therefore, the decision rule is

$$\text{Reject } H_0 \text{ if } Z > +1.96$$
$$\text{or if } Z < -1.96;$$
$$\text{otherwise do not reject } H_0.$$

Suppose that the sample of 25 cereal boxes indicates a sample mean $\bar{X} = 372.5$ grams and the population standard deviation σ is assumed to be 15 grams. Using Equation (1):

$$Z = \frac{\bar{X} - \mu}{\frac{\sigma}{\sqrt{n}}} = \frac{372.5 - 368}{\frac{15}{\sqrt{25}}} = +1.50$$

Because the test statistic $Z = +1.50$, and $-1.96 < +1.50 < +1.96$, the decision is not to reject H_0 (see Figure 3). The conclusion is reached that the mean fill amount is 368 grams. Alternatively, to take into account the possibility of a Type II error, the conclusion can be stated as "there is insufficient evidence that the mean fill is different from 368 grams."

FIGURE 3
Testing a hypothesis about the mean (σ known) at 0.05 level of significance

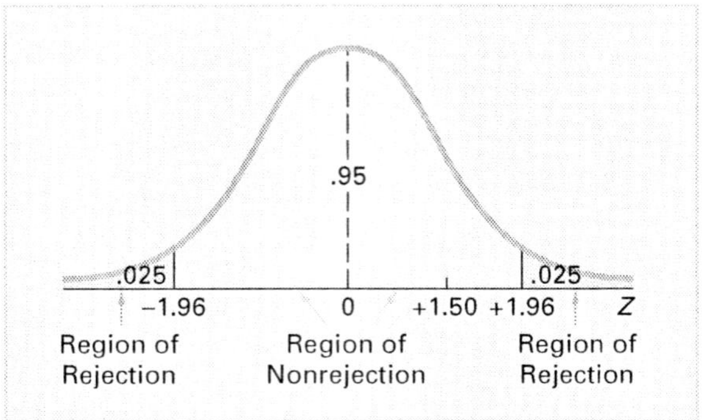

Now that hypothesis-testing methodology has been used to draw a conclusion about the population mean in situations where the population standard deviation is known, the steps involved are summarized in Exhibit 2.

EXHIBIT 2 THE TEN-STEP METHOD OF HYPOTHESIS TESTING

1. State the null hypothesis, H_0. The null hypothesis must be stated in statistical terms using population parameters. In testing whether the mean amount of cereal filled is 368 grams, the null hypothesis states that μ equals 368.
2. State the alternative hypothesis, H_1. The alternative hypothesis must be stated in statistical terms using population parameters. In testing whether the mean amount filled is 368 grams, the alternative hypothesis states that μ is not equal to 368 grams.
3. Choose the level of significance, α. The level of significance is specified according to the relative importance of the risks of committing Type I and Type II errors in the problem. In this example $\alpha = 0.05$.
4. Choose the sample size, n. The sample size is determined after taking into account the specified risks of committing Type I and Type II errors (i.e., selected levels of α and β) and considering budget constraints in carrying out the study. In the cereal example, 25 cereal boxes were randomly selected.
5. Determine the appropriate statistical technique and corresponding test statistic to use. Because σ is known from information about the filling process, a Z test was selected for the cereal example.
6. Set up the critical values that divide the rejection and nonrejection regions. Once the null and alternative hypotheses are specified and the level of significance and the sample size are determined, the critical values for the appropriate statistical distribution can be found so that the rejection and nonrejection regions can be specified. In the cereal example the values +1.96 and −1.96 were used to define these regions because the Z-test statistic refers to the standardized normal distribution.
7. Collect the data and compute the sample value of the appropriate test statistic. In the cereal example, $\bar{X} = 372.5$, so $Z = +1.50$.
8. Determine whether the test statistic has fallen into the rejection or the nonrejection region. The computed value of the test statistic is compared with the critical values for the appropriate sampling distribution to determine whether it falls into the rejection or nonrejection region. For the cereal example, $Z = +1.50$ was in the region of nonrejection, because $-1.96 < Z = +1.50 < +1.96$.
9. Make the statistical decision. If the test statistic falls into the nonrejection region, the null hypothesis H_0 cannot be rejected. If the test statistic falls into the rejection region, the null hypothesis is rejected. In the cereal example, H_0 was not rejected.
10. Express the statistical decision in the context of the problem. In the cereal-filling example, the conclusion reached is that there was insufficient evidence that the average amount filled was different from 368 grams.

The *p*-Value Approach to Hypothesis Testing

p-Value
The p-value is the probability of obtaining a test statistic equal to or more extreme than the result obtained from the sample data, given that the null hypothesis H_0 is true.

In recent years, with the advent of widely available statistical and spreadsheet software, the concept of the ***p*-value** as an approach to hypothesis testing has increasingly gained acceptance. The p-value is often referred to as the *observed level of significance*, which is the smallest level at which H_0 can be rejected for a given set of data. The decision rules for rejecting H_0 in the p-value approach follows.

- If the p-value is greater than or equal to α, the null hypothesis is not rejected.
- If the p-value is less than α, the null hypothesis is rejected.

To understand the p-value approach, consider the cereal-filling-process example. You tested whether or not the mean fill amount was equal to 368 grams. A Z value of +1.50 was obtained and the null hypothesis was not rejected because +1.50 was less than the upper critical value of +1.96 and more than the lower critical value of −1.96.

Now the p-value approach is used. For the *two-tail test*, you find the probability of obtaining a test statistic Z that is equal to or *more extreme than* 1.50 standard deviation units from the center of a standardized normal distribution. This means that you need to compute the probability of obtaining a Z value greater than +1.50 along with the probability of obtaining a Z value less than −1.50. The Cumulative Standardized Normal Distribution table shows that the probability of obtaining a Z value below −1.50 is 0.0668. The probability of obtaining a value below +1.50 is 0.9332. Therefore, the probability of obtaining a value above +1.50 is 1 – 0.9332 = 0.0668. Thus, the *p*-value for this two-tail test is 0.0668 + 0.0668 = 0.1336 (see Figure 4). This result is interpreted to mean that the probability of obtaining a result equal to or more extreme than the one observed is 0.1336. Because 0.1336 is greater than $\alpha = 0.05$, the null hypothesis is not rejected.

FIGURE 4
Finding a *p*-value for a two-tail test

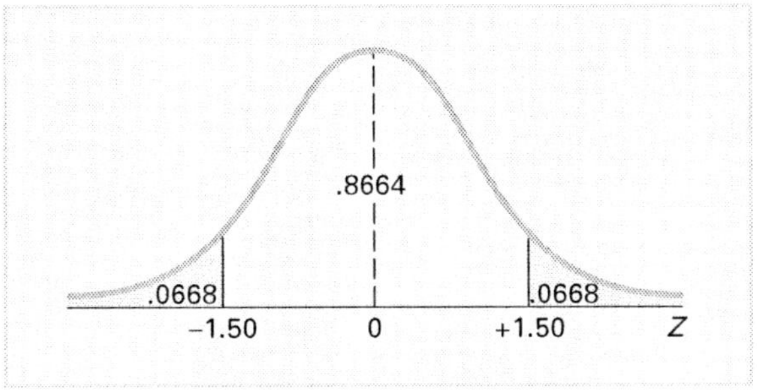

A thorough interpretation of the *p*-value is an important component of effective data analysis when hypothesis testing is used. Recall that the *p*-value is the probability of obtaining a test statistic equal to or more extreme than the result obtained in the sample. In the previous example, the observed sample mean is 372.5 grams, 4.5 grams above the hypothesized value and the *p*-value is 0.1336. Thus, if in fact the population mean is 368 grams, there is a 13.36% chance of obtaining a sample mean more than 4.5 grams away from 368 (i.e., greater than or equal to 372.5 grams or less than or equal to 363.5 grams). Therefore, while 372.5 is above the hypothesized value of 368, a result as extreme or more extreme than 372.5 is not highly unlikely when the population mean is truly 368.

Unless you are dealing with a test statistic that follows the normal distribution, the computation of the *p*-value can be very difficult. However, Microsoft Excel routinely presents the *p*-value as part of the output for hypothesis-testing procedures. Figure 5 displays Microsoft Excel output for the cereal-filling example discussed in this section. Note that the Microsoft Excel output indicates the computed *Z* value of +1.50, the *p*-value of 0.1336, and the decision made.

FIGURE 5
Microsoft Excel *Z*-test output for the cereal-filling example

	A	B
1	Cereal-Filling Process Hypothesis Test	
2		
3	Data	
4	Null Hypothesis μ=	368
5	Level of Significance	0.05
6	Population Standard Deviation	15
7	Sample Size	25
8	Sample Mean	372.5
9		
10	Intermediate Calculations	
11	Standard Error of the Mean	3
12	Z Test Statistic	1.5
13		
14	Two-Tail Test	
15	Lower Critical Value	-1.959962787
16	Upper Critical Value	1.959962787
17	*p*-Value	0.133614458
18	Do not reject the null hypothesis	

A summary of the *p*-value approach for hypothesis testing is displayed in Exhibit 3.

EXHIBIT 3 THE TEN STEPS OF HYPOTHESIS TESTING USING THE *p*-VALUE APPROACH

1. State the null hypothesis, H_0.
2. State the alternative hypothesis, H_1.
3. Choose the level of significance, α.
4. Choose the sample size, *n*.
5. Determine the appropriate statistical technique and corresponding test statistic.
6. Collect the data and compute the sample value of the appropriate test statistic.

7. Calculate the p-value based on the test statistic. This involves
   a. Sketching the distribution under the null hypothesis H_0.
   b. Placing the test statistic on the horizontal axis.
   c. Shading in the appropriate area under the curve, based on the alternative hypothesis H_1.
8. Compare the p-value to α.
9. Make the statistical decision. If the p-value is greater than or equal to α, the null hypothesis is not rejected. If the p-value is less than α, the null hypothesis is rejected.
10. Express the statistical decision in the context of the problem.

Excel Strategies Performing the Z Test of Hypothesis for the Mean (σ Known)

CHAPTER 8.xls

*Retrieve the Figure 8.5 worksheet of the **Chapter 8.xls** workbook to view the test of the hypothesis for the mean (σ known).*

You implement a worksheet that features the **NORMSINV** and **NORMSDIST** functions to perform a Z test of the hypothesis for the mean (σ known). PHStat2 can construct this worksheet for you in a single step.

For example, to perform the Z test of the hypothesis for the mean for the cereal-filling process problem, shown in Figure 5, use one of these strategies:

Using Excel with PHStat2

Use the PHStat2 Z Test for the Mean, sigma known, procedure to perform a Z test of the hypothesis for the mean (σ known).

Select **PHStat | One-Sample Test | Z Test for the Mean, sigma known**.

In the Z Test for the Mean, sigma known, dialog box (shown at right):

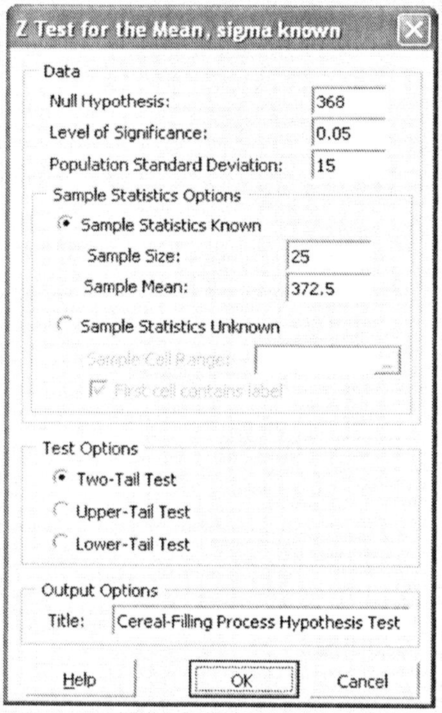

Enter **368** in the **Null Hypothesis** edit box.

Enter **0.05** in the **Level of Significance** edit box.

Enter **15** in the **Population Standard Deviation** edit box.

Select the **Sample Statistics Known** option button and enter **25** in the **Sample Size** and **372.5** in the **Sample Mean** edit boxes.

Select the **Two-Tail Test** option button.

Enter a title in the **Title** edit box.

Click the **OK** button.

*For problems in which the sample mean is not known and needs to be calculated, select the **Sample Statistics Unknown** option button and enter the cell range of the sample data in the **Sample Cell Range** edit box (dimmed in the illustration).*

*For problems that require a one-tailed test (see section 3), select the **Upper-Tail Test** or **Lower-Tail Test** option button, as appropriate, when completing this dialog box.*

Using Excel

Follow the instructions of section EH1 at the end of this chapter to manually implement a worksheet to perform a Z test of the hypothesis for the mean (σ known).

A Connection between Confidence Interval Estimation and Hypothesis Testing

Confidence interval estimation and hypothesis testing are based on the same set of concepts, but they are used for different purposes. Confidence intervals are used to estimate parameters, and provide the user with a range of values in which the parameter is located with a certain known probability. In this chapter, hypothesis testing is used for making decisions about specified values of population parameters. Hypothesis tests are used when trying to prove that a parameter is less than, more than, or not equal to a specified value. Proper interpretation of a confidence interval, however, can also indicate whether a parameter is less than, more than, or not equal to a specified value. Moreover, the confidence interval provides the interval estimate of the parameter in question. An advantage of hypothesis testing is the added insight provided by interpreting the p-value.

For example, in this section you tested whether the population mean fill amount was different from 368 grams by using Equation (1):

$$Z = \frac{\bar{X} - \mu}{\frac{\sigma}{\sqrt{n}}}$$

Instead of testing the null hypothesis that $\mu = 368$ grams, the same conclusion can be reached by obtaining a confidence interval estimate of μ. If the hypothesized value of $\mu = 368$ falls into the interval, the null hypothesis is not rejected because 368 would not be considered an unusual value. On the other hand, if the hypothesized value does not fall into the interval, the null hypothesis is rejected, because "368 grams" is then considered an unusual value. The confidence interval estimate is set up from the following data:

$$n = 25,\ \bar{X} = 372.5 \text{ grams},\ \sigma = 15 \text{ grams (specified by the company)}$$

For a confidence level of 95% (corresponding to a 0.05 level of significance—i.e., $\alpha = .05$),

$$\bar{X} \pm Z\frac{\sigma}{\sqrt{n}}$$

$$372.5 \pm (1.96)\frac{15}{\sqrt{25}}$$

$$372.5 \pm 5.88$$

so that

$$366.62 \leq \mu \leq 378.38$$

Because the interval includes the hypothesized value of 368 grams, the null hypothesis is not rejected. There is insufficient evidence that the mean fill amount over the entire filling process is not 368 grams. This is the same decision reached by using the hypothesis-testing methodology.

PROBLEMS FOR SECTION 2

Learning the Basics

18 If a 0.05 level of significance is used in a (two-tail) hypothesis test, what will you decide if the computed value of the test statistic Z is +2.21?

19 If a 0.10 level of significance is used in a (two-tail) hypothesis test, what will be your decision rule for rejecting a null hypothesis that the population mean is 500 if you use the Z test?

20 If a 0.01 level of significance were used in a (two-tail) hypothesis test, what would be your decision rule for rejecting H_0: $\mu = 12.5$ if you were to use the Z test?

21 What would be your decision in problem 20 if the computed value of the test statistic Z were −2.61?

22 Suppose that in a two-tail hypothesis test you compute the value of the test statistic Z as +2.00. What is the p-value?

23 In problem 22, what is your statistical decision if you test the null hypothesis at the 0.10 level of significance?

24 Suppose that in a two-tail hypothesis test you compute the value of the test statistic Z as −1.38. What is the p-value?

25 In problem 24, what is your statistical decision if you test the null hypothesis at the 0.01 level of significance?

Applying the Concepts

26 The director of manufacturing at a clothing factory needs to determine whether a new machine is producing a particular type of cloth according to the manufacturer's specifications, which indicate that the cloth should have a mean breaking strength of 70 pounds and a standard deviation of 3.5 pounds. A sample of 49 pieces of cloth reveals a sample mean breaking strength of 69.1 pounds.

a. State the null and alternative hypotheses.
b. Is there evidence that the machine is not meeting the manufacturer's specifications for average breaking strength? (Use a 0.05 level of significance.)
c. Compute the p-value and interpret its meaning.
d. What would be your answer in (b) if the standard deviation were specified as 1.75 pounds?
e. What would be your answer in (b) if the sample mean were 69 pounds and the standard deviation is 3.5 pounds?

27 The manager of a paint supply store wants to determine whether the amount of paint contained in 1-gallon cans purchased from a nationally known manufacturer actually averages 1 gallon. It is known from the manufacturer's specifications that the standard deviation of the amount of paint is equal to 0.02 gallon. A random sample of 50 cans is selected, and the mean amount of paint per 1-gallon can is found to be 0.995 gallon.

a. State the null and alternative hypotheses.
b. Is there evidence that the mean amount is different from 1.0 gallon (use $\alpha = 0.01$)?
c. Compute the p-value and interpret its meaning.
d. Set up a 99% confidence interval estimate of the population mean amount of paint.
e. Compare the results of (b) and (d). What conclusions do you reach?

28 The quality-control manager at a lightbulb factory needs to determine whether the mean life of a large shipment of lightbulbs is equal to the specified value of 375 hours. The process standard deviation is known to be 100 hours. A random sample of 64 lightbulbs indicates a sample mean life of 350 hours.

a. State the null and alternative hypotheses.
b. At the 0.05 level of significance is there evidence that the mean life is different from 375 hours?
c. Compute the p-value and interpret its meaning.
d. Set up a 95% confidence interval estimate of the population mean life of the lightbulbs.
e. Compare the results of (b) and (d). What conclusions do you reach?

29 The inspection division of the Lee County Weights and Measures Department is interested in determining whether the proper amount of soft drink has been placed in 2-liter bottles at the local bottling plant of a large nationally known soft-drink company. The bottling plant has informed the inspection division that the standard deviation for 2-liter bottles is 0.05 liter. A random sample of one hundred 2-liter bottles obtained from this bottling plant indicates a sample mean of 1.99 liters.

a. State the null and alternative hypotheses.
b. At the 0.05 level of significance is there evidence that the mean amount in the bottles is different from 2.0 liters?
c. Compute the p-value and interpret its meaning.
d. Set up a 95% confidence interval estimate of the population mean amount in the bottles.
e. Compare the results of (b) and (d). What conclusions do you reach?

30 A manufacturer of salad dressings uses machines to dispense liquid ingredients into bottles that move along a filling line. The machine that dispenses dressings is working properly when 8 ounces are dispensed. The standard deviation of the process is 0.15 ounce. A sample of 50 bottles is selected periodically, and the filling line is stopped if there is evidence that the mean amount dispensed is different from 8 ounces. Suppose that the mean amount dispensed in a particular sample of 50 bottles is 7.983 ounces.

a. State the null and alternative hypotheses.
b. Is there evidence that the population average amount is different from 8 ounces? (Use a 0.05 level of significance.)
c. Compute the p-value and interpret its meaning.
d. What will be your answer in (b) if the standard deviation is specified as 0.05 ounce?
e. What will be your answer in (b) if the sample mean is 7.952 ounces and the standard deviation is 0.15 ounce?

31 ATMs must be stocked with enough cash to satisfy customers making withdrawals over an entire weekend. But if too much cash is unnecessarily kept in the ATMs, the bank is forgoing the opportunity of investing the money and earning interest. Suppose that at a particular branch the expected (i.e., population) mean amount of money withdrawn from ATMs per customer transaction over the weekend is \$160 with an expected (i.e., population) standard deviation of \$30.

a. State the null and alternative hypotheses.
b. If a random sample of 36 customer transactions is examined and the sample mean withdrawal is \$172, is there evidence to believe that the population average withdrawal is no longer \$160? (Use a 0.05 level of significance.)
c. Compute the p-value and interpret its meaning.
d. What will be your answer in (b) if you use a 0.01 level of significance?
e. What will be your answer in (b) if the standard deviation is \$24?

3 ONE-TAIL TESTS

So far, hypothesis-testing methodology has been used to examine the question of whether or not the population mean amount of cereal filled is 368 grams. The alternative hypothesis (H_1: $\mu \neq 368$) contains two possibilities: Either the mean is less than 368 grams, or the mean is more than 368 grams. For this reason, the rejection region is divided into the two tails of the sampling distribution of the mean.

In many situations, however, the alternative hypothesis focuses on a *particular direction*. One such situation occurs in the following application. A company that makes processed cheese is interested in determining whether some suppliers that provide milk for the processing operation are adding water to their milk to increase the amount supplied to the processing operation. It is known that excess water reduces the freezing point of the milk. The freezing point of natural milk is normally distributed with a mean of $-0.545°$ Celsius (C). The standard deviation of the freezing temperature of natural milk is known to be 0.008°C. Because the cheese company is only interested in determining whether the freezing point of the milk is less than what would be expected from natural milk, the entire rejection region is located in the lower tail of the distribution.

Critical Value Approach

Suppose you wish to prove that the freezing point of milk is less than $-0.545°$. To perform this one-tail hypothesis test, the ten-step method listed in Exhibit 2 is used.

Steps 1 and 2: H_0: $\mu \geq -0.545°$

H_1: $\mu < -0.545°$

Note that the alternative hypothesis contains the statement you are trying to prove. If the null hypothesis is rejected, you will have statistical proof that the average freezing point of the milk provided is less than the natural freezing point of $-0.545°$. If the conclusion of the test is "do not reject H_0," then the conclusion is that there is insufficient evidence to prove that the freezing point is below the natural freezing point of $-0.545°$.

Step 3: $\alpha = 0.05$

Step 4: $n = 25$

Step 5: A Z test is used since the population standard deviation of the natural freezing point of milk is known.

Step 6: The rejection region is entirely contained in the lower tail of the sampling distribution of the mean since you want to reject H_0 only when the sample mean is significantly below $-0.545°$. When the entire rejection region is contained in one tail of the sampling distribution of the test statistic, the test is called a **one-tail** or **directional test**. When the alternative hypothesis includes the less than sign, the critical value on the Z distribution must be less than zero. As shown from Table 2 and Figure 6, because the entire rejection region is in the lower tail of the standardized normal distribution and contains an area of 0.05, the area below the critical value must be 0.05; thus, the critical value of the Z-test statistic is -1.645, the average of -1.64 and -1.65.

TABLE 2

Obtaining the critical value of the Z-test statistic from the standardized normal distribution for a one-tail test with $\alpha = 0.05$

Z	.00	.01	.02	.03	.04	.05	.06	.07	.08	.09
⋮	⋮	⋮	⋮	⋮	⋮	⋮	⋮	⋮	⋮	⋮
−1.8	.0359	.0351	.0344	.0336	.0329	.0322	.0314	.0307	.0301	.0294
−1.7	.0446	.0436	.0427	.0418	.0409	.0401	.0392	.0384	.0375	.0367
−1.6	.0548	.0537	.0526	.0516	.0505	.0495	.0485	.0475	.0465	.0455

Source: Extracted from the Cumulative Standardized Normal table.

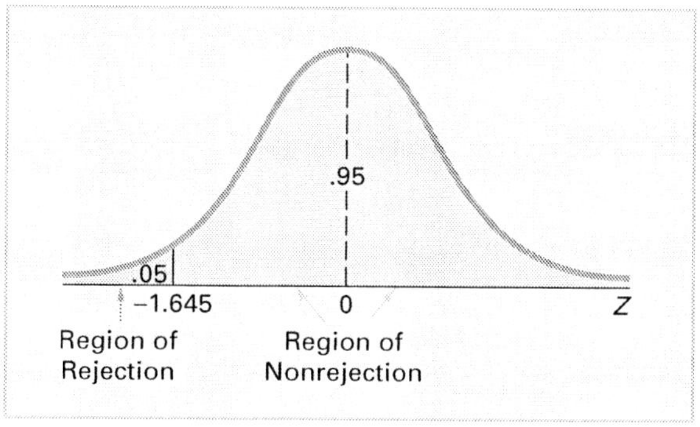

FIGURE 6
One-tail test of hypothesis for a mean (σ known) at the 0.05 level of significance

The decision rule is

$$\text{Reject } H_0 \text{ if } Z < -1.645;$$
$$\text{otherwise do not reject } H_0.$$

Step 7: If a sample of 25 containers of milk is selected and the sample average freezing point is determined to be $-0.550°$, using the Z test given by Equation (1),

$$n = 25, \quad \bar{X} = -0.550°, \quad \sigma = 0.008°$$

and

$$Z = \frac{\bar{X} - \mu}{\frac{\sigma}{\sqrt{n}}} = \frac{-0.550 - (-0.545)}{\frac{0.008}{\sqrt{25}}} = -3.125$$

Step 8: Since $Z = -3.125 < -1.645$, the observed statistic is in the region of rejection (see Figure 6).

Step 9: Reject H_0.

Step 10: Conclude that the mean freezing point of the milk provided is below $-0.545°$. The company should pursue an investigation of the milk supplier because the freezing point is significantly below what could be expected to occur by chance if water has not been added to the milk.

p-Value Approach

The ten steps listed in Exhibit 3 are now used to illustrate the test on the previous pages using the p-value approach.

Steps 1–5: These steps are the same as in the critical value approach.

Step 6: $Z = -3.125$ (see step 7 of the critical value approach).

Step 7: To obtain the p-value, since the alternative hypothesis indicates a rejection region entirely in the *lower* tail of the sampling distribution of the Z-test statistic, you need to find the probability of obtaining a Z value *below* the test statistic of -3.125. From the Cumulative Standardized Normal table, the probability of obtaining a Z value below -3.125 is 0.0009 (see Figure 7).

Step 8: The p-value of 0.0009 is less than $\alpha = 0.05$.

Step 9: Reject H_0.

Step 10: Conclude that the mean freezing point of the milk provided is below $-0.545°$. The company should pursue an investigation of the milk supplier because the freezing point is significantly below what could be expected to occur by chance if water has not been added to the milk.

Moreover, the p-value of 0.0009 indicates the probability of obtaining a sample mean of -0.550 or less if in fact the population mean is $-0.545°$. Because this probability is so small, it is unlikely that the hypothesized value of $-0.545°$ is correct.

Figure 8 displays output from Microsoft Excel for this example.

FIGURE 7
Determining the p-value for a one-tail test

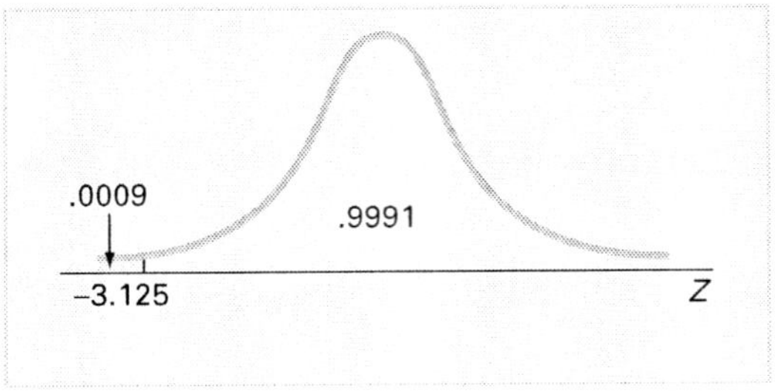

FIGURE 8
Microsoft Excel Z-test output for the milk production example

	A		B
1	**Milk Production Hypothesis**		
2			
3	**Data**		
4	**Null Hypothesis**	μ=	-0.545
5	**Level of Significance**		0.05
6	**Population Standard Deviation**		0.008
7	**Sample Size**		25
8	**Sample Mean**		-0.55
9			
10	Intermediate Calculations		
11	Standard Error of the Mean		0.0016
12	**Z Test Statistic**		-3.125
13			
14	**Lower-Tail Test**		
15	**Lower Critical Value**		-1.644853476
16	***p*-Value**		0.000889093
17	**Reject the null hypothesis**		

To perform one-tail tests of hypotheses, you must properly formulate H_0 and H_1. A summary of the null and alternative hypotheses for one-tail tests is presented in Exhibit 4.

EXHIBIT 4 THE NULL AND ALTERNATIVE HYPOTHESES IN ONE-TAIL TESTS

1. The null hypothesis H_0 represents the status quo or the current belief in a situation.
2. The alternative hypothesis H_1 is the opposite of the null hypothesis and represents a research claim or specific inference you would like to prove.
3. If you reject the null hypothesis, you have statistical proof that the alternative hypothesis is correct.
4. If you do not reject the null hypothesis, then you have failed to prove the alternative hypothesis. The failure to prove the alternative hypothesis, however, does not mean that you have proven the null hypothesis.
5. The null hypothesis (H_0) always refers to a specified value of the *population parameter* (such as μ), not to a *sample statistic* (such as $\bar{X}$).
6. The statement of the null hypothesis *always* contains an equal sign regarding the specified value of the parameter (e.g., H_0: $\mu \geq -0.545°C$).
7. The statement of the alternative hypothesis *never* contains an equal sign regarding the specified value of the parameter (e.g., H_1: $\mu < -0.545°C$).

PROBLEMS FOR SECTION 3

Learning the Basics

32 What is the *upper-tail* critical value of the Z-test statistic at the 0.01 level of significance?

33 In problem 32, what would be your statistical decision if the computed value of the Z-test statistic were 2.39?

34 What is the *lower-tail* critical value of the Z-test statistic at the 0.01 level of significance?

35 In problem 34, what would be your statistical decision if the computed value of the Z-test statistic were -1.15?

36 Suppose that in a one-tail hypothesis test where you reject H_0 only in the *upper* tail, you compute the value of the test statistic Z to be $+2.00$. What is the p-value?

37 In problem 36, what would be your statistical decision if you tested the null hypothesis at the 0.05 level of significance?

38 Suppose that in a one-tail hypothesis test where you reject H_0 only in the *lower* tail, you compute the value of the test statistic Z as -1.38. What is the p-value?

39 In problem 38, what would be your statistical decision if you tested the null hypothesis at the 0.01 level of significance?

40 Suppose that in a one-tail hypothesis test where you reject H_0 only in the *lower* tail, you compute the value of the test statistic Z as $+1.38$. What is the p-value?

41 In problem 40, what would be your statistical decision if you tested the null hypothesis at the 0.01 level of significance?

Applying the Concepts

42 The Glen Valley Steel Company manufactures steel bars. If the production process is working properly, it turns out steel bars with mean length of *at least* 2.8 feet with a standard deviation of 0.20 foot (as determined from engineering specifications on the production equipment involved). Longer steel bars can be used or altered, but shorter bars must be scrapped. A sample of 25 bars is selected from the production line. The sample indicates a mean length of 2.73 feet. The company wants to determine whether the production equipment needs to be adjusted.

a. State the null and alternative hypotheses.
b. If the company wants to test the hypothesis at the 0.05 level of significance, what decision would be made using the critical value approach to hypothesis testing?
c. If the company wants to test the hypothesis at the 0.05 level of significance, what decision would be made using the p-value approach to hypothesis testing?
d. Interpret the meaning of the p-value in this problem.
e. Compare your conclusions in (b) and (c).

43 The director of manufacturing at a clothing factory needs to determine whether a new machine is producing a particular type of cloth according to the manufacturer's specifications, which indicate that the cloth should have a mean breaking strength of at least 70 pounds and a standard deviation of 3.5 pounds. The director is concerned that if the mean breaking strength is actually *less* than 70 pounds, the company will face too many lawsuits. A sample of 49 pieces of cloth reveals a sample mean of 69.1 pounds.

a. State the null and alternative hypotheses.
b. At the 0.05 level of significance, using the critical value approach to hypothesis testing, is there evidence that the mean breaking strength is less than 70 pounds?
c. At the 0.05 level of significance, using the p-value approach to hypothesis testing, is there evidence that the mean breaking strength is less than 70 pounds?
d. Interpret the meaning of the p-value in this problem.
e. Compare your conclusions in (b) and (c).
f. Repeat (a)–(e) if the sample of 49 pieces of cloth reveals a sample mean of 70.4 pounds.

44 A manufacturer of salad dressings uses machines to dispense liquid ingredients into bottles that move along a filling line. The machine that dispenses dressings is working properly when 8 ounces are dispensed. The manufacturer is particularly concerned that the bottles do not have an average of less than 8 ounces. The standard deviation of the process is 0.15 ounce. A sample of 50 bottles is selected periodically, and the filling line is stopped if there is evidence that the mean amount dispensed is actually *less* than 8 ounces. Suppose that the average amount dispensed in a particular sample of 50 bottles is 7.983 ounces.

a. State the null and alternative hypotheses.
b. At the 0.05 level of significance, using the critical value approach to hypothesis testing, is there evidence that the mean amount dispensed is less than 8 ounces?
c. At the 0.05 level of significance, using the p-value approach to hypothesis testing, is there evidence that the mean amount dispensed is less than 8 ounces?
d. Interpret the meaning of the p-value in this problem.
e. Compare your conclusions in (b) and (c).

45 The policy of a particular bank branch is that its ATMs must be stocked with enough cash to satisfy customers making withdrawals over an entire weekend. Customer goodwill depends on such services meeting customer needs. At this branch the expected (i.e., population) mean amount of money withdrawn from ATMs per customer transaction over the weekend is \$160 with an expected (i.e., population) standard deviation of \$30. Suppose that a random sample of 36 customer transactions is examined, and it is observed that the sample mean withdrawal is \$172.

a. At the 0.05 level of significance, using the critical value approach to hypothesis testing, is there evidence to believe that the true mean withdrawal is greater than \$160?
b. At the 0.05 level of significance, using the p-value approach to hypothesis testing, is there evidence to believe that the true mean withdrawal is greater than \$160?
c. Interpret the meaning of the p-value in this problem.
d. Compare your conclusions in (a) and (b).

4 t TEST OF HYPOTHESIS FOR THE MEAN (σ UNKNOWN)

In most hypothesis-testing situations dealing with numerical data, the standard deviation σ of the population is unknown. Instead, the actual standard deviation of the population is estimated by computing S, the standard deviation of the sample. If the population is assumed to be normally distributed, you may recall that the sampling distribution of the mean will follow a t distribution with $n - 1$ degrees of freedom. Equation (2) defines the test statistic t for determining the difference between the sample mean $\bar{X}$ and the population mean μ when the sample standard deviation S is used.

t TEST OF HYPOTHESIS FOR THE MEAN (σ UNKNOWN)

$$t = \frac{\bar{X} - \mu}{\frac{S}{\sqrt{n}}} \tag{2}$$

where the test statistic t follows a t distribution having $n - 1$ degrees of freedom.

To illustrate the use of this t test, consider the Using Statistics scenario concerning the Saxon Home Improvement Company. Over the past five years, the mean amount per sales invoice is \$120. As an accountant for the company, you need to be able to inform the finance department if this amount changes. In other words, the hypothesis test is used to try to prove that the mean amount per sales invoices is increasing or decreasing.

Critical Value Approach To perform this two-tail hypothesis test, the ten-step method listed in Exhibit 2 is used.

Steps 1 and 2: H_0: $\mu = \$120$

H_1: $\mu \neq \$120$

Note that the alternative hypothesis contains the statement you are trying to prove. If the null hypothesis is rejected, you will have statistical proof that the mean amount per sales invoices is no longer \$120. If the conclusion of the test is "do not reject H_0," then there is insufficient evidence to prove that the mean amount differs from the long-term average of \$120.

Step 3: Select $\alpha = 0.05$.

Step 4: A random sample of $n = 12$ invoices will be used.

Step 5: Assuming the population is normally distributed, a t test is used since the population standard deviation of the amounts listed on the sales invoices is unknown.

Step 6: For a given sample size n, the test statistic t follows a t distribution with $n - 1$ degrees of freedom. If a level of significance of $\alpha = 0.05$ is selected, the critical values of the t distribution with $12 - 1 = 11$ degrees of freedom can be obtained from the Critical Values of t table, as illustrated in Figure 9 and Table 3. Because the alternative hypothesis H_1 that $\mu \neq \$120$ is *nondirectional*, the area in the rejection region of the t distribution's left (lower) tail is 0.025, and the area in the rejection region of the t distribution's right (upper) tail is also 0.025.

From the t table as given in the Critical Values of t table, a portion of which is shown in Table 3, the critical values are ± 2.2010. The decision rule is

Reject H_0 if $t < -t_{11} = -2.2010$

or if $t > t_{11} = +2.2010$;

otherwise do not reject H_0.

Step 7: The following data are the amounts (in dollars) in a random sample of 12 sales invoices.

108.98 152.22 111.45 110.59 127.46 107.26 93.32 91.97 111.56 75.71 128.58 135.11

FIGURE 9
Testing a hypothesis about mean (σ unknown) at 0.05 level of significance with 11 degrees of freedom

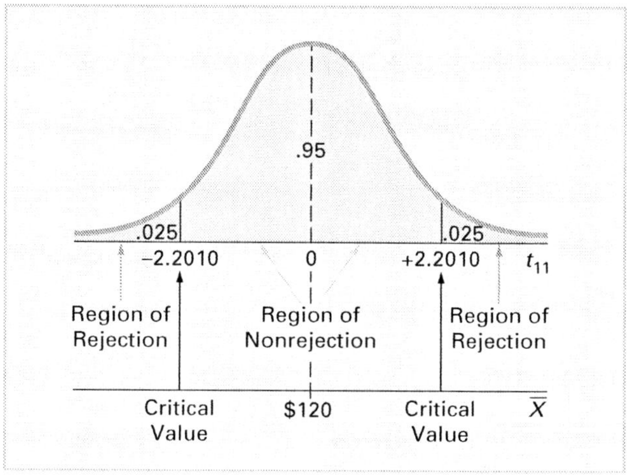

TABLE 3
Determining the critical value from the *t* table for an area of 0.025 in each tail with 11 degrees of freedom

	Upper-Tail Areas					
Degrees of Freedom	**.25**	**.10**	**.05**	**.025**	**.01**	**.005**
1	1.0000	3.0777	6.3138	12.7062	31.8207	63.6574
2	0.8165	1.8856	2.9200	4.3027	6.9646	9.9248
3	0.7649	1.6377	2.3534	3.1824	4.5407	5.8409
4	0.7407	1.5332	2.1318	2.7764	3.7469	4.6041
5	0.7267	1.4759	2.0150	2.5706	3.3649	4.0322
6	0.7176	1.4398	1.9432	2.4469	3.1427	3.7074
7	0.7111	1.4149	1.8946	2.3646	2.9980	3.4995
8	0.7064	1.3968	1.8595	2.3060	2.8965	3.3554
9	0.7027	1.3830	1.8331	2.2622	2.8214	3.2498
10	0.6998	1.3722	1.8125	2.2281	2.7638	3.1693
11	0.6974	1.3634	1.7959	2.2010	2.7181	3.1058

Source: Extracted from the Critical Values of *t* table.

INVOICES.xls

For the data set pertaining to the random sample of $n = 12$ sales invoices, using Equations (A) and (B), or the Microsoft Excel output of Figure 10.

ARITHMETIC MEAN

The arithmetic mean is the sum of the values divided by the number of values.

$$\bar{X} = \frac{\sum_{i=1}^{n} X_i}{n} \quad \textbf{(A)}$$

where

$\bar{X}$ = arithmetic mean
n = number of observations or sample size
X_i = ith observation of the variable X
$\sum_{i=1}^{n} X_i$ = summation of all X_i values in the sample

SAMPLE STANDARD DEVIATION

The sample standard deviation is the square root of the sum of the squared differences around the arithmetic mean divided by the sample size minus one.

$$S = \sqrt{S^2} = \sqrt{\frac{\sum_{i=1}^{n}(X_i - \overline{X})^2}{n-1}} \qquad \textbf{(B)}$$

$$\overline{X} = \frac{\sum_{i=1}^{n} X_i}{n} = \$112.85 \text{ and } \quad S = \sqrt{\frac{\sum_{i=1}^{n}(X_i - \overline{X})^2}{n-1}} = \$20.80$$

FIGURE 10
Microsoft Excel output for the one-sample *t* test of sales invoices

	A	B
1	**Mean Amount Per Invoice Hypothesis**	
2		
3	**Data**	
4	**Null Hypothesis** μ=	120
5	**Level of Significance**	0.05
6	**Sample Size**	12
7	**Sample Mean**	112.8508333
8	**Sample Standard Deviation**	20.7979918
9		
10	Intermediate Calculations	
11	Standard Error of the Mean	6.003863082
12	Degrees of Freedom	11
13	***t* Test Statistic**	-1.19076111
14		
15	**Two-Tail Test**	
16	**Lower Critical Value**	-2.200986273
17	**Upper Critical Value**	2.200986273
18	***p*-Value**	0.258809315
19	**Do not reject the null hypothesis**	

From Equation (2),

$$t = \frac{\overline{X} - \mu}{\frac{S}{\sqrt{n}}} = \frac{112.85 - 120}{\frac{20.80}{\sqrt{12}}} = -1.19$$

Step 8: Since $-2.201 < t = -1.19 < 2.201$, the observed statistic is in the region of nonrejection (see Figure 9).

Step 9: Do not reject H_0.

Step 10: The data provide insufficient evidence to conclude that the mean amount per sales invoice differs from \$120. You should inform the finance department that the audit suggests that the mean amount per invoice has not changed.

p-Value Approach

Steps 1–5: These steps are the same as in the critical value approach.

Step 6: $t = -1.19$ (see step 7 of the critical value approach).

Step 7: Microsoft Excel provides p-values for hypothesis-testing procedures. Figure 10 lists the p-value for this two-tail test as 0.26.

Step 8: The p-value of 0.26 is greater than $\alpha = 0.05$.

Step 9: Do not reject H_0.

Step 10: The data provide insufficient evidence to conclude that the mean amount per sales invoice differs from \$120. You should inform the finance department that the audit suggests that the mean amount per invoice has not changed. Moreover, the p-value indicates that if the null hypothesis were true, the probability that a sample of 12 invoices could have a monthly mean that differs by \$7.15 or more from the stated \$120 is 0.26. In other words, if the mean amount per sales invoice is truly \$120, then there is a 26% chance of observing a sample mean below \$112.85 or above \$127.15.

Note that in the above example it is incorrect to state that there is a 26% chance that the null hypothesis is true. This misinterpretation of the p-value is sometimes used by those not properly trained in statistics. Remember that the p-value is a conditional probability, calculated by *assuming* that the null hypothesis is true. In general, it is proper to state the following. If the null hypothesis is true, then there is a (p-value)*100% chance of observing a sample result at least as contradictory to the null hypothesis as the result observed.

The one-sample t test is used when the population standard deviation σ is not known and is estimated[2] using the sample standard deviation S. The t test is considered a *classical parametric* procedure, one that makes a variety of stringent assumptions that must hold if you are to be assured that the results obtained from employing the test are valid. Assumptions of the one-sample t test are presented in the following box.

2When a large sample size is available, S estimates σ precisely enough that there is little difference between the t and Z distributions. Therefore, a Z test can be used instead of a t test when the sample size is greater than 120.

ASSUMPTIONS OF THE ONE-SAMPLE t TEST

To use the one-sample t test, the obtained numerical data are assumed to represent a random sample from a population that is normally distributed. In practice, as long as the sample size is not very small and the population is not very skewed, the t distribution provides a good approximation to the sampling distribution of the mean when s is unknown.

CHAPTER 8.xls

Retrieve the Figure 8.10 worksheet of the ***Chapter 8.xls*** *workbook to view the t test of the hypothesis for the mean (σ unknown).*

Excel Strategies Performing the *t* Test of Hypothesis for the Mean (σ Unknown)

You implement a worksheet that features the **TINV** and **TDIST** functions to perform a *t* test of the hypothesis for the mean (σ unknown). PHStat2 can construct this worksheet for you in a single step.

For example, to perform the *t* test of the hypothesis for the mean amount per sales invoice for the Saxon Home Improvement Company, shown in Figure 10, open to the **Data** worksheet of the **Chapter 8.xls** workbook and use one of these strategies:

Using Excel with PHStat2

Use the PHStat2 t Test for the Mean, sigma unknown procedure to perform a *t* test of the hypothesis for the mean (σ unknown).

Select **PHStat | One-Sample Tests | t Test for the Mean, sigma unknown**.

In the t Test for the Mean, sigma unknown, dialog box (shown at right):

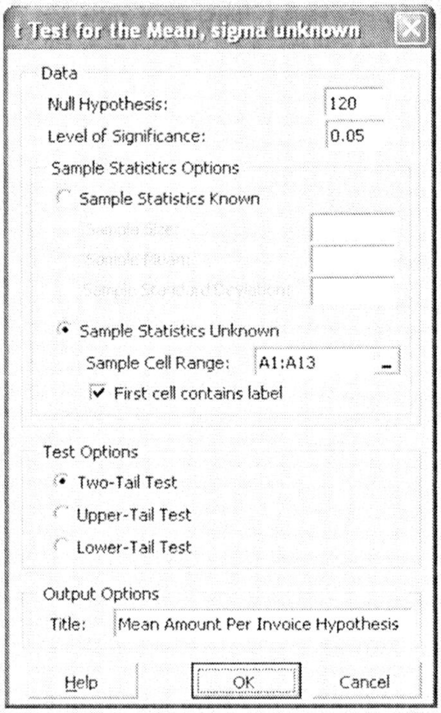

Enter **120** in the **Null Hypothesis** edit box.

Enter **0.05** in the **Level of Significance** edit box.

Select the **Sample Statistics Unknown** option button and enter **A1:A13** in the **Sample Cell Range** edit box and select the **First cell contains label** check box.

Select the **Two-Tail Test** option button.

Enter a title in the **Title** edit box.

Click the **OK** button.

*For problems in which the sample size, sample mean, and sample standard deviation are known, select the **Sample Statistics Known** option button and enter those statistics in the appropriate edit boxes. (Make no entry in the Sample Cell Range edit box, which will appear dimmed at that point.)*

Using Excel

Follow the instructions of section EH2 at the end of this chapter to manually implement a worksheet to perform a t test of the hypothesis for the mean (σ unknown).

Microsoft Excel can be used to evaluate the assumptions necessary for using the t test. The normality assumption can be checked in several ways. A determination of how closely the actual data match the normal distribution's theoretical properties can be made through a descriptive analysis of the obtained statistics along with a graphical analysis using a histogram, a stem-and-leaf display, a box-and-whisker plot, and a normal probability plot.

Figures 11, 12, and 13 present the descriptive summary measures, normal probability plot, and box-and-whisker plot obtained from Microsoft Excel for the invoice amounts data.

FIGURE 11

Microsoft Excel output of descriptive statistics for invoice amounts data

	A	B
1	*Invoice Amount*	
2		
3	Mean	112.8508333
4	Standard Error	6.003863082
5	Median	111.02
6	Mode	#N/A
7	Standard Deviation	20.7979918
8	Sample Variance	432.5564629
9	Kurtosis	0.172707598
10	Skewness	0.13363802
11	Range	76.51
12	Minimum	75.71
13	Maximum	152.22
14	Sum	1354.21
15	Count	12
16	Largest(1)	152.22
17	Smallest(1)	75.71

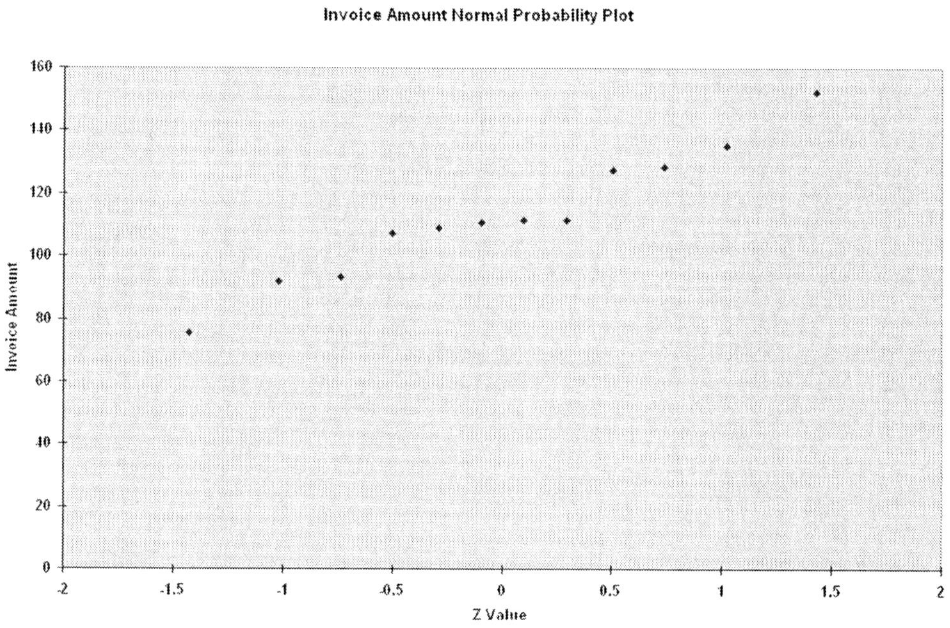

FIGURE 12
Normal probability plot obtained from Microsoft Excel for the invoices amount data

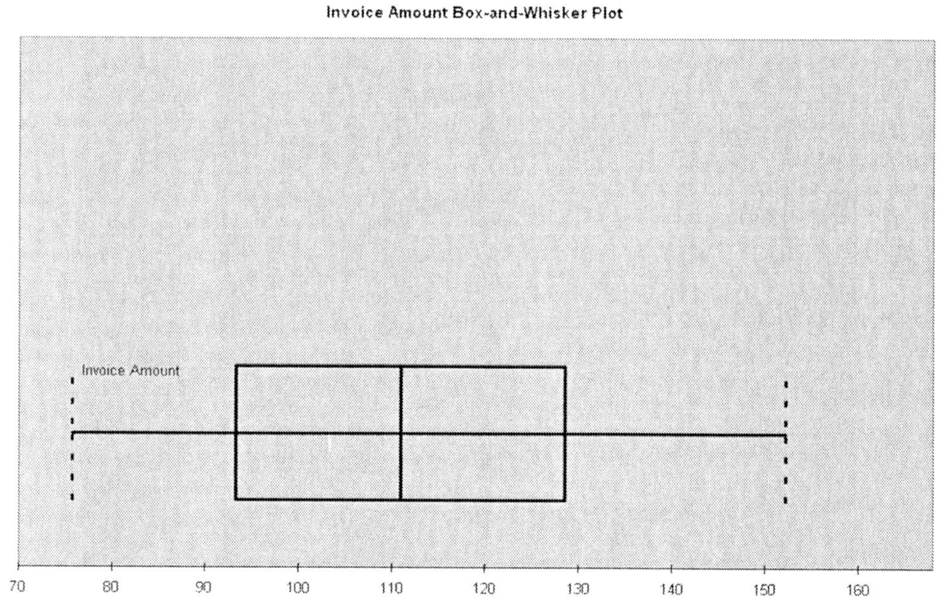

FIGURE 13
Box-and-whisker plot obtained from Microsoft Excel for the invoice amount data

Because the mean is very close to the median and the points on the normal probability plot appear to be increasing approximately in a straight line and the box-and-whisker plot appears symmetrical, there is no reason to believe that the assumption of underlying population normality of the sales invoice data is violated to any great extent. You can conclude that the results obtained by the auditor are valid.

The t test is a **robust** test. It does not lose power if the shape of the population from which the sample is drawn departs somewhat from a normal distribution, particularly when the sample size is large enough to enable the test statistic t to be influenced by the central limit theorem. However, erroneous conclusions can be drawn and statistical power can be lost if the t test is used incorrectly. If the sample size n is small (i.e., less than 30) and you cannot easily make the assumption that the underlying population from which the sample was taken is at least approximately normally distributed, other, *nonparametric* testing procedures are more appropriate (see references 1 and 2).

PROBLEMS FOR SECTION 4

Learning the Basics

46 If, in a sample of size $n = 16$ selected from an underlying normal population, the sample mean $\bar{X} = 56$ and the sample standard deviation is $S = 12$, what is the value of the t-test statistic if you are testing the null hypothesis H_0 that $\mu = 50$?

47 In problem 46, how many degrees of freedom are there in the one-sample t test?

48 In problems 46 and 47, what are the critical values from the t table if the level of significance $\alpha = 0.05$ and the alternative hypothesis H_1 is as follows:

a. $\mu \neq 50$? **b.** $\mu > 50$?

49 In problems 46, 47, and 48, what is your statistical decision if the alternative hypothesis H_1 is as follows:

a. $\mu \neq 50$? **b.** $\mu > 50$?

50 If, in a sample of size $n = 16$ selected from a left-skewed population, the sample mean $\bar{X} = 65$ and the sample standard deviation $S = 21$, would you use the t test to test the null hypothesis H_0 that $\mu = 60$? Discuss.

51 If, in a sample of size $n = 160$ selected from a left-skewed population, the sample mean $\bar{X} = 65$ and the sample standard deviation $S = 21$, would you use the t test to test the null hypothesis H_0 that $\mu = 60$? Discuss.

Applying the Concepts

Problems 52–54 can be solved manually or by using Microsoft Excel. We recommend that problems 55–61 be solved using Microsoft Excel.

52 The director of admissions at a large university advises parents of incoming students about the cost of textbooks during a typical semester. A sample of 100 students enrolled in the university indicates a sample mean cost of \$315.40 with a sample standard deviation of \$43.20.

a. Using the 0.10 level of significance, is there evidence that the population mean is above \$300?

b. What is your answer in (a) if the standard deviation is \$75 and the 0.05 level of significance is used?

c. What is your answer in (a) if the sample mean is \$305.11 and the sample standard deviation is \$43.20?

53 A manufacturer of flashlight batteries took a sample of 13 batteries from a day's production and used them continuously until they failed to work. The life as measured by the number of hours until failure was: **BATTERIES.xls**

342 426 317 545 264 451 1,049 631 512 266 492 562 298

a. At the 0.05 level of significance, is there evidence that the mean life of the batteries is more than 400 hours?

b. Determine the p-value in (a) and interpret its meaning.

c. Using the information above, what would you advise if the manufacturer wanted to be able to say in advertisements that these batteries "should last more than 400 hours"?

d. Suppose that the first value was 1,342 instead of 342. Repeat (a)–(c), using this value. Comment on the difference in the results.

54 In a recent article (Nanci Hellmich, "'Supermarket Guru' Has a Simple Mantra," *USA Today*, June 19, 2002, 7D) it was claimed that the average supermarket trip takes 22 minutes. Suppose that, in an effort to test this claim, a sample of 50 shoppers at a local supermarket were studied. The mean shopping time for the sample of 50 shoppers was 25.36 minutes with a standard deviation of 7.24 minutes. Using the 0.10 level of significance, is there evidence that the mean shopping time at the local supermarket is different from the claimed value of 22 minutes?

55 The following data represent the amount of soft drink filled in a sample of 50 consecutive 2-liter bottles. The results, listed horizontally in the order of being filled, were: **DRINK.xls**

2.109 2.086 2.066 2.075 2.065 2.057 2.052 2.044 2.036 2.038
2.031 2.029 2.025 2.029 2.023 2.020 2.015 2.014 2.013 2.014
2.012 2.012 2.012 2.010 2.005 2.003 1.999 1.996 1.997 1.992
1.994 1.986 1.984 1.981 1.973 1.975 1.971 1.969 1.966 1.967
1.963 1.957 1.951 1.951 1.947 1.941 1.941 1.938 1.908 1.894

a. At the 0.05 level of significance, is there evidence that the mean amount of soft drink filled is different from 2.0 liters?

b. Determine the p-value in (a) and interpret its meaning.

c. What assumption about the amount of soft drink filled must be made in (a)?

d. Evaluate the assumption in (c) graphically. Are the results obtained in (a) valid? Why?

e. Examine the values of the 50 bottles in their sequential order as given in the problem. Is there a pattern to the results? If so, what impact might this pattern have on the validity of the results obtained in (a)?

56 One of the major measures of the quality of service provided by any organization is the speed with which it responds to customer complaints. A large family-held department store selling furniture and flooring including carpeting had undergone a major expansion in the past several years. In particular, the flooring department had expanded from two installation crews to an installation supervisor, a measurer, and 15 installation crews. During a recent year there were 50 complaints concerning carpeting installation. The following data **FURNITURE.xls** represent the number of days between the receipt of the complaint and the resolution of the complaint.

54 5 35 137 31 27 152 2 123 81 74 27 11 19 126 110 110 29
61 35 94 31 26 5 12 4 165 32 29 28 29 26 25 1 14 13 13 10 5
27 4 52 30 22 36 26 20 23 33 68

a. The installation supervisor claims that the mean number of days between the receipt of the complaint and the resolution of the complaint is 20 days or less. At the 0.05 level of significance, is there evidence that the claim is not true (i.e., that the average number of days is greater than 20)?

b. What assumption about the population distribution must be made in (a)?

c. Do you think that the assumption made in (b) has been seriously violated? Explain.

d. What effect might your conclusion in (c) have on the validity of the results obtained in (a)?

57 In an article in *Quality Engineering*, the viscosity (resistance to flow) of a chemical product produced in batches was examined. The data for 120 batches are in the data file **CHEMICAL.xls**.

Source: Holmes and Mergen, "Parabolic Control Limits for the Exponentially Weighted Moving Average Control Charts," (1992), Quality Engineering, *4(4): 487–495.*

a. In the past, the mean viscosity was 15.5. At the 0.10 level of significance, is there evidence that the mean viscosity has changed from 15.5?

b. What assumption about the population distribution must be made in (a)?

c. Do you think that the assumption made in (b) has been seriously violated? Explain.

58 In New York State, savings banks are permitted to sell a form of life insurance called Savings Bank Life Insurance (SBLI). The approval process consists of underwriting, which includes a review of the application, a medical information bureau check, possible requests for additional medical information and medical exams, and a policy compilation stage where the policy pages are generated and sent to the bank for delivery. The ability to deliver approved policies to customers in a timely manner is critical to the profitability of this service to the bank. During a period of 1 month, a random sample of 27 approved policies was selected **INSURANCE.xls** and the total processing time in days was recorded with the following results:

73 19 16 64 28 28 31 90 60 56 31 56 22 18
45 48 17 17 17 91 92 63 50 51 69 16 17

a. In the past, suppose that mean processing time averaged 45 days. At the 0.05 level of significance, is there evidence that the mean processing time has changed from 45 days?

b. What assumption about the population distribution must be made in (a)?

c. Do you think that the assumption made in (b) has been seriously violated? Explain.

59 One operation of a steel mill is to cut pieces of steel into parts that will later be used as the frame for front seats in an automotive plant. The steel is cut with a diamond saw and requires the resulting parts to be within ±0.005 inch of the length specified by the automobile company. The data in the data file **STEEL.xls** come from a sample of 100 steel parts. The measurement reported is the difference in inches between the actual length of the steel part, as measured by a laser measurement device, and the specified length of the steel part. For example, an observation of −0.002 represents a steel part that is 0.002 inch shorter than the specified length.

a. At the 0.05 level of significance, is there evidence that the mean difference is not equal to 0.0 inches?

b. Determine the p-value in (a) and interpret its meaning.

c. What assumption about the differences between the actual length of the steel part, as measured by a laser measurement device, and the specified length of the steel part must be made in (a)?

d. Evaluate the assumption in (c) graphically. Are the results obtained in (a) valid? Why?

60 Consider a tea bag filling operation. An important quality characteristic of interest for this process is the weight of the tea in the individual bags. The data in the data file **TEABAGS.xls** is an ordered array of the weight, in grams, of a sample of 50 tea bags produced during an eight-hour shift.

a. Is there evidence that the mean amount of tea per bag is different from 5.5 grams (use $\alpha = 0.01$)?

b. Set up a 99% confidence interval estimate of the population mean amount of tea per bag. Interpret this interval.

c. Compare the conclusions reached in (a) and (b). Are they the same?

61 The data in the file **CHANGE2003.xls** contains a random sample of 30 mutual funds taken from the mutual funds reported in the *Wall Street Journal* on March 7, 2003. For each mutual fund, "Change" is the change (in dollars) in fund value from trading on March 6, 2003.

a. Is there evidence that the mean fund value for mutual funds changed on March 6, 2003? Use a level of significance of 0.05.

b. What assumptions are made to perform the test in (a)?

c. Determine the p-value and interpret its meaning.

5 Z TEST OF HYPOTHESIS FOR THE PROPORTION

In some situations, you want to test a hypothesis pertaining to the population proportion p of values that are in a particular category rather than the population mean value. A random sample can be selected from the population and the **sample proportion**, $p_s = X/n$, can be computed. The value of this statistic is then compared to the hypothesized value of the parameter p so that a decision can be made about the hypothesis.

If the number of successes (X) and the number of failures ($n - X$) are each at least five, the sampling distribution of a proportion approximately follows a standardized normal distribution. To perform the hypothesis test in order to evaluate the magnitude of the difference between the sample proportion p_s and the hypothesized population proportion p, the **Z test for the proportion** given in Equation (3) is used.

ONE-SAMPLE Z TEST FOR THE PROPORTION

$$Z \cong \frac{p_s - p}{\sqrt{\dfrac{p(1-p)}{n}}} \qquad \textbf{(3)}$$

where

$$p_s = \frac{X}{n} = \frac{\text{number of successes in the sample}}{\text{sample size}}$$

= observed proportion of successes

p = hypothesized proportion of successes in the population

The test statistic Z approximately follows a standardized normal distribution.

Alternatively, the Z-test statistic can be written in terms of the number of successes X as in Equation (4).

Z TEST FOR THE PROPORTION IN TERMS OF THE NUMBER OF SUCCESSES

$$Z \cong \frac{X - np}{\sqrt{np(1-p)}} \qquad \textbf{(4)}$$

A study reported in the *Wall Street Journal* can serve to illustrate the (one-sample) Z test for a hypothesized proportion. In the study, the question posed was "are an equal number of home-based businesses owned by men and women?" The study of 899 home-based businesses reported that 369 were owned by women (Eleena De Lisser and Dan Morse, "More Men Work at Home than Women, Study Shows," *Wall Street Journal*, May 18, 1999, B2).

In terms of proportions, the null and alternative hypotheses can be stated as follows:

H_0: $p = 0.50$ (i.e., the proportion of home-based businesses owned by females is 0.50)

H_1: $p \neq 0.50$ (i.e., the proportion of home-based businesses owned by females is not 0.50)

Critical Value Approach Because you are interested in whether the proportion of home-based businesses owned by females is 0.50 (and that owned by males is 0.50), a two-tail test is used. If a level of significance α of 0.05 is selected, the rejection and nonrejection regions are set up as in Figure 14, and the decision rule is

Reject H_0 if $Z < -1.96$ or if $Z > +1.96$;

otherwise do not reject H_0.

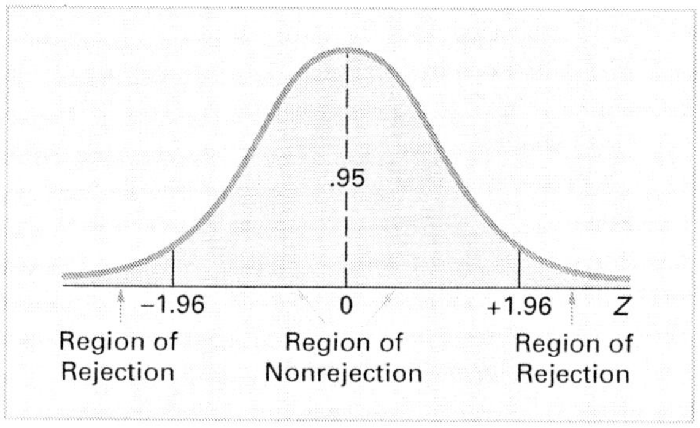

FIGURE 14
Two-tail test of hypothesis for the proportion at the 0.05 level of significance

From the data, since 369 of the 899 home-based businesses are owned by females,

$$p_S = \frac{369}{899} = 0.41046$$

Using Equation (3),

$$Z \cong \frac{p_S - p}{\sqrt{\dfrac{p(1-p)}{n}}} = \frac{0.41046 - 0.50}{\sqrt{\dfrac{0.50(1-0.50)}{899}}} = \frac{-0.08954}{0.0167} = -5.37$$

or, using Equation (4),

$$Z \cong \frac{X - np}{\sqrt{np(1-p)}} = \frac{369 - (899)(0.50)}{\sqrt{899(0.50)(0.50)}} = \frac{-80.5}{14.99} = -5.37$$

Because $-5.37 < -1.96$, you reject H_0. Thus, there is evidence that the proportion of home-based businesses owned by females is not 0.50. Figure 15 presents Microsoft Excel output for these data.

FIGURE 15
Microsoft Excel output for the study on home-based business ownership

	A	B
1	**Ownership Proportion Hypothesis**	
2		
3	**Data**	
4	**Null Hypothesis** *p*=	0.5
5	**Level of Significance**	0.05
6	**Number of Successes**	369
7	**Sample Size**	899
8		
9	Intermediate Calculations	
10	Sample Proportion	0.410456062
11	Standard Error	0.016675934
12	**Z Test Statistic**	-5.369650635
13		
14	**Two-Tail Test**	
15	**Lower Critical Value**	-1.959962787
16	**Upper Critical value**	1.959962787
17	***p*-Value**	7.9064E-08
18	**Reject the null hypothesis**	

p-Value Approach As an alternative approach toward making a hypothesis-testing decision, the p-value can be computed. Because a two-tail test is involved in which the rejection region is located in the lower tail and the upper tail, you need to find the area below a Z value of -5.37 and a Z value above $+5.37$. Figure 15 shows that this probability is 0.000000079064 (7.9064E–08 in scientific notation). Because this value is less than the *selected* level of significance ($\alpha = 0.05$), the null hypothesis is rejected. This extremely small p-value indicates that there is virtually no chance of obtaining a sample proportion of 0.41046 if in fact the population proportion is 0.50.

Excel Strategies Performing the *Z* Test of Hypothesis for the Proportion

CHAPTER 8.xls

*Retrieve the Figure 8.15 worksheet of the **Chapter 8.xls** workbook to view the Z test of the hypothesis for the proportion shown in Figure 15.*

You implement a worksheet that features the **NORMSINV** and **NORMSDIST** functions to perform a *Z* test of the hypothesis for the proportion. PHStat2 can construct this worksheet for you in a single step.

For example, to perform a *Z* test of the hypothesis for the proportion of home-based business owned by females, shown in Figure 15, use one of these strategies:

Using Excel with PHStat2

Use the PHStat2 *Z* Test for the Proportion procedure to perform a *Z* test of the hypothesis for the proportion.

Select **PHStat | One-Sample Tests | Z Test for the Proportion.**

In the Z Test for the Proportion dialog box (shown at right):

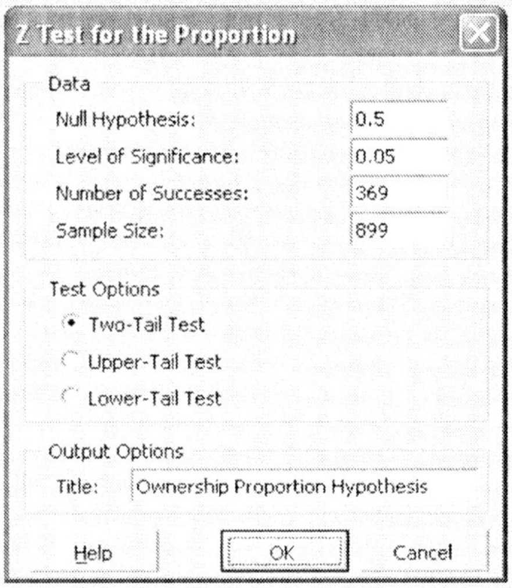

Enter **0.5** in the **Null Hypothesis** edit box.
Enter **0.05** in the **Level of Significance** edit box.
Enter **369** in the **Number of Successes** edit box.
Enter **899** in the **Sample Size** edit box.
Select the **Two-Tail Test** option button.
Enter a title in the **Title** edit box.
Click the **OK** button.

*For problems that require a one-tailed test, select the **Upper-Tail Test** or **Lower-Tail Test** option button, as appropriate, when completing this dialog box.*

Using Excel

Follow the instructions of section EH3 at the end of this chapter to manually implement a worksheet to perform a *Z* test of the hypothesis for the proportion.

PROBLEMS FOR SECTION 5

Learning the Basics

62 If, in a random sample of 400 items, 88 are found to be defective, what is the sample proportion of defective items?

63 In problem 62, if the null hypothesis is that 20% of the items in the population are defective, what is the value of the *Z*-test statistic?

64 In problems 62 and 63, suppose you are testing the null hypothesis H_0: $p = 0.20$ against the two-tail alternative hypothesis H_1: $p \neq 0.20$ and you choose the level of significance of $\alpha = 0.05$. What is your statistical decision?

Applying the Concepts

65 An article in the *Wall Street Journal* implies that more than half of all Americans would prefer being given $100 rather than a day off from work. This statement is based on a survey conducted by American Express Incentive Services, in which 593 of 1,040 respondents indicated that they would rather have the $100 (Carlos Tejada, "Work Week," *Wall Street Journal*, July 25, 2000, A1).

a. At the 0.05 level of significance, is there evidence based on the survey data that more than half of all Americans would rather have $100 than a day off from work?

b. Compute the p-value and interpret its meaning.

66 In a national poll of 811 personal computer owners, Peter D. Hart Research Associates found that 44% (357) of the PC owners ranked sharing their credit card information as the number one concern in online shopping. The survey also indicated that 72% (584) of PC owners would purchase a more secure computer if available. When given an actual dollar amount the added security would cost, 57% (462) indicated that they would pay an extra $75 for a new PC delivering a more secure online experience ("Hart Poll Finds 72% of PC Owners Would Purchase a More Secure Computer if Available," *Business Wire*, Washington D.C., September 11, 2001).

a. Test the null hypothesis that 50% of all PC owners in the United States rank sharing their credit card information as the number one concern in online shopping versus the alternative that the percentage is not equal to 50% (use $\alpha = 0.05$).

b. Compute the p-value in (a) and interpret its meaning.

c. At the 0.05 level of significance, is there evidence that more than half of all PC owners in the United States would pay an extra $75 for a new PC delivering a more secure online experience?

d. Compute the p-value in (c) and interpret its meaning.

e. At the 0.05 level of significance, is there evidence that more than 55% of all PC owners in the United States would pay an extra $75 for a new PC delivering a more secure online experience?

f. Compute the p-value in (e) and interpret its meaning.

67 To handle the increased necessity of storing and organizing huge amounts of data, many companies are making large expenditures for increased data-storage capability. The slowdown in the U.S. economy, however, has many companies delaying data-storage expenditures. In July 2001, it was reported that 38% of the companies surveyed have delayed expenditures on storage deployments because of the economic slowdown. The sample size for this survey was not disclosed (Jeff Mead, "The Real Cost of Storage," *eWEEK*, October 1, 2001, 40).

a. Suppose that the above results were based on the responses of 50 companies. Is there evidence at the 0.01 level of significance that less than half of all companies are delaying data-storage expenditures?

b. Compute the p-value in (a) and interpret its meaning.

c. Suppose that the above results were based on the responses of 100 companies. Is there evidence at the 0.01 level of significance that less than half of all companies are delaying data-storage expenditures?

d. Compute the p-value in (c) and interpret its meaning.

e. Compare your answers in (a) and (b) with your answers to (c) and (d). Explain the effect that sample size has on statistical significance.

f. What ethical issues are raised when one fails to report the sample size used in a survey?

68 One of the biggest issues facing e-retailers is the ability to turn browsers into buyers (M. Totty, "Making the Sale," *Wall Street Journal*, September 24, 2001, R6). This is measured by the conversion rate, the percentage of browsers who buy something in their visit to a site. This article reported that the conversion rate for llbean.com was 10.1% and for victoriasecret.com was 8.2%. Suppose that each of these sites were redesigned in an attempt to increase their conversion rates. Samples of 200 browsers at each redesigned site were selected. Suppose that 24 browsers at llbean.com made a purchase and 25 browsers at victoriasecret.com made a purchase.

a. Is there evidence of an increased conversion rate at llbean.com at the 0.05 level of significance?

b. Is there evidence of an increased conversion rate at victoriasecret.com at the 0.05 level of significance?

69 More professional women than ever before are foregoing motherhood because of the time constraints of their careers. Yet, many women still manage to find time to climb the corporate ladder and set time aside to have children. A survey of 187 attendees at *Fortune Magazine's* Most Powerful Women in Business summit in March 2002 found that 133 had at least one child (Carol Hymowitz, "Women Plotting Mix of Work and Family Won't Find Perfect Plan," *Wall Street Journal*, June 11, 2002, B1). Assume that the group of 187 women is a random sample from the population of all successful women executives.

a. What is the sample proportion of successful women executives who have children?

b. At the 0.05 level of significance, can you state that more than half of all successful women executives have children?

c. At the 0.05 level of significance, can you state that more than two-thirds of all successful women executives have children?

d. Do you think the random sample assumption is valid? Explain.

70 In the spring of 2002, Office Depot entered into its biggest brand recognition campaign in company history. A major thrust of the campaign was a series of new television advertisements featuring well-known entertainers and sports figures including former NFL coach Bill Parcells, supermodel Kathy Ireland, and Olympic ice skater Tara Lipinski. Company officials had mixed feelings on the success of these star-studded advertisements. A key metric for the success of television advertisements is the proportion of viewers who "like the ads a lot." Harris Ad Research Service conducted a study of 1,189 adults who viewed the ads, and reported that 18% indicated that they "like the ads a lot." According to Harris, the proportion of a typical television advertisement receiving the "like the ads a lot" score is believed to be 22% (Theresa Howard, "Stars Don't Mean Hits for Ads," **www.usatoday.com**, April 22, 2002).

a. Using a 0.01 level of significance, is there evidence that the Home Depot ads are less successful than the typical ad (i.e., is the population proportion of "like the ads a lot" for the Home Depot ads less than 0.22)?

b. Compute the p-value and interpret its meaning.

71 A sample of 400 college educated 35- to 64-year-olds with household incomes more than \$100,000 were asked if they agreed with the following statement. "Government should be more involved in oversight and regulation of private enterprise." Fifty-two percent of the respondents agreed with the statement ("USA Today Snapshots," *USA Today*, July 16, 2002, B1). Use the ten-step p-value approach to test if there is evidence that more than half of the population of college-educated 35- to 64-year-olds with household incomes more than \$100,000 agrees that government should be more involved in oversight and regulation of private enterprise.

6 POTENTIAL HYPOTHESIS-TESTING PITFALLS AND ETHICAL ISSUES

To this point, you have studied the fundamental concepts of hypothesis-testing methodology. Hypothesis testing has been used for analyzing differences between sample estimates (i.e., statistics) and hypothesized population characteristics (i.e., parameters) in order to make decisions about the underlying characteristics. You have also learned how to evaluate the risks involved in making these decisions.

When planning to carry out a test of the hypothesis based on a survey, research study, or designed experiment, several questions must be asked to ensure that proper methodology is used. Questions like the ones in Exhibit 5 need to be raised and answered in the planning stage. Therefore, a person with substantial statistical training should be consulted and involved early in the process. All too often such an individual is consulted far too late in the process, after the data have been collected. Typically, all that can be done at such a late stage is to choose the statistical test procedure that would be best for the obtained data. You are forced to assume that certain biases built into the study (because of poor planning) are negligible. But this is a large assumption. Good research involves good planning. To avoid biases, adequate controls must be built in from the beginning.

EXHIBIT 5 QUESTIONS TO CONSIDER IN THE PLANNING STAGE OF HYPOTHESIS TESTING

1. What is the goal of the survey, study, or experiment? Can it be translated into a null hypothesis and an alternative hypothesis?
2. Is the hypothesis test going to be a two-tail test or one-tail test?
3. Can a random sample be drawn from the underlying population of interest?
4. What kinds of measurements will be obtained from the sample? Are the sampled outcomes going to be numerical or categorical?
5. At what significance level, or risk of committing a Type I error, should the hypothesis test be conducted?
6. Is the intended sample size large enough to achieve the desired power of the test for the level of significance chosen?
7. What statistical test procedure is to be used on the sampled data and why?
8. What kinds of conclusions and interpretations can be drawn from the results of the hypothesis test?

You need to distinguish between poor research methodology and unethical behavior. Ethical considerations arise when there is a manipulation of the hypothesis-testing process. Some of the ethical issues that arise when dealing with hypothesis-testing methodology include the data collection method, informed consent from human subjects being "treated," the type of test—two-tail or one-tail—the choice of level of significance α, data snooping, the cleansing and discarding of data, and the reporting of findings.

Data Collection Method—Randomization To eliminate the possibility of potential biases in the results, proper data collection methods must be used. To draw meaningful conclusions, the data obtained must be the outcome of a random sample from a population or from an experiment in which a **randomization** process was employed. Potential respondents should not be permitted to self-select for a study nor should they be purposely selected. Aside from the potential ethical issues that may be raised, such a lack of randomization can result in serious coverage errors or selection biases that destroy the value of the study.

Informed Consent from Human Respondents Being "Treated" Ethical considerations require that any individual who is to be subjected to some "treatment" in an experiment be made aware of the research endeavor and any potential behavioral or physical side effects. The subject should also provide informed consent with respect to participation.

Type of Test—Two-Tail or One-Tail If prior information is available that leads you to test the null hypothesis against a specifically directed alternative, then a one-tail test will be more powerful than a two-tail test. On the other hand, you should realize that if you are interested only in *differences* from the null hypothesis, not in the *direction* of the difference, the two-tail test is the appropriate procedure to use. For example, if previous research and statistical testing have already established the difference in a particular direction, or if an established scientific theory states that it is possible for results to occur in only one direction, then a one-tail or directional test can be used.

Choice of Level of Significance α In a well-designed study, the level of significance α is selected before data collection occurs. You cannot be permitted to alter the level of significance, after the fact, to achieve a specific result. This would be data snooping. One answer to this issue is to always report the p-value, not just the conclusions of the hypothesis test.

Data Snooping **Data snooping** is never permissible. It is unethical to perform a hypothesis test on a set of data, look at the results, and then select whether the test should be a two-tail test or a one-tail test and/or choose the level of significance. These steps must be done first, as part of the study, before the data are collected in order for the conclusions drawn to have meaning. In those situations in which a statistician is consulted by a researcher late in the process, with data already available, it is imperative that the null and alternative hypotheses be established and the level of significance be chosen prior to carrying out the hypothesis test. Moreover, extreme or unusual observations cannot be arbitrarily changed or discarded in order to alter the results of the hypothesis tests.

Cleansing and Discarding of Data Data cleansing is not data snooping. In the data preparation stage of editing, coding, and transcribing, you have an opportunity to review the data for any observation whose measurement seems to be extreme or unusual. After this has been done, the outcomes of the numerical variables in the data set should be organized into stem-and-leaf displays and box-and-whisker plots in preparation for further data presentation and *confirmatory analysis*. This *exploratory data analysis* stage gives you another opportunity to cleanse the data set by flagging outlier observations that need to be checked against the original data. In addition, the exploratory data analysis enables you to examine the data graphically with respect to the assumptions underlying a particular hypothesis test procedure.

The process of data cleansing raises a major ethical question. Should an observation ever be removed from a study? The answer is a qualified yes. If it can be determined that a measurement is incomplete or grossly in error because of some equipment problem or unusual behavioral occurrence unrelated to the study, a decision to discard the observation may be made. Sometimes there is no choice—an individual may decide to quit a particular study he or she has been participating in before a final measurement can be made. In a well-designed experiment or study, the researcher would decide, in advance, on all rules regarding the possible discarding of data.

Reporting of Findings In conducting research, it is vitally important to document both good and bad results so that individuals who follow up on such research do not have to start all over again. It is inappropriate to report the results of hypothesis tests that show statistical significance but not those for which there was insufficient evidence in the findings. In those instances where there was insufficient evidence to reject H_0, it must be made clear that this does not prove that the null hypothesis is true. What the result does indicate is that with the sample size used, there was not enough information to *disprove* the null hypothesis.

Statistical Significance versus Practical Significance The individual making a decision based on the results of a test of hypothesis needs to make a distinction between the existence of a statistically significant result and its practical significance in the context within a field of application. It is sometimes the case that due to a very large sample size, a result that has little practical significance will be deemed to be statistically significant. For example, suppose that prior to a national marketing campaign focusing on a series of expensive television commercials, it was believed that the proportion of people who recognized your brand was 0.30. At the completion of the campaign, a survey of 20,000 people indicates that 6,168 recognized your brand. A one-tail test trying to prove that the proportion is now greater than 0.30 results in a p-value of 0.0047 and the correct statistical conclusion is that the proportion of consumers recognizing your brand name has now increased. Was the campaign successful? The result of the hypothesis test indicates a statistically significant increase in brand awareness, but is this increase practically important? Note that the population proportion is now estimated at $6,168/20,000 = 0.3084$ or 30.84%. This increase is less than 1% more than the hypothesized value of 30%. Did the large expenses associated with the marketing campaign produce a result with a meaningful increase in brand awareness? Because of the minimal real-world impact an increase of less than 1% has on the overall marketing strategy, and the huge expenses associated with the marketing campaign, you should conclude that the campaign was not successful. On the other hand, if the campaign increased brand awareness by 20%, you could conclude that the campaign was indeed successful.

To summarize, in discussing ethical issues concerning hypothesis-testing methodology, the key is *intent*. You must distinguish between poor data analysis and unethical practice. Unethical behavior occurs when someone willfully causes a selection bias in data collection, manipulates the treatment of human subjects without informed consent, uses data snooping to select the type of test (two-tail or one-tail) and/or level of significance to his or her advantage, hides the facts by discarding observations that do not support a stated hypothesis, or fails to report pertinent findings.

7 THE POWER OF A TEST (CD-ROM TOPIC)

section8.7.pdf

In section 1 the power of the test was defined as the probability of rejecting the null hypothesis when it is false. In this section on the CD-ROM, the concept of the power of the test is developed in greater depth.

SUMMARY

As observed in the summary flowchart, this chapter presented the fundamental underpinnings of hypothesis-testing methodology. You learned how to perform Z and t tests on population means, and Z tests on population proportions, and you learned how an operations manager of a production facility can use these tests to monitor and improve a cereal-filling process. The three chapters that follow build on the foundations of hypothesis testing that have been discussed here.

Chapter summary flowchart

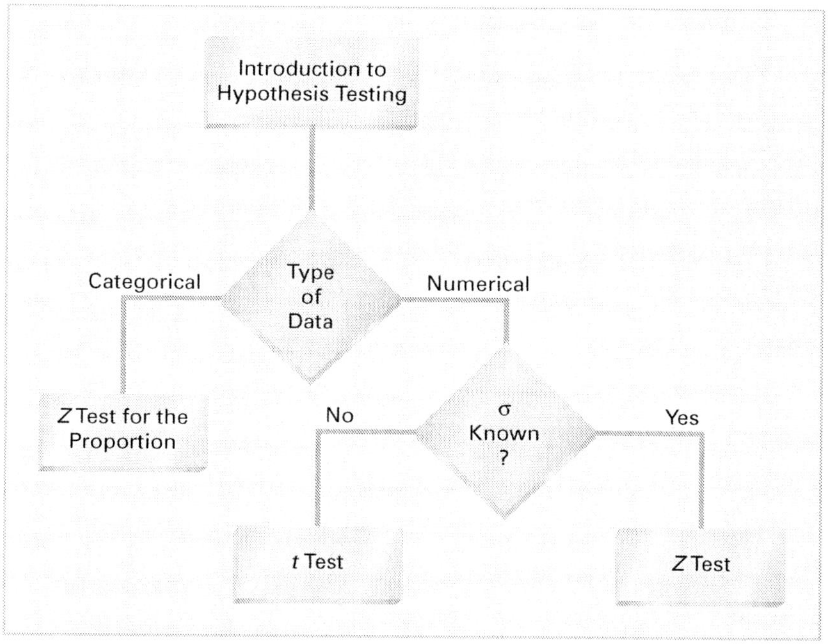

KEY TERMS

α (level of significance)
alternative hypothesis (H_1)
β risk
confidence coefficient ($1 - \alpha$)
confidence level
critical region
critical value
data snooping
directional test
hypothesis testing
hypothesis-testing methodology
level of significance (α)
null hypothesis (H_0)
one-tail test
p-value
power of a statistical test
randomization
region of nonrejection
region of rejection
robust
sample proportion
t test of hypothesis for a mean
test statistic
two-tail test
Type I error
Type II error
Z test of hypothesis for the mean
Z test for the proportion
Z-test statistic

CHAPTER REVIEW PROBLEMS

Checking Your Understanding

72 What is the difference between a null hypothesis H_0 and an alternative hypothesis H_1?

73 What is the difference between a Type I and a Type II error?

74 What is meant by the power of a test?

75 What is the difference between a one-tail and a two-tail test?

76 What is meant by a p-value?

77 How can a confidence interval estimate for the population mean provide conclusions to the corresponding hypothesis test for the population mean?

78 What is the step-by-step hypothesis-testing methodology?

79 What are some of the ethical issues to be concerned with in performing a hypothesis test?

80 In planning to carry out a test of hypothesis based on a designed experiment or research study under investigation, what are some of the questions that need to be raised in order to ensure that proper methodology will be used?

Applying the Concepts

Problems 81–86 can be solved manually or by using Microsoft Excel. We recommend that problems 87–93 be solved using Microsoft Excel.

81 An article in *Marketing News* (Thomas T. Semon, "Consider a Statistical Insignificance Test," *Marketing News*, February 1, 1999) argues that the level of significance used when comparing two products is often too low, i.e., sometimes you should be using an α value greater than 0.05. Specifically, the article recounts testing the proportion of potential customers with a preference for product 1 over product 2. The null hypothesis is that the population proportion of potential customers preferring product 1 is 0.5, and the alternative hypothesis is that it is not equal to 0.5. The p-value for the test is 0.22. The article suggests that in some cases this should be enough evidence to reject the null hypothesis.

a. State the null and alternative hypotheses in statistical terms.
b. Explain the risks associated with Type I and Type II errors.
c. What would be the consequences if you rejected the null hypothesis for a p-value of 0.22?
d. Why do you think the article suggests raising the value of α?
e. What would you do in this situation?
f. What would be your answer in (e) if the p-value were actually 0.12? What if it were 0.06?

82 La Quinta Motor Inns developed a computer model to help predict the profitability of sites that are being considered as locations for new hotels. If the computer model predicts large profits, La Quinta buys the proposed site and builds a new hotel. If the computer model predicts small or moderate profits, La Quinta chooses not to proceed with that site (Sheryl E. Kimes and James A. Fitzsimmons, "Selecting Profitable Hotel Sites at La Quinta Motor Inns," *Interfaces*, Vol. 20, March–April 1990, 12–20). This decision-making procedure can be expressed in the hypothesis-testing framework. The null hypothesis is that the site is not a profitable location. The alternative hypothesis is that the site is a profitable location.

a. Explain the risks associated with committing a Type I error.
b. Explain the risks associated with committing a Type II error.
c. Which type of error do you think the executives at La Quinta Motor Inns are trying hard to avoid? Explain.
d. How do changes in the rejection criterion affect the probabilities of committing Type I and Type II errors?

83 A 1999 General Accounting Office (GAO) study found that about a third of the 23.4 million retirees 65 or older supplemented Medicare with some form of employer coverage (Carlos Tejada, "Work Week," *Wall Street Journal*, June 26, 2002, B5). The article suggests that this proportion is increasing. Suppose that in a current study, a random sample of 500 retirees 65 or older indicated that 185 supplemented Medicare with some form of employer coverage.

a. At the 0.01 level of significance, is there evidence that the proportion of retirees 65 or older that supplement Medicare with some form of employer coverage is now greater than one-third?
b. Compute the p-value and interpret its meaning.

84 The owner of a gasoline station wants to study gasoline purchasing habits by motorists at his station. A random sample of 60 motorists during a certain week is selected with the following results:

- Amount purchased: $\bar{X} = 11.3$ gallons, $S = 3.1$ gallons.
- 11 motorists purchased premium grade gasoline.

a. At the 0.05 level of significance, is there evidence that the mean purchase is different from 10 gallons?
b. Find the p-value in (a).
c. At the 0.05 level of significance, is there evidence that fewer than 20% of the motorists purchase premium grade gasoline?
d. What would be your answer to (a) if the sample mean was 10.3 gallons?
e. What is your answer to (c) if seven motorists purchased premium grade gasoline?

85 An auditor for a government agency is assigned the task of evaluating reimbursement for office visits to physicians paid by Medicare. The audit is to be conducted for all Medicare payments in a particular geographic area during a certain month. Suppose the audit is conducted on a sample of 75 of the reimbursements with the following result:

- In 12 of the office visits, an incorrect amount of reimbursement was provided.
- The amount of reimbursement was: $\bar{X} = \$93.70$, $S = \$34.55$.

a. At the 0.05 level of significance, is there evidence that the mean reimbursement is less than $100?
b. At the 0.05 level of significance, is there evidence that the proportion of incorrect reimbursements in the population is greater than 0.10?
c. Discuss the underlying assumptions of the test used in (a).
d. What would be your answer to (a) if the sample mean were $90?
e. What would be your answer to (b) if 15 office visits had incorrect reimbursements?

86 A bank branch located in a commercial district of a city has developed an improved process for serving customers during the noon to 1:00 P.M. peak lunch period. The waiting time (defined as the time the customer enters the line until he or she is served) of a random sample of 15 customers during this hour is recorded over a period of 1 week and the results are as follows: **BANK1.xls**

4.21 5.55 3.02 5.13 4.77 2.34 3.54 3.20 4.50 6.10 0.38
5.12 6.46 6.19 3.79

a. At the 0.05 level of significance, is there evidence that the mean waiting time is less than 5 minutes?
b. What assumption must hold in order to perform the test in (a)?
c. Evaluate this assumption through a graphical approach. Discuss.
d. As a customer walks into the branch office during the lunch hour, she asks the branch manager how long she

can expect to wait. The branch manager replies, "Almost certainly not longer than 5 minutes." On the basis of the results of (a), evaluate this statement.

87 One of the major measures of the quality of service provided by an organization is the speed with which it responds to customer complaints. A large family-held store that sells furniture and flooring, including carpet, had undergone a major expansion in the past several years. In particular, the flooring department had expanded from two installation crews to an installation supervisor, a measurer, and 15 installation crews. A sample of 50 complaints in a recent year concerning carpet installation was selected. The following data represent the number of days between the receipt of the complaint and the resolution of the complaint. **FURNITURE.xls**

54	5	35	137	31	27	152	2	123	81	74	27
11	19	126	110	110	29	61	35	94	31	26	5
12	4	165	32	29	28	29	26	25	1	14	13
13	10	5	27	4	52	30	22	36	26	20	23
33	68										

Suppose a customer calls the store with a complaint after the carpet has been installed. She asks the flooring department manager how long she can expect to wait to have her complaint resolved. The flooring department manager replies, "Almost certainly not longer than 20 days." Evaluate this statement.

88 In New York State, savings banks are permitted to sell a form of life insurance called Savings Bank Life Insurance (SBLI). The approval process consists of underwriting, which includes a review of the application, a medical information bureau check, possible requests for additional medical information and medical exams, and a policy compilation stage in which the policy pages are generated and sent to the bank for delivery. The ability to deliver approved policies to customers in a timely manner is critical to the profitability of this service to the bank. During a period of 1 month, a random sample of 27 approved policies was selected and the total processing time in days was recorded with the following results: **INSURANCE.xls**

73	19	16	64	28	28	31	90	60	56	31	56	22	18
45	48	17	17	17	91	92	63	50	51	69	16	17	

Suppose a customer calls the bank and asks how long he can expect to wait before the policy is approved. The bank manager replies, "About 30 days." Evaluate this statement.

89 A manufacturing company produces electrical insulators. If the insulators break when in use, a short circuit is likely to occur. To test the strength of the insulators, destructive testing is carried out in high-powered labs to determine how much *force* is required to break the insulators. Force is measured by observing how many pounds must be applied to the insulator before it breaks. The following data are from 30 observations from this experiment. **FORCE.xls**

Force (in the Number of Pounds Required to Break the Insulator)

1870	1728	1656	1610	1634	1784	1522	1696	1592	1662
1866	1764	1734	1662	1734	1774	1550	1756	1762	1866
1820	1744	1788	1688	1810	1752	1680	1810	1652	1736

a. At the 0.05 level of significance, is there evidence that the mean force is greater than 1,500 pounds?
b. What assumption must hold in order to perform the test in (a)?
c. Evaluate this assumption through a graphical approach. Discuss.
d. Based on (a), what can you conclude about the strength of the insulators?

90 An important quality characteristic used by the manufacturer of "Boston" and "Vermont" asphalt shingles is the amount of moisture the shingles contain when they are packaged. Customers may feel that they have purchased a product lacking in quality if they find moisture and wet shingles inside the packaging. In some cases, excessive moisture can cause the granules attached to the shingle for texture and coloring purposes to fall off the shingle, resulting in appearance problems. To monitor the amount of moisture present, the company conducts moisture tests. A shingle is weighed and then dried. The shingle is then reweighed and, based on the amount of moisture taken out of the product, the pounds of moisture per 100 square feet are calculated. The company would like to show that the average moisture content is less than 0.35 pounds per 100 square feet. The data file **MOISTURE.xls** includes 36 measurements (in pounds per 100 square feet) for the "Boston" shingles and 31 for "Vermont" shingles.

a. For the "Boston" shingles, is there evidence at the 0.05 level of significance that the mean moisture content is less than 0.35 pounds per 100 square feet?
b. Interpret the meaning of the p-value in (a).
c. For the "Vermont" shingles, is there evidence at the 0.05 level of significance that the mean moisture content is less than 0.35 pounds per 100 square feet?
d. Interpret the meaning of the p-value in (c).
e. What assumption must hold in order to perform the tests in (a) and (c)?
f. Evaluate the assumption for the "Boston" shingles and the "Vermont" shingles by using a graphical approach. Discuss.

91 Studies conducted by a manufacturer of "Boston" and "Vermont" asphalt shingles have shown product weight to be a major factor in the customer's perception of quality. Moreover, the weight represents the amount of raw materials being used and is therefore very important to the company from a cost standpoint. The last stage of the assembly line packages the shingles before the packages are placed on wooden pallets.

Once a pallet is full (a pallet for most brands holds 16 squares of shingles) it is weighed and the measurement is recorded. The data file **PALLET.xls** contains the weight (in pounds) from a sample of 368 pallets of "Boston" shingles and 330 pallets of "Vermont" shingles.

a. For the "Boston" shingles, is there evidence that the mean weight is different from 3,150 pounds.
b. Interpret the meaning of the p-value in (a).
c. For the "Vermont" shingles, is there evidence that the mean weight is different from 3,700 pounds.
d. Interpret the meaning of the p-value in (c).
e. Evaluate whether the assumption needed for (a) and (c) have been seriously violated.

92 The manufacturer of "Boston" and "Vermont" asphalt shingles provide their customers with a 20-year warranty on most of their products. To determine whether a shingle will last as long as the warranty period, accelerated-life testing is conducted at the manufacturing plant. Accelerated-life testing exposes the shingle to the stresses it would be subject to in a lifetime of normal use in a laboratory setting via an experiment that takes only a few minutes to conduct. In this test, a shingle is repeatedly scraped with a brush for a short period of time and the amount of shingle granules that are removed by the brushing is weighed (in grams). Shingles that experience low amounts of granule loss are expected to last longer in normal use than shingles that experience high amounts of granule loss. The data file **GRANULE.xls** contains a sample of 170 measurements made on the company's "Boston" shingles, and 140 measurements made on "Vermont" shingles.

a. For the "Boston" shingles, is there evidence that the mean granule loss is different from 0.50 grams.
b. Interpret the meaning of the p-value in (a).
c. For the "Vermont" shingles, is there evidence that the mean granule loss is different from 0.50 grams.
d. Interpret the meaning of the p-value in (a).
e. Evaluate whether the assumption needed for (a) and (c) have been seriously violated.

Report Writing Exercises

93 Referring to the results you obtained in problems 90–92 concerning the "Boston" and "Vermont" shingles, write a report that evaluates the moisture level, weight, and granule loss of the two types of shingles. Be sure to incorporate into the report tables and charts obtained using Microsoft Excel and prepare a PowerPoint slide presentation (see the Using Microsoft Office discussion in the appendix on Preparing Data for Reports and Presentations Using Microsoft Office).

Internet Exercises

94 Go to the Web site for this text

www.prenhall.com/levine

Select Chapter 8 and then click on Internet exercises.

RUNNING CASE MANAGING THE *SPRINGVILLE HERALD*

Continuing its monitoring of the blackness of the newspaper print, the production department of the newspaper wants to ensure that the mean blackness of the print for all newspapers is at least 0.97 on a standard scale in which the target value is 1.0. A random sample of 50 newspapers has been selected **SH8.xls** and the blackness of each paper has been measured. Calculate the sample statistics and determine if there is evidence that the mean blackness is less than 0.97. Write a memo to management that summarizes your conclusions.

Blackness of 50 Newspapers

0.854	1.023	1.005	1.030	1.219	0.977	1.044	0.778	1.122	1.114
1.091	1.086	1.141	0.931	0.723	0.934	1.060	1.047	0.800	0.889
1.012	0.695	0.869	0.734	1.131	0.993	0.762	0.814	1.108	0.805
1.223	1.024	0.884	0.799	0.870	0.898	0.621	0.818	1.113	1.286
1.052	0.678	1.162	0.808	1.012	0.859	0.951	1.112	1.003	0.972

WEB CASE

Apply your knowledge about hypothesis testing in this Web Case that continues the cereal-fill-packaging dispute Web Case.

Oxford Cereals recently conducted a public experiment in which it claims it has successfully debunked the statements of groups such as the TriCities Consumers Concerned About Cereal Companies That Cheat (TCCACCTC) that claimed that Oxford Cereals was cheating consumers by packaging cereals at less than labeled weights. Review the Oxford Cereals' press release and supporting documents that describe the experiment at the company's Web site (**www.prenhall.com/Springville/OC_WinTrust.htm**) and then answer the following:

1. Are the results of the independent testing valid? Why, or why not? If you were conducting the experiment, is there anything you would change?
2. Do the results support the claim that Oxford Cereals is not cheating its customers?
3. Is the claim of the Oxford CEO that many cereal boxes contain *more* than 368 grams surprising? True?
4. Could there ever be a circumstance in which the results of the public experiment *and* the TCCACCTC's results are both correct? Explain.

REFERENCES

1. Bradley, J. V., *Distribution-Free Statistical Tests* (Englewood Cliffs, NJ: Prentice Hall, 1968).
2. Daniel, W., *Applied Nonparametric Statistics*, 2nd ed. (Boston, MA: Houghton Mifflin, 1990).
3. *Microsoft Excel 2002* (Redmond, WA: Microsoft Corporation, 2001).

Answers to Selected Even-Numbered Problems

For more detailed solutions including explanations, interpretations, and Excel output, see the *Student Solutions Manual*.

2 H_1 is used to denote the alternative hypothesis.

4 β is used to denote the consumer's risk, or the chance of committing a Type II error.

6 α is the probability of making a Type I error.

8 The power of a test is the complement of the probability β of making a Type II error.

10 It is possible to incorrectly fail to reject a false null hypothesis because it is possible that the mean of a single sample will fall in the nonrejection region even though the hypothesized population mean is false.

12 Other things being equal, the closer the *hypothesized* mean is to the *actual* mean, the larger is the risk of committing a Type II error.

14 Under the French judicial system, unlike the one in the United States, the null hypothesis is that the defendant is guilty, the alternative hypothesis is that the defendant is innocent. The meaning of α and β risks would also be switched.

16 H_0: $\mu = 20$ minutes.
H_1: $\mu \neq 20$ minutes.

18 Reject H_0.

20 Reject H_0 if $Z < -2.58$ or $Z > +2.58$.

22 0.0456.

24 0.1676.

26 (a) H_0: $\mu = 70$ pounds. H_1: $\mu \neq 70$ pounds. **(b)** Reject H_0 if $Z < -1.96$ or $Z > +1.96$. Since $Z_{calc} = -1.80$ is between the critical bounds of $\pm$ 1.96, do not reject H_0. **(c)** 0.0718 **(d)** Since $Z_{calc} = -3.60$ is less than the lower critical bound of -1.96, reject H_0. **(e)** Reject H_0 if $Z < -1.96$ or $Z > +1.96$. Since $Z_{calc} = -2.00$ is less than the lower critical bound of -1.96, reject H_0.

28 (a) H_0: $\mu = 375$ hours. H_1: $\mu \neq 375$ hours. **(b)** Since $Z_{calc} = -2.00$ is below the critical bound of -1.96, reject H_0. **(c)** 0.0456 **(d)** $325.50 \leq \mu \leq 374.50$ **(e)** The results are the same.

30 (a) H_0: $\mu = 8$, H_1: $\mu \neq 8$ **(b)** Reject H_0 if $Z <$ 1.96 or $Z >$ 1.96. Since $Z = 0.8$ is between the critical bounds of $\pm$ 1.96, do not reject H_0. **(c)** 0.4229. **(d)** Reject H_0 if $Z < -1.96$ or $Z >$ +1.96. Since $Z_{calc} = -2.40$ is less than the lower critical bound of -1.96, reject H_0. **(e)** Reject H_0 if $Z < -1.96$ or $Z > +1.96$. Since $Z_{calc} = -2.26$ is less than the lower critical bound of -1.96, reject H_0.

32 2.33.

34 -2.33.

36 0.0228.

38 0.0838.

40 0.9162.

42 (a) H_0: 2.8 feet. H_1: $\mu < 2.8$ feet. **(b)** If $Z < -$ 1.645, reject H_0. Since $Z_{calc} = -1.75$ is less than $Z_{crit} = -1.645$, reject H_0. **(c)** If p value < 0.05, reject H_0. Since p value $= 0.0401$ is less than $\alpha = 0.05$, reject H_0. **(d)** The probability of obtaining a sample whose mean is 2.73 feet or less when the null hypothesis is true is 0.0401. **(e)** The conclusions are the same.

44 (a) H_0: $\mu \geq 8$ ounces. H_1: $\mu < 8$ ounces. **(b)** If $Z < -1.645$, reject H_0. Since $Z_{calc} = -0.80$ is greater than $Z_{crit} = -1.645$, do not reject H_0. **(c)** If p value < 0.05, reject H_0. Since p value $= 0.2119$ is greater than $\alpha = 0.05$, do not reject H_0. **(d)** The probability of obtaining a sample whose mean is 7.983 ounces or less when the null hypothesis is true is 0.2119. **(e)** The conclusions are the same.

46 2.00.

48 (a) $t_{crit} = \pm 2.1315$. **(b)** $t_{crit} = +1.7531$.

50 No, you should not use the t test to test the null hypothesis that $\mu = 60$ on a population that is left-skewed because the sample size ($n = 16$) is less than 30. The t test assumes that, if the underlying population is not normally distributed, the sample size is sufficiently large to enable the test statistic t to be influenced by the central limit theorem. If sample sizes are small ($n < 30$), the t test should not be used because the sampling distribution does not meet the requirements of the central limit theorem.

52 (a) H_0: $\mu \leq \$300$. H_1: $\mu > \$300$. If $t >$ 1.2902, reject H_0. Since $t_{calc} = 3.5648$ is above the critical bound of $t = 1.2902$, reject H_0. **(b)** H_0: $\mu \leq \$300$. H_1: $\mu > \$300$. If $t > 1.6604$, reject H_0. Since $t_{calc} = 2.0533$ is above the critical bound of $t = 1.6604$, reject H_0. **(c)** H_0: $\mu \leq \$300$. H_1: $\mu > \$300$. If $t > 1.2902$, reject H_0. Since $t_{calc} = 1.1829$ is below the critical bound of $t = 1.2902$, do not reject H_0.

54 H_0: $\mu = 22.2$, H_1: $\mu \neq 22.2$. Reject H_0 if $|t| > 1.6766$. Since $|t| > 1.6766$, reject H_0.

56 (a) H_0: $\mu \leq 20$, H_1: $\mu > 20$. Reject H_0 if $t >$ 1.6766. Since $t > 1.6766$, reject H_0. **(b)** The population distribution needs to be normal. **(c)** The normal probability plot indicates that the distribution is skewed to the right. **(d)** Even though the population distribution is probably not normally distributed, the result obtained in (a) should still be valid due to the central limit theorem as a result of the relatively large sample size of 50.

58 (a) H_0: $\mu = 45$, H_1: $\mu \neq 45$. Reject H_0 if $|t| > 2.0555$. Since $|t| < 2.0555$, do not reject H_0. **(b)** The population distribution needs to be normal. **(c)** The box-and-whisker plot indicates that the distribution is not symmetrical and is skewed to the right. **(d)** The conclusion reached in (a) is consistent with the findings in problem 3.61.

60 (a) H_0: $\mu = 5.5$, H_1: $\mu \neq 5.5$. Reject H_0 if $|t| > 2.680$. Since $|t| < 2.680$, do not reject H_0. **(b)** $5.46 < \mu < 5.54$. With 99% confidence, one can conclude that the population average amount of tea per bag is somewhere between 5.46 and 5.54 grams. **(c)** The conclusions are the same.

62 0.22.

64 H_0: $p = 0.20$, H_1: $p \neq 0.20$. If $Z < -1.96$ or $Z > 1.96$, reject H_0. Since $Z_{calc} = 1.00$ is between the critical bounds of $Z = \pm 1.96$, do not reject H_0.

66 (a) H_0: $p = 0.50$, H_1: $p \neq 0.50$. If $Z <$ -1.96 or $Z > 1.96$, reject H_0. Since $Z_{calc} =$ 3.4061 is less than the lower critical bounds of $Z = 1.96$, reject H_0. **(b)** 0.00066. **(c)** H_0: $p \leq$ 0.50, H_1: $p > 0.50$. If $Z > 1.645$, reject H_0. Since $Z_{calc} = 3.968$ is greater than the critical bound of $Z = 1.645$, reject H_0. **(d)** 3.6260E-5. **(e)** H_0: $p \leq 0.55$, H_1: $p > 0.55$. If $Z > 1.645$, reject H_0. Since $Z_{calc} = 1.13$ falls below the critical bound of 1.645, do not reject H_0. **(f)** 0.1301.

68 (a) H_0: $p \leq 0.101$, H_1: $p > 0.101$. If $Z >$ 1.645, reject H_0. Since $Z_{calc} = 0.8917$ is below the critical bound of 1.645, do not reject H_0. **(b)** H_0: $p \leq 0.082$, H_1: $p > 0.082$.

If $Z > 1.645$, reject H_0. Since $Z_{calc} = 2.2164$ is above the critical bound of 1.645, reject H_0.

70 (a) $H_0: p \geq 0.22$, $H_1: p < 0.22$. If $Z < -2.3263$, reject H_0. Since $Z_{calc} = -3.3296$ is below the critical bound of $Z = -2.3263$, reject H_0. **(b)** 0.00043.

82 (a) La Quinta Motor Inns commits a Type I error when it purchases a site that is not profitable. If a Type I error has been committed, its cost will be the amount of lost profit the Inns could have earned by using the money to purchase another profitable site. **(b)** Type II error occurs when La Quinta Motor Inns fails to purchase a profitable site. The cost to La Quinta Motor Inns when a Type II error is committed is the loss on the potential amount of profit the site could have generated had the Inns decided to purchase the site. **(c)** The executives at La Quinta Motor Inns are trying to avoid a Type I error by adopting a very stringent decision criterion. Only sites that are classified as capable of generating high profit will be purchased. Sites classified as capable of generating moderate profit will have a much higher likelihood of not being profitable. **(d)** If the executives adopt a less stringent rejection criterion by buying sites that the computer model predicts moderate or large profit, the probability of committing a Type I error will increase. Many more of the sites the computer model predicts that will generate moderate profit may end up not being profitable at all. On the other hand, the less stringent rejection criterion will lower the probability of committing a Type II error since now more potentially profitable sites will be purchased.

84 (a) $H_0: \mu = 10.0$ gallons. $H_1: \mu \neq 10.0$ gallons. If $t < -2.0010$ or $t > 2.0010$, reject H_0. Since the test statistic of $t_{calc} = 3.2483$ is above the upper critical value of $t = 2.0010$, reject H_0. **(b)** 0.0019. **(c)** $H_0: p \geq 0.20$. $H_1: p < 0.20$. If $Z < -1.645$, reject H_0. Since the test statistic of $Z_{calc} = -0.32$ is above the critical bound of $Z = -1.645$, do not reject H_0. **(d)** $H_0: \mu = 10.0$ gallons. $H_1: \mu \neq 10.0$ gallons. If $t < -2.0010$ or $t > 2.0010$, reject H_0. Since the test statistic of $t_{calc} = 0.7496$ is between the critical bounds of $t = \pm 2.0010$, do not reject H_0. **(e)** $H_0: p \geq 0.20$. $H_1: p < 0.20$. If $Z < -1.645$, reject H_0. Since the test statistic of $Z_{calc} = -1.61$ is above the critical bound of $Z = -1.645$, do not reject H_0.

86 (a) $H_0: \mu \geq 5$ minutes. $H_1: \mu < 5$ minutes. If $t < -1.7613$, reject H_0. Since the test statistic of $t_{calc} = -1.6867$ is above the critical bound of $t = -1.7613$, do not reject H_0. **(b)** To perform the t-test on the population mean, you must assume that the observed sequence in which the data were collected is random and that the data are approximately normally distributed. **(c)** With the exception of one extreme point, the data are approximately normally distributed. **(d)** 0.0569.

88 (a) $H_0: \mu = 30$, $H_1: \mu \neq 30$. Reject H_0 if $|t| > 2.0555$, $d.f. = 26$. Since $|t| > 2.0555$, reject H_0. **(b)** In order for the t-test to be valid, the data are assumed to be independently drawn from a population that is normally distributed. **(c)** The box-and-whisker plot suggests that the distribution of the data is skewed to the right. With a sample size of 27, the t distribution will not provide a good approximation to the sampling distribution of the sample mean. **(d)** The right-skewed distribution of the data makes the t-test in part (a) invalid. The manager should be very careful not to make any misleading statement and should, instead, request another test with a much larger data set to be performed in order for the central limit theorem to have a chance to operate.

90 (a) $H_0: \mu \geq 0.35$, $H_1: \mu < 0.35$. Reject H_0 if $t < -1.690$, $d.f. = 35$. Since $t = -1.4735 > 1.690$, do not reject H_0. **(b)** 0.0748. **(c)** $H_0: \mu \geq 0.35$, $H_1: \mu < 0.35$. Reject H_0 if $t < -1.6973$, $d.f. = 30$. Since $t = -3.10 < -1.6973$, reject H_0. **(d)** 0.0021. **(e)** In order for the t-test to be valid, the data are assumed to be independently drawn from a population that is normally distributed. Since the sample sizes are 36 and 31, respectively, which are considered large enough, the t distribution will provide a good approximation to the sampling distribution of the mean as long as the population distribution is not very skewed. **(f)** Both box-and-whisker plots suggest that the data are skewed slightly to the right, more so for the Boston shingles. To be more conservative, larger sample sizes should be used in both samples.

92 (a) $H_0: \mu = 0.5$, $H_1: \mu \neq 0.5$. Reject H_0 if $|t| > 1.9741$. Since $t = -21.60 < 1.9741$, reject H_0. **(b)** p-value is virtually zero. **(c)** $H_0: \mu = 0.5$, $H_1: \mu \neq 0.5$. Reject H_0 if $|t| > 1.977$, $d.f. = 139$. Since $t = -27.19 < -1.977$, reject H_0. **(d)** p-value is virtually zero. **(e)** In order for the t-test to be valid, the data are assumed to be independently drawn from a population that is normally distributed. Since the sample sizes are 170 and 140, respectively, which are considered large enough, the t distribution will provide a good approximation to the sampling distribution of the mean even if the population is not normally distributed.

Excel Handbook for Hypothesis Testing: One Sample Tests

EH1 PERFORMING THE Z TEST OF HYPOTHESIS FOR THE MEAN (σ KNOWN)

To perform a Z test of the hypothesis for the mean (σ known), implement a worksheet that features the **NORMSINV** and **NORMSDIST** functions. These functions are entered as **NORMSINV ($P< X$)** where $P < X$ is the area under the curve that is less than X, and **NORMSDIST(Z *value*)**.

Table EH1 contains the design for a **Z Test** worksheet that performs a Z test of the hypothesis for the mean for the cereal-filling process problem, shown in Figure 5. This design uses the NORMSINV function to determine the lower and upper critical values and uses the NORMSDIST function to determine the p-value from the Z value calculated in cell B12. This design displays a message advising whether or not to reject the null hypothesis in cell A18 by using the IF function to compare the p-value in cell B17 to the level of significance in cell B5.

When implementing this design, enter the formula for cell A18, typeset in Table EH1 as three lines, as one continuous line.

Table EH1
Z Test worksheet design

	A	B
1	Cereal-Filling Hypothesis Test	
2		
3	Data	
4	Null Hypothesis μ=	368
5	Level of Significance	0.05
6	Population Standard Deviation	15
7	Sample Size	25
8	Sample Mean	372.5
9		
10	Intermediate Calculations	
11	Standard Error of the Mean	=B6/SQRT(B7)
12	Z Test Statistic	=(B8 – B4)/B11
13		
14	Two-Tailed Test	
15	Lower Critical Value	=NORMSINV(B5/2)
16	Upper Critical Value	=NORMSINV(1 – B5/2)
17	*p*-Value	=2 * (1 – NORMSDIST(ABS(B12)))
18	=IF(B17 < B5, "Reject the null hypothesis", "Do not reject the null hypothesis")	

For problems that require one-tailed tests, use the alternative entries for rows 14 through 17 shown in either Table EH2L or Table EH2U (Row 18 is left empty for both one-tail tests.) These alternatives use the functions found in rows 14 through 18 in Table EH1 in similar ways to determine whether or not to reject the null hypothesis. When implementing one of these alternatives, enter the formula containing the IF function in cell A17, typeset as three lines, as one continuous line.

Table EH2L
Lower-tail alternate entries for *Z* Test worksheet design

	A	B
14	Lower-Tail Test	
15	Lower Critical Value	=NORMSINV(B5)
16	*p*-Value	=NORMSDIST(B12)
17	=IF(B16 < B5, "Reject the null hypothesis", "Do not reject the null hypothesis")	

Table EH2U
Upper-tail alternate entries for *Z* Test worksheet design

	A	B
14	Upper-Tail Test	
15	Upper Critical Value	=NORMSINV(1 – B5)
16	*p*-Value	=1 – NORMSDIST(B12)
17	=IF(B16 < B5, "Reject the null hypothesis", "Do not reject the null hypothesis")	

EH2 PERFORMING THE *t* TEST OF HYPOTHESIS FOR THE MEAN (σ UNKNOWN)

To perform a *t* test of the hypothesis for the mean (σ unknown), implement a worksheet that features the **TINV** and **TDIST** functions. These functions are entered as **TINV(1-*confidence level, degrees of freedom*)**, and **TDIST(ABS(*t*), *degrees of freedom, tails*)**, where ABS(*t*) is the absolute value of the *t* test statistic, and *tails* is either 1, for a one-tail test, or 2 for a two-tail test.

Table EH2 contains the design for a ***t* Test** worksheet that performs a *t* test of the hypothesis for the mean amount per sales invoice for Saxon Home Improvement Company, shown in Figure 10. This design assumes that the invoice sample data have been entered into column A of a worksheet named **Data**. This design uses the TINV function to return the *t* values for the lower and upper critical values

Table EH3
t Test worksheet design

	A	B
1	Mean Amount Per Invoice Hypothesis	
2		
3	Data	
4	Null Hypothesis μ=	120
5	Level of Significance	0.05
6	Sample Size	=COUNT(Data!A:A)
7	Sample Mean	=AVERAGE(Data!A:A)
8	Sample Standard Deviation	=STDEV(Data!A:A)
9		
10	Intermediate Calculations	
11	Standard Error of the Mean	=B8/SQRT(B6)
12	Degrees of Freedom	=B6 – 1
13	*t* Test Statistic	=(B7 – B4)/B11
14		
15	Two-Tail Test	
16	Lower Critical Value	=–(TINV(B5, B12))
17	Upper Critical Value	=TINV(B5, B12)
18	*p*-Value	=TDIST(ABS(B13), B12, 2)
19	=IF(B18 < B5, "Reject the null hypothesis", "Do not reject the null hypothesis")	

and uses the TDIST function to return probability values. This design displays a message advising whether or not to reject the null hypothesis in cell A18 by using the IF function to compare the *p*-value in cell B18 to the level of significance in cell B5.

When implementing this design, enter the formula for cell A19, typeset as three lines, as one continuous line and use the Symbol font to enter the μ symbol in cell A4.

For problems that require one-tailed tests, implement the additional entries for cell range D15:E18 shown in Table EH4 and use the alternative entries for rows 15 through 18 shown in either Table EH5L or Table EH5U. (Row 19 is left empty for both one-tail tests.) These alternatives use the functions found in rows 15 through 19 in Table EH3 in similar ways to determine whether or not to reject the null hypothesis. (Note that *tails* is set to 1 in TDIST function used in cell E17.) When implementing one of these alternatives, enter the formula containing the IF function in cell A18, typeset as three lines, as one continuous line.

Table EH4
Cell range D15:E18 additions to *t* Test worksheet design, required for all one-tail *t* Tests (column C is blank)

	D	E
15	Calculations Area	
16	For one-tailed tests:	
17	TDIST value	=TDIST(ABS(B13), B12, 1)
18	1 – TDIST value	=1 – E17

Table EH5L
Lower-tail alternate entries for *t* Test worksheet design

	A	B
15	Lower-Tail Test	
16	Lower Critical Value	= –(TINV(2 * B5, B12))
17	*p*-Value	=IF(B13 < 0, E17, E18)
18	=IF(B17 < B5, "Reject the null hypothesis", "Do not reject the null hypothesis")	

Table EH5U
Upper-tail alternate entries for *t* Test worksheet design

	A	B
15	Upper-Tail Test	
16	Upper Critical Value	=(TINV(2 * B5, B12))
17	*p*-Value	=IF(B13 < 0, E18, E17)
18	=IF(B17 < B5, "Reject the null hypothesis", "Do not reject the null hypothesis")	

EH3 PERFORMING THE *Z* TEST OF HYPOTHESIS FOR THE PROPORTION

To perform a *Z* test of hypothesis for the proportion, implement a worksheet that features the **NORMSINV** and **NORMSDIST** functions. These functions are entered as **NORMSINV(*P* < *X*)**, where $P < X$ is the area under the curve that is less than X, and **NORMSDIST(Z *value*)**.

Table EH6 contains the design for a ***Z* Test** worksheet that performs a *Z* test of the hypothesis for the proportion of home-based business owned by females, shown in Figure 15. Similar to the design discussed in section EH1, this design uses the NORMSINV function to determine the lower and upper critical values and uses the NORMSDIST function to determine the *p*-value from the *Z* value calculated in cell B12. This design displays a message advising whether or not to reject the null hypothesis in cell A19 by using the IF function to compare the *p*-value in cell B17 to the level of significance in cell B5.

Table EH6
Z Test sheet design

	A	B
1	Ownership Proportion Hypothesis	
2		
3	Data	
4	Null Hypothesis *p*=	0.5
5	Level of Significance	0.05
6	Number of Successes	369
7	Sample Size	899
8		
9	Intermediate Calculations	
10	Sample Proportion	=B6/B7
11	Standard Error	=SQRT(B4 * (1 – B4)/B7)
12	Z Test Statistic	=(B10 – B4)/B11
13		
14	Two-Tail Test	
15	Lower Critical Value	=NORMSINV(B5/2)
16	Upper Critical Value	=NORMSINV(1 – B5/2)
17	*p*-Value	=2 * (1 – NORMSDIST(ABS(B12)))
18	=IF(B17 < B5, "Reject the null hypothesis", "Do not reject the null hypothesis")	

When implementing this design, enter the formula for cell A18, typeset in Table EH6 as three lines, as one continuous line.

For problems that require one-tailed tests, use the alternative entries for rows 14 through 17 shown in either Table EH7L or Table EH7U. (Row 18 is left empty for both one-tail tests.) These alternatives use the functions found in rows 14 through 18 in Table EH6 in similar ways to determine whether or not to reject the null hypothesis. When implementing one of these alternatives, enter the formula containing the IF function in cell A17, typeset as three lines, as one continuous line.

Table EH7L
Lower-tail alternate entries for *Z* Test worksheet design

	A	B
14	Lower-Tail Test	
15	Lower Critical Value	=NORMSINV(B5)
16	*p*-Value	=NORMSDIST(B12)
17	=IF(B16 < B5, "Reject the null hypothesis", "Do not reject the null hypothesis")	

Table EH7U
Upper-tail alternate entries for *Z* Test worksheet design

	A	B
14	Upper-Tail Test	
15	Upper Critical Value	=NORMSINV(1 – B5)
16	*p*-Value	=1 – NORMSDIST(B12)
17	=IF(B16 < B5, "Reject the null hypothesis", "Do not reject the null hypothesis")	

Simple Linear Regression

USING STATISTICS: Forecasting Sales for a Clothing Store

LEARNING OBJECTIVES

- To use regression analysis to predict the value of a dependent variable based on an independent variable
- To understand the meaning of the regression coefficients b_0 and b_1
- To evaluate the assumptions of regression analysis and know what to do if the assumptions are violated
- To make inferences about the slope and correlation coefficient
- To estimate mean values and predict individual values

USING STATISTICS

Forecasting Sales for a Clothing Store

Sunflowers, a chain of women's clothing stores, has improved its market share over the past 25 years by increasing the number of stores in the chain. Currently, however, the chain does not have a systematic approach to selecting new sites. Instead, sites are selected subjectively, based primarily on the availability of a great lease or the perception of an ideal location. As the director of special projects and planning, you need to develop a strategic plan for opening several new stores. This plan must be able to forecast annual sales for all potential stores under consideration. You believe that the size of the store is significantly related to its success and want to incorporate this information into the decision-making process. How can you develop a statistical model that will allow you to forecast annual sales based on the size of the proposed new stores?

INTRODUCTION

In this chapter, one or more variables will be used to obtain a prediction of a numerical variable of interest.

Regression analysis is used primarily for the purpose of prediction. In this chapter you will learn how to develop a regression model to predict the values of a **dependent** or **response variable** based on the values of one **explanatory** or **independent variable**. In addition to prediction, regression analysis is used to study the relationship between a dependent variable and an independent variable and to quantify the effect that changes in the independent variable have on the dependent variable. In this chapter the focus is on **simple linear regression**—a statistical technique that uses a *single* numerical independent variable X to predict the numerical dependent variable Y.[1]

[1]Regression models in which the dependent variable is categorical involve the use of logistic regression (see reference 4).

1 TYPES OF REGRESSION MODELS

The **scatter diagram** is used to plot the relationship between an X variable on the horizontal axis and a Y variable on the vertical axis. The nature of the relationship between two variables can take many forms, ranging from simple to extremely complicated mathematical functions. The simplest relationship consists of a straight-line or **linear relationship**. An example of this relationship is shown in Figure 1.

FIGURE 1
A positive straight-line relationship

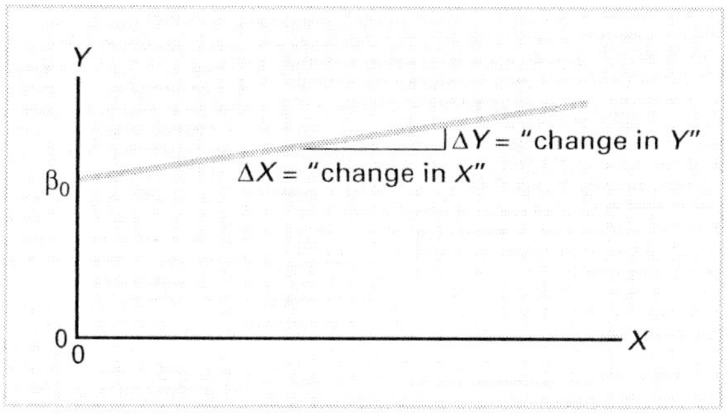

The straight-line (linear) model can be represented as shown in Equation (1).

SIMPLE LINEAR REGRESSION MODEL

$$Y_i = \beta_0 + \beta_1 X_i + \varepsilon_i \tag{1}$$

where

β_0 = Y intercept for the population
β_1 = slope for the population
ε_i = random error in Y for observation i

In this model, the **slope** of the line, β_1, represents the expected change in Y per unit change in X. It represents the average amount that Y changes (either positively or negatively) for a particular unit change in X. The ***Y* intercept** β_0 represents the average value of Y when X equals 0. The last component of the model, ε_i, represents the random error in Y for each observation i that occurs. In other words, ε_i is the vertical distance Y_i is above or below the line of regression.

The selection of the proper mathematical model depends on the distribution of the X and Y values on the scatter diagram. This can be seen from an examination of panels A–F in Figure 2.

In panel A note that the values of Y are generally increasing linearly as X increases. This panel is similar to Figure 3, which illustrates the positive relationship between the square footage (i.e., store size available) and the annual sales at branches of the Sunflowers women's clothing store.

Panel B is an example of a negative linear relationship. As X increases, the values of Y are generally decreasing. An example of this type of relationship might be the price of a particular product and the amount of sales.

The data in panel C show a positive curvilinear relationship between X and Y. The values of Y increase as X increases, but this increase tapers off beyond certain values of X. An example of this positive curvilinear relationship might be the age and maintenance cost of a machine. As a machine gets older, the maintenance cost may rise rapidly at first but then level off beyond a certain number of years.

Panel D shows a parabolic or U-shaped relationship between X and Y. As X increases, at first Y generally decreases; but as X continues to increase, Y not only stops decreasing but actually increases above its minimum value. An example of this type of relationship might be the number of errors per hour at a task and the number of hours worked. The number of errors per hour decreases as the individual becomes more proficient at the task but then it increases beyond a certain point because of factors such as fatigue and boredom.

Panel E indicates an exponential relationship between X and Y. In this case, Y, in general, decreases very rapidly as X first increases, but then it decreases much less rapidly as X increases further. An example of this exponential relationship could be the resale value of an automobile and its age. In the first year the resale value drops drastically from its original price; however, the resale value then decreases much less rapidly in subsequent years.

FIGURE 2
Examples of types of relationships found in scatter diagrams

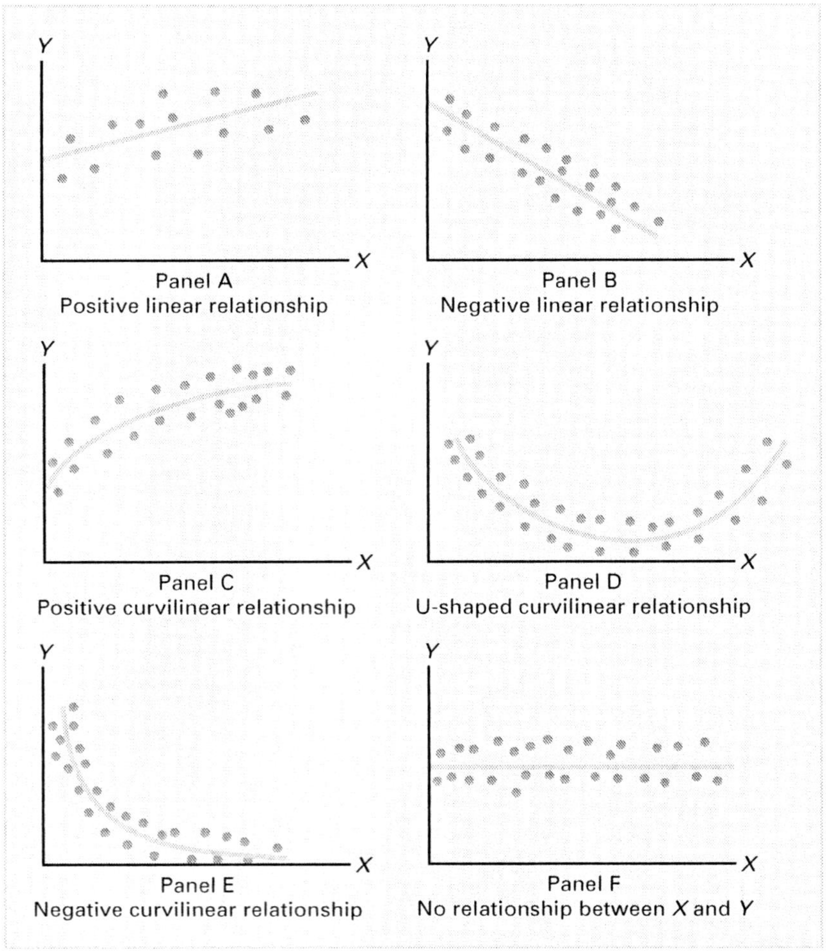

FIGURE 3
Scatter diagram obtained from Microsoft Excel for the site selection data

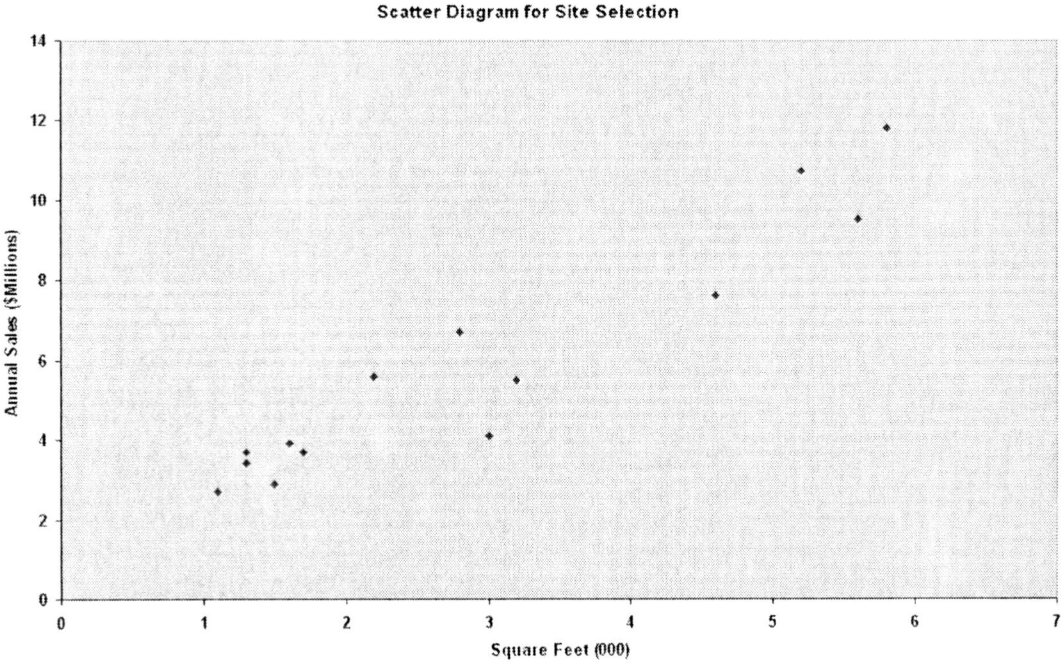

Finally panel F shows a set of data in which there is very little or no relationship between X and Y. High and low values of Y appear at each value of X.

In this section a variety of different models that could be used to represent the relationship between two variables has been examined briefly. Although scatter diagrams can be useful in showing visually the mathematical form of a relationship, more sophisticated statistical procedures are available to determine the most appropriate model for a set of variables. The rest of this chapter discusses the models that fit linear relationships between variables.

2 DETERMINING THE SIMPLE LINEAR REGRESSION EQUATION

In the Using Statistics scenario, the stated goal is to forecast annual sales for all new stores based on store size. To examine the relationship between the store size (i.e., square footage) and its annual sales, a sample of 14 stores was selected. The results for these 14 stores are summarized in Table 1.

TABLE 1

Square footage (thousands of square feet) and annual sales (in millions of dollars) for sample of 14 branches of the Sunflowers women's clothing store chain

SITE.xls

Store	Square Feet (000)	Annual Sales (in Millions of Dollars)	Store	Square Feet (000)	Annual Sales (in Millions of Dollars)
1	1.7	3.7	8	1.1	2.7
2	1.6	3.9	9	3.2	5.5
3	2.8	6.7	10	1.5	2.9
4	5.6	9.5	11	5.2	10.7
5	1.3	3.4	12	4.6	7.6
6	2.2	5.6	13	5.8	11.8
7	1.3	3.7	14	3.0	4.1

The scatter diagram for the data in Table 1 is shown in Figure 3. An examination of Figure 3 indicates an increasing relationship between square feet (X) and annual sales (Y). As the size of the store as measured by its square footage increases, annual sales increase approximately as a straight line. Based on this, you can assume that a straight line provides a useful mathematical model of this relationship. Now you need to determine the specific straight line or linear model that is the *best* fit to these data.

The Least-Squares Method

In the preceding section, a statistical model is hypothesized to represent the relationship between two variables, square footage and sales, in the Sunflowers chain of women's clothing stores. However, as shown in Table 1 above, data have been obtained from only a random sample of the population of stores. If certain assumptions are valid (see section 4), the sample Y intercept b_0 and the sample slope b_1 can be used as estimates of the respective population parameters β_0 and β_1. Thus, the simple linear regression equation used to estimate the linear regression model is shown in Equation (2).

SIMPLE LINEAR REGRESSION EQUATION

The predicted value of Y equals the Y intercept plus the slope times the value of X.

$$\hat{Y}_i = b_0 + b_1 X_i \quad \textbf{(2)}$$

where

$\hat{Y}_i$ = predicted value of Y for observation i
X_i = value of X for observation i

Equation (2) requires the determination of two **regression coefficients**—b_0 (the sample Y intercept) and b_1 (the sample slope)—in order to predict values of Y. Once b_0 and b_1 are obtained, the straight line is known and can be plotted on the scatter diagram. Then a visual comparison can be made of how well this particular straight line fits the original data by observing whether the original data lie close to the line or deviate greatly from the line.

Simple linear regression analysis is concerned with finding the straight line that fits the data best. The best fit could be defined in a variety of ways Perhaps the simplest way might involve finding the straight line for which the differences between the actual values (Y_i) and the values that would be predicted from the line of regression ($\hat{Y}_i$) are as small as possible. However, because these differences are positive for some observations and negative for other observations instead, an approach called the least squares method that minimizes the sum of the squared differences is used:

Since $\hat{Y}_i = b_0 + b_1X_i$,

$$\sum_{i=1}^{n}(Y_i - \hat{Y}_i)^2 = \sum_{i=1}^{n}[Y_i - (b_0 + b_1X_i)]^2$$

Since this equation has two unknowns, b_0 and b_1, the sum of the squared differences is a function of the sample Y-intercept b_0 and the sample slope b_1. The **least-squares method** determines the values of b_0 and b_1 that minimize the sum of squared differences. Any values for b_0 and b_1 other than those determined by the least-squares method result in a greater sum of squared differences between the actual value of Y and the predicted value of Y.

In this text, Excel spreadsheet software is used to perform the calculations involved in the least-squares method. However, to understand how the results displayed in the Excel output have been computed, see section 10 where many of the computations involved are illustrated. Figure 4 represents output from Microsoft Excel for the data of Table 1.

FIGURE 4
Microsoft Excel output for the site selection problem

	A	B	C	D	E	F	G
1	**Site Selection Analysis**						
2							
3	*Regression Statistics*						
4	**Multiple R**	0.95088					
5	**R Square**	0.90418					
6	**Adjusted R Square**	0.89619					
7	**Standard Error**	0.96638 (S_{YX})					
8	**Observations**	14 (n)					
9							
10	**ANOVA**						
11		*df*	*SS*	*MS*	*F*	*Significance F* (p-value)	
12	**Regression**	1	105.74761 (SSR)	105.74761	113.23351	1.82269E-07	
13	**Residual**	12	11.20668 (SSE)	0.93389			
14	**Total**	13	116.95429 (SST)				
15							
16		*Coefficients*	*Standard Error*	*t Stat*	*P-value*	*Lower 95%*	*Upper 95%*
17	**Intercept**	0.96447 (b_0)	0.52619	1.83293	0.09173	-0.18200	2.11095
18	**Square Feet**	1.66986 (b_1)	0.15693	10.64112	0.00000	1.32795	2.01177

VISUAL EXPLORATIONS: Exploring Simple Linear Regression Coefficients

Use the Visual Explorations Simple Linear Regression procedure to produce a fitted line of regression that is as close as possible to the least-squares regression line. Open the **Visual Explorations.xla** macro workbook and:

Select **VisualExplorations | Simple Linear Regression** from the Microsoft Excel menu bar.

When a scatter diagram of the site selection data of Table 1 with an unfitted line of regression appears (shown below):

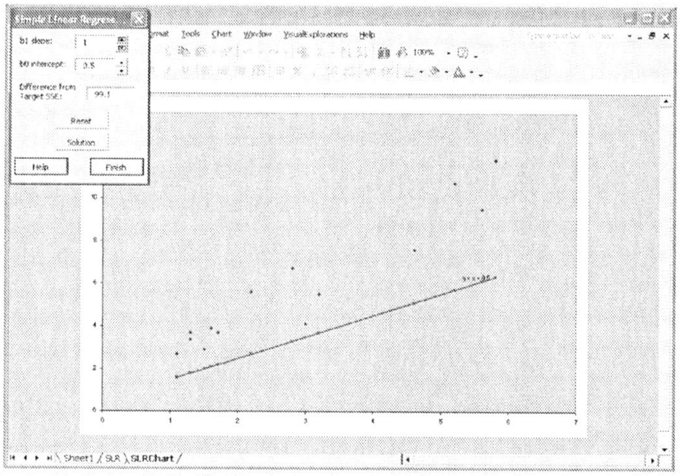

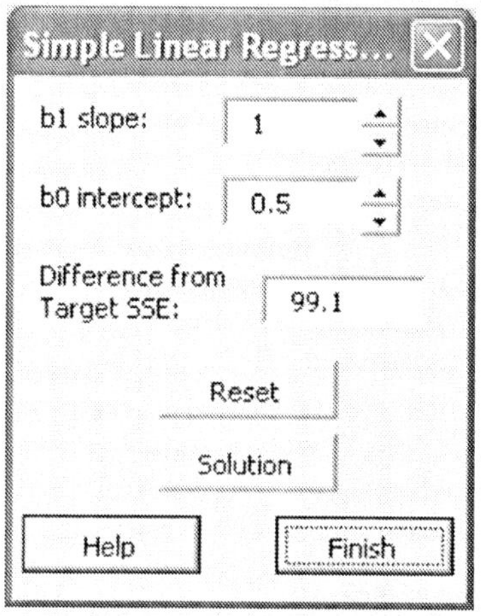

Click the spinner buttons in the floating control panel (see closeup above) to change the values for b_1, the slope of the line, and b_0, the Y intercept of the line of regression.

Try to produce a fitted line of regression that is as close as possible to the least-squares regression line, using the chart display and the Difference from Target SSE value as feedback (see further on for an explanation of *SSE*).

Click **Finish** when you are done with this exploration.

You can also click the **Reset** button to reset the values in the floating control panel, **Help** for more information about the problem, or **Solution** to reveal the actual fitted line of regression.

Using your own regression data. You can also use Visual Explorations to explore fitting a line of regression that is as close as possible to the least-squares regression line for your own set of data. To do this, open the **Visual Explorations.xla** workbook (if it is not already open) and then:

Select **VisualExplorations | Simple Linear Regression with your worksheet data**.

In the Simple Linear Regression (your data) dialog box (shown below):

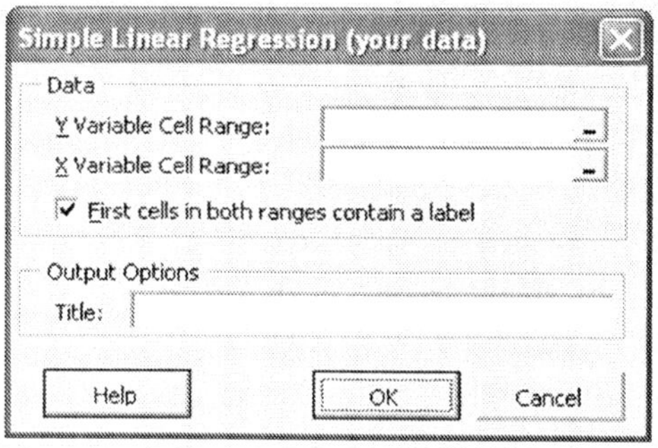

Enter the *Y* variable cell range in the **Y Variable Cell Range** edit box.

Enter the *X* variable cell range in the **X Variable Cell Range** edit box.

Select the **First cells in both ranges contain a label** check box, if appropriate.

Enter a title in the **Title** edit box.

Click the **OK** button.

When the scatter diagram of your data with an unfitted line of regression appears, follow the instructions in the first part of this section to produce a fitted line of regression that is as close as possible to the least-squares regression line.

From Figure 4, observe that $b_1 = 1.670$ and $b_0 = 0.964$. Thus the equation for the best straight line [see Equation (2)] for these data is

$$\hat{Y}_i = 0.964 + 1.670X_i$$

The slope b_1 was computed as +1.670. This means that for each increase of 1 unit in X, the average value of Y is estimated to increase by 1.670 units. In other words, for each increase of 1.0 thousand square feet in the size of the store, the expected annual sales are estimated to increase by 1.670 millions of dollars. Thus, the slope represents the portion of the annual sales that are estimated to vary according to the size of the store.

The Y intercept b_0 was computed to be +0.964 (millions of dollars). The Y intercept represents the average value of Y when X equals 0. Because the square footage size of the store cannot be 0, this Y intercept has no practical interpretation. Moreover, the Y intercept for this example is outside the range of the observed values of the X variable, and therefore interpretations of the value of b_0 should be made cautiously. The line of regression for these data, along with the actual observations, is depicted in Figure 5.

FIGURE 5

Scatter diagram and line of regression obtained from Microsoft Excel for site selection data

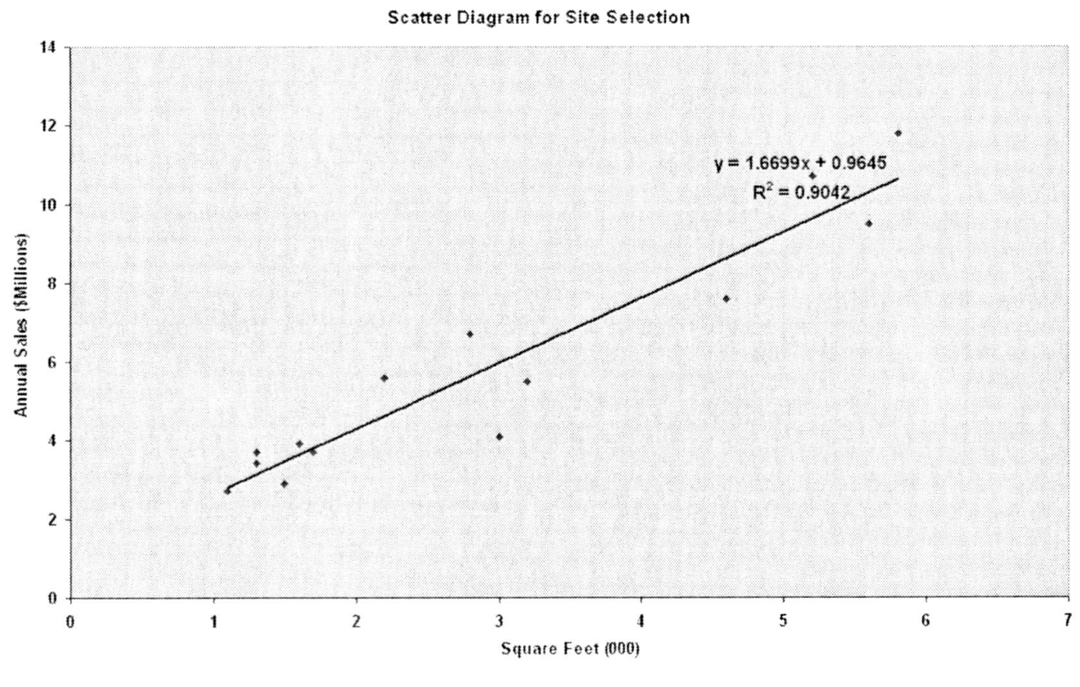

To illustrate a situation where there is a direct interpretation for the Y intercept b_0, see Example 1.

EXAMPLE 1

INTERPRETING THE Y INTERCEPT b_0 AND THE SLOPE b_1

Suppose that an economist wanted to use the yearly rate of productivity growth in the United States (X) to predict the percentage change in the Standard & Poor's index of 500 stocks. A regression model was fit based upon annual data for a period of 50 years with the following results:

$$\hat{Y}_i = -5.0 + 7X_i$$

What is the interpretation of the Y intercept b_0 and the slope b_1?

SOLUTION

The Y intercept $b_0 = -5.0$ indicates that when the rate of productivity growth is zero, the expected percentage change in the Standard & Poor's stock index is −5.0, meaning that the index is predicted to decrease by 5% during a year in which the productivity growth is zero. The slope $b_1 = 7$ indicates that for each increase in productivity of 1%, the expected change in the Standard & Poor's stock index is predicted to be +7.0, meaning that the index is predicted to increase by 7% for each 1% increase in productivity.

Return to the Using Statistics scenario concerning the Sunflowers clothing stores. The regression model that has been fit to the site selection data can now be used to predict the average annual sales as illustrated in Example 2.

EXAMPLE 2

PREDICTING AVERAGE ANNUAL SALES BASED ON SQUARE FOOTAGE

Use the regression equation to predict the average annual sales for a store with 4,000 square feet.

SOLUTION

You can determine the predicted value by substituting $X = 4$ (thousands of square feet) into the regression equation,

$$\hat{Y}_i = 0.964 + 1.670X_i$$
$$\hat{Y}_i = 0.964 + 1.670(4) = 7.644 \text{ or } \$7{,}644{,}000$$

Thus, the predicted average annual sales of a store with 4,000 square feet is $7,644,000.

Predictions in Regression Analysis: Interpolation versus Extrapolation

When using a regression model for prediction purposes, it is important that you consider only the **relevant range** of the independent variable in making predictions. This relevant range includes all values from the smallest to the largest X used in developing the regression model. Hence, when predicting Y for a given value of X, you can interpolate within this relevant range of the X values, but you should not extrapolate beyond the range of X values. When you use the square footage to predict annual sales, note from Table 1 that the square footage (in thousands of square feet) varies from 1.1 to 5.8. Therefore, predictions of annual sales should be made *only* for stores whose size is between 1.1 and 5.8 thousands of square feet. Any prediction of annual sales for stores whose size is outside this range presumes that the fitted relationship holds outside the range of 1.1 to 5.8 thousands of square feet. For example, you cannot extrapolate the linear relationship beyond 5,800 square feet in Example 1. It would be improper to use the regression equation to forecast the sales for a new store containing 8,000 square feet. It is quite possible that store size has a point of diminishing returns. If that were true as square footage increases beyond 5,800 square feet, the effect on sales might become smaller and smaller.

CHAPTER 12.xls

*Retrieve the Figure 12.3, Figure 12.4, and Figure 12.5 worksheets of the **Chapter 12.xls** workbook to view scatter diagrams and regression analysis worksheets for the site selection data of Table 1 similar to the ones on the previous pages.*

Excel Strategies Performing Simple Linear Regression

You perform a simple linear regression analysis and generate a scatter diagram with a fitted line of regression by using the combination of the Data Analysis Regression procedure and the Chart Wizard and then modifying the chart produced to include a line of regression. PHStat2 can do all but the last task for you in a single step. (Some of the regression statistics produced are discussed in section 3.)

For example, to perform a simple linear regression analysis for the site selection data of Table 1, open to the **Data** worksheet of the **Chapter 12.xls** workbook and use one of these strategies:

Using Excel with PHStat2

Use the PHStat2 Simple Linear Regression procedure to calculate the regression statistics and to generate a scatter diagram.

Select **PHStat | Regression | Simple Linear Regression**.

In the Simple Linear Regression dialog box (shown at right):

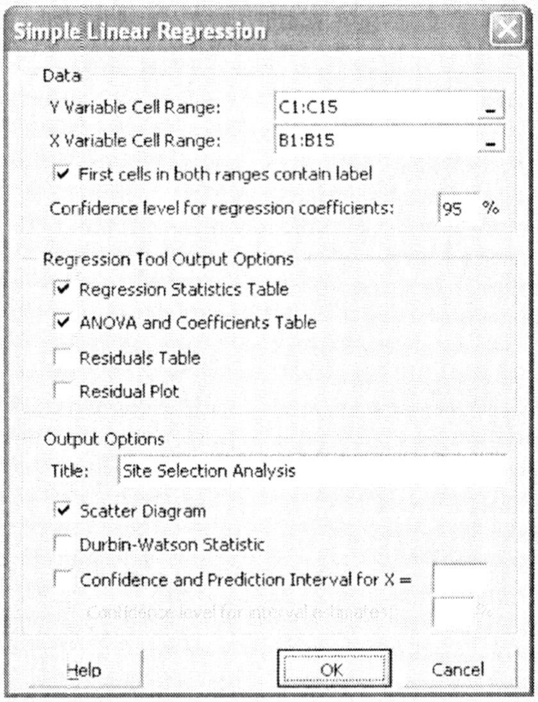

Enter **C1:C15** in the **Y Variable Cell Range** edit box.

Enter **B1:B15** in the **X Variable Cell Range** edit box.

Select the **First cells in both ranges contain label** check box.

Enter **95** in the **Confidence level for regression coefficients** edit box.

Select the **Regression Statistics Table** and the **ANOVA and Coefficients Table** check boxes.

Enter a title in the **Title** edit box.

Select the **Scatter Diagram** check box.

Click the **OK** button.

This procedure generates a worksheet that does ***not*** *dynamically change. Therefore, you will need to rerun the procedure if you make any changes to the underlying sample data in order to update the results.*

To add a line of regression to the new scatter diagram, follow the instructions in section EH2 at the end of this chapter.

Using Excel

Follow the instructions for the tasks listed below to perform a simple linear regression analysis and generate a scatter diagram with a fitted line of regression. Generating simple linear regression analysis and generating a scatter diagram are not dependent on each other and can be done alone or at different times.

Perform Simple Linear Regression Analysis Task. Follow the instructions of section EH1 to perform a simple linear regression analysis for the site selection data of Table 1.

Generate Scatter Diagram Task. Use the Chart Wizard to generate a scatter diagram. Open to the **Data** worksheet of the **Chapter 12.xls** workbook, select **Insert | Chart** and make these entries in the Chart Wizard dialog boxes:

Step 1 dialog box. Select the **Standard Types** tab and then select **XY (Scatter)** from the Chart type: list box. Select the first (top) **Chart sub-type** choice, labeled as **Scatter. Compares pairs of values**, when selected, and click the **Next** button.

Step 2 dialog box. Select the **Data Range** tab. Enter **B1:C15** in the Data range edit box. Select the **Columns** option button in the **Series in** group and click **Next**.

Step 3 dialog box. Select the **Titles** tab. Enter **Scatter Diagram** as the **Chart title, Square Feet** in the **Value (X) axis** edit box, and **Annual Sales ($Millions)** in the **Value (Y) axis** edit box. Select, in turn, the **Axes, Gridlines, Legend**, and **Data Table** tabs and adjust settings as discussed in Exhibit EP6 of the Excel Primer, and click **Next.** (Consult your instructor if you require the Excel Primer.)

Step 4 dialog box. Select the **As new sheet** option button, enter a descriptive and unique sheet name, and click the **Finish** button to generate the chart.

The Chart Wizard always assumes that the first column in the Data range cell range contains values for the X variable (as it does in the preceding example). For similar problems in which the values for the Y variable appear first, copy the Y variable values to a column to the right of the X values column before using the Chart Wizard. If the scatter diagram contains Y values that are less than zero, see the end of this chapter for instructions to relocate the X axis of the chart.

Adding Line of Regression Task. Follow the instructions of section EH2 to add a fitted line of regression to the scatter diagram produced in the previous task.

PROBLEMS FOR SECTION 2

Learning the Basics

1 Fitting a straight line to a set of data yields the following regression equation

$$\hat{Y}_i = 2 + 5X_i$$

a. Interpret the meaning of the Y intercept b_0.
b. Interpret the meaning of the slope b_1.
c. Predict the average value of Y for $X = 3$.
If the values of X range from 2 to 25, should you use this model to predict the average value of Y when X equals
d. 3?
e. −3?
f. 0?
g. 24?
h. 26?

2 Fitting a straight line to a set of data yields the following regression equation

$$\hat{Y}_i = 16 - 0.5X_i$$

a. Interpret the meaning of the Y intercept b_0.
b. Interpret the meaning of the slope b_1.
c. Predict the average value of Y for $X = 6$.

Applying the Concepts

Problem 3 can be solved manually or by using Microsoft Excel. We recommend that Microsoft Excel be used to solve Problems 4–8.

3 The marketing manager of a large supermarket chain would like to determine the effect of shelf space on the sales of pet food. A random sample of 12 equal-sized stores is selected, with the following results: **PETFOOD.xls**

Store	Shelf Space X (Feet)	Weekly Sales, Y (Hundreds of Dollars)
1	5	1.6
2	5	2.2
3	5	1.4
4	10	1.9
5	10	2.4
6	10	2.6
7	15	2.3
8	15	2.7
9	15	2.8
10	20	2.6
11	20	2.9
12	20	3.1

a. Set up a scatter diagram.
b. Assuming a linear relationship, use the least-squares method to find the regression coefficients b_0 and b_1.
c. Interpret the meaning of the slope b_1 in this problem.
d. Predict the average weekly sales (in hundreds of dollars) of pet food for stores with 8 feet of shelf space for pet food.
e. Suppose that sales in store 12 are 2.6. Repeat (b)–(d) with this value and compare the results to your original results.
f. How much shelf space would you recommend that the marketing manager allocate to pet food? Explain.

4 The owner of an intracity moving company typically has his most experienced manager predict the total number of labor hours that will be required to complete an upcoming move. This approach has proved useful in the past, but he would like to be able to develop a more accurate method of predicting the labor hours by using the amount of cubic feet moved. In a preliminary effort to provide a more accurate method, he has collected data for 36 moves MOVING.xls in which the travel time was an insignificant portion of the labor hours worked.

a. Set up a scatter diagram.

b. Assuming a linear relationship, use the least-squares method to find the regression coefficients b_0 and b_1.

c. Interpret the meaning of the slope b_1 in this problem.

d. Predict the labor hours for moving 500 cubic feet.

e. What factors besides the cubic feet moved might affect labor hours?

5 A large mail-order house believes that there is an association between the weight of the mail it receives and the number of orders to be filled. It would like to investigate the relationship in order to predict the number of orders based on the weight of the mail. From an operational perspective, knowledge of the number of orders will help in the planning of the order-fulfillment process. A sample of 25 mail shipments is selected within a range of 200 to 700 pounds. The results are as follows. **MAIL.xls**

Weight of Mail (Pounds)	Orders (In Thousands)	Weight of Mail (Pounds)	Orders (In Thousands)
216	6.1	432	13.6
283	9.1	409	12.8
237	7.2	553	16.5
203	7.5	572	17.1
259	6.9	506	15.0
374	11.5	528	16.2
342	10.3	501	15.8
301	9.5	628	19.0
365	9.2	677	19.4
384	10.6	602	19.1
404	12.5	630	18.0
426	12.9	652	20.2
482	14.5		

a. Set up a scatter diagram.

b. Assuming a linear relationship, use the least-squares method to find the regression coefficients b_0 and b_1.

c. Interpret the meaning of the slope b_1 in this problem.

d. Predict the average number of orders when the weight of the mail is 500 pounds.

6 A company that has the distribution rights to home video sales of previously released movies would like to be able to estimate the number of units that it can expect to sell. Data are available for 30 movies **MOVIE.xls** that indicate the box office gross (in millions of dollars) and the number of home videos sold (in thousands).

a. Set up a scatter diagram.

b. Use the least-squares method to find the regression coefficients b_0 and b_1.

c. State the simple linear regression equation.

d. Interpret the meaning of b_0 and b_1 in this problem.

e. Predict the video unit sales for a movie that had a box office gross of $20 million.

f. What other factors in addition to box office gross might be useful in predicting video unit sales?

7 An agent for a residential real estate company in a large city would like to be able to predict the monthly rental cost for apartments based on the size of the apartment as defined by square footage. A sample of 25 apartments in a particular residential neighborhood was selected, and the information gathered revealed the following: **RENT.xls**

Apartment	Monthly Rent ($)	Size (Square Feet)	Apartment	Monthly Rent ($)	Size (Square Feet)
1	950	850	14	1,800	1,369
2	1,600	1,450	15	1,400	1,175
3	1,200	1,085	16	1,450	1,225
4	1,500	1,232	17	1,100	1,245
5	950	718	18	1,700	1,259
6	1,700	1,485	19	1,200	1,150
7	1,650	1,136	20	1,150	896
8	935	726	21	1,600	1,361
9	875	700	22	1,650	1,040
10	1,150	956	23	1,200	755
11	1,400	1,100	24	800	1,000
12	1,650	1,285	25	1,750	1,200
13	2,300	1,985			

a. Set up a scatter diagram.

b. Use the least-squares method to find the regression coefficients b_0 and b_1.

c. State the simple linear regression equation.

d. Interpret the meaning of b_0 and b_1 in this problem.

e. Predict the monthly rental cost for an apartment that has 1,000 square feet.

f. Why would it not be appropriate to use the model to predict the monthly rental for apartments that have 500 square feet?

g. Your friends Jim and Jennifer are considering signing a lease for an apartment in this residential neighborhood. They are trying to decide between two apartments, one with 1,000 square feet for a monthly rent of $1,275 and the other with 1,200 square feet for a monthly rent of $1,425. What would you recommend to them? Why?

8 The data in the file **HARDNESS.xls** provide measurements on the hardness and tensile strength for 35 specimens of die-cast aluminum. It is believed that hardness (measured in Rockwell E units) can be used to predict tensile strength (measured in thousands of pounds per square inch).

a. Set up a scatter diagram.

b. Assuming a linear relationship, use the least-squares method to find the regression coefficients b_0 and b_1.

c. Interpret the meaning of the slope b_1 in this problem.

d. Predict the average tensile strength for die-cast aluminum that has a hardness of 30 Rockwell E units.

3 MEASURES OF VARIATION

Obtaining the Sum of Squares

To examine the ability of the independent variable to predict the dependent variable in the statistical model, several measures of variation need to be developed. The first measure, the **total sum of squares (*SST*)**, is a measure of variation of the Y_i values around their mean $\bar{Y}$. In a regression analysis, the **total variation** or total sum of squares can be subdivided into **explained variation** or **regression sum of squares (*SSR*)**, that which is attributable to the relationship between *X* and *Y*, and **unexplained variation** or **error sum of squares (*SSE*)**, that which is attributable to factors other than the relationship between *X* and *Y*. These different measures of variation are shown in Figure 6.

FIGURE 6
Measures of variation

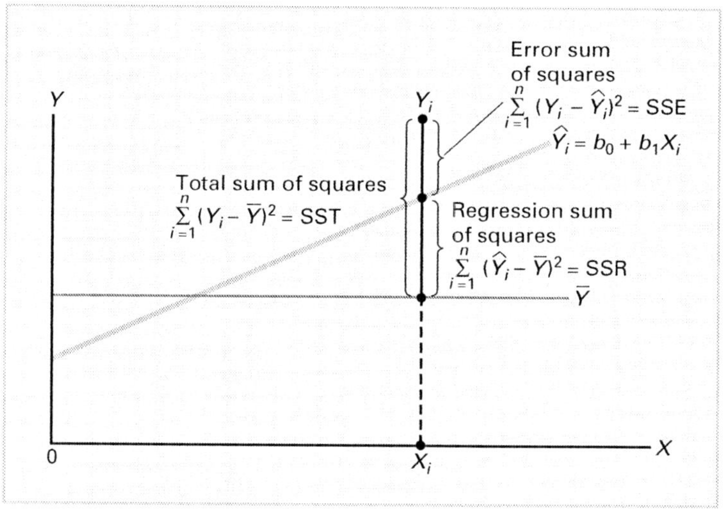

The regression sum of squares (*SSR*) represents the difference between $\hat{Y}_i$ (the value of *Y* that is predicted from the regression equation) and $\bar{Y}$ (the average value of *Y*). The error sum of squares (*SSE*) represents the part of the variation in *Y* that is not explained by the regression. It is based on the difference between Y_i and $\hat{Y}_i$. These measures of variation are defined as shown in Equations (3), (4), (5), and (6).

MEASURES OF VARIATION IN REGRESSION

Total sum of squares = regression sum of squares + error sum of squares.

$$SST = SSR + SSE \tag{3}$$

TOTAL SUM OF SQUARES (*SST*)

The total sum of squares (*SST*) is equal to the sum of the squared differences between each observed *Y* value and $\bar{Y}$, the average value of *Y*.

$$SST = \text{total variation or total sum of squares} = \sum_{i=1}^{n}(Y_i - \bar{Y})^2 \tag{4}$$

REGRESSION SUM OF SQUARES (*SSR*)

The regression sum of squares (*SSR*) is equal to the sum of the squared differences between the predicted value of *Y* and $\overline{Y}$, the average value of *Y*.

$$SSR = \text{explained variation or regression sum of squares} \qquad (5)$$
$$= \sum_{i=1}^{n} (\hat{Y}_i - \overline{Y})^2$$

ERROR SUM OF SQUARES (*SSE*)

The error sum of squares (*SSE*) is equal to the sum of the squared differences between the observed value of *Y* and the predicted value of *Y*.

$$SSE = \text{unexplained variation or error sum of squares} \qquad (6)$$
$$= \sum_{i=1}^{n} (Y_i - \hat{Y}_i)^2$$

Figure 7 represents the sum of squares portion of the Microsoft Excel output for the site selection problem.

FIGURE 7

Sum of squares obtained from Microsoft Excel for the site selection problem

SSR

10	**ANOVA**					
11		*df*	*SS*	*MS*	*F*	*Significance F*
12	**Regression**	1	105.74761	105.74761	113.23351	1.82269E-07
13	**Residual**	12	11.20668	0.93389		
14	**Total**	13	116.95429			

SST SSE

Observe that

$$SSR = 105.7476, \quad SSE = 11.2067, \quad \text{and } SST = 116.9543$$

Note also, from Equation (3), that

$$SST = SSR + SSE$$
$$116.9543 = 105.7476 + 11.2067$$

The *SST* is equal to 116.9543. This amount is subdivided into the sum of squares that is explained by the regression (*SSR*), equal to 105.7476, and the sum of squares that is unexplained by the regression (*SSE*), equal to 11.2067.

SCIENTIFIC NOTATION

In some data sets with a large number of significant digits, the output may be displayed using a numerical format known as *scientific notation*. This type of format is used to display very small or very large values. The number after the letter E represents the number of digits that the decimal point needs to be moved to the left (for a negative number) or to the right (for a positive number). For example, the number 3.7431E+02 means that the decimal point should be moved two places to the right, producing the number 374.31. The number 3.7431E–02 means that the decimal point should be moved two places to the left, producing the number 0.037431. When scientific notation is used, fewer significant digits are usually displayed, and the numbers may appear to be rounded.

The Coefficient of Determination

By themselves, SSR, SSE, and SST provide little that can be directly interpreted. However, the ratio of the regression sum of squares (SSR) to the total sum of squares (SST) provides a measure of the usefulness of the regression equation. This ratio is called the **coefficient of determination** r^2 and is defined in Equation (7).

COEFFICIENT OF DETERMINATION

The coefficient of determination is equal to the regression sum of squares (i.e., explained variation) divided by the total sum of squares (i.e., total variation).

$$r^2 = \frac{\text{regression sum of squares}}{\text{total sum of squares}} = \frac{SSR}{SST} \tag{7}$$

The coefficient of determination measures the proportion of variation in Y that is explained by the independent variable X in the regression model. For the site selection example, with $SSR = 105.7476$; $SSE = 11.2067$; and $SST = 116.9543$;

$$r^2 = \frac{105.7476}{116.9543} = 0.904$$

Therefore, 90.4% of the variation in annual sales can be explained by the variability in the size of the store as measured by the square footage. This is an example of a strong positive linear relationship between two variables because the use of a regression model has reduced the variability in predicting annual sales by 90.4%. Only 9.6% of the sample variability in annual sales is due to factors other than what is accounted for by the linear regression model that uses only square footage.

Figure 8 represents the coefficient of determination portion of the Microsoft Excel output for the site selection problem.

FIGURE 8

Partial regression output obtained from Microsoft Excel for the site selection problem

3	*Regression Statistics*	
4	**Multiple R**	**0.95088**
5	**R Square**	**0.90418**
6	**Adjusted R Square**	**0.89619**
7	**Standard Error**	**0.96638**
8	**Observations**	**14.00000**

S_{YX}

Standard Error of the Estimate

Although the least-squares method results in the line that fits the data with the minimum amount of variation, unless all the observed data points fall on a straight line, the regression equation is not a perfect predictor. Just as all data values cannot be expected to be exactly equal to their arithmetic mean, neither can they be expected to fall exactly on the regression line. Therefore, a statistic that measures the variability of the actual Y values from the predicted Y values needs to be developed, in the same way that the standard deviation is developed as a measure of the variability of each observation around its mean. This standard deviation around the line of regression is called the **standard error of the estimate**.

The variability around the line of regression is illustrated in Figure 5 for the site selection data. You can see from Figure 5 that, although many of the actual values of Y fall near the predicted line of regression, there are several values above the line of regression as well as below the line of regression.

The standard error of the estimate, represented by the symbol S_{YX}, is defined in Equation (8).

STANDARD ERROR OF THE ESTIMATE

$$S_{YX} = \sqrt{\frac{SSE}{n-2}} = \sqrt{\frac{\sum_{i=1}^{n}(Y_i - \hat{Y}_i)^2}{n-2}} \quad \textbf{(8)}$$

where

Y_i = actual value of Y for a given X_i
$\hat{Y}_i$ = predicted value of Y for a given X_i
SSE = error sum of squares

From Equation (8), with $SSE = 11.2067$,

$$S_{YX} = \sqrt{\frac{11.2067}{14-2}} = 0.9664$$

This standard error of the estimate, equal to 0.9664 millions of dollars (i.e., \$966,400), is labeled Standard Error on the Microsoft Excel output of Figure 8. The standard error of the estimate represents a measure of the variation around the line of regression. It is measured in the same units used by the dependent variable Y. The interpretation of the standard error of the estimate is similar to that of the standard deviation. Just as the standard deviation measures variability around the arithmetic mean, the standard error of the estimate measures variability around the line of regression. As you will see in sections 7 and 8, the standard error of the estimate can be used to determine whether a statistically significant relationship exists between the two variables and also to make inferences about future values of Y.

PROBLEMS FOR SECTION 3

Learning the Basics

9 What does it mean if the coefficient of determination r^2 is equal to 0.80?

10 If $SSR = 36$ and $SSE = 4$, find SST, and then compute the coefficient of determination r^2 and interpret its meaning.

11 If $SSR = 66$ and $SST = 88$, compute the coefficient of determination r^2 and interpret its meaning.

12 If $SSE = 10$ and $SSR = 30$, compute the coefficient of determination r^2 and interpret its meaning.

13 If $SSR = 120$, why is it impossible for SST to equal 110?

Applying the Concepts

Problem 14 can be solved manually or using Microsoft Excel. We recommend that problems 15–19 be solved using Microsoft Excel.

14 In problem 3, the marketing manager used shelf space for pet food to predict weekly sales. **PETFOOD.xls** Using the computer output you obtained to solve that problem,

a. Determine the coefficient of determination r^2 and interpret its meaning.
b. Determine the standard error of the estimate.
c. How useful do you think this regression model is for predicting sales?

15 In problem 4, an owner of a moving company wanted to predict labor hours based on the cubic feet moved. **MOVING.xls** Using the computer output you obtained to solve that problem,

a. Determine the coefficient of determination r^2 and interpret its meaning.
b. Determine the standard error of the estimate.
c. How useful do you think this regression model is for predicting labor hours?

16 In problem 5, the weight of mail was used to predict the number of orders received. **MAIL.xls** Using the computer output you obtained to solve that problem,

a. Determine the coefficient of determination r^2 and interpret its meaning.
b. Find the standard error of the estimate.
c. How useful do you think this regression model is for predicting the number of orders?

17 In problem 6, a company wanted to predict home video sales based on the box office gross of movies. **MOVIE.xls** Using the computer output you obtained to solve that problem,

a. Determine the coefficient of determination r^2 and interpret its meaning.
b. Determine the standard error of the estimate.
c. How useful do you think this regression model is for predicting sales?

18 In problem 7, an agent for a real estate company wanted to predict the monthly rent for apartments based on the size of the apartment. **RENT.xls** Using the computer output you obtained to solve that problem,

a. Determine the coefficient of determination r^2 and interpret its meaning.
b. Determine the standard error of the estimate.
c. How useful do you think this regression model is for predicting monthly rent?

19 In problem 8, hardness was used to predict the tensile strength of die-cast aluminum. **HARDNESS.xls** Using the computer output you obtained to solve that problem,

a. Determine the coefficient of determination r^2 and interpret its meaning.
b. Find the standard error of the estimate.
c. How useful do you think this regression model is for predicting the tensile strength of die-cast aluminum?

4 ASSUMPTIONS

The discussion of hypothesis testing and the analysis of variance emphasized the importance of the assumptions to the validity of any conclusions reached. The assumptions necessary for regression are similar to those of the analysis of variance because both topics fall under the general heading of *linear models* (reference 6).

The three **assumptions of regression** are listed in Exhibit 1.

EXHIBIT 1 ASSUMPTIONS OF REGRESSION

1. Normality of error
2. Homoscedasticity
3. Independence of errors

The first assumption, **normality**, requires that the error around the line of regression be normally distributed at each value of X (see Figure 9 below). Like the t test and the ANOVA F test, regression analysis is fairly robust against departures from the normality assumption. As long as the distribution of the errors around the line of regression at each level of X is not extremely different from a normal distribution, inferences about the line of regression and the regression coefficients will not be seriously affected.

FIGURE 9
Assumptions of regression

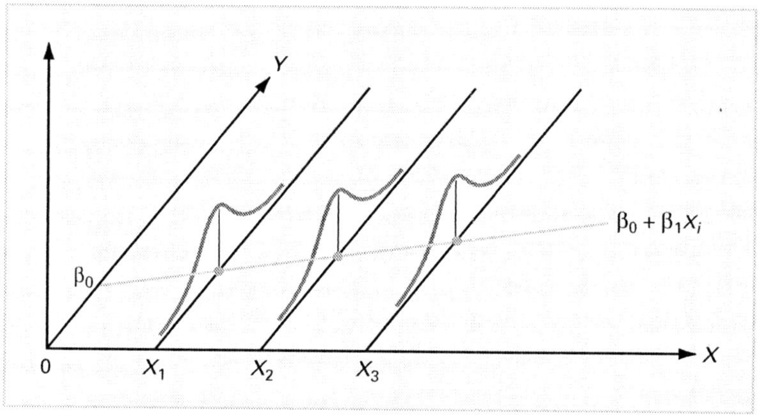

The second assumption, **homoscedasticity**, requires that the variation around the line of regression be constant for all values of X. This means that the errors vary the same amount when X is a low value as when X is a high value (see Figure 9). The homoscedasticity assumption is important for using the least-squares method of determining the regression coefficients. If there are serious departures from this assumption, either data transformations or weighted least-squares methods (see reference 6) can be applied.

The third assumption, **independence of errors**, requires that the errors around the regression line be independent for each value of X. This assumption is particularly important when data are collected over a period of time. In such situations, the errors for a specific time period are often correlated with those of the previous time period.

5 RESIDUAL ANALYSIS

In the preceding discussion of the site selection data, a simple linear regression model has been used. In this section, a graphical approach called **residual analysis** is developed to evaluate whether the regression model that has been fitted to the data is an appropriate model. In addition, residual analysis also enables potential violations of the assumptions of the regression model to be evaluated.

Evaluating the Aptness of the Fitted Model

The **residual** or estimated error value e_i is defined as the difference between the observed (Y_i) and predicted ($\hat{Y}_i$) values of the dependent variable for a given value of X_i. Graphically a residual is depicted on a scatter diagram as the vertical distance between an observed value of Y and the line defined by the simple regression equation. Numerically the residual is defined in Equation (9).

THE RESIDUAL

The residual is equal to the difference between the observed value of *Y* and the predicted value of *Y*.

$$e_i = Y_i - \hat{Y}_i \quad \textbf{(9)}$$

The aptness of the fitted regression model is evaluated by plotting the residuals on the vertical axis against the corresponding X_i values of the independent variable on the horizontal axis. If the fitted model is appropriate for the data, there will be no apparent pattern in this plot. However, if the fitted model is not appropriate, there will be a relationship between the X_i values and the residuals e_i. Such a pattern can be observed in Figure 10. Panel A depicts a situation in which, although

FIGURE 10
Studying the appropriateness of the simple linear regression model

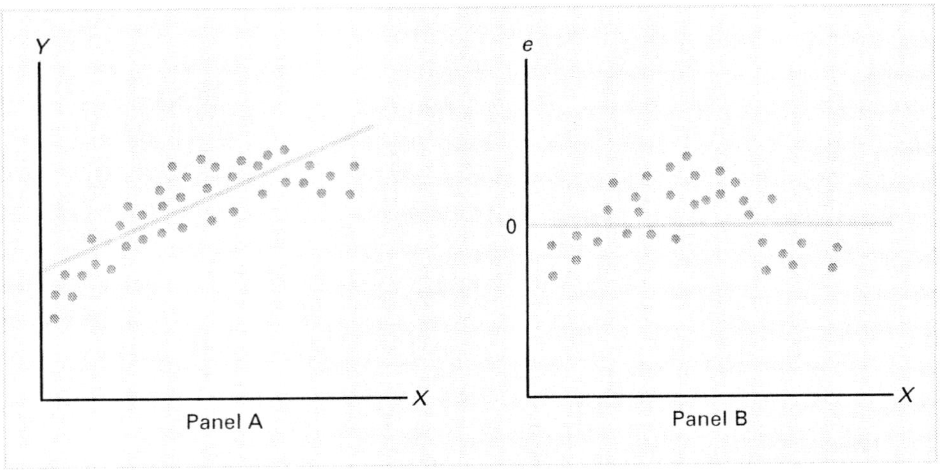

there is an increasing trend in Y as X increases, the relationship seems curvilinear because the upward trend decreases for increasing values of X. Thus, a curvilinear or quadratic model between the two variables seems more appropriate than a simple linear regression model. This quadratic effect is highlighted in panel B where there is a clear relationship between X_i and e_i. By plotting the residuals, the linear trend of X with Y has been filtered out or removed, thereby exposing the lack of fit in the simple linear model. Thus, a quadratic model is a better fit and should be used in place of the simple linear model.

To determine whether the simple linear regression model is appropriate, return to the evaluation of the site selection data. Figure 11 provides the predicted and residual values of the response variable (annual sales) obtained from Microsoft Excel.

FIGURE 11
Residual statistics obtained from Microsoft Excel for the site selection problem

22	**RESIDUAL OUTPUT**		
23			
24	*Observation*	*Predicted Annual Sales*	*Residuals*
25	1	3.803239598	-0.103239598
26	2	3.636253367	0.263746633
27	3	5.640088147	1.059911853
28	4	10.31570263	-0.815702635
29	5	3.135294672	0.264705328
30	6	4.638170757	0.961829243
31	7	3.135294672	0.564705328
32	8	2.801322208	-0.101322208
33	9	6.308033074	-0.808033074
34	10	3.469267135	-0.569267135
35	11	9.647757708	1.052242292
36	12	8.645840318	-1.045840318
37	13	10.6496751	1.150324902
38	14	5.974060611	-1.874060611

To determine whether the linear model is appropriate for these data, the residuals have been plotted against the independent variable (store size in thousands of square feet) in Figure 12.

FIGURE 12
Plot obtained from Microsoft Excel of residuals against the square footage of a store for the site selection problem

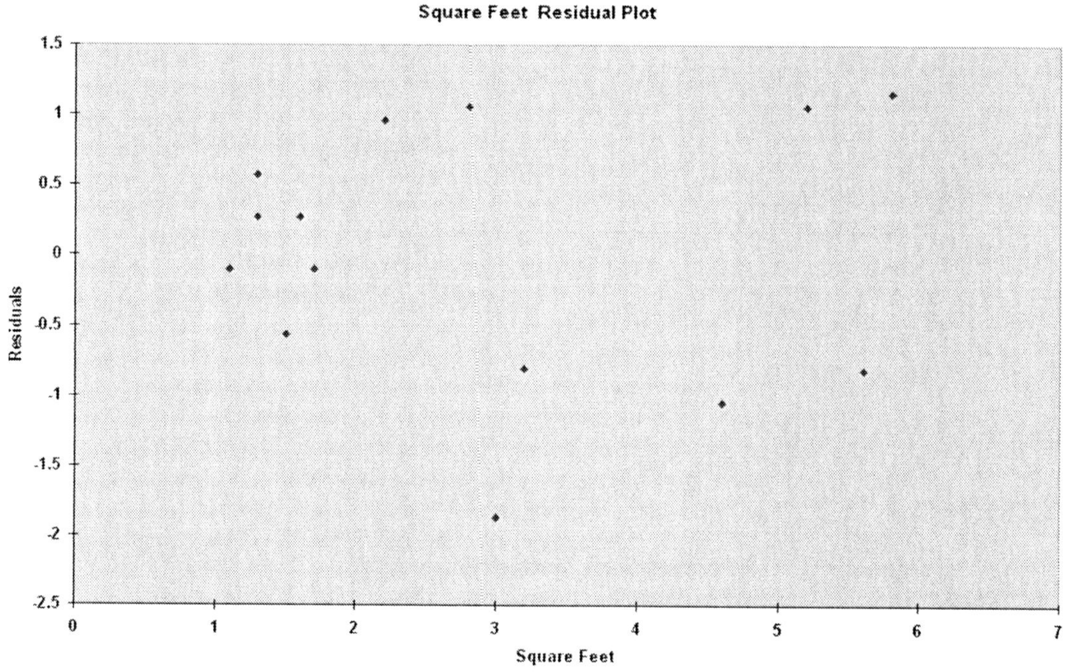

Observe that although there is widespread scatter in the residual plot, there is no apparent pattern or relationship between the residuals and X_i. The residuals appear to be evenly spread above and below 0 for the differing values of X. This result enables you to conclude that the straight-line model is appropriate for the site selection sales data.

Excel Strategies Generating Residual Analyses

You modify the procedure to generate a simple linear regression analysis to generate a residual analysis plot on a separate chart sheet.

For example, to perform a simple linear regression analysis for the site selection data of Table 1, open to the **Data** worksheet of the **Chapter 12.xls** workbook and use one of these modifications:

Using Excel with PHStat2

Follow the "Using Excel with PHStat2" instructions, modifying the instructions to select all four check boxes of the **Regression Tool Output Options** group (**Regression Statistics Table**, **ANOVA and Coefficients Table**, **Residuals Table**, and **Residual Plot**) as is shown below at the left.

Using Excel

Modify the instructions of section EH1 (at the end of this chapter), by selecting the **Residuals** and **Residual Plots** check boxes in the Regression dialog box as is shown below at the right. Then, if appropriate, follow the instructions of section EH3 to modify the residual plot generated if necessary.

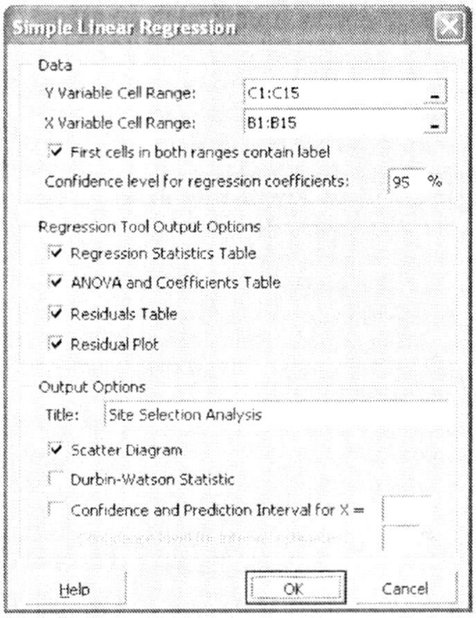

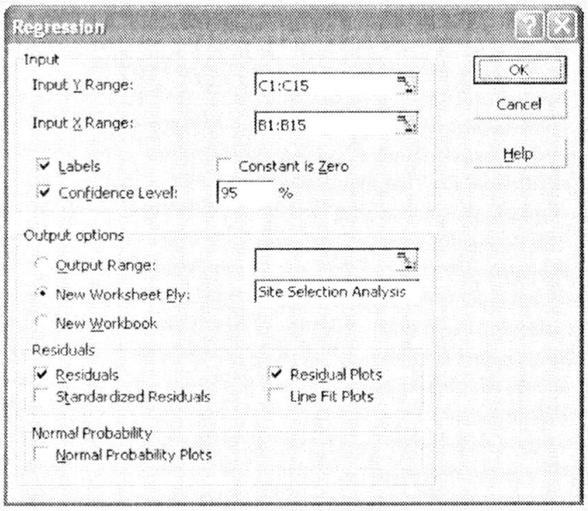

Evaluating the Assumptions

Homoscedasticity The assumption of homoscedasticity can also be evaluated from a plot of the residuals with X_i. For the site selection data of Figure 12 there do not appear to be major differences in the variability of the residuals for different X_i values. Thus, you can conclude that, for this fitted model, there is no apparent violation in the assumption of equal variance at each level of X.

To observe a case in which the homoscedasticity assumption is violated, examine the hypothetical plot of the residuals with X_i in Figure 13. In this plot there appears to be a *fanning* effect in which the variability of the residuals increases as X increases, demonstrating the lack of homogeneity in the variances of Y_i at each level of X.

FIGURE 13
Violation of homoscedasticity

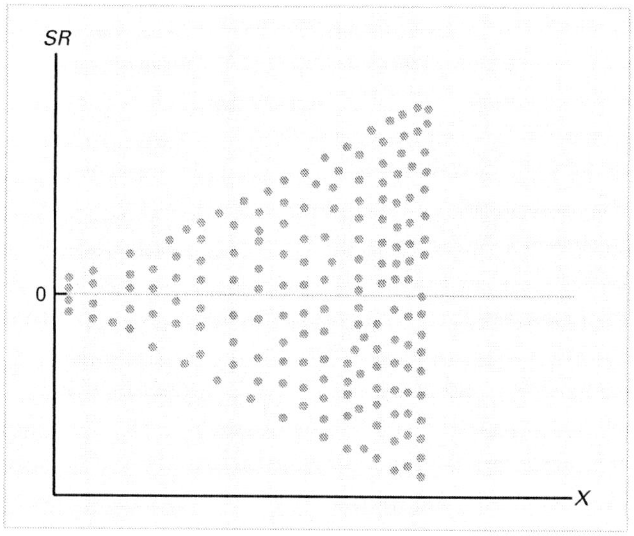

Normality The assumption of normality in the errors around the line of regression can be evaluated from a residual analysis by tallying the residuals into a frequency distribution and displaying the results in a histogram. For the site selection data, the residuals have been tallied into a frequency distribution as indicated in Table 2. (There are an insufficient number of observations to construct a histogram.) The normality assumption can also be evaluated by comparing the actual versus theoretical values of the residuals, or by constructing a normal probability plot of the residuals. Figure 14 contains a normal probability plot of the residuals for the site selection problem.

TABLE 2
Frequency distribution of 14 residual values for the site selection data

Residuals	Frequency
−2.25 but less than −1.75	1
−1.75 but less than −1.25	0
−1.25 but less than −0.75	3
−0.75 but less than −0.25	1
−0.25 but less than +0.25	2
+0.25 but less than +0.75	3
+0.75 but less than +1.25	4
Total	14

It is difficult to evaluate the normality assumption for a sample of only 14 observations regardless of whether a histogram, stem-and-leaf display, box-and-whisker plot, or normal probability plot is obtained. You can see from Figure 14 that the data do not appear to depart substantially from a normal distribution. The robustness of regression analysis to modest departures from normality, along with the small sample size, leads one to conclude that you should not be overly concerned about departures from this normality assumption in the site selection data.

FIGURE 14
Normal probability plot of residuals obtained from Microsoft Excel for the site selection data

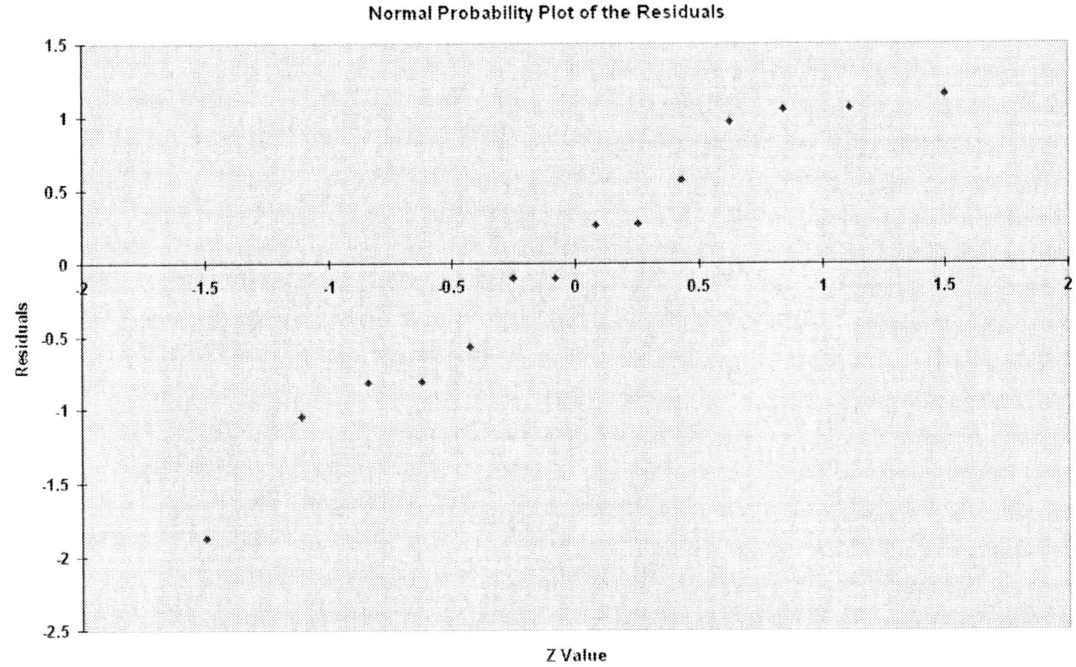

Independence The assumption of independence of the errors can be evaluated by plotting the residuals in the order or sequence in which the observed data were obtained. Data collected over periods of time sometimes exhibit an *autocorrelation* effect among successive observations. In these instances, there exists a relationship between consecutive residuals. Such a relationship, if it exists (which violates the assumption of independence), will be apparent in the plot of the residuals versus the time in which they were collected. This effect can be measured by the Durbin-Watson statistic, which is the subject of section 6. For the site selection data considered thus far in this chapter, the data were collected during the same time period. Therefore the independence assumption does not need to be evaluated.

PROBLEMS FOR SECTION 5

Learning the Basics

20 The following represents the residuals and X values obtained from a regression analysis along with the accompanying residual plot:

X	Residuals
1	0.70
2	-0.78
3	1.03
4	0.33
5	2.39
6	-0.67
7	0.16
8	1.65
9	-1.19
10	0.84
11	0.29
12	-1.28
13	1.21
14	-0.37
15	1.02
16	-0.16
17	1.42
18	-0.71
19	-0.63
20	0.67

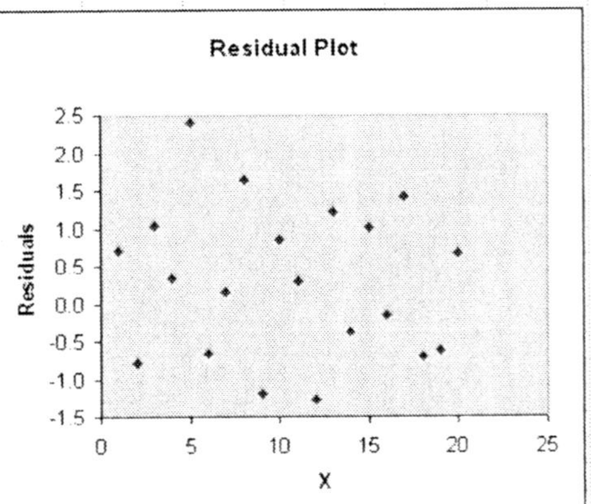

Is there any evidence of a pattern in the residuals? Explain.

21 The following represents the residuals and X values obtained from a regression analysis along with the accompanying residual plot:

X	Residuals
1	0.70
2	1.58
3	1.03
4	0.33
5	-0.39
6	-0.67
7	-0.56
8	-0.65
9	-1.19
10	-0.84
11	-0.29
12	-1.28
13	-0.21
14	-0.37
15	0.22
16	-0.16
17	0.82

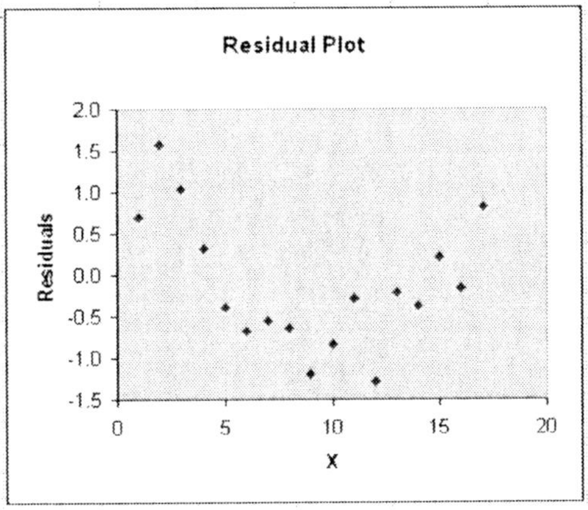

Is there any evidence of a pattern in the residuals? Explain.

Applying the Concepts

Note: We recommend that problems 22–27 be solved using Microsoft Excel.

22 In problem 3, the marketing manager used shelf space for pet food to predict weekly sales. Perform a residual analysis for these data. **PETFOOD.xls** Based on the results obtained,

a. Determine the adequacy of the fit of the model.
b. Evaluate whether the assumptions of regression have been seriously violated.

23 In problem 4, the owner of a moving company wanted to predict labor hours based on the cubic feet moved. Perform a residual analysis for these data. **MOVING.xls** Based on the results obtained,

a. Determine the adequacy of the fit of the model.
b. Evaluate whether the assumptions of regression have been seriously violated.

24 In problem 5, the weight of mail was used to predict the number of orders received. Perform a residual analysis for these data. **MAIL.xls** Based on the results obtained,

a. Determine the adequacy of the fit of the model.
b. Evaluate whether the assumptions of regression have been seriously violated.

25 In problem 6, a company wanted to predict home video sales based on the box office gross. Perform a residual analysis for these data. **MOVIE.xls** Based on the results obtained,

a. Determine the adequacy of the fit of the model.
b. Evaluate whether the assumptions of regression have been seriously violated.

26 In problem 7, an agent for a real estate company wanted to predict the monthly rent for apartments based on the size of the apartment. Perform a residual analysis for these data. **RENT.xls** Based on the results obtained,

a. Determine the adequacy of the fit of the model.
b. Evaluate whether the assumptions of regression have been seriously violated.

27 In problem 8, the hardness was used to predict the tensile strength of die-cast aluminum. Perform a residual analysis for these data. **HARDNESS.xls** Based on the results obtained,

a. Determine the adequacy of the fit of the model.
b. Evaluate whether the assumptions of regression have been seriously violated.

6 MEASURING AUTOCORRELATION: THE DURBIN-WATSON STATISTIC

One of the basic assumptions of the regression model is the independence of the errors. This assumption is often violated when data are collected over sequential periods of time because a residual at any one point in time may tend to be similar to residuals at adjacent points in time. Such a pattern in the residuals is called **autocorrelation**. When substantial autocorrelation is present in a set of data, the validity of a regression model can be in serious doubt.

Residual Plots to Detect Autocorrelation

As mentioned in section 5, one way to detect autocorrelation in a set of data is to plot the residuals in time order. If a positive autocorrelation effect is present, clusters of residuals with the same sign will be present and an apparent pattern will be readily detected. If negative autocorrelation exists, residuals will tend to jump back and forth from positive to negative to positive, and so on. This type of pattern is very rarely seen in regression analysis; thus, the focus of this section is on positive autocorrelation. To illustrate positive autocorrelation, consider the following example.

The manager of a package delivery store wants to predict weekly sales based on the number of customers making purchases for a period of 15 weeks. In this situation, because data are collected over a period of 15 consecutive weeks at the same store, you need to determine whether autocorrelation is present. The data for this store are summarized in Table 3. Figure 15 represents partial Excel output.

TABLE 3

Customers and sales for period of 15 consecutive weeks

CUSTSALE.xls

Week	Customers	Sales (in thousands of dollars)	Week	Customers	Sales (in thousands of dollars)
1	794	9.33	9	880	12.07
2	799	8.26	10	905	12.55
3	837	7.48	11	886	11.92
4	855	9.08	12	843	10.27
5	845	9.83	13	904	11.80
6	844	10.09	14	950	12.15
7	863	11.01	15	841	9.64
8	875	11.49			

FIGURE 15

Microsoft Excel output for the package delivery store data of Table 3

	A	B	C	D	E	F	G
1	Package Delivery Store Sales Analysis						
2							
3	*Regression Statistics*						
4	Multiple R	0.81083					
5	R Square	0.65745					
6	Adjusted R Square	0.63109					
7	Standard Error	0.93604					
8	Observations	15					
9							
10	ANOVA						
11		*df*	*SS*	*MS*	*F*	*Significance F*	
12	Regression	1	21.86043	21.86043	24.95014	0.00025	
13	Residual	13	11.39014	0.87616			
14	Total	14	33.25057333				
15							
16		*Coefficients*	*Standard Error*	*t Stat*	*P-value*	*Lower 95%*	*Upper 95%*
17	Intercept	-16.03219	5.31017	-3.01915	0.00987	-27.50411	-4.56028
18	Customers	0.03076	0.00616	4.99501	0.00025	0.01746	0.04406

b_0 b_1

Note from Figure 15, that r^2 is 0.657, indicating that 65.7% of the variation in sales can be explained by variation in the number of customers. In addition, the Y intercept b_0 is -16.032, and the slope b_1 is 0.03076. However, before using this model for prediction, you must undertake proper analyses of the residuals. Because the data have been collected over a consecutive period of 15 weeks, in addition to checking the normality and homoscedasticity assumptions, you must investigate the independence of errors assumption. The residuals are plotted versus time in Figure 16 to see whether a pattern exists.

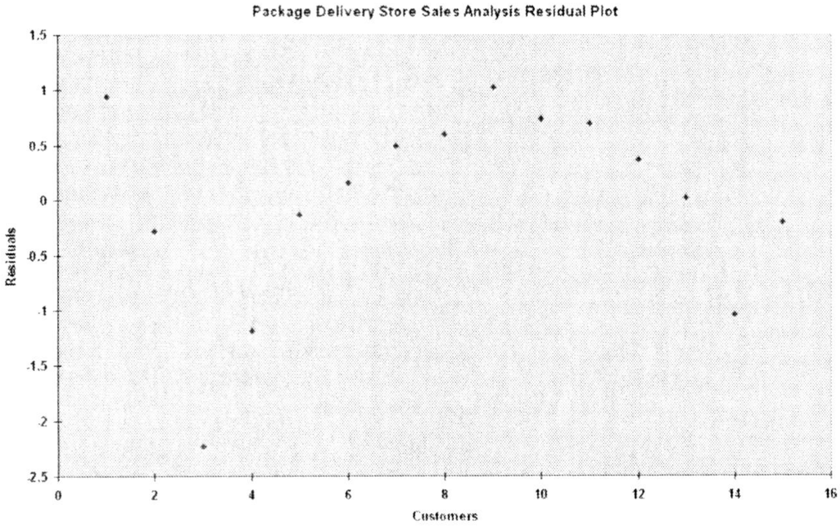

FIGURE 16

Microsoft Excel residual plot over time for the package delivery store data of Table 3

From Figure 16, observe that the points tend to fluctuate up and down in a cyclical pattern. This cyclical pattern provides strong cause for concern about the autocorrelation of the residuals and, hence, a violation of the assumption of independence of the residuals.

The Durbin-Watson Statistic

In addition to residual plots, autocorrelation can also be detected and measured by using the **Durbin-Watson statistic**. This statistic measures the correlation between each residual and the residual for the time period immediately preceding the one of interest. The Durbin-Watson statistic D is defined in Equation (10).

DURBIN-WATSON STATISTIC

$$D = \frac{\sum_{i=2}^{n}(e_i - e_{i-1})^2}{\sum_{i=1}^{n} e_i^2} \tag{10}$$

where

e_i = residual at the time period i

To better understand the Durbin-Watson statistic, you need to examine the composition of the D statistic presented in Equation (10). The numerator $\sum_{i=2}^{n}(e_i - e_{i-1})^2$ represents the squared difference between two successive residuals, summed from the second observation to the nth observation. The denominator $\sum_{i=1}^{n} e_i^2$ represents the sum of the squared residuals. When successive residuals are positively autocorrelated, the value of D will approach 0. If the residuals are not correlated, the value of D will be close to 2. (If there is negative autocorrelation, D will be greater than 2 and could even approach its maximum value of 4.) For the package delivery store data, the Durbin-Watson statistic, $D = 0.883$, is obtained from Microsoft Excel as illustrated in Figure 17.

FIGURE 17

Microsoft Excel output of the Durbin-Watson statistic for the sales data

	A	B
1	**Durbin-Watson Calculations**	
2		
3	Sum of Squared Difference of Residuals	10.05752
4	Sum of Squared Residuals	11.39014
5		
6	**Durbin-Watson Statistic**	**0.88300**

The main issue in using the Durbin-Watson statistic is to determine when the autocorrelation is large enough to make the D statistic fall sufficiently below 2 to conclude that there is significant positive autocorrelation. Whether D is significant is dependent on n, the number of observations being analyzed, and k, the number of independent variables in the model (in simple linear regression, $k = 1$). Table 4 has been extracted from the table of the Durbin-Watson statistic.

TABLE 4

Finding critical values of the Durbin-Watson statistic

	$\alpha = .05$									
	$k = 1$		$k = 2$		$k = 3$		$k = 4$		$k = 5$	
n	d_L	d_U	d_L	d_U	d_L	d_U	d_L	d_U	d_L	d_U
15	1.08	1.36	.95	1.54	.82	1.75	.69	1.97	.56	2.21
16	1.10	1.37	.98	1.54	.86	1.73	.74	1.93	.62	2.15
17	1.13	1.38	1.02	1.54	.90	1.71	.78	1.90	.67	2.10
18	1.16	1.39	1.05	1.53	.93	1.69	.82	1.87	.71	2.06

From Table 4 observe that two values are shown for each combination of α (level of significance), n (sample size), and k (number of independent variables in the model). The first value, d_L, represents the lower critical value. If D is below d_L, you conclude that there is evidence of positive autocorrelation among the residuals. Under such a circumstance, the least-squares method used in this chapter are inappropriate, and alternative methods need to be used (see reference 6). The second value, d_U, represents the upper critical value of D, above which you would conclude that there is no evidence of positive autocorrelation among the residuals. If D is between d_L and d_U, you are unable to arrive at a definite conclusion.

Thus, for the data concerning the package delivery stores, with one independent variable ($k = 1$) and 15 observations ($n = 15$), $d_L = 1.08$ and $d_U = 1.36$. Because $D = 0.883 < 1.08$, you conclude that there is positive autocorrelation among the residuals. The least-squares regression analysis of the data is inappropriate because of the presence of significant positive autocorrelation among the residuals. Alternative approaches discussed in reference 6 need to be considered.

Excel Strategies Calculating the Durbin-Watson Statistic

You perform a simple linear regression analysis by using the Data Analysis Regression procedure and then implement a worksheet that features the **SUMXMY2** and **SUMSQ** functions to calculate the Durbin-Watson statistic for a simple linear regression. PHStat2 can do these tasks for you in a single step.

For example, to calculate this statistic for the simple linear regression analysis for package delivery store sales data in Table 3, open to the **Sales Data** worksheet of the **Chapter 12.xls** workbook and use one of these strategies:

CHAPTER 12.xls

Retrieve the Figure 12.17 worksheet of the ***Chapter 12.xls*** *workbook to view the Durbin-Watson statistic calculations shown on the previous page.*

Using Excel with PHStat2

Use the PHStat2 Simple Linear Regression procedure to calculate the Durbin-Watson statistic for a simple linear regression.

Select **PHStat | Regression | Simple Linear Regression**.

In the Simple Linear Regression dialog box (shown at right):

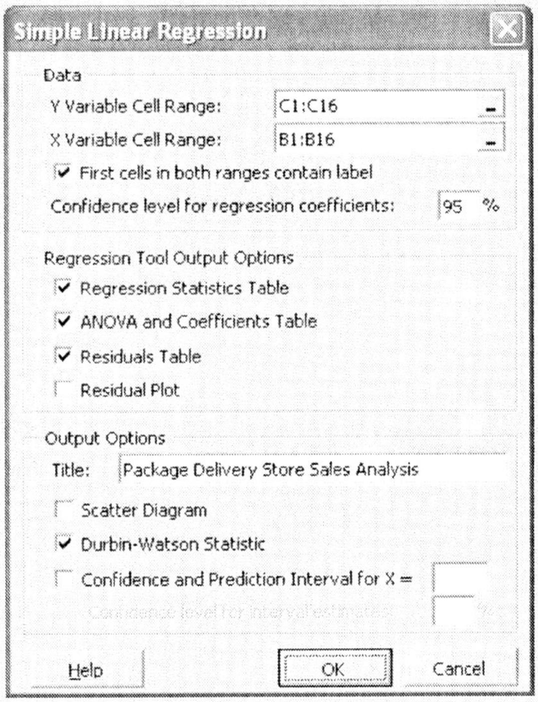

Enter **C1:C16** in the **Y Variable Cell Range** edit box.

Enter **B1:B16** in the **X Variable Cell Range** edit box.

Select the **First cells in both ranges contain label** check box.

Enter **95** in the **Confidence level for regression coefficients** edit box.

Select the **Regression Statistics Table**, **ANOVA and Coefficients Table**, and **Residuals Table** check boxes.

Enter a title in the **Title** edit box.

Select the **Durbin-Watson Statistic** check box.

Click the **OK** button

This procedure generates separate worksheets for the regression statistics and the Durbin-Watson statistic calculations.

This procedure generates a worksheet that does ***not*** *dynamically change. Therefore, you will need to rerun the procedure if you make any changes to the underlying sample data in order to update the Durbin-Watson statistic.*

Using Excel

Follow the instructions of section EH4 at the end of this chapter to manually implement a worksheet to calculate the Durbin-Watson statistic from a worksheet that contains regression statistics (see section EH1).

PROBLEMS FOR SECTION 6

Learning the Basics

28 The residuals for a set of data collected over 10 consecutive time periods are as follows:

Time Period	Residual	Time Period	Residual
1	−5	6	+1
2	−4	7	+2
3	−3	8	+3
4	−2	9	+4
5	−1	10	+5

a. Plot the residuals over time. What conclusions can you reach about the pattern of the residuals over time?
b. Based on (a), what conclusion can you reach about the autocorrelation of the residuals?

29 The residuals for a set of data collected over 15 consecutive time periods are as follows:

Time Period	Residual	Time Period	Residual
1	+4	9	+6
2	−6	10	−3
3	−1	11	+1
4	−5	12	+3
5	+2	13	0
6	+5	14	−4
7	−2	15	−7
8	+7		

a. Plot the residuals over time. What conclusion can you reach about the pattern of the residuals over time?
b. Compute the Durbin-Watson statistic. At the 0.05 level of significance, is there evidence of positive autocorrelation among the residuals?
c. Based on (a) and (b), what conclusion can you reach about the autocorrelation of the residuals?

Applying the Concepts

We recommend that problems 31–34 be solved using Microsoft Excel.

30 In problem 3 (pet food sales), the marketing manager used shelf space for pet food to predict weekly sales.
a. Is it necessary to compute the Durbin-Watson statistic? Explain.
b. Under what circumstances would it be necessary to compute the Durbin-Watson statistic before proceeding with the least-squares method of regression analysis?

31 The owner of a single-family home in a suburban county in the northeastern United States would like to develop a model to predict electricity consumption in his all-electric house (lights, fans, heat, appliances, and so on) based on outdoor atmospheric temperature (in degrees Fahrenheit). Monthly billing data and temperature information were available for a period of 24 consecutive months in the file: **ELECUSE.xls**
a. Set up a scatter diagram.
b. Assuming a linear relationship, use the least-squares method to find the regression coefficients b_0 and b_1.
c. Interpret the meaning of the slope b_1 in this problem.
d. Predict the average kilowatt usage when the average atmospheric temperature is 50 degrees Fahrenheit.
e. Compute the coefficient of determination r^2 and interpret its meaning.
f. Compute the standard error of the estimate.
g. Plot the residuals versus the average atmospheric temperature.
h. Plot the residuals versus the time period.
i. Compute the Durbin-Watson statistic. At the 0.05 level of significance, is there evidence of positive autocorrelation among the residuals?
j. Based on the results of (g)–(i), is there reason to question the validity of the model?

32 A mail-order catalog business that sells personal computer supplies, software, and hardware maintains a centralized warehouse for the distribution of products ordered. Management is currently examining the process of distribution from the warehouse and is interested in studying the factors that affect warehouse distribution costs. Currently, a small handling fee is added to the order, regardless of the amount of the order. Data have been collected over the past 24 months indicating the warehouse distribution costs and the number of orders received. The results are as follows: **WARECOST.xls**

Months	Distribution Cost (Thousands of Dollars)	Number of Orders
1	52.95	4,015
2	71.66	3,806
3	85.58	5,309
4	63.69	4,262
5	72.81	4,296
6	58.44	4,097
7	52.46	3,213
8	70.77	4,809
9	82.03	5,237
10	74.39	4,732
11	70.84	4,413
12	54.08	2,921
13	62.98	3,977
14	72.30	4,428
15	58.99	3,964
16	79.38	4,582
17	94.44	5,582
18	59.74	3,450
19	90.50	5,079
20	93.24	5,735
21	69.33	4,269
22	53.71	3,708
23	89.18	5,387
24	66.80	4,161

a. Set up a scatter diagram.
b. Assuming a linear relationship, use the least-squares method to find the regression coefficients b_0 and b_1.
c. Interpret the meaning of the slope b_1 in this problem.
d. Predict the monthly warehouse distribution costs when the number of orders is 4,500.
e. Compute the coefficient of determination r^2 and interpret its meaning.
f. Compute the standard error of the estimate.
g. Plot the residuals versus the number of orders.
h. Plot the residuals versus the time period.
i. Compute the Durbin-Watson statistic. At the 0.05 level of significance, is there evidence of positive autocorrelation among the residuals?
j. Based on the results of (g)–(i), is there reason to question the validity of the model?

33 A freshly brewed shot of espresso has three distinct components, the heart, body, and cream. The separation of these three components typically lasts only 10–20 seconds. To use the espresso shot in making a latte, cappuccino, or other drinks, the shot must be poured into the beverage during the separation of the heart, body, and cream. If the shot is used after the separation occurs, the drink becomes excessively bitter and acidic, ruining the final drink. Thus, a longer separation time allows the drink-maker more time to pour the shot and ensure that the beverage will meet expectations. An employee at a coffee shop hypothesized that the harder the espresso grounds were tamped down into the portafilter before brewing, the longer the separation time would be. An experiment using 24 observations was conducted to test this relationship. The independent variable Tamp measures the distance in inches between the espresso grounds and the top of the portafilter (i.e., the harder the tamp the larger the distance). The dependent variable Time is the number of seconds the heart, body, and cream are separated (i.e., the amount of time after the shot is poured before it must be used for the customer's beverage). **ESPRESSO.xls**

Shot	Tamp	Time	Shot	Tamp	Time
1	0.20	14	13	0.50	18
2	0.50	14	14	0.50	13
3	0.50	18	15	0.35	19
4	0.20	16	16	0.35	19
5	0.20	16	17	0.20	17
6	0.50	13	18	0.20	18
7	0.20	12	19	0.20	15
8	0.35	15	20	0.20	16
9	0.50	9	21	0.35	18
10	0.35	15	22	0.35	16
11	0.50	11	23	0.35	14
12	0.50	16	24	0.35	16

a. Determine the simple linear regression equation using Time as the dependent variable and Tamp as the independent variable.
b. Interpret the slope (b_1) in this problem.
c. Plot the residuals versus the time order of experimentation. Are there any noticeable patterns?
d. Compute the Durbin-Watson statistic. At the 0.05 level of significance, is there evidence of positive autocorrelation among the residuals?

34 The owner of a large chain of ice cream stores would like to study the effect of atmospheric temperature on sales during the summer season. A sample of 21 consecutive days is selected, with the results stored in the data file: **ICECREAM.xls**

(*Hint:* Determine which are the independent and dependent variables.)

a. Set up a scatter diagram.
b. Assuming a linear relationship, use the least-squares method to find the regression coefficients b_0 and b_1.
c. Interpret the meaning of the slope b_1 in this problem.
d. Predict the sales per store for a day in which the temperature is 83°F.
e. Compute the standard error of the estimate.
f. Compute the coefficient of determination r^2 and interpret its meaning in this problem.
g. Plot the residuals versus the temperature.
h. Plot the residuals versus the time period.
i. Compute the Durbin-Watson statistic. At the 0.05 level of significance, is there evidence of positive autocorrelation among the residuals?
j. Based on the results of (g)–(i), is there reason to question the validity of the model?
k. Suppose that the amount of sales on day 21 was 1.75. Repeat (a)–(j) and compare the differences in the results.

7 INFERENCES ABOUT THE SLOPE AND CORRELATION COEFFICIENT

In sections 1 through 3, regression is used solely for the purpose of description. The least-squares method is used to determine the regression coefficients and to predict the value of Y from a given value of X. In addition, the standard error of the estimate and the coefficient of determination are discussed.

When residual analysis, as discussed in section 5, indicates that the assumptions of a least-squares regression model have not been seriously violated and that the straight-line model is appropriate, inferences about the linear relationship between the variables in a population can be made based on the sample results.

t Test for the Slope

To determine the existence of a significant linear relationship between the X and Y variables, a hypothesis test concerning whether β_1 (the population slope) is equal to 0 is performed. The null and alternative hypotheses are stated as follows:

$$H_0: \beta_1 = 0 \text{ (There is no linear relationship.)}$$
$$H_1: \beta_1 \neq 0 \text{ (There is a linear relationship.)}$$

If the null hypothesis is rejected, you can conclude that there is evidence of a linear relationship. The test statistic for this hypothesis test is defined in Equation (11).

TESTING A HYPOTHESIS FOR A POPULATION SLOPE β_1 USING THE t TEST

The t statistic equals the difference between the sample slope and hypothesized value of the population slope divided by the standard error of the slope.

$$t = \frac{b_1 - \beta_1}{S_{b_1}} \quad \textbf{(11)}$$

where

$$S_{b_1} = \frac{S_{YX}}{\sqrt{SSX}}$$
$$SSX = \sum_{i=1}^{n}(X_i - \bar{X})^2$$

The test statistic t follows a t distribution with $n - 2$ degrees of freedom.

[2] *More detailed computations of the t-test statistic are provided in section 10.*

Returning to the Using Statistics scenario concerning the site selection example, to test whether there is a significant relationship between the size of the store and the annual sales at the 0.05 level of significance, refer to the Microsoft Excel output for the t test presented in Figure 18.[2]

FIGURE 18
t test obtained from Microsoft Excel for the site selection problem

16		Coefficients	Standard Error	t Stat	P-value	Lower 95%	Upper 95%
17	Intercept	0.96447	0.52619	1.83293	0.09173	-0.18200	2.11095
18	Square Feet	1.66986	0.15693	10.64112	0.00000	1.32795	2.01177

t statistic for β_1

Therefore, to test the existence of a linear relationship at the 0.05 level of significance,

$$b_1 = +1.670 \qquad n = 14 \qquad S_{b_1} = 0.157$$

and

$$t = \frac{b_1 - \beta_1}{S_{b_1}}$$

$$= \frac{1.670 - 0}{0.157} = 10.64$$

This t statistic is provided in the column titled t Stat by Microsoft Excel (see Figure 18). Because $t = 10.64 > 2.1788$ (see Figure 19), you reject H_0. Using the p-value, you reject H_0 because the p-value is approximately zero. A p-value of approximately zero means the probability is almost zero of seeing this strong (or stronger) of a linear relationship if in fact there is no linear relationship between annual sales and the size of the stores. Hence, you can conclude that there is a significant linear relationship between average annual sales and the size of the store.

FIGURE 19
Testing a hypothesis about the population slope at the 0.05 level of significance with 12 degrees of freedom

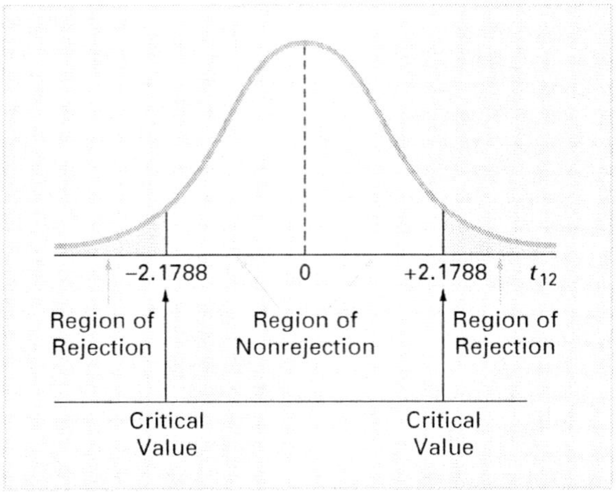

F Test for the Slope

An alternative approach for testing whether the slope in simple linear regression is statistically significant is to use an F test. Recall that the F test is used to test the ratio of two variances. In testing for the significance of the slope, the F test, defined in Equation (12) is the ratio of the variance that is due to the regression (MSR) divided by the error variance ($MSE = S_{YX}^2$).

TESTING A HYPOTHESIS FOR A POPULATION SLOPE β_1 USING THE F TEST

The F statistic is equal to the regression mean square (MSR) divided by the error mean square (MSE).

$$F = \frac{MSR}{MSE} \tag{12}$$

where

$$MSR = \frac{SSR}{k}$$

$$MSE = \frac{SSE}{n - k - 1}$$

k = number of explanatory variables in the regression model

The test statistic F follows an F distribution with k and $n - k - 1$ degrees of freedom.

Using a level of significance α, the decision rule is

Reject H_0 if $F > F_U$,
otherwise do not reject H_0.

The complete set of results is organized into an ANOVA table as illustrated in Table 5.

TABLE 5

ANOVA table for testing the significance of a regression coefficient

Source	df	Sums of Squares	Mean Square (Variance)	F
Regression	k	SSR	$MSR = \frac{SSR}{k}$	$F = \frac{MSR}{MSE}$
Error	$n - k - 1$	SSE	$MSE = \frac{SSE}{n - k - 1}$	
Total	$n - 1$	SST		

The completed ANOVA table is also available as part of the output from Microsoft Excel (shown in Figure 20).

FIGURE 20

F test obtained from Microsoft Excel for the site selection problem

MSR

10	**ANOVA**					
11		*df*	*SS*	*MS*	*F*	*Significance F*
12	**Regression**	**1**	**105.74761**	**105.74761**	**113.23351**	**1.82269E-07**
13	**Residual**	**12**	**11.20668**	**0.93389**		
14	**Total**	**13**	**116.95429**			

MSE

Observe in Figure 20 that the computed F statistic is 113.23 and the p-value is less than 0.001 (Excel computes the p-value as 0.000000182).

If a level of significance of 0.05 is chosen, from the Critical Values of F table the critical value of the F distribution (with 1 and 12 degrees of freedom) is 4.75, as depicted in Figure 21. Because $F = 113.23 > 4.75$ or because the p-value $= 0.000000182 < 0.05$, you reject H_0 and conclude that the size of the store is significantly related to annual sales. Note that the p-value for the F test given in Figure 20 is identical to the p-value for the t test given in Figures 18 and the computed F test statistic equals the square of the computed t test statistic $[F = 113.23 = t^2 = (10.64)^2]$.

FIGURE 21

Regions of rejection and nonrejection when testing for significance of slope at the 0.05 level of significance with 1 and 12 degrees of freedom

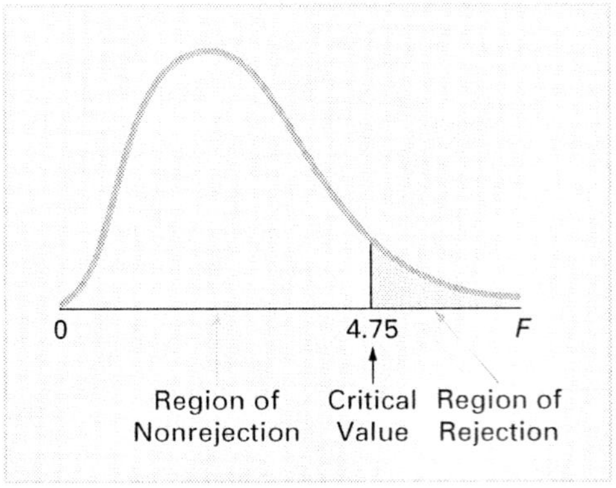

Confidence Interval Estimate of the Slope (β_1)

An alternative to testing the existence of a linear relationship between the variables is to set up a confidence interval estimate of β_1 and to determine whether the hypothesized value ($\beta_1 = 0$) is included in the interval. The confidence interval estimate of β_1 is obtained as shown in Equation (13).

CONFIDENCE INTERVAL ESTIMATE OF THE SLOPE β_1

The confidence interval estimate for the slope can be obtained by taking the sample slope b_1 and adding and subtracting the critical t value multiplied by the standard error of the slope.

$$b_1 \pm t_{n-2} S_{b_1} \qquad \textbf{(13)}$$

From the Microsoft Excel output of Figure 18,

$$b_1 = +1.670 \qquad n = 14 \qquad S_{b_1} = 0.157$$

and from the Critical Values of t table, $t_{12} = 2.1788$. Thus,

$$\begin{aligned} b_1 \pm t_{n-2} S_{b_1} &= +1.670 \pm (2.1788)(0.157) \\ &= +1.670 \pm 0.342 \\ &+1.328 \leq \beta_1 \leq +2.012 \end{aligned}$$

From Equation (13), the population slope is estimated with 95% confidence to be between +1.328 and +2.012 (i.e., \$1,328,000 to \$2,012,000). Because these values are above 0, you conclude that there is a significant linear relationship between annual sales and square footage size of the store. Had the interval included 0, the conclusion would have been that no significant relationship exists between the variables. Moreover, the confidence interval indicates that for each increase of 1,000 square feet, average annual sales are estimated to increase by at least \$1,328,000 but less than \$2,012,000.

t Test for a Correlation Coefficient

The **correlation coefficient** r is computed to measure the strength of the relationship between two numerical variables. The correlation coefficient can be used to determine whether there is any evidence of a statistically significant association between these variables. The population correlation coefficient ρ is hypothesized to be equal to 0. Thus, the null and alternative hypotheses are

$$H_0: \rho = 0 \text{ (No correlation)}$$

$$H_1: \rho \neq 0 \text{ (Correlation)}$$

The test statistic for determining the existence of a significant correlation is given in Equation (14).

TESTING FOR THE EXISTENCE OF CORRELATION

$$t = \frac{r - \rho}{\sqrt{\frac{1 - r^2}{n - 2}}} \quad \textbf{(14)}$$

where

$$r = +\sqrt{r^2} \text{ if } b_1 > 0$$

or

$$r = -\sqrt{r^2} \text{ if } b_1 < 0$$

The test statistic t follows a t distribution with $n - 2$ degrees of freedom.

In the site selection problem, $r^2 = 0.904$ and $b_1 = +1.670$ (see Figure 4). Since $b_1 > 0$, the correlation coefficient for annual sales and store size is the positive square root of r^2, i.e., $r^2 = +\sqrt{0.904} = +0.951$. Testing the null hypothesis that there is no correlation between these two variables results in the following observed t statistic:

$$t = \frac{r - 0}{\sqrt{\frac{1 - r^2}{n - 2}}}$$

$$= \frac{0.951 - 0}{\sqrt{\frac{1 - (0.951)^2}{14 - 2}}} = 10.64$$

Using the 0.05 level of significance, since $t = 10.64 > 2.1788$, the null hypothesis is rejected. You can conclude that there is evidence of an association between annual sales and store size. Note that this t statistic is equivalent to the t statistic found when testing whether the population slope β_1 is equal to zero (Figure 18).

When inferences concerning the population slope were discussed, confidence intervals and tests of hypothesis were used interchangeably. However, developing a confidence interval for the correlation coefficient is more complicated because the shape of the sampling distribution of the statistic r varies for different values of the population correlation coefficient. Methods for developing a confidence interval estimate for the correlation coefficient are presented in reference 6.

PROBLEMS FOR SECTION 7

Learning the Basics

35 Suppose that you are testing the null hypothesis that there is no relationship between two variables X and Y. From your sample of $n = 18$ you determine that $b_1 = +4.5$ and $S_{b_1} = 1.5$.

a. What is the value of the t-test statistic?

b. At the $\alpha = 0.05$ level of significance, what are the critical values?

c. Based on your answers to (a) and (b), what statistical decision should be made?

d. Set up a 95% confidence interval estimate of the population slope β_1.

36 Suppose that you are testing the null hypothesis that there is no relationship between two variables X and Y. From your sample of $n = 20$, you determine that $SSR = 60$ and $SSE = 40$.

a. What is the value of the F-test statistic?

b. At the $\alpha = 0.05$ level of significance, what is the critical value?

c. Based on your answers to (a) and (b), what statistical decision should be made?

d. Calculate the correlation coefficient by first calculating r^2 and assuming b_1 is negative.

e. At the 0.05 level of significance, is there a significant correlation between X and Y?

Applying the Concepts

Problems 37–39 can be solved manually or using Microsoft Excel. We recommend that problems 40–48 be solved using Microsoft Excel.

37 In problem 3, the marketing manager used shelf space for pet food to predict weekly sales. **PETFOOD.xls** Using the computer output you obtained to solve that problem,

a. At the 0.05 level of significance, is there evidence of a linear relationship between shelf space and sales?

b. Set up a 95% confidence interval estimate of the population slope β_1.

38 The volatility of a stock is often measured by its beta value. You can estimate the beta value of a stock by performing a simple linear regression model using the percentage weekly change in the stock as the dependent variable and the percentage weekly change in a market index as the independent variable. The Standard & Poor's (S&P) 500 Index is a common index to use. For example, if you wanted to estimate the beta for IBM, you could use the following model, which is sometimes referred to as a *market model*.

$$(\text{\% weekly change in IBM}) = \beta_0 + \beta_1(\text{\% weekly change in S\&P 500 index}) + \varepsilon$$

The least-squares regression estimate of the slope b_1 is the estimate of the beta for IBM. Note that a stock with a beta of 1.0 tends to move the same as the overall market. A stock with a beta value of 1.5 tends to move 50% more than the overall market, and a stock with a beta of 0.6 tends to move only 60% as much as the overall market. Stocks with negative betas tend to move in a direction opposite to that of the overall market. The following table gives some beta values for some widely held stocks.

Company	Beta
Procter and Gamble	0.626
Ford Motor Company	1.074
IBM	1.132
LSI Logic	1.705

a. For each of the four companies, interpret the value of the beta.

b. How can investors use the beta value as a guide for investing?

39 Index funds are mutual funds that try to mimic the movement of leading indexes such as the S&P 500 index, the NASDAQ index, or the Russell 2000 Index. The beta values for these funds (as described in problem 38) are therefore approximately 1.0. The estimated market models for these funds are approximately:

$$(\text{\% weekly change in index fund}) = b_0 + 1.0(\text{\% weekly change in the index})$$

Leveraged index funds are designed to magnify the movement of major indexes. An article in *Mutual Funds* (Lynn O'Shaughnessy, "Reach for Higher Returns," *Mutual Funds*, July 1999, 44–49) described some of the risks and rewards associated with these funds and gave details on some of the most popular leveraged funds including those in the following table.

Name (Ticker Symbol)	Fund Description
Potomac Small Cap Plus (POSCX)	125% of Russell 2000 Index
Rydex "Inv" Nova (RYNVX)	150% of the S&P 500 Index
ProFund UltraOTC "Inv" (UOPIX)	Double (200%) the NASDAQ 100 Index

Thus, estimated market models for these funds are approximately:

$$(\text{\% weekly change in POSCX}) = b_0 + 1.25(\text{\% weekly change in the Russell 2000 index})$$
$$(\text{\% weekly change in RYNVX}) = b_0 + 1.50(\text{\% weekly change in the S\&P 500 index})$$
$$(\text{\% weekly change in UOPIX fund}) = b_0 + 2.0(\text{\% weekly change in the NASDAQ 100 index})$$

Thus, if the Russell 2000 Index gains 10% over a period of time, the leveraged mutual fund POSCX gains approximately 12.5%. On the downside, if the same index loses 20%, POSCX loses approximately 25%.

a. Consider the leveraged mutual fund ProFund UltraBull "Inv" (ULPIX), whose description is 200% of the performance of the S&P 500 Index. What is its approximate market model?

b. If the S&P gains 30% in a year, what do you expect ULPIX to do?

c. If the S&P loses 35% in a year, what do you expect ULPIX to do?

d. What type of investors should be attracted to leveraged funds? Which type of investors should stay away from these funds?

40 In problem 4, the owner of a moving company wanted to predict labor hours based on the number of cubic feet moved. **MOVING.xls** Using the computer output you obtained to solve that problem,

a. At the 0.05 level of significance, is there evidence of a linear relationship between the number of cubic feet moved and labor hours?

b. Set up a 95% confidence interval estimate of the population slope β_1.

41 In problem 5, the weight of mail was used to predict the number of orders received. **MAIL.xls** Using the computer output you obtained to solve that problem,

a. At the 0.05 level of significance, is there evidence of a linear relationship between the weight of mail and the number of orders received?

b. Set up a 95% confidence interval estimate of the population slope β_1.

42 In problem 6, a company wanted to predict home video sales based on the box office gross of movies. **MOVIE.xls** Using the computer output you obtained to solve that problem,

a. At the 0.05 level of significance, is there evidence of a linear relationship between box office gross and home video sales?

b. Set up a 95% confidence interval estimate of the population slope β_1.

43 In problem 7, an agent for a real estate company wanted to predict the monthly rent for apartments based on the size of the apartment. **RENT.xls** Using the computer output you obtained to solve that problem,

a. At the 0.05 level of significance, is there evidence of a linear relationship between the size of the apartment and the monthly rent?

b. Set up a 95% confidence interval estimate of the population slope β_1.

44 In problem 8, hardness was used to predict the tensile strength of die-cast aluminum. **HARDNESS.xls** Using the computer output you obtained to solve that problem,

a. At the 0.05 level of significance, is there evidence of a linear relationship between hardness and tensile strength?

b. Set up a 95% confidence interval estimate of the population slope β_1.

45 The data in the file **REFRIGERATOR.xls** represent the approximate retail price and the energy cost per year of 10 medium-size top-freezer refrigerators.

Source: Refrigerators. Copyright © 2002 by Consumers Union of U.S., Inc. Adapted from Consumer Reports, *August 2002, 26, by permission of Consumers Union U.S., Inc., Yonkers NY 10703–1057.*

a. Compute the coefficient of correlation r.

b. At the 0.05 level of significance, is there a significant linear relationship between the retail price (in \$) and the energy cost per year (in \$) of medium-size top-freezer refrigerators?

46 The data in the file **SECURITY.xls** represent the turnover rate of pre-boarding screeners at airports in 1998–1999 and the security violations detected per million passengers.

Source: Alan B. Krueger, "A Small Dose of Common Sense Would Help Congress Break the Gridlock over Airport Security." The New York Times, *November 15, 2001, C2.*

a. Compute the coefficient of correlation r.

b. At the 0.05 level of significance, is there a significant linear relationship between the turnover rate of pre-boarding screeners and the security violations detected?

c. What conclusions can you reach about the relationship between the turnover rate of pre-boarding screeners and the security violations detected?

47 The data in the file **CELLPHONE.xls** represents the digital-mode talk time in hours and the battery capacity in milliampere-hours of cellphones.

Talk Time	Battery Capacity	Talk Time	Battery Capacity
4.50	800	1.50	450
4.00	1500	2.25	900
3.00	1300	2.25	900
2.00	1550	3.25	900
2.75	900	2.25	700
1.75	875	2.25	800
1.75	750	2.50	800
2.25	1100	2.25	900
1.75	850	2.00	900

Source: "Service Shortcomings." Copyright 2002 by Consumers Union of U.S., Inc. Adapted from Consumer Reports, *February 2002, 25, by permission of Consumers Union of U.S., Inc., Yonkers, NY 10703–1057.*

a. Compute the coefficient of correlation r.

b. At the 0.05 level of significance, is there a significant linear relationship between the battery capacity and the digital-mode talk time?

c. What conclusions can you reach about the relationship between the battery capacity and the digital-mode talk time?

d. You would expect the cellphones with higher battery capacity to have a higher talk time. Is this borne out by the data?

48 The data in the file **BATTERIES2.xls** represents the price and cold-cranking amps (which denotes the starting current the battery can deliver) of automobile batteries.

Source: "Leading the Charge." Copyright 2001 by Consumers Union of U.S., Inc. Adapted from Consumer Reports, *October 2001, 25, by permission of Consumers Union of U.S., Inc., Yonkers, NY 10703–1057.*

a. Compute the coefficient of correlation r.

b. At the 0.05 level of significance, is there a significant linear relationship between the cold-cranking amps and the price?

c. What conclusions can you reach about the relationship between the cold-cranking amps and the price?

d. You would expect the batteries with higher cold-cranking amps to have a higher price. Is this borne out by the data?

8 ESTIMATION OF MEAN VALUES AND PREDICTION OF INDIVIDUAL VALUES

In this section, methods of making inferences about the mean of Y and the prediction of individual values of Y are presented.

Obtaining the Confidence Interval Estimate

In Example 2, the regression equation was used to make predictions about the value of Y for a given X. The average yearly sales for stores with 4,000 square feet was predicted to be 7.644 millions of dollars ($7,644,000). This estimate, however, is a *point estimate* of the population average value. A **confidence interval estimate for the mean response** can now be developed to make inferences about the average value of Y for a given X.

CONFIDENCE INTERVAL ESTIMATE FOR THE MEAN OF Y

$$\hat{Y}_i \pm t_{n-2} S_{YX} \sqrt{h_i}$$
$$\hat{Y}_i - t_{n-2} S_{YX} \sqrt{h_i} \leq \mu_{Y|X=X_i} \leq \hat{Y}_i + t_{n-2} S_{YX} \sqrt{h_i} \qquad \textbf{(15)}$$

where

$$h_i = \frac{1}{n} + \frac{(X_i - \bar{X})^2}{SSX}$$

$\hat{Y}_i$ = predicted value of Y; $\hat{Y}_i = b_0 + b_1 X_i$

S_{YX} = standard error of the estimate

n = sample size

X_i = given value of X

$\mu_{Y|X=X_i}$ = mean value of Y when $X = X_i$

$$SSX = \sum_{i=1}^{n} (X_i - \bar{X})^2$$

An examination of Equation (15) indicates that the width of the confidence interval is dependent on several factors. For a given level of confidence, increased variation around the line of regression, as measured by the standard error of the estimate, results in a wider interval. However, as would be expected, increased sample size reduces the width of the interval. In addition, the width of the interval also varies at different values of X. When predicting Y for values of X close to $\bar{X}$, the interval is narrower than for predictions for X values more distant from the mean.

In the site selection example, suppose you want to obtain a 95% confidence interval estimate of the population average annual sales for all stores that contain 4,000 square feet ($X = 4$). Using the simple linear regression equation:

$$\begin{aligned}\hat{Y}_i &= 0.964 + 1.670X_i \\ &= 0.964 + 1.670(4) = 7.644 \text{ (millions of dollars)}\end{aligned}$$

Also, given the following

$$\bar{X} = 2.9214 \qquad S_{YX} = 0.9664$$
$$SSX = \sum_{i=1}^{n} (X_i - \bar{X})^2 = 37.9236$$

From the Critical Values of t table, $t_{12} = 2.1788$. Thus,

$$\hat{Y}_i \pm t_{n-2} S_{YX} \sqrt{h_i}$$

where

$$h_i = \frac{1}{n} + \frac{(X_i - \overline{X})^2}{SSX}$$

so that

$$\begin{aligned}
&\hat{Y}_i \pm t_{n-2} S_{YX} \sqrt{\frac{1}{n} + \frac{(X_i - \overline{X})^2}{SSX}} \\
&= 7.644 \pm (2.1788)(0.9664)\sqrt{\frac{1}{14} + \frac{(4 - 2.9214)^2}{37.9236}} \\
&= 7.644 \pm 0.673
\end{aligned}$$

so

$$6.971 \le \mu_{Y|X=4} \le 8.317$$

Therefore, the 95% confidence interval estimate is that the population average annual sales are between 6.971 and 8.317 (millions of dollars) for stores with 4,000 square feet of space.

Obtaining the Prediction Interval

In addition to the need to obtain a confidence interval estimate for the average value, it is often important to predict the response for an individual value. Although the form of the prediction interval is similar to the confidence interval estimate of Equation (15), the prediction interval is predicting an individual value, not estimating a parameter. The **prediction interval for an individual response** Y, at a particular value X_i, denoted by $Y_{X=X_i}$ is defined in Equation (16).

PREDICTION INTERVAL FOR AN INDIVIDUAL RESPONSE Y

$$\hat{Y}_i \pm t_{n-2} S_{YX} \sqrt{1 + h_i}$$

$$\hat{Y}_i - t_{n-2} S_{YX} \sqrt{1 + h_i} \le Y_{X=X_i} \le \hat{Y}_i + t_{n-2} S_{YX} \sqrt{1 + h_i} \quad \textbf{(16)}$$

where h_i, $\hat{Y}_i$, S_{YX}, n, and X_i are defined as in Equation (15). And $Y_{X=X_i}$ = a future value of Y when $X = X_i$.

Suppose you wanted to set up a 95% prediction interval of the annual sales for an individual store that contains 4,000 square feet ($X = 4$). Using the simple linear regression equation:

$$\begin{aligned}
\hat{Y}_i &= 0.964 + 1.670X_i \\
&= 0.964 + 1.670(4) \\
&= 7.644 \text{ (millions of dollars)}
\end{aligned}$$

Also, given the following

$$\overline{X} = 2.9214 \qquad S_{YX} = 0.9664$$

$$SSX = \sum_{i=1}^{n} (X_i - \overline{X})^2 = 37.9236$$

From the Critical Values of t table, $t_{12} = 2.1788$. Thus,

$$\hat{Y}_i \pm t_{n-2} S_{YX} \sqrt{1 + h_i}$$

where

$$h_i = \frac{1}{n} + \frac{(X_i - \bar{X})^2}{\sum_{i=1}^{n}(X_i - \bar{X})^2}$$

so that

$$\hat{Y}_i \pm t_{n-2} S_{YX} \sqrt{1 + \frac{1}{n} + \frac{(X_i - \bar{X})^2}{SSX}}$$

$$= 7.644 \pm (2.1788)(0.9664)\sqrt{1 + \frac{1}{14} + \frac{(4 - 2.9214)^2}{37.9236}}$$

$$= 7.644 \pm 2.210$$

so

$$5.433 \le Y_{X=4} \le 9.854$$

Therefore, with 95% confidence you predict that the annual sales for an individual store with 4,000 square feet of space is between \$5,433,000 and \$9,854,000. Figure 22 represents the confidence interval estimate and the prediction interval obtained from Microsoft Excel for the site selection problem. If you compare the results of the confidence interval estimate and the prediction interval, observe that the width of the prediction interval for an individual store is much wider than the confidence interval estimate for the average store. This is because there will be much more variation in predicting an individual value than in estimating an average value.

FIGURE 22
Confidence interval estimate and prediction interval obtained from Microsoft Excel for the site selection problem

	A	B
1	**Site Selection Analysis**	
2		
3	**Data**	
4	**X Value**	**4**
5	**Confidence Level**	**95%**
6		
7	Intermediate Calculations	
8	Sample Size	14
9	Degrees of Freedom	12
10	t Value	2.178813
11	Sample Mean	2.921429
12	Sum of Squared Difference	37.92357
13	Standard Error of the Estimate	0.96638
14	h Statistic	0.102104
15	Predicted Y (YHat)	7.643923
16		
17	**For Average Y**	
18	Interval Half Width	0.672804
19	**Confidence Interval Lower Limit**	**6.971119**
20	**Confidence Interval Upper Limit**	**8.316727**
21		
22	**For Individual Response Y**	
23	Interval Half Width	2.210441
24	**Prediction Interval Lower Limit**	**5.433482**
25	**Prediction Interval Upper Limit**	**9.854364**

Excel Strategies Calculating the Confidence Interval Estimate and Prediction Interval

You perform a simple linear regression analysis by using the Data Analysis Regression procedure and then implement a worksheet that features the **TINV** and **TREND** functions to calculate the confidence interval for the mean response and the prediction interval for an individual response. PHStat2 can do these tasks for you in a single step.

For example, to calculate these intervals for the simple linear regression analysis of the site selection data of Table 1, open to the **Data** worksheet of the **Chapter 12.xls** workbook and use one of these strategies:

CHAPTER 12.xls

Retrieve the Figure 12.22 worksheet of the ***Chapter 12.xls*** *workbook to view the confidence interval estimate and prediction interval worksheet shown on the previous page.*

Using Excel with PHStat2

Use the PHStat2 Simple Linear Regression procedure to calculate the intervals.

Select **PHStat | Regression | Simple Linear Regression**.

In the Simple Linear Regression dialog box (shown at right):

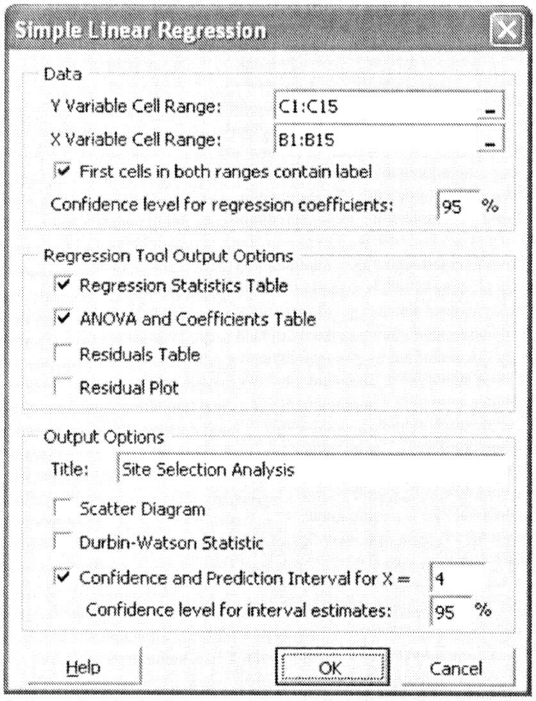

Enter **C1:C15** in the **Y Variable Cell Range** edit box.

Enter **B1:B15** in the **X Variable Cell Range** edit box.

Select the **First cells in both ranges contain label** check box.

Enter **95** in the **Confidence level for regression coefficients** edit box.

Select the **Regression Statistics Table** and **ANOVA and Coefficients Table** check boxes.

Enter a title in the **Title** edit box.

Select the **Confidence and Prediction Interval for X =** check box and enter **4** in its edit box.

Enter **95** in the **Confidence level for interval estimates** edit box.

Click the **OK** button.

Using Excel

Follow the instructions of section EH5 at the end of this chapter to manually implement a worksheet to calculate the confidence interval for the mean response and the prediction interval for an individual response.

PROBLEMS FOR SECTION 8

Learning the Basics

49 Based on a sample of 20 observations, the least-squares method was used to obtain the following linear regression equation: $\hat{Y}_i = 5 + 3X_i$. In addition,

$$S_{YX} = 1.0, \bar{X} = 2, \text{ and } \sum_{i=1}^{n}(X_i - \bar{X})^2 = 20$$

a. Set up a 95% confidence interval estimate of the population average response for $X = 2$.
b. Set up a 95% prediction interval of the individual response for $X = 2$.

50 Based on a sample of 20 observations, the least-squares method was used to obtain the following linear regression equation: $\hat{Y}_i = 5 + 3X_i$. In addition,

$$S_{YX} = 1.0, \bar{X} = 2, \text{ and } \sum_{i=1}^{n}(X_i - \bar{X})^2 = 20$$

a. Set up a 95% confidence interval estimate of the population average response for $X = 4$.
b. Set up a 95% prediction interval of the individual response for $X = 4$.
c. Compare the results of (a) and (b) with those of problem 49 (a) and (b). Which interval is wider? Why?

Applying the Concepts

We recommend that problems 51–56 be solved using Microsoft Excel.

51 In problem 3, the marketing manager used shelf space for pet food to predict weekly sales. **PETFOOD.xls**
a. Set up a 95% confidence interval estimate of the average weekly sales for all stores that have 8 feet of shelf space for pet food.
b. Set up a 95% prediction interval of the weekly sales of an individual store that has 8 feet of shelf space for pet food.
c. Explain the difference in the results obtained in (a) and (b).

52 In problem 4, the owner of a moving company wanted to predict labor hours based on the number of cubic feet moved. **MOVING.xls**
a. Set up a 95% confidence interval estimate of the average labor hours for all moves of 500 cubic feet.
b. Set up a 95% prediction interval of the weekly sales of a move that has 500 cubic feet.
c. Explain the difference in the results obtained in (a) and (b).

53 In problem 5, the weight of mail was used to predict the number of orders received. **MAIL.xls**
a. Set up a 95% confidence interval estimate of the population average number of orders received for a weight of 500 pounds.
b. Set up a 95% prediction interval of the number of orders received for an individual package with a weight of 500 pounds.
c. Explain the difference in the results obtained in (a) and (b).

54 In problem 6, a company wanted to predict home video sales based on the box office gross of movies. **MOVIE.xls**
a. Set up a 95% confidence interval estimate of the average video sales for all movies that gross 10 million dollars at the box office.
b. Set up a 95% prediction interval of the video sales of an individual movie that grosses 10 million dollars at the box office.
c. Explain the difference in the results obtained in (a) and (b).

55 In problem 7, an agent for a real estate company wanted to predict the monthly rent for apartments based on the size of the apartment. **RENT.xls**
a. Set up a 95% confidence interval estimate of the average monthly rental for all apartments that are 1,000 square feet in size.
b. Set up a 95% prediction interval of the monthly rental of an individual apartment that is 1,000 square feet in size.
c. Explain the difference in the results obtained in (a) and (b).

56 In problem 8, the hardness was used to predict the tensile strength of die-cast aluminum. **HARDNESS.xls**
a. Set up a 95% confidence interval estimate of the population average tensile strength for a hardness of 30 Rockwell E units.
b. Set up a 95% prediction interval of the tensile strength for an individual specimen that has a hardness of 30 Rockwell E units.
c. Explain the difference in the results obtained in (a) and (b).

9 PITFALLS IN REGRESSION AND ETHICAL ISSUES

Some of the pitfalls involved in using regression analysis are summarized in Exhibit 2.

EXHIBIT 2 PITFALLS IN USING REGRESSION

1. Lacking an awareness of the assumptions of least-squares regression
2. Not knowing how to evaluate the assumptions of least-squares regression
3. Not knowing what the alternatives to least-squares regression are if a particular assumption is violated
4. Using a regression model without knowledge of the subject matter
5. Extrapolating outside the relevant range
6. Concluding that a significant relationship identified in an observational study is due to a cause-and-effect relationship

The widespread availability of spreadsheet and statistical software has made the use of regression analysis common place. With this positive development of enhanced technology comes the realization that, for many users, this access has not been accompanied by an understanding of how to use regression analysis properly. How can a user be expected to know what the alternatives to least-squares regression are if a particular assumption is violated, when he or she in many instances is not even aware of the assumptions of regression, let alone how the assumptions can be evaluated?

The necessity of going beyond the basic number crunching—of computing the Y intercept, the slope, and r^2—can be illustrated by referring to Table 6, a classical pedagogical piece of statistical literature that deals with the importance of observation through scatter plots and residual analysis.

TABLE 6
Four sets of artificial data

ANSCOMBE.xls

Data Set A		Data Set B		Data Set C		Data Set D	
X_i	Y_i	X_i	Y_i	X_i	Y_i	X_i	Y_i
10	8.04	10	9.14	10	7.46	8	6.58
14	9.96	14	8.10	14	8.84	8	5.76
5	5.68	5	4.74	5	5.73	8	7.71
8	6.95	8	8.14	8	6.77	8	8.84
9	8.81	9	8.77	9	7.11	8	8.47
12	10.84	12	9.13	12	8.15	8	7.04
4	4.26	4	3.10	4	5.39	8	5.25
7	4.82	7	7.26	7	6.42	19	12.50
11	8.33	11	9.26	11	7.81	8	5.56
13	7.58	13	8.74	13	12.74	8	7.91
6	7.24	6	6.13	6	6.08	8	6.89

Source: F. J. Anscombe, "Graphs in Statistical Analysis," American Statistician, Vol. 27 (1973), 17–21.

Anscombe (reference 1) showed that for all four data sets given in Table 6, the following identical results are obtained:

$$\hat{Y}_i = 3.0 + 0.5X_i$$
$$S_{YX} = 1.237$$
$$S_{b_1} = 0.118$$
$$r^2 = 0.667$$

$$SSR = \text{explained variation} = \sum_{i=1}^{n}(\hat{Y}_i - \bar{Y})^2 = 27.51$$

$$SSE = \text{unexplained variation} = \sum_{i=1}^{n}(Y_i - \hat{Y}_i)^2 = 13.76$$

$$SST = \text{total variation} = \sum_{i=1}^{n}(Y_i - \bar{Y})^2 = 41.27$$

Thus, with respect to these statistics associated with a simple linear regression, the four data sets are identical. Were the analysis to stop at this point, valuable information in the data would be lost. By examining Figure 23, which represents scatter diagrams for the four data sets, and Figure 24, which represents residual plots for the four data sets, it is clear that each of the four data sets has a unique relationship between X and Y.

FIGURE 23
Scatter diagrams for four data sets

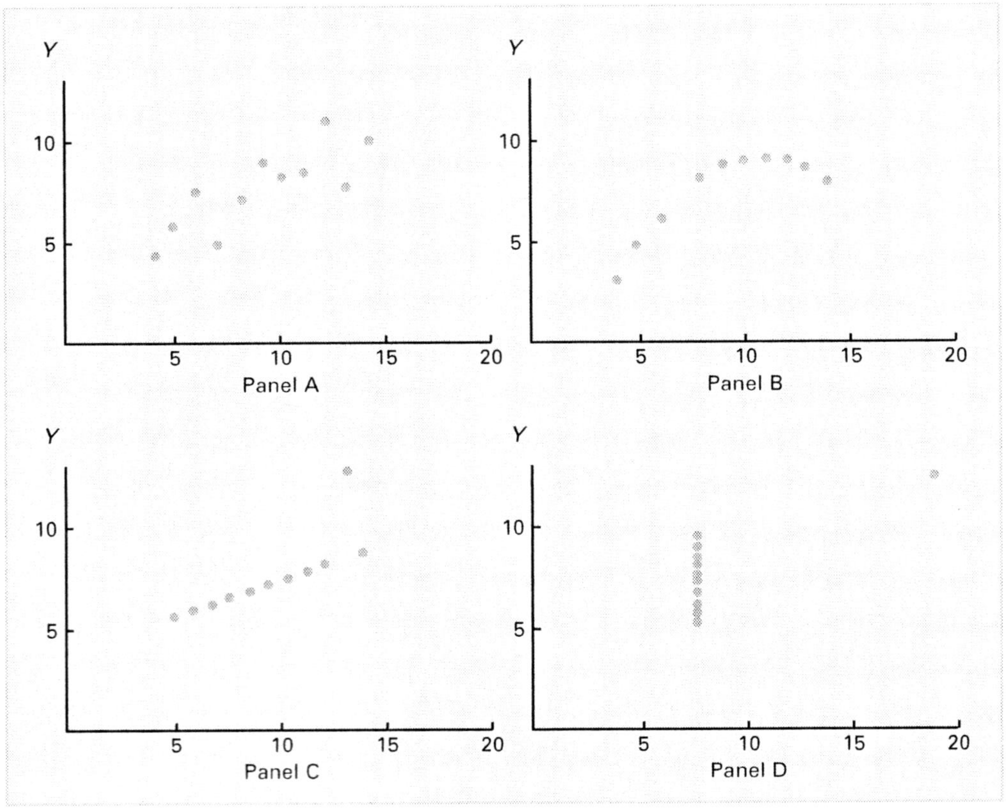

From the scatter diagrams of Figure 23 and the residual plots of Figure 24, observe how different the data sets are. The only data set that seems to follow an approximate straight line is data set A. The residual plot for data set A does not show any obvious patterns or outlying residuals. This is certainly not the case for data sets B, C, and D. The scatter plot for data set B shows that a quadratic regression model should be considered. This conclusion is reinforced by the clear parabolic form of the residual plot for B. The scatter diagram and the residual plot for data set C clearly depicts what is an outlying observation. If this is the case, you may want to remove the outlier and reestimate the basic model. Methodology that allows you to study whether the removal of observations is appropriate is called influence analysis (see reference 6). The result of reestimating the model might be a relationship much different from what was originally uncovered. Similarly, the scatter diagram for data set D also represents the situation in which the fitted model is heavily dependent on the outcome of a single response ($X_8 = 19$ and $Y_8 = 12.50$). Any regression model would have to be evaluated cautiously since its regression coefficients are heavily dependent on a single observation.

In summary, scatter diagrams and residual plots are of vital importance to a complete regression analysis. The information they provide is so basic to a credible analysis that these graphical methods should always be included as part of a regression analysis. Thus, a strategy that can be used to help avoid the pitfalls of regression is summarized in Exhibit 3.

EXHIBIT 3 STRATEGY FOR AVOIDING THE PITFALLS OF REGRESSION

1. Always start with a scatter plot to observe the possible relationship between X and Y.
2. Check the assumptions of regression after the regression model has been fit, before moving on to using the results of the model.

3. Plot the residuals versus the independent variable. This will enable you to determine whether the model fit to the data is an appropriate one and will allow you to check visually for violations of the homoscedasticity assumption.
4. Use a histogram, stem-and-leaf display, box-and-whisker plot, or normal probability plot of the residuals to graphically evaluate whether the normality assumption has been seriously violated.
5. If the evaluation done in 3 and 4 indicates violations in the assumptions, use alternative methods to least-squares regression or alternative least-squares models (quadratic or multiple regression), depending on what the evaluation has indicated.
6. If the evaluation done in 3 and 4 does not indicate violations in the assumptions, then the inferential aspects of the regression analysis can be undertaken. Tests for the significance of the regression coefficients can be done and confidence and prediction intervals can be developed.
7. Avoid making predictions and forecasts outside the relevant range of the independent variable.
8. Always note that the relationships identified in observational studies may or may not be due to a cause-and-effect relationship. Remember that while causation implies correlation, correlation does not imply causation.

FIGURE 24
Residual plots for four data sets

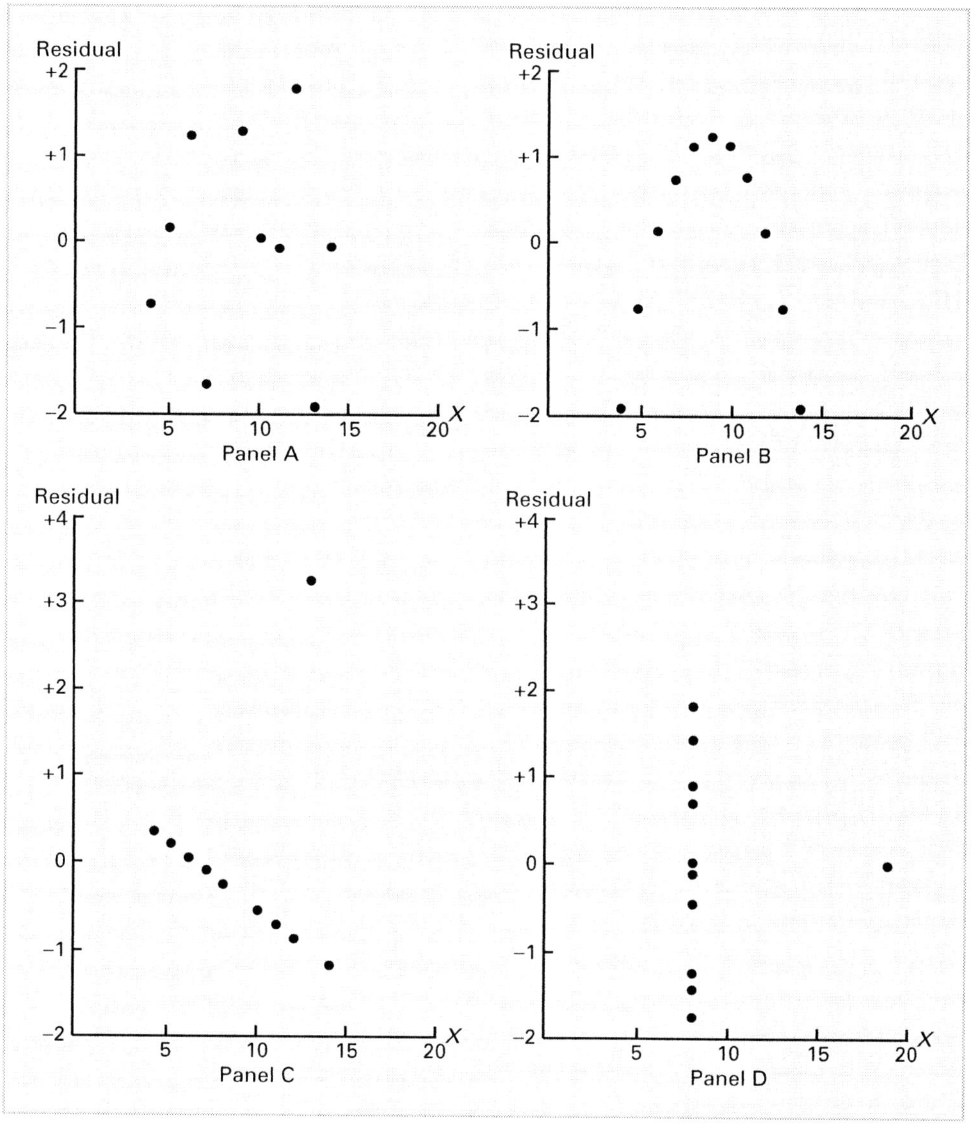

10 COMPUTATIONS IN SIMPLE LINEAR REGRESSION

In developing the simple linear regression model, the primary focus has been on using the output of Microsoft Excel. In this section, the computations involved in developing many of the statistics obtained for the simple linear regression model are illustrated.

Computing the Y Intercept b_0 and the Slope b_1

Using the least-squares method, the sum of squared errors (SSE) is minimized. In Equation (17) note that SSE is written as a function of b_0 and b_1.

ERROR SUM OF SQUARES

$$SSE = \sum_{i=1}^{n} (Y_i - \hat{Y}_i)^2$$

$$= \sum_{i=1}^{n} \left[Y_i - (b_0 + b_1 X_i)\right]^2 \quad \textbf{(17)}$$

The values of b_0 and b_1, which minimize Equation (17), are given in Equations (18) and (19). For details, see reference 6.

COMPUTATIONAL FORMULA FOR THE SLOPE b_1

$$b_1 = \frac{SSXY}{SSX} \quad \textbf{(18)}$$

where

$$SSXY = \sum_{i=1}^{n} (X_i - \bar{X})(Y_i - \bar{Y}) = \sum_{i=1}^{r} X_i Y_i - \frac{\left(\sum_{i=1}^{n} X_i\right)\left(\sum_{i=1}^{n} Y_i\right)}{n}$$

$$SSX = \sum_{i=1}^{n} (X_i - \bar{X})^2 = \sum_{i=1}^{n} X_i^2 - \frac{\left(\sum_{i=1}^{n} X_i\right)^2}{n}$$

and

COMPUTATIONAL FORMULA FOR THE Y INTERCEPT b_0

$$b_0 = \bar{Y} - b_1 \bar{X} \quad \textbf{(19)}$$

where

$$\bar{Y} = \frac{\sum_{i=1}^{n} Y_i}{n} \quad \text{and} \quad \bar{X} = \frac{\sum_{i=1}^{n} X_i}{n}$$

Examining Equations (18) and (19), you see that five quantities must be calculated to determine b_1 and b_0. These are n, the sample size; $\sum_{i=1}^{n} X_i$, the sum of the X values; $\sum_{i=1}^{n} Y_i$, the sum of the Y values; $\sum_{i=1}^{n} X_i^2$, the sum of the squared X values, and $\sum_{i=1}^{n} X_i Y_i$, the sum of the cross-product of X and Y. For the site selection data, the number of square feet is used to predict the annual sales in a store. The computation of the various sums needed (including $\sum_{i=1}^{n} Y_i^2$, the sum of the squared Y values that will be used to compute the SST) are presented in Figure 25.

FIGURE 25
Computations obtained from Microsoft Excel for the site selection problem

Store	Square Feet(X)	Annual Sales(Y)	X²	Y²	XY
1	1.7	3.7	2.89	13.69	6.29
2	1.6	3.9	2.56	15.21	6.24
3	2.8	6.7	7.84	44.89	18.76
4	5.6	9.5	31.36	90.25	53.2
5	1.3	3.4	1.69	11.56	4.42
6	2.2	5.6	4.84	31.36	12.32
7	1.3	3.7	1.69	13.69	4.81
8	1.1	2.7	1.21	7.29	2.97
9	3.2	5.5	10.24	30.25	17.6
10	1.5	2.9	2.25	8.41	4.35
11	5.2	10.7	27.04	114.49	55.64
12	4.6	7.6	21.16	57.76	34.96
13	5.8	11.8	33.64	139.24	68.44
14	3	4.1	9	16.81	12.3
Totals	40.9	81.8	157.41	594.9	302.3

Using Equations (18) and (19), you can compute the values of b_0 and b_1:

$$b_1 = \frac{SSXY}{SSX}$$

$$SSXY = \sum_{i=1}^{n}(X_i - \bar{X})(Y_i - \bar{Y}) = \sum_{i=1}^{n} X_i Y_i - \frac{\left(\sum_{i=1}^{n} X_i\right)\left(\sum_{i=1}^{n} Y_i\right)}{n}$$

$$SSXY = 302.3 - \frac{(40.9)(81.8)}{14}$$
$$= 302.3 - 238.97285$$
$$= 63.32715$$

$$SSX = \sum_{i=1}^{n}(X_i - \bar{X})^2 = \sum_{i=1}^{n} X_i^2 - \frac{\left(\sum_{i=1}^{n} X_i\right)^2}{n}$$
$$= 157.41 - \frac{(40.9)^2}{14}$$
$$= 157.41 - 119.48642$$
$$= 37.92358$$

so that

$$b_1 = \frac{63.32715}{37.92358} = 1.66986$$

and

$$b_0 = \overline{Y} - b_1\overline{X}$$

$$\overline{Y} = \frac{\sum_{i=1}^{n} Y_i}{n} = \frac{81.8}{14} = 5.842857$$

$$\overline{X} = \frac{\sum_{i=1}^{n} X_i}{n} = \frac{40.9}{14} = 2.92143$$

$$b_0 = 5.842857 - (1.66986)(2.92143) = 0.964478$$

Computing the Measures of Variation

Computational formulas can be developed to compute *SST*, *SSR*, and *SSE* that were defined in Equations (4), (5) and (6).

COMPUTATIONAL FORMULA FOR *SST*

$$SST = \sum_{i=1}^{n}(Y_i - \overline{Y})^2 = \sum_{i=1}^{n} Y_i^2 - \frac{\left(\sum_{i=1}^{n} Y_i\right)^2}{n} \quad \textbf{(20)}$$

COMPUTATIONAL FORMULA FOR *SSR*

$$SSR = \sum_{i=1}^{n}(\hat{Y}_i - \overline{Y})^2 = b_0\sum_{i=1}^{n} Y_i + b_1\sum_{i=1}^{n} X_iY_i - \frac{\left(\sum_{i=1}^{n} Y_i\right)^2}{n} \quad \textbf{(21)}$$

COMPUTATIONAL FORMULA FOR *SSE*

$$SSE = \sum_{i=1}^{n}(Y_i - \hat{Y})^2 = \sum_{i=1}^{n} Y_i^2 - b_0\sum_{i=1}^{n} Y_i - b_1\sum_{i=1}^{n} X_iY_i \quad \textbf{(22)}$$

Using the summary results from Figure 25,

$$SST = \sum_{i=1}^{n}(Y_i - \bar{Y})^2 = \sum_{i=1}^{n} Y_i^2 - \frac{\left(\sum_{i=1}^{n} Y_i\right)^2}{n}$$

$$= 594.9 - \frac{(81.8)^2}{14}$$

$$= 594.9 - 477.94571$$

$$= 116.95429$$

$$SSR = \sum_{i=1}^{n}(\hat{Y}_i - \bar{Y})^2$$

$$= b_0 \sum_{i=1}^{n} Y_i + b_1 \sum_{i=1}^{n} X_i Y_i - \frac{\left(\sum_{i=1}^{n} Y_i\right)^2}{n}$$

$$= (0.964478)(81.8) + (1.66986)(302.3) - \frac{(81.8)^2}{14}$$

$$= 105.74726$$

$$SSE = \sum_{i=1}^{n}(Y_i - \hat{Y}_i)^2$$

$$= \sum_{i=1}^{n} Y_i^2 - b_0 \sum_{i=1}^{n} Y_i - b_1 \sum_{i=1}^{n} X_i Y_i$$

$$= 594.9 - (0.964478)(81.8) - (1.66986)(302.3)$$

$$= 11.20703$$

Computing the Standard Error of the Slope

In section 7, the standard error of the slope was used to test the existence of a relationship between the X and Y variables. The computational formula can be developed as follows:

$$S_{b_1} = \frac{S_{YX}}{\sqrt{SSX}}$$

$$SSX = \sum_{i=1}^{n}(X_i - \bar{X})^2$$

$$= \sum_{i=1}^{n} X_i^2 - \frac{\left(\sum_{i=1}^{n} X_i\right)^2}{n}$$

$$= 157.41 - \frac{(40.9)^2}{14}$$

$$= 37.92358$$

$$S_{b_1} = \frac{0.96638}{\sqrt{37.92358}}$$

$$= 0.156925$$

A second illustration of the computations involved in regression is shown in Example 3.

EXAMPLE 3

COMPUTING, b_0, b_1, SST, SSR, SSE, r^2, r, AND S_{YX}

In Table 6, four data sets were considered. Data set *A* consisted of the following values:

X_i	Y_i	X_i	Y_i
10	8.04	4	4.26
14	9.96	7	4.82
5	5.68	11	8.33
8	6.95	13	7.58
9	8.81	6	7.24
12	10.84		

For these data, compute b_0, b_1, SST, SSR, SSE, r^2, r, and S_{YX}.

SOLUTION

Five quantities must be calculated to determine b_1 and b_0. These are n, the sample size; $\sum_{i=1}^{n} X_i$, the sum of the X values; $\sum_{i=1}^{n} Y_i$, the sum of the Y values; $\sum_{i=1}^{n} X_i^2$, the sum of the squared X values, and $\sum_{i=1}^{n} X_iY_i$, the sum of the cross-products of X and Y. In addition, $\sum_{i=1}^{n} Y_i^2$, the sum of the squared Y values, is needed to compute SST. The computation of these sums has been obtained from Microsoft Excel and is presented in Table 7.

TABLE 7
Microsoft Excel computations for data set *A*

	A	B	C	D	E	F
1		X	Y	X Squared	Y Squared	XY
2		10	8.04	100	64.6416	80.4
3		14	9.96	196	99.2016	139.44
4		5	5.68	25	32.2624	28.4
5		8	6.95	64	48.3025	55.6
6		9	8.81	81	77.6161	79.29
7		12	10.84	144	117.5056	130.08
8		4	4.26	16	18.1476	17.04
9		7	4.82	49	23.2324	33.74
10		11	8.33	121	69.3889	91.63
11		13	7.58	169	57.4564	98.54
12		6	7.24	36	52.4176	43.44
13	Sums	99	82.51	1001	660.1727	797.6

Using Equations (18) and (19), the values of b_0 and b_1 are computed as follows:

$$b_1 = \frac{SSXY}{SSX}$$

$$SSXY = \sum_{i=1}^{n}(X_i - \bar{X})(Y_i - \bar{Y}) = \sum_{i=1}^{n} X_iY_i - \frac{\left(\sum_{i=1}^{n} X_i\right)\left(\sum_{i=1}^{n} Y_i\right)}{n}$$

$$SSXY = 797.6 - \frac{(99)(82.51)}{11}$$

$$= 797.6 - 742.59$$

$$= 55.01$$

$$SSX = \sum_{i=1}^{n}(X_i - \overline{X})^2 = \sum_{i=1}^{n} X_i^2 - \frac{\left(\sum_{i=1}^{n} X_i\right)^2}{n}$$
$$= 1{,}001 - \frac{(99)^2}{11}$$
$$= 1{,}001 - 891$$
$$= 110$$

so that

$$b_1 = \frac{55.01}{110}$$
$$= 0.50009$$

and $$b_0 = \overline{Y} - b_1\overline{X}$$

$$\overline{Y} = \frac{\sum_{i=1}^{n} Y_i}{n} = \frac{82.51}{11} = 7.5009$$
$$\overline{X} = \frac{\sum_{i=1}^{n} X_i}{n} = \frac{99}{11} = 9.0$$
$$b_0 = 7.5009 - (0.50009)(9.0)$$
$$= 3.00009$$

Using the summary results,

$$SST = \sum_{i=1}^{n}(Y_i - \overline{Y})^2 = \sum_{i=1}^{n} Y_i^2 - \frac{\left(\sum_{i=1}^{n} Y_i\right)^2}{n}$$
$$= 660.1727 - \frac{(82.51)^2}{11}$$
$$= 660.1727 - 618.9$$
$$= 41.2727$$

$$SSR = \sum_{i=1}^{n}(\hat{Y}_i - \overline{Y})^2$$
$$= b_0\sum_{i=1}^{n} Y_i + b_1\sum_{i=1}^{n} X_iY_i - \frac{\left(\sum_{i=1}^{n} Y_i\right)^2}{n}$$
$$= (3.00009)(82.51) + (0.50009)(797.6) - \frac{(82.51)^2}{11}$$
$$= 27.51$$

$$SSE = \sum_{i=1}^{n}(Y_i - \hat{Y}_i)^2$$
$$= \sum_{i=1}^{n} Y_i^2 - b_0\sum_{i=1}^{n} Y_i - b_1\sum_{i=1}^{n} X_iY_i$$
$$= 660.1727 - (3.00009)(82.51) - (.50009)(797.6)$$
$$= 13.7627$$

Using Equation (7),

$$r^2 = \frac{SSR}{SST} = \frac{27.51}{41.2727} = 0.667$$

Since $b_1 = +0.50$, $\sqrt{r^2} = +\sqrt{0.667} = +0.816$

Using Equation (8),

$$S_{YX} = \sqrt{\frac{SSE}{n-2}} = \sqrt{\frac{13.76}{11-2}}$$
$$= 1.237$$

SUMMARY

As you can see from the summary flowchart, this chapter develops the simple linear regression model, discusses the assumptions of the model, and shows how these assumptions could be evaluated. Then the t test for the significance of the slope was developed and the regression model was used for prediction. You have learned how the director of special projects and planning for a clothing store can use a regression model to help investigate the relationship between the size of a store and its annual sales. You have used the information obtained in the analysis of this model to make better decisions when selecting new sites for stores, as well as forecasting sales for existing stores.

KEY TERMS

assumptions of regression
autocorrelation
coefficient of determination
confidence interval estimate for the mean response
confidence interval estimate of the slope
correlation coefficient
dependent variable
Durbin-Watson statistic
error sum of squares (*SSE*)
explained variation
explanatory variable
F test for the slope
homoscedasticity
independence of errors
independent variable
least-squares method
linear relationship
normality
prediction interval for an individual response *Y*
regression analysis
regression coefficients
regression sum of squares (*SSR*)
relevant range
residual
residual analysis
response variable
scatter diagram
simple linear regression
slope
standard error of the estimate
t test for a correlation coefficient
t test for the slope
total sum of squares (*SST*)
total variation
unexplained variation
Y intercept

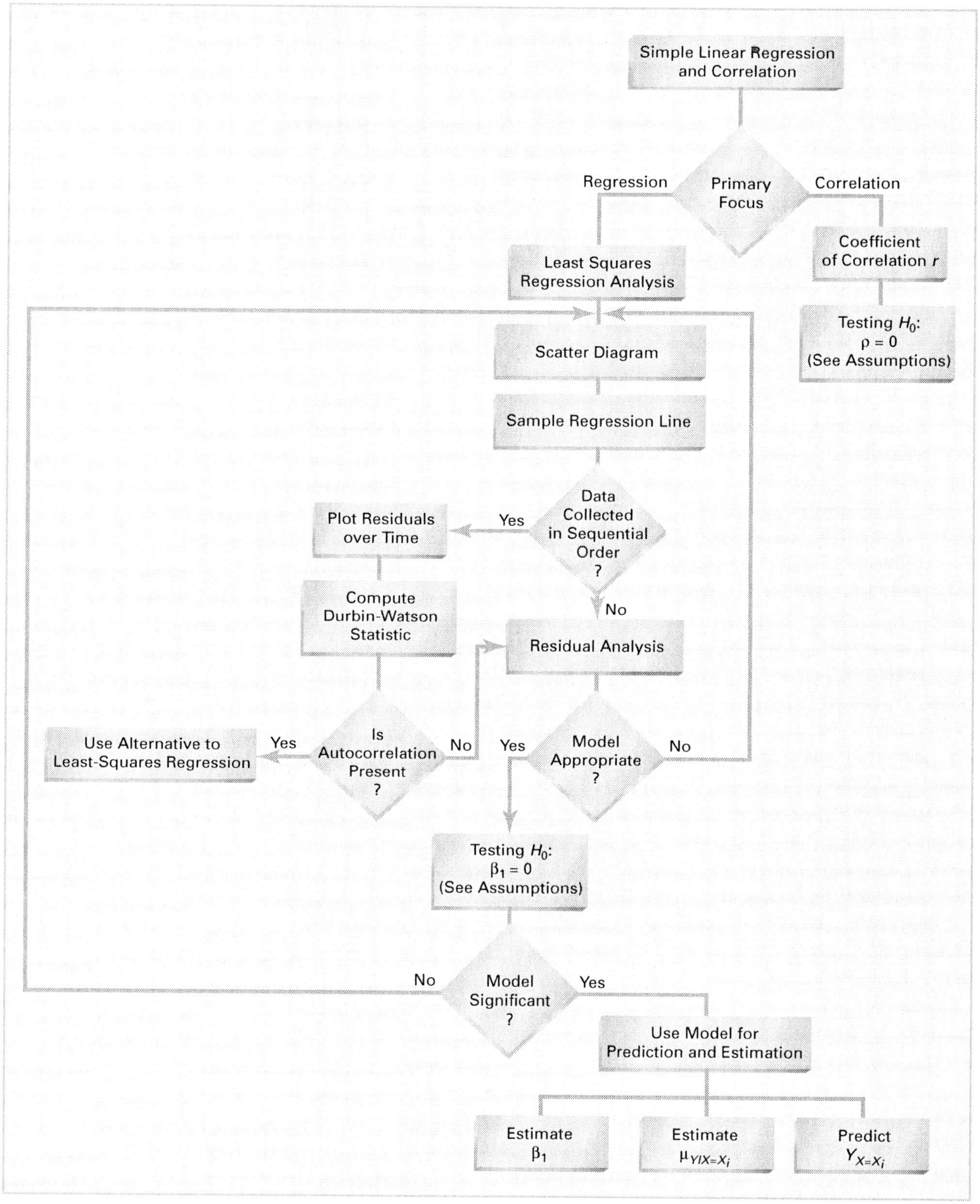

Chapter summary flowchart

CHAPTER REVIEW PROBLEMS

Checking Your Understanding

57 What is the interpretation of the Y intercept and the slope in a regression model?

58 What is the interpretation of the coefficient of determination?

59 When will the unexplained variation or error sum of squares be equal to 0?

60 When will the explained variation or sum of squares due to regression be equal to 0?

61 Why should a residual analysis always be done as part of the development of a regression model?

62 What are the assumptions of regression analysis and how can they be evaluated?

63 What is the Durbin-Watson statistic and when and how should it be used in regression analysis?

64 Under what circumstances is it important to compute the Durbin-Watson statistic? Explain.

65 What is the difference between a confidence interval estimate of the mean response $\mu_{Y|X=X_i}$ and a prediction interval of $Y_{X=X_i}$?

Applying the Concepts

We recommend that Microsoft Excel be used to solve problems 66–82.

66 Management of a soft-drink bottling company wished to develop a method for allocating delivery costs to customers. Although one cost clearly relates to travel time within a particular route, another variable cost reflects the time required to unload the cases of soft drink at the delivery point. A sample of 20 customers was selected from routes within a territory and the delivery time and the number of cases delivered were measured with the following results: **DELIVERY.xls**

Customer	Number of Cases	Delivery Time (Minutes)	Customer	Number of Cases	Delivery Time (Minutes)
1	52	32.1	11	161	43.0
2	64	34.8	12	184	49.4
3	73	36.2	13	202	57.2
4	85	37.8	14	218	56.8
5	95	37.8	15	243	60.6
6	103	39.7	16	254	61.2
7	116	38.5	17	267	58.2
8	121	41.9	18	275	63.1
9	143	44.2	19	287	65.6
10	157	47.1	20	298	67.3

Assume that you wanted to develop a model to predict delivery time based on the number of cases delivered.

a. Set up a scatter diagram.
b. Use the least-squares method to find the regression coefficients b_0 and b_1.
c. State the regression equation.
d. Interpret the meaning of b_0 and b_1 in this problem.
e. Predict the delivery time for a customer who is receiving 150 cases of soft drink.
f. Would it be appropriate to use the model to predict the delivery time for a customer who is receiving 500 cases of soft drink? Why?
g. Determine the coefficient of determination r^2 and explain its meaning in this problem.
h. Determine the coefficient of correlation.
i. Determine the standard error of the estimate.
j. Perform a residual analysis. Is there any evidence of a pattern in the residuals? Explain.
k. At the 0.05 level of significance, is there evidence of a linear relationship between delivery time and the number of cases delivered?
l. Set up a 95% confidence interval estimate of the average delivery time for customers that receive 150 cases of soft drink.
m. Set up a 95% prediction interval of the delivery time for an individual customer who is receiving 150 cases of soft drink.
n. Set up a 95% confidence interval estimate of the population slope.
o. Explain how the results obtained in (a)–(n) can help allocate delivery costs to customers.

67 A brokerage house would like to be able to predict the number of trade executions per day and has decided to use the number of incoming phone calls as a predictor variable. Data were collected over a period of 35 days. **TRADES.xls**

a. Set up a scatter diagram.
b. Use the least-squares method to find the regression coefficients b_0 and b_1.
c. State the regression equation.
d. Interpret the meaning of b_0 and b_1 in this problem.
e. Predict the number of trades executed for a day in which the number of incoming calls is 2,000.
f. Would it be appropriate to use the model to predict the number of trades executed for a day in which the number of incoming calls is 5,000? Why?
g. Determine the coefficient of determination r^2 and explain its meaning in this problem.
h. Determine the coefficient of correlation.
i. Determine the standard error of the estimate.
j. Plot the residuals against the number of incoming calls and also against the days. Is there any evidence of a pattern in the residuals with either of these variables? Explain.
k. Determine the Durbin-Watson statistic for these data.

l. Based on the results of (j) and (k), is there reason to question the validity of the model? Explain.
m. At the 0.05 level of significance, is there evidence of a linear relationship between the volume of trade executions and the number of incoming calls?
n. Set up a 95% confidence interval estimate of the average number of trades executed for days in which the number of incoming calls is 2,000.
o. Set up a 95% prediction interval of the number of trades executed for a particular day in which the number of incoming calls is 2,000.
p. Set up a 95% confidence interval estimate of the population slope.
q. Based on the results of (a)–(p), do you think the brokerage house should focus on a strategy of increasing the total number of incoming calls or on a strategy that relies on trading by a small number of heavy traders? Explain.

68 Suppose you want to develop a model to predict selling price of homes based on assessed value. A sample of 30 recently sold single-family houses in a small city is selected to study the relationship between selling price (in $000) and assessed value (in $000). The houses in the city had been reassessed at full value 1 year prior to the study. The results are in the file: **HOUSE1.xls**

(*Hint:* First determine which are the independent and dependent variables.)

a. Plot a scatter diagram and, assuming a linear relationship, use the least-squares method to find the regression coefficients b_0 and b_1.
b. Interpret the meaning of the Y intercept b_0 and the slope b_1 in this problem.
c. Use the regression equation developed in (a) to predict the selling price for a house whose assessed value is $70,000.
d. Determine the standard error of the estimate.
e. Determine the coefficient of determination r^2 and interpret its meaning in this problem.
f. Determine the coefficient of correlation r.
g. Perform a residual analysis on your results and determine the adequacy of the fit of the model.
h. At the 0.05 level of significance, is there evidence of a linear relationship between selling price and assessed value?
i. Set up a 95% confidence interval estimate of the average selling price for houses with an assessed value of $70,000.
j. Set up a 95% prediction interval of the selling price of an individual house with an assessed value of $70,000.
k. Set up a 95% confidence interval estimate of the population slope.

69 Suppose you want to develop a model to predict assessed value based on heating area. A sample of 15 single-family houses is selected in a city. The assessed value (in thousands of dollars) and the heating area of the houses (in thousands of square feet) are recorded with the following results: **HOUSE2.xls**

House	Assessed Value ($000)	Heating Area of Dwelling (Thousands of Square Feet)
1	84.4	2.00
2	77.4	1.71
3	75.7	1.45
4	85.9	1.76
5	79.1	1.93
6	70.4	1.20
7	75.8	1.55
8	85.9	1.93
9	78.5	1.59
10	79.2	1.50
11	86.7	1.90
12	79.3	1.39
13	74.5	1.54
14	83.8	1.89
15	76.8	1.59

(*Hint:* First determine which are the independent and dependent variables.)

a. Plot a scatter diagram and, assuming a linear relationship, use the least-squares method to find the regression coefficients b_0 and b_1.
b. Interpret the meaning of the Y intercept b_0 and the slope b_1 in this problem.
c. Use the regression equation developed in (a) to predict the assessed value for a house whose heating area is 1,750 square feet.
d. Determine the standard error of the estimate.
e. Determine the coefficient of determination r^2 and interpret its meaning in this problem.
f. Determine the coefficient of correlation r.
g. Perform a residual analysis on your results and determine the adequacy of the fit of the model.
h. At the 0.05 level of significance, is there evidence of a linear relationship between assessed value and heating area?
i. Set up a 95% confidence interval estimate of the average assessed value for houses with a heating area of 1,750 square feet.
j. Set up a 95% prediction interval of the assessed value of an individual house with a heating area of 1,750 square feet.
k. Set up a 95% confidence interval estimate of the population slope.
l. Suppose that the assessed value for the fourth house was $79,700. Repeat (a)–(k) and compare the results with your original results.

70 The director of graduate studies at a large college of business would like to be able to predict the grade point index (GPI) of students in an MBA program based on the Graduate Management Aptitude Test (GMAT) score. A sample of 20 students who had completed 2 years in the program is selected; the results are as follows: **GPIGMAT.xls**

Observation	GMAT Score	GPI	Observation	GMAT Score	GPI
1	688	3.72	11	567	3.07
2	647	3.44	12	542	2.86
3	652	3.21	13	551	2.91
4	608	3.29	14	573	2.79
5	680	3.91	15	536	3.00
6	617	3.28	16	639	3.55
7	557	3.02	17	619	3.47
8	599	3.13	18	694	3.60
9	616	3.45	19	718	3.88
10	594	3.33	20	759	3.76

(*Hint:* First determine which are the independent and dependent variables.)

a. Plot a scatter diagram and, assuming a linear relationship, use the least-squares method to find the regression coefficients b_0 and b_1.

b. Interpret the meaning of the Y intercept b_0 and the slope b_1 in this problem.

c. Use the regression equation developed in (a) to predict the GPI for a student with a GMAT score of 600.

d. Determine the standard error of the estimate.

e. Determine the coefficient of determination r^2 and interpret its meaning in this problem.

f. Determine the coefficient of correlation r.

g. Perform a residual analysis on your results and determine the adequacy of the fit of the model.

h. At the 0.05 level of significance, is there evidence of a linear relationship between GMAT score and GPI?

i. Set up a 95% confidence interval estimate for the average GPI of students with a GMAT score of 600.

j. Set up a 95% prediction interval for a particular student with a GMAT score of 600.

k. Set up a 95% confidence interval estimate of the population slope.

l. Suppose the GPIs of the 19th and 20th students were incorrectly entered. The GPI for student 19 should be 3.76, and the GPI for student 20 should be 3.88. Repeat (a)–(k) and compare the results with your original results.

71 The manager of the purchasing department of a large banking organization would like to develop a model to predict the amount of time it takes to process invoices. Data are collected from a sample of 30 days, and the number of invoices processed and completion time in hours is recorded. **INVOICE.xls**

(*Hint:* First determine which are the independent and dependent variables.)

a. Set up a scatter diagram.

b. Assuming a linear relationship, use the least-squares method to find the regression coefficients b_0 and b_1.

c. Interpret the meaning of the Y intercept b_0 and the slope b_1 in this problem.

d. Use the regression equation developed in (b) to predict the amount of time it would take to process 150 invoices.

e. Determine the standard error of the estimate.

f. Determine the coefficient of determination r^2 and interpret its meaning.

g. Determine the coefficient of correlation r.

h. Perform a residual analysis of your results.

i. Based on the plots in (h), does the model seem appropriate?

j. Compute the Durbin-Watson statistic and, at the 0.05 level of significance, determine whether there is any autocorrelation in the residuals.

k. Based on the results of (h)–(j), what conclusions can you reach concerning the validity of the model fit in (b)?

l. At the 0.05 level of significance, is there evidence of a linear relationship between the amount of time and the number of invoices processed?

m. Set up a 95% confidence interval estimate of the average amount of time taken to process 150 invoices.

n. Set up a 95% prediction interval of the amount of time it would take to process 150 invoices on a particular day.

72 On January 28, 1986, the space shuttle *Challenger* exploded and seven astronauts were killed. Prior to the launch, when predicted atmospheric temperature was for freezing weather at the launch site, engineers for Morton Thiokol (the manufacturer of the rocket motor) prepared charts to make the case that the launch should not take place due to the cold weather. These arguments were rejected and the launch tragically took place. Upon investigation after the tragedy, experts agreed that the disaster occurred because of leaky rubber O-rings that did not seal properly due to the cold temperature. Data indicating the atmospheric temperature at the time of 23 previous launches and the O-ring damage index are as follows: **O-RING.xls**

Flight Number	Temperature (°F)	O-Ring Damage Index
1	66	0
2	70	4
3	69	0
5	68	0
6	67	0
7	72	0
8	73	0
9	70	0
41-B	57	4
41-C	63	2
41-D	70	4
41-G	78	0
51-A	67	0
51-B	75	0
51-C	53	11
51-D	67	0
51-F	81	0
51-G	70	0
51-I	67	0
51-J	79	0
61-A	75	4
61-B	76	0
61-C	58	4

Note: Data from flight 4 is omitted due to unknown O-ring condition.

Sources: Primary: Report of the Presidential Commission on the Space Shuttle Challenger Accident, Washington, DC, 1986, Vol. II (H1–H3) and Vol. IV (664), *Post Challenger Evaluation of Space Shuttle Risk Assessment and Management,* Washington, DC, 1988, 135–136. *Secondary: E. R. Tufte,* Visual and Statistical Thinking: Displays of Evidence for Making Decisions *(Cheshire, CT: Graphics Press, 1997).*

a. Set up a scatter diagram for the seven flights in which there was O-ring damage (O-ring damage index ≠ 0). What conclusions, if any, can you draw about the relationship between atmospheric temperature and O-ring damage?
b. Set up a scatter diagram for all 23 flights.
c. Explain any differences in the interpretation of the relationship between atmospheric temperature and O-ring damage in (a) and (b).
d. Based on the scatter diagram in (b), provide reasons for why a prediction should not be made for an atmospheric temperature of 31°F, the temperature on the morning of the launch of the *Challenger*.
e. Although the assumption of a linear relationship between atmospheric temperature may not be valid, fit a simple linear regression model to predict O-ring damage based on atmospheric temperature.
f. Plot the straight line (e) on the scatter diagram developed in (b).
g. Based on the results of (f), do you think a straight line is an appropriate model for these data? Explain.
h. Perform a residual analysis of the linear relationship fit in (f). What conclusions do you reach?

73 Brett Trueman, a professor in the business school at the University of California at Berkeley, studied the relationship between the number of visitors to an Internet company's Web site and the company's gross profit (Matt Krantz, "Net Investors Follow Stats," *USA Today*, January 20, 2000, 1B). The data in the file **PAGEVIEW.xls** summarizes Professor Trueman's findings for the 10 largest Internet companies.

Source: Extracted from USA Today, *January 20, 2000, 1B.*

Use gross profits (in millions of dollars) as the dependent variable and page views (in thousands of monthly visitors) as the independent variable.

a. Construct and interpret a scatter diagram.
b. Use the least-squares method to find the regression coefficients b_0 and b_1.
c. Interpret the coefficients in (b).
d. Construct and interpret a 95% confidence interval for the slope parameter.
e. State and interpret the coefficient of determination.
f. State and interpret the standard error of the estimate.
g. Are there any potential outliers in the data? If so, identify the company or companies and discuss your findings.
h. Remove Amazon.com from the data and reanalyze the data. Compare the results obtained with those of (a)–(g). What conclusions can you reach about the effect of Amazon.com on your findings?

74 During the fall harvest season in the United States, pumpkins are sold in large quantities at farm stands. Often, instead of weighing the pumpkins prior to sale, the farm stand operator will just place the pumpkin in the appropriate circular cutout on the counter. When asked why this was done, one farmer replied, "I can tell the weight of the pumpkin from its circumference." To determine whether this was really true, a sample of 23 pumpkins were measured for circumference and weighed with the following results. **PUMPKIN.xls**

Circumference (CM)	Weight (Grams)	Circumference (CM)	Weight (Grams)
50	1200	57	2000
55	2000	66	2500
54	1500	82	4600
52	1700	83	4600
37	500	70	3100
52	1000	34	600
53	1500	51	1500
47	1400	50	1500
51	1500	49	1600
63	2500	60	2300
33	500	59	2100
43	1000		

a. Set up a scatter diagram.
b. Assuming a linear relationship, use the least-squares method to find the regression coefficients b_0 and b_1.
c. Interpret the meaning of the slope b_1 in this problem.
d. Predict the average weight for a pumpkin that is 60 centimeters in circumference.
e. Do you think it is a good idea for the farmer to sell pumpkins by circumference instead of weight? Explain.
f. Determine the coefficient of determination r^2 and interpret its meaning.
g. Find the standard error of the estimate.
h. Perform a residual analysis for these data and determine the adequacy of the fit of the model.
i. At the 0.05 level of significance, is there evidence of a linear relationship between the circumference and the weight of a pumpkin?
j. Set up a 95% confidence interval estimate of the population slope β_1.
k. Set up a 95% confidence interval estimate of the population average weight for pumpkins that have a circumference of 60 centimeters.
l. Set up a 95% prediction interval of the weight for an individual pumpkin that has a circumference of 60 centimeters.

75 Crazy Dave, a well-known baseball analyst, would like to study various team statistics for the 2002 baseball season to determine which variables might be useful in predicting the number of wins achieved by teams during a season. He has decided to begin by using the team earned run average (ERA), a measure of pitching performance, to predict the number of wins. The data for the 30 major league teams are in the file: **BB2002.xls**

(*Hint:* First determine which are the independent and dependent variables.)

a. Set up a scatter diagram.
b. Assuming a linear relationship, use the least-squares method to find the regression coefficients b_0 and b_1.
c. Interpret the meaning of the Y intercept b_0 and the slope b_1 in this problem.
d. Use the regression equation developed in (b) to predict the number of wins for a team with an ERA of 4.50.
e. Compute the standard error of the estimate.
f. Compute the coefficient of determination r^2 and interpret its meaning.
g. Compute the coefficient of correlation.
h. Perform a residual analysis on your results and determine the adequacy of the fit of the model.
i. At the 0.05 level of significance, is there evidence of a linear relationship between the number of wins and the ERA?
j. Set up a 95% confidence interval estimate of the average number of wins expected for teams with an ERA of 4.50.
k. Set up a 95% prediction interval of the number of wins for an individual team that has an ERA of 4.50.
l. Set up a 95% confidence interval estimate of the slope.
m. The 30 teams constitute a population. In order to use statistical inference [as in (i)–(l)], the data must be assumed to represent a random sample. What "population" would this sample be drawing conclusions about?
n. What other independent variables might be considered for inclusion in the model?

76 Zagat's publishes restaurant ratings for various locations in the United States. The data file **RESTRATE.xls** contains the Zagat rating for food, décor, service, and the price per person for a sample of 50 restaurants located in New York City and 50 restaurants located on Long Island. Suppose you wanted to develop a regression model to predict the price per person based on a variable that represents the sum of the ratings for food, décor, and service.

Source: Extracted from Zagat Survey 2002 New York City Restaurants and Zagat Survey 2001–2002, Long Island Restaurants.

a. Set up a scatter diagram.
b. Assuming a linear relationship, use the least-squares method to find the regression coefficients b_0 and b_1.
c. Interpret the meaning of the Y intercept b_0 and the slope b_1 in this problem.
d. Use the regression equation developed in (b) to predict the price per person for a restaurant with a summated rating of 50.
e. Compute the standard error of the estimate.
f. Compute the coefficient of determination r^2 and interpret its meaning.
g. Compute the coefficient of correlation.
h. Perform a residual analysis on your results and determine the adequacy of the fit of the model.
i. At the 0.05 level of significance, is there evidence of a linear relationship between the price per person and the summated rating?
j. Set up a 95% confidence interval estimate of the average price per person for restaurants with a summated rating of 50.
k. Set up a 95% prediction interval of the price per person for a restaurant with a summated rating of 50.
l. Set up a 95% confidence interval estimate of the slope.
m. How useful do you think the summated rating is as a predictor of price? Explain.

77 Can demographic information be helpful in predicting the sales for sporting goods stores? The data stored in **SPORTING.xls** are the monthly sales totals from a random sample of 38 stores in a large chain of nationwide sporting goods stores. All stores in the franchise, and thus within the sample, are approximately the same size and carry the same merchandize. The county, or in some cases counties, in which the store draws the majority of its customers is referred to here as the customer base. For each of the 38 stores, demographic information about the customer base is provided. The data are real but the name of the franchise is not used at the request of the company. The variables in the data set are:

Sales: Latest one-month sales total (dollars)
Age: Median age of customer base (years)
HS: Percentage of customer base with a high school diploma
College: Percentage of customer base with a college diploma
Growth: Annual population growth rate of customer base over the past 10 years
Income: Median family income of customer base (dollars)

a. Set up a scatter diagram using sales as the dependent variable and median family income as the independent variable. Discuss the scatter diagram.
b. Assuming a linear relationship, use the least-squares method to find the regression coefficients b_0 and b_1.
c. Interpret the meaning of the Y intercept b_0 and the slope b_1 in this problem.
d. Compute the standard error of the estimate.
e. Compute the coefficient of determination r^2 and interpret its meaning.
f. Compute the coefficient of correlation r and interpret its meaning.
g. Perform a residual analysis on your results and determine the adequacy of the fit of the model.
h. At the 0.05 level of significance, is there evidence of a linear relationship between the independent variable and the dependent variable?
i. Set up a 95% confidence interval estimate of the slope and interpret its meaning.
j. Repeat (a)–(i) using age as the independent variable.

k. Repeat (a)–(i) using high school graduation rate as the independent variable.
l. Repeat (a)–(i) using college graduation rate as the independent variable.
m. Repeat (a)–(i) using growth as the independent variable.
n. Which of the five models do you think would be the best for predicting sales at an individual store location?
o. Write a short summary of your findings.

78 Each year ninth-grade students in Ohio must take a proficiency test. The data file **SCHOOLS.xls** contains data from 47 school districts in Ohio for the 1994 to 1995 school year. The variables in the data set are:

School District: Name of school district
Percentage Passing: Percentage of students passing the ninth-grade proficiency test
Percentage Attendance: Daily average of the percentage of students attending class
Salary: Average teacher salary (dollars)
Spending: Instructional spending per pupil (dollars)

Source: Mark Skertic, "School Spending Doesn't Add Up," Cincinnati Enquirer, *October 22, 1995, A1.*

a. Set up a scatter diagram using the percentage passing the proficiency test as the dependent variable and daily attendance as the independent variable. Discuss the scatter diagram.
b. Assuming a linear relationship, use the least-squares method to find the regression coefficients b_0 and b_1.
c. Interpret the meaning of the Y intercept b_0 and the slope b_1 in this problem.
d. Compute the standard error of the estimate.
e. Compute the coefficient of determination r^2 and interpret its meaning.
f. Compute the coefficient of correlation r and interpret its meaning.
g. Perform a residual analysis on your results and determine the adequacy of the fit of the model.
h. At the 0.05 level of significance, is there evidence of a linear relationship between the independent variable and the dependent variable?
i. Set up a 95% confidence interval estimate of the slope and interpret its meaning.
j. Repeat (a)–(i) using average teacher salary as the independent variable.
k. Repeat (a)–(i) using instructional spending as the independent variable.
l. Which of the three models is best at predicting the percentage of students who will pass the ninth-grade proficiency tests?
m. Write a short summary of your findings.

79 Refer to the discussion of beta values and market models in problems 38 and 39. The data file **SP500.xls** contains one year of data recorded weekly ending May 14, 2003. Note that the *weekly change* for both the S&P 500 and the four individual stocks is measured as the percentage change from the previous week's closing value to the current week's closing value. The variables included are:

Week: Current week
SP500: Weekly change in the S&P 500 Index
IAL: Weekly change in stock price of International Aluminum
SEARS: Weekly change in stock price of Sears
BancONE: Weekly change in stock price of BancOne Corporation of Ohio
GM: Weekly change in stock price of General Motors

Source: Finance.Yahoo.com, *May 15, 2003.*

a. Estimate the market model for IAL (*Hint*: Use the change in the S&P 500 Index as the independent variable and the change in IAL's stock price as the dependent variable.)
b. Interpret the beta value for IAL.
c. Repeat (a)–(b) for Sears.
d. Repeat (a)–(b) for BancOne Corporation of Ohio.
e. Repeat (a)–(b) for General Motors.
f. Write a brief summary of your findings.

80 The data file **RETURNS.xls** contains the stock price of four companies collected weekly for 53 consecutive weeks ending May 14, 2003. The variables are:

Week: Closing date for stock prices
GM: Stock price of General Motors
Ford: Stock price of Ford
IAL: Stock price of International Aluminum
MSFT: Microsoft Corporation

Source: Finance.Yahoo.com, *May 15, 2003.*

a. Calculate the correlation coefficient r for each pair of stocks. (There are six of them.)
b. Interpret the meaning of r for each pair.
c. Is it a good idea to have all the stocks in an individual's portfolio be strongly, positively correlated among each other? Explain.

81 Is the daily performance of the stock market correlated to changes in interest rates? The data file **BONDRATE.xls** contains information concerning interest rates and the Dow Jones Industrial Average for the 60 consecutive business days ending May 14, 2003. The variables included are:

Date: Current day
10-Year Bond: Change in the interest rate for U.S. Treasury 10-year bonds (measured as the percentage change from previous day's closing rate to current day's closing rate)
DJIA: Change in the Dow Jones Industrial Average (measured as the percentage change from previous day's closing number to current day's closing number)

Source: Finance.Yahoo.com, *May 15, 2003.*

a. Compute and interpret the correlation coefficient r for daily change in the DJIA and daily change in the interest rate for 10-year bonds.
b. At the 0.05 level of significance, is there a relationship between these two variables? Explain.

c. Using a level of significance of 0.10, is there a relationship between these two variables? Explain.
d. Discuss why these two variables might be correlated.

Report Writing Exercises

82 In problem 77 you developed simple linear regression models to predict monthly sales at a sporting goods store. Now, write a report based on the models you developed. Appended to your report should be all appropriate charts and statistical information obtained from the data. Be sure to incorporate tables and charts you obtained into the report using Microsoft Office as discussed in the appendix. In addition, you might want to develop an oral presentation using PowerPoint presentation tools (see the appendix on Preparing Data for Reports and Presentations Using Microsoft Office).

Internet Exercises

83 Go to the Web site for this text

www.prenhall.com/levine

Select Chapter 12 and then click on Internet exercises.

RUNNING CASE MANAGING THE *SPRINGVILLE HERALD*

To ensure that as many trial subscriptions as possible are converted to regular subscriptions, the *Herald* marketing department works closely with the distribution department to accomplish a smooth initial delivery process for the trial subscription customers. To assist in this effort, the marketing department needs to be able to better forecast the number of new regular subscriptions for the coming months.

A team consisting of managers from the marketing and distribution departments was convened to develop a better method of forecasting new subscriptions. Previously, after examining new subscription data for the previous 2 or 3 months, a group of three managers would develop a consensus on what the final forecast should be. Lauren Hall, who was recently hired by the company to provide special skills in quantitative forecasting methods, suggested that the department look for factors that might be helpful in predicting new subscriptions.

Members of the team noted that the forecasts in the last year had been particularly inaccurate because in some months much more time was spent on telemarketing than in other months. In particular, in the last month, only 1,055 hours were completed since callers were busy during the first week of the month attending training sessions on the personal but formal greeting style and a new standard presentation guide. Lauren suggested that the data for the number of new subscriptions and the number of hours spent on telemarketing for new subscriptions for each month for the past 2 years be obtained from company records. (see **SH12.xls**)

EXERCISES

SH1 What criticism can you make concerning the method of forecasting that involved taking the new subscriptions for the past 3 months as the basis for future projections?

SH2 What factors other than number of telemarketing hours spent might be useful in predicting the number of new subscriptions? Explain.

SH3 a. Analyze the data and develop a statistical model to predict the average number of new subscriptions for a month based on the number of hours spent on telemarketing for new subscriptions. Write a report giving detailed findings concerning the model that has been fit to the data.
b. If there are expected to be 1,200 hours spent on telemarketing in the coming month, estimate the average number of new subscriptions expected for the month. Indicate the assumptions upon which this prediction is based. Do you think these assumptions are valid? Explain.
c. What would be the danger of estimating the average number of new subscriptions for a month in which 2,000 hours were spent on telemarketing.

WEB CASE

Apply your knowledge of simple linear regression in this Web Case that extends the Sunflowers Clothing Stores Using Statistics *scenario from this chapter.*

Leasing agents from the Triangle Mall Management Corporation have suggested that Sunflowers consider several locations in some of Triangle's newly renovated "lifestyle" malls located in areas of higher than average disposable income. Although the locations would be smaller than the average size of a typical Sunflowers location, the leasing agents argue that higher than average disposable income in the surrounding community is a better predictor of higher sales than store size. The leasing agents maintain that sample data from 14 Sunflowers stores proves that this is true.

Review the leasing agents' proposal and supporting documents that describe the data at the company's Web site **www.prenhall.com/Springville/Triangle_Sunflower.htm** and then answer the following:

1. Should average disposable income be used to predict sales based on the sample of 14 Sunflowers stores?
2. Should the management of Sunflowers accept the claims of Triangle's leasing agents? Why, or why not?
3. Is it possible that the average disposable income of the surrounding area is not an important factor in leasing new locations? Explain.
4. Are there any other factors not mentioned by the leasing agents that might be relevant to the store leasing decision?

REFERENCES

1. Anscombe, F. J., "Graphs in Statistical Analysis," *The American Statistician* 27 (1973): 17–21.
2. Hoaglin, D. C., and R. Welsch, "The Hat Matrix in Regression and ANOVA," *The American Statistician* 32 (1978): 17–22.
3. Hocking, R. R., "Developments in Linear Regression Methodology: 1959–1982," *Technometrics* 25 (1983): 219–250.
4. Hosmer, D. W., and S. Lemeshow, *Applied Logistic Regression*, 2nd ed. (New York: Wiley, 2001).
5. *Microsoft Excel 2002* (Redmond, WA: Microsoft Corporation, 2001).
6. Neter, J., M. H. Kutner, C. J. Nachtsheim, and W. Wasserman, *Applied Linear Statistical Models*, 4th ed. (Homewood, IL: Irwin, 1996).

Answers to Selected Even-Numbered Problems

For more detailed solutions including explanations, interpretations, and Excel output, see the *Student Solutions Manual*.

2 (a) When $X = 0$, the estimated expected value of Y is 16. **(b)** For increase in the value X by 1 unit, we can expect a decrease in an estimated 0.5 units in the value of Y. **(c)** 13.

4 (b) $b_0 = -2.3697$, $b_1 = 0.0501$ **(c)** The estimated average amount of labor will increase by 0.05 hour for each additional cubic foot moved. **(d)** 22.6705.

6 (b), **(c)** $\hat{Y} = 76.54 + 4.3331X$. **(d)** For each increase of 1 million dollars in box office gross, expected home video units sold are estimated to increase by 4.3331 thousand, or 4333.1 units. **(e)** 163,202 units **(f)** Some other factors that might be useful in predicting video unit sales are (i) the number of days the movie was screened, (ii) the rating of the movie by critics, (iii) the amount of advertising spent on the video release, etc.

8 (b) $\hat{Y} = 6.0483 + 2.0191X$. **(c)** For each increase of one additional Rockwell E unit in hardness, the estimated average tensile strength will increase by 2.0191 thousand pounds per square inch. **(d)** 147.382 thousand pounds per square inch.

10 $SST = 40$ and $r^2 = 0.90$. So, 90% of the variation in the dependent variable can be explained by the variation in the independent variable.

12 $r^2 = 0.75$. So, 75% of the variation in the dependent variable can be explained by the variation in the independent variable.

14 (a) $r^2 = 0.684$. So, 68.4% of the variation in the dependent variable can be explained by the variation in the independent variable. **(b)** 0.308 **(c)** Based on (a) and (b), the model should be very useful for predicting sales.

16 (a) $r^2 = 0.9731$. So, 97.31% of the variation in the dependent variable can be explained by the variation in the independent variable. **(b)** 0.7258 **(c)** Based on (a) and (b), the model should be very useful for predicting the number of order.

18 (a) $r^2 = 0.723$. So, 72.3% of the variation in the dependent variable can be explained by the variation in the independent variable. **(b)** 194.6 **(c)** Based on (a) and (b), the model should be very useful for predicting monthly rent.

20 A residual analysis of the data indicates no apparent pattern. The assumptions of regression appear to be met.

22 (a)–(b) Based on a residual analysis, the model appears to be adequate.

24 (a) The residual plot does not reveal any obvious pattern. So a linear fit appears to be adequate. **(b)** The residual plot does not reveal any possible violation of the homoscedasticity assumption. The normal probability plot shows that the distribution has a thicker left tail than a normal distribution but there is no sign of severe skewness.

26 (a)–(b) Based on a residual analysis of the residuals versus size, the model appears to be adequate. From the normal probability plot, it appears that the normality assumption is violated.

28 (a) An increasing linear relationship exists. The critical values of the Durbin-Watson statistic are $d_L = 1.08$ and $d_U = 1.36$ **(b)** $D = 0.109$ **(c)** Since $D = 0.109 < d_L = 1.08$, there is enough evidence to conclude that there is strong positive autocorrelation among the residuals.

30 (a) No, since the data have been collected for a single period for a set of stores. **(b)** If a single store was studied over a period of time and the amount of shelf space varied over time, computation of the Durbin-Watson statistic would be necessary.

32 (b) $b_0 = 0.458$, $b_1 = 0.0161$ **(c)** For each increase of one order, the expected distribution cost is estimated to increase by 0.0161 thousand dollars, or \$16.10. **(d)** \$72,908 **(e)** $r^2 = 0.844$. So, 84.4% of the variation in distribution cost can be explained by the variation in the number of orders. **(f)** 5.218 **(i)** $D = 2.08 > 1.45$. There is no evidence of positive autocorrelation among the residuals. **(j)** Based on a residual analysis, the model appears to be adequate.

34 (b) $b_0 = -2.535$, $b_1 = 0.060728$ **(c)** For each increase of one degree Fahrenheit in the high temperature, expected sales are estimated to increase by 0.060728 thousand dollars, or \$60.73. **(d)** \$2505.40 **(e)** 0.1461 **(f)** $r^2 = 0.94$. So, 94% of the variation in sales per store can be explained by the variation in the daily high temperature. **(i)** $D = 1.64 > 1.42$. There is no evidence of positive autocorrelation among the residuals. **(j)** The plot of the residuals versus time period shows some clustering of positive and negative residuals for intervals in the domain, suggesting a nonlinear model might be better. Otherwise, the model appears to be adequate. **(k)** $b_0 = -2.6281$, $b_1 = 0.061713$. For each increase of one degree Fahrenheit in the high temperature, expected sales are estimated to increase by 0.061713 thousand dollars, or \$61.71. $\hat{Y} = 2.4941$ or \$2494.10. $r^2 = 0.929$. 92.9% of the variation in sales per store can be explained by the variation in the daily high temperature. $s_{YX} = 0.1623$, $D = 1.24$. The test of the Durbin-Watson statistic is inconclusive as to whether there is positive autocorrelation among the residuals. The plot of the residuals versus time period shows some clustering of positive and negative residuals for intervals in the domain, suggesting a nonlinear model might be better. Otherwise, the model appears to be adequate. The results are similar to those in (a)–(j).

36 (a) $MSR = 60$, $MSE = 2.222$, $F = 27$ **(b)** $F_{1,18} = 4.41$ **(c)** Reject H_0. **(d)** $r^2 = 0.6$ $r = -0.7746$ **(e)** Reject H_0 if $|t_{cal}| > 2.1009$. Since $t_{cal} = -5.196$ is below the lower critical bound of -2.1009, reject H_0.

38 (a) For Proctor and Gamble, the estimated value of its stock will increase by 0.626% on average when the S & P 500 index increases by 1%. For Ford Motor Company, the estimated value of its stock will increase by 1.074% on average when the S & P 500 index increases by 1%. For IBM, the estimated value of its stock will increase by 1.132% on average when the S & P 500 index increases by 1%. For LSI Logic, the estimated value of its stock will increase by 1.705% on average when the S & P 500 index increases by 1%. **(b)** A stock is riskier than the market if the estimated absolute value of the beta exceeds one. This can be used to gauge the volatility of a stock in relation to how the market behaves in general.

40 (a) $t = 16.5223 > t_{34} = 2.0322$. Reject H_0. **(b)** $0.0439 \le \beta_1 \le 0.0562$.

42 (a) $t = 8.65 > t_{28} = 2.0484$. Reject H_0. **(b)** $3.3073 \leq \beta_1 \leq 5.3589$.

44 (a) Since p-value = 7.26497E-06 < 0.05. Reject H_0. **(b)** $1.2463 \leq \beta_1 \leq 2.7918$.

46 (a) $r = -0.4014$. **(b)** $t = -1.8071$, p-value = 0.0885 > 0.05. Do not reject H_0. **(c)** There is not sufficient evidence to conclude that there is a linear relationship between the turnover rate of pre-boarding screeners and the security violations detected.

48 (a) $r = 0.4838$. **(b)** $t = 2.5926$, p-value = 0.0166 < 0.05. Reject H_0. **(c)** The higher the price of a battery is, the higher is its cold-cranking amps. **(d)** Yes, the expectation that batteries with higher cranking amps to have a higher price is borne out by the data.

50 (a) $15.95 \leq \mu_{YX} \leq 18.05$ **(b)** $14.651 \leq Y_I \leq 19.349$. **(c)** The intervals in this problem are wider because the value of X is farther from $\bar{X}$.

52 (a) $20.7990 \leq \mu_{Y|X} \leq 24.5419$ **(b)** $12.2755 \leq Y_I \leq 33.0654$ **(c)** Part (b) provides an estimate for an individual response and Part (a) provides an estimate for an average predicted value.

54 (a) $100.96 \leq \mu_{Y|X} \leq 138.77$ **(b)** $20.01 \leq Y_I \leq 219.72$ **(c)** Part (b) provides an estimate for an individual response and Part (a) provides an estimate for an average predicted value.

56 (a) $116.7082 \leq \mu_{Y|X} \leq 178.0564$ **(b)** $111.5942 \leq Y_I \leq 183.1704$ **(c)** Part (b) provides an estimate for an individual response and Part (a) provides an estimate for an average predicted value.

66 (b) $b_0 = 24.84$, $b_1 = 0.14$ **(c)** $\hat{Y} = 24.84 + 0.14X$ **(d)** For each additional case, the estimated delivery time increases by 0.14 minutes. **(e)** $\hat{Y} = 45.84$. **(f)** No, 500 cases is outside the relevant range of the data used to fit the regression equation. **(g)** $r^2 = 0.972$. So, 97.2% of the variation in delivery time can be explained by the variation in the number of cases. **(h)** Since b_1 is positive, $r = 0.986$ **(i)** $s_{YX} = 1.987$ **(j)** Based on a visual inspection of the graphs of the distribution of residuals and the residuals versus the number of cases, there is no pattern. The model appears to be adequate. **(k)** $t = 24.88 > t_{18} = 2.1009$. Reject H_0. **(l)** $44.88 \leq \mu_{YX} \leq 46.80$ **(m)** $41.56 \leq Y_I \leq 50.12$ **(n)** $0.1282 \leq \beta_1 \leq 0.1518$.

68 (a) $b_0 = -44.172$, $b_1 = 1.78171$ **(b)** For each additional dollar in assessed value, the estimated selling price increases by \$1.78. **(c)** $\hat{Y} = 80.458$ or \$80,458 **(d)** $s_{YX} = 3.475$ **(e)** $r^2 = 0.926$. 92.6% of the variation in selling price can be explained by the variation in the assessed value. **(f)** $r = 0.962$ **(g)** Based on a visual inspection of the graphs of the distribution of residuals and the residuals versus the assessed value, there is no pattern. The model appears to be adequate. **(h)** $t = 18.66 > t_{28} = 2.0484$. Reject H_0. **(i)** $78.707 \leq \mu_{YX} \leq 82.388$ **(j)** $73.195 \leq Y_I \leq 87.900$ **(k)** $1.5862 \leq \beta_1 \leq 1.9772$.

70 (a) $b_0 = 0.30$, $b_1 = 0.00487$ **(b)** For each additional point on the GMAT score, the estimated GPI increases by 0.00487. **(c)** $\hat{Y} = 3.2225$ **(d)** $s_{YX} = 0.1559$ **(e)** $r^2 = 0.7978$. 79.78% of the variation in the GPI can be explained by the variation in the GMAT score. **(f)** $r = 0.893$ **(g)** Based on a visual inspection of the graphs of the distribution of residuals and the residuals versus the GMAT score, there is no pattern. The model appears to be adequate. **(h)** $t = 8.428 > t_{18} = 2.1009$. Reject H_0. **(i)** $3.144 \leq \mu_{YX} \leq 3.301$ **(j)** $2.886 \leq Y_I \leq 3.559$ **(k)** $0.00366 \leq \beta_1 \leq 0.00608$ **(l)** $b_0 = 0.258$, $b_1 = 0.00494$. For each additional point on the GMAT score, the estimated GPI increases by 0.00494. $\hat{Y} = 3.221$. $s_{YX} = 0.147$, $r^2 = 0.820$. 82.0% of the variation in the GPI can be explained by the variation in the GMAT score. $r = 0.906$. Based on a visual inspection of the graphs of the distribution of residuals and the residuals versus the GMAT score, there is no pattern. The model appears to be adequate. $t = 9.06 > t_{18} = 2.1009$. Reject H_0. $3.147 \leq \mu_{YX} \leq 3.295$ $2.903 \leq Y_I \leq 3.539$ $0.00380 \leq \beta_1 \leq 0.00609$.

72 (a) There is not any clear relationship between atmospheric temperature and O-ring damage from the scatter plot. **(c)** In (b), there are 16 observations with an O-ring damage index of 0 for a variety of temperature. If one concentrates on these observations with no O-ring damage, there is obviously no relationship between O-ring damage index and temperature. If all observations are used, the observations with no O-ring damage will bias the estimated relationship. If the intention is to investigate the relationship between the degrees of O-ring damage to atmospheric temperature, it makes sense to focus only on the flight in which there was O-ring damage. **(d)** Prediction should not be made for an atmospheric temperature of 31°F because it is outside the range of the temperature variable in the data. **(e)** $\hat{Y} = 18.036 - 0.240X$ **(g)** A nonlinear model is more appropriate for these data. **(h)** The string of negative residuals and positive residuals that lie on a straight line with a positive slope in the lower-right corner of the plot is a strong indication that a nonlinear model should be used if all 23 observations are to be used in the fit.

74 (b) $\hat{Y} = -2629.222 + 82.4717X$ **(c)** For each increase in one additional cm in circumference, the estimated average weight of a pumpkin will increase by 82.4717 grams. **(d)** $\hat{Y} = 2319.080$ grams. **(e)** There appears to be a positive relationship between weight and circumference of a pumpkin. **(f)** $r^2 = 0.9373$. 93.73% of the variation in pumpkin weight can be explained by the variation in circumference. **(g)** $S_{YX} = 277.7495$. **(h)** There appears to be a nonlinear relationship between circumference and weight. **(i)** p-value is virtually 0. Reject H_0. **(j)** $72.7875 < \beta_1 < 92.1559$ **(k)** $2186.9589 < \mu_{Y|X} < 2451.2020$ **(l)** $1726.5508 < Y_I < 2911.6101$.

76 (b) $\hat{Y} = -13.6561 + 0.8932X$ **(c)** It is not meaningful to interpret b_0. For each additional unit of increase in summated rating, the estimated average price per person will increase by \$0.8932. **(d)** $\hat{Y} = \$31.01$ **(e)** $S_{YX} = 7.0167$ **(f)** $r^2 = 0.4246$. 42.46% of the variation in price per person can be explained by the variation in summated rating. **(g)** $r = 0.6516$. **(h)** Based on a visual inspection of the residual plot of summated rating, there may be a violation of the homoscedasticity assumption. **(i)** p-value is virtually 0. Reject H_0. **(j)** $\$29.07 < \mu_{Y|X} < \$32.94$. **(k)** $\$16.95 < Y_I < \$45.06$ **(l)** $0.6848 < \beta_1 < 1.1017$. **(m)** The linear regression model appears to have provided an adequate fit and shown a significant linear relationship between price per person and summated rating.

78 (a) There is a very obvious positive relationship between % of students passing the proficiency test and the daily average of the percentage of students attending class. **(b)** $b_0 = -771.5868$, $b_1 = 8.8447$ $\hat{Y} = -771.5869 + 8.8447X$ **(c)** $b_1 = 8.8447$ implies that as daily average percentage of students attending class increases by 1%, the estimated average percentage of students passing the ninth-grade proficiency test will increase by 8.8447%. **(d)** $S_{YX} = 10.5787$. **(e)** $r^2 = 0.6024$. 60.24% of the total variation in % passing the proficiency test can be explained by % attendance. **(f)** $r = 0.7762$. There is a rather strong positive linear relationship between % of students passing the proficiency test and daily average of the % of students attending class. **(g)** The residuals are evenly distributed across the range of % attendance. There is no obvious violation of the homoscedasticity assumption. The distribution of the residuals is left-skewed. However, with the exception of two extremely negative residuals, the histogram is not too badly skewed. **(h)** Reject H_0 when $|t| > 2.0141$. Since $t = 8.2578$ is above the upper critical bound 2.0141, reject H_0. **(i)** 6.6874 <

$\beta_1 < 11.0020$ **(j) (a)** There seems to be a slightly positive relationship between % of students passing the proficiency test and average teacher salary. **(b)** $\hat{Y} = 23.065 + 0.0011X$ **(c)** $b_1 = 0.0011$ implies that as average teacher salary increase by \$1, the estimated average percentage of students passing the ninth-grade proficiency test will increase by 0.0011%. **(d)** $S_{YX} = 16.3755$ **(e)** $r^2 = 0.0474$. Only 4.74% of the total variation in % passing the proficiency test can be explained by average teacher salary. **(f)** $r = 0.2177$. There seems to be a rather weak positive linear relationship between % of students passing the proficiency test and average teacher salary. **(g)** The residuals are evenly distributed across difference range of % attendance. There is no obvious violation of the homoscedasticity assumption. The distribution of the residuals is slightly left-skewed but not too far from a normal distribution. **(h)** Reject H_0 when $|t| > 2.0141$. Since $t = 1.496$ is below the upper critical bound 2.0141, do not reject H_0. **(i)** $-0.000375 < \beta_1 < 0.002542$ **(k) (a)** There seems to be a slightly positive relationship between % of students passing the proficiency test and spending per pupil. **(b)** $\hat{Y} = 35.7843 + 0.0109X$ **(c)** $b_1 = 0.0109$ implies that as spending per pupil increases by \$1, the estimated average percentage of students passing the ninth-grade proficiency test will increase by 0.019%. **(d)** $S_{YX} = 15.9984$ **(e)** $r^2 = 0.0907$. Only 9.07% of the total variation in % passing the proficiency test can be explained by spending per pupil. **(f)** $r = 0.3012$. There seems to be a rather weak positive linear relationship between % of students passing the proficiency test and spending per pupil. The residuals are evenly distributed across difference range of % attendance. There is no obvious violation of the homoscedasticity assumption.

12.78 (k) (g) The distribution of the residuals is slightly left-skewed. Excluding the largest negative residual, the histogram is symmetric. **(h)** Reject H_0 when $|t| > 2.0141$. Since $t = 2.1192$ is above the upper critical bound 2.0141, reject H_0. **(i)** $0.00054 < \beta_1 < 0.02129$. **(l)** The model with % attendance is the best model to use for predicting % passing since it has the highest R-square of 60.24%.

80 (a) GM and Ford: $r = 0.947235$, GM and IAL: $r = 0.33972$, GM and Microsoft: $r = 0.177661$, Ford and IAL: $r = 0.402414$, Ford and Microsoft: $r = 0.25265$, IAL and Microsoft: $r = 0.29521$. **(b)** There is a strong positive correlation of $r = 0.9472$ between the stock prices of GM and Ford, a moderately positive correlation of 0.4024 between the prices of Ford and IAL, a weak positive correlation of $r = 0.3397$ between the prices of GM and IAL, a weak positive correlation of $r = 0.2527$ between the prices of Ford and Microsoft, a weak positive correlation of $r = 0.2952$ between the prices of IAL and Microsoft and a very weak positive correlation of $r = 0.1777$ between GM and Microsoft. **(c)** It is not a good idea to have all the stocks in an individual's portfolio be strongly positively correlated for that will increase the variance, a measure of risk, of the portfolio. Some negatively correlated stock prices in a portfolio can reduce the combined variance (portfolio risk).

Excel Handbook for Simple Linear Regression

EH1 PERFORMING SIMPLE LINEAR REGRESSION ANALYSIS

To perform a simple linear regression analysis, use the Data Analysis Regression procedure. For example, to perform a simple linear regression analysis for the site selection data of Table 1, open to the **Data** worksheet of the **Chapter 12.xls** workbook and:

Select **Tools | Data Analysis**.

Select **Regression** from the list box in the Data Analysis dialog box and click the **OK** button.

In the Regression dialog box (shown at right):

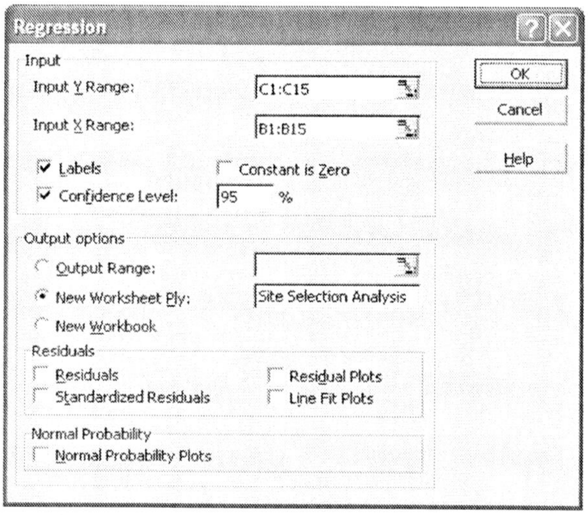

Enter **C1:C15** in the **Input Y Range** edit box.

Enter **B1:B15** in the **Input X Range** edit box.

Select the **Labels** check box.

Select the **Confidence Level check box** and enter **95** in its edit box.

Select the **New Worksheet Ply** option button and enter a name for the new sheet.

Click the **OK** button.

*This procedure generates a worksheet that does **not** dynamically change. Therefore, you will need to rerun the procedure if you make any changes to the underlying sample data in order to update the results.*

EH2 ADDING A LINE OF REGRESSION TO A SCATTER DIAGRAM

To add a fitted line of regression to a scatter diagram, use the Excel Add Trendline command. For example, to add a line of regression to a scatter diagram for the site selection data of Table 1, first follow the "Using Excel with PHStat2" or the "Using Excel: Generate Scatter Diagram Task" instructions. With the workbook open to the new scatter diagram chart sheet, select **Chart | Add Trendline**. In the Add Trendline dialog box:

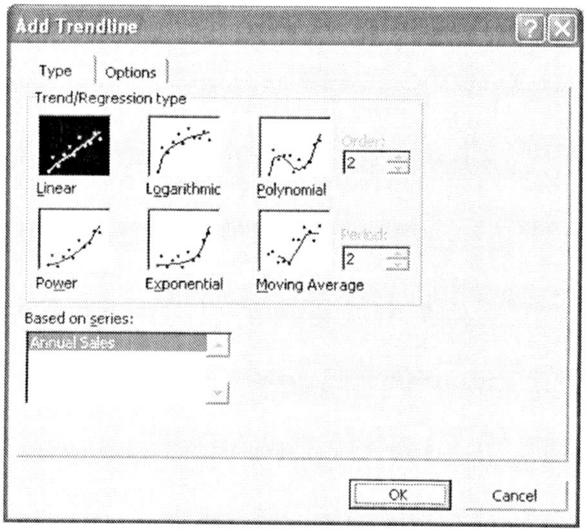

Select the **Type** tab and select the **Linear** choice in the Trend/ Regression type group (shown at right).

Select the **Options** tab and select the **Automatic** option button and the **Display equation on chart** and **Display R-squared value on chart** check boxes (shown at right).

Click the **OK** button.

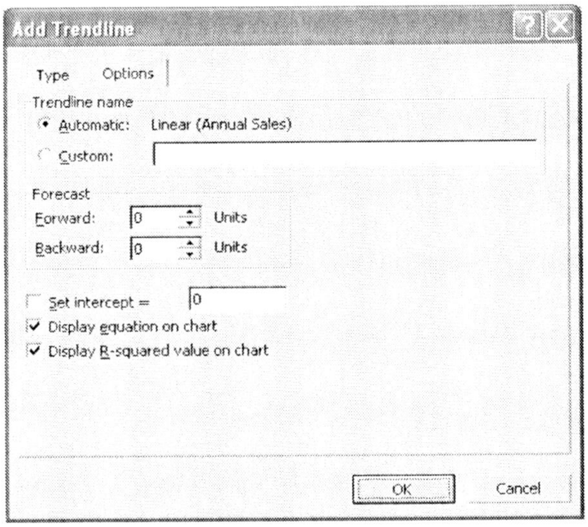

EH3 MODIFYING RESIDUAL PLOTS AND SCATTER DIAGRAMS

Limitations in the Chart Wizard and Data Analysis Regression tool sometimes produce scatter diagrams and residual plots that are awkwardly formatted. Use the following procedures, as appropriate, to enhance the formatting of these charts, if necessary.

Converting a chart object into a chart sheet. The Data Analysis Regression tool produces residual plots as chart objects, superimposed over a worksheet, and not as chart sheets as is done in instructions throughout this text. To convert a chart object into a chart sheet, select the residual plot chart, then select **Chart** | **Location**. In the Chart Location dialog box (shown at right), select the **As new sheet** option button, enter a descriptive and unique sheet name, and click the **OK** button to generate the chart.

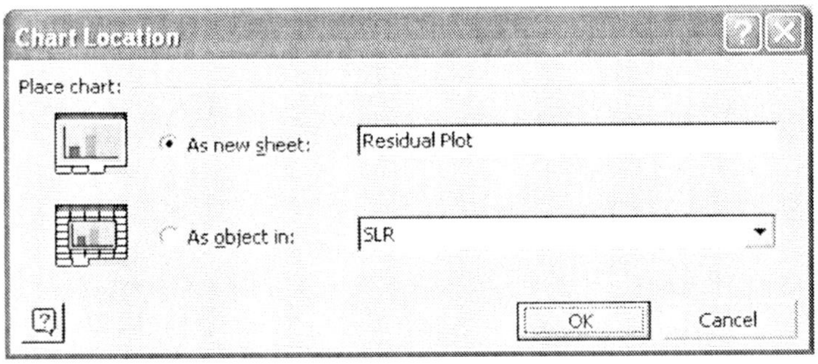

Relocating an X-axis to the bottom of a chart. If there are Y values on a residual plot or scatter diagram that are less than zero, Microsoft Excel will place the X-axis at the point $Y = 0$, possibly obscuring some of the data points. To relocate the X-axis to the bottom of the chart, select the chart and:

Right-click the **Y-axis**. (The tool tip "Value (Y) axis" appears when the mouse pointer is properly positioned over this axis (shown at right).

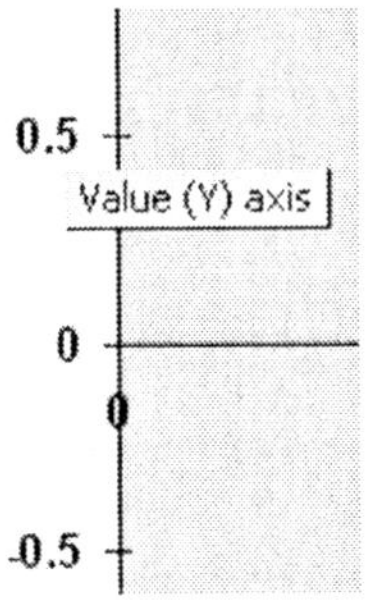

Select **Format Axis** from the shortcut menu.

In the Format Axis dialog box (shown at right), select the **Scale** tab and enter the value found in the **Minimum** edit box in the **Value (X) axis Crosses at** edit box. As you enter this value, the check box for this entry is deselected automatically. You can also optionally change the values for the minimum and maximum values for the Y-axis.

Click the **OK** button.

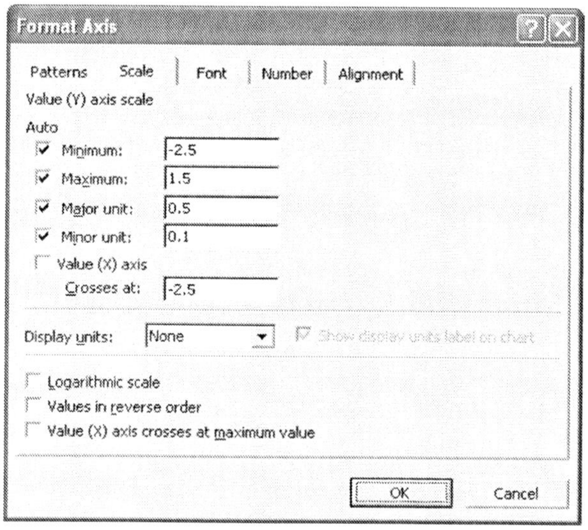

EH4 CALCULATING THE DURBIN-WATSON STATISTIC

To calculate the Durbin-Watson statistic, first perform a simple linear regression analysis on your data (see section EH1) and then implement a worksheet that features the **SUMXMY2** and **SUMSQ** functions. These functions are entered as **SUMXMY2(*variable 1 cell range*, *variable 2 cell range*)** and **SUMSQ(*variable cell range*)**.

Table EH1 contains the design for a **Durbin Watson** worksheet that calculates this statistic for the simple linear regression analysis of the package delivery sales data of Table 3. This design calculates the sum of squared differences between the set of e_i and e_{i-1} values, and the sum of the squared values for all residual values, using the SUMXMY2 and SUMSQ functions, respectively. This design assumes that the residuals appear on a worksheet named SLR in the cell range C25:C39. (Both the PHStat2 Simple Linear Regression procedure and the Data Analysis Regression tool place the calculated residuals in the cell range C25:C39.)

Table EH1
Durbin-Watson worksheet design

	A	B
1	Durbin-Watson Calculations	
2		
3	Sum of Squared Difference of Residuals	=SUMXMY2(SLR!C26:C39,SLR!C25:C38)
4	Sum of Squared Residuals	=SUMSQ(SLR!C25:C39)
5		
6	Durbin-Watson Statistic	=B3/B4

EH5 CALCULATING CONFIDENCE INTERVAL ESTIMATES AND PREDICTION INTERVALS

To calculate the confidence interval for the mean response and the prediction interval for an individual response, first perform a simple linear regression analysis on your data (see section EH1) and then implement two interrelated worksheets, one that features the **TINV(*1-confidence level*, *degrees of freedom*)** and **TREND(*Y variable cell range*, *X variable cell range*, *X value*)**.

Table EH2 contains the design for an **Intervals** worksheet that calculates the confidence interval for the mean response and the prediction interval for an individual response for the simple linear regression analysis of the site selection data of Table 1. This design calculates the *t* statistic value using the TINV function and calculates the average predicted *Y* for a given *X* value using the TREND function. This design assumes that the standard error of the estimate S_{YX} appears on a worksheet named *SLR* in cell B7. (Both the PHStat2 Simple Linear Regression procedure and the Data Analysis Regression tool place the standard error in cell B7.)

Table EH2
Intervals worksheet design

	A	B
1	Site Selection Analysis	
2		
3	Data	
4	X Value	4
5	Confidence Level	0.95
6		
7	Intermediate Calculations	
8	Sample Size	=COUNT(Data!B:B)
9	Degrees of Freedom	=B8 – 2
10	t Value	=TINV(1 – B5, B9)
11	Sample Mean	=AVERAGE(Data!B:B)
12	Sum of Squared Difference	=SUM(Data!D:D)
13	Standard Error of the Estimate	=SLR!B7
14	h Statistic	=1/B8 + (B4 – B11)^2/B12
15	Average Predicted Y (YHat)	=TREND(Data!C2:C15, DATA!B2:B15, B4)
16		
17	For Average Y	
18	Interval Half Width	=B10 * B13 * SQRT(B14)
19	Confidence Interval Lower Limit	=B15 – B18
20	Confidence Interval Upper Limit	=B15 + B18
21		
22	For Individual Response Y	
23	Interval Half Width	=B10 * B13 * SQRT(1 + B14)
24	Prediction Interval Lower Limit	=B15 – B23
25	Prediction Interval Upper Limit	=B15 + B23

The design also assumes that the site selection data of Table 1 appears in a **Data** worksheet in columns B and C (as it does in **CHAPTER 12.xls**) and that column D of that worksheet calculates the squares of the differences for each X value.

When implementing this design, implement the Intervals worksheet first and then add the column D entries to the Data worksheet using the procedure above. Do not worry about any #DIV/0! error messages that may appear in cells as you implement Table EH2. These will disappear when you add the column D entries to the Data worksheet. To do this, click the **Data** sheet tab and enter the heading **(X-XBar)^2** in cell **D1**. Then enter the formula **=(B2–Intervals$B$11)^2** in cell **D2** and copy this formula down through **row 15**.

Introduction to Multiple Regression

USING STATISTICS: Predicting OmniPower Sales

LEARNING OBJECTIVES

- To develop a multiple regression model
- To interpret the regression coefficients
- To determine which independent variables should be included in the regression model
- To determine which independent variables are more important in predicting a dependent variable
- To use categorical variables in a regression model

USING STATISTICS

Predicting OmniPower Sales

You are the marketing manager for Omni Foods, a large food products company that is interested in introducing a low-priced, high-energy bar called OmniPower. High-energy bars, loaded with fats, carbohydrates, and calories, are designed to provide quick energy for runners, mountain climbers, and other athletes involved in long, strenuous activities. Sales of high-energy bars have skyrocketed in recent years, and the grocery store chain believes that there is a potentially strong market for OmniPower. Before introducing the bar nationwide, you need to determine the effect that price and in-store promotions will have on the sales of OmniPower. A sample of 34 stores in a supermarket chain is selected for a test-market study, and you need to construct a regression model in order to analyze the data obtained from the study. How can you incorporate the effects of price and promotion into this zmodel? How can you use this model to improve the success of the nationwide introduction of OmniPower?

INTRODUCTION

In simple regression, the focus is on a model in which one numerical independent or explanatory variable X is used to predict the value of a numerical dependent or response variable Y. It is often the case that a better-fitting model can be developed if more than one explanatory variable is considered. Thus, in this chapter, discussion is extended to consider **multiple regression** models in which several explanatory variables can be used to predict the value of a dependent variable.

1 DEVELOPING THE MULTIPLE REGRESSION MODEL

A sample of 34 stores in a chain is selected for a test-market study of OmniPower. All the stores selected have approximately the same monthly sales volume. Two independent variables are considered here—the price of an OmniPower bar as measured in cents (X_1) and the monthly budget for in-store promotional expenditures measured in dollars (X_2). In-store promotional expenditures typically include signs and displays, in-store coupons, and free samples. The dependent variable Y is the number of OmniPower bars sold in a month. The results are presented in Table 1.

Interpreting the Regression Coefficients

When several explanatory variables are present, a simple linear regression model can be extended by assuming a linear relationship between each explanatory variable and the dependent variable. For example, with k explanatory variables, the multiple regression model is expressed as shown in Equation (1).

TABLE 1
Monthly OmniPower sales, price, and promotional expenditures

OMNI.xls

Store	Sales	Price	Promotion	Store	Sales	Price	Promotion
1	4,141	59	200	18	2,730	79	400
2	3,842	59	200	19	2,618	79	400
3	3,056	59	200	20	4,421	79	400
4	3,519	59	200	21	4,113	79	600
5	4,226	59	400	22	3,746	79	600
6	4,630	59	400	23	3,532	79	600
7	3,507	59	400	24	3,825	79	600
8	3,754	59	400	25	1,096	99	200
9	5,000	59	600	26	761	99	200
10	5,120	59	600	27	2,088	99	200
11	4,011	59	600	28	820	99	200
12	5,015	59	600	29	2,114	99	400
13	1,916	79	200	30	1,882	99	400
14	675	79	200	31	2,159	99	400
15	3,636	79	200	32	1,602	99	400
16	3,224	79	200	33	3,354	99	600
17	2,295	79	400	34	2,927	99	600

MULTIPLE REGRESSION MODEL WITH *k* INDEPENDENT VARIABLES

$$Y_i = \beta_0 + \beta_1 X_{1i} + \beta_2 X_{2i} + \beta_3 X_{3i} + \cdots + \beta_k X_{ki} + \varepsilon_i \tag{1}$$

where

β_0 = Y intercept
β_1 = slope of Y with variable X_1 holding variables $X_2, X_3, \ldots, X_k$ constant
β_2 = slope of Y with variable X_2 holding variables $X_1, X_3, \ldots, X_k$ constant
β_3 = slope of Y with variable X_3 holding variables $X_1, X_2, \ldots, X_k$ constant
.
.
.
β_k = slope of Y with variable X_k holding variables $X_1, X_2, X_3, \ldots, X_{k-1}$ constant
ε_i = random error in Y for observation i

Equation (2) defines the multiple regression model with two explanatory variables.

MULTIPLE REGRESSION MODEL WITH 2 INDEPENDENT VARIABLES

$$Y_i = \beta_0 + \beta_1 X_{1i} + \beta_2 X_{2i} + \varepsilon_i \tag{2}$$

where

β_0 = Y intercept
β_1 = slope of Y with variable X_1 holding variable X_2 constant
β_2 = slope of Y with variable X_2 holding variable X_1 constant
ε_i = random error in Y for observation i

This multiple regression model can be compared with the simple linear regression model, expressed as

$$Y_i = \beta_0 + \beta_1 X_i + \varepsilon_i$$

In the simple regression model, note that the slope β_1 represents the change in the mean of Y per unit change in X and does not take into account any other variables besides the single independent variable included in the model. In the multiple regression model with two independent variables [Equation (2)], the slope β_1 represents the change in the mean of Y per unit change in X_1, taking into account the effect of X_2. β_1 is referred to as a **net regression coefficient**.[1]

[1] *Net regression coefficients are sometimes referred to as partial regression coefficients.*

As in the case of simple regression, the sample regression coefficients (b_0, b_1, and b_2) are used as estimates of the population parameters (β_0, β_1, and β_2). The regression equation for a multiple regression model with two explanatory variables is given in Equation (3).

MULTIPLE REGRESSION EQUATION WITH 2 INDEPENDENT VARIABLES

$$\hat{Y}_i = b_0 + b_1 X_{1i} + b_2 X_{2i} \tag{3}$$

Microsoft Excel can be used to obtain the values of the three regression coefficients using the least-squares method. Figure 1 presents partial output for the OmniPower sales data from Microsoft Excel. From Figure 1, observe that the computed values of the regression coefficients are

$$b_0 = 5{,}837.52 \quad b_1 = -53.2173 \quad b_2 = 3.6131$$

Therefore, the multiple regression equation can be expressed as

$$\hat{Y}_i = 5{,}837.52 - 53.2173 X_{1i} + 3.6131 X_{2i}$$

where

$\hat{Y}_i$ = predicted average monthly sales of OmniPower bars for store i
X_{1i} = price of OmniPower bar (in cents) for store i
X_{2i} = monthly in-store promotional expenditures (in dollars) for store i

FIGURE 1
Partial output obtained from Microsoft Excel for OmniPower sales data

	A	B	C	D	E	F	G
1	**OmniPower Sales Analysis**						
2							
3	*Regression Statistics*						
4	Multiple R	0.870475					
5	R Square	0.757726					
6	Adjusted R Square	0.742095					
7	Standard Error	638.06529					
8	Observations	34					
9							
10	ANOVA						
11		*df*	*SS*	*MS*	*F*	*Significance F*	
12	Regression	2	39472730.77	19736365.387	48.47713433	2.86258E-10	
13	Residual	31	12620946.67	407127.312			
14	Total	33	52093677.44				
15							
16		*Coefficients*	*Standard Error*	*t Stat*	*P-value*	*Lower 95%*	*Upper 95%*
17	Intercept	5837.5208	628.150	9.29319	1.79101E-10	4556.39921	7118.64230
18	Price	-53.21734	6.85222	-7.76644	9.20016E-09	-67.19254	-39.24213
19	Promotion	3.61306	0.68522	5.27283	9.82196E-06	2.21554	5.01058

The sample Y intercept b_0, computed as 5,837.52, estimates the expected number of OmniPower bars sold in a month if the price is \$0.00 and the total amount spent on promotional expenditures is also \$0.00. Because these values of price and promotion are outside the range of price and promotion observed and are nonsensical, the value of b_0 has no practical interpretation.

The slope of price with OmniPower sales (b_1, computed as −53.2173) means that, for a given amount of monthly promotional expenditures, the expected sales of OmniPower are estimated to decrease by 53.2173 bars per month for each 1-cent increase in the price. The slope of monthly promotional expenditures with OmniPower sales (b_2, computed as 3.6131) means that, for a given price, the expected sales of OmniPower are estimated to increase by 3.6131 bars for each additional \$1 spent on promotions. These estimates allow the marketing department to better understand the likely effect that price and promotion decisions will have in the marketplace. For example, a 10-cent decrease in price is estimated to increase sales by 532.173 bars, with a fixed amount of monthly promotional expenditures, whereas a \$100 increase in promotional expenditures is estimated to increase sales by 361.31 bars, for a given price.

INTERPRETING THE SLOPES IN MULTIPLE REGRESSION

Regression coefficients in multiple regression are called net regression coefficients and measure the average change in Y per unit change in a particular X, *holding constant the effect of the other X variables*. For example, in the study of OmniPower bar sales, for a store with a given amount of promotional expenditures, the expected sales are estimated to decrease by 53.22 bars per month for each 1-cent increase in the price of the OmniPower bar. Another way to interpret this is to think of similar stores with an equal amount of promotional expenditures. For such stores (with the same promotional expenditures), expected sales are predicted to decrease by 53.22 bars per month for each 1-cent increase in the price of the OmniPower bar.

In a similar manner, the slope of sales with promotional expenditures can be viewed from the perspective of two similar stores (except for the amount of promotional expenditures) with the same price for an OmniPower bar. For these stores, the expected sales are estimated to increase by 3.61 bars per month for each additional dollar of promotional expenditures. It is this conditional nature of the interpretation that is critical to understanding the magnitude of each slope.

Predicting the Dependent Variable Y

Now that the multiple regression model has been fitted to these data, you can predict the average monthly sales of OmniPower bars and develop a confidence interval estimate and a prediction interval, assuming that the regression model fitted is an appropriate one.

Suppose you want to predict the average number of bars of OmniPower sold for a store that has a sales price of 79 cents during a month in which promotional expenditures are \$400. Using the multiple regression equation

$$\hat{Y}_i = 5{,}837.52 - 53.2173X_{1i} + 3.6131X_{2i}$$

with $X_{1i} = 79$ and $X_{2i} = 400$,

$$\hat{Y}_i = 5{,}837.52 - 53.2173(79) + 3.6131(400)$$

and thus

$$\hat{Y}_i = 3{,}078.57$$

Therefore, you estimate that an average of 3,078.57 OmniPower bars would be sold in stores that have a price of 79 cents per bar and \$400 in promotional expenditures.

After the prediction of Y has been obtained, and a residual analysis (see section 2) has been conducted, the next step involves developing a confidence interval estimate of the mean response and a prediction interval for an individual response. Confidence and prediction intervals obtained from Microsoft Excel for the OmniPower bar sales are presented in Figure 2.

The 95% confidence interval estimate of the average OmniPower bar sales under these circumstances is between 2,854.07 and 3,303.08 bars. The prediction interval for an individual store is between 1,758.01 and 4,399.14 bars.

FIGURE 2
Confidence interval estimate and prediction interval obtained from Microsoft Excel for the OmniPower example

	A	B	C	D
1	Confidence and Prediction Estimate Intervals			
2				
3	Data			
4	Confidence Level	95%		
5		1		
6	Price given value	79		
7	Promotion given value	400		
8				
9	X'X	34	2646	13200
10		2646	214674	1018800
11		13200	1018800	6000000
12				
13	Inverse of X'X	0.969163	-0.00941	-0.00053
14		-0.00941	0.000115	1.12E-06
15		-0.00053	1.12E-06	1.15E-06
16				
17	X'G times Inverse of X'X	0.012054	0.000149	1.49E-05
18				
19	[X'G times Inverse of X'X] times XG	0.029762		
20	t Statistic	2.039515		
21	Predicted Y (YHat)	3078.574		
22				
23	For Average Predicted Y (YHat)			
24	Interval Half Width	224.5031		
25	Confidence Interval Lower Limit	2854.071		
26	Confidence Interval Upper Limit	3303.077		
27				
28	For Individual Response Y			
29	Interval Half Width	1320.567		
30	Prediction Interval Lower Limit	1758.008		
31	Prediction Interval Upper Limit	4399.141		

Coefficients of Multiple Determination

The coefficient of determination r^2 measures the variation in Y that is explained by the independent variable X in the simple linear regression model. In multiple regression, because there are at least two explanatory variables, the **coefficient of multiple determination** represents the proportion of the variation in Y that is explained by the set of explanatory variables selected. Equation (4) defines the coefficient of multiple determination for a multiple regression model with two or more explanatory variables.

THE COEFFICIENT OF MULTIPLE DETERMINATION

The coefficient of multiple determination is equal to the regression sum of squares (*SSR*) divided by the total sum of squares (*SST*).

$$r^2_{Y.12\ldots k} = \frac{SSR}{SST} \quad (4)$$

where

SSR = regression sum of squares
SST = total sum of squares

In the OmniPower example, from Figure 1, $SSR = 39{,}472{,}730.77$, $SST = 52{,}093{,}677.44$, and $k = 2$. Thus,

$$r^2_{Y.12} = \frac{SSR}{SST} = \frac{39{,}472{,}730.77}{52{,}093{,}677.44} = 0.7577$$

This coefficient of multiple determination, computed as 0.7577, means that 75.77% of the variation in sales can be explained by the variation in the price and the variation in the promotional expenditures.

However, when dealing with multiple regression models, some statisticians suggest that the **adjusted r^2** should be computed to reflect both the number of explanatory variables in the model and the sample size. This is especially necessary when you are comparing two or more regression models that predict the same dependent variable but have a different number of explanatory variables. Equation (5) defines the adjusted r^2.

ADJUSTED r^2

$$r^2_{\text{adj}} = 1 - \left[(1 - r^2_{Y.12\ldots k})\frac{n-1}{n-k-1}\right] \tag{5}$$

where k is the number of explanatory variables in the regression equation.

Thus, for the OmniPower bar data, because $r^2_{Y.12} = 0.7577$, $n = 34$, and $k = 2$,

$$\begin{aligned} r^2_{\text{adj}} &= 1 - \left[(1 - r^2_{Y.12})\frac{(34-1)}{(34-2-1)}\right] \\ &= 1 - \left[(1 - 0.7577)\frac{33}{31}\right] \\ &= 1 - 0.2579 \\ &= 0.7421 \end{aligned}$$

Hence, 74.21% of the variation in sales can be explained by the multiple regression model—adjusted for number of predictors and sample size.

Excel Strategies Performing Multiple Regression Analysis

You perform a multiple regression analysis and calculate a confidence interval estimate and prediction interval by first using the Data Analysis Regression procedure and then implementing a worksheet that features the **TINV** and several advanced mathematical functions. PHStat2 can do these tasks for you in a single step.

For example, to perform a multiple regression analysis for the OmniPower sales data of Table 1, open to the **Data** worksheet of the **Chapter 13.xls** workbook and use one of these strategies:

CHAPTER 13.xls

Retrieve the Figure 13.1 and Figure 13.2 worksheets of the ***Chapter 13.xls*** *workbook to view the multiple regression model and confidence interval estimate and prediction interval shown on the preceding pages.*

Using Excel with PHStat2

Use the PHStat2 Multiple Regression procedure to perform a multiple regression analysis.

Select **PHStat2 | Regression | Multiple Regression**.

In the Multiple Regression dialog box (shown at right):

Enter **A1:A35** in the **Y Variable Cell Range** edit box.

Enter **B1:C35** in the **X Variables Cell Range** edit box.

Select the **First cells in both ranges contain label** check box.

Enter **95** in the **Confidence level for regression coefficients** edit box.

Select the **Regression Statistics Table** and the **ANOVA and Coefficients Table** check boxes.

Enter a title in the **Title** edit box.

Select the **Confidence Interval Estimate & Prediction Interval** check box and enter **95** in the **Confidence level for interval estimates** edit box.

Click the **OK** button.

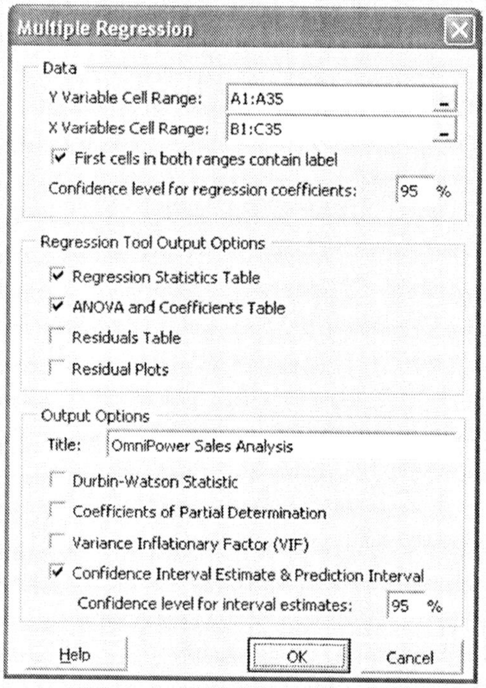

To complete the analysis, enter the values for each of the X variables in the appropriate column B cells in the worksheet generated to calculate the confidence interval estimate and prediction interval.

*This procedure generates a multiple regression statistics worksheet that does **not** dynamically change. Therefore, you will need to rerun the procedure if you make any changes to the underlying sample data in order to update the results.*

Using Excel

Generate Multiple Regression Model Task. Follow the instructions of section EH1 (at the end of this chapter) to generate the multiple regression model.

Calculate Confidence Interval Estimate and Prediction Interval Task. Follow the instructions of section EH2 to manually implement worksheets that calculate a confidence interval estimate and prediction interval for the multiple regression model.

PROBLEMS FOR SECTION 1

Learning the Basics

1 For this problem use the following multiple regression equation:

$$\hat{Y}_i = 10 + 5X_{1i} + 3X_{2i} \text{ and } r^2_{Y.12} = 0.60$$

a. Interpret the meaning of the slopes.
b. Interpret the meaning of the Y intercept.
c. Interpret the meaning of the coefficient of multiple determination $r^2_{Y.12}$.

2 For this problem use the following multiple regression equation:

$$\hat{Y}_i = 50 - 2X_{1i} + 7X_{2i} \text{ and } r^2_{Y.12} = 0.40$$

a. Interpret the meaning of the slopes.
b. Interpret the meaning of the Y intercept.
c. Interpret the meaning of the coefficient of multiple determination $r^2_{Y.12}$.

Applying the Concepts

Problems 3 and 4 can be solved manually. Problems 5–8 can be solved using Microsoft Excel.

3 A marketing analyst for a major shoe manufacturer is considering the development of a new brand of running shoes. The marketing analyst wants to determine which variables can be used in predicting durability (or the effect of long-term impact). Two independent variables are to be considered, X_1 (FOREIMP), a measurement of the forefoot shock-absorbing capability, and X_2 (MIDSOLE), a measurement of the change in impact properties over time, along with the dependent variable Y (LTIMP), which is a measure of the long-term ability to absorb shock after a repeated impact test. A random sample of 15 types of currently manufactured running shoes was selected for testing. The following (partial) output is obtained:

ANOVA	*df*	*SS*	*MS*	*F*	Significance *F*
Regression	2	12.61020	6.30510	97.69	0.0001
Error	12	0.77453	0.06454		
Total	14	13.38473			

Variable	Coefficients	Standard Error	*t* Stat	*p* Value
Intercept	−0.02686	0.06905	−0.39	0.7034
Foreimp	0.79116	0.06295	12.57	0.0000
Midsole	0.60484	0.07174	8.43	0.0000

a. Assuming that each independent variable is linearly related to long-term impact, state the multiple regression equation.
b. Interpret the meaning of the slopes in this problem.
c. Compute the coefficient of multiple determination $r^2_{Y.12}$ and interpret its meaning.
d. Compute the adjusted r^2.

4 Eileen M. Van Aken and Brian M. Kleiner, professors at Virginia Polytechnic Institute and State University, investigated the factors that contribute to the effectiveness of teams ("Determinants of Effectiveness for Cross-Functional Organizational Design Teams," *Quality Management Journal*, 1997, 4, 51–79). The researchers studied 34 independent variables such as team skills, diversity, meeting frequency, and clarity in expectations. For each of the teams studied, each of the variables was given a value of 1 through 100 based on the results of interviews and survey data, where 100 represents the highest rating. The dependent variable, team performance, was also given a value of 1 through 100, with 100 being the highest rating. Many different regression models were explored, including the following:

Model 1

$$\text{Team Performance} = \beta_0 + \beta_1 \text{ (Team Skills)} + \varepsilon,$$
$$r^2_{adj} = 0.68$$

Model 2

$$\text{Team Performance} = \beta_0 + \beta_1 \text{ (Clarity in Expectations)} + \varepsilon,$$
$$r^2_{adj} = 0.78$$

Model 3

$$\text{Team Performance} = \beta_0 + \beta_1 \text{ (Team Skills)} + \beta_2 \text{ (Clarity in Expectations)} + \varepsilon,$$
$$r^2_{adj} = 0.97$$

a. Interpret the adjusted r^2 for each of the three models.
b. Which of these three models do you think is the best predictor of team performance?

5 A mail-order catalog business selling personal computer supplies, software, and hardware maintains a centralized warehouse. Management is currently examining the process of distribution from the warehouse and wants to study the factors that affect warehouse distribution costs. Currently, a small handling fee is added to each order, regardless of the amount of the order. Data collected over the past 24 months indicate the warehouse distribution costs (in thousands of dollars), the sales (in thousands of dollars), and the number of orders received. **WARECOST.xls**

a. State the multiple regression equation.
b. Interpret the meaning of the slopes b_1 and b_2 in this problem.
c. Explain why the regression coefficient b_0 has no practical meaning in the context of this problem.
d. Predict the average monthly warehouse distribution cost when sales are $400,000 and the number of orders is 4,500.
e. Set up a 95% confidence interval estimate for the average monthly warehouse distribution cost when sales are $400,000 and the number of orders is 4,500.
f. Set up a 95% prediction interval for the monthly warehouse distribution cost at a particular warehouse when sales are $400,000 and the number of orders is 4,500.
g. Determine the coefficient of multiple determination $r^2_{Y.12}$ and interpret its meaning.
h. Determine the adjusted r^2.

6 A consumer organization wants to develop a regression model to predict gasoline mileage as measured by miles per gallon based on the horsepower of the car's engine and the weight of the car. A sample of 50 recent car models was selected and the results recorded. **AUTO.xls**

a. State the multiple regression equation.
b. Interpret the meaning of the slopes b_1 and b_2 in this problem.
c. Explain why the regression coefficient b_0 has no practical meaning in the context of this problem.
d. Predict the average miles per gallon for cars that have 60 horsepower and weighs 2,000 pounds.
e. Set up a 95% confidence interval estimate for the average miles per gallon for cars that have 60 horsepower and weigh 2,000 pounds.
f. Set up a 95% prediction interval for the miles per gallon for an individual car that has 60 horsepower and weighs 2,000 pounds.
g. Determine the coefficient of multiple determination $r^2_{Y.12}$ and interpret its meaning.
h. Determine the adjusted r^2.

7 A large consumer products company wants to measure the effectiveness of different types of advertising media in the promotion of its products. Specifically, two types of advertising media are to be considered: radio advertising and newspaper advertising (including the cost of discount coupons). A sample of 22 cities with approximately equal populations is selected for study during a test period of one month. Each city is allocated a specific expenditure level both for radio advertising and for newspaper advertising. The sales of the product (in thousands of dollars) and also the levels of media expenditure (in thousands of dollars) during the test month are recorded with the following results: **ADVERTISE.xls**

City	Sales ($000)	Radio Advertising ($000)	Newspaper Advertising ($000)
1	973	0	40
2	1,119	0	40
3	875	25	25
4	625	25	25
5	910	30	30
6	971	30	30
7	931	35	35
8	1,177	35	35
9	882	40	25
10	982	40	25
11	1,628	45	45
12	1,577	45	45
13	1,044	50	0
14	914	50	0
15	1,329	55	25
16	1,330	55	25
17	1,405	60	30
18	1,436	60	30
19	1,521	65	35
20	1,741	65	35
21	1,866	70	40
22	1,717	70	40

On the basis of the results obtained:

a. State the multiple regression equation.

b. Interpret the meaning of the slopes b_1 and b_2 in this problem.

c. Interpret the meaning of the regression coefficient b_0.

d. Predict the average sales for a city in which radio advertising is \$20,000 and newspaper advertising is \$20,000.

e. Set up a 95% confidence interval estimate for the average sales for cities in which radio advertising is \$20,000 and newspaper advertising is \$20,000.

f. Set up a 95% prediction interval for the sales for an individual city in which radio advertising is \$20,000 and newspaper advertising is \$20,000.

g. Determine the coefficient of multiple determination $r^2_{Y.12}$ and interpret its meaning.

h. Determine the adjusted r^2.

8 The director of broadcasting operations for a television station wants to study the issue of standby hours, hours in which unionized graphic artists at the station are paid but are not actually involved in any activity. The variables to be considered are:

Standby hours (Y)—the total number of standby hours per week

Total staff present (X_1)—the weekly total of people-days over a 7-day week.

Remote hours (X_2)—the total number of hours worked by employees at locations away from the central plant

The results for a period of 26 weeks are in the data file: **STANDBY.xls**

On the basis of the results obtained:

a. State the multiple regression equation.

b. Interpret the meaning of the slopes b_1 and b_2 in this problem.

c. Explain why the regression coefficient b_0 has no practical meaning in the context of this problem.

d. Predict the average standby hours for a week in which the total staff present is 310 people-days and the remote hours are 400.

e. Set up a 95% confidence interval estimate for the average standby hours for weeks in which the total staff present is 310 people-days and the remote hours are 400.

f. Set up a 95% prediction interval for the standby hours for a single week in which the total staff present is 310 people-days and the remote hours are 400.

g. Determine the coefficient of multiple determination $r^2_{Y.12}$ and interpret its meaning.

h. Determine the adjusted r^2.

2 RESIDUAL ANALYSIS FOR THE MULTIPLE REGRESSION MODEL

Residual analysis can be used to evaluate whether the simple linear regression model is appropriate for the set of data being studied. In examining a multiple regression model with two explanatory variables, the residual plots listed in Exhibit 1 are of particular interest.

EXHIBIT 1 RESIDUAL PLOTS USED IN MULTIPLE REGRESSION

1. Residuals versus $\hat{Y}_i$
2. Residuals versus X_{1i}
3. Residuals versus X_{2i}
4. Residuals versus time

The first residual plot examines the pattern of residuals versus the predicted values of Y. If the residuals show a pattern for different predicted values of Y, this provides evidence of a possible quadratic effect in at least one explanatory variable, a possible violation of the assumption of equal variance, and/or the need to transform the Y variable. The second and third residual plots involve the explanatory variables. Patterns in the plot of the residuals versus an explanatory variable may indicate the existence of a quadratic effect and, therefore, indicate the need to add a quadratic explanatory variable to the multiple regression model. The fourth type of plot is used to investigate patterns in the residuals in order to validate the independence assumption when the data have been collected in time order. Associated with the residual plot versus time, the Durbin-Watson statistic can be computed and the existence of positive autocorrelation among the residuals can be determined.

Figure 3 consists of the residual plots obtained from Microsoft Excel for the OmniPower sales example. Note in Figure 3 that there appears to be very little or no pattern in the relationship between the residuals and the value of X_1 (price), the value of X_2 (promotional expenditures), or the predicted value of Y. Thus, you can conclude that the multiple regression model is appropriate for predicting sales.

FIGURE 3
Residual plots obtained from Microsoft Excel for the OmniPower bar model: panel A, residuals versus predicted Y; panel B, residuals versus price; panel C, residuals versus promotional expenditures

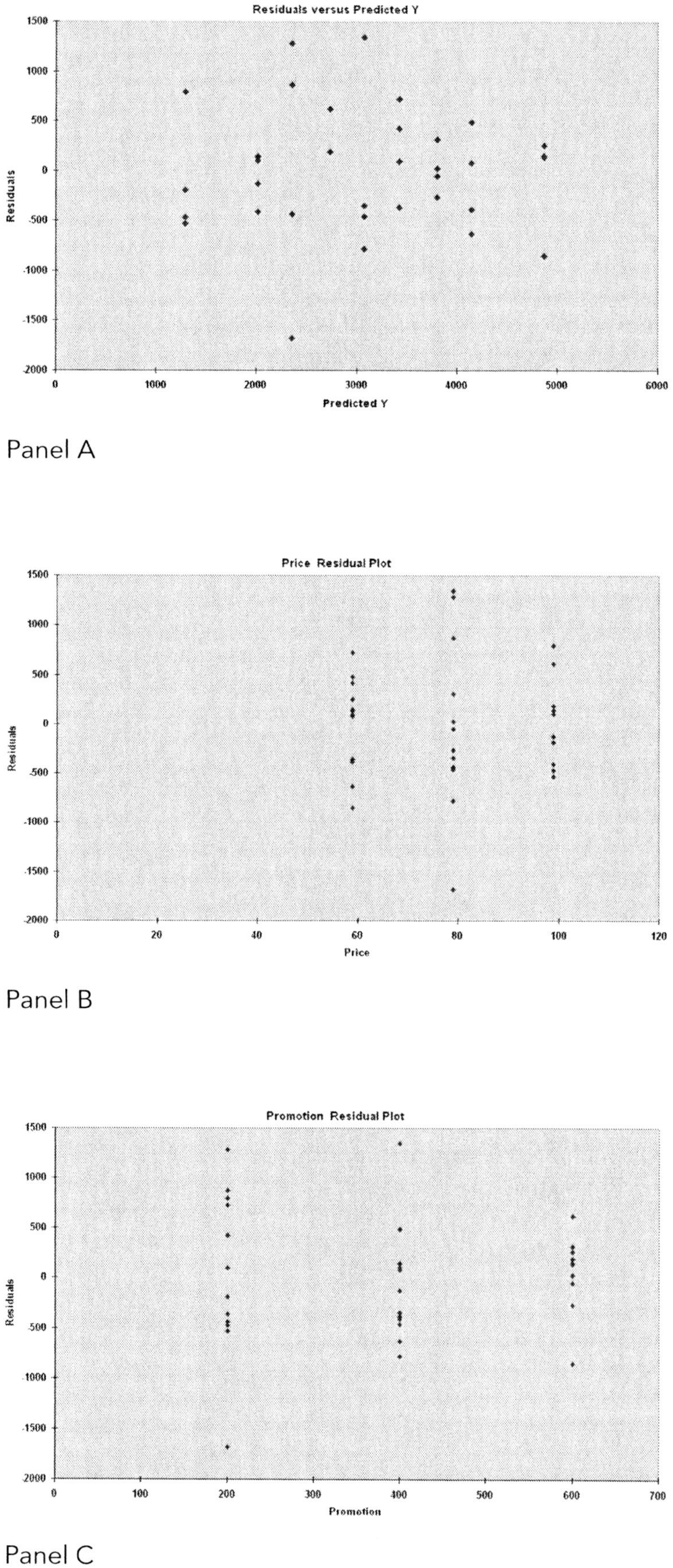

Excel Strategies Generating Residual Analyses

You modify the procedure to perform a multiple regression analysis to generate a residual analysis plot on a separate chart sheet.

For example, to generate residual analysis plots for the OmniPower sales data of Table 1, open to the **Data** worksheet of the **Chapter 13.xls** workbook and use one of these modifications:

Using Excel with PHStat2

Follow the "Using Excel with PHStat2" instructions, modifying the instructions to select all four check boxes of the **Regression Tool Output Options** group (**Regression Statistics Table**, **ANOVA and Coefficients Table**, **Residuals Table**, and **Residual Plot**) as is shown at right.

To generate a residual plot that plots residuals versus predicted values of *Y*, follow the instructions of section EH3 after running the PHStat2 procedure.

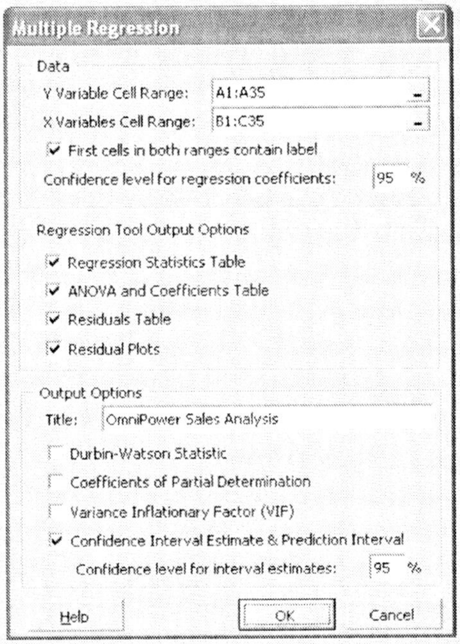

Using Excel

Modify the instructions of section EH1 at the end of this chapter, by selecting the **Residuals** and **Residual Plots** check boxes in the Regression dialog box as is shown at right. Then, if appropriate, follow the instructions of section EH3 to modify the residual plot generated as is necessary.

To generate a residual plot that plots residuals versus predicted values of *Y*, follow the instructions of section EH3 after running the Data Analysis Regression procedure.

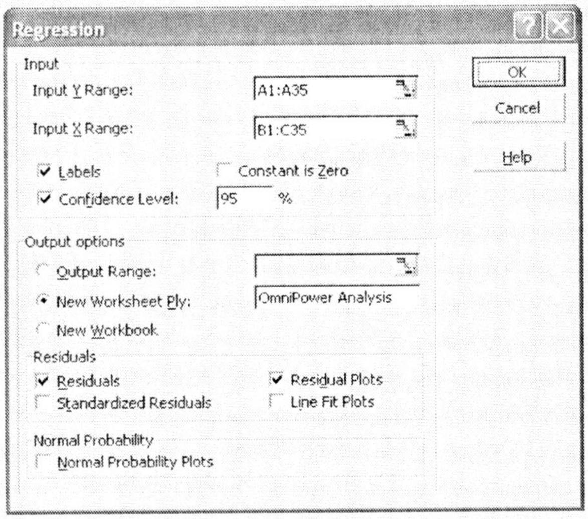

PROBLEMS FOR SECTION 2

Applying the Concepts

Problems 9–12 can be solved using Microsoft Excel.

9 In problem 5, sales and number of orders were used to predict distribution costs at a mail-order catalog business. **WARECOST.xls**

a. Perform a residual analysis on your results and determine the adequacy of the fit of the model.
b. Plot the residuals against the months. Is there any evidence of a pattern in the residuals? Explain.
c. Determine the Durbin-Watson statistic.
d. At the 0.05 level of significance, is there evidence of positive autocorrelation in the residuals?

10 In problem 6, horsepower and weight were used to predict gasoline mileage. Perform a residual analysis on your results and determine the adequacy of the fit of the model. **AUTO.xls**

11 In problem 7, the amount of radio advertising and newspaper advertising was used to predict sales. Perform a residual analysis on your results and determine the adequacy of the fit of the model. **ADVERTISE.xls**

12 In problem 8, the total staff present and remote hours were used to predict standby hours. **STANDBY**

a. Perform a residual analysis on your results and determine the adequacy of the fit of the model.
b. Plot the residuals against the weeks. Is there evidence of a pattern in the residuals? Explain.
c. Determine the Durbin-Watson statistic.
d. At the 0.05 level of significance, is there evidence of positive autocorrelation in the residuals?

3 TESTING FOR THE SIGNIFICANCE OF THE MULTIPLE REGRESSION MODEL

Now that residual analysis has been used to determine whether the multiple regression model is appropriate, you can determine whether there is a significant relationship between the dependent variable and the set of explanatory variables. Because there is more than one explanatory variable, the null and alternative hypotheses are as follows:

H_0: $\beta_1 = \beta_2 = \cdots = \beta_k = 0$ (No linear relationship between the dependent variable and the explanatory variables.)

H_1: At least one $\beta_j \neq 0$ (Linear relationship between the dependent variable and at least one of the explanatory variables.)

This null hypothesis is tested with an F test as shown in Equation (6) and summarized in Table 2.

F TEST FOR THE ENTIRE REGRESSION MODEL IN MULTIPLE REGRESSION

The F statistic is equal to the regression mean square (MSR) divided by the error mean square (MSE).

$$F = \frac{MSR}{MSE} \tag{6}$$

where

k = number of explanatory variables in the regression model
F = test statistic from an F distribution with k and $n - k - 1$ degrees of freedom

TABLE 2

ANOVA summary table for testing the significance of a set of regression coefficients in a multiple regression model with k explanatory variables

Source	Degrees of Freedom	Sum of Squares	Mean Square (Variance)	F
Regression	k	SSR	$MSR = \frac{SSR}{k}$	$F = \frac{MSR}{MSE}$
Error	$n - k - 1$	SSE	$MSE = \frac{SSE}{n - k - 1}$	
Total	$n - 1$	SST		

The decision rule is

Reject H_0 at the α level of significance if $F > F_{U(k,n-k-1)}$;

otherwise, do not reject H_0.

If a 0.05 level of significance is used, the critical value of the F distribution with 2 and 31 degrees of freedom obtained from the Critical Values of F table is approximately 3.32 (see Figure 4). From Figure 1 the F statistic given in the ANOVA summary table is 48.48. Because $48.48 > F_U = 3.32$, or because the p-value $= 0.000 < 0.05$, you reject H_0 and conclude that at least one of the explanatory variables (price and/or promotional expenditures) is related to sales.

FIGURE 4
Testing for significance of a set of regression coefficients at the 0.05 level of significance with 2 and 31 degrees of freedom

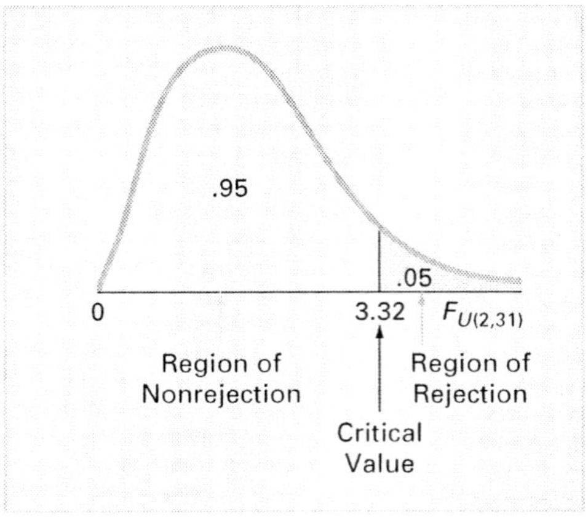

PROBLEMS FOR SECTION 3

Learning the Basics

13 The following ANOVA summary table was obtained from a multiple regression model with two independent variables.

Source	Degrees of Freedom	Sum of Squares	Mean Squares	F
Regression	2	60		
Error	18	120		
Total	20	180		

a. Determine the mean square that is due to regression and the mean square that is due to error.
b. Compute the F statistic.
c. Determine whether there is a significant relationship between Y and the two explanatory variables at the 0.05 level of significance.

14 The following ANOVA summary table was obtained from a multiple regression model with two independent variables.

Source	Degrees of Freedom	Sum of Squares	Mean Squares	F
Regression	2	30		
Error	10	120		
Total	12	150		

a. Determine the mean square that is due to regression and the mean square that is due to error.
b. Compute the F statistic.
c. Determine whether there is a significant relationship between Y and the two explanatory variables at the 0.05 level of significance.

Applying the Concepts

Problem 15 can be solved manually. Problems 16–19 can be solved using Microsoft Excel.

15 In problem 3, the durability of a brand of running shoe was predicted based on a measurement of the forefoot shock-absorbing capability and a measurement of the change in impact properties over time. The following ANOVA summary table was obtained:

ANOVA	Degrees of Freedom	SS	MS	F	Significance
Regression	2	12.61020	6.30510	97.69	0.0001
Error	12	10.77453	0.06454		
Total	14	13.38473			

a. Determine whether there is a significant relationship between long-term impact and the two explanatory variables at the 0.05 level of significance.
b. Interpret the meaning of the p-value.

16 In problem 5, sales and number of orders were used to predict distribution costs at a mail-order catalog business. Use the computer output you obtained to solve that problem: **WARECOST.xls**

a. Determine whether there is a significant relationship between distribution costs and the two explanatory variables (sales and number of orders) at the 0.05 level of significance.

b. Interpret the meaning of the *p*-value.

17 In problem 6, horsepower and weight were used to predict gasoline mileage. Use the computer output you obtained to solve that problem. **AUTO.xls**

a. Determine whether there is a significant relationship between gasoline mileage and the two explanatory variables (horsepower and weight) at the 0.05 level of significance.

b. Interpret the meaning of the *p*-value.

18 In problem 7, the amount of radio advertising and newspaper advertising was used to predict sales. Use the computer output you obtained to solve that problem. **ADVERTISE.xls**

a. Determine whether there is a significant relationship between sales and the two explanatory variables (radio advertising and newspaper advertising) at the 0.05 level of significance.

b. Interpret the meaning of the *p*-value.

19 In problem 8, the total staff present and remote hours were used to predict standby hours. Use the computer output you obtained to solve that problem. **STANDBY.xls**

a. Determine whether there is a significant relationship between standby hours and the two explanatory variables (total staff present and remote hours) at the 0.05 level of significance.

b. Interpret the meaning of the *p*-value.

4 INFERENCES CONCERNING THE POPULATION REGRESSION COEFFICIENTS

Atest of hypothesis is performed on the slope in a simple linear regression model to determine the significance of the relationship between X and Y. In addition, a confidence interval is used to estimate the population slope. In this section these procedures are extended to situations involving multiple regression.

Tests of Hypothesis

In a simple linear regression model to test a hypothesis concerning the population slope β_1, the following equation is used:

$$t = \frac{b_1 - \beta_1}{S_{b_1}}$$

This equation can be generalized for multiple regression as shown in Equation (7).

TESTING FOR THE SLOPE IN MULTIPLE REGRESSION

$$t = \frac{b_j - \beta_j}{S_{b_j}} \qquad (7)$$

where

b_j = slope of variable j with Y, holding constant the effects of all other independent variables

S_{b_j} = standard error of the regression coefficient b_j

t = test statistic for a t distribution with $n - k - 1$ degrees of freedom

k = number of explanatory variables in the regression equation

β_j = hypothesized value of the population slope for variable j, holding constant the effects of all other independent variables

The results of the t test for each of the independent variables included in the regression model are provided as part of the output obtained in Figure 1.

Thus, to determine whether variable X_2 (amount of promotional expenditures) has a significant effect on sales, taking into account the price of OmniPower bars, the null and alternative hypotheses are

$$H_0: \beta_2 = 0$$
$$H_1: \beta_2 \neq 0$$

From Equation (7), and Figure 1,

$$t = \frac{b_2 - \beta_2}{S_{b_2}}$$
$$= \frac{3.6131 - 0}{0.6852} = 5.27$$

If a level of significance of 0.05 is selected, the critical values of t for 31 degrees of freedom obtained from the Critical Values of t table are −2.0395 and +2.0395 (see Figure 5).

FIGURE 5
Testing for significance of a regression coefficient at the 0.05 level of significance with 31 degrees of freedom

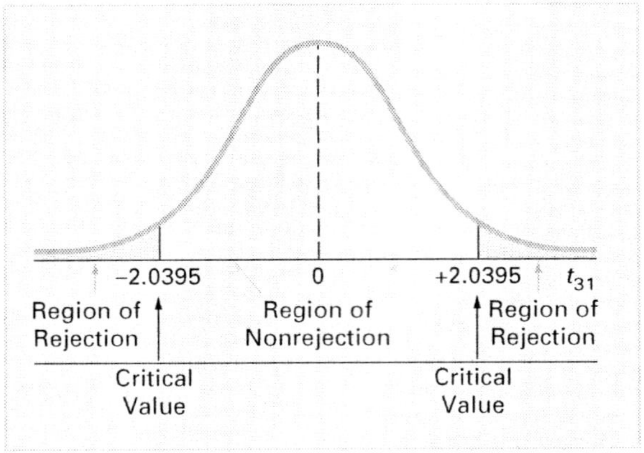

From Figure 1, observe that the p-value is 0.00000982 (or 9.82E-06 in scientific notation). Because $t = 5.27 > 2.0395$ or the p-value of $0.00000982 < 0.05$, you reject H_0 and conclude that there is a significant relationship between variable X_2 (promotional expenditures) and sales, taking into account the price X_1. Moreover, the p-value indicates that if in fact there is no linear relationship between sales and promotional expenditures, the probability of observing a relationship between sales and promotional expenditures that is as strong or stronger than that observed in the sample data is only 0.00000982. Thus, this extremely small p-value allows you to strongly reject the null hypothesis that there is no linear relationship between sales and promotional expenditures.

In a similar manner, in Example 1 you can test for the significance of β_1, the slope of sales with price.

EXAMPLE 1

TESTING FOR THE SIGNIFICANCE OF THE SLOPE OF SALES AND PRICE

At the 0.05 level of significance, is there evidence that the slope of sales with price is different from zero?

SOLUTION

From Figure 1, $t = -7.766 < -2.0395$ (the critical value for $\alpha = 0.05$) or the p-value $= 0.0000000092 < 0.05$. Therefore, there is a significant relationship between price X_1 and sales, taking into account the promotional expenditures X_2.

As observed with each of these two X variables, the test of significance for a particular regression coefficient is actually a test for the significance of adding a particular variable into a regression model given that the other variable has been included. Therefore, the t test for the regression coefficient is equivalent to testing for the contribution of each explanatory variable.

Confidence Interval Estimation

Instead of testing the significance of a population slope, you may be more concerned with estimating the value of a population slope. In multiple regression analysis, a confidence interval estimate for a population slope can be obtained from Equation (8).

CONFIDENCE INTERVAL ESTIMATE FOR THE SLOPE

$$b_j \pm t_{n-k-1} S_{b_j} \tag{8}$$

For example, if you want to obtain a 95% confidence interval estimate of the population slope β_1 (the effect of price X_1 on sales Y, holding constant the effect of promotional expenditures X_2), from Equation (8) and Figure 1,

$$b_1 \pm t_{n-k-1} S_{b_1}$$

Because the critical value of t at the 95% confidence level with 31 degrees of freedom is 2.0395 (see the Critical Values of t table),

$$-53.2173 \pm (2.0395)(6.8522)$$

$$-53.2173 \pm 13.9752$$

$$-67.1925 \le \beta_1 \le -39.2421$$

Thus, taking into account the effect of promotional expenditures, the estimated effect of each one-cent increase in price is to reduce average sales by between approximately 39.2 and 67.2 bars. You have 95% confidence that this interval correctly estimates the true relationship between these variables.

From a hypothesis-testing viewpoint, because this confidence interval does not include 0, you conclude that the regression coefficient β_1 has a significant effect. A confidence interval estimate for the slope of sales with promotional expenditures is developed in Example 2.

EXAMPLE 2

OBTAINING A CONFIDENCE INTERVAL ESTIMATE FOR THE SLOPE OF SALES WITH PROMOTIONAL EXPENDITURES

Set up a 95% confidence interval estimate of the population slope of sales with promotional expenditures.

SOLUTION

Because the critical value of t at the 95% confidence level with 31 degrees of freedom is 2.0395 (see the Critical Values of t table),

$$3.6131 \pm (2.0395)(0.6852)$$

$$3.6131 \pm 1.3975$$

$$2.2156 \le \beta_2 \le 5.0106$$

Thus, taking into account the effect of price, the estimated effect of each additional dollar of promotional expenditures is to increase average sales by between approximately 2.2 and 5 bars. You have 95% confidence that this interval correctly estimates the true relationship between these variables. From a hypothesis-testing viewpoint, because this confidence interval does not include 0, you can conclude that the regression coefficient β_2 has a significant effect.

PROBLEMS FOR SECTION 4

Learning the Basics

20 Given the following information from a multiple regression analysis

$$n = 25, b_1 = 5, b_2 = 10, S_{b_1} = 2, S_{b_2} = 8$$

a. Which variable has the largest slope in units of a t statistic?
b. Set up a 95% confidence interval estimate of the population slope β_1.
c. At the 0.05 level of significance, determine whether each explanatory variable makes a significant contribution to the regression model. On the basis of these results, indicate the independent variables that should be included in this model.

21 Given the following information from a multiple regression analysis

$$n = 20, b_1 = 4, b_2 = 3, S_{b_1} = 1.2, S_{b_2} = 0.8$$

a. Which variable has the largest slope in units of a t statistic?
b. Set up a 95% confidence interval estimate of the population slope.
c. At the 0.05 level of significance, determine whether each explanatory variable makes a significant contribution to the regression model. On the basis of these results, indicate the independent variables that should be included in this model.

Applying the Concepts

Problem 22 can be solved manually. Problems 23–26 can be solved using Microsoft Excel.

22 In problem 3 the durability of a brand of running shoe was predicted based on a measurement of the forefoot shock-absorbing capability and a measurement of the change in impact properties over time for a sample of 15 pairs of shoes. Use the following results:

Variable	Coefficients	Standard Error	t Stat	p-Value
Intercept	−0.02686	0.06905	−0.39	
Foreimp	0.79116	0.06295	12.57	0.0000
Midsole	0.60484	0.07174	8.43	0.0000

a. Set up a 95% confidence interval estimate of the population slope between long-term impact and forefoot impact.
b. At the 0.05 level of significance, determine whether each explanatory variable makes a significant contribution to the regression model. On the basis of these results, indicate the independent variables that should be included in this model.

23 In problem 5, sales and number of orders were used to predict distribution costs at a mail-order catalog business. Use the computer output you obtained to solve that problem. **WARECOST.xls**

a. Set up a 95% confidence interval estimate of the population slope between distribution cost and sales.
b. At the 0.05 level of significance, determine whether each explanatory variable makes a significant contribution to the regression model. On the basis of these results, indicate the independent variables that should be included in this model.

24 In problem 6, horsepower and weight were used to predict gasoline mileage. Use the computer output you obtained to solve that problem. **AUTO.xls**

a. Set up a 95% confidence interval estimate of the population slope between gasoline mileage and horsepower.
b. At the 0.05 level of significance, determine whether each explanatory variable makes a significant contribution to the regression model. On the basis of these results, indicate the independent variables that should be included in this model.

25 In problem 7, the amount of radio advertising and newspaper advertising was used to predict sales. Use the computer output you obtained to solve that problem. **ADVERTISE.xls**

a. Set up a 95% confidence interval estimate of the population slope between sales and radio advertising.
b. At the 0.05 level of significance, determine whether each explanatory variable makes a significant contribution to the regression model. On the basis of these results, indicate the independent variables that should be included in this model.

26 In problem 8, the total number of staff present and remote hours were used to predict standby hours. Use the computer output you obtained to solve that problem. **STANDBY.xls**

a. Set up a 95% confidence interval estimate of the population slope between standby hours and total number of staff present.
b. At the 0.05 level of significance, determine whether each explanatory variable makes a significant contribution to the regression model. On the basis of these results, indicate the independent variables that should be included in this model.

5 TESTING PORTIONS OF THE MULTIPLE REGRESSION MODEL

In developing a multiple regression model, one objective is to use only those explanatory variables that are useful in predicting the value of a dependent variable. If an explanatory variable is not helpful in making this prediction, it could be deleted from the multiple regression model and a model with fewer explanatory variables could be used in its place.

An alternative method to the t test discussed in section 4 for determining the contribution of an explanatory variable is called the **partial F-test statistic**. It involves determining the contribution to the regression sum of squares made by each explanatory variable after all the other explanatory variables have been included in the model. The new explanatory variable is included only if it significantly improves the model.

To apply the partial F-test criterion in the OmniPower bar sales example, you need to evaluate the contribution of promotional expenditures (X_2) after price (X_1) has been included in the model, and, conversely, you must also evaluate the contribution of price (X_1) after promotional expenditures (X_2) have been included in the model.

In general, if there are several explanatory variables, the contribution of each explanatory variable to be included in the model can be determined by taking into account the regression sum of squares of a model that includes all explanatory variables except the one of interest, SSR (all variables except j). Thus, to determine the contribution of variable j, assuming that all other variables are already included, begin by using Equation (9) below.

DETERMINING THE CONTRIBUTION OF AN INDEPENDENT VARIABLE TO THE REGRESSION MODEL

$$SSR(X_j \mid \text{all variables } except\ j) = SSR(\text{all variables } including\ j) - SSR\ (\text{all variables } except\ j) \quad \textbf{(9)}$$

If, as in the OmniPower bar sales example, there are two explanatory variables, the contribution of each can be determined from Equations (10a) and (10b).

Contribution of variable X_1 given that X_2 has been included:

$$SSR(X_1 \mid X_2) = SSR(X_1 \text{ and } X_2) - SSR(X_2) \quad \textbf{(10a)}$$

Contribution of variable X_2 given that X_1 has been included:

$$SSR(X_2 \mid X_1) = SSR(X_1 \text{ and } X_2) - SSR(X_1) \quad \textbf{(10b)}$$

The terms $SSR(X_2)$ and $SSR(X_1)$, respectively, represent the sum of squares that is due to regression for a model that includes only the explanatory variable X_2 (promotional expenditures) and only the explanatory variable X_1 (price). Output obtained from Microsoft Excel for these two models is presented in Figures 6 and 7.

FIGURE 6

Partial output obtained from Microsoft Excel of simple linear regression model for sales and promotional expenditures $SSR(X_2)$

	A	B	C	D	E	F	G
1	Sales & Promotional Expenses Analysis						
2							
3	*Regression Statistics*						
4	Multiple R	0.535095					
5	R Square	0.286327					
6	Adjusted R Square	0.264024					
7	Standard Error	1077.872084					
8	Observations	34					
9							
10	ANOVA						
11		*df*	*SS*	*MS*	*F*	*Significance F*	
12	Regression	1	14915814.102	14915814.102	12.83845	0.0011115	
13	Residual	32	37177863.339	1161808.229			
14	Total	33	52093677.441				
15							
16		*Coefficients*	*Standard Error*	*t Stat*	*P-value*	*Lower 95%*	*Upper 95%*
17	Intercept	1496.01613	483.978853	3.09107747	0.004111	510.1843006	2481.847958
18	Promotion	4.12806	1.152100	3.58307795	0.001111	1.7813154	6.474814

FIGURE 7

Partial output obtained from Microsoft Excel of simple linear regression model for sales and price $SSR(X_1)$

	A	B	C	D	E	F	G
1	Sales & Price Analysis						
2							
3	*Regression Statistics*						
4	Multiple R	0.735146					
5	R Square	0.540440					
6	Adjusted R Square	0.526078					
7	Standard Error	864.945650					
8	Observations	34					
9							
10	ANOVA						
11		*df*	*SS*	*MS*	*F*	*Significance F*	
12	Regression	1	28153486.15	28153486.15	37.63176099	7.35855E-07	
13	Residual	32	23940191.29	748130.98			
14	Total	33	52093677.44				
15							
16		*Coefficients*	*Standard Error*	*t Stat*	*P-value*	*Lower 95%*	*Upper 95%*
17	Intercept	7512.34798	734.6188701	10.22618434	1.30793E-11	6015.97958	9008.716388
18	Price	-56.71384	9.2451043	-6.13447316	7.35855E-07	-75.54549	-37.882199

Observe from Figure 6 that $SSR(X_2) = 14{,}915{,}814.10$ and from Figure 1, $SSR(X_1 \text{ and } X_2) = 39{,}472{,}730.77$. Therefore, from Equation (10a),

$$\begin{aligned} SSR(X_1 \mid X_2) &= SSR(X_1 \text{ and } X_2) - SSR(X_2) \\ &= 39{,}472{,}730.77 - 14{,}915{,}814.10 \\ &= 24{,}556{,}916.67 \end{aligned}$$

To determine whether X_1 significantly improves the model after X_2 has been included, you can now subdivide the regression sum of squares into two component parts as shown in Table 3.

TABLE 3

ANOVA table dividing the regression sum of squares into components to determine the contribution of variable X_1

Source	Degrees of Freedom	Sum of Squares	Mean Square (Variance)	F
Regression	2	39,472,730.77	19,736,365.39	
$\left\{ \begin{matrix} X_2 \\ X_1 \mid X_2 \end{matrix} \right\}$	$\left\{ \begin{matrix} 1 \\ 1 \end{matrix} \right\}$	$\left\{ \begin{matrix} 14{,}915{,}814.10 \\ 24{,}556{,}916.67 \end{matrix} \right\}$	24,556,916.67	60.32
Error	31	12,620,946.67	407,127.31	
Total	33	52,093,677.44		

The null and alternative hypotheses to test for the contribution of X_1 to the model are

H_0: Variable X_1 does not significantly improve the model after variable X_2 has been included.
H_1: Variable X_1 significantly improves the model after variable X_2 has been included.

The partial F-test statistic is defined in Equation (11).

THE PARTIAL F-TEST STATISTIC FOR DETERMINING THE CONTRIBUTION OF AN INDEPENDENT VARIABLE

$$F = \frac{SSR(X_j \mid \text{all variables } except\ j)}{MSE} \qquad \textbf{(11)}$$

The partial F-test statistic follows an F distribution with 1 and $n - k - 1$ degrees of freedom.

Thus, from Table 3,

$$F = \frac{24{,}556{,}916.67}{407{,}127.31} = 60.32$$

Because there are 1 and 31 degrees of freedom, if a level of significance of 0.05 is selected, observe from the Critical Values of F table that the critical value is approximately 4.17 (see Figure 8).

FIGURE 8

Testing for contribution of regression coefficient to multiple regression model at 0.05 level of significance with 1 and 31 degrees of freedom

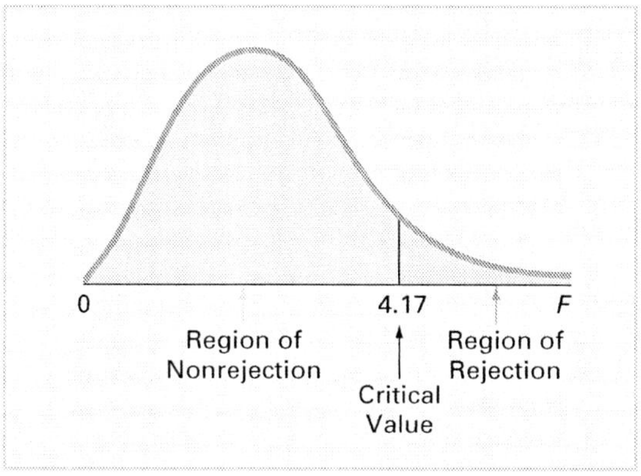

Because the partial F-test statistic is greater than this critical F value ($60.32 > 4.17$), the decision is to reject H_0 and conclude that the addition of variable X_1 (price) significantly improves a regression model that already contains variable X_2 (promotional expenditures).

To evaluate the contribution of variable X_2 (promotional expenditures) to a model in which variable X_1 (price) has been included, you need to use Equation (10b):

$$SSR(X_2 | X_1) = SSR(X_1 \text{ and } X_2) - SSR(X_1)$$

Observe from Figure 7, that $SSR(X_1) = 28{,}153{,}486.15$ and from Table 3, $SSR(X_1 \text{ and } X_2) = 39{,}472{,}730.77$.

Therefore, from Equation (10b)

$$SSR(X_2 | X_1) = 39{,}472{,}730.77 - 28{,}153{,}486.15 = 11{,}319{,}244.62$$

Thus, to determine whether X_2 significantly improves a model after X_1 has been included, the regression sum of squares can be subdivided into two component parts as shown in Table 4.

TABLE 4

ANOVA table dividing the regression sum of squares into components to determine the contribution of variable X_2

Source	Degrees of Freedom	Sum of Squares	Mean Square (Variance)	F
Regression	2	39,472,730.77	19,736,365.39	
X_1	1	28,153,486.15		
$X_2 \| X_1$	1	11,319,244.62	11,319,244.62	27.80
Error	31	12,620,946.67	407,127.31	
Total	33	52,093,677.44		

The null and alternative hypotheses to test for the contribution of X_2 to the model are

H_0: Variable X_2 does not significantly improve the model after variable X_1 has been included.

H_1: Variable X_2 significantly improves the model after variable X_1 has been included.

Using Equation (11) and Table 4, you obtain

$$F = \frac{11{,}319{,}244.62}{407{,}127.31} = 27.80$$

Because there are 1 and 31 degrees of freedom, if a 0.05 level of significance is selected, observe from Figure 8 that the critical value of F is approximately 4.17.

Because the partial F-test statistic is greater than this critical value (27.80 > 4.17), the decision is to reject H_0 and conclude that the addition of variable X_2 (promotional expenditures) significantly improves the multiple regression model already containing X_1 (price).

Thus, by testing for the contribution of each explanatory variable after the other has been included in the model, you determine that each of the two explanatory variables significantly improves the model. Therefore, the multiple regression model should include both price X_1 and promotional expenditures X_2 in predicting the sales of OmniPower bars.

Focusing on the interpretation of these conclusions, note that there is a relationship between the value of the t-test statistic obtained from Equation (7) and the partial F-test statistic [Equation (11)] used to determine the contributions of X_1 and X_2 to the multiple regression model. The t-values were computed to be −7.77 and +5.27, and the corresponding values of F were 60.32 and 27.80. These values illustrate the relationship between t and F shown in Equation (12).

THE RELATIONSHIP BETWEEN A t STATISTIC AND AN F STATISTIC

$$t_a^2 = F_{1,a} \qquad \textbf{(12)}$$

where

a = number of degrees of freedom

Coefficient of Partial Determination

In section 1 the coefficient of multiple determination ($r_{Y.12}^2$), which measures the proportion of the variation in Y that is explained by variation in the two explanatory variables, was discussed. Now that the contribution of each explanatory variable to the multiple regression model has been examined, the **coefficients of partial determination** ($r_{Y1.2}^2$ and $r_{Y2.1}^2$) can be computed. The coefficients measure the proportion of the variation in the dependent variable that is explained by each explanatory variable while controlling for, or holding constant, the other explanatory variable(s). Equation (13) defines the coefficients of partial determination for a multiple regression model with two explanatory variables.

COEFFICIENTS OF PARTIAL DETERMINATION FOR A MULTIPLE REGRESSION MODEL CONTAINING TWO INDEPENDENT VARIABLES

$$r_{Y1.2}^2 = \frac{SSR(X_1 | X_2)}{SST - SSR(X_1 \text{ and } X_2) + SSR(X_1 | X_2)} \qquad \textbf{(13a)}$$

and

$$r_{Y2.1}^2 = \frac{SSR(X_2 | X_1)}{SST - SSR(X_1 \text{ and } X_2) + SSR(X_2 | X_1)} \qquad \textbf{(13b)}$$

where

$SSR(X_1 \mid X_2)$ = sum of squares of the contribution of variable X_1 to the regression model given that variable X_2 has been included in the model

SST = total sum of squares for Y

$SSR(X_1 \text{ and } X_2)$ = regression sum of squares when variables X_1 and X_2 are both included in the multiple regression model

$SSR(X_2 \mid X_1)$ = sum of squares of the contribution of variable X_2 to the regression model given that variable X_1 has been included in the model

In a multiple regression model containing several (k) explanatory variables, the coefficient of partial determination for the jth variable is defined in Equation (14).

COEFFICIENT OF PARTIAL DETERMINATION FOR A MULTIPLE REGRESSION MODEL CONTAINING *k* INDEPENDENT VARIABLES

$$r^2_{Yj.(\text{all variables } except\, j)} = \frac{SSR(X_j \mid \text{all variables } except\, j)}{SST - SSR(\text{all variables } including\, j) + SSR(X_j \mid \text{all variables } except\, j)} \quad \textbf{(14)}$$

For the OmniPower sales example,

$$r^2_{Y1.2} = \frac{24{,}556{,}916.67}{52{,}093{,}677.44 - 39{,}472{,}730.77 + 24{,}556{,}916.67} = 0.6605$$

and

$$r^2_{Y2.1} = \frac{11{,}319{,}244.62}{52{,}093{,}677.24 - 39{,}472{,}730.77 + 11{,}319{,}244.62} = 0.4728$$

The coefficient of partial determination of variable Y with X_1 while holding X_2 constant ($r^2_{Y1.2}$) means that for a fixed (constant) amount of promotional expenditures, 66.05% of the variation in OmniPower sales can be explained by the variation in the price. The coefficient of partial determination of variable Y with X_2 while holding X_1 constant ($r^2_{Y2.1}$) means that for a given (constant) price, 47.28% of the variation in sales of OmniPower bars can be explained by variation in the amount of promotional expenditures.

Excel Strategies Calculating Coefficients of Partial Determination

You modify the procedure to perform a multiple regression analysis to calculate the coefficients of partial determination.

For example, to calculate the coefficients of partial determination for the multiple regression model for the OmniPower sales data of Table 1, open to the **Data** worksheet of the **Chapter 13.xls** workbook and use one of these modifications:

Using Excel with PHStat2
Follow the "Using Excel with PHStat2" instructions, modifying the instructions to select the **Coefficients of Partial Determination** check box in the Output Options group (shown at right).

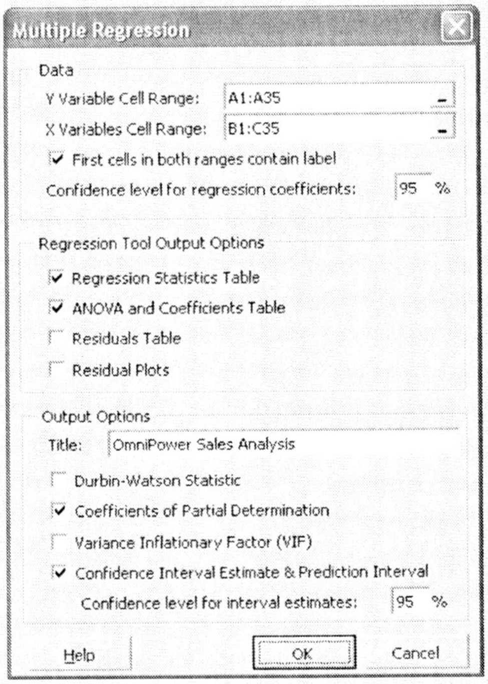

Using Excel
Follow the instructions of section EH4 at the end of this chapter to manually implement worksheets for the coefficients of partial determination calculations.

PROBLEMS FOR SECTION 5

Learning the Basics

27 The following ANOVA summary table was obtained for a multiple regression model with two independent variables:

Source	Degrees of Freedom	Sum of Squares	Mean Squares	F
Regression	2	60		
Error	18	120		
Total	20	180		

If $SSR(X_1) = 45$ and $SSR(X_2) = 25$:

a. Determine whether there is a significant relationship between Y and each of the explanatory variables at the 0.05 level of significance.
b. Compute the coefficients of partial determination $r^2_{Y1.2}$ and $r^2_{Y2.1}$ and interpret their meaning.

28 The following ANOVA summary table was obtained for a multiple regression model with two independent variables:

Source	Degrees of Freedom	Sum of Squares	Mean Squares	F
Regression	2	30		
Error	10	120		
Total	12	150		

If $SSR(X_1) = 20$ and $SSR(X_2) = 15$:

a. Determine whether there is a significant relationship between Y and each of the explanatory variables at the 0.05 level of significance.
b. Compute the coefficients of partial determination $r^2_{Y1.2}$ and $r^2_{Y2.1}$ and interpret their meaning.

Applying the Concepts

Problems 29–32 can be solved using Microsoft Excel.

29 In problem 5, sales and number of orders were used to predict distribution costs at a mail-order catalog business. Use the computer output you obtained to solve that problem. **WARECOST.xls**
a. At the 0.05 level of significance, determine whether each explanatory variable makes a significant contribution to the regression model. On the basis of these results, indicate the regression model that should be used in the problem.
b. Compute the coefficients of partial determination $r^2_{Y1.2}$ and $r^2_{Y2.1}$ and interpret their meaning.

30 In problem 6, horsepower and weight were used to predict gasoline mileage. Use the computer output you obtained to solve that problem. **AUTO.xls**
a. At the 0.05 level of significance, determine whether each explanatory variable makes a significant contribution to the regression model. On the basis of these results, indicate the regression model that should be used in the problem.
b. Compute the coefficients of partial determination $r^2_{Y1.2}$ and $r^2_{Y2.1}$ and interpret their meaning.

31 In problem 7, the amount of radio advertising and newspaper advertising was used to predict sales. Use the computer output you obtained to solve that problem. **ADVERTISE.xls**

a. At the 0.05 level of significance, determine whether each explanatory variable makes a significant contribution to the regression model. On the basis of these results, indicate the regression model that should be used in the problem.

b. Compute the coefficients of partial determination $r^2_{Y1.2}$ and $r^2_{Y2.1}$ and interpret their meaning.

32 In problem 8, the total staff present and remote hours were used to predict standby hours. Use the computer output you obtained to solve that problem. **STANDBY.xls**

a. At the 0.05 level of significance, determine whether each explanatory variable makes a significant contribution to the regression model. On the basis of these results, indicate the regression model that should be used in the problem.

b. Compute the coefficients of partial determination $r^2_{Y1.2}$ and $r^2_{Y2.1}$ and interpret their meaning.

6 USING DUMMY VARIABLES AND INTERACTION TERMS IN REGRESSION MODELS

In the discussion of multiple regression models, the assumption has been made that each explanatory (or independent) variable is numerical. However, there are many occasions in which categorical variables need to be included in a regression model. For example, in section 1 price and promotional expenditures were used to predict the average monthly sales of OmniPower high-energy bars. In addition to these numerical independent variables, you may want to include the effect of the location in the store where the bars are shelved (for example, end-aisle display or no end-aisle display) when developing a model to predict OmniPower sales.

The use of **dummy variables** allows for the consideration of categorical explanatory variables as part of the regression model. If a given categorical explanatory variable has two categories, then only one dummy variable will be needed to represent the two categories. A particular dummy variable X_d, is defined as

$$X_d = 0 \text{ if the observation is in category 1}$$

$$X_d = 1 \text{ if the observation is in category 2}$$

To illustrate the application of dummy variables in regression, a model for predicting the average assessed value from a sample of 15 houses will be developed based on the size of the house (in thousands of square feet) and whether or not the house has a fireplace. The data are presented in Table 5. A dummy variable for fireplace (X_2) can be defined as

$$X_2 = 0 \text{ if the house does not have a fireplace}$$

$$X_2 = 1 \text{ if the house has a fireplace}$$

TABLE 5

Predicting assessed value based on size of the house and presence of a fireplace

HOUSE3.xls

House	Assessed Value ($000)	Size of Dwelling (Thousands of Square Feet)	Fire-Place	House	Assessed Value ($000)	Size of Dwelling (Thousands of Square Feet)	Fire-Place
1	84.4	2.00	Yes	9	78.5	1.59	Yes
2	77.4	1.71	No	10	79.2	1.50	Yes
3	75.7	1.45	No	11	86.7	1.90	Yes
4	85.9	1.76	Yes	12	79.3	1.39	Yes
5	79.1	1.93	No	13	74.5	1.54	No
6	70.4	1.20	Yes	14	83.8	1.89	Yes
7	75.8	1.55	Yes	15	76.8	1.59	No
8	85.9	1.93	Yes				

Assuming that the slope of assessed value with the size of the house is the same for houses that have and do not have a fireplace, the multiple regression model is

$$Y_i = \beta_0 + \beta_1 X_{1i} + \beta_2 X_{2i} + \varepsilon_i$$

where

Y_i = assessed value in thousands of dollars for house i
β_0 = Y intercept
X_{1i} = size of the house in thousands of square feet for house i
β_1 = slope of assessed value with size of the house holding constant the effect of the presence of a fireplace
X_{2i} = dummy variable representing the presence or absence of a fireplace for house i
β_2 = incremental effect of the presence of a fireplace holding constant the effect of the size of the house
ε_i = random error in Y for house i

Figure 9 illustrates the output for this model obtained from Microsoft Excel.

FIGURE 9
Microsoft Excel output for the regression model that includes size of the house and presence of fireplace

	A	B	C	D	E	F	G
1	Assessed Value Analysis						
2							
3	*Regression Statistics*						
4	Multiple R	0.90059					
5	R Square	0.81106					
6	Adjusted R Square	0.77957					
7	Standard Error	2.26260					
8	Observations	15					
9							
10	ANOVA						
11		*df*	*SS*	*MS*	*F*	*Significance F*	
12	Regression	2	263.70391	131.85196	25.75565	4.54968E-05	
13	Residual	12	61.43209	5.11934			
14	Total	14	325.136				
15							
16		*Coefficients*	*Standard Error*	*t Stat*	*P-value*	*Lower 95%*	*Upper 95%*
17	Intercept	50.09049	4.351658	11.510668	7.67943E-08	40.60904	59.57194
18	Size	16.18583	2.574442	6.287124	4.02437E-05	10.57661	21.79506
19	Fireplace	3.85298	1.241223	3.104183	0.00912	1.14859	6.55737

From Figure 9, the regression equation is

$$\hat{Y}_i = 50.09 + 16.186X_{1i} + 3.853X_{2i}$$

For houses without a fireplace, this reduces to

$$\hat{Y}_i = 50.09 + 16.186X_{1i}, \text{ because } X_2 = 0$$

while for houses with a fireplace, the regression equation is

$$\hat{Y}_i = 53.943 + 16.186X_{1i}$$

because $X_2 = 1$, so 3.853 is added to 50.09. In this model, the regression coefficients are interpreted as follows:

1. Holding constant whether or not a house has a fireplace, for each increase of 1.0 thousand square feet in the size of the house, the average assessed value is predicted to increase by 16.186 thousands (or \$16,186).
2. Holding constant the size of the house, the presence of a fireplace is predicted to increase the assessed value of the house by an average of 3.853 thousand dollars (or \$3,853).

Note from Figure 9 that the t statistic for the slope of the size of the house with assessed value is 6.29 and the p-value is approximately 0.000; the t statistic for presence of a fireplace is 3.10 and the p-value is 0.009. Thus, each of the two variables is making a significant contribution to the model at a level of significance of 0.01. In addition, the coefficient of multiple determination indicates that 81.1% of the variation in assessed value is explained by variation in the size of the house and whether or not the house has a fireplace.

EXAMPLE 3

MODELING A THREE-LEVEL CATEGORICAL VARIABLE

Define a multiple regression model using sales as the dependent variable and package-design and price as dependent variables. Package-design is a three-level categorical variable with designs *A*, *B*, or *C*.

SOLUTION

To model a three-level categorical variable, two dummy variables are needed:

$$X_{1i} = 1 \text{ if package design } A \text{ is used in observation } i, 0 \text{ otherwise}$$
$$X_{2i} = 1 \text{ if package design } B \text{ is used in observation } i, 0 \text{ otherwise}$$

Note that if observation i is for package-design A, then $X_{1i} = 1$ and $X_{2i} = 0$; for package-design B, then $X_{1i} = 0$ and $X_{2i} = 1$; and for package-design C, then $X_{1i} = X_{2i} = 0$. A third independent variable is used for price:

$$X_{3i} = \text{price for observation } i$$

Thus, the following is a suitable regression model for this example:

$$Y_i = \beta_0 + \beta_1 X_{1i} + \beta_2 X_{2i} + \beta_3 X_{3i} + \varepsilon_i$$

where

Y_i = sales for observation i
β_0 = Y intercept
β_1 = difference between the mean of design A and mean of design C, holding the price constant
β_2 = difference between the mean of design B and mean of design C, holding the price constant
β_3 = slope of sales with price, holding the package design constant
ε_i = random error in Y for observation i

Interactions

In all the regression models discussed so far, it is assumed that the effect that an independent variable has on the dependent variable is statistically independent of the other independent variables in the model. An **interaction** occurs if the effect of an independent variable on the response variable is dependent on the value of a second independent variable. For example, it is possible for advertising to have a large effect on the sales of a product when the price of a product is small. However, if the price of the product is too high, increases in advertising will not dramatically change sales. In this case, sales and advertising are said to interact. In other words, you cannot make general statements about the effect of advertising on sales. The effect that advertising has on sales is *dependent* on the price. To model an interaction effect in a regression model an **interaction term** (sometimes referred to as a **cross-product term**) is used. To illustrate the concept of interaction and use of an interaction term, return to the example concerning the assessment values of homes discussed on previous pages.

In the regression model on the previous page, it is assumed that the effect the size of the home has on the assessed value is independent of whether or not the house has a fireplace. In other words, it is assumed that the slope of assessed value with size is the same for houses with fireplaces as it is for houses without fireplaces. If these two slopes are different, an interaction between size of the home and fireplace exists.

A hypothesis of equal slopes of a Y variable with X can be evaluated by defining an interaction term that consists of the product of the explanatory variable X_1 and the dummy variable X_2 and then testing whether this interaction variable makes a significant contribution to a regression model that contains the other X variables. If the interaction is significant, you cannot use the original model for prediction. For the data of Table 5, let

$$X_3 = X_1 * X_2$$

The Microsoft Excel output for this regression model, which includes the size of the house X_1, the presence of a fireplace X_2, and the interaction of X_1 and X_2 (which is defined as X_3), is provided in Figure 10.

FIGURE 10
Microsoft Excel output for a regression model that includes size, presence of fireplace, and interaction of size and presence of fireplace

	A	B	C	D	E	F	G
1	Assessed Value Analysis						
2							
3	*Regression Statistics*						
4	Multiple R	0.91791					
5	R Square	0.84255					
6	Adjusted R Square	0.79961					
7	Standard Error	2.15727					
8	Observations	15					
9							
10	ANOVA						
11		*df*	*SS*	*MS*	*F*	*Significance F*	
12	Regression	3	273.94410	91.31470	19.62150	0.00010	
13	Residual	11	51.19190	4.65381			
14	Total	14	325.136				
15							
16		*Coefficients*	*Standard Error*	*t Stat*	*P-value*	*Lower 95%*	*Upper 95%*
17	Intercept	62.95218	9.61218	6.54921	4.13993E-05	41.79591	84.10845
18	Size	8.36242	5.81730	1.43751	0.17841	-4.44137	21.16621
19	Fireplace	-11.84036	10.64550	-1.11224	0.28975	-35.27097	11.59024
20	Size * Fireplace	9.51800	6.41647	1.48337	0.16605	-4.60456	23.64056

To test the null hypothesis H_0: $\beta_3 = 0$ versus the alternative hypothesis H_1: $\beta_3 \neq 0$, from Figure 10, observe that the t statistic for the interaction of size and presence of a fireplace is 1.48. Because the p-value = 0.166 > 0.05, the null hypothesis is not rejected. Therefore, the interaction term does not make a significant contribution to the model given that size and presence of a fireplace are already included.

Regression models can have several explanatory variables. Example 4 illustrates a regression model in which there are two numerical explanatory variables as well as a categorical independent variable.

EXAMPLE 4

STUDYING A REGRESSION MODEL THAT CONTAINS A DUMMY VARIABLE

A real estate developer wants to predict heating oil consumption based on atmospheric temperature X_1 and the amount of attic insulation X_2. Suppose that, of 15 houses selected, houses 1, 4, 6, 7, 8, 10, and 12 are ranch-style houses. Fit the appropriate regression model based on these three independent variables, X_1, X_2, and X_3 (the dummy variable for ranch-style houses).

HTNGOIL.xls

SOLUTION

Define X_3, a dummy variable for ranch-style house as follows

$$X_3 = 0 \text{ if the style is not ranch}$$
$$X_3 = 1 \text{ if the style is ranch}$$

Assuming that the slope between home heating oil consumption and atmospheric temperature X_1 and between home heating oil consumption and the amount of attic insulation X_2 is the same for both styles of houses, the regression model is:

$$Y_i = \beta_0 + \beta_1 X_{1i} + \beta_2 X_{2i} + \beta_3 X_{3i} + \varepsilon_i$$

where

Y_i = monthly heating oil consumption in gallons for house i
β_0 = Y intercept
β_1 = slope of heating oil consumption with atmospheric temperature, holding constant the effect of attic insulation and the style of the house
β_2 = slope of heating oil consumption with attic insulation, holding constant the effect of atmospheric temperature and the style of the house
β_3 = incremental effect of the presence of a ranch-style house, holding constant the effect of atmospheric temperature and attic insulation
ε_i = random error in Y for house i

Figure 11 displays partial output obtained from Microsoft Excel.

FIGURE 11

Microsoft Excel output for a regression model that includes temperature, insulation, and style for the heating oil data

	A	B	C	D	E	F	G
1	**Heating Oil Consumption Analysis**						
2							
3	*Regression Statistics*						
4	Multiple R	0.99421					
5	R Square	0.98845					
6	Adjusted R Square	0.98529					
7	Standard Error	15.74894					
8	Observations	15					
9							
10	ANOVA						
11		*df*	*SS*	*MS*	*F*	*Significance F*	
12	Regression	3	233406.90935	77802.30312	313.68217	6.21548E-11	
13	Residual	11	2728.31998	248.02909			
14	Total	14	236135.22933				
15							
16		*Coefficients*	*Standard Error*	*t Stat*	*P-value*	*Lower 95%*	*Upper 95%*
17	Intercept	592.54012	14.33698	41.32948	2.02317E-13	560.98461	624.09562
18	Temperature	-5.52510	0.20443	-27.02670	2.07188E-11	-5.97505	-5.07515
19	Insulation	-21.37613	1.44802	-14.76232	1.34816E-08	-24.56320	-18.18906
20	Ranch-style	-38.97267	8.35844	-4.66267	0.00069	-57.36947	-20.57586

From the output in Figure 11, the regression equation is:

$$\hat{Y}_i = 592.5401 - 5.5251X_{1i} - 21.3761X_{2i} - 38.9727X_{3i}$$

For houses that are not ranch-style, this reduces to

$$\hat{Y}_i = 592.5401 - 5.5251X_{1i} - 21.3761X_{2i}$$

since $X_3 = 0$. For houses that are ranch-style, this reduces to

$$\hat{Y}_i = 553.5674 - 5.5251X_{1i} - 21.3761X_{2i}$$

since $X_3 = 1$.

In addition, note the following:

1. Holding constant the effect of attic insulation and the house style, for each additional 1°F increase in atmospheric temperature, the average oil consumption is predicted to decrease by 5.5251 gallons.
2. Holding constant the effect of atmospheric temperature and the house style, for each additional 1-inch increase in attic insulation, the average oil consumption is predicted to decrease by 21.3761 gallons.
3. b_3 measures the effect on oil consumption of having a ranch-style house ($X_3 = 1$) compared with having a house that is not ranch-style ($X_3 = 0$). Thus, with atmospheric temperature and attic insulation held constant, a ranch-style house is estimated to use an average of 38.973 fewer gallons of heating oil per month than a house that is not ranch-style.

Note from the Excel output in Figure 11 above that the three t statistics representing the slopes for temperature, insulation, and presence of a ranch-style house are –27.03, –14.76, and –4.66. Each of the corresponding p-values is extremely small, all being less than 0.001. Thus, each of the three variables is making a significant contribution to the model. In addition, the coefficient of multiple determination indicates that 98.8% of the variation in oil usage is explained by variation in the temperature, insulation, and whether the house is ranch-style.

Before you can use the model in Example 4, you need to determine whether the independent variables interact with each other. In Example 5, three interaction terms are added to the model used in Example 4.

EXAMPLE 5

EVALUATING A REGRESSION MODEL WITH SEVERAL INTERACTIONS

For the data of Example 4, determine whether adding the interaction terms make a significant contribution to the regression model.

SOLUTION

To evaluate possible interactions between the independent variables, three interaction terms are constructed. Let $X_4 = X_1 * X_2$, $X_5 = X_1 * X_3$, and $X_6 = X_2 * X_3$. The regression model is now

$$Y_i = \beta_0 + \beta_1 X_{1i} + \beta_2 X_{2i} + \beta_3 X_{3i} + \beta_4 X_{4i} + \beta_5 X_{5i} + \beta_6 X_{6i} + \varepsilon_i$$

where X_1 is temperature, X_2 is insulation, X_3 is whether the house is ranch-style, X_4 is the interaction term between temperature and insulation, X_5 is the interaction term between temperature and ranch-style, and X_6 is the interaction term between insulation and ranch-style.

To test whether the three interaction terms significantly improve the regression model, the partial F test for the contribution of a variable to a model defined in Equation (11) is extended. To test for the simultaneous contribution of all three variables, the null and alternative hypotheses are:

H_0: $\beta_4 = \beta_5 = \beta_6 = 0$ (There are no interactions among X_1, X_2, and X_3.)
H_1: $\beta_4 \neq 0$ and/or $\beta_5 \neq 0$ and/or $\beta_6 \neq 0$ (X_1 interacts with X_2, and/or X_1 interacts with X_3, and/or X_2 interacts with X_3.)

Observe from Figure 12 that

$$SSR(X_1, X_2, X_3, X_4, X_5, X_6) = 234{,}510.58 \text{ with 6 degrees of freedom}$$

and from Figure 11 that $SSR(X_1, X_2, X_3) = 233{,}406.91$ with 3 degrees of freedom.

FIGURE 12
Microsoft Excel output for a regression model that includes temperature X_1, insulation X_2, whether or not the house is ranch-style X_3, the interaction of temperature and insulation X_4, the interaction of temperature and ranch-style X_5, and the interaction of insulation and ranch-style X_6

	A	B	C	D	E	F	G
1	Heating Oil Consumption Analysis						
2							
3	*Regression Statistics*						
4	Multiple R	0.99655					
5	R Square	0.99312					
6	Adjusted R Square	0.98796					
7	Standard Error	14.25065					
8	Observations	15					
9							
10	ANOVA						
11		*df*	*SS*	*MS*	*F*	*Significance F*	
12	Regression	6	234510.58185	39085.09697	192.46069	3.32423E-08	
13	Residual	8	1624.64749	203.08094			
14	Total	14	236135.22933				
15							
16		*Coefficients*	*Standard Error*	*t Stat*	*P-value*	*Lower 95%*	*Upper 95%*
17	Intercept	642.88670	26.70590	24.07283	9.45284E-09	581.30273	704.47066
18	Temperature	-6.92627	0.75311	-9.19687	1.58014E-05	-8.66295	-5.18959
19	Insulation	-27.88251	3.58011	-7.78818	5.29456E-05	-36.13826	-19.62677
20	Style	-84.60882	29.99556	-2.82071	0.02247	-153.77875	-15.43889
21	Temperature * Insulation	0.17021	0.08863	1.92039	0.09106	-0.03418	0.37460
22	Temperature * Ranch-style	0.65957	0.46168	1.42862	0.19097	-0.40507	1.72420
23	Insulation * Ranch-style	4.98698	3.51368	1.41930	0.19358	-3.11559	13.08955

Thus, $SSR(X_1, X_2, X_3, X_4, X_5, X_6) - SSR(X_1, X_2, X_3) = 234{,}510.58 - 233{,}406.91 = 1{,}103.67$, and the difference in degrees of freedom is $6 - 3 = 3$.

To extend Equation (11), using the partial F test for the simultaneous contribution of three variables to a model[2], the null hypothesis is tested by

$$F = \frac{[SSR(X_1, X_2, X_3, X_4, X_5, X_6) - SSR(X_1, X_2, X_3)]/3}{MSE(X_1, X_2, X_3, X_4, X_5, X_6)} = \frac{1{,}103.67/3}{203.08} = 1.81$$

The observed F statistic of 1.81 is compared to the F-value for 3 and 8 degrees of freedom using a level of significance of 0.05. Because $1.81 < 4.07$, you conclude that the interaction terms do not make a significant contribution to the model, given that temperature X_1, insulation X_2, and whether the house is ranch-style X_3 are already included. Therefore, the multiple regression model using X_1, X_2, and X_3 but no interaction terms is the better model. Had you rejected this null hypothesis, you would then test the contribution of each interaction separately in order to determine which interaction terms should be included in the model.

[2] In general, if a model has several independent variables and you are interested in testing whether an additional set of independent variables contribute to the model, the numerator of the F test is the difference between SSR (for all independent variables) –SSR (for the initial set of variables) divided by the number of independent variables whose contribution is being tested.

Excel Strategies Creating Dummy Variables and Interaction Terms

You create dummy variables and interaction terms by adding columns containing formulas to the worksheet that contains your sample data. Once created, you can include these columns as part of the **X Variable Cell Range** (PHStat2 Multiple Regression procedure) or **Input X Range** (Data Analysis Regression procedure).

Create Dummy Variables Task. To change a two-category categorical variable into a dummy variable with the values 0 and 1, use the Microsoft Excel **Edit | Replace** command. For example, to change the two-category fireplace variable of Table 5 into a dummy variable in which 0 represents the value No and 1 represents Yes, open to the **Data** worksheet of the **House3.xls** workbook and:

Copy the cell range **C1:C16** to cell **D1** for later double-checking of your work.

Select the cell range **C2:C16** that contains the fireplace categorical responses, Yes and No.

Select **Edit | Replace**.

In the Replace dialog box (shown below):

Enter **Yes** in the **Find what** edit box and enter **1** in the **Replace with** edit box.
Click the **Replace All** button. If a message box confirming replacements appears, click the **OK** button.

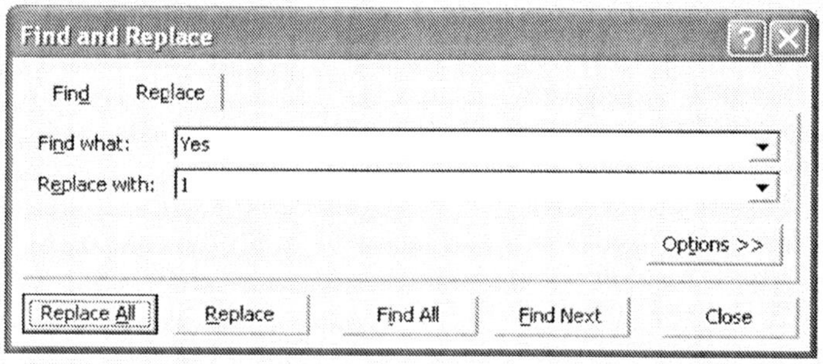

With the cell range C2:C16 still selected, select **Edit | Replace** a second time.

In the Replace dialog box:

Enter **No** in the **Find what** edit box and enter **0** in the **Replace with** edit box.
Click the **Replace All** button.

Compare values in column C with the values in column D. Make sure that all 1 values in column C have a corresponding Yes value in column D and that all 0 values in column C have a corresponding No value in column D.

Select column **D** and then select **Edit | Delete** to delete the double-checking column.

Create Interaction Terms Task. To create interaction terms, enter formulas in the form ***=cell1*cell2*** in a new column. The table on the next page shows the new column D formulas for the size and fireplace interaction for the Data worksheet modified by the previous task.

	A	B	C	D
1	Value	Size	Fireplace	Size * Fireplace
2	84.4	2.00	1	=B2 * C2
3	77.4	1.71	0	=B3 * C3
4	75.7	1.45	0	=B4 * C4
5	85.9	1.76	1	=B5 * C5
6	79.1	1.93	0	=B6 * C6
7	70.4	1.20	1	=B7 * C7
8	75.8	1.55	1	=B8 * C8
9	85.9	1.93	1	=B9 * C9
10	78.5	1.59	1	=B10 * C10
11	79.2	1.50	1	=B11 * C11
12	86.7	1.90	1	=B12 * C12
13	79.3	1.39	1	=B13 * C13
14	74.5	1.54	0	=B14 * C14
15	83.8	1.89	1	=B15 * C15
16	76.8	1.59	0	=B16 * C16

PROBLEMS FOR SECTION 6

Learning the Basics

33 Suppose X_1 is a numerical variable and X_2 is a dummy variable and the following regression equation for a sample of $n = 20$ is:

$$\hat{Y}_i = 6 + 4X_{1i} + 2X_{2i}$$

a. Interpret the meaning of the slope for variable X_1.

b. Interpret the meaning of the slope for variable X_2.

c. Suppose that the t statistic for testing the contribution of variable X_2 is 3.27. At the 0.05 level of significance, is there evidence that variable X_2 makes a significant contribution to the model?

Applying the Concepts

Problem 34 can be solved manually. Problems 35–44 can be solved using Microsoft Excel.

34 The chair of the accounting department of a large public university wants to develop a regression model to predict the grade-point average in accounting for students who are graduating as accounting majors based on total SAT score for the student and whether or not the student received a grade of B or higher in the introductory statistics course (0 = no and 1 = yes).

a. Explain the steps involved in developing a regression model for these data. Be sure to indicate the particular models that need to be evaluated and compared.

b. If the regression coefficient for the variable of whether or not the student received a grade of B or higher in the introductory statistics course was +0.30, how would this be interpreted?

35 The marketing manager of a large supermarket chain would like to determine the effect of shelf space and whether the product was placed at the front or back of the aisle on the sales of pet food. A random sample of 12 equal-sized stores is selected with the following results: **PETFOOD.xls**

Store	Shelf Space (Feet)	Location	Weekly Sales (Hundreds of Dollars)
1	5	Back	1.6
2	5	Front	2.2
3	5	Back	1.4
4	10	Back	1.9
5	10	Back	2.4
6	10	Front	2.6
7	15	Back	2.3
8	15	Back	2.7
9	15	Front	2.8
10	20	Back	2.6
11	20	Back	2.9
12	20	Front	3.1

a. State the multiple regression equation.
b. Interpret the meaning of the slopes in this problem.
c. Predict the average weekly sales of pet food for a store with 8 feet of shelf space situated at the back of the aisle and set up a 95% confidence interval estimate and a 95% prediction interval.
d. Perform a residual analysis on the results and determine the adequacy of the fit of the model.
e. Determine whether there is a significant relationship between sales and the two explanatory variables (shelf space and aisle position) at the 0.05 level of significance.
f. At the 0.05 level of significance, determine whether each explanatory variable makes a contribution to the regression model. On the basis of these results, indicate the regression model that should be used.
g. Set up 95% confidence interval estimates of the population slope for the relationship between sales and shelf space and between sales and aisle location.
h. Interpret the meaning of the coefficient of multiple determination $r^2_{Y.12}$.
i. Compute the adjusted r^2.
j. Compute the coefficients of partial determination and interpret their meaning.
k. What assumption about the slope of shelf space with sales must be made in this problem?
l. Include an interaction term in the model, and at the 0.05 level of significance, determine whether it makes a significant contribution to the model.
m. On the basis of the results of (f) and (l), which model is more appropriate? Explain.

36 A real estate association in a suburban community would like to study the relationship between the size of a single-family house (as measured by the number of rooms) and the selling price of the house (in thousands of dollars). The study is to be carried out in two different neighborhoods, one on the east side of the community (=0) and the other on the west side (=1). A random sample of 20 houses was selected with the following results given in the file: **NEIGHBOR.xls**

a. State the multiple regression equation.
b. Interpret the meaning of the slopes in this problem.
c. Predict the average selling price for a house with nine rooms that is located in an east side neighborhood and set up a 95% confidence interval estimate and a 95% prediction interval.
d. Perform a residual analysis on the results, and determine the adequacy of the fit of the model.
e. Determine whether there is a significant relationship between selling price and the two explanatory variables (rooms and neighborhood) at the 0.05 level of significance.
f. At the 0.05 level of significance, determine whether each explanatory variable makes a contribution to the regression model. On the basis of these results, indicate the regression model that should be used.
g. Set up 95% confidence interval estimates of the population slope for the relationship between selling price and number of rooms and between selling price and neighborhood.
h. Interpret the meaning of the coefficient of multiple determination.
i. Compute the adjusted r^2.
j. Compute the coefficients of partial determination and interpret their meaning.
k. What assumption must be made about the slope of selling price with number of rooms?
l. Include an interaction term in the model, and, at the 0.05 level of significance, determine whether it makes a significant contribution to the model.
m. On the basis of the results of (f) and (l), which model is more appropriate? Explain.

37 The file **COLLEGES2002.xls** contains data on 80 colleges and universities. Among the variables included are the annual total cost (in thousands of dollars), the first quartile score on the Scholastic Aptitude Test (SAT), and whether the school is public or private (0 = public; 1 = private). Develop a model to predict the annual total cost based on first quartile SAT score and whether the school is public or private:

a. State the multiple regression equation.
b. Interpret the meaning of the slopes in this problem.
c. Predict the average total cost for a school with a first quartile SAT score of 1,000 that is a public institution and set up a 95% confidence interval estimate and a 95% prediction interval.
d. Perform a residual analysis on the results and determine the adequacy of the fit of the model.
e. Determine whether there is a significant relationship between annual total cost and the two explanatory variables (first quartile SAT score and whether the school is public or private) at the 0.05 level of significance.
f. At the 0.05 level of significance, determine whether each explanatory variable makes a contribution to the regression model. On the basis of these results, indicate the regression model that should be used in this problem.
g. Set up 95% confidence interval estimates of the population slope for the relationship between annual total cost and first quartile SAT score and between annual total cost and whether the school is public or private.
h. Interpret the meaning of the coefficient of multiple determination.
i. Compute the adjusted r^2.
j. Compute the coefficients of partial determination and interpret their meaning.
k. What assumption about the slope of annual total cost with first quartile SAT score must be made in this problem?
l. Include an interaction term in the model and, at the 0.05 level of significance, determine whether it makes a significant contribution to the model.
m. On the basis of the results of (f) and (l), which model is more appropriate? Explain.

38 In mining engineering, holes are often drilled through rock using drill bits. As the drill hole gets deeper, additional rods are added to the drill bit to enable additional drilling to take place. It is expected that drilling time increases with depth. This increased drilling time could be caused by several factors, including the mass of the drill rods that are strung together. A key question relates to whether drilling is faster using dry drilling holes or wet drilling holes. Dry drilling holes involve forcing compressed air down the drill rods to flush the cuttings and drive the hammer. Using wet drilling holes involves forcing water rather than air down the hole. The data file **DRILL.xls** contains measurements of the time to drill each additional five feet (in minutes), the depth (in feet), and whether the hole was a dry drilling hole or a wet drilling hole for a sample of 50 drill holes. Develop a model to predict additional drilling time based on depth and type of drilling hole (dry or wet).

Source: R. Penner and D. G. Watts, "Mining Information," The American Statistician *45, 1991, 4–9.*

a. State the multiple regression equation.
b. Interpret the meaning of the slopes in this problem.
c. Predict the average additional drilling time for a dry drilling hole at a depth of 100 feet and set up a 95% confidence interval estimate and a 95% prediction interval.
d. Perform a residual analysis on the results and determine the adequacy of the fit of the model.
e. Determine whether there is a significant relationship between additional drilling time and the two explanatory variables (depth and type of hole) at the 0.05 level of significance.
f. At the 0.05 level of significance, determine whether each explanatory variable makes a contribution to the regression model. On the basis of these results, indicate the regression model that should be used.
g. Set up 95% confidence interval estimates of the population slope for the relationship between additional drilling time and depth and between additional drilling time and type of hole.
h. Interpret the meaning of the coefficient of multiple determination.
i. Compute the adjusted r^2.
j. Compute the coefficients of partial determination and interpret their meaning.
k. What assumption about the slope of additional drilling time with depth must be made in this problem?
l. Include an interaction term in the model and, at the 0.05 level of significance, determine whether it makes a significant contribution to the model.
m. On the basis of the results of (f) and (l), which model is more appropriate? Explain.

39 Zagat's publishes restaurant ratings for various locations in the United States. The data file **RESTRATE.xls** contains the Zagat rating for food, décor, service, and the price per person for a sample of 50 restaurants located in New York City ($X_d = 0$) and 50 restaurants located on Long Island ($X_d = 1$). Suppose you wanted to develop a regression model to predict the price per person based on a variable that represents the sum of the ratings for food, décor, and service, and on location (New York City or Long Island).

Source: Extracted from Zagat Survey 2002 New York City Restaurants *and* Zagat Survey 2001–2002 Long Island Restaurants.

a. State the multiple regression equation.
b. Interpret the meaning of the slopes in this problem.
c. Predict the average price for a restaurant with a summated rating of 60 that is located in New York City and set up a 95% confidence interval estimate and 95% prediction interval.
d. Perform a residual analysis on the results and determine the adequacy of the fit of the model.
e. Determine whether there is a significant relationship between price and the two explanatory variables (summated rating and location) at the 0.05 level of significance.
f. At the 0.05 level of significance, determine whether each explanatory variable makes a contribution to the regression model. On the basis of these results, indicate the regression model that should be used in this problem.
g. Set up 95% confidence interval estimates of the population slope for the relationship between price and summated rating and between price and location.
h. Interpret the meaning of the coefficient of multiple determination $r^2_{Y.12}$.
i. Compute the adjusted r^2.
j. Compute the coefficients of partial determination and interpret their meaning.
k. What assumption about the slope of price with summated rating must be made in this problem?
l. Include an interaction term in the model and, at the 0.05 level of significance, determine whether it makes a significant contribution to the model.
m. On the basis of the results of (f) and (l), which model is more appropriate? Explain.

40 In problem 5 sales and orders were used to predict distribution cost. Develop a regression model that includes the interaction of sales and orders in addition to sales and orders to predict distribution cost.

a. At the 0.05 level of significance, is there evidence that the interaction term makes a significant contribution to the model?
b. Which regression model should be used, the one used in this problem or the one used in problem 5? Explain.

41 In problem 6 horsepower and weight were used to predict miles per gallon. Develop a regression model that includes the interaction of horsepower and weight in addition to horsepower and weight to predict miles per gallon.

a. At the 0.05 level of significance, is there evidence that the interaction term makes a significant contribution to the model?

b. Which regression model should be used, the one used in this problem or the one used in problem 6? Explain.

42 In problem 7 radio advertising and newspaper advertising were used to predict sales. Develop a regression model that includes the interaction of radio advertising and newspaper advertising in addition to radio advertising and newspaper advertising to predict sales.

a. At the 0.05 level of significance, is there evidence that the interaction term makes a significant contribution to the model?

b. Which regression model should be used, the one used in this problem or the one used in problem 7? Explain.

43 In problem 8 total staff present and remote hours were used to predict standby hours. Develop a regression model that includes the interaction of total staff present and remote hours in addition to total staff present and remote hours to predict standby hours.

a. At the 0.05 level of significance, is there evidence that the interaction term makes a significant contribution to the model?

b. Which regression model should be used, the one used in this problem or the one used in problem 8? Explain.

44 The director of a training program for a large insurance company wanted to compare three different methods of training new underwriters. The three methods are traditional, CD-ROM-based, and Web-based. She divides 30 trainees into three randomly assigned groups of 10. Before the start of the training, each trainee is given a proficiency exam that measures mathematics and computer skills. At the end of the training, all students take the same end-of-training exam. The results **UNDERWRITING.xls** were as follows.

Proficiency Exam	End-of-Training Exam	Method
94	14	Traditional
96	19	Traditional
98	17	Traditional
100	38	Traditional
102	40	Traditional
105	26	Traditional
109	41	Traditional
110	28	Traditional
111	36	Traditional
130	66	Traditional
80	38	CD-ROM-based
84	34	CD-ROM-based
90	43	CD-ROM-based
97	43	CD-ROM-based
97	61	CD-ROM-based
112	63	CD-ROM-based
115	93	CD-ROM-based
118	74	CD-ROM-based
120	76	CD-ROM-based
120	79	CD-ROM-based
92	55	Web-based
96	53	Web-based
99	55	Web-based
101	52	Web-based
102	35	Web-based
104	46	Web-based
107	57	Web-based
110	55	Web-based
111	42	Web-based
118	81	Web-based

Develop a multiple regression model to predict the score on the end-of-training exam based on the score on the proficiency exam and the method of training used.

a. State the multiple regression equation.

b. Interpret the meaning of the slopes in this problem.

c. Predict the average end-of-training exam score for a student with a proficiency exam score of 100 who has Web-based training.

d. Perform a residual analysis on your results and determine the adequacy of the fit of the model.

e. Determine whether there is a significant relationship between the end-of-training exam score and the explanatory variables (proficiency score and training method) at the 0.05 level of significance.

f. At the 0.05 level of significance, determine whether each explanatory variable makes a contribution to the regression model. On the basis of these results, indicate the regression model that should be used in this problem.

g. Set up 95% confidence interval estimates of the population slope for the relationship between end-of-training exam score and each explanatory variable.

h. Interpret the meaning of the coefficient of multiple determination $r^2_{Y.123}$.

i. Compute the adjusted r^2.

j. Compute the coefficients of partial determination, and interpret their meaning.

k. What assumption about the slope of proficiency score with end-of-training exam score must be made in this problem?

l. Include interaction terms in the model, and at the 0.05 level of significance determine whether any interaction terms make a significant contribution to the model.

m. On the basis of the results of (f) and (l), which model is more appropriate? Explain.

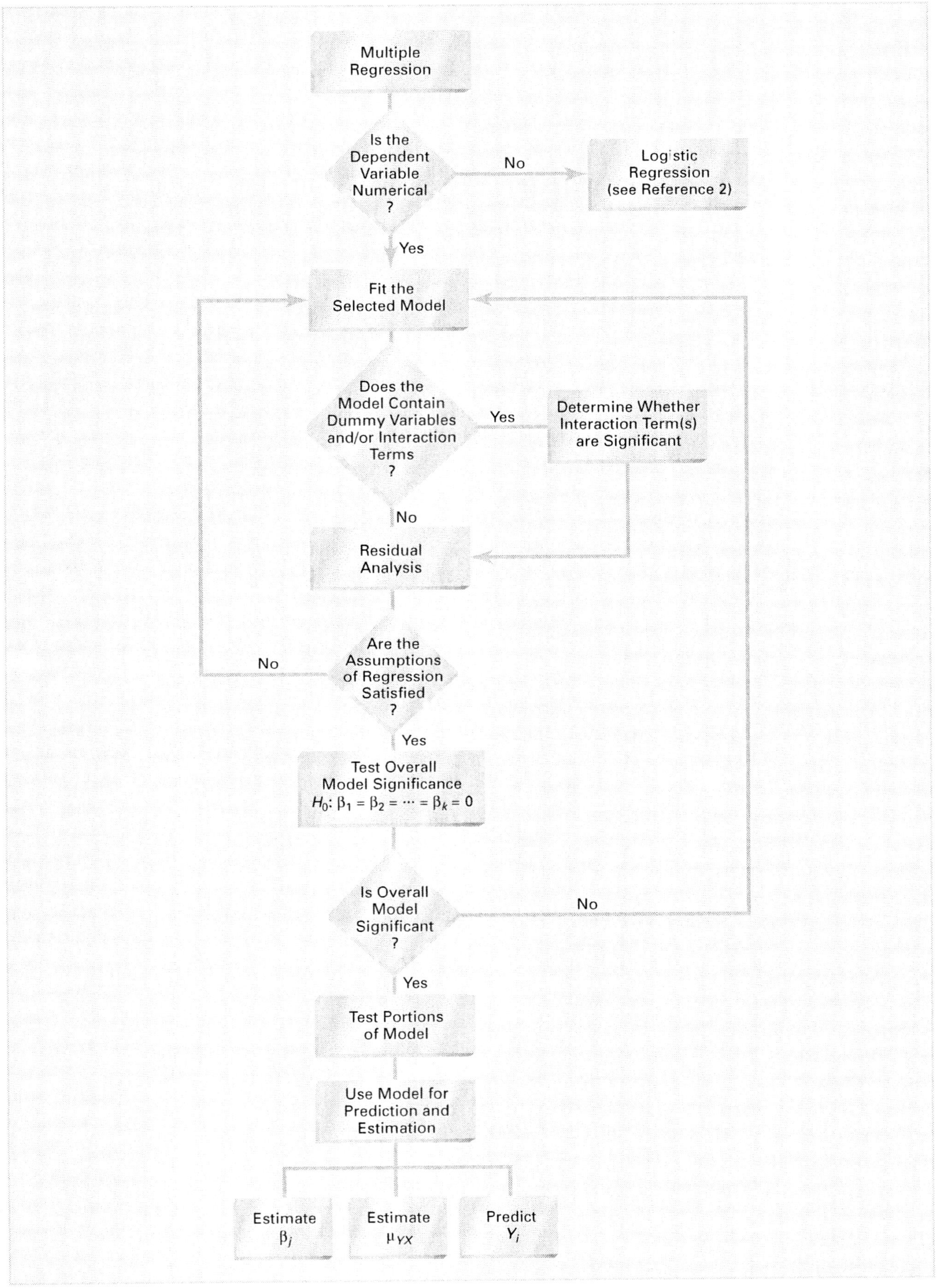

Chapter summary flowchart

SUMMARY

In this chapter, you learned how a marketing manager can use multiple regression analysis to understand the effects of price and promotional expenses on the sales of a new product. In addition, categorical independent variables and interaction terms were used in regression models.

KEY TERMS

adjusted r^2
coefficient of multiple determination
coefficients of partial determination
cross-product term
dummy variables
interaction
interaction term
multiple regression
net regression coefficient
partial F-test statistic

CHAPTER REVIEW PROBLEMS

Checking Your Understanding

45 How does the interpretation of the regression coefficients differ in multiple regression and simple regression?

46 How does testing the significance of the entire regression model differ from testing the contribution of each independent variable in the multiple regression model?

47 How do the coefficients of partial determination differ from the coefficient of multiple determination?

48 Why and how are dummy variables used?

49 How can you evaluate whether the slope of the response variable with an independent variable is the same for each level of the dummy variable?

50 Under what circumstances would you want to include a dummy variable in a regression model?

51 What assumption concerning the slope between the response variable Y and the numerical explanatory variable X must be made when a dummy variable is included in a regression model?

Applying the Concepts

Problems 52–58 should be solved using Microsoft Excel.

52 A sample of 30 recently sold single-family houses in a small city in the western part of the United States is selected. Develop a model to predict the selling price (in thousands of dollars) using the assessed value (in thousands of dollars) as well as time period (in months since reassessment). The houses in the city had been reassessed at full value 1 year prior to the study. The results are contained in the file: **HOUSE1.xls**

a. State the multiple regression equation.
b. Interpret the meaning of the slopes in this equation.
c. Predict the average selling price for a house that has an assessed value of $70,000 and was sold in time period 12.
d. Perform a residual analysis on your results, and determine the adequacy of the fit of the model.
e. Determine whether there is a significant relationship between selling price and the two explanatory variables (assessed value and time period) at the 0.05 level of significance.
f. Determine the p-value in (e) and interpret its meaning.
g. Interpret the meaning of the coefficient of multiple determination in this problem.
h. Determine the adjusted r^2.
i. At the 0.05 level of significance, determine whether each explanatory variable makes a significant contribution to the regression model. On the basis of these results, indicate the regression model that should be used in this problem.
j. Determine the p-values in (i) and interpret their meaning.
k. Compute the coefficients of partial determination and interpret their meaning?

53 Measuring the height of a California redwood tree is a very difficult undertaking because these trees grow to heights of over 300 feet. It is understood by people familiar with these trees that the height of a California redwood tree is related to other characteristics of the tree, including the diameter of the tree at the breast height of a person and the thickness of the bark of the tree. The data in the file **REDWOOD.xls** represent the height, diameter at breast height of a person, and bark thickness for a sample of 21 California redwood trees.

a. State the multiple regression equation.
b. Interpret the meaning of the slopes in this equation.
c. Predict the average height for a tree that has a breast diameter of 25 inches and a bark thickness of 2 inches.
d. Interpret the meaning of the coefficient of multiple determination $r^2_{Y.12}$ in this problem.
e. Perform a residual analysis on the results and determine the adequacy of the fit of the model.
f. Determine whether there is a significant relationship between height of redwood trees and the two explanatory variables (breast diameter and the bark thickness) at the 0.05 level of significance.

g. Set up a 95% confidence interval estimate of the population slope between the height of the redwood trees and breast diameter and between the height of redwood trees and the bark thickness.
h. At the 0.05 level of significance, determine whether each explanatory variable makes a significant contribution to the regression model. On the basis of these results, indicate the independent variables that should be included in this model.
i. Set up a 95% confidence interval estimate of the average height for a tree that has a breast diameter of 25 inches and a bark thickness of 2 inches along with a prediction interval.
j. Compute the coefficients of partial determination $r^2_{Y1.2}$ and $r^2_{Y2.1}$ and interpret their meaning.

54 Develop a model to predict the assessed value (in thousands of dollars) using the size of the houses (in thousands of square feet) and the age of the houses (in years) from the following table: **HOUSE2.xls**

House	Assessed Value ($000)	Size of Dwelling (Thousands of Square Feet)	Age (Years)
1	84.4	2.00	3.42
2	77.4	1.71	11.50
3	75.7	1.45	8.33
4	85.9	1.76	0.00
5	79.1	1.93	7.42
6	70.4	1.20	32.00
7	75.8	1.55	16.00
8	85.9	1.93	2.00
9	78.5	1.59	1.75
10	79.2	1.50	2.75
11	86.7	1.90	0.00
12	79.3	1.39	0.00
13	74.5	1.54	12.58
14	83.8	1.89	2.75
15	76.8	1.59	7.17

a. State the multiple regression equation.
b. Interpret the meaning of the slopes in this equation.
c. Predict the average assessed value for a house that has a size of 1,750 square feet and is 10 years old.
d. Perform a residual analysis on the results and determine the adequacy of the fit of the model.
e. Determine whether there is a significant relationship between assessed value and the two explanatory variables (size and age) at the 0.05 level of significance.
f. Determine the p-value in (e) and interpret its meaning.
g. Interpret the meaning of the coefficient of multiple determination in this problem.
h. Determine the adjusted r^2.
i. At the 0.05 level of significance, determine whether each explanatory variable makes a significant contribution to the regression model. On the basis of these results, indicate the regression model that should be used in this problem.
j. Determine the p-values in (i) and interpret their meaning.
k. Compute the coefficients of partial determination ($r^2_{Y1.2}$ and $r^2_{Y2.1}$) and interpret their meaning.

55 The file **COLLEGES2002.xls** contains data on 80 colleges and universities. Among the variables included are the annual total cost (in thousands of dollars), the first quartile (Q_1) and third quartile (Q_3) score on the Scholastic Aptitude Test (SAT), and the room and board expenses (in thousands of dollars). Develop a model to predict the annual total cost based on first quartile SAT score and room and board expenses.
a. State the multiple regression equation.
b. Interpret the meaning of the slopes in this equation.
c. Predict the average annual total cost for a school that has a first quartile SAT score of 1,100 and a room and board expense of $5,000.
d. Perform a residual analysis on the results and determine the adequacy of the fit of the model.
e. Determine whether there is a significant relationship between annual total cost and the two explanatory variables (first quartile SAT score and room and board expenses) at the 0.05 level of significance.
f. Determine the p-value in (e) and interpret its meaning.
g. Interpret the meaning of the coefficient of multiple determination in this problem.
h. Determine the adjusted r^2.
i. At the 0.05 level of significance, determine whether each explanatory variable makes a significant contribution to the regression model. On the basis of these results, indicate the regression model that should be used in this problem.
j. Determine the p-values in (i) and interpret their meaning.
k. Set up a 95% confidence interval estimate of the population slope between annual total cost and first quartile SAT score.
l. Compute the coefficients of partial determination ($r^2_{Y1.2}$ and $r^2_{Y2.1}$) and interpret their meaning.
m. Explain why the slope for total annual cost with room and board expenses seems substantially different from 1.0.
n. What other factors that are not included in the model might account for the strong positive relationship between total cost and first quartile SAT score?

56 The file **AUTO2002.xls** contains data on 121 automobile models from the year 2002. Among the variables included are the gasoline mileage, the length (in inches), and the weight (in pounds) of each automobile. Develop a model to predict the gasoline mileage based on the length and weight of each automobile.

a. State the multiple regression equation.
b. Interpret the meaning of the slopes in this equation.
c. Predict the average gasoline mileage for an automobile that has a length of 195 inches and a weight of 3,000 pounds.
d. Perform a residual analysis on the results and determine the adequacy of the fit of the model.
e. Determine whether there is a significant relationship between gasoline mileage and the two explanatory variables (length and weight) at the 0.05 level of significance.
f. Determine the p-value in (e) and interpret its meaning.
g. Interpret the meaning of the coefficient of multiple determination in this problem.
h. Determine the adjusted r^2.
i. At the 0.05 level of significance, determine whether each explanatory variable makes a significant contribution to the regression model. On the basis of these results, indicate the regression model that should be used in this problem.
j. Determine the p-values in (i) and interpret their meaning.
k. Set up a 95% confidence interval estimate of the population slope between gasoline mileage and weight.
l. Compute the coefficients of partial determination ($r^2_{Y1.2}$ and $r^2_{Y2.1}$) and interpret their meaning.

57 Crazy Dave, the well-known baseball analyst, wants to determine which variables are important in predicting a team's wins in a given season. He has collected data related to wins, earned run average (ERA), and runs scored for the 2002 season (stored in the file **BB2002.xls**). Develop a model to predict the number of wins based on ERA and runs scored.

a. State the multiple regression equation.
b. Interpret the meaning of the slopes in this equation.
c. Predict the average number of wins for a team that has an ERA of 4.5 and has scored 750 runs.
d. Perform a residual analysis on the results and determine the adequacy of the fit of the model.
e. Determine whether there is a significant relationship between number of wins and the two explanatory variables (ERA and runs scored) at the 0.05 level of significance.
f. Determine the p-value in (e) and interpret its meaning.
g. Interpret the meaning of the coefficient of multiple determination in this problem.
h. Determine the adjusted r^2.
i. At the 0.05 level of significance, determine whether each explanatory variable makes a significant contribution to the regression model. On the basis of these results, indicate the regression model that should be used in this problem.
j. Determine the p-values in (i) and interpret their meaning.
k. Set up a 95% confidence interval estimate of the population slope between wins and ERA.
l. Compute the coefficients of partial determination ($r^2_{Y1.2}$ and $r^2_{Y2.1}$) and interpret their meaning.
m. Which seems to be more important in predicting wins, pitching as measured by ERA or offense as measured by runs scored? Explain.

58 Referring to problem 57, suppose that in addition to using earned run average (ERA) to predict the number of wins, Crazy Dave wants to include the league (American versus National) as an explanatory variable. Develop a model to predict wins based on ERA and league: **BB2002.xls**

a. State the multiple regression equation.
b. Interpret the meaning of the slopes in this problem.
c. Predict the average number of wins for a team with an ERA of 4.5 in the American League. Set up a 95% confidence interval estimate and a 95% prediction interval.
d. Perform a residual analysis on the results, and determine the adequacy of the fit of the model.
e. Determine whether there is a significant relationship between wins and the two explanatory variables (ERA and league) at the 0.05 level of significance.
f. At the 0.05 level of significance, determine whether each explanatory variable makes a contribution to the regression model. On the basis of these results, indicate the regression model that should be used in this problem.
g. Set up 95% confidence interval estimates of the population slope for the relationship between wins and ERA and between wins and league.
h. Interpret the meaning of the coefficient of multiple determination.
i. Determine the adjusted r^2.
j. Compute the coefficients of partial determination ($r^2_{Y1.2}$ and $r^2_{Y2.1}$) and interpret their meaning.
k. What assumption about the slope of wins with ERA must be made in this problem?
l. Include an interaction term in the model, and, at the 0.05 level of significance, determine whether it makes a significant contribution to the model.
m. On the basis of the results of (f) and (l), which model is more appropriate? Explain.

Internet Exercises

59 Go to the Web site for this text

www.prenhall.com/levine

Select Chapter 13 and then click on Internet exercises.

RUNNING CASE MANAGING THE *SPRINGVILLE HERALD*

In its continuing study of the home-delivery subscription solicitation process, a marketing department team wants to test the effects of two types of structured sales presentations (personal formal and personal informal) and the number of hours spent on telemarketing on the number of new subscriptions. For the past several months, the staff has recorded these data which can be found at **http://www.prenhall.com/HeraldCase/EffectsData.htm** and in the **EffectsData.htm** file in the HeraldCase folder on the CD that accompanies this text **SH13.xls**.

Analyze these data and develop a statistical model to predict the number of new subscriptions for a week based on the number of hours spent on telemarketing and the sales presentation type. Write a report giving detailed findings concerning the regression model used.

WEB CASE

Apply your knowledge of multiple regression models in this Web Case that extends the Using Statistics *OmniPower scenario from this chapter.*

To ensure a successful test-marketing of its OmniPower energy bars, the marketing department of OmniFoods has arranged for the In-Store Placements Group (ISPG), a merchandising consultancy, to work with the grocery store chain conducting the test-market study. Using the same 34-store sample used to better understand the relationship between price and promotional dollars, ISPG claims that both product shelf locations and the presence of in-store OmniPower coupon dispensers increases sales of the energy bars.

Review the ISPG claims and supporting data at OmniFoods internal Web site (**www.prenhall.com/Springville/Omni_ISPGMemo.htm**) and then answer the following:

1. Are the supporting data consistent with ISPG's claims? Perform an appropriate statistical analysis that would confirm the relationship between sales and product shelf locations and the presence of in-store OmniPower coupon dispensers.
2. If you were advising OmniFoods, would you recommend using both special shelf locations and in-store coupon dispensers to sell OmniPower bars?
3. What additional data would be relevant to determining the effectiveness of the sales promotion techniques used by ISPG?

REFERENCES

1. Hocking, R. R., "Developments in Linear Regression Methodology: 1959–1982," *Technometrics* 25 (1983): 219–250.
2. Hosmer, D. W., and S. Lemeshow, *Applied Logistic Regression*, 2nd ed. (New York: Wiley, 2001).
3. *Microsoft Excel 2002* (Redmond, WA: Microsoft Corp., 2001).
4. Neter, J., M. Kutner, C. Nachtsheim, and W. Wasserman, *Applied Linear Statistical Models*, 4th ed. (Homewood, IL: Irwin, 1996).

Answers to Selected Even-Numbered Problems

For more detailed solutions including explanations, interpretations, and Excel output, see the *Student Solutions Manual*.

2 (a) Holding constant the effect of X_2, for each additional unit of X_1 the response variable Y is expected to decrease on average by 2 units. Holding constant the effect of X_1, for each additional unit of X_2 the response variable Y is expected to increase on average by 7 units. **(b)** The Y-intercept 50 estimates the value of Y if X_1 and X_2 are both 0. **(c)** 40% of the variation in Y can be explained or accounted for by the variation in X_1 and the variation in X_2.

4 (a) 68% of the total variability in team performance can be explained by team skills after adjusting for the number of predictors and sample size. 78% of the total variability in team performance can be explained by clarity in expectation after adjusting for the number of predictors and sample size. 97% of the total variability in team performance can be explained by both team skills and clarity in expectations after adjusting for the number of predictors and sample size. **(b)** Model 3 is the best predictor of team performance since it has the highest adjusted r^2.

6 (a) $\hat{Y} = 58.15708 - 0.11753X_1 - 0.00687X_2$ **(b)** For a given weight, each increase by one unit in horsepower is expected to result in an average decrease in MPG by 0.11753. For a given horsepower, each increase of one unit in weight is expected to result in the average decrease in MPG by 0.00687. **(c)** The interpretation of b_0 has no practical meaning here because it would have meant the estimated average gasoline mileage when a car has 0 horsepower and 0 weight. **(d)** $\hat{Y}_i = 37.365$ MPG **(e)** $35.453 < \mu_{Y|X} < 39.276$ **(f)** $28.747 < Y_I < 45.981$ **(g)** $r^2_{Y.12} = 0.7494$. So, 74.94% of the variation in MPG can be explained by variation in horsepower and variation in weight. **(h)** $r^2_{adj} = 0.7388$.

8 (a) $\hat{Y} = -330.675 + 1.764865\,X_1 - 0.13897\,X_2$ **(b)** For a given amount of remote hours, each increase by one unit in total staff present is expected to result in an average increase in standby hours by 1.764865. For a given amount of total staff present, each increase by one unit in remote hours is expected to result in the average decrease in standby hours by 0.13897. **(c)** The interpretation of b_0 has no practical meaning here because it would have meant the estimated average standby hours when there was no weekly total of people-days over a 7-day week and staff present and zero total number of hours worked by employees at locations away from the central plant. **(d)** $\hat{Y}_i = 160.845$. **(e)** $141.7856 < \mu_{Y|X} < 179.9074$. **(f)** $85.2014 < Y_I < 236.4915$ **(g)** $r^2_{Y.12} = 0.4899$. So, 48.99% of the variation in sales can be explained by variation in radio and television advertising and variation in newspaper advertising. **(h)** $r^2_{adj} = 0.4456$.

10 There appears to be a quadratic relationship in the plot of the residuals against the predicted values of MPG, the horsepower, and the weight. Thus, variable transformations or quadratic terms for the explanatory variables should be considered for inclusion in the model.

12 (a) Based upon a residual analysis, the model appears adequate. **(b)** There is no evidence of a pattern over time. **(c)** D = 1.79 **(d)** D = 1.79 > 1.55. There is no evidence of positive autocorrelation in the residuals.

14 (a) $MSR = 15$, $MSE = 12$ **(b)** $F = 1.25$ **(c)** $F = 1.25 < F_{U(2,13-2-1)} = 4.103$. Do not reject H_0.

16 (a) $MSR = 1684$, $MSE = 22.7$, $F = 74.13$, $F = 74.13 > F_{U(2,24-2-1)} = 3.467$. Reject H_0. **(b)** The probability of obtaining an F-test statistic based on 2 and 21 degrees when H_0 is true is less than 0.001.

18 (a) $MSR = 1014016$, $MSE = 25251$, $F = 40.16$, $F = 40.16 > F_{U(2,22-2-1)} = 3.522$. Reject H_0. **(b)** The probability of obtaining an F-test statistic based on 2 and 19 degrees when H_0 is true is less than 0.001.

20 (a) Variable X_1 has a larger slope in terms of the t-statistic of 2.5 than variable X_2, which has a smaller slope in terms of the t-statistic of 1.25. **(b)** $0.85225 \le \beta_1 \le 9.14775$. **(c)** For X_1: $t = 2.50 > t_{22} = 2.0739$. Reject H_0. For X_2: $t = 1.25 < t_{22} = 2.0739$. Do not reject H_0. Only variable X_1 should be included in the model.

22 (a) $0.65400 \le \beta_1 \le 0.92832$ **(b)** For X_1: $t = 12.57 > t_{12} = 2.1788$. Reject H_0. For X_2: $t = 8.43 > t_{12} = 2.1788$. Reject H_0. Both variables X_1 and X_2 should be included in the model.

24 (a) $-0.18311 \le \beta_1 \le -0.05195$ **(b)** For X_1: $t = -3.605 < -t_{47} = -2.0117$. Reject H_0. For X_2: $t = -4.91 < -t_{47} = -2.0117$. Reject H_0. Both variables X_1 and X_2 should be included in the model.

26 (a) $0.9809 \le \beta_1 \le 2.5489$ **(b)** For X_1: $t = 4.66 > t_{23} = 2.0687$. Reject H_0. For X_2: $t = -2.36 < -t_{23} = -2.0687$. Reject H_0. Both variables X_1 and X_2 should be included in the model.

28 (a) For X_1: $F = 1.25 < F_{U(1,10)} = 4.965$. Do not reject H_0. For $F = 0.833 < F_{U(1,10)} = 4.965$. Do not reject H_0. Neither variable should be included in the model and other variables should be investigated. **(b)** $r^2_{Y1.2} = 0.1111$. Holding constant the effect of variable X_2, 11.11% of the variation in Y can be explained by the variation in variable X_1. $r^2_{Y2.1} = 0.0769$. Holding constant the effect of variable X_1, 7.69% of the variation in Y can be explained by the variation in variable X_2.

30 (a) For X_1: $F = 12.96 > F_{U(1,47)} = 4.047$. Reject H_0. For X_2: $F = 24.04 > F_{U(1,47)} = 4.047$. Reject H_0. Both variables should be included in the model. **(b)** $r^2_{Y1.2} = 0.2162$. Holding constant the effect of weight, 21.62% of the variation in Y can be explained by the variation in horsepower. $r^2_{Y2.1} = 0.3384$. Holding constant the effect of horsepower, 33.84% of the variation in Y can be explained by the variation in weight.

32 (a) For X_1: $F = 21.68 > F_{U(1,23)} = 4.279$. Reject H_0. For X_2: $F = 5.586 > F_{U(1,23)} = 4.279$. Reject H_0. Both variables should be included in the model. **(b)** $r^2_{Y1.2} = 0.4852$. Holding constant the effect of remote hours, 48.52% of the variation in Y can be explained by the variation in total staff present. $r^2_{Y2.1} = 0.1954$. Holding constant the effect of total staff present, 19.54% of the variation in Y can be explained by the variation in remote hours.

34 (a) First, develop a multiple regression model using X_1 as the variable for the SAT score and X_2 as a dummy variable with $X_2 = 1$ if a student had a grade of B or better in the introductory statistics course. If the dummy variable coefficient is significantly different than zero, you need to develop a model with the interaction term X_1X_2 to make sure that the coefficient of X_1 is not significantly different if $X_2 = 0$ or $X_2 = 1$. **(b)** If a student received a grade of B or better in the introductory statistics course, the student would be expected to have a grade point average in accountancy that is 0.30 higher than a student who had the same SAT score, but did not get a grade of B or better in the introductory statistics course.

36 (a) $\hat{Y} = 43.737 + 9.219X_1 + 12.697X_2$, where X_1 = number of rooms and X_2 = neighborhood (east = 0). **(b)** Holding constant the effect of neighborhood, for each additional room, the selling price is expected to increase on average by 9.219 thousands of dollars, or \$9219. For a given number of rooms, a west neighborhood is expected to increase selling price over an east neighborhood by 12.697 thousands of dollars, or \$12,697. **(c)** \$126,710, $109.5600 < Y_{X=X_i} < 143.8551$, $121.4714 < \mu_{Y|X=X_i} < 131.9437$. **(d)** Based on a residual analysis, the model appears adequate. **(e)** $F = 55.39 > F_{2,17} = 3.5915$. Reject H_0. **(f)** For X_1: $t = 8.95 > t_{17} = 2.1098$. Reject H_0. For X_2: $t = 3.59 > t_{17} = 2.1098$. Reject H_0. The regression model with the two independent variables should be used. **(g)** $7.0466 \le \beta_1 \le 11.3913$, $5.2377 \le \beta_2 \le 20.1557$ **(h)** $r^2_{Y.12} = 0.867$. 86.7% of the variation in selling price can be explained by variation in number of rooms and variation in neighborhood. **(i)** $r^2_{adj} = 0.851$ **(j)** $r^2_{Y1.2} = 0.825$. Holding constant the effect of neighborhood, 82.5% of the variation in selling price can be explained by variation in number of rooms. $r^2_{Y2.1} = 0.431$. Holding constant the effect of number of rooms, 43.1% of the variation in selling price can be explained by variation in neighborhood. **(k)** The slope of selling price with number of rooms is the same regardless of whether the house is located in an east or west neighborhood. **(l)** $\hat{Y} = 53.95 + 8.032X_1 - 5.90X_2 + 2.089X_1X_2$. For X_1X_2: the p-value is 0.330. Do not reject H_0. **(m)** The two-variable model in (a) should be used.

38 (a) $\hat{Y} = 8.0100 + 0.0052X_1 - 2.1052X_2$, where X_1 = depth (in feet) and X_2 = type of drilling (wet = 0, dry = 1). **(b)** Holding constant the effect of type of drilling, for each foot increase in depth of the hole, the additional drilling time is estimated to increase on average by 0.0052 minutes. For a given depth, dry drilling is estimated to reduce average additional drilling time over wet drilling by 2.1052 minutes. **(c)** Dry drilling: $\hat{Y} = 6.4276$ minutes. $6.2096 < \mu_{Y|X} < 6.6457$, $4.92304 < Y_I < 7.9322$ **(d)** Based on a residual analysis, the model appears adequate. **(e)** $F = 111.109$, $F_{2,97} = 3.09$ using Excel. p-value is virtually 0. Reject H_0. **(f)** For X_1: $t = 5.0289 > t_{97} = 1.9847$. Reject H_0. For X_2: $t = -14.0331 < t_{97} = -1.9847$. Reject H_0. The regression model with the two independent variables should be used. **(g)** $0.0032 \le \beta_1 \le 0.0073$, $-2.4029 \le \beta_2 \le -1.8075$ **(h)** $r^2_{Y.12} = 0.6961$. 69.61% of the variation in additional drilling time can be explained by the depth of the hole and variation in type of drilling. **(i)** $r^2_{adj} = 0.6899$ **(j)** $r^2_{Y1.2} = 0.2068$. Holding constant the effect of type of drilling, 20.68% of the variation in additional drilling time can be explained by variation in depth of the hole. $r^2_{Y2.1} = 0.6700$. Holding constant the effect of the depth of the hole, 67% of the variation in additional drilling time can be explained by variation in type of drilling. **(k)** The slope of additional drilling time with depth of the hole is the same regardless of whether it is dry drilling hole or wet drilling hole. **(l)** $\hat{Y} = 7.9120 + 0.0060X_1 - 1.9091X_2 - 0.0015X_1X_2$. For X_1X_2: the p-value is $0.4624 > 0.05$. Do not reject H_0. **(m)** The two-variable model in (a) should be used.

40 (a) $\hat{Y} = 31.5594 + 0.0296X_1 + 0.0041X_2 + 1.7159 \cdot 10^{-5}X_1X_2$, where X_1 = sales, X_2 = orders, $X_3 = X_1X_2$. For X_1X_2: the p-value is $0.3249 > 0.05$. Do not reject H_0. **(b)** The model in problem 13.5 should be used.

42 (a) $\hat{Y} = -1293.3105 + 43.6600X_1 + 56.9335X_2 - 0.8430X_1X_2$, where X_1 = radio advertisement, X_2 = newspaper advertisement, $X_3 = X_1X_2$. For X_1X_2: the p-value is $0.0018 < 0.05$. Reject H_0. **(b)** The model in this problem should be used.

44 (a) $\hat{Y} = -63.9813 + 1.1258X_1 - 22.2887X_2 + 8.0880X_3$ where X_1 = proficiency exam, X_2 = traditional method dummy, X_3 = CD-ROM-based dummy. **(b)** Holding constant the effect of training method, for each point increase in proficiency exam score, the end-of-training exam score is estimated to increase on average by 1.1258 points. For a given proficiency exam score, the end-of-training exam score of a trainee who has been trained by the traditional method will have an estimated average score that is 22.2887 points below a trainee that has been trained using the Web-based method. For a given proficiency exam score, the end-of-training exam score of a trainee who has been trained by the CD-ROM-based method will have an estimated average score that is 8.0880 points above a trainee that has been trained using the Web-based method. **(c)** $\hat{Y} = 48.5969$. **(d)** There appears to be a quadratic effect from the residual plots. There is no severe departure from the normality assumption from the normal probability plot. **(e)** $F = 31.77$. The p-value is virtually 0. Reject H_0. **(f)** For X_1: $t = 7.0868$ and the p-value is virtually 0. Reject H_0. For X_2: $t = -5.1649$ and the p-value is virtually 0. Reject H_0. For X_3: $t = 1.8765$ and the p-value = 0.07186. Do not reject H_0. The regression model should use the proficiency exam score and the traditional dummy variable. **(g)** $0.7992 \le \beta_1 \le 1.4523$, $-31.1591 \le \beta_2 \le -13.4182$, $-0.7719 \le \beta_2 \le 16.9480$. **(h)** $r^2_{Y.12} = 0.7857$. 78.57% of the variation in the end-of-training exam score can be explained by the proficiency exam score and whether the trainee is trained by the traditional or Web-based method. **(i)** $r^2_{adj} = 0.7610$ **(j)** $r^2_{Y1.23} = 0.6589$. Holding constant the effect of training method, 65.89% of the variation in end-of-training exam score can be explained by variation in the proficiency exam score. $r^2_{Y2.13} = 0.5064$. Holding constant the effect of proficiency exam score, 50.64% of the variation in end-of-training exam score can be explained by the difference between traditional and Web-based methods. $r^2_{Y3.12} = 0.1193$. Holding constant the effect of proficiency exam score, 11.93% of the variation in end-of-training exam score can be explained by the difference between CD-ROM-based and Web-based methods. **(k)** The slope of proficiency score with end-of-training exam score is the same regardless of the proficiency exam score. **(l)** $F = 0.8122$. The p-value = $0.46 > 0.05$. Do not reject H_0. **(m)** The regression model should use the proficiency exam score and the traditional dummy variable.

46 Testing the significance of the entire regression model involves a simultaneous test of whether any of the independent variables are significant. Testing the contribution of each independent variable tests the contribution of that independent variable after accounting for the effect of the other independent variables in the model.

52 (a) $\hat{Y} = -44.988 + 1.7506X_1 + 0.368X_2$, where X_1 = assessed value (in thousands of dollars) and X_2 = time period (in months). **(b)** Holding constant the effects of time period, for each additional thousand dollars in assessed value the selling price of the house is expected to increase on the average by 1.7506 thousands of dollars, or \$1,750.60. Holding constant the effects of assessed value, for each additional month the selling price of the house is expected to increase on the average by 0.368 thousands of dollars, or \$368. **(c)** \$81,969 **(d)** All four residual plots indicate that the fitted model appears to be adequate. **(e)** $F = 223.46 > F_{U(2,27)} = 3.35$. Reject H_0. **(f)** The p-value is less than 0.001.

(g) $r^2_{Y.12} = 0.943$. So, 94.3% of the variation in selling price can be explained by the variation in assessed value and the variation in time period. **(h)** $r^2_{adj} = 0.939$ **(i)** For X_1: $t = 20.41 > t_{27} = 2.0518$. Reject H_0. For X_2: $t = 2.873 > t_{27} = 2.0518$. Reject H_0. Both variables should be included in the model. **(j)** For X_1, the p-value is less than 0.001. For X_2, the p-value is 0.008. **(k)** $r^2_{Y1.2} = 0.9392$. For a given time period, 93.92% of the variation in selling price can be explained by variation in assessed value. $r^2_{Y2.1} = 0.2342$. For a given assessed value, 23.42% of the variation in selling price can be explained by variation in time period.

54 (a) $\hat{Y} = 63.7751 + 10.7252X_1 - 0.2843X_2$, where X_1 = size (in thousands of square feet) and X_2 = age (in years). **(b)** Holding constant the effects of age, for each additional thousand square feet the assessed value of the house is expected to increase on the average by 10.7252 thousands of dollars, or $10,725.20. Holding constant the effects of size, for each year of age the assessed value of the house is expected to decrease on the average by 0.2843 thousands of dollars, or $284.30. **(c)** $79,702 **(d)** The residual plot against age indicates a potential pattern that may require the addition of nonlinear terms. One value appears to be an outlier in all four plots. **(e)** $F = 28.58 > F_{U(2,12)} = 3.89$. Reject H_0. **(f)** The p-value is less than 0.001. **(g)** $r^2_{Y.12} = 0.8265$. 82.65% of the variation in assessed value can be explained by the variation in size and the variation in age. **(h)** $r^2_{adj} = 0.7976$. **(i)** For X_1: $t = 3.558 > t_{12} = 2.1788$. Reject H_0. For X_2: $t = -3.400 < -t_{12} = -2.1788$. Reject H_0. Both variables should be included in the model.

(j) For X_1, the p-value is 0.004. For X_2, the p-value is 0.005. **(k)** $r^2_{Y1.2} = 0.5134$. For a given age of the house, 51.34% of the variation in assessed value can be explained by variation in size. $r^2_{Y2.1} = 0.4907$. For a given amount of size in square feet, 49.07% of the variation in assessed value can be explained by variation in age.

56 (a) $\hat{Y} = 40.8765 - 0.0121$ length $-$ 0.0050 weight. **(b)** $b_1 = -0.0121$: Holding weight fixed, the estimated average mileage of a car will decrease by 0.0121 miles per gallon as the length of the car increases by one inch. $b_2 = -.0050$: Holding length fixed, the estimate average mileage of a car will decrease by .0050 miles per gallon as the weight of the car increases by one pound. **(c)** 23.6603 miles per gallon. **(d)** According to the residual plot of length, the homoscedasticity assumption seems to have been violated. From the residual plot of weight, there seems to be a quadratic relationship between mileage and weight. **(e)** Yes, there is a significant relationship between gasoline mileage and the two explanatory variables at the 0.05 level of significance because the p-value of the F-test is essentially zero. **(f)** The p-value is essentially zero. **(g)** 61.17% of the total variation in gasoline mileage can be explained by length and weight of a car. **(h)** $r^2_{adj} = 0.6051$. **(i)** The model should include only weight as the explanatory variable. **(j)** The p-value for length is 0.6474. The p-value for weight is essentially zero. **(k)** [−0.0059, −0.0040]. **(l)** $r^2_{Y1\cdot2} = 0.0018$, $r^2_{Y2\cdot1} = 0.4706$. Holding weight constant, 0.18% of the variation in mileage can be explained by length. Holding length constant, 47.06% of the variation in mileage can be explained by weight.

58 (a) $\hat{Y} = 170.8022 - 3.0654X_1 - 19.9941X_2$, where X_1 = league dummy (0 = American, 1 = National) and X_2 = ERA. **(b)** Holding constant the effect of ERA, the estimated average number of wins for a team in the American League is 3.0654 above that of the National League. Holding constant the effect of league, for each unit increase in ERA, the estimated average number of wins is estimated to decrease by 19.9941. **(c)** Approximately 81wins. **(d)** Based on a residual analysis, the model appears adequate. **(e)** $F = 20.257$. p-value = 4.23207E-06 < 0.05. Reject H_0. **(f)** For X_1: $t = -0.9755$. p-value = 0.3380 > 0.05. Do not reject H_0. For X_2: $t = -6.3616$. p-value = 8.20671E-07 < 0.05. Reject H_0. The model should include ERA but not the league dummy. **(g)** $-9.5130 \le \beta_1 \le 3.3823$, $-26.4429 \le \beta_2 \le -13.5453$. **(h)** $r^2_{Y.12} = 0.6001$. 60.01% of the variation in number of wins can be explained by variation in type of league and variation in ERA. **(i)** $r^2_{adj} = 0.5705$. **(j)** $r^2_{Y1.2} = 0.0340$. Holding constant the effect of ERA, 3.4% of the variation in number of wins can be explained by variation in the type of league. $r^2_{Y2.1} = 0.5998$. Holding constant the effect of league, 59.98% of the variation in number of wins can be explained by variation in ERA. **(k)** The slope of number of wins with ERA is the same regardless of whether the team is in the American or National League. **(l)** The p-value is 0.7299. Do not reject H_0. **(m)** The model with only ERA should be used.

Excel Handbook for Introduction to Multiple Regression

EH1 PERFORMING MULTIPLE REGRESSION ANALYSIS

To perform a multiple regression analysis, use the Data Analysis Regression procedure. For example, to perform a multiple regression analysis for the OmniPower sales data of Table 1, open to the **Data** worksheet of the **Chapter 13.xls** workbook and:

Select **Tools | Data Analysis**.

Select **Regression** from the list box in the Data Analysis dialog box and click the **OK** button.

In the Regression dialog box (shown at right):

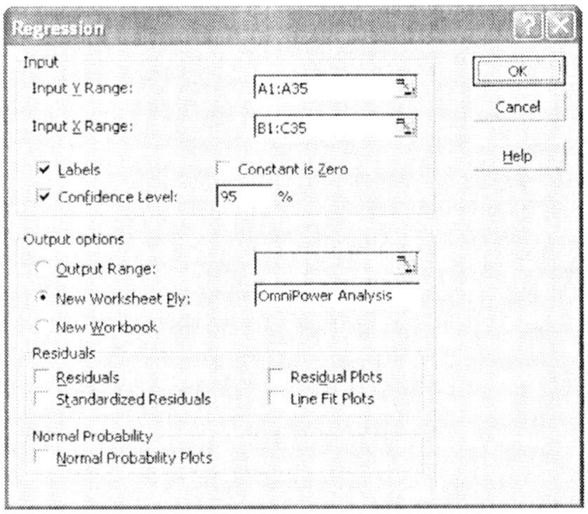

Enter **A1:A35** in the **Input Y Range** edit box.

Enter **B1:C35** in the **Input X Range** edit box.

Select the **Labels** check box.

Select the **Confidence Level check box** and enter **95** in its edit box.

Select the **New Worksheet Ply** option button and enter a name for the new sheet.

Click the **OK** button.

This procedure generates a worksheet that does ***not*** *dynamically change. Therefore, you will need to rerun the procedure if you make any changes to the underlying sample data in order to update the results.*

EH2 CALCULATING CONFIDENCE INTERVAL ESTIMATES AND PREDICTION INTERVALS

To calculate the confidence interval estimate and prediction interval for a multiple regression model, follow the instructions of section EH1 to perform a multiple regression analysis and then implement a worksheet that features the **TINV** and several matrix-related functions to calculate the confidence interval estimate and the prediction interval.

Tables EH1 and EH2 contain the design for an **Intervals** worksheet that calculates the confidence interval estimate and prediction interval for the OmniPower sales data shown in Figure 2. This design requires that a three-column worksheet named **XMatrix** that contains all ones in the cell range A2:A35 and the values for the two X variables in the cell range B2:C35 be created and that a worksheet containing multiple regression statistics has been generated by using the instructions of section EH1.

The design calculates the interval half width using, in part, matrix calculations that are beyond the scope of this text to explain. These calculations use the TRANSPOSE, MMULT, and MINVERSE functions, entered as **TRANSPOSE(*cell range*)**, **MMULT(*cell range 1, cell range 2*)**, and **MINVERSE(*cell range*)**. The design also calculates the t statistic using the TINV function, entered as **TINV(1-*confidence level, degrees of freedom*)**.

Table EH1
Intervals worksheet design for columns A and B

	A	B
1	Confidence and Prediction Estimate Intervals	
2		
3	Data	
4	Confidence Level	0.95
5		1
6	Price given value	79
7	Promotion given value	400
8		
9	X′X	=MMULT(TRANSPOSE(XMatrix!A2:C35), XMatrix!A2:C35)
10		=MMULT(TRANSPOSE(XMatrix!A2:C35), XMatrix!A2:C35)
11		=MMULT(TRANSPOSE(XMatrix!A2:C35), XMatrix!A2:C35)
12		
13	Inverse of X′X	=MINVERSE(B9:D11)
14		=MINVERSE(B9:D11)
15		=MINVERSE(B9:D11)
16		
17	X′G times Inverse of X′X	=MMULT(TRANSPOSE(B5:B7), B13:D15)
18		
19	[X′G times Inverse of X′X] time XG	=MMULT(B17:D17, B5:B7)
20	t Statistic	=TINV(1 – B4, MR!B13)
21	Predicted Y (YHat)	=MMULT(TRANSPOSE(B5:B7), MR!B17:B19)
22		
23	For Average Predicted Y (YHat)	
24	Interval Half Width	=B20 * SQRT(B19) * MR!B7
25	Confidence Interval Lower Limit	=B21 – B24
26	Confidence Interval Upper Limit	=B21 + B24
27		
28	For Individual Response Y	
29	Interval Half Width	=B20 * SQRT(1 + B19) * MR!B7
30	Prediction Interval Lower Limit	=B21 – B29
31	Prediction Interval Upper Limit	=B21 + B29

Table EH2
Intervals worksheet design for columns C and D (rows 1 through 8 are blank)

	C	D
9	=MMULT(TRANSPOSE(Xmatrix!A2:C35), Xmatrix!A2:C35)	=MMULT(TRANSPOSE(XMatrix!A2:C35), XMatrix!A2:C35)
10	=MMULT(TRANSPOSE(Xmatrix!A2:C35), Xmatrix!A2:C35)	=MMULT(TRANSPOSE(XMatrix!A2:C35), XMatrix!A2:C35)
11	=MMULT(TRANSPOSE(Xmatrix!A2:C35), Xmatrix!A2:C35)	=MMULT(TRANSPOSE(XMatrix!A2:C35), XMatrix!A2:C35)
12		
13	=MINVERSE(B9:D11)	=MINVERSE(B9:D11)
14	=MINVERSE(B9:D11)	=MINVERSE(B9:D11)
15	=MINVERSE(B9:D11)	=MINVERSE(B9:D11)
16		
17	=MMULT(TRANSPOSE(B5:B7), B13:D15)	=MMULT(TRANSPOSE(B5:B7), B13:D15)

To implement this design, first create the XMatrix worksheet and perform a multiple regression analysis. Rename the worksheet produced by the Data Analysis Regression procedure **MR** to facilitate formula entry. Enter the formulas that are typeset as two lines, as single continuous lines. The five sets of duplicated formulas in the cell ranges B9:D11, B13:D15, and B17:D17 in Table EH2 are all array formulas and must be entered as follows:

Select the cell range to contain a duplicated formula.

Type the formula into the first cell of the range, but do not press the **Enter** key.

While holding down the **Control** and **Shift** keys, press the **Enter** key.

EH3 GENERATING A SCATTER DIAGRAM OF THE RESIDUALS VERSUS PREDICTED *Y*

To generate a scatter diagram of the residuals versus the predicted *Y*, follow the instructions for one of the strategies to generate residual analyses and then use the Chart Wizard to generate the scatter diagram.

For example, to generate the residuals versus predicted *Y* scatter diagram for the OmniPower sales data of Table 1, open to the worksheet that contains the multiple regression statistics and residuals, select **Insert | Chart** and make these entries in the Chart Wizard dialog boxes:

Step 1 dialog box. Select the **Standard Types** tab and then select **XY (Scatter)** from the Chart type: list box. Select the first (top) **Chart sub-type** choice, labeled as **Scatter. Compares pairs of values**, when selected, and click the **Next** button.

Step 2 dialog box. Select the **Data Range** tab. Enter **C26:C59** in the **Data range** edit box and select the **Columns** option button. Select the **Series** tab. Enter the *formula* **=MR!B26:B59** in the X Values edit box and click **Next.** (This entry assumes that the worksheet that contains multiple regression statistics is named MR. If your worksheet has another name, adjust the entry to reflect that name.)

Step 3 dialog box. Select the **Titles** tab. Enter **Residuals versus Predicted Y** as the **Chart title, Predicted Y** in the **Value (X) axis** edit box, and **Residuals** in the **Value (Y) axis** edit box. Select, in turn, the **Axes**, **Gridlines**, **Legend**, and **Data Table** tabs and adjust settings as discussed in Exhibit EP6 in the Excel Primer, and click **Next.** (Consult your instructor if you require the Excel Primer.)

Step 4 dialog box. Select the **As new sheet** option button, enter a descriptive and unique sheet name, and click the **Finish** button to generate the chart.

If necessary, relocate the X-axis to the bottom of the scatter diagram.

EH4 CALCULATING THE COEFFICIENTS OF PARTIAL DETERMINATION

To calculate the coefficients of partial determination, follow the instructions of section EH1 to perform a multiple regression analysis and then implement a worksheet that uses simple arithmetic formulas and the results of various regression models.

Table EH3 contains the design for a **CPD** worksheet that calculates the coefficients of partial determination for the OmniPower sales data of Table 1. The design assumes that either the PHStat2 Multiple Regression or Data Analysis Regression tool had been used to generate three regression model **worksheets**, the MR (the full regression), NOTX1 (regression excluding price), and NOTX2 (regression excluding promotion) worksheets, that contain the regression sum of squares values in cell C12. The design also assumes that the MR sheet contains the total sum of squares in cell C14, as would be the case if either PHStat2 or the Data Analysis Regression tool were used. (If your worksheets have names other than MR, NOTX1, and NOTX2, make the appropriate adjustments to the formula entries.)

Table EH3
CPD worksheet design

	A	B	C	D
1	OmniPower Sales Analysis			
2	Coefficients of Partial Determination			
3				
4	Intermediate Calculations			
5	SSR(X1,X2)	=MR!C12		
6	SST	=MR!C14		
7	SSR(X2)	=NOTX1!C12	SSR(X1 | X2)	=B5 – B7
8	SSR(X1)	=NOTX2!C12	SSR(X2 | X1)	=B5 – B8
9				
10	Coefficients			
11	r2 Y1.2	=D7/(B6 – B5 + D7)		
12	r2 Y2.1	=D8/(B6 – B5 + D8)		

Decision Making

USING STATISTICS: Selecting a Stock

LEARNING OBJECTIVES

- To use payoff tables and decision trees to evaluate alternative courses of action
- To use several criteria to select an alternative course of action
- To use Bayes' theorem to revise probabilities in light of sample information
- To understand the concept of utility

USING STATISTICS

Selecting a Stock

As the manager of a stock mutual fund you are responsible for purchasing and selling stocks for the fund. The investors in your fund expect a large return on their investment and, at the same time, they want to minimize their risk. At the present time, you need to decide between two stocks to purchase. An economist for your company has evaluated the potential one-year returns for both stocks under four economic conditions: recession, stability, moderate growth, and boom. She has also estimated the probability of each economic condition occurring. How can you use the information provided by the economist to determine which stock to choose in order to maximize return and minimize risk?

INTRODUCTION

In this chapter these probability rules and probability distributions are applied to a decision-making process for evaluating whether a specific course of action should or should not be taken. In this context, you can consider the four basic features of a decision-making situation:

1. **Alternative courses of action.** The decision-maker must have two or more possible choices to evaluate prior to selecting one course of action. For example, as a manager of a mutual fund in the Using Statistics scenario, you must decide whether to purchase stock A or stock B.
2. **Events.** The decision-maker must list the events that can occur and consider each event's probability of occurring. To aid in selecting which stock to purchase in the Using Statistics scenario, an economist for your company has listed four possible economic conditions and the probability of each occurring in the next year.
3. **Payoffs.** In order to evaluate each course of action, the decision-maker must associate a value or payoff with the result of each event. In business applications, this payoff is usually expressed in terms of profits or costs, although other payoffs such as units of satisfaction or utility may be considered. In the Using Statistics scenario, the payoff is the return on investment.
4. **Decision criteria.** The decision-maker must determine how the best course of action is to be selected. Several criteria will be discussed in this chapter.

1 PAYOFF TABLES AND DECISION TREES

In order to evaluate the various alternative courses of action for the complete set of events, you need to develop a payoff table or construct a decision tree. A **payoff table** contains each possible event that can occur for each alternative course of action. Furthermore, you must associate a value or payoff for each combination of an event and course of action. Example 1 provides an application of the payoff table concerning a marketing manager trying to decide whether or not to introduce a new model of a television set.

EXAMPLE 1

A PAYOFF TABLE FOR DECIDING WHETHER TO MARKET A TELEVISION SET

The marketing manager of a consumer electronics company is considering whether or not a particular large screen television set should be introduced into the market. The manager is aware that there are risks in deciding whether to market this television set. For example, it is possible that the television set will be marketed and it will be unsuccessful. Alternatively, a decision could be made not to market a television set that would have been successful. There is a fixed cost of \$3 (millions of dollars) incurred prior to making a final decision to market the television set. Based on past experience, if the television set is successful, a profit of \$45 (millions of dollars) would be obtained. If the television set is not successful, a loss of \$36 million would be incurred. Set up a payoff table for these two alternative courses of action.

SOLUTION

Table 1 is a payoff table for the television set marketing example.

TABLE 1
Payoff table for the television set marketing example (in millions of dollars)

	Alternative Courses of Action (Millions of Dollars)	
Event E_i	**Market, A_1**	**Do Not Market, A_2**
Successful television set, E_1	+\$45	−\$3
Unsuccessful television set, E_2	−\$36	−\$3

A **decision tree** is another way of representing the events for each alternative course of action. The decision tree pictorially represents the events and courses of action through a set of branches and nodes. A decision tree is illustrated in Example 2.

EXAMPLE 2

THE DECISION TREE FOR THE TELEVISION SET MARKETING DECISION

Given the payoff table for the television marketing example, set up a decision tree.

SOLUTION

Figure 1 is the decision tree for the payoff table of Example 1. Observe that the first set of branches relates to the two alternative courses of action, market the television set or do not market the television set. The second set of branches represents the possible events of successful television set and unsuccessful television set. These events occur for each of the alternative courses of action on the decision tree.

FIGURE 1
Decision tree for the television set marketing example

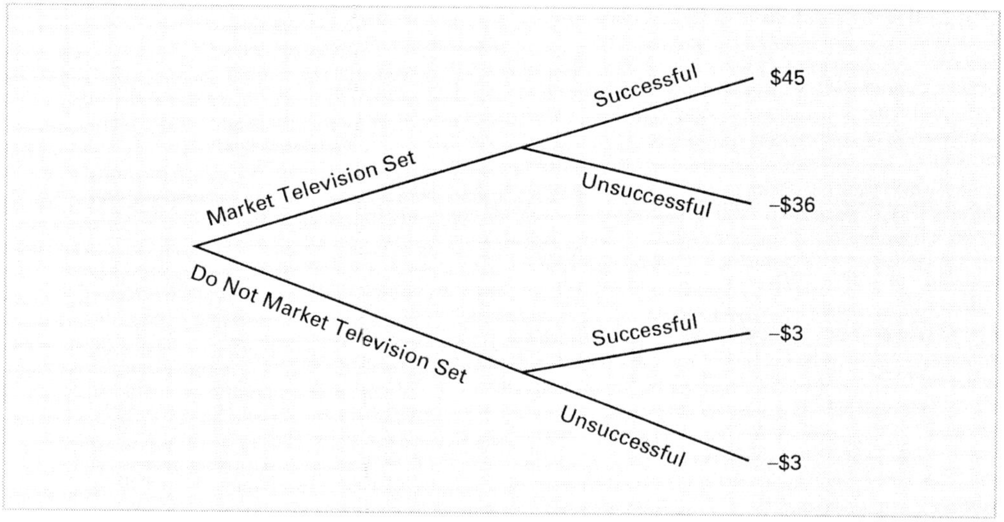

The decision structure for the television set marketing example contains only two possible alternative courses of action and two possible events. In general, there can be any number of alternative courses of action and events. As a manager of a mutual fund in the Using Statistics scenario, you need to decide between two stocks to purchase for short-term investment of up to one year. An economist in the company has predicted returns for the two stocks under the four economic conditions—recession, stability, moderate growth, and boom. The predicted 1-year return of a $1,000 investment in each stock under each economic condition is presented in Table 2. The decision tree for this payoff table is depicted in Figure 2. The decision (which stock to purchase) is the first branch of the tree and the four events (the economic conditions) are represented by the second set of branches.

TABLE 2

Predicted 1-year return on investment of $1,000 in each of two stocks under four economic conditions

	Stocks	
Economic Conditions	**A**	**B**
Recession	$ 30	$−50
Stable economy	70	30
Moderate growth	100	250
Boom	150	400

FIGURE 2

Decision tree for the stock selection payoff table

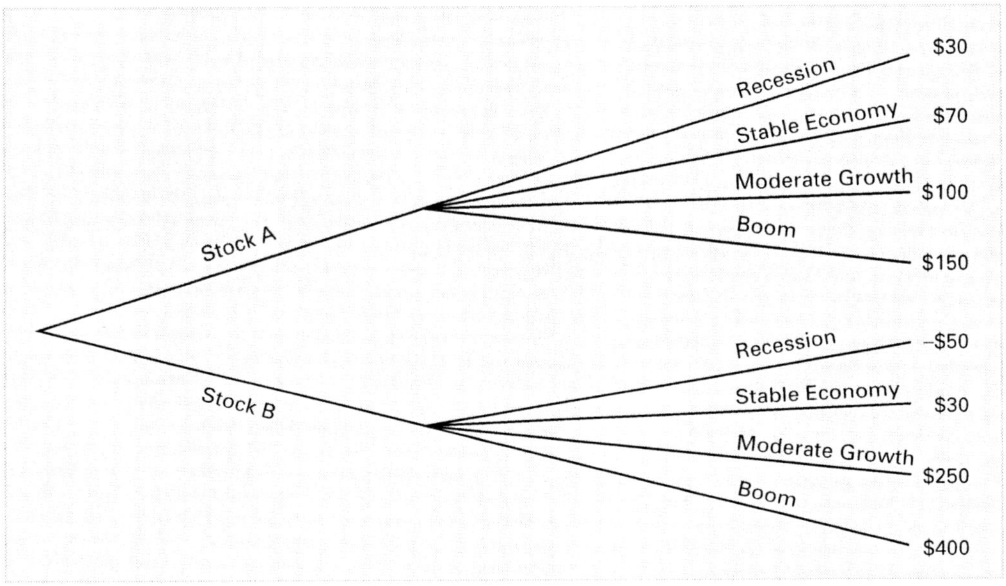

Opportunity Loss
The opportunity loss is the difference between the highest possible profit for an event and the actual profit obtained for an action taken.

Payoff tables and decision trees are used as decision-making tools to help to determine a course of action. For example, when deciding whether to market a television set, of course you would market it if you knew that the television set was going to be successful. Conversely, you would not market it if you knew that it was not going to be successful. For each event, you can determine the amount of profit that will be lost if the best alternative course of action is not taken. This is called opportunity loss. Opportunity loss is illustrated in Example 3.

EXAMPLE 3

FINDING OPPORTUNITY LOSS IN THE TELEVISION SET MARKETING EXAMPLE

Using the payoff table from Example 1, set up an opportunity loss table.

SOLUTION

For the event "successful television set," the maximum profit is achieved when the product is marketed (+$45 millions). The opportunity that is lost by not marketing the television set is the difference between $45 million and −$3 million, which is $48 million. If the television is unsuccessful, the best action is not to market the television set (−$3 million profit). The opportunity that is lost by making the incorrect decision of marketing the television set is −$3 − (−$36) = $33 million. Note that the opportunity loss will *always be a nonnegative number*, because it represents the difference between the profit under the best action and any other course of action that is taken for the particular event. The complete opportunity loss table for the television marketing example is shown in Table 3.

TABLE 3
Opportunity loss table for the television marketing example (in millions of dollars)

			Alternative Courses of Action	
Event E_i	Optimum Action	Profit of Optimum Action	Market	Do Not Market
Successful television	Market	\$45	\$45 – \$45 = \$0	\$45 – (–\$3) = \$48
Unsuccessful television	Do not market	–\$3	–\$3 – (–\$36) = \$33	–\$3 – (–\$3) = \$0

CHAPTER 16.xls

Retrieve the Figure 16.3 worksheet of the ***Chapter 16.xls*** *workbook to view the opportunity loss analysis shown on the next page.*

Excel Strategies Performing Opportunity Loss Analysis

You implement a worksheet that features the **INDEX** and **MATCH** functions to perform an opportunity loss analysis. PHStat2 can construct this worksheet for you in a single step.

For example, to generate the opportunity loss analysis for the television set marketing payoff table of Table 1, open to an empty worksheet and use one of these strategies:

Using Excel with PHStat2

Use the PHStat2 Opportunity Loss procedure to perform an opportunity loss analysis.

Select **PHStat | Decision-Making | Opportunity Loss**.

In the Opportunity Loss Table dialog box (show at right):

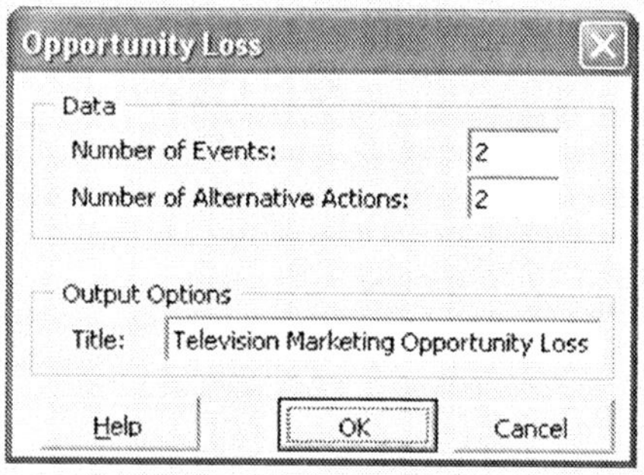

Enter **2** in the **Number of Events** edit box.

Enter **2** in the **Number of Alternative Actions** edit box.

Enter a title in the **Title** edit box.

Click the **OK** button.

In the empty payoff table of the new worksheet generated by PHStat2 (shown below):

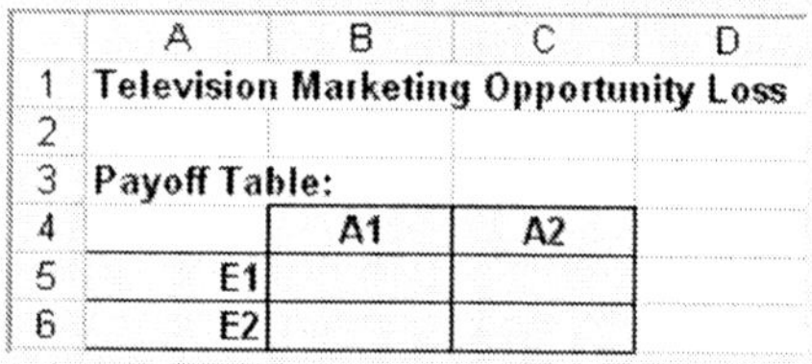

	A	B	C	D
1	Television Marketing Opportunity Loss			
2				
3	Payoff Table:			
4		A1	A2	
5	E1			
6	E2			

Enter **Successful** in cell **A5** and **Unsuccessful** in cell **A6** as replacements for the E1 and E2 labels and adjust the width of column A so that both labels are fully visible.

Enter **Market** in cell **B4** and **Do not market** in cell **C4** as replacements for the A1 and A2 labels and increase the widths of columns B and C so that both labels are fully visible.

Enter **45** in cell **B5**, **–36** in cell **B6**, and **–3** in cells **C5** and **C6**.

Adjust the width of column B so that both optimum action labels are fully visible.

Using Excel

Follow the instructions of section EH1 at the end of this chapter to manually implement a worksheet to perform an opportunity loss analysis.

Figure 3 represents an opportunity loss table obtained from Microsoft Excel.

FIGURE 3

Opportunity loss table obtained from Microsoft Excel

	A	B	C	D	E
1	**Television Marketing Opportunity Loss**				
2					
3	**Payoff Table:**				
4		Market	Do not market		
5	Successful	45	-3		
6	Unsuccessful	-36	-3		
7					
8					
9	**Opportunity Loss Table:**				
10		Optimum	Optimum	Alternatives	
11		Action	Profit	Market	Do not market
12	Successful	Market	45	0	48
13	Unsuccessful	Do not market	-3	33	0

You can also develop an opportunity loss table for the stock selection problem in the Using Statistics scenario. Here, there are four possible events or economic conditions that will affect the 1-year return for each of the two stocks. In a recession, stock *A* is best, providing a return of \$30 as compared to a loss of \$50 from stock *B*. In a stable economy, stock *A* again is better than stock *B* because it provides a return of \$70 compared to \$30 for stock *B*. However, under conditions of moderate growth or boom, stock *B* is superior to stock *A*. In a moderate growth period, stock *B* provides a return of \$250 as compared to \$100 from stock *A*, while in boom conditions the disparity between stocks is even greater with stock *B* providing a return of \$400 as compared to \$150 for stock *A*. The complete set of opportunity losses is summarized in Table 4.

TABLE 4

Opportunity loss table for two stocks under four economic conditions

			Alternative Courses of Action	
Event E_i	Optimum Action	Profit of Optimum Action	A	B
Recession	A	\$ 30	30 – 30 = 0	30 – (–50) = 80
Stable economy	A	70	70 – 70 = 0	70 – 30 = 40
Moderate growth	B	250	250 – 100 = 150	250 – 250 = 0
Boom	B	400	400 – 150 = 250	400 – 400 = 0

PROBLEMS FOR SECTION 1

Learning the Basics

1 For this problem, use the following payoff table:

	Action	
Event	A (\$)	B (\$)
1	50	100
2	200	125

a. Set up an opportunity loss table.
b. Construct a decision tree.

2 For this problem, use the following payoff table:

	Action	
Event	A (\$)	B (\$)
1	50	10
2	300	100
3	500	200

a. Set up an opportunity loss table.
b. Construct a decision tree.

Applying the Concepts

3 A manufacturer of designer jeans must decide whether to build a large factory or a small factory in a particular location. The profit per pair of jeans manufactured is estimated as \$10. A small factory will have an amortized annual cost of \$200,000, with a production capacity of 50,000 jeans per year. A large factory will have an amortized annual cost of \$400,000 with a production capacity of 100,000 jeans per year. Four levels of manufacturing demand are considered likely: 10,000, 20,000, 50,000, and 100,000 pairs of jeans per year.

a. Determine the possible levels of production for a small factory and the payoffs for each possible level of production.
b. Determine the possible levels of production for a large factory and the payoffs for each possible level of production.
c. Based on the results of (a) and (b), set up a payoff table indicating the events and alternative courses of action.
d. Set up a decision tree.
e. Set up an opportunity loss table.

4 An author is trying to choose between two publishing companies that are competing for the marketing rights to her new novel. Company A has offered the author \$10,000 plus \$2 per book sold. Company B has offered the author \$2,000 plus \$4 per book sold. The author believes that five levels of demand for the book are possible: 1,000, 2,000, 5,000, 10,000, and 50,000 books sold.

a. Compute the payoffs for each level of demand for company A and company B.
b. Set up a payoff table indicating the events and alternative courses of action.
c. Set up a decision tree.
d. Set up an opportunity loss table.

5 The LeFleur Garden Center chain purchases and sells Christmas trees during the holiday season. It purchases the trees for \$10 each and sells them for \$20 each. Any trees not sold by Christmas Day can be sold for \$2 each to a company that makes wood chips. The garden center estimates that four levels of demand are possible, 100, 200, 500, and 1,000 trees.

a. Compute the payoffs for purchasing 100, 200, 500, or 1,000 trees for each of the four levels of demand.
b. Set up a payoff table indicating the events and alternative courses of action.
c. Set up a decision tree.
d. Set up an opportunity loss table.

2 CRITERIA FOR DECISION MAKING

After the profit and opportunity loss for each event under each alternative course of action have been obtained in the payoff and opportunity loss tables, you need to determine the criteria for selecting the most desirable course of action. To determine which alternative to choose, you first assign a probability to each event. The probability assigned is based on information available from past data, from the opinions of the decision-maker, or from knowledge about the probability distribution that the event may follow. Using these probabilities, along with the payoffs or opportunity losses of each event–action combination, the best course of action is then selected according to a particular criterion. In this section, three decision criteria are presented—expected monetary value, expected opportunity loss, and the return-to-risk ratio.

Expected Monetary Value

The formula to compute the expected value of a probability distribution is extended to compute the expected monetary value for each alternative course of action. The **expected monetary value (*EMV*)** for a course of action j is the payoff (x_{ij}) for each combination of event i and action j times P_i, the probability of occurrence of the event i, summed over all events [see Equation (1)].

EXPECTED MONETARY VALUE

$$EMV(j) = \sum_{i=1}^{N} x_{ij} P_i \qquad (1)$$

where

$EMV(j)$ = expected monetary value of action j
x_{ij} = payoff that occurs when course of action j is selected and event i occurs
P_i = probability of occurrence of event i

Criterion: Select the course of action with the largest *EMV*.

The application of expected monetary value to the television set marketing example is illustrated in Example 4.

EXAMPLE 4

COMPUTING THE EXPECTED MONETARY VALUE IN THE TELEVISION SET MARKETING EXAMPLE

Returning to the payoff table for deciding whether to market a television set (Example 1), suppose that a probability of 0.40 is assigned to the event that the television will be successful (so that a probability of 0.60 is assigned to the complementary event that the television will not be successful). Compute the expected monetary value for each alternative course of action and determine whether the television set should be marketed.

SOLUTION

The expected monetary value for each alternative course of action can be determined by using Equation (1). These computations are summarized in Table 5.

TABLE 5

Expected monetary value (in millions of dollars) for each alternative for the television set marketing example

		Alternative Courses of Action			
Event E_i	P_i	**Market, A_1**	$x_{ij}P_i$	**Do Not Market, A_2**	$x_{ij}P_i$
Successful television, E_1	0.40	+\$45	\$45(0.4) = \$18	−\$3	−\$3(0.4) = −\$1.2
Unsuccessful television, E_2	0.60	−\$36	−\$36(0.6) = −\$21.6	−\$3	−\$3(0.6) = −\$1.8
			$EMV(A_1) = -\$3.6$		$EMV(A_2) = -\$3$

The expected monetary value for marketing the television is −\$3.6 millions, and the expected monetary value for not marketing the television set is −\$3 millions. Thus, if your objective is to choose the action that maximizes the expected monetary value, you would choose the action of not marketing the television set because its profit is highest (or in this case its loss is lowest). Note that if the probability the television is successful, P_1, is slightly greater than the assumed value of 0.40, a different decision is made. Specifically, if $P_1 = 0.41$, then $EMV(A_1) = -\$2.79$ million, $EMV(A_2) = -\$3$ million, and the best decision is to market the television. This change in the optimal decision when such a small change in the assumed probability of success occurs, illustrates the importance of accuracy when determining the probabilities. Moreover, you need to consider the *closeness* of the decision-making criterion before making a final conclusion concerning introducing the new television set.

As a second application of expected monetary value, return to the Using Statistics scenario and the payoff table presented in Table 2. Suppose the company economist assigns the following probabilities to the different economic conditions:

$$P(\text{Recession}) = 0.10$$
$$P(\text{Stable economy}) = 0.40$$
$$P(\text{Moderate growth}) = 0.30$$
$$P(\text{Boom}) = 0.20$$

Using the information provided in Table 2, the expected monetary value for each of the two stocks is computed as shown in Table 6.

TABLE 6

Expected monetary value for each alternative action for each of two stocks under four economic conditions

		Alternative Courses of Action			
Event E_i	P_i	**A**	$x_{ij}P_i$	**B**	$x_{ij}P_i$
Recession	0.10	30	30(0.1) = 3	−50	−50(0.1) = −5
Stable economy	0.40	70	70(0.4) = 28	30	30(0.4) = 12
Moderate growth	0.30	100	100(0.3) = 30	250	250(0.3) = 75
Boom	0.20	150	150(0.2) = 30	400	400(0.2) = 80
			$EMV(A) = 91$		$EMV(B) = 162$

Thus, the expected monetary value or profit for stock A is \$91, and the expected monetary value or profit for stock B is \$162. Using these results, you should choose stock B because the expected rate of return on stock B is 162/1,000 or 16.2%, almost twice that of stock A, which has an expected rate of return of 91/1,000 or 9.1% on the \$1,000 investment.

Expected Opportunity Loss

Earlier, you learned how to use the expected monetary value criterion when making a decision. An equivalent criterion, based on opportunity losses, is introduced next. Note that payoffs and opportunity losses can be viewed as two sides of the same coin. It all depends on whether you wish to view the problem in terms of *maximizing* expected monetary value or *minimizing* expected opportunity loss. The **expected opportunity loss (*EOL*)** of action j is the loss L_{ij} for each combination of event i and action j times P_i, the probability of occurrence of the event i, summed over all events [see Equation (2)].

EXPECTED OPPORTUNITY LOSS

$$EOL(j) = \sum_{i=1}^{N} L_{ij} P_i \quad (2)$$

where

L_{ij} = opportunity loss that occurs when course of action j is selected and event i occurs

P_i = probability of occurrence of event i

Criterion: Select the course of action with the smallest *EOL*. Selecting the course of action with the smallest *EOL* is equivalent to selecting the course of action with the largest *EMV*. See Equation (1).

The application of opportunity loss to the television set marketing example is illustrated in Example 5.

EXAMPLE 5

COMPUTING THE EXPECTED OPPORTUNITY LOSS FOR THE TELEVISION SET MARKETING EXAMPLE

Referring to the opportunity loss table given in Table 3, and assuming that a probability of 0.40 is assigned to the event that the television set will be successful, compute the expected opportunity loss for each alternative course of action and determine whether the television should be marketed (Table 7).

TABLE 7

Expected opportunity loss in millions of dollars for each alternative for the television set marketing example

		Alternative Courses of Action			
Event E_i	P_i	Market, A_1	$L_{ij}P_i$	Do Not Market, A_2	$L_{ij}P_i$
Successful television, E_1	0.40	0	0(0.4) = 0	\$48	\$48(0.4) = \$19.2
Unsuccessful television, E_2	0.60	\$33	\$33(0.6) = \$19.8	0	0(0.6) = 0
			$EOL(A_1)$ = \$19.8		$EOL(A_2)$ = \$19.2

SOLUTION

The expected opportunity loss is lower for not marketing the television set (\$19.2 million) than for marketing the television (\$19.8 million). Therefore, using the *EOL* criterion, the optimal decision is not to market the television set. This outcome is expected since the equivalent *EMV* criterion produced the same optimal strategy. Note once again that if the probability the television set is successful, P_1, is slightly greater than the assumed value of 0.40, a different decision is made. Specifically, if $P_1 = 0.41$ then $EOL(A_1)$ = \$19.47 million, $EOL(A_2)$ = \$19.68 million, and the best decision is to market the television set.

The expected opportunity loss from the best decision has a special meaning in the context of making decisions. It is defined as the **expected value of perfect information (*EVPI*)**, and is calculated in Equation (3).

EXPECTED VALUE OF PERFECT INFORMATION

$$EVPI = \text{expected profit under certainty} - \text{expected monetary value of the best alternative} \quad (3)$$

The **expected profit under certainty** represents the expected profit that you could make if you have perfect information about which even will occur. To illustrate the expected value of perfect information, turn to Example 6.

EXAMPLE 6

COMPUTING THE EXPECTED VALUE OF PERFECT INFORMATION IN THE TELEVISION SET MARKETING EXAMPLE

Referring to Example 5, compute the expected profit under certainty and the expected value of perfect information ($EVPI$).

SOLUTION

If the marketing manager in the television example could always predict the future, a profit of \$45 million would be made for the 40% of the televisions that are successful, and a loss of \$3 million would be incurred for the 60% of the televisions that would not be successful. Thus,

$$\begin{aligned}\text{Expected profit under certainty} &= 0.40(\$45) + 0.60(-\$3)\\ &= \$18 - \$1.80\\ &= \$16.2\end{aligned}$$

This value, \$16.2 million, represents the profit that could be made if the marketing manager knew with *certainty* whether the television set was going to be successful. The expected value of perfect information can be obtained by using Equation (3):

$$\begin{aligned}EVPI &= \text{expected profit under certainty} - \text{expected monetary value of the best alternative}\\ &= \$16.2 - (-\$3) = \$19.2\end{aligned}$$

This $EVPI$ value of \$19.2 million represents the maximum amount that the marketing manager should be willing to pay to obtain perfect information. Of course, perfect information can never be obtained and you should never pay the entire $EVPI$ for more information. Rather, the $EVPI$ provides a guideline for an upper bound on to how much you might consider paying for better information. The $EVPI$ is also the expected opportunity loss of not marketing the television set.

Return to the Using Statistics scenario and the opportunity loss table presented in Table 4. The computations to determine the expected opportunity loss for stock A and stock B are presented in Table 8 below.

TABLE 8

Expected opportunity loss for each alternative for the stock selection example

		Alternative Courses of Action			
Event E_i	P_i	A	$L_{ij}P_i$	B	$L_{ij}P_i$
Recession	0.10	0	0(0.1) = 0	80	80(0.1) = 8
Stable economy	0.40	0	0(0.4) = 0	40	40(0.4) = 16
Moderate growth	0.30	150	150(0.3) = 45	0	0(0.3) = 0
Boom	0.20	250	250(0.2) = 50	0	0(0.2) = 0
			$EOL(A) = 95$		$EOL(B) = EVPI = 24$

The expected opportunity loss is lower for stock B than for stock A, so consistent with the decision made using expected monetary value, stock B should be chosen. The expected value of perfect information is \$24 (per \$1,000 invested), meaning that you should be willing to pay up to \$24 to obtain perfect information.

Return-to-Risk Ratio

Unfortunately, neither the expected monetary value nor the expected opportunity loss criterion takes into account the variability of the payoffs of alternative courses of action under different events. From Table 2 observe that the return for stock A varies from \$30 in a recession to \$150 in an economic boom, whereas stock B (the one chosen according to the expected monetary value and expected opportunity loss criteria) varies from a loss of \$50 in a recession to a profit of \$400 in an economic boom.

To take into account the variability of the events (in this case, the different economic conditions), you can compute the variance and standard deviation of each stock using the following equations. Using the information presented in Table 6, for stock A, EMV(A) = $\mu_A = 91$ and the variance is equal to

$$\begin{aligned}\sigma_A^2 &= \sum_{i=1}^{N}(X_i - \mu)^2 P(X_i)\\ &= (30-91)^2(0.1) + (70-91)^2(0.4)\\ &\quad + (100-91)^2(0.3) + (150-91)^2(0.2)\\ &= 1{,}269\end{aligned}$$

and the standard deviation of stock A is $\sigma_A = \sqrt{1{,}269} = \$35.62$. For stock B, EMV(B) = $\mu_B = 162$ and the variance is

$$\begin{aligned}\sigma_B^2 &= \sum_{i=1}^{N}(X_i - \mu)^2 P(X_i)\\ &= (-50-162)^2(0.1) + (30-162)^2(0.4)\\ &\quad + (250-162)^2(0.3) + (400-162)^2(0.2)\\ &= 25{,}116\end{aligned}$$

and the standard deviation of stock B is $\sigma_B = \sqrt{25{,}116} = \$158.48$.

Because you are comparing two sets of data with vastly different means, you should evaluate the relative risk associated with each stock. Once you have obtained the standard deviation of the return from each stock, the coefficient of variation can be computed. Substituting σ for S in this equation, you find that the coefficient of variation for stock A is equal to

$$\begin{aligned}CV_A &= \left(\frac{\sigma_A}{EMV_A}\right)100\%\\ &= \left(\frac{35.62}{91}\right)100\% = 39.1\%\end{aligned}$$

while the coefficient of variation for portfolio B is equal to

$$\begin{aligned}CV_B &= \left(\frac{\sigma_B}{EMV_B}\right)100\%\\ &= \left(\frac{158.48}{162}\right)100\% = 97.8\%\end{aligned}$$

Thus, there is much more variation in return for stock B than for stock A.

Since the coefficient of variation shows the relative size of the variation compared to the arithmetic mean (or expected monetary value), a criterion other than *EMV* or *EOL* is needed to express the relationship between the return (or payoff) and the *risk* (as expressed by the standard deviation). One such criterion is the **return-to-risk ratio (*RTRR*)**. The return-to-risk ratio, defined in Equation (4), represents the expected monetary value of action *j* divided by the standard deviation of action *j*.

RETURN-TO-RISK RATIO

$$RTRR(j) = \frac{EMV(j)}{\sigma_j} \tag{4}$$

where

$EMV(j)$ = expected monetary value for alternative course of action j

σ_j = standard deviation for alternative course of action j

Criterion: Select the course of action with the largest *RTRR*.

For each of the two stocks discussed previously, the return-to-risk ratios are computed as follows. For stock *A*, the return-to-risk ratio is equal to

$$RTRR(A) = \frac{91}{35.62} = 2.55$$

For stock *B*, the return-to-risk ratio is equal to

$$RTRR(B) = \frac{162}{158.48} = 1.02$$

Thus, relative to the risk as expressed by the standard deviation, the return seems much higher for stock *A* than for stock *B*. Stock *A* has a smaller expected monetary value than stock *B*, but also had a much smaller risk than stock *B*. The return-to-risk ratio shows *A* to be preferable to *B*. Figure 4 represents output from Microsoft Excel.

FIGURE 4
Expected value worksheet obtained from Microsoft Excel

	A	B	C	D	E	F	G	H
1	**Stock Selection Analysis**							
2								
3	**Probabilities & Payoffs Table:**							
4		P	Stock A	Stock B				
5	Recession	0.1	30	-50				
6	Stable economy	0.4	70	30		Calculations Area		
7	Moderate growth	0.3	100	250		For variance and std. deviation		
8	Boom	0.2	150	400		Stock A	Stock B	
9						3721	44944	
10	Statistics for:		Stock A	Stock B		441	17424	
11	Expected Monetary Value		91	162		81	7744	
12	Variance		1269	25116		3481	56644	
13	Standard Deviation		35.6230	158.4803				
14	Coefficient of Variation		0.3915	0.9783				
15	Return to Risk Ratio		2.5545	1.0222				
16								
17	Opportunity Loss Table:							
18		Optimum	Optimum	Alternatives				
19		Action	Profit	Stock A	Stock B			
20	Recession	Stock A	30	0	80			
21	Stable economy	Stock A	70	0	40			
22	Moderate growth	Stock B	250	150	0			
23	Boom	Stock B	400	250	0			
24				Stock A	Stock B			
25	Expected Opportunity Loss			95	24			
26					EVPI			

CHAPTER 16.xls

*Retrieve the Figure 16.4 worksheet of the **Chapter 16.xls** workbook to view the criteria for decision making shown on the previous page.*

Excel Strategies Calculating Criteria for Decision Making

You implement a worksheet that features the **SUMPRODUCT**, **INDEX**, and **MATCH** functions to calculate expected monetary values, expected opportunity losses, and measures of variation from payoff table data and event probabilities. PHStat2 can construct this worksheet for you in a single step.

For example, to calculate these criteria for the stock selection example of the Using Statistics scenario of this chapter, use one of these strategies:

Using Excel with PHStat2

Use the PHStat2 Expected Monetary Value procedure to calculate criteria for decision making.

Select **PHStat | Decision-Making | Expected Monetary Value**.

In the Expected Monetary Value dialog box (shown at right):

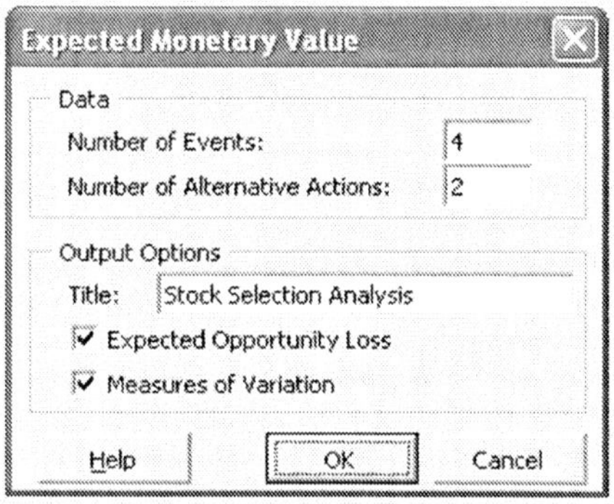

Enter **4** in the **Number of Events** edit box.

Enter **2** in the **Number of Alternative Actions** edit box.

Enter a title in the **Title** edit box.

Select the **Expected Opportunity Loss** and **Measures of Variation** check boxes.

Click the **OK** button.

In the empty payoff table of new worksheet generated by PHStat2 (shown below):

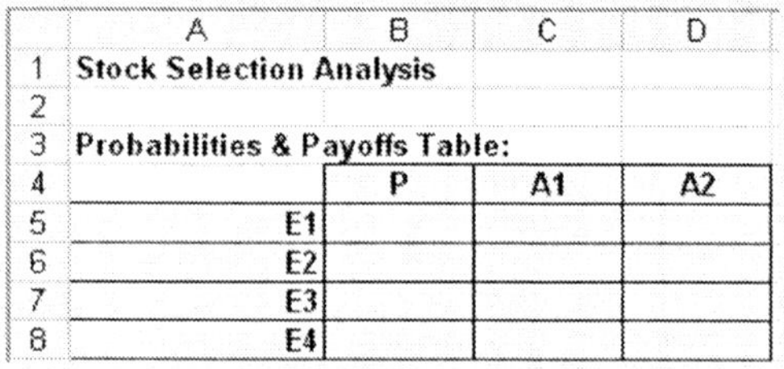

Enter **Recession** in cell **A5**, **Stable economy** in cell **A6**, **Moderate growth** in cell **A7**, and **Boom** in cell **A8** as replacements for the E1 through E4 labels and increase the width of column A so that both labels are fully visible.

Enter **Stock A** in cell **C4** and **Stock B** in cell **D4** as replacements for the A1 and A2 labels and increase the widths of columns B and C so that both labels are fully visible.

Enter the event probabilities **0.1** in cell **B5, 0.4** in cell **B6, 0.3** in cell **B7**, and **0.2** in cell **B8**.

Enter **30** in cell **C5, 70** in cell **C6, 100** in cell **C7, 150** in cell **C8, –50** in cell **D5, 30** in cell **D6, 250** in cell **D7**, and **400** in cell **D8**.

*If you have already calculated the opportunity losses for the alternative courses of action, you can use the PHStat2 Expected Opportunity Loss procedure to calculate expected opportunity loss. Select **PHStat | Decision-Making | Expected Opportunity Loss** and in the procedure's dialog box enter the number of events and number of alternative courses of action as is done in the above.*

Using Excel

Follow the instructions of section EH2 at the end of this chapter to manually implement a worksheet to calculate criteria for decision making.

PROBLEMS FOR SECTION 2

Learning the Basics

6 For this problem use the following payoff table:

	Action	
Event	*A*	*B*
1	50	100
2	200	125

The probability of event 1 is 0.5 and the probability of event 2 is also 0.5.

a. Compute the expected monetary value (*EMV*) for actions *A* and *B*.
b. Compute the expected opportunity loss (*EOL*) for actions *A* and *B*.
c. Explain the meaning of the expected value of perfect information (*EVPI*) in this problem.
d. Based on the results of (a) or (b), which action would you choose? Why?
e. Compute the coefficient of variation for each action.
f. Compute the return-to-risk ratio for each action.
g. Based on (e) and (f), what action would you choose? Why?
h. Compare the results of (d) and (g) and explain any differences.

7 For the following payoff table:

	Action	
Event	*A*	*B*
1	50	10
2	300	100
3	500	200

The probability of event 1 is 0.8, the probability of event 2 is 0.1, and the probability of event 3 is 0.1.

a. Compute the expected monetary value (*EMV*) for actions *A* and *B*.
b. Compute the expected opportunity loss (*EOL*) for actions *A* and *B*.
c. Explain the meaning of the expected value of perfect information (*EVPI*) in this problem.
d. Based on the results of (a) or (b), which action would you choose? Why?
e. Compute the coefficient of variation for each action.
f. Compute the return-to-risk ratio for each action.
g. Based on (e) and (f), what action would you choose? Why?
h. Compare the results of (d) and (g) and explain any differences.
i. Would your answers to (d) and (g) be different if the probabilities for the three events were 0.1, 0.1, and 0.8 respectively? Discuss.

8 For a potential investment of $1,000, if a stock has an *EMV* of $100 and a standard deviation of $25, what is the

a. rate of return?
b. coefficient of variation?
c. return-to-risk ratio?

9 If a stock has the following returns under the following economic conditions,

Economic Condition	Probability	Return
Recession	0.30	$ 50
Stable economy	0.30	100
Moderate growth	0.30	120
Boom	0.10	200

compute the

a. expected monetary value.
b. standard deviation.
c. coefficient of variation.
d. return-to-risk ratio.

10 The following are the results for two stocks:

	A	*B*
Expected monetary value	$90	$60
Standard deviation	10	10

Which stock would you choose and why?

11 The following are the results for two stocks:

	A	*B*
Expected monetary value	$60	$60
Standard deviation	20	10

Which stock would you choose and why?

Applying the Concepts

12 A vendor at a local baseball stadium must determine whether to sell ice cream or soft drinks at today's game. The vendor believes that the profit made will depend on the weather. The payoff table is as follows:

	Action	
Event	Sell Soft Drinks	Sell Ice Cream
Cool weather	$50	$30
Warm weather	60	90

Based on her past experience at this time of year, the vendor estimates the probability of warm weather as 0.60.

a. Compute the expected monetary value (*EMV*) for selling soft drinks and selling ice cream.
b. Compute the expected opportunity loss (*EOL*) for selling soft drinks and selling ice cream.
c. Explain the meaning of the expected value of perfect information (*EVPI*) in this problem.
d. Based on the results of (a) or (b), which would you choose to sell, soft drinks or ice cream? Why?
e. Compute the coefficient of variation for selling soft drinks and for selling ice cream.
f. Compute the return-to-risk ratio for selling soft drinks and selling ice cream.
g. Based on (e) and (f), what would you choose to sell, soft drinks or ice cream? Why?
h. Compare the results of (d) and (g) and explain any differences.

13 The Islander Fishing Company purchases clams for $1.50 per pound from Peconic Bay fishermen and sells them to various New York restaurants for $2.50 per pound. Any clams not sold to the restaurants by the end of the week can be sold to a local soup company for $0.50 per pound. The probabilities of various levels of demand are as follows:

Demand (Pounds)	Probability
500	0.2
1,000	0.4
2,000	0.4

(*Hint:* The company can purchase 500, 1,000, or 2,000 pounds.)
a. For each possible purchase level (500, 1,000, or 2,000 pounds) compute the profit (or loss) for each level of demand.
b. Using the expected monetary value (*EMV*) criterion, determine the optimal number of pounds of clams the company should purchase from the fishermen. Discuss.
c. Compute the standard deviation for each possible purchase level.
d. Compute the expected opportunity loss (*EOL*) for purchasing 500, 1,000, and 2,000 pounds of clams.
e. Explain the meaning of the expected value of perfect information (*EVPI*) in this problem.
f. Compute the coefficient of variation for purchasing 500, 1,000, and 2,000 pounds of clams. Discuss.
g. Compute the return-to-risk ratio for purchasing 500, 1,000, and 2,000 pounds of clams. Discuss.
h. Based on (b) and (d), what would you choose to sell, 500, 1,000, or 2,000 pounds of clams? Why?
i. Compare the results of (b), (d), (f), and (g) and explain any differences.
j. Suppose that clams can be sold for $3 per pound. Repeat (a)–(h) with this selling price for clams and compare the results with those obtained in (h).
k. What would be the effect on the results in (a)–(i) if the probability of the demand for 500, 1,000, and 2,000 clams were 0.4, 0.4, and 0.2, respectively?

14 An investor has a certain amount of money available to invest now. Three alternative investments are available. The estimated profits of each investment under each economic condition are indicated in the following payoff table:

	Investment Selection		
Event	***A***	***B***	***C***
Economy declines	$500	−$2,000	−$7,000
No change	$1,000	$2,000	−$1,000
Economy expands	$2,000	$5,000	$20,000

Based on his own past experience, the investor assigns the following probabilities to each economic condition:

$P(\text{economy declines}) = 0.30$
$P(\text{no change}) = 0.50$
$P(\text{economy expands}) = 0.20$

a. Determine the best investment according to the expected monetary value (*EMV*) criterion. Discuss.
b. Compute the standard deviation for each possible investment selection.
c. Compute the expected opportunity loss (*EOL*) for investments *A*, *B*, and *C*.
d. Explain the meaning of the expected value of perfect information (*EVPI*) in this problem.
e. Compute the coefficient of variation for investments *A*, *B*, and *C*.
f. Compute the return-to-risk ratio for investments *A*, *B*, and *C*.
g. Based on (e) and (f), what would you choose, investments *A*, *B*, or *C*? Why?
h. Compare the results of (a) and (g) and explain any differences.
i. Suppose the probabilities of the different economic conditions were as follows:
(1) 0.1, 0.6, and 0.3
(2) 0.1, 0.3, and 0.6
(3) 0.4, 0.4, and 0.2
(4) 0.6, 0.3, and 0.1
Repeat (a)–(h) with each of these sets of probabilities and compare the results with those originally obtained in (h). Discuss.

15 In problem 3, a payoff table was developed for building a small factory and a large factory for manufacturing designer jeans. Given the results obtained in that problem, suppose that the probability of the levels of manufacturing demand are as follows:

Demand	Probability
10,000	0.1
20,000	0.4
50,000	0.2
100,000	0.3

a. Compute the expected monetary value (*EMV*) for building a small factory and building a large factory.

b. Compute the expected opportunity loss (*EOL*) for building a small factory and building a large factory.
c. Explain the meaning of the expected value of perfect information (*EVPI*) in this problem.
d. Based on the results of (a) or (b), which would you choose to build, a small factory or a large factory? Why?
e. Compute the coefficient of variation for building a small factory and for building a large factory.
f. Compute the return-to-risk ratio for building a small factory and for building a large factory.
g. Based on (e) and (f), what would you choose to build, a small factory or a large factory? Why?
h. Compare the results of (d) and (g) and explain any differences.
i. Suppose that the probabilities of demand were 0.4, 0.2, 0.2, and 0.2, respectively. Repeat (a)–(h) with these probabilities and compare the results with those of (a)–(h).

16 In problem 4, a payoff table was developed to assist an author in choosing between signing with company *A* and with company *B*. Given the results obtained in that problem, suppose that the probabilities of the levels of demand for the novel are

Demand	Probability
1,000	0.45
2,000	0.20
5,000	0.15
10,000	0.10
50,000	0.10

a. Compute the expected monetary value (*EMV*) for signing with company *A* and with company *B*.
b. Compute the expected opportunity loss (*EOL*) for signing with company *A* and with company *B*.
c. Explain the meaning of the expected value of perfect information (*EVPI*) in this problem.
d. Based on the results of (a) or (b), if you were the author, which company would you choose to sign with, company *A* or company *B*? Why?
e. Compute the coefficient of variation for signing with company *A* and for signing with company *B*.
f. Compute the return-to-risk ratio for signing with company *A* and for signing with company *B*.
g. Based on (e) and (f), which company would you choose to sign with, company *A* or company *B*? Why?
h. Compare the results of (d) and (g) and explain any differences.
i. Suppose that the probabilities of demand were 0.3, 0.2, 0.2, 0.1, and 0.2, respectively. Repeat (a)–(h) with these probabilities and compare the results with those for (a)–(h).

17 In problem 5, a payoff table is developed for purchasing 100, 200, 500, and 1,000 Christmas trees. Given the results obtained in that problem, suppose that the probabilities of the demand for the different number of trees is as follows

Demand (Number of Trees)	Probability
100	0.20
200	0.50
500	0.20
1,000	0.10

a. Compute the expected monetary value (*EMV*) for purchasing 100, 200, 500, and 1,000 trees.
b. Compute the expected opportunity loss (*EOL*) for purchasing 100, 200, 500, and 1,000 trees.
c. Explain the meaning of the expected value of perfect information (*EVPI*) in this problem.
d. Based on the results of (a) or (b), which would you choose to purchase 100, 200, 500, or 1,000 trees? Why?
e. Compute the coefficient of variation for purchasing 100, 200, 500, and 1,000 trees.
f. Compute the return-to-risk ratio for purchasing 100, 200, 500, and 1,000 trees.
g. Based on (e) and (f), what would you choose to purchase, 100, 200, 500, or 1,000 trees? Why?
h. Compare the results of (d) and (g) and explain any differences.
i. Suppose that the probabilities of demand were 0.4, 0.2, 0.2, and 0.2, respectively. Repeat (a)–(h) with these probabilities and compare the results with those for (a)–(h).

3 DECISION MAKING WITH SAMPLE INFORMATION

In sections 1 and 2 the framework for making decisions when there are two or more courses of action was developed. Different criteria for choosing between alternatives were used and the expected value of perfect information was discussed. For each criterion, the probabilities of the various events were obtained using the past experience and/or the subjective judgment of the decision-maker. Bayes' theorem can be used to revise the prior probabilities based on sample information. Decision making with sample information is illustrated in Example 7.

EXAMPLE 7

DECISION MAKING USING SAMPLE INFORMATION FOR THE TELEVISION SET MARKETING EXAMPLE

In a previous example, you may have found that the probability of a successful television, given that a favorable report was received, is 0.64. Thus, the probability of an unsuccessful television, given that a favorable report was received, is 1 – 0.64 = 0.36. Given that a favorable report has been received, compute the expected monetary value for each alternative course of action and determine whether the television should be marketed.

SOLUTION

Because the original subjective probabilities were used in Example 4 to determine the best decision based on the expected monetary value criterion, the expected profit of each alternative must be reevaluated by using the revised probabilities, which are illustrated in Table 9.

TABLE 9

Expected monetary value in millions of dollars using revised probabilities for each alternative in the television set marketing example

		Alternative Courses of Action			
Event E_i	**P_i**	**Market, A_1**	**$x_{ij}P_i$**	**Do Not Market, A_2**	**$x_{ij}P_i$**
Successful television, E_1	0.64	+\$45	\$45(0.64) = \$28.8	–\$3	–\$3(0.64) = –\$1.92
Unsuccessful television, E_2	0.36	–\$36	–\$36(0.36) = –\$12.96	–\$3	–\$3(0.36) = –\$1.08
			$EMV(A_1)$ = \$15.84		$EMV(A_2)$ = –\$3

In this case, the optimal decision is to market the product, because an average profit of \$15.84 million can be expected as compared to a loss of \$3 million if the television set is not marketed. This decision is different from the one considered optimal prior to the collection of the sample information in the form of the market research report. The favorable recommendation contained in the report greatly increases the probability that the television set will be successful.

Because the relative desirability of the two stocks under consideration in the Using Statistics scenario is directly affected by economic conditions, it is useful to obtain a forecast of the economic conditions in the upcoming year. Suppose that a forecast can be obtained that predicts either an expanding economy (F_1) or a declining or stagnant economy (F_2). Past experience indicates that, when there is a recession, prior forecasts predicted an expanding economy 20% of the time. When there has been a stable economy, prior forecasts predicted an expanding economy 40% of the time. When there is moderate growth, prior forecasts predicted an expanding economy 70% of the time. Finally, when there is a boom economy, prior forecasts predicted an expanding economy 90% of the time. If the forecast is for an expanding economy, the prior probabilities of economic conditions can be revised using Bayes' theorem. Let

event E_1 = recession — event F_1 = expanding economy is predicted

event E_2 = stable economy — event F_2 = declining or stagnant economy is predicted

event E_3 = moderate growth

event E_4 = boom economy

and

$$P(E_1) = 0.10 \qquad P(F_1 \mid E_1) = 0.20$$
$$P(E_2) = 0.40 \qquad P(F_1 \mid E_2) = 0.40$$
$$P(E_3) = 0.30 \qquad P(F_1 \mid E_3) = 0.70$$
$$P(E_4) = 0.20 \qquad P(F_1 \mid E_4) = 0.90$$

Then, using Bayes' theorem

$$P(E_1 \mid F_1) = \frac{P(F_1 \mid E_1)P(E_1)}{P(F_1 \mid E_1)P(E_1) + P(F_1 \mid E_2)P(E_2) + P(F_1 \mid E_3)P(E_3) + P(F_1 \mid E_4)P(E_4)}$$
$$= \frac{(0.20)(0.10)}{(0.20)(0.10) + (0.40)(0.40) + (0.70)(0.30) + (0.90)(0.20)}$$
$$= \frac{0.02}{0.57} = 0.035$$

$$P(E_2 \mid F_1) = \frac{P(F_1 \mid E_2)P(E_2)}{P(F_1 \mid E_1)P(E_1) + P(F_1 \mid E_2)P(E_2) + P(F_1 \mid E_3)P(E_3) + P(F_1 \mid E_4)P(E_4)}$$
$$= \frac{(0.40)(0.40)}{(0.20)(0.10) + (0.40)(0.40) + (0.70)(0.30) + (0.90)(0.20)}$$
$$= \frac{0.16}{0.57} = 0.281$$

$$P(E_3 \mid F_1) = \frac{P(F_1 \mid E_3)P(E_3)}{P(F_1 \mid E_1)P(E_1) + P(F_1 \mid E_2)P(E_2) + P(F_1 \mid E_3)P(E_3) + P(F_1 \mid E_4)P(E_4)}$$
$$= \frac{(0.70)(0.30)}{(0.20)(0.10) + (0.40)(0.40) + (0.70)(0.30) + (0.90)(0.20)}$$
$$= \frac{0.21}{0.57} = 0.368$$

$$P(E_4 \mid F_1) = \frac{P(F_1 \mid E_4)P(E_4)}{P(F_1 \mid E_1)P(E_1) + P(F_1 \mid E_2)P(E_2) + P(F_1 \mid E_3)P(E_3) + P(F_1 \mid E_4)P(E_4)}$$
$$= \frac{(0.90)(0.20)}{(0.20)(0.10) + (0.40)(0.40) + (0.70)(0.30) + (0.90)(0.20)}$$
$$= \frac{0.18}{0.57} = 0.316$$

The computation of these probabilities is summarized in Table 10 and displayed in the form of a decision tree in Figure 5.

TABLE 10

Bayes' theorem calculations for the stock funds

Event, E_i	Prior Probability, $P(E_i)$	Conditional Probability, $P(F_1 \mid E_i)$	Joint Probability, $P(F_1 \mid E_i)P(E_i)$	Revised Probability, $P(E_i \mid F_1)$
E_1 = Recession	0.10	0.20	0.02	$0.02/0.57 = 0.035 = P(E_1 \mid F_1)$
E_2 = Stable economy	0.40	0.40	0.16	$0.16/0.57 = 0.281 = P(E_2 \mid F_1)$
E_3 = Moderate growth	0.30	0.70	0.21	$0.21/0.57 = 0.368 = P(E_3 \mid F_1)$
E_4 = Boom	0.20	0.90	0.18	$0.18/0.57 = 0.316 = P(E_4 \mid F_1)$
			0.57	

Because the original probabilities were used in Table 6 to determine the best decision based on the expected monetary value criterion, the expected profit of each alternative is reevaluated by using the revised probabilities in Table 10. The revised expected monetary value computations are illustrated in Table 11.

TABLE 11

Expected monetary value using revised probabilities for each alternative for each of two stocks under four economic conditions

		Alternative Courses of Action			
Event E_i	P_i	A	$x_{ij}P_i$	B	$x_{ij}P_i$
Recession	0.035	30	30(0.035) = 1.05	$-50	−50(0.035) = −1.75
Stable economy	0.281	70	70(0.281) = 19.67	30	30(0.281) = 8.43
Moderate growth	0.368	100	100(0.368) = 36.80	250	250(0.368) = 92.00
Boom	0.316	150	150(0.316) = 47.40	400	400(0.316) = 126.40
			$EMV(A)$ = $104.92		$EMV(B)$ = $225.08

FIGURE 5
Decision tree with revised probabilities for stock selection analysis

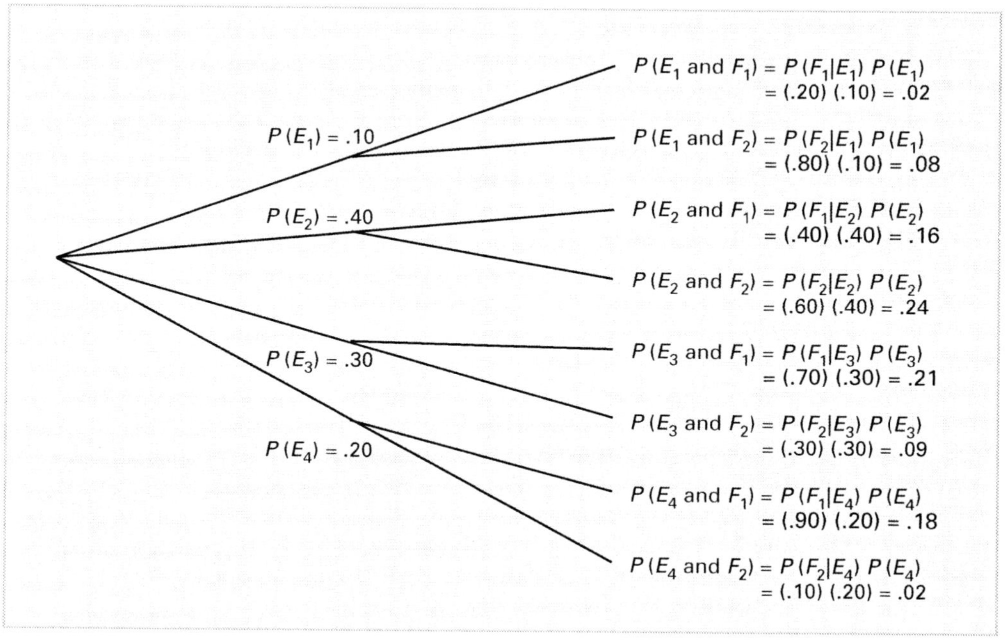

Thus, the expected monetary value or profit for stock A is \$104.92, and the expected monetary value or profit for stock B is \$225.08. Using this criterion, you should once again choose stock B, since the expected monetary value is much higher for this stock. However, you should also examine the return-to-risk ratio in light of these revised probabilities. Using the following equations, for stock A since $EMV(A) = \mu_A = \$104.92$,

$$\begin{aligned}\sigma_A^2 &= \sum_{i=1}^{N}(X_i - \mu)^2 P(X_i)\\ &= (30 - 104.92)^2(0.035) + (70 - 104.92)^2(0.281)\\ &\quad + (100 - 104.92)^2(0.368) + (150 - 104.92)^2(0.316)\\ &= 1{,}190.194\end{aligned}$$

The standard deviation of stock A is $\sigma_A = \sqrt{1{,}190.194} = \$34.50$.

For stock B since $EMV(B) = \mu_B = \$225.08$,

$$\begin{aligned}\sigma_B^2 &= \sum_{i=1}^{N}(X_i - \mu)^2 P(X_i)\\ \sigma_B^2 &= (-50 - 225.08)^2(0.035) + (30 - 225.08)^2(0.281)\\ &\quad + (250 - 225.08)^2(0.368) + (400 - 225.08)^2(0.316)\\ \sigma_B^2 &= 23{,}239.39\end{aligned}$$

The standard deviation of stock B is $\sigma_B = \sqrt{23{,}239.39} = \$152.445$.

Now that the standard deviation of the return from each stock has been obtained, the coefficient of variation can be computed. Substituting σ for S and EMV for $\bar{X}$ in the following equation, the coefficient of variation for stock A is equal to

$$CV_A = \left(\frac{\sigma_A}{EMV_A}\right)100\%$$

$$CV_A = \left(\frac{34.50}{104.92}\right)100\% = 32.88\%$$

while the coefficient of variation for stock B is equal to

$$CV_B = \left(\frac{\sigma_B}{EMV_B}\right)100\%$$

$$CV_B = \left(\frac{152.445}{225.08}\right)100\% = 67.73\%$$

Thus, you can see that there is still much more variation in the returns from stock B than from stock A.

For each of these two stocks, the return-to-risk ratios are calculated as follows. For stock A, the return-to-risk ratio is equal to

$$RTRR(A) = \frac{104.92}{34.50} = 3.041$$

For stock B, the return-to-risk ratio is equal to

$$RTRR(B) = \frac{225.08}{152.445} = 1.476$$

Thus, using the return-to-risk ratio, you should select stock A. Note that this is a different decision than that reached by using expected monetary value (or the equivalent expected opportunity loss). What stock should you buy? Your final decision will depend on whether you believe that it is more important to maximize the expected return on investment (select stock B) or to control the relative risk (select stock A). A closer examination of the objective of the mutual fund is warranted.

PROBLEMS FOR SECTION 3

Learning the Basics

18 In the following payoff table:

	Action	
Event	A	B
1	50	100
2	200	125

Suppose $P(E_1)$, the probability of event 1, is equal to 0.5 and $P(E_2)$, the probability of event 2, is also equal to 0.5. Suppose that $P(F|E_1) = 0.6$ and $P(F|E_2) = 0.4$ and event F occurs.

a. Revise the probabilities $P(E_1)$ and $P(E_2)$ in light of this information.

b. Compute the expected monetary value of action A and action B.

c. Compute the expected opportunity loss of action A and action B.

d. Explain the meaning of the expected value of perfect information ($EVPI$) in this problem.

e. On the basis of (b) or (c), which action should you choose? Why?

f. Compute the coefficient of variation for each action.

g. Compute the return-to-risk ratio for each action.

h. On the basis of (f) and (g), which action should you choose? Why?

i. Compare the results of (e) and (h), and explain any differences.

19 For this problem, use the following payoff table:

	Action	
Event	A	B
1	50	10
2	300	100
3	500	200

Suppose $P(E_1)$, the probability of event 1, is equal to 0.8, $P(E_2)$, the probability of event 2, is equal to 0.1, and $P(E_3)$, the probability of event 3, is equal to 0.1. Suppose that $P(F|E_1) = 0.2$, $P(F|E_2) = 0.4$, and $P(F|E_3) = 0.4$ and event F occurs.

a. Revise the probabilities $P(E_1)$, $P(E_2)$, and $P(E_3)$ in light of this information.

Based on these revised probabilities

b. Compute the expected monetary value of action A and action B.

c. Compute the expected opportunity loss of action A and action B.

d. Explain the meaning of the expected value of perfect information ($EVPI$) in this problem.

e. On the basis of (b) and (c), which action should you choose? Why?

f. Compute the coefficient of variation for each action.

g. Compute the return-to-risk ratio for each action.

h. On the basis of (f) and (g), which action should you choose? Why?

i. Compare the results of (e) and (h) and explain any differences.

Applying the Concepts

20 In problem 12, a vendor at a baseball stadium was deciding on whether to sell ice cream or soft drinks at today's game. Suppose that prior to making her decision, she decides to hear the forecast of the local weather reporter. In the past, when it has been cool, the weather reporter has forecast cool weather 80% of the time. When it has been warm, the weather reporter has forecast warm weather 70% of the time. If today's forecast is for cool weather,

a. revise the prior probabilities of the vendor in light of this information.
b. use these revised probabilities to do problem 12.
c. compare the results obtained in (b) to those of problem 12.

21 In problem 14, an investor is trying to determine the optimal investment decision among three investment opportunities. Suppose that prior to making his investment decision, the investor decides to consult with his stockbroker. In the past when the economy has declined, the stockbroker has given a rosy forecast 20% of the time (with a gloomy forecast 80% of the time). When there has been no change in the economy, the stockbroker has given a rosy forecast 40% of the time. When there has been an expanding economy, the stockbroker has given a rosy forecast 70% of the time. The stockbroker in this case gives a gloomy forecast for the economy.

a. Revise the probabilities of the investor in light of this economic forecast by the stockbroker.
b. Use these revised probabilities to do problem 14.
c. Compare the results obtained in (b) to those of problem 14.

22 In problem 16, an author is deciding which of two competing publishing companies to select to publish her new novel. Suppose that prior to making a final decision, the author decides to have an experienced reviewer examine her novel. This reviewer has an outstanding reputation for predicting the success of a novel. In the past, for novels that sold 1,000 copies, only 1% received favorable reviews. Of novels that sold 5,000 copies, 25% received favorable reviews. Of novels that sold 10,000 copies, 60% received favorable reviews. Of novels that sold 50,000 copies, 99% received favorable reviews. After examining the author's novel, the reviewer gives it an unfavorable review.

a. Revise the probabilities of the number of books sold in light of the reviewer's unfavorable review.
b. Use these revised probabilities to do problem 16.
c. Compare the results obtained in (b) to those of problem 16.

4 UTILITY

Thus far the assumption has been made that each incremental amount of profit or loss has the same value as the previous amounts of profits attained or losses incurred. In fact, under many circumstances this is not the case in the business world. Most individuals, as well as many companies, make special efforts to avoid large losses. At the same time, many individuals, place less value on extremely large profits as compared to initial profits. Such differential evaluation of incremental profits or losses is referred to as **utility**, a concept first discussed by Daniel Bernoulli in the 18th century (see reference 1). To illustrate this concept, suppose that you are faced with the following two choices:

Choice 1 A fair coin is to be tossed; if it lands on heads you will receive \$0.60, if it lands on tails you will pay \$0.40.

Choice 2 Do not play the game.

What decision should you choose? The expected value of playing this game is (0.60)(0.50) + (−0.40)(0.50) = +\$0.10, and the expected value of not playing the game is 0.

Most people will decide to play the game, since the expected value is positive and only small amounts of money are involved. Suppose, however, that the game is formulated with a payoff of \$600,000 when the coin lands on heads and a loss of \$400,000 when the coin lands on tails. The expected value of playing the game is now +\$100,000. With these payoffs, even though the expected value is positive, most individuals will not play the game because of the severe negative consequences of losing \$400,000. Each additional dollar amount of either profit or loss does not have the same utility as the previous amount. Large negative amounts for most individuals have severely negative utility; conversely, the extra value of each incremental dollar of profit decreases, when high enough profit levels are reached.

An important part of the decision-making problem, which is beyond the scope of this text (see references 2 and 3), is to develop a utility curve for the decision-maker that represents the utility of each specified dollar amount.

There are three basic types of utility curves: those of the risk averter, the risk seeker, and the risk-neutral person (see Figure 6).

FIGURE 6

Three types of utility curves: (a) risk averter, (b) risk seeker, (c) risk neutral

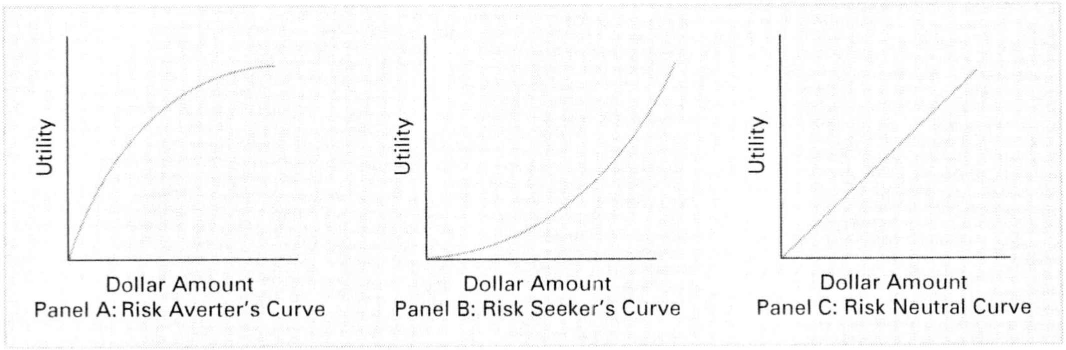

The **risk averter's curve** shows a rapid increase in utility for initial amounts of money followed by a gradual leveling off for increasing dollar amounts. This curve is appropriate for most individuals because the value of each additional dollar is not as great after large amounts of money have been earned.

The **risk seeker's curve** represents the utility of one who enjoys taking risks. The utility is greater for large dollar amounts. This curve represents an individual who is interested only in "striking it rich" and is willing to take large risks to obtain the opportunity of making large profits.

The **risk-neutral curve** represents the expected monetary value approach. Each additional dollar of profit has the same value as the previous dollar.

After a utility curve has been developed for a particular decision-maker in a specific situation, the dollar amounts are converted to utilities and the decision-maker uses the utility of each alternative course of action along with the decision criteria of expected utility, expected opportunity loss, and return-to-risk ratio to make a decision.

PROBLEMS FOR SECTION 4

Applying the Concepts

23 Do you consider yourself a risk seeker, a risk averter or a risk-neutral person? Explain.

24 Refer to problems 3–5 and 12–17. In which problems do you think the expected monetary value (risk-neutral) criteria may be inappropriate? Why?

SUMMARY

As you can see in the summary flowchart, this chapter is about decision making. You have learned how to develop payoff tables and decision trees, to use various criteria to choose between alternative courses of action, and to revise probabilities in the light of sample information using Bayes' theorem.

In the Using Statistics scenario, you learned how a manager of a mutual fund could use these tools to decide whether to purchase stock *A* or stock *B*. You found that stock *B* had a higher expected monetary value, a lower expected opportunity loss, but a lower return-to-risk ratio.

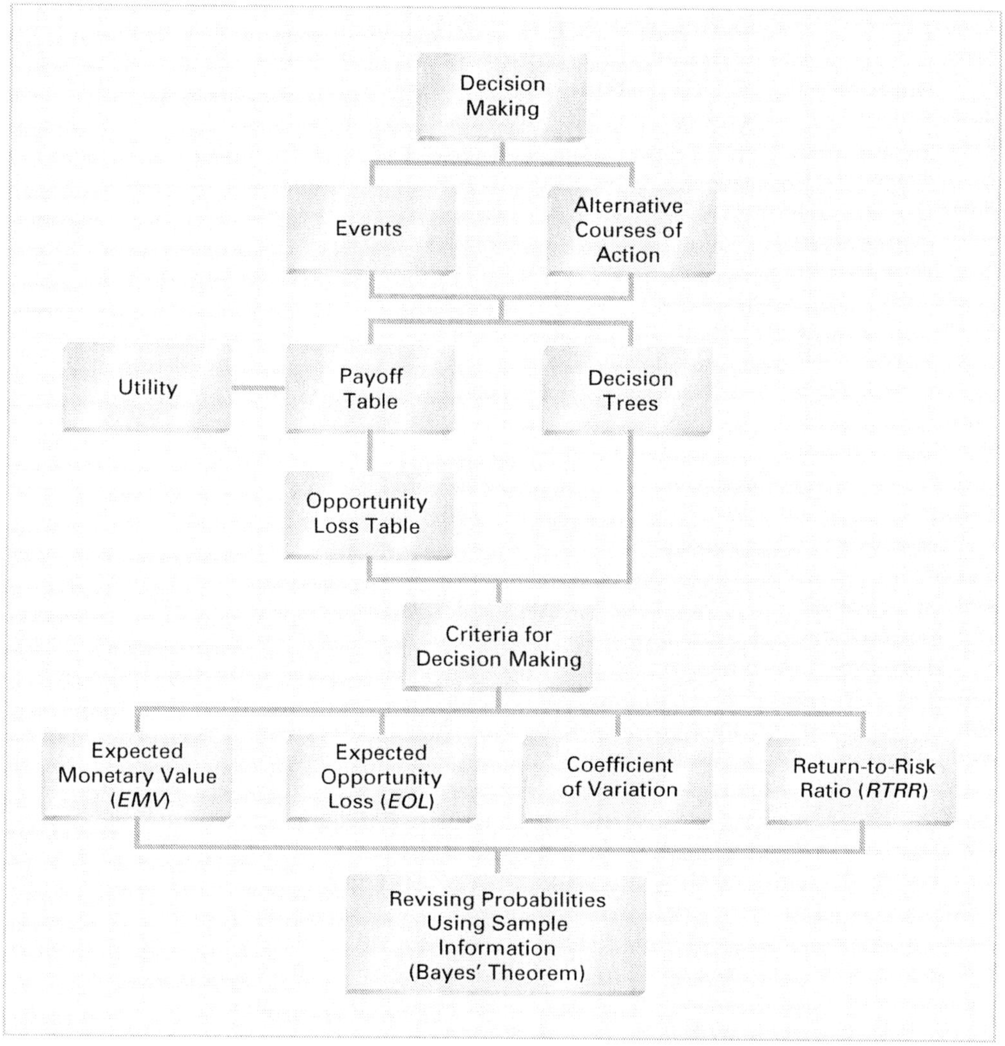

Chapter summary flowchart

KEY TERMS

alternative courses of action
decision criteria
decision tree
events or states of the world
expected monetary value (*EMV*)
expected opportunity loss (*EOL*)
expected profit under certainty
expected value of perfect information (*EVPI*)
opportunity loss
payoffs
payoff table
return-to-risk ratio (*RTRR*)
risk averter's curve
risk neutral curve
risk seeker's curve
utility

CHAPTER REVIEW PROBLEMS

Checking Your Understanding

25 What is the difference between an event and an alternative course of action?

26 What are the advantages and disadvantages of a payoff table as compared to a decision tree?

27 How are opportunity losses obtained from payoffs?

28 Why can't an opportunity loss be negative?

29 How does expected monetary value differ from expected opportunity loss?

30 What is the meaning of the expected value of perfect information?

31 How does the expected value of perfect information differ from the expected profit under certainty?

32 What are the advantages and disadvantages of using expected monetary value as compared to the return-to-risk ratio?

33 How is Bayes' theorem used to revise probabilities in light of the sample information?

34 What is the difference between a risk averter and a risk seeker?

35 Why should utilities be used instead of payoffs in certain circumstances?

Applying the Concepts

36 The Shop-Quik Supermarkets purchase large quantities of white bread for sale during a week. The stores purchase the bread for $0.75 per loaf and sell it for $1.10 per loaf. Any loaves not sold by the end of the week can be sold to a local thrift shop for $0.40. Based on past demand, the probability of various levels of demand is as follows:

Demand (Loaves)	Probability
6,000	0.10
8,000	0.50
10,000	0.30
12,000	0.10

a. Set up the payoff table indicating the events and alternative courses of action.
b. Set up the decision tree.
c. Compute the expected monetary value (*EMV*) for purchasing 6,000, 8,000, 10,000, and 12,000 loaves.
d. Compute the expected opportunity loss (*EOL*) for purchasing 6,000, 8,000, 10,000, and 12,000 loaves.
e. Explain the meaning of the expected value of perfect information (*EVPI*) in this problem.
f. Based on the results of (c) or (d), how many loaves would you purchase? Why?
g. Compute the coefficient of variation for each purchase level.
h. Compute the return-to-risk ratio for each purchase level.
i. Based on (g) and (h), what action would you choose? Why?
j. Compare the results of (f) and (i) and explain any differences.
k. Suppose that the probabilities of the demand level for loaves are as follows:

Demand (Loaves)	Probability
6,000	0.30
8,000	0.40
10,000	0.20
12,000	0.10

Repeat (c)–(j) of this problem with these new probabilities. Compare the results obtained with these new probabilities to those of (c)–(j).

37 The owner of a home heating oil delivery company would like to determine whether to offer a solar heating installation service to its customers. The owner of the company has determined that a startup cost of $150,000 would be necessary, but a profit of $2,000 can be made on each solar heating system installed. The owner estimates the probability of various demand levels as follows:

Number of Units Installed	Probability
50	0.40
100	0.30
200	0.30

a. Set up the payoff table indicating the events and alternative courses of action.
b. Set up the decision tree.
c. Set up the opportunity loss table.
d. Compute the expected monetary value (*EMV*) for offering this solar heating system installation service.
e. Compute the expected opportunity loss (*EOL*) for offering this solar heating system installation service.
f. Explain the meaning of the expected value of perfect information (*EVPI*) in this problem.
g. Compute the return-to-risk ratio for offering this solar heating system installation service.
h. Based on the results of (d) or (e), and (g), should the company offer this solar heating system installation service? Why?
i. How would your answers to (a)–(h) be affected if the startup cost were $200,000?

38 The manufacturer of a nationally distributed brand of potato chips would like to determine the feasibility of changing the product package from a cellophane bag to an unbreakable container. The product manager believes that there would be three possible national market responses to a change in product package: weak, moderate, and strong. The projected payoffs, in millions of dollars, in increased or decreased profit compared to the current package are as follows:

	Strategy	
Event	Use New Package	Keep Old Package
Weak national response	−$4	0
Moderate national response	1	0
Strong national response	5	0

Based on past experience, the product manager assigns the following probabilities to the different levels of national response:

P(Weak national response) = 0.30
P(Moderate national response) = 0.60
P(Strong national response) = 0.10

a. Set up the decision tree.
b. Set up the opportunity loss table.
c. Compute the expected monetary value (EMV) for offering this new product package.
d. Compute the expected opportunity loss (EOL) for offering this new product package.
e. Explain the meaning of the expected value of perfect information ($EVPI$) in this problem.
f. Compute the return-to-risk ratio for offering this new product package.
g. Based on the results of (c) or (d), and (f), should the company offer this new product package? Why?
h. What would be your answers to parts (c)–(g) if the probabilities were 0.6, 0.3, and 0.1, respectively?
i. What would be your answers to parts (c)–(g) if the probabilities were 0.1, 0.3, and 0.6, respectively.

Before making a final decision, the product manager would like to test market the new package in a selected city. In this selected city, the new package is substituted for the old package and a determination is made as to whether sales have increased, decreased, or stayed the same in a specified period of time. In previous test marketing of other products, when there has been a subsequent weak national response, sales in the test city have decreased 60% of the time, stayed the same 30% of the time, and increased 10% of the time. Where there has been a moderate national response, sales in the test city have decreased 20% of the time, stayed the same 40% of the time, and increased 40% of the time. When there has been a strong national response, sales in the test city have decreased 5% of the time, stayed the same 35% of the time, and increased 60% of the time.

j. If sales in the test city stayed the same, revise the original probabilities in light of this new information.
k. Use the revised probabilities obtained in (j) to repeat (c)–(g).
l. If sales in the test city decreased, revise the original probabilities in light of this new information.
m. Use the revised probabilities obtained in (l) to repeat (c)–(g).

39 An entrepreneur would like to determine whether it would be profitable to establish a gardening service in a local suburb. The entrepreneur believes that there are four possible levels of demand for this gardening service:

1. Very low demand—1% of the households would use the service.
2. Low demand—5% of the households would use the service.
3. Moderate demand—10% of the households would use the service.
4. High demand—25% of the households would use the service.

Based on past experiences in other suburbs, the entrepreneur assigns the following probabilities to the various demand levels:

P(very low demand) = 0.20
P(low demand) = 0.50
P(moderate demand) = 0.20
P(high demand) = 0.10

The entrepreneur has calculated the following profits or losses of this garden service for each demand level (over a period of 1 year):

	Action	
Demand	**Provide Garden Service ($)**	**Do Not Provide Garden Service**
Very low (p = .01)	–$50,000	0
Low (p = 0.05)	$60,000	0
Moderate (p = 0.10)	$130,000	0
High (p = 0.25)	$300,000	0

a. Set up a decision tree.
b. Set up an opportunity loss table.
c. Compute the expected monetary value (EMV) for offering this garden service.
d. Compute the expected opportunity loss (EOL) for offering this garden service.
e. Explain the meaning of the expected value of perfect information ($EVPI$) in this problem.
f. Compute the return-to-risk ratio for offering this garden service.
g. Based on the results of (c) or (d), and (f), should the entrepreneur offer this garden service? Why?

The entrepreneur decides that before making a final decision, a survey of households in this suburb should be taken to determine demand for the gardening service. A random sample of 20 households is selected and 3 indicate that they would use this gardening service.

h. Revise the prior probabilities in light of this sample information.

(*Hint:* Use the binomial distribution to determine the probability of the outcome that occurred given a particular level of demand.)

i. Use the revised probabilities obtained in (h) to repeat (c)–(g).

40 A manufacturer of a brand of inexpensive felt tip pens maintains a production process that produces 10,000 pens per day. In order to maintain the highest quality of this product, the manufacturer guarantees free replacement of any defective pen sold. It has been calculated that each defective pen produced costs 20 cents for the manufacturer to replace. Based on past experience, four rates of producing defective pens are possible:

Very low—1% of the pens manufactured will be defective.
Low—5% of the pens manufactured will be defective.
Moderate—10% of the pens manufactured will be defective.
High—20% of the pens manufactured will be defective.

The manufacturer can reduce the rate of defective pens produced by having a mechanic fix the machines at the end of each day. This mechanic can reduce the rate to 1%, but his services will cost $80.

A payoff table based on the daily production of 10,000 pens, indicating the replacement costs for each of the two alternatives (calling in the mechanic and not calling in the mechanic), is as follows:

	Action	
Defective Rate	**Do Not Call Mechanic**	**Call Mechanic**
Very low (1%)	$20	$100
Low (5%)	$100	$100
Moderate (10%)	$200	$100
High (20%)	$400	$100

Based on past experience, each defective rate is assumed to be equally likely to occur.

a. Set up a decision tree.
b. Set up an opportunity loss table.
c. Compute the expected monetary value (*EMV*) for calling and for not calling the mechanic.
d. Compute the expected opportunity loss (*EOL*) for calling and for not calling the mechanic.
e. Explain the meaning of the expected value of perfect information (*EVPI*) in this problem.
f. Compute the return-to-risk ratio for not calling the mechanic.
g. Based on the results of (c) or (d), and (f), should the company call the mechanic? Why?

At the end of a day's production, a sample of 15 pens is selected, of which 2 are defective.

h. Revise the prior probabilities in light of this sample information.

(*Hint:* Use the binomial distribution to determine the probability of the outcome that occurred given a particular defective rate.)

i. Use the revised probabilities obtained in (h) to repeat (c)–(g).

Internet Exercises

41 Go to the Web site for the text

www.prenhall.com/levine

Select Chapter 16 and click on Internet exercises.

WEB CASE

Apply your knowledge of decision-making techniques in this Web Case that extends the StockTout Web case from earlier chapters.

StraightArrow Banking & Investments is a Tri-Cities competitor of StockTout that is currently advertising its StraightArrow StraightDeal fund.

Visit the StraightArrow Web site (**www.prenhall.com/Springville/SA_Home.htm**) and examine the claims and supporting data for the fund. Compare those claims and data to the supporting data found on the StockTout Happy Bull and Worried Bear Funds Web page (**www.prenhall.com/Springville/ST_BullsandBears.htm**). Then answer the following:

1. Is the StraightArrow StraightDeal fund a better investment than either of the StockTout funds? Support your answer by performing and summarizing an appropriate analysis.

2. Before making a decision about which fund makes a better investment, you decide that you need to obtain a reliable forecast for the direction of the economy in the next year. After further investigation you find that there is a forecast made by a consensus of leading economists that the economy will be expanding in the next year. You also find out that in the past, when there has been a recession, the consensus of leading economists predicted an expanding economy 10% of the time. When there was a stable economy, they predicted an expanding economy 50% of the time, and when there was an expanding economy, they predicted an expanding economy 75% of the time. When there was a rapidly expanding economy, they predicted an expanding economy 90% of the time.

Does this information change your answer to question 1? Why, or why not?

REFERENCES

1. Bernstein, P. L. *Against the Gods: The Remarkable Story of Risk* (New York: John Wiley, 1996).
2. Render, B., R. M. Stair, and M. Hanna. *Quantitative Analysis for Management*, 8th ed. (Upper Saddle River, NJ: Prentice Hall, 2003).
3. Tversky, A., and D. Kahneman, "Rationale Choice and the Framing of Decisions," *Journal of Business*, 59 (1986) 251–278.

Answers to Selected Even-Numbered Problems

For more detailed solutions including explanations, interpretations, and Excel output, see the *Student Solutions Manual*.

4 (a)–(b) Payoff table: Event 1 \$12,000, \$6,000, Event 2 \$14,000, \$10,000, Event 3 \$20,000, \$22,000, Event 4 \$30,000, \$42,000, Event 5 \$110,000, \$202,000.

6 (a) 125, 112.50 **(b)** 25, 37.50 **(c)** Perfect information would correctly forecast which event, 1 or 2, will occur. The value of perfect information is the increase in the expected value if you knew which of the events 1 or 2 would occur prior to making a decision between actions. It allows us to select the optimum action given a correct forecast. *EMV* with perfect information = 150, *EVPI* = 25 **(d)** Action A **(e)** 60%, 11.11% **(f)** 1.667, 9.0 **(g)** Action B **(h)** The best decision depends on the decision criteria.

8 (a) 10% **(b)** 25% **(c)** 4.0.

10 Select portfolio A.

12 (a) 56, 66 **(b)** 18, 8 **(c)** *EVPI* is the maximum amount of money the vendor is willing to pay for the information about which event will occur. **(d)** Sell ice cream. **(e)** 8.748%, 44.536% **(f)** 11.431, 2.245.

14 (a) 1,050, 1,400, 1,400 **(b)** 522.02, 2498.00, 9656.09 **(c)** 4100, 3750, 3750 **(d)** *EVPI* = 3,750. The investor should not be willing to pay more than \$3,750 for a perfect forecast. **(e)** 49.72%, 178.43%, 689.92% **(f)** 2.01, 0.56, 0.14 **(g)–(h)** Actions *B* and *C* optimize the expected monetary value, but action *A* minimizes the coefficient of variation and maximizes the investor's return to risk.

16 (a) 25200, 32400 **(b)** 10700, 3500 **(c)** 3500 **(d)** Sign with company *B* to maximize the expected monetary value (\$32,400) and minimize the expected opportunity loss (\$3,500). **(e)** 114.25%, 177.73% **(f)** 0.8752, 0.5627 **(g)** Signing with company *A* will minimize the author's risk and yield the higher return to risk. **(h)** Company *B* has a higher *EMV* than *A*, but choosing company *B* also entails more risk and has a lower return to risk ratio than *A*.

18 (a) 0.6, 0.4 **(b)** 110, 110 **(c)** 30, 30 **(d)** 30 **(e)** Both have the same *EMV*. **(f)** 66.8%, 11.1% **(g)** 1.497, 8.981 **(h)** Action *B* has a better return to risk ratio. **(i)** Both have the same *EMV*, but action *B* has a better return to risk ratio.

20 (a) 0.64, 0.36 **(b)** *EMV*: 53.6, 51.6; *EOL*: 10.8, 12.8; *EMV* with perfect information = 64.4; *EVPI* = 10.8. The vendor should not be willing to pay more than \$10.80 for a perfect forecast of the weather. The vendor should sell soft drinks to maximize value and minimize loss. *CV*: 8.96%, 55.81%. Return to risk ratio: 11.1667, 1.7917. Based on these revised probabilities, the vendor's decision changes because of the increased likelihood of cool weather given a forecast for cool. Under these conditions, she should sell soft drinks to maximize the expected monetary value and minimize her expected opportunity loss.

22 (a) 0.5590, 0.2484, 0.1412, 0.0502, 0.0013 **(c)** The author's decision is affected by the changed probabilities. Under the new circumstances, signing with company *A* maximizes the expected monetary value (\$14,658.60), minimizes the expected opportunity loss (\$1,004.40), minimizes risk with a smaller coefficient of variation, and yields a higher return to risk than choosing company *B*.

36 (c) 2100, 2660, 2520, 1960 **(d)** 980, 420, 560, 1120 **(e)** *EVPI* = 420 **(f)** buy 8000 loaves **(g)** 0, 15.79%, 35.57%, 57.14% **(h)** undefined, 6.333, 2.811, 1.750 **(i)** buy 8000 loaves **(k)** repeat part (c) 2100, 2380, 2100, 1540 repeat part (d) 700, 490, 770, 1330 repeat part (e) *EVPI* = 490 repeat part (f) buy 8000 loaves repeat part (g) 0, 26.96%, 51.64%, 85.76% repeat part (h) undefined, 3.710, 1.937, 1.166 repeat part (i) buy 8000 loaves.

38 (c) −100000, 0 **(d)** 1200000, 1100000 **(e)** *EVPI* = 1100000 **(f)** −0.0356, undefined **(g)** continue using old packaging **(h)** repeat part (c) −1600000, 0 repeat part (d) 2400000, 800000 repeat part (e) *EVPI* = 800000 repeat part (f) −0.5101, undefined repeat part (g) continue using old packaging **(i)** repeat part (c) 2900000, 0 repeat part (d) 400000, 3300000 repeat part (e) *EVPI* = 400000 repeat part (f) 0.9953, undefined repeat part (g) use the new packaging **(j)** 0.2466, 0.6575, 0.0959 **(k)** repeat part (c) 150600, 0 repeat part (d) 986400, 1137000 repeat part (e) *EVPI* = 986400 repeat part (f) 0.0570, undefined repeat part (g) use the new packaging **(l)** 0.5902, 0.3934, 0.0164 **(m)** repeat part (c) −1885400, 0 repeat part (d) 2360800, 475400 repeat part (e) *EVPI* = 475400 repeat part (f) −0.7288, undefined repeat part (g) use the old packaging.

40 (c) 180, 100 **(d)** 20, 100 **(e)** *EVPI* = 20 **(f)** 1.2665, undefined **(g)** call the mechanic **(h)** 0.0143, 0.2100, 0.4159, 0.3598 **(i)** repeat part (c) 248, 100 repeat part (d) 1.15, 149.53 repeat part (e) *EVPI* = 1.15 repeat part (f) 2.0544, undefined repeat part (g) call the mechanic.

Excel Handbook for Decision Making

EH1 PERFORMING OPPORTUNITY LOSS ANALYSIS

To perform an opportunity loss analysis, implement a worksheet that features the **INDEX** and **MATCH** functions. These functions are entered as **INDEX(*cell range,* 1, *column number*)**, where **1** and *column number* specifies the row (1) and the column number that is relative to the start of the *cell range*; and **MATCH(*lookup cell, lookup cell range,* 0)**, where ***lookup cell*** is the cell containing the lookup value and *lookup cell range* is the cell range in which to look for a matching value.

Tables EH1 and EH2 contain the design for an **Opportunity Loss** worksheet that performs an opportunity loss analysis for the television set marketing payoff table of Table 1. This design uses the MAX function to determine the optimum profit for each event. In turn, the optimum profit values are used by the MATCH function to help the INDEX function select the alternative course of action label from the payoff table cell range B4:C4.

When implementing this design, enter the formulas for cells B12 and B13, typeset as two lines each, as single continuous lines, with the mix of absolute and relative cell references as shown.

For similar problems with a different number of events, insert rows inside both the payoff and opportunity loss tables by first selecting the last rows of the tables, then selecting **Insert | Rows**, as is necessary, and then copying formulas down into the new blank rows. For problems with a different number of alternative courses of actions, select columns C and E and, in turn, select **Insert | Columns**. In the opportunity loss table, leave the new column C blank, but copy formulas from column D cells to the cells of the new column F.

Table EH1
Opportunity Loss worksheet payoff table range design

	A	B	C
1	Television Marketing Opportunity Loss		
2			
3	Payoff Table:		
4		Market	Do not market
5	Successful	45	–3
6	Unsuccessful	–36	–3

Table EH2
Opportunity Loss worksheet opportunity loss table range design (rows 7 and 8 are blank)

	A	B	C	D	E
9	Opportunity Loss Table:				
10		Optimum	Optimum	Alternatives	
11		Action	Profit	=B4	=C4
12	=A5	=INDEX($B$4:$C$4, 1, MATCH(C12, B5:C5, 0))	=MAX(B5:C5)	=$C12 – B5	=$C12 – C5
13	=A6	=INDEX($B$4:$C$4, 1, MATCH(C13, B6:C6, 0))	=MAX(B6:C6)	=$C13 – B6	=$C13 – C6

EH2 CALCULATING CRITERIA FOR DECISION MAKING

To calculate expected monetary values, expected opportunity losses, and measures of variation from payoff table data and event probabilities, implement a worksheet that features the **SUMPRODUCT**, **INDEX**, and **MATCH** functions. SUMPRODUCT is entered as **SUMPRODUCT (*multiplier cell range, multiplicand cell range*)**, where *multiplier cell range* is the cell range containing the probabilities, and *multiplicand cell range* is the cell range containing one of the alternative courses of action. (See the previous section for the formats for the INDEX and MATCH functions.)

Tables EH3 through EH7 contain the design for a **Criteria** worksheet that calculates decision-making criteria for the stock selection example of the Using Statistics scenario of this chapter. This design uses the SUMPRODUCT function to calculate the *EMV*, the variance, and the *EOL*. The design uses the INDEX and MATCH function in the same way as it is used in section EH1 to determine the optimum action for each event.

When implementing this design, enter the formulas in rows 11, 12, 20 through 23, and 25 and 26, typeset as two lines each, as single continuous lines. Also be sure to enter the mix of relative and absolute cell references for the formulas that contain both and note that the formulas for cells D26 and E26 contain consecutive double quotation marks. Enter the labels for rows 10 through 15 in column C and enter the cell C25 label as a single line.

For similar problems, adapt the design by inserting rows and columns inside both the probabilities & payoffs, calculations area, and opportunity loss table ranges and by copying and adjusting formulas as necessary.

Table EH3
Criteria worksheet design for Probabilities & Payoffs Table range

	A	B	C	D
1	Expected Monetary Value			
2				
3	Probabilities & Payoffs Table:			
4		P	A1	A2
5	Recession	0.1	30	–50
6	Stable economy	0.4	70	30
7	Moderate growth	0.3	100	250
8	Boom	0.2	150	400

Table EH4
Criteria worksheet design for cell range A10:D15 (row 9 is blank)

	A	B	C	D
10		Statistics for:	=C4	=D4
11	Expected Monetary Value		=SUMPRODUCT($B$5:$B$8, C5:C8)	=SUMPRODUCT($B$5:$B$8, D5:D8)
12		Variance	=SUMPRODUCT($B$5:$B$8, F9:F12)	=SUMPRODUCT($B$5:$B$8, G9:G12)
13		Standard Deviation	=SQRT(C12)	=SQRT(D12)
14		Coefficient of Variation	=C13/C11	=D13/D11
15		Return to Risk Ratio	=C11/C13	=D11/D13

Table EH5
Criteria worksheet design for columns F:G (rows 1 through 5 in these columns are blank)

	F	G
6	Calculations Area	
7	For variance and std. deviation	
8	=C4	=D4
9	=(C5 – C$11) ^2	=(D5 – D$11) ^2
10	=(C6 – C$11) ^2	=(D6 – D$11) ^2
11	=(C7 – C$11) ^2	=(D7 – D$11) ^2
12	=(C8 – C$11) ^2	=(D8 – D$11) ^2

Table EH6
Criteria worksheet design for rows 17:23 (row 16 should be left blank)

	A	B	C	D	E
17	Opportunity Loss Table:				
18		Optimum	Optimum	Alternatives	
19		Action	Profit	=C4	=D4
20	=A5	=INDEX($C$4:$D$4, 1, MATCH(C20, C5:D5, 0))	=MAX(C5:D5)	=$C20 – C5	=$C20 – D5
21	=A6	=INDEX($C$4:$D$4, 1, MATCH(C21, C6:D6, 0))	=MAX(C6:D6)	=$C21 – C6	=$C21 – D6
22	=A7	=INDEX($C$4:$D$4, 1 MATCH(C22, C7:D7, 0))	=MAX(C7:D7)	=$C22 – C7	=$C22 – D7
23	=A8	=INDEX($C$4:$D$4, 1, MATCH(C23, C8:D8, 0))	=MAX(C8:D8)	=$C23 – C8	=$C23 – D8

Table EH7
Criteria worksheet design for rows 24:26

	A	B	C	D	E
24				=C4	=D4
25	Expected Opportunity Loss			=SUMPRODUCT($B$5:$B$8, D20:D23)	=SUMPRODUCT($B$5:$B$8, E20:E23)
26				=IF(D25 = MIN($D$25:$E$25), "EVPI", "")	=IF(E25 = MIN($D$25:$E$25), "EVPI", "")

TABLES

Tables

TABLE 1

Table of Random Numbers

	COLUMN							
Row	00000 12345	00001 67890	11111 12345	11112 67890	22222 12345	22223 67890	33333 12345	33334 67890
01	49280	88924	35779	00283	81163	07275	89863	02348
02	61870	41657	07468	08612	98083	97349	20775	45091
03	43898	65923	25078	86129	78496	97653	91550	08078
04	62993	93912	30454	84598	56095	20664	12872	64647
05	33850	58555	51438	85507	71865	79488	76783	31708
06	97340	03364	88472	04334	63919	36394	11095	92470
07	70543	29776	10087	10072	55980	64688	68239	20461
08	89382	93809	00796	95945	34101	81277	66090	88872
09	37818	72142	67140	50785	22380	16703	53362	44940
10	60430	22834	14130	96593	23298	56203	92671	15925
11	82975	66158	84731	19436	55790	69229	28661	13675
12	39087	71938	40355	54324	08401	26299	49420	59208
13	55700	24586	93247	32596	11865	63397	44251	43189
14	14756	23997	78643	75912	83832	32768	18928	57070
15	32166	53251	70654	92827	63491	04233	33825	69662
16	23236	73751	31888	81718	06546	83246	47651	04877
17	45794	26926	15130	82455	78305	55058	52551	47182
18	09893	20505	14225	68514	46427	56788	96297	78822
19	54382	74598	91499	14523	68479	27686	46162	83554
20	94750	89923	37089	20048	80336	94598	26940	36858
21	70297	34135	53140	33340	42050	82341	44104	82949
22	85157	47954	32979	26575	57600	40881	12250	73742
23	11100	02340	12860	74697	96644	89439	28707	25815
24	36871	50775	30592	57143	17381	68856	25853	35041
25	23913	48357	63308	16090	51690	54607	72407	55538
26	79348	36085	27973	65157	07456	22255	25626	57054
27	92074	54641	53673	54421	18130	60103	69593	49464
28	06873	21440	75593	41373	49502	17972	82578	16364
29	12478	37622	99659	31065	83613	69889	58869	29571
30	57175	55564	65411	42547	70457	03426	72937	83792
31	91616	11075	80103	07831	59309	13276	26710	73000
32	78025	73539	14621	39044	47450	03197	12787	47709
33	27587	67228	80145	10175	12822	86687	65530	49325
34	16690	20427	04251	64477	73709	73945	92396	68263
35	70183	58065	65489	31833	82093	16747	10386	59293
36	90730	35385	15679	99742	50866	78028	75573	67257
37	10934	93242	13431	24590	02770	48582	00906	58595
38	82462	30166	79613	47416	13389	80268	05085	96666
39	27463	10433	07606	16285	93699	60912	94532	95632
40	02979	52997	09079	92709	90110	47506	53693	49892
41	46888	69929	75233	52507	32097	37594	10067	67327
42	53638	83161	08289	12639	08141	12640	28437	09268
43	82433	61427	17239	89160	19666	08814	37841	12847
44	35766	31672	50082	22795	66948	65581	84393	15890
45	10853	42581	08792	13257	61973	24450	52351	16602
46	20341	27398	72906	63955	17276	10646	74692	48438
47	54458	90542	77563	51839	52901	53355	83281	19177
48	26337	66530	16687	35179	46560	00123	44546	79896
49	34314	23729	85264	05575	96855	23820	11091	79821
50	28603	10708	68933	34189	92166	15181	66628	58599

continued

TABLE 1

Table of Random Numbers (*Continued*)

	COLUMN							
Row	00000 12345	00001 67890	11111 12345	11112 67890	22222 12345	22223 67890	33333 12345	33334 67890
51	66194	28926	99547	16625	45515	67953	12108	57846
52	78240	43195	24837	32511	70880	22070	52622	61881
53	00833	88000	67299	68215	11274	55624	32991	17436
54	12111	86683	61270	58036	64192	90611	15145	01748
55	47189	99951	05755	03834	43782	90599	40282	51417
56	76396	72486	62423	27618	84184	78922	73561	52818
57	46409	17469	32483	09083	76175	19985	26309	91536
58	74626	22111	87286	46772	42243	68046	44250	42439
59	34450	81974	93723	49023	58432	67083	36876	93391
60	36327	72135	33005	28701	34710	49359	50693	89311
61	74185	77536	84825	09934	99103	09325	67389	45869
62	12296	41623	62873	37943	25584	09609	63360	47270
63	90822	60280	88925	99610	42772	60561	76873	04117
64	72121	79152	96591	90305	10189	79778	68016	13747
65	95268	41377	25684	08151	61816	58555	54305	86189
66	92603	09091	75884	93424	72586	88903	30061	14457
67	18813	90291	05275	01223	79607	95426	34900	09778
68	38840	26903	28624	67157	51986	42865	14508	49315
69	05959	33836	53758	16562	41081	38012	41230	20528
70	85141	21155	99212	32685	51403	31926	69813	58781
71	75047	59643	31074	38172	03718	32119	69506	67143
72	30752	95260	68032	62871	58781	34143	68790	69766
73	22986	82575	42187	62295	84295	30634	66562	31442
74	99439	86692	90348	66036	48399	73451	26698	39437
75	20389	93029	11881	71685	65452	89047	63669	02656
76	39249	05173	68256	36359	20250	68686	05947	09335
77	96777	33605	29481	20063	09398	01843	35139	61344
78	04860	32918	10798	50492	52655	33359	94713	28393
79	41613	42375	00403	03656	77580	87772	86877	57085
80	17930	00794	53836	53692	67135	98102	61912	11246
81	24649	31845	25736	75231	83808	98917	93829	99430
82	79899	34061	54308	59358	56462	58166	97302	86828
83	76801	49594	81002	30397	52728	15101	72070	33706
84	36239	63636	38140	65731	39788	06872	38971	53363
85	07392	64449	17886	63632	53995	17574	22247	62607
86	67133	04181	33874	98835	67453	59734	76381	63455
87	77759	31504	32832	70861	15152	29733	75371	39174
88	85992	72268	42920	20810	29361	51423	90306	73574
89	79553	75952	54116	65553	47139	60579	09165	85490
90	41101	17336	48951	53674	17880	45260	08575	49321
91	36191	17095	32123	91576	84221	78902	82010	30847
92	62329	63898	23268	74283	26091	68409	69704	82267
93	14751	13151	93115	01437	56945	89661	67680	79790
94	48462	59278	44185	29616	76537	19589	83139	28454
95	29435	88105	59651	44391	74588	55114	80834	85686
96	28340	29285	12965	14821	80425	16602	44653	70467
97	02167	58940	27149	80242	10587	79786	34959	75339
98	17864	00991	39557	54981	23588	81914	37609	13128
99	79675	80605	60059	35862	00254	36546	21545	78179
00	72335	82037	92003	34100	29879	46613	89720	13274

Source: Partially extracted from the Rand Corporation. A Million Random Digits with 100,000 Normal Deviates. *(Glencoe, IL, The Free Press, 1955).*

TABLE 2

The Cumulative Standardized Normal Distribution

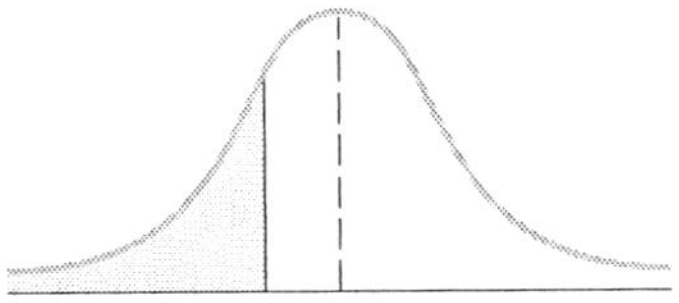

Entry represents area under the cumulative standardized normal distribution from −∞ to Z

Z	0.00	0.01	0.02	0.03	0.04	0.05	0.06	0.07	0.08	0.09
−3.9	0.00005	0.00005	0.00004	0.00004	0.00004	0.00004	0.00004	0.00004	0.00003	0.00003
−3.8	0.00007	0.00007	0.00007	0.00006	0.00006	0.00006	0.00006	0.00005	0.00005	0.00005
−3.7	0.00011	0.00010	0.00010	0.00010	0.00009	0.00009	0.00008	0.00008	0.00008	0.00008
−3.6	0.00016	0.00015	0.00015	0.00014	0.00014	0.00013	0.00013	0.00012	0.00012	0.00011
−3.5	0.00023	0.00022	0.00022	0.00021	0.00020	0.00019	0.00019	0.00018	0.00017	0.00017
−3.4	0.00034	0.00032	0.00031	0.00030	0.00029	0.00028	0.00027	0.00026	0.00025	0.00024
−3.3	0.00048	0.00047	0.00045	0.00043	0.00042	0.00040	0.00039	0.00038	0.00036	0.00035
−3.2	0.00069	0.00066	0.00064	0.00062	0.00060	0.00058	0.00056	0.00054	0.00052	0.00050
−3.1	0.00097	0.00094	0.00090	0.00087	0.00084	0.00082	0.00079	0.00076	0.00074	0.00071
−3.0	0.00135	0.00131	0.00126	0.00122	0.00118	0.00114	0.00111	0.00107	0.00103	0.00100
−2.9	0.0019	0.0018	0.0018	0.0017	0.0016	0.0016	0.0015	0.0015	0.0014	0.0014
−2.8	0.0026	0.0025	0.0024	0.0023	0.0023	0.0022	0.0021	0.0021	0.0020	0.0019
−2.7	0.0035	0.0034	0.0033	0.0032	0.0031	0.0030	0.0029	0.0028	0.0027	0.0026
−2.6	0.0047	0.0045	0.0044	0.0043	0.0041	0.0040	0.0039	0.0038	0.0037	0.0036
−2.5	0.0062	0.0060	0.0059	0.0057	0.0055	0.0054	0.0052	0.0051	0.0049	0.0048
−2.4	0.0082	0.0080	0.0078	0.0075	0.0073	0.0071	0.0069	0.0068	0.0066	0.0064
−2.3	0.0107	0.0104	0.0102	0.0099	0.0096	0.0094	0.0091	0.0089	0.0087	0.0084
−2.2	0.0139	0.0136	0.0132	0.0129	0.0125	0.0122	0.0119	0.0116	0.0113	0.0110
−2.1	0.0179	0.0174	0.0170	0.0166	0.0162	0.0158	0.0154	0.0150	0.0146	0.0143
−2.0	0.0228	0.0222	0.0217	0.0212	0.0207	0.0202	0.0197	0.0192	0.0188	0.0183
−1.9	0.0287	0.0281	0.0274	0.0268	0.0262	0.0256	0.0250	0.0244	0.0239	0.0233
−1.8	0.0359	0.0351	0.0344	0.0336	0.0329	0.0322	0.0314	0.0307	0.0301	0.0294
−1.7	0.0446	0.0436	0.0427	0.0418	0.0409	0.0401	0.0392	0.0384	0.0375	0.0367
−1.6	0.0548	0.0537	0.0526	0.0516	0.0505	0.0495	0.0485	0.0475	0.0465	0.0455
−1.5	0.0668	0.0655	0.0643	0.0630	0.0618	0.0606	0.0594	0.0582	0.0571	0.0559
−1.4	0.0808	0.0793	0.0778	0.0764	0.0749	0.0735	0.0721	0.0708	0.0694	0.0681
−1.3	0.0968	0.0951	0.0934	0.0918	0.0901	0.0885	0.0869	0.0853	0.0838	0.0823
−1.2	0.1151	0.1131	0.1112	0.1093	0.1075	0.1056	0.1038	0.1020	0.1003	0.0985
−1.1	0.1357	0.1335	0.1314	0.1292	0.1271	0.1251	0.1230	0.1210	0.1190	0.1170
−1.0	0.1587	0.1562	0.1539	0.1515	0.1492	0.1469	0.1446	0.1423	0.1401	0.1379
−0.9	0.1841	0.1814	0.1788	0.1762	0.1736	0.1711	0.1685	0.1660	0.1635	0.1611
−0.8	0.2119	0.2090	0.2061	0.2033	0.2005	0.1977	0.1949	0.1922	0.1894	0.1867
−0.7	0.2420	0.2388	0.2358	0.2327	0.2296	0.2266	0.2236	0.2206	0.2177	0.2148
−0.6	0.2743	0.2709	0.2676	0.2643	0.2611	0.2578	0.2546	0.2514	0.2482	0.2451
−0.5	0.3085	0.3050	0.3015	0.2981	0.2946	0.2912	0.2877	0.2843	0.2810	0.2776
−0.4	0.3446	0.3409	0.3372	0.3336	0.3300	0.3264	0.3228	0.3192	0.3156	0.3121
−0.3	0.3821	0.3783	0.3745	0.3707	0.3669	0.3632	0.3594	0.3557	0.3520	0.3483
−0.2	0.4207	0.4168	0.4129	0.4090	0.4052	0.4013	0.3974	0.3936	0.3897	0.3859
−0.1	0.4602	0.4562	0.4522	0.4483	0.4443	0.4404	0.4364	0.4325	0.4286	0.4247
−0.0	0.5000	0.4960	0.4920	0.4880	0.4840	0.4801	0.4761	0.4721	0.4681	0.4641

continued

TABLE 2

The Cumulative Standardized Normal Distribution (*Continued*)

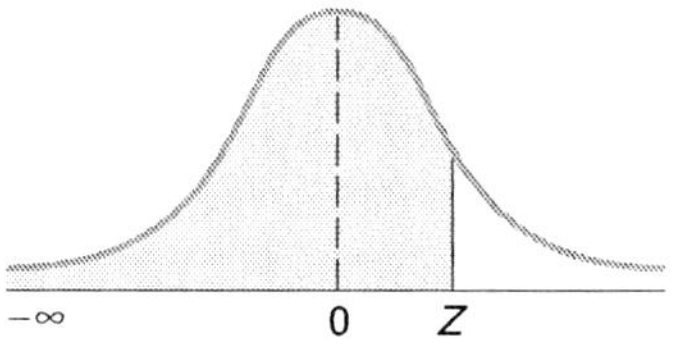

Entry represents area under the standardized normal distribution from −∞ to Z

Z	0.00	0.01	0.02	0.03	0.04	0.05	0.06	0.07	0.08	0.09
0.0	0.5000	0.5040	0.5080	0.5120	0.5160	0.5199	0.5239	0.5279	0.5319	0.5359
0.1	0.5398	0.5438	0.5478	0.5517	0.5557	0.5596	0.5636	0.5675	0.5714	0.5753
0.2	0.5793	0.5832	0.5871	0.5910	0.5948	0.5987	0.6026	0.6064	0.6103	0.6141
0.3	0.6179	0.6217	0.6255	0.6293	0.6331	0.6368	0.6406	0.6443	0.6480	0.6517
0.4	0.6554	0.6591	0.6628	0.6664	0.6700	0.6736	0.6772	0.6808	0.6844	0.6879
0.5	0.6915	0.6950	0.6985	0.7019	0.7054	0.7088	0.7123	0.7157	0.7190	0.7224
0.6	0.7257	0.7291	0.7324	0.7357	0.7389	0.7422	0.7454	0.7486	0.7518	0.7549
0.7	0.7580	0.7612	0.7642	0.7673	0.7704	0.7734	0.7764	0.7794	0.7823	0.7852
0.8	0.7881	0.7910	0.7939	0.7967	0.7995	0.8023	0.8051	0.8078	0.8106	0.8133
0.9	0.8159	0.8186	0.8212	0.8238	0.8264	0.8289	0.8315	0.8340	0.8365	0.8389
1.0	0.8413	0.8438	0.8461	0.8485	0.8508	0.8531	0.8554	0.8577	0.8599	0.8621
1.1	0.8643	0.8665	0.8686	0.8708	0.8729	0.8749	0.8770	0.8790	0.8810	0.8830
1.2	0.8849	0.8869	0.8888	0.8907	0.8925	0.8944	0.8962	0.8980	0.8997	0.9015
1.3	0.9032	0.9049	0.9066	0.9082	0.9099	0.9115	0.9131	0.9147	0.9162	0.9177
1.4	0.9192	0.9207	0.9222	0.9236	0.9251	0.9265	0.9279	0.9292	0.9306	0.9319
1.5	0.9332	0.9345	0.9357	0.9370	0.9382	0.9394	0.9406	0.9418	0.9429	0.9441
1.6	0.9452	0.9463	0.9474	0.9484	0.9495	0.9505	0.9515	0.9525	0.9535	0.9545
1.7	0.9554	0.9564	0.9573	0.9582	0.9591	0.9599	0.9608	0.9616	0.9625	0.9633
1.8	0.9641	0.9649	0.9656	0.9664	0.9671	0.9678	0.9686	0.9693	0.9699	0.9706
1.9	0.9713	0.9719	0.9726	0.9732	0.9738	0.9744	0.9750	0.9756	0.9761	0.9767
2.0	0.9772	0.9778	0.9783	0.9788	0.9793	0.9798	0.9803	0.9808	0.9812	0.9817
2.1	0.9821	0.9826	0.9830	0.9834	0.9838	0.9842	0.9846	0.9850	0.9854	0.9857
2.2	0.9861	0.9864	0.9868	0.9871	0.9875	0.9878	0.9881	0.9884	0.9887	0.9890
2.3	0.9893	0.9896	0.9898	0.9901	0.9904	0.9906	0.9909	0.9911	0.9913	0.9916
2.4	0.9918	0.9920	0.9922	0.9925	0.9927	0.9929	0.9931	0.9932	0.9934	0.9936
2.5	0.9938	0.9940	0.9941	0.9943	0.9945	0.9946	0.9948	0.9949	0.9951	0.9952
2.6	0.9953	0.9955	0.9956	0.9957	0.9959	0.9960	0.9961	0.9962	0.9963	0.9964
2.7	0.9965	0.9966	0.9967	0.9968	0.9969	0.9970	0.9971	0.9972	0.9973	0.9974
2.8	0.9974	0.9975	0.9976	0.9977	0.9977	0.9978	0.9979	0.9979	0.9980	0.9981
2.9	0.9981	0.9982	0.9982	0.9983	0.9984	0.9984	0.9985	0.9985	0.9986	0.9986
3.0	0.99865	0.99869	0.99874	0.99878	0.99882	0.99886	0.99889	0.99893	0.99897	0.99900
3.1	0.99903	0.99906	0.99910	0.99913	0.99916	0.99918	0.99921	0.99924	0.99926	0.99929
3.2	0.99931	0.99934	0.99936	0.99938	0.99940	0.99942	0.99944	0.99946	0.99948	0.99950
3.3	0.99952	0.99953	0.99955	0.99957	0.99958	0.99960	0.99961	0.99962	0.99964	0.99965
3.4	0.99966	0.99968	0.99969	0.99970	0.99971	0.99972	0.99973	0.99974	0.99975	0.99976
3.5	0.99977	0.99978	0.99978	0.99979	0.99980	0.99981	0.99981	0.99982	0.99983	0.99983
3.6	0.99984	0.99985	0.99985	0.99986	0.99986	0.99987	0.99987	0.99988	0.99988	0.99989
3.7	0.99989	0.99990	0.99990	0.99990	0.99991	0.99991	0.99992	0.99992	0.99992	0.99992
3.8	0.99993	0.99993	0.99993	0.99994	0.99994	0.99994	0.99994	0.99995	0.99995	0.99995
3.9	0.99995	0.99995	0.99996	0.99996	0.99996	0.99996	0.99996	0.99996	0.99997	0.99997
4.0	0.99996832									
4.5	0.99999660									
5.0	0.99999971									
5.5	0.99999998									
6.0	0.99999999									

TABLE 3

Critical Values of *t*

For a particular number of degrees of freedom, entry represents the critical value of t *corresponding to a specified upper-tail area* (α)

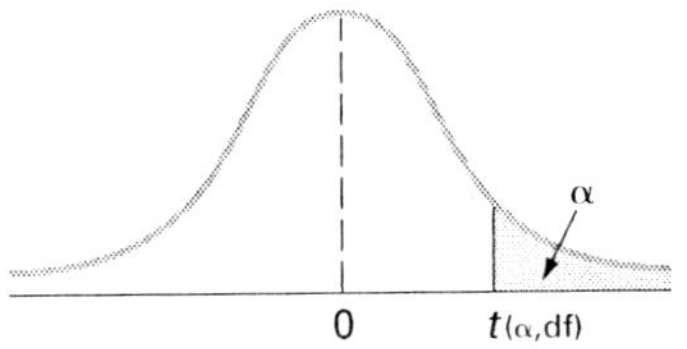

Degrees of Freedom	UPPER-TAIL AREAS 0.25	0.10	0.05	0.025	0.01	0.005
1	1.0000	3.0777	6.3138	12.7062	31.8207	63.6574
2	0.8165	1.8856	2.9200	4.3027	6.9646	9.9248
3	0.7649	1.6377	2.3534	3.1824	4.5407	5.8409
4	0.7407	1.5332	2.1318	2.7764	3.7469	4.6041
5	0.7267	1.4759	2.0150	2.5706	3.3649	4.0322
6	0.7176	1.4398	1.9432	2.4469	3.1427	3.7074
7	0.7111	1.4149	1.8946	2.3646	2.9980	3.4995
8	0.7064	1.3968	1.8595	2.3060	2.8965	3.3554
9	0.7027	1.3830	1.8331	2.2622	2.8214	3.2498
10	0.6998	1.3722	1.8125	2.2281	2.7638	3.1693
11	0.6974	1.3634	1.7959	2.2010	2.7181	3.1058
12	0.6955	1.3562	1.7823	2.1788	2.6810	3.0545
13	0.6938	1.3502	1.7709	2.1604	2.6503	3.0123
14	0.6924	1.3450	1.7613	2.1448	2.6245	2.9768
15	0.6912	1.3406	1.7531	2.1315	2.6025	2.9467
16	0.6901	1.3368	1.7459	2.1199	2.5835	2.9208
17	0.6892	1.3334	1.7396	2.1098	2.5669	2.8982
18	0.6884	1.3304	1.7341	2.1009	2.5524	2.8784
19	0.6876	1.3277	1.7291	2.0930	2.5395	2.8609
20	0.6870	1.3253	1.7247	2.0860	2.5280	2.8453
21	0.6864	1.3232	1.7207	2.0796	2.5177	2.8314
22	0.6858	1.3212	1.7171	2.0739	2.5083	2.8188
23	0.6853	1.3195	1.7139	2.0687	2.4999	2.8073
24	0.6848	1.3178	1.7109	2.0639	2.4922	2.7969
25	0.6844	1.3163	1.7081	2.0595	2.4851	2.7874
26	0.6840	1.3150	1.7056	2.0555	2.4786	2.7787
27	0.6837	1.3137	1.7033	2.0518	2.4727	2.7707
28	0.6834	1.3125	1.7011	2.0484	2.4671	2.7633
29	0.6830	1.3114	1.6991	2.0452	2.4620	2.7564
30	0.6828	1.3104	1.6973	2.0423	2.4573	2.7500
31	0.6825	1.3095	1.6955	2.0395	2.4528	2.7740
32	0.6822	1.3086	1.6939	2.0369	2.4487	2.7385
33	0.6820	1.3077	1.6924	2.0345	2.4448	2.7333
34	0.6818	1.3070	1.6909	2.0322	2.4411	2.7284
35	0.6816	1.3062	1.6896	2.0301	2.4377	2.7238
36	0.6814	1.3055	1.6883	2.0281	2.4345	2.7195
37	0.6812	1.3049	1.6871	2.0262	2.4314	2.7154
38	0.6810	1.3042	1.6860	2.0244	2.4286	2.7116
39	0.6808	1.3036	1.6849	2.0227	2.4258	2.7079
40	0.6807	1.3031	1.6839	2.0211	2.4233	2.7045
41	0.6805	1.3025	1.6829	2.0195	2.4208	2.7012
42	0.6804	1.3020	1.6820	2.0181	2.4185	2.6981
43	0.6802	1.3016	1.6811	2.0167	2.4163	2.6951
44	0.6801	1.3011	1.6802	2.0154	2.4141	2.6923
45	0.6800	1.3006	1.6794	2.0141	2.4121	2.6896
46	0.6799	1.3022	1.6787	2.0129	2.4102	2.6870
47	0.6797	1.2998	1.6779	2.0117	2.4083	2.6846
48	0.6796	1.2994	1.6772	2.0106	2.4066	2.6822

continued

TABLE 3

Critical Values of *t* (*Continued*)

Degrees of Freedom	UPPER-TAIL AREAS 0.25	0.10	0.05	0.025	0.01	0.005
49	0.6795	1.2991	1.6766	2.0096	2.4049	2.6800
50	0.6794	1.2987	1.6759	2.0086	2.4033	2.6778
51	0.6793	1.2984	1.6753	2.0076	2.4017	2.6757
52	0.6792	1.2980	1.6747	2.0066	2.4002	2.6737
53	0.6791	1.2977	1.6741	2.0057	2.3988	2.6718
54	0.6791	1.2974	1.6736	2.0049	2.3974	2.6700
55	0.6790	1.2971	1.6730	2.0040	2.3961	2.6682
56	0.6789	1.2969	1.6725	2.0032	2.3948	2.6665
57	0.6788	1.2966	1.6720	2.0025	2.3936	2.6649
58	0.6787	1.2963	1.6716	2.0017	2.3924	2.6633
59	0.6787	1.2961	1.6711	2.0010	2.3912	2.6618
60	0.6786	1.2958	1.6706	2.0003	2.3901	2.6603
61	0.6785	1.2956	1.6702	1.9996	2.3890	2.6589
62	0.6785	1.2954	1.6698	1.9990	2.3880	2.6575
63	0.6784	1.2951	1.6694	1.9983	2.3870	2.6561
64	0.6783	1.2949	1.6690	1.9977	2.3860	2.6549
65	0.6783	1.2947	1.6686	1.9971	2.3851	2.6536
66	0.6782	1.2945	1.6683	1.9966	2.3842	2.6524
67	0.6782	1.2943	1.6679	1.9960	2.3833	2.6512
68	0.6781	1.2941	1.6676	1.9955	2.3824	2.6501
69	0.6781	1.2939	1.6672	1.9949	2.3816	2.6490
70	0.6780	1.2938	1.6669	1.9944	2.3808	2.6479
71	0.6780	1.2936	1.6666	1.9939	2.3800	2.6469
72	0.6779	1.2934	1.6663	1.9935	2.3793	2.6459
73	0.6779	1.2933	1.6660	1.9930	2.3785	2.6449
74	0.6778	1.2931	1.6657	1.9925	2.3778	2.6439
75	0.6778	1.2929	1.6654	1.9921	2.3771	2.6430
76	0.6777	1.2928	1.6652	1.9917	2.3764	2.6421
77	0.6777	1.2926	1.6649	1.9913	2.3758	2.6412
78	0.6776	1.2925	1.6646	1.9908	2.3751	2.6403
79	0.6776	1.2924	1.6644	1.9905	2.3745	2.6395
80	0.6776	1.2922	1.6641	1.9901	2.3739	2.6387
81	0.6775	1.2921	1.6639	1.9897	2.3733	2.6379
82	0.6775	1.2920	1.6636	1.9893	2.3727	2.6371
83	0.6775	1.2918	1.6634	1.9890	2.3721	2.6364
84	0.6774	1.2917	1.6632	1.9886	2.3716	2.6356
85	0.6774	1.2916	1.6630	1.9883	2.3710	2.6349
86	0.6774	1.2915	1.6628	1.9879	2.3705	2.6342
87	0.6773	1.2914	1.6626	1.9876	2.3700	2.6335
88	0.6773	1.2912	1.6624	1.9873	2.3695	2.6329
89	0.6773	1.2911	1.6622	1.9870	2.3690	2.6322
90	0.6772	1.2910	1.6620	1.9867	2.3685	2.6316
91	0.6772	1.2909	1.6618	1.9864	2.3680	2.6309
92	0.6772	1.2908	1.6616	1.9861	2.3676	2.6303
93	0.6771	1.2907	1.6614	1.9858	2.3671	2.6297
94	0.6771	1.2906	1.6612	1.9855	2.3667	2.6291
95	0.6771	1.2905	1.6611	1.9853	2.3662	2.6286
96	0.6771	1.2904	1.6609	1.9850	2.3658	2.6280
97	0.6770	1.2903	1.6607	1.9847	2.3654	2.6275
98	0.6770	1.2902	1.6606	1.9845	2.3650	2.6269
99	0.6770	1.2902	1.6604	1.9842	2.3646	2.6264
100	0.6770	1.2901	1.6602	1.9840	2.3642	2.6259
110	0.6767	1.2893	1.6588	1.9818	2.3607	2.6213
120	0.6765	1.2886	1.6577	1.9799	2.3578	2.6174
∞	0.6745	1.2816	1.6449	1.9600	2.3263	2.5758

TABLE 4

Critical Values of χ^2

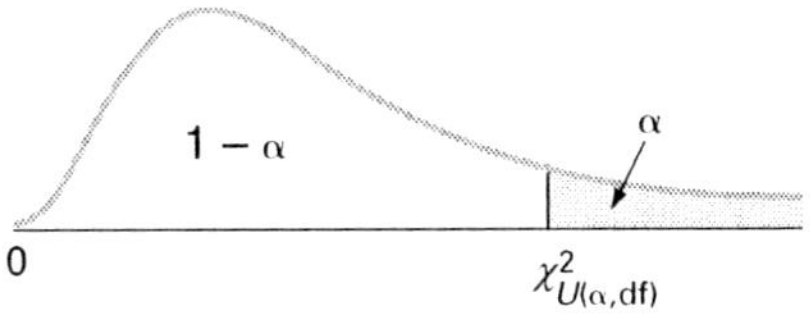

For a particular number of degrees of freedom, entry represents the critical value of χ^2 corresponding to a specified upper-tail area (α).

	UPPER TAIL AREAS (α)											
Degrees of Freedom	0.995	0.99	0.975	0.95	0.90	0.75	0.25	0.10	0.05	0.025	0.01	0.005
1			0.001	0.004	0.016	0.102	1.323	2.706	3.841	5.024	6.635	7.879
2	0.010	0.020	0.051	0.103	0.211	0.575	2.773	4.605	5.991	7.378	9.210	10.597
3	0.072	0.115	0.216	0.352	0.584	1.213	4.108	6.251	7.815	9.348	11.345	12.838
4	0.207	0.297	0.484	0.711	1.064	1.923	5.385	7.779	9.488	11.143	13.277	14.860
5	0.412	0.554	0.831	1.145	1.610	2.675	6.626	9.236	11.071	12.833	15.086	16.750
6	0.676	0.872	1.237	1.635	2.204	3.455	7.841	10.645	12.592	14.449	16.812	18.458
7	0.989	1.239	1.690	2.167	2.833	4.255	9.037	12.017	14.067	16.013	18.475	20.278
8	1.344	1.646	2.180	2.733	3.490	5.071	10.219	13.362	15.507	17.535	20.090	21.955
9	1.735	2.088	2.700	3.325	4.168	5.899	11.389	14.684	16.919	19.023	21.666	23.589
10	2.156	2.558	3.247	3.940	4.865	6.737	12.549	15.987	18.307	20.483	23.209	25.188
11	2.603	3.053	3.816	4.575	5.578	7.584	13.701	17.275	19.675	21.920	24.725	26.757
12	3.074	3.571	4.404	5.226	6.304	8.438	14.845	18.549	21.026	23.337	26.217	28.299
13	3.565	4.107	5.009	5.892	7.042	9.299	15.984	19.812	22.362	24.736	27.688	29.819
14	4.075	4.660	5.629	6.571	7.790	10.165	17.117	21.064	23.685	26.119	29.141	31.319
15	4.601	5.229	6.262	7.261	8.547	11.037	18.245	22.307	24.996	27.488	30.578	32.801
16	5.142	5.812	6.908	7.962	9.312	11.912	19.369	23.542	26.296	28.845	32.000	34.267
17	5.697	6.408	7.564	8.672	10.085	12.792	20.489	24.769	27.587	30.191	33.409	35.718
18	6.265	7.015	8.231	9.390	10.865	13.675	21.605	25.989	28.869	31.526	34.805	37.156
19	6.844	7.633	8.907	10.117	11.651	14.562	22.718	27.204	30.144	32.852	36.191	38.582
20	7.434	8.260	9.591	10.851	12.443	15.452	23.828	28.412	31.410	34.170	37.566	39.997
21	8.034	8.897	10.283	11.591	13.240	16.344	24.935	29.615	32.671	35.479	38.932	41.401
22	8.643	9.542	10.982	12.338	14.042	17.240	26.039	30.813	33.924	36.781	40.289	42.796
23	9.260	10.196	11.689	13.091	14.848	18.137	27.141	32.007	35.172	38.076	41.638	44.181
24	9.886	10.856	12.401	13.848	15.659	19.037	28.241	33.196	36.415	39.364	42.980	45.559
25	10.520	11.524	13.120	14.611	16.473	19.939	29.339	34.382	37.652	40.646	44.314	46.928
26	11.160	12.198	13.844	15.379	17.292	20.843	30.435	35.563	38.885	41.923	45.642	48.290
27	11.808	12.879	14.573	16.151	18.114	21.749	31.528	36.741	40.113	43.194	46.963	49.645
28	12.461	13.565	15.308	16.928	18.939	22.657	32.620	37.916	41.337	44.461	48.278	50.993
29	13.121	14.257	16.047	17.708	19.768	23.567	33.711	39.087	42.557	45.722	49.588	52.336
30	13.787	14.954	16.791	18.493	20.599	24.478	34.800	40.256	43.773	46.979	50.892	53.672

For larger values of degrees of freedom (df) the expression $Z = \sqrt{2\chi^2} - \sqrt{2(df) - 1}$ may be used and the resulting upper-tail area can be obtained from the table of the cumulative standardized normal distribution (Table E.2).

TABLE 5

Critical Values of F

For a particular combination of numerator and denominator degrees of freedom, entry represents the critical values of F *corresponding to a specified upper-tail area* (α).

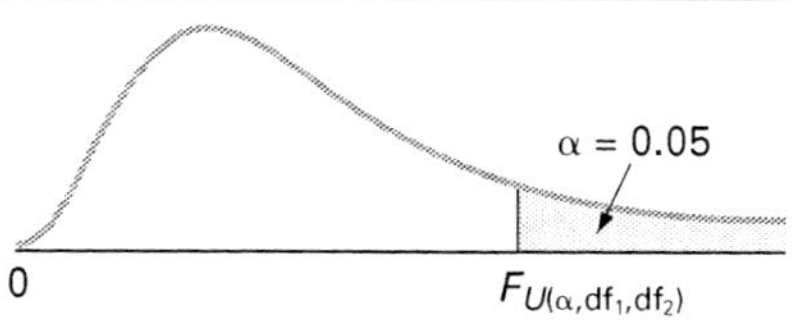

Denominator df_2	NUMERATOR, df_1 1	2	3	4	5	6	7	8	9	10	12	15	20	24	30	40	60	120	∞
1	161.40	199.50	215.70	224.60	230.20	234.00	236.80	238.90	240.50	241.90	243.90	245.90	248.00	249.10	250.10	251.10	252.20	253.30	254.30
2	18.51	19.00	19.16	19.25	19.30	19.33	19.35	19.37	19.38	19.40	19.41	19.43	19.45	19.45	19.46	19.47	19.48	19.49	19.50
3	10.13	9.55	9.28	9.12	9.01	8.94	8.89	8.85	8.81	8.79	8.74	8.70	8.66	8.64	8.62	8.59	8.57	8.55	8.53
4	7.71	6.94	6.59	6.39	6.26	6.16	6.09	6.04	6.00	5.96	5.91	5.86	5.80	5.77	5.75	5.72	5.69	5.66	5.63
5	6.61	5.79	5.41	5.19	5.05	4.95	4.88	4.82	4.77	4.74	4.68	4.62	4.56	4.53	4.50	4.46	4.43	4.40	4.36
6	5.99	5.14	4.76	4.53	4.39	4.28	4.21	4.15	4.10	4.06	4.00	3.94	3.87	3.84	3.81	3.77	3.74	3.70	3.67
7	5.59	4.74	4.35	4.12	3.97	3.87	3.79	3.73	3.68	3.64	3.57	3.51	3.44	3.41	3.38	3.34	3.30	3.27	3.23
8	5.32	4.46	4.07	3.84	3.69	3.58	3.50	3.44	3.39	3.35	3.28	3.22	3.15	3.12	3.08	3.04	3.01	2.97	2.93
9	5.12	4.26	3.86	3.63	3.48	3.37	3.29	3.23	3.18	3.14	3.07	3.01	2.94	2.90	2.86	2.83	2.79	2.75	2.71
10	4.96	4.10	3.71	3.48	3.33	3.22	3.14	3.07	3.02	2.98	2.91	2.85	2.77	2.74	2.70	2.66	2.62	2.58	2.54
11	4.84	3.98	3.59	3.36	3.20	3.09	3.01	2.95	2.90	2.85	2.79	2.72	2.65	2.61	2.57	2.53	2.49	2.45	2.40
12	4.75	3.89	3.49	3.26	3.11	3.00	2.91	2.85	2.80	2.75	2.69	2.62	2.54	2.51	2.47	2.43	2.38	2.34	2.30
13	4.67	3.81	3.41	3.18	3.03	2.92	2.83	2.77	2.71	2.67	2.60	2.53	2.46	2.42	2.38	2.34	2.30	2.25	2.21
14	4.60	3.74	3.34	3.11	2.96	2.85	2.76	2.70	2.65	2.60	2.53	2.46	2.39	2.35	2.31	2.27	2.22	2.18	2.13
15	4.54	3.68	3.29	3.06	2.90	2.79	2.71	2.64	2.59	2.54	2.48	2.40	2.33	2.29	2.25	2.20	2.16	2.11	2.07
16	4.49	3.63	3.24	3.01	2.85	2.74	2.66	2.59	2.54	2.49	2.42	2.35	2.28	2.24	2.19	2.15	2.11	2.06	2.01
17	4.45	3.59	3.20	2.96	2.81	2.70	2.61	2.55	2.49	2.45	2.38	2.31	2.23	2.19	2.15	2.10	2.06	2.01	1.96
18	4.41	3.55	3.16	2.93	2.77	2.66	2.58	2.51	2.46	2.41	2.34	2.27	2.19	2.15	2.11	2.06	2.02	1.97	1.92
19	4.38	3.52	3.13	2.90	2.74	2.63	2.54	2.48	2.42	2.38	2.31	2.23	2.16	2.11	2.07	2.03	1.98	1.93	1.88
20	4.35	3.49	3.10	2.87	2.71	2.60	2.51	2.45	2.39	2.35	2.28	2.20	2.12	2.08	2.04	1.99	1.95	1.90	1.84
21	4.32	3.47	3.07	2.84	2.68	2.57	2.49	2.42	2.37	2.32	2.25	2.18	2.10	2.05	2.01	1.96	1.92	1.87	1.81
22	4.30	3.44	3.05	2.82	2.66	2.55	2.46	2.40	2.34	2.30	2.23	2.15	2.07	2.03	1.98	1.91	1.89	1.84	1.78
23	4.28	3.42	3.03	2.80	2.64	2.53	2.44	2.37	2.32	2.27	2.20	2.13	2.05	2.01	1.96	1.91	1.86	1.81	1.76
24	4.26	3.40	3.01	2.78	2.62	2.51	2.42	2.36	2.30	2.25	2.18	2.11	2.03	1.98	1.94	1.89	1.84	1.79	1.73
25	4.24	3.39	2.99	2.76	2.60	2.49	2.40	2.34	2.28	2.24	2.16	2.09	2.01	1.96	1.92	1.87	1.82	1.77	1.71
26	4.23	3.37	2.98	2.74	2.59	2.47	2.39	2.32	2.27	2.22	2.15	2.07	1.99	1.95	1.90	1.85	1.80	1.75	1.69
27	4.21	3.35	2.96	2.73	2.57	2.46	2.37	2.31	2.25	2.20	2.13	2.06	1.97	1.93	1.88	1.84	1.79	1.73	1.67
28	4.20	3.34	2.95	2.71	2.56	2.45	2.36	2.29	2.24	2.19	2.12	2.04	1.96	1.91	1.87	1.82	1.77	1.71	1.65
29	4.18	3.33	2.93	2.70	2.55	2.43	2.35	2.28	2.22	2.18	2.10	2.03	1.94	1.90	1.85	1.81	1.75	1.70	1.64
30	4.17	3.32	2.92	2.69	2.53	2.42	2.33	2.27	2.21	2.16	2.09	2.01	1.93	1.89	1.84	1.79	1.74	1.68	1.62
40	4.08	3.23	2.84	2.61	2.45	2.34	2.25	2.18	2.12	2.08	2.00	1.92	1.84	1.79	1.74	1.69	1.64	1.58	1.51
60	4.00	3.15	2.76	2.53	2.37	2.25	2.17	2.10	2.04	1.99	1.92	1.84	1.75	1.70	1.65	1.59	1.53	1.47	1.39
120	3.92	3.07	2.68	2.45	2.29	2.17	2.09	2.02	1.96	1.91	1.83	1.75	1.66	1.61	1.55	1.50	1.43	1.35	1.25
∞	3.84	3.00	2.60	2.37	2.21	2.10	2.01	1.94	1.88	1.83	1.75	1.67	1.57	1.52	1.46	1.39	1.32	1.22	1.00

continued

TABLE 5

Critical Values of F (*Continued*)

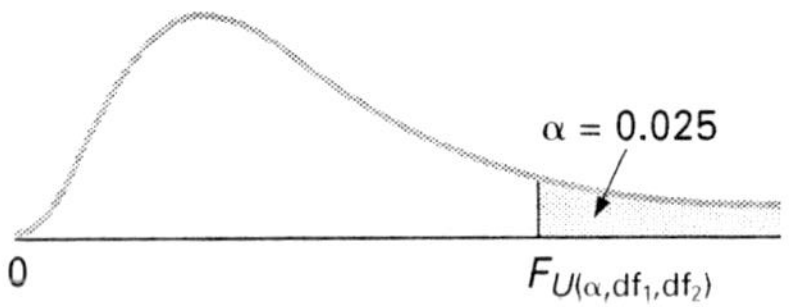

Denominator df_2	NUMERATOR, df_1 1	2	3	4	5	6	7	8	9	10	12	15	20	24	30	40	60	120	∞
1	647.80	799.50	864.20	899.60	921.80	937.10	948.20	956.70	963.30	968.60	976.70	984.90	993.10	997.20	1,001.00	1,006.00	1,010.00	1,014.00	1,018.00
2	38.51	39.00	39.17	39.25	39.30	39.33	39.36	39.39	39.39	39.40	39.41	39.43	39.45	39.46	39.46	39.47	39.48	39.49	39.50
3	17.44	16.04	15.44	15.10	14.88	14.73	14.62	14.54	14.47	14.42	14.34	14.25	14.17	14.12	14.08	14.04	13.99	13.95	13.90
4	12.22	10.65	9.98	9.60	9.36	9.20	9.07	8.98	8.90	8.84	8.75	8.66	8.56	8.51	8.46	8.41	8.36	8.31	8.26
5	10.01	8.43	7.76	7.39	7.15	6.98	6.85	6.76	6.68	6.62	6.52	6.43	6.33	6.28	6.23	6.18	6.12	6.07	6.02
6	8.81	7.26	6.60	6.23	5.99	5.82	5.70	5.60	5.52	5.46	5.37	5.27	5.17	5.12	5.07	5.01	4.96	4.90	4.85
7	8.07	6.54	5.89	5.52	5.29	5.12	4.99	4.90	4.82	4.76	4.67	4.57	4.47	4.42	4.36	4.31	4.25	4.20	4.14
8	7.57	6.06	5.42	5.05	4.82	4.65	4.53	4.43	4.36	4.30	4.20	4.10	4.00	3.95	3.89	3.84	3.78	3.73	3.67
9	7.21	5.71	5.08	4.72	4.48	4.32	4.20	4.10	4.03	3.96	3.87	3.77	3.67	3.61	3.56	3.51	3.45	3.39	3.33
10	6.94	5.46	4.83	4.47	4.24	4.07	3.95	3.85	3.78	3.72	3.62	3.52	3.42	3.37	3.31	3.26	3.20	3.14	3.08
11	6.72	5.26	4.63	4.28	4.04	3.88	3.76	3.66	3.59	3.53	3.43	3.33	3.23	3.17	3.12	3.06	3.00	2.94	2.88
12	6.55	5.10	4.47	4.12	3.89	3.73	3.61	3.51	3.44	3.37	3.28	3.18	3.07	3.02	2.96	2.91	2.85	2.79	2.72
13	6.41	4.97	4.35	4.00	3.77	3.60	3.48	3.39	3.31	3.25	3.15	3.05	2.95	2.89	2.84	2.78	2.72	2.66	2.60
14	6.30	4.86	4.24	3.89	3.66	3.50	3.38	3.29	3.21	3.15	3.05	2.95	2.84	2.79	2.73	2.67	2.61	2.55	2.49
15	6.20	4.77	4.15	3.80	3.58	3.41	3.29	3.20	3.12	3.06	2.96	2.86	2.76	2.70	2.64	2.59	2.52	2.46	2.40
16	6.12	4.69	4.08	3.73	3.50	3.34	3.22	3.12	3.05	2.99	2.89	2.79	2.68	2.63	2.57	2.51	2.45	2.38	2.32
17	6.04	4.62	4.01	3.66	3.44	3.28	3.16	3.06	2.98	2.92	2.82	2.72	2.62	2.56	2.50	2.44	2.38	2.32	2.25
18	5.98	4.56	3.95	3.61	3.38	3.22	3.10	3.01	2.93	2.87	2.77	2.67	2.56	2.50	2.44	2.38	2.32	2.26	2.19
19	5.92	4.51	3.90	3.56	3.33	3.17	3.05	2.96	2.88	2.82	2.72	2.62	2.51	2.45	2.39	2.33	2.27	2.20	2.13
20	5.87	4.46	3.86	3.51	3.29	3.13	3.01	2.91	2.84	2.77	2.68	2.57	2.46	2.41	2.35	2.29	2.22	2.16	2.09
21	5.83	4.42	3.82	3.48	3.25	3.09	2.97	2.87	2.80	2.73	2.64	2.53	2.42	2.37	2.31	2.25	2.18	2.11	2.04
22	5.79	4.38	3.78	3.44	3.22	3.05	2.93	2.84	2.76	2.70	2.60	2.50	2.39	2.33	2.27	2.21	2.14	2.08	2.00
23	5.75	4.35	3.75	3.41	3.18	3.02	2.90	2.81	2.73	2.67	2.57	2.47	2.36	2.30	2.24	2.18	2.11	2.04	1.97
24	5.72	4.32	3.72	3.38	3.15	2.99	2.87	2.78	2.70	2.64	2.54	2.44	2.33	2.27	2.21	2.15	2.08	2.01	1.94
25	5.69	4.29	3.69	3.35	3.13	2.97	2.85	2.75	2.68	2.61	2.51	2.41	2.30	2.24	2.18	2.12	2.05	1.98	1.91
26	5.66	4.27	3.67	3.33	3.10	2.94	2.82	2.73	2.65	2.59	2.49	2.39	2.28	2.22	2.16	2.09	2.03	1.95	1.88
27	5.63	4.24	3.65	3.31	3.08	2.92	2.80	2.71	2.63	2.57	2.47	2.36	2.25	2.19	2.13	2.07	2.00	1.93	1.85
28	5.61	4.22	3.63	3.29	3.06	2.90	2.78	2.69	2.61	2.55	2.45	2.34	2.23	2.17	2.11	2.05	1.98	1.91	1.83
29	5.59	4.20	3.61	3.27	3.04	2.88	2.76	2.67	2.59	2.53	2.43	2.32	2.21	2.15	2.09	2.03	1.96	1.89	1.81
30	5.57	4.18	3.59	3.25	3.03	2.87	2.75	2.65	2.57	2.51	2.41	2.31	2.20	2.14	2.07	2.01	1.94	1.87	1.79
40	5.42	4.05	3.46	3.13	2.90	2.74	2.62	2.53	2.45	2.39	2.29	2.18	2.07	2.01	1.94	1.88	1.80	1.72	1.64
60	5.29	3.93	3.34	3.01	2.79	2.63	2.51	2.41	2.33	2.27	2.17	2.06	1.94	1.88	1.82	1.74	1.67	1.58	1.48
120	5.15	3.80	3.23	2.89	2.67	2.52	2.39	2.30	2.22	2.16	2.05	1.94	1.82	1.76	1.69	1.61	1.53	1.43	1.31
∞	5.02	3.69	3.12	2.79	2.57	2.41	2.29	2.19	2.11	2.05	1.94	1.83	1.71	1.64	1.57	1.48	1.39	1.27	1.00

continued

TABLE 5

Critical Values of *F* (*Continued*)

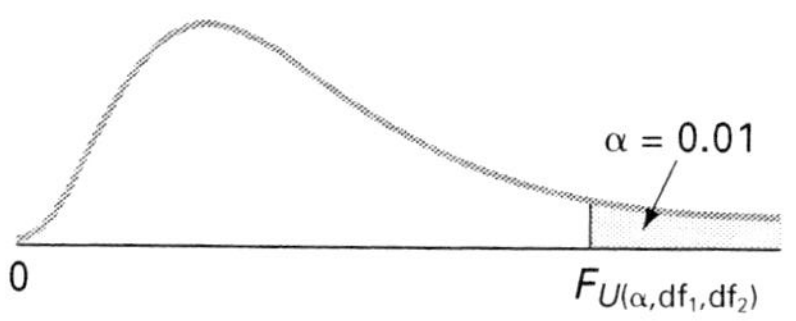

NUMERATOR, df_1

Denominator df_2	1	2	3	4	5	6	7	8	9	10
1	4,052.00	4,999.50	5,403.00	5,625.00	5,764.00	5,859.00	5,928.00	5,982.00	6,022.00	6,056.00
2	98.50	99.00	99.17	99.25	99.30	99.33	99.36	99.37	99.39	99.40
3	34.12	30.82	29.46	28.71	28.24	27.91	27.67	27.49	27.35	27.23
4	21.20	18.00	16.69	15.98	15.52	15.21	14.98	14.80	14.66	14.55
5	16.26	13.27	12.06	11.39	10.97	10.67	10.46	10.29	10.16	10.05
6	13.75	10.92	9.78	9.15	8.75	8.47	8.26	8.10	7.98	7.87
7	12.25	9.55	8.45	7.85	7.46	7.19	6.99	6.84	6.72	6.62
8	11.26	8.65	7.59	7.01	6.63	6.37	6.18	6.03	5.91	5.81
9	10.56	8.02	6.99	6.42	6.06	5.80	5.61	5.47	5.35	5.26
10	10.04	7.56	6.55	5.99	5.64	5.39	5.20	5.06	4.94	4.85
11	9.65	7.21	6.22	5.67	5.32	5.07	4.89	4.74	4.63	4.54
12	9.33	6.93	5.95	5.41	5.06	4.82	4.64	4.50	4.39	4.30
13	9.07	6.70	5.74	4.21	4.86	4.62	4.44	4.30	4.19	4.10
14	8.86	6.51	5.56	5.04	4.69	4.46	4.28	4.14	4.03	3.94
15	8.68	6.36	5.42	4.89	4.56	4.32	4.14	4.00	3.89	3.80
16	8.53	6.23	5.29	4.77	4.44	4.20	4.03	3.89	3.78	3.69
17	8.40	6.11	5.18	4.67	4.34	4.10	3.93	3.79	3.68	3.59
18	8.29	6.01	5.09	4.58	4.25	4.01	3.84	3.71	3.60	3.51
19	8.18	5.93	5.01	4.50	4.17	3.94	3.77	3.63	3.52	3.43
20	8.10	5.85	4.94	4.43	4.10	3.87	3.70	3.56	3.46	3.37
21	8.02	5.78	4.87	4.37	4.04	3.81	3.64	3.51	3.40	3.31
22	7.95	5.72	4.82	4.31	3.99	3.76	3.59	3.45	3.35	3.26
23	7.88	5.66	4.76	4.26	3.94	3.71	3.54	3.41	3.30	3.21
24	7.82	5.61	4.72	4.22	3.90	3.67	3.50	3.36	3.26	3.17
25	7.77	5.57	4.68	4.18	3.85	3.63	3.46	3.32	3.22	3.13
26	7.72	5.53	4.64	4.14	3.82	3.59	3.42	3.29	3.18	3.09
27	7.68	5.49	4.60	4.11	3.78	3.56	3.39	3.26	3.15	3.06
28	7.64	5.45	4.57	4.07	3.75	3.53	3.36	3.23	3.12	3.03
29	7.60	5.42	4.54	4.04	3.73	3.50	3.33	3.20	3.09	3.00
30	7.56	5.39	4.51	4.02	3.70	3.47	3.30	3.17	3.07	2.98
40	7.31	5.18	4.31	3.83	3.51	3.29	3.12	2.99	2.89	2.80
60	7.08	4.98	4.13	3.65	3.34	3.12	2.95	2.82	2.72	2.63
120	6.85	4.79	3.95	3.48	3.17	2.96	2.79	2.66	2.56	2.47
∞	6.63	4.61	3.78	3.32	3.02	2.80	2.64	2.51	2.41	2.32

Denominator df_2	12	15	20	24	30	40	60	120	∞
1	6,106.00	6,157.00	6,209.00	6,235.00	6,261.00	6,287.00	6,313.00	6,339.00	6,366.00
2	99.42	99.43	99.45	99.46	99.47	99.47	99.48	99.49	99.50
3	27.05	26.87	26.69	26.60	26.50	26.41	26.32	26.22	26.13
4	14.37	14.20	14.02	13.93	13.84	13.75	13.65	13.56	13.46
5	9.89	9.72	9.55	9.47	9.38	9.29	9.20	9.11	9.02
6	7.72	7.56	7.40	7.31	7.23	7.14	7.06	6.97	6.88
7	6.47	6.31	6.16	6.07	5.99	5.91	5.82	5.74	5.65
8	5.67	5.52	5.36	5.28	5.20	5.12	5.03	4.95	4.86
9	5.11	4.96	4.81	4.73	4.65	4.57	4.48	4.40	4.31
10	4.71	4.56	4.41	4.33	4.25	4.17	4.08	4.00	3.91
11	4.40	4.25	4.10	4.02	3.94	3.86	3.78	3.69	3.60
12	4.16	4.01	3.86	3.78	3.70	3.62	3.54	3.45	3.36
13	3.96	3.82	3.66	3.59	3.51	3.43	3.34	3.25	3.17
14	3.80	3.66	3.51	3.43	3.35	3.27	3.18	3.09	3.00
15	3.67	3.52	3.37	3.29	3.21	3.13	3.05	2.96	2.87
16	3.55	3.41	3.26	3.18	3.10	3.02	2.93	2.81	2.75
17	3.46	3.31	3.16	3.08	3.00	2.92	2.83	2.75	2.65
18	3.37	3.23	3.08	3.00	2.92	2.84	2.75	2.66	2.57
19	3.30	3.15	3.00	2.92	2.84	2.76	2.67	2.58	2.49
20	3.23	3.09	2.94	2.86	2.78	2.69	2.61	2.52	2.42
21	3.17	3.03	2.88	2.80	2.72	2.64	2.55	2.46	2.36
22	3.12	2.98	2.83	2.75	2.67	2.58	2.50	2.40	2.31
23	3.07	2.93	2.78	2.70	2.62	2.54	2.45	2.35	2.26
24	3.03	2.89	2.74	2.66	2.58	2.49	2.40	2.31	2.21
25	2.99	2.85	2.70	2.62	2.54	2.45	2.36	2.27	2.17
26	2.96	2.81	2.66	2.58	2.50	2.42	2.33	2.23	2.13
27	2.93	2.78	2.63	2.55	2.47	2.38	2.29	2.20	2.10
28	2.90	2.75	2.60	2.52	2.44	2.35	2.26	2.17	2.06
29	2.87	2.73	2.57	2.49	2.41	2.33	2.23	2.14	2.03
30	2.84	2.70	2.55	2.47	2.39	2.30	2.21	2.11	2.01
40	2.66	2.52	2.37	2.29	2.20	2.11	2.02	1.92	1.80
60	2.50	2.35	2.20	2.12	2.03	1.94	1.84	1.73	1.60
120	2.34	2.19	2.03	1.95	1.86	1.76	1.66	1.53	1.38
∞	2.18	2.04	1.88	1.79	1.70	1.59	1.47	1.32	1.00

continued

TABLE 5

Critical Values of *F* (*Continued*)

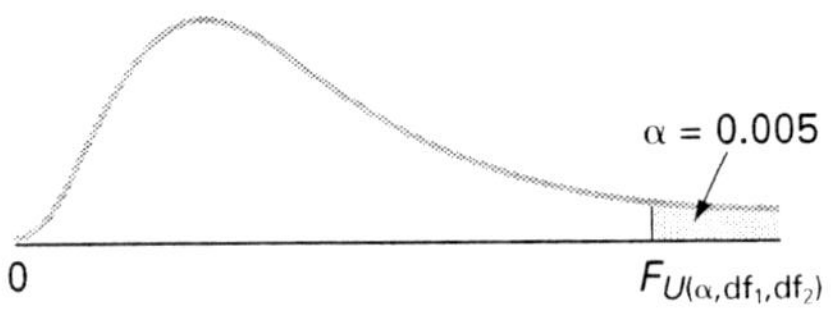

Denominator df_2	NUMERATOR, df_1: 1	2	3	4	5	6	7	8	9	10	12	15	20	24	30	40	60	120	∞
1	16,211.00	20,000.00	21,615.00	22,500.00	23,056.00	23,437.00	23,715.00	23,925.00	24,091.00	24,224.00	24,426.00	24,630.00	24,836.00	24,910.00	25,044.00	25,148.00	25,253.00	25,359.00	25,465.00
2	198.50	199.00	199.20	199.20	199.30	199.30	199.40	199.40	199.40	199.40	199.40	199.40	199.40	199.50	199.50	199.50	199.50	199.50	199.50
3	55.55	49.80	47.47	46.19	45.39	44.84	44.43	44.13	43.88	43.69	43.39	43.08	42.78	42.62	42.47	42.31	42.15	41.99	41.83
4	31.33	26.28	24.26	23.15	22.46	21.97	21.62	21.35	21.14	20.97	20.70	20.44	20.17	20.03	19.89	19.75	19.61	19.47	19.32
5	22.78	18.31	16.53	15.56	14.94	14.51	14.20	13.96	13.77	13.62	13.38	13.15	12.90	12.78	12.66	12.53	12.40	12.27	12.11
6	18.63	14.54	12.92	12.03	11.46	11.07	10.79	10.57	10.39	10.25	10.03	9.81	9.59	9.47	9.36	9.24	9.12	9.00	8.88
7	16.24	12.40	10.88	10.05	9.52	9.16	8.89	8.68	8.51	8.38	8.18	7.97	7.75	7.65	7.53	7.42	7.31	7.19	7.08
8	14.69	11.04	9.60	8.81	8.30	7.95	7.69	7.50	7.34	7.21	7.01	6.81	6.61	6.50	6.40	6.29	6.18	6.06	5.95
9	13.61	10.11	8.72	7.96	7.47	7.13	6.88	6.69	6.54	6.42	6.23	6.03	5.83	5.73	5.62	5.52	5.41	5.30	5.19
10	12.83	9.43	8.08	7.34	6.87	6.54	6.30	6.12	5.97	5.85	5.66	5.47	5.27	5.17	5.07	4.97	4.86	4.75	1.61
11	12.23	8.91	7.60	6.88	6.42	6.10	5.86	5.68	5.54	5.42	5.24	5.05	4.86	4.75	4.65	4.55	4.44	4.34	4.23
12	11.75	8.51	7.23	6.52	6.07	5.76	5.52	5.35	5.20	5.09	4.91	4.72	4.53	4.43	4.33	4.23	4.12	4.01	3.90
13	11.37	8.19	6.93	6.23	5.79	5.48	5.25	5.08	4.94	4.82	4.64	4.46	4.27	4.17	4.07	3.97	3.87	3.76	3.65
14	11.06	7.92	6.68	6.00	5.56	5.26	5.03	4.86	4.72	4.60	4.43	4.25	4.06	3.96	3.86	3.76	3.66	3.55	3.41
15	10.80	7.70	6.48	5.80	5.37	5.07	4.85	4.67	4.54	4.42	4.25	4.07	3.88	3.79	3.69	3.58	3.48	3.37	3.26
16	10.58	7.51	6.30	5.64	5.21	4.91	4.69	4.52	4.38	4.27	4.10	3.92	3.73	3.64	3.54	3.44	3.33	3.22	3.11
17	10.38	7.35	6.16	5.50	5.07	4.78	4.56	4.39	4.25	4.14	3.97	3.79	3.61	3.51	3.41	3.31	3.21	3.10	2.98
18	10.22	7.21	6.03	5.37	4.96	4.66	4.44	4.28	4.14	4.03	3.86	3.68	3.50	3.40	3.30	3.20	3.10	2.89	2.87
19	10.07	7.09	5.92	5.27	4.85	4.56	4.34	4.18	4.04	3.93	3.76	3.59	3.40	3.31	3.21	3.11	3.00	2.89	2.78
20	9.94	6.99	5.82	5.17	4.76	4.47	4.26	4.09	3.96	3.85	3.68	3.50	3.32	3.22	3.12	3.02	2.92	2.81	2.69
21	9.83	6.89	5.73	5.09	4.68	4.39	4.18	4.02	3.88	3.77	3.60	3.43	3.24	3.15	3.05	2.95	2.84	2.73	2.61
22	9.73	6.81	5.65	5.02	4.61	4.32	4.11	3.94	3.81	3.70	3.54	3.36	3.18	3.08	2.98	2.88	2.77	2.66	2.55
23	9.63	6.73	5.58	4.95	4.54	4.26	4.05	3.88	3.75	3.64	3.47	3.30	3.12	3.02	2.92	2.82	2.71	2.60	2.48
24	9.55	6.66	5.52	4.89	4.49	4.20	3.99	3.83	3.69	3.59	3.42	3.25	3.06	2.97	2.87	2.77	2.66	2.55	2.43
25	9.48	6.60	5.46	4.84	4.43	4.15	3.94	3.78	3.64	3.54	3.37	3.20	3.01	2.92	2.82	2.72	2.61	2.50	2.38
26	9.41	6.54	5.41	4.79	4.38	4.10	3.89	3.73	3.60	3.49	3.33	3.15	2.97	2.87	2.77	2.67	2.56	2.45	2.33
27	9.34	6.49	5.36	4.74	4.34	4.06	3.85	3.69	3.56	3.45	3.28	3.11	2.93	2.83	2.73	2.63	2.52	2.41	2.29
28	9.28	6.44	5.32	4.70	4.30	4.02	3.81	3.65	3.52	3.41	3.25	3.07	2.89	2.79	2.69	2.59	2.48	2.37	2.25
29	9.23	6.40	5.28	4.66	4.26	3.98	3.77	3.61	3.48	3.38	3.21	3.04	2.86	2.76	2.66	2.56	2.45	2.33	2.21
30	9.18	6.35	5.24	4.62	4.23	3.95	3.74	3.58	3.45	3.34	3.18	3.01	2.82	2.73	2.63	2.52	2.42	2.30	2.18
40	8.83	6.07	4.98	4.37	3.99	3.71	3.51	3.35	3.22	3.12	2.95	2.78	2.60	2.50	2.40	2.30	2.18	2.06	1.93
60	8.49	5.79	4.73	4.14	3.76	3.49	3.29	3.13	3.01	2.90	2.74	2.57	2.39	2.29	2.19	2.08	1.96	1.83	1.69
120	8.18	5.54	4.50	3.92	3.55	3.28	3.09	2.93	2.81	2.71	2.54	2.37	2.19	2.09	1.98	1.87	1.75	1.61	1.43
∞	7.88	5.30	4.28	3.72	3.35	3.09	2.90	2.74	2.62	2.52	2.36	2.19	2.00	1.90	1.79	1.67	1.53	1.36	1.00

Source: Reprinted from E. S. Pearson and H. O. Hartley, eds., Biometrika Tables for Statisticians, *3rd ed., 1966, by permission of the* Biometrika *Trustees.*

TABLE 6

Table of Binomial Probabilities

(begins on the following page)

TABLE 6

Table of Binomial Probabilities

For a given combination of n *and* p, *entry indicates the probability of obtaining a specified value of* X. *To locate entry:* ***when p ≤ .50****, read* p *across the top heading and both* n *and* X *down the left margin;* ***when p ≥ .50****, read* p *across the bottom heading and both* n *and* X *up the right margin.*

n	*X*	0.01	0.02	0.03	0.04	0.05	0.06	0.07	0.08	0.09	0.10	0.15	0.20	0.25	0.30	0.35	0.40	0.45	0.50	*X*	*n*
2	0	0.9801	0.9604	0.9409	0.9216	0.9025	0.8836	0.8649	0.8464	0.8281	0.8100	0.7225	0.6400	0.5625	0.4900	0.4225	0.3600	0.3025	0.2500	2	
	1	0.0198	0.0392	0.0582	0.0768	0.0950	0.1128	0.1302	0.1472	0.1638	0.1800	0.2550	0.3200	0.3750	0.4200	0.4550	0.4800	0.4950	0.5000	1	
	2	0.0001	0.0004	0.0009	0.0016	0.0025	0.0036	0.0049	0.0064	0.0081	0.0100	0.0225	0.0400	0.0625	0.0900	0.1225	0.1600	0.2025	0.2500	0	2
3	0	0.9703	0.9412	0.9127	0.8847	0.8574	0.8306	0.8044	0.7787	0.7536	0.7290	0.6141	0.5120	0.4219	0.3430	0.2746	0.2160	0.1664	0.1250	3	
	1	0.0294	0.0576	0.0847	0.1106	0.1354	0.1590	0.1816	0.2031	0.2236	0.2430	0.3251	0.3840	0.4219	0.4410	0.4436	0.4320	0.4084	0.3750	2	
	2	0.0003	0.0012	0.0026	0.0046	0.0071	0.0102	0.0137	0.0177	0.0221	0.0270	0.0574	0.0960	0.1406	0.1890	0.2389	0.2880	0.3341	0.3750	1	
	3	0.0000	0.0000	0.0000	0.0001	0.0001	0.0002	0.0003	0.0005	0.0007	0.0010	0.0034	0.0080	0.0156	0.0270	0.0429	0.0640	0.0911	0.1250	0	3
4	0	0.9606	0.9224	0.8853	0.8493	0.8145	0.7807	0.7481	0.7164	0.6857	0.6561	0.5220	0.4096	0.3164	0.2401	0.1785	0.1296	0.0915	0.0625	4	
	1	0.0388	0.0753	0.1095	0.1416	0.1715	0.1993	0.2252	0.2492	0.2713	0.2916	0.3685	0.4096	0.4219	0.4116	0.3845	0.3456	0.2995	0.2500	3	
	2	0.0006	0.0023	0.0051	0.0088	0.0135	0.0191	0.0254	0.0325	0.0402	0.0486	0.0975	0.1536	0.2109	0.2646	0.3105	0.3456	0.3675	0.3750	2	
	3	0.0000	0.0000	0.0001	0.0002	0.0005	0.0008	0.0013	0.0019	0.0027	0.0036	0.0115	0.0256	0.0469	0.0756	0.1115	0.1536	0.2005	0.2500	1	
	4	—	—	0.0000	0.0000	0.0000	0.0000	0.0000	0.0000	0.0001	0.0001	0.0005	0.0016	0.0039	0.0081	0.0150	0.0256	0.0410	0.0625	0	4
5	0	0.9510	0.9039	0.8587	0.8154	0.7738	0.7339	0.6957	0.6591	0.6240	0.5905	0.4437	0.3277	0.2373	0.1681	0.1160	0.0778	0.0503	0.0312	5	
	1	0.0480	0.0922	0.1328	0.1699	0.2036	0.2342	0.2618	0.2866	0.3086	0.3280	0.3915	0.4096	0.3955	0.3601	0.3124	0.2592	0.2059	0.1562	4	
	2	0.0010	0.0038	0.0082	0.0142	0.0214	0.0299	0.0394	0.0498	0.0610	0.0729	0.1382	0.2048	0.2637	0.3087	0.3364	0.3456	0.3369	0.3125	3	
	3	0.0000	0.0001	0.0003	0.0006	0.0011	0.0019	0.0030	0.0043	0.0060	0.0081	0.0244	0.0512	0.0879	0.1323	0.1811	0.2304	0.2757	0.3125	2	
	4	—	0.0000	0.0000	0.0000	0.0000	0.0001	0.0001	0.0002	0.0003	0.0004	0.0022	0.0064	0.0146	0.0283	0.0488	0.0768	0.1128	0.1562	1	
	5	—	—	—	—	—	0.0000	0.0000	0.0000	0.0000	0.0000	0.0001	0.0003	0.0010	0.0024	0.0053	0.0102	0.0185	0.0312	0	5
6	0	0.9415	0.8858	0.8330	0.7828	0.7351	0.6899	0.6470	0.6064	0.5679	0.5314	0.3771	0.2621	0.1780	0.1176	0.0754	0.0467	0.0277	0.0156	6	
	1	0.0571	0.1085	0.1546	0.1957	0.2321	0.2642	0.2922	0.3164	0.3370	0.3543	0.3993	0.3932	0.3560	0.3025	0.2437	0.1866	0.1359	0.0937	5	
	2	0.0014	0.0055	0.0120	0.0204	0.0305	0.0422	0.0550	0.0688	0.0833	0.0984	0.1762	0.2458	0.2966	0.3241	0.3280	0.3110	0.2780	0.2344	4	
	3	0.0000	0.0002	0.0005	0.0011	0.0021	0.0036	0.0055	0.0080	0.0110	0.0146	0.0415	0.0819	0.1318	0.1852	0.2355	0.2765	0.3032	0.3125	3	
	4	—	0.0000	0.0000	0.0000	0.0001	0.0002	0.0003	0.0005	0.0008	0.0012	0.0055	0.0154	0.0330	0.0595	0.0951	0.1372	0.1861	0.2344	2	
	5	—	—	—	—	0.0000	0.0000	0.0000	0.0000	0.0000	0.0001	0.0004	0.0015	0.0044	0.0102	0.0205	0.0369	0.0609	0.0937	1	
	6	—	—	—	—	—	—	—	—	—	0.0000	0.0000	0.0001	0.0002	0.0007	0.0018	0.0041	0.0083	0.0156	0	6

n	X	0.99	0.98	0.97	0.96	0.95	0.94	0.93	0.92	0.91	0.90	0.85	0.80	0.75	0.70	0.65	0.60	0.55	0.50	X	n
7	0	0.9321	0.8681	0.8080	0.7514	0.6983	0.6485	0.6017	0.5578	0.5168	0.4783	0.3206	0.2097	0.1335	0.0824	0.0490	0.0280	0.0152	0.0078	7	
	1	0.0659	0.1240	0.1749	0.2192	0.2573	0.2897	0.3170	0.3396	0.3578	0.3720	0.3960	0.3670	0.3115	0.2471	0.1848	0.1306	0.0872	0.0547	6	
	2	0.0020	0.0076	0.0162	0.0274	0.0406	0.0555	0.0716	0.0886	0.1061	0.1240	0.2097	0.2753	0.3115	0.3177	0.2985	0.2613	0.2140	0.1641	5	
	3	0.0000	0.0003	0.0008	0.0019	0.0036	0.0059	0.0090	0.0128	0.0175	0.0230	0.0617	0.1147	0.1730	0.2269	0.2679	0.2903	0.2918	0.2734	4	
	4	—	0.0000	0.0000	0.0001	0.0002	0.0004	0.0007	0.0011	0.0017	0.0026	0.0109	0.0287	0.0577	0.0972	0.1442	0.1935	0.2388	0.2734	3	
	5	—	—	—	0.0000	0.0000	0.0000	0.0000	0.0001	0.0001	0.0002	0.0012	0.0043	0.0115	0.0250	0.0466	0.0774	0.1172	0.1641	2	
	6	—	—	—	—	—	—	—	0.0000	0.0000	0.0000	0.0001	0.0004	0.0013	0.0036	0.0084	0.0172	0.0320	0.0547	1	
	7	—	—	—	—	—	—	—	—	—	—	0.0000	0.0000	0.0001	0.0002	0.0006	0.0016	0.0037	0.0078	0	7
8	0	0.9227	0.8508	0.7837	0.7214	0.6634	0.6096	0.5596	0.5132	0.4703	0.4305	0.2725	0.1678	0.1001	0.0576	0.0319	0.0168	0.0084	0.0039	8	
	1	0.0746	0.1389	0.1939	0.2405	0.2793	0.3113	0.3370	0.3570	0.3721	0.3826	0.3847	0.3355	0.2670	0.1977	0.1373	0.0896	0.0548	0.0312	7	
	2	0.0026	0.0099	0.0210	0.0351	0.0515	0.0695	0.0888	0.1087	0.1288	0.1488	0.2376	0.2936	0.3115	0.2965	0.2587	0.2090	0.1569	0.1094	6	
	3	0.0001	0.0004	0.0013	0.0029	0.0054	0.0089	0.0134	0.0189	0.0255	0.0331	0.0839	0.1468	0.2076	0.2541	0.2786	0.2787	0.2568	0.2187	5	
	4	0.0000	0.0000	0.0001	0.0002	0.0004	0.0007	0.0013	0.0021	0.0031	0.0046	0.0185	0.0459	0.0865	0.1361	0.1875	0.2322	0.2627	0.2734	4	
	5	—	—	0.0000	0.0000	0.0000	0.0000	0.0001	0.0001	0.0002	0.0004	0.0026	0.0092	0.0231	0.0467	0.0808	0.1239	0.1719	0.2187	3	
	6	—	—	—	—	—	—	0.0000	0.0000	0.0000	0.0000	0.0002	0.0011	0.0038	0.0100	0.0217	0.0413	0.0703	0.1094	2	
	7	—	—	—	—	—	—	—	—	—	—	0.0000	0.0001	0.0004	0.0012	0.0033	0.0079	0.0164	0.0312	1	
	8	—	—	—	—	—	—	—	—	—	—	—	0.0000	0.0000	0.0001	0.0002	0.0007	0.0017	0.0039	0	8
9	0	0.9135	0.8337	0.7602	0.6925	0.6302	0.5730	0.5204	0.4722	0.4279	0.3874	0.2316	0.1342	0.0751	0.0404	0.0207	0.0101	0.0046	0.0020	9	
	1	0.0830	0.1531	0.2116	0.2597	0.2985	0.3292	0.3525	0.3695	0.3809	0.3874	0.3679	0.3020	0.2253	0.1556	0.1004	0.0605	0.0339	0.0176	8	
	2	0.0034	0.0125	0.0262	0.0433	0.0629	0.0840	0.1061	0.1285	0.1507	0.1722	0.2597	0.3020	0.3003	0.2668	0.2162	0.1612	0.1110	0.0703	7	
	3	0.0001	0.0006	0.0019	0.0042	0.0077	0.0125	0.0186	0.0261	0.0348	0.0446	0.1069	0.1762	0.2336	0.2668	0.2716	0.2508	0.2119	0.1641	6	
	4	0.0000	0.0000	0.0001	0.0003	0.0006	0.0012	0.0021	0.0034	0.0052	0.0074	0.0283	0.0661	0.1168	0.1715	0.2194	0.2508	0.2600	0.2461	5	
	5	—	—	0.0000	0.0000	0.0000	0.0001	0.0002	0.0003	0.0005	0.0008	0.0050	0.0165	0.0390	0.0735	0.1181	0.1672	0.2128	0.2461	4	
	6	—	—	—	—	—	0.0000	0.0000	0.0000	0.0000	0.0001	0.0006	0.0028	0.0087	0.0210	0.0424	0.0743	0.1160	0.1641	3	
	7	—	—	—	—	—	—	—	—	—	0.0000	0.0000	0.0003	0.0012	0.0039	0.0098	0.0212	0.0407	0.0703	2	
	8	—	—	—	—	—	—	—	—	—	—	—	0.0000	0.0001	0.0004	0.0013	0.0035	0.0083	0.0176	1	
	9	—	—	—	—	—	—	—	—	—	—	—	—	0.0000	0.0000	0.0001	0.0003	0.0008	0.0020	0	9
10	0	0.9044	0.8171	0.7374	0.6648	0.5987	0.5386	0.4840	0.4344	0.3894	0.3487	0.1969	0.1074	0.0563	0.0282	0.0135	0.0060	0.0025	0.0010	10	
	1	0.0914	0.1667	0.2281	0.2770	0.3151	0.3438	0.3643	0.3777	0.3851	0.3874	0.3474	0.2684	0.1877	0.1211	0.0725	0.0403	0.0207	0.0098	9	
	2	0.0042	0.0153	0.0317	0.0519	0.0746	0.0988	0.1234	0.1478	0.1714	0.1937	0.2759	0.3020	0.2816	0.2335	0.1757	0.1209	0.0763	0.0439	8	
	3	0.0001	0.0008	0.0026	0.0058	0.0105	0.0168	0.0248	0.0343	0.0452	0.0574	0.1298	0.2013	0.2503	0.2668	0.2522	0.2150	0.1665	0.1172	7	
	4	0.0000	0.0000	0.0001	0.0004	0.0010	0.0019	0.0033	0.0052	0.0078	0.0112	0.0401	0.0881	0.1460	0.2001	0.2377	0.2508	0.2384	0.2051	6	
	5	—	—	0.0000	0.0000	0.0001	0.0001	0.0003	0.0005	0.0009	0.0015	0.0085	0.0264	0.0584	0.1029	0.1536	0.2007	0.2340	0.2461	5	
	6	—	—	—	—	0.0000	0.0000	0.0000	0.0000	0.0001	0.0001	0.0012	0.0055	0.0162	0.0368	0.0689	0.1115	0.1596	0.2051	4	
	7	—	—	—	—	—	—	—	—	0.0000	0.0000	0.0001	0.0008	0.0031	0.0090	0.0212	0.0425	0.0746	0.1172	3	
	8	—	—	—	—	—	—	—	—	—	—	0.0000	0.0001	0.0004	0.0014	0.0043	0.0106	0.0229	0.0439	2	
	9	—	—	—	—	—	—	—	—	—	—	—	0.0000	0.0000	0.0001	0.0005	0.0016	0.0042	0.0098	1	
	10	—	—	—	—	—	—	—	—	—	—	—	—	—	0.0000	0.0000	0.0001	0.0003	0.0010	0	10

continued

TABLE 6

Table of Binomial Probabilities (*Continued*)

		p																			
n	*X*	0.01	0.02	0.03	0.04	0.05	0.06	0.07	0.08	0.09	0.10	0.15	0.20	0.25	0.30	0.35	0.40	0.45	0.50	*X*	*n*
20	0	0.8179	0.6676	0.5438	0.4420	0.3585	0.2901	0.2342	0.1887	0.1516	0.1216	0.0388	0.0115	0.0032	0.0008	0.0002	0.0000	0.0000	—	20	
	1	0.1652	0.2725	0.3364	0.3683	0.3774	0.3703	0.3526	0.3282	0.3000	0.2702	0.1368	0.0576	0.0211	0.0068	0.0020	0.0005	0.0001	0.0000	19	
	2	0.0159	0.0528	0.0988	0.1458	0.1887	0.2246	0.2521	0.2711	0.2818	0.2852	0.2293	0.1369	0.0699	0.0278	0.0100	0.0031	0.0008	0.0002	18	
	3	0.0010	0.0065	0.0183	0.0364	0.0596	0.0860	0.1139	0.1414	0.1672	0.1901	0.2428	0.2054	0.1339	0.0716	0.0323	0.0123	0.0040	0.0011	17	
	4	0.0000	0.0006	0.0024	0.0065	0.0133	0.0233	0.0364	0.0523	0.0703	0.0898	0.1821	0.2182	0.1897	0.1304	0.0738	0.0350	0.0139	0.0046	16	
	5	—	0.0000	0.0002	0.0009	0.0022	0.0048	0.0088	0.0145	0.0222	0.0319	0.1028	0.1746	0.2023	0.1789	0.1272	0.0746	0.0365	0.0148	15	
	6	—	—	0.0000	0.0001	0.0003	0.0008	0.0017	0.0032	0.0055	0.0089	0.0454	0.1091	0.1686	0.1916	0.1712	0.1244	0.0746	0.0370	14	
	7	—	—	—	0.0000	0.0000	0.0001	0.0002	0.0005	0.0011	0.0020	0.0160	0.0545	0.1124	0.1643	0.1844	0.1659	0.1221	0.0739	13	
	8	—	—	—	—	—	0.0000	0.0000	0.0001	0.0002	0.0004	0.0046	0.0222	0.0609	0.1144	0.1614	0.1797	0.1623	0.1201	12	
	9	—	—	—	—	—	—	—	0.0000	0.0000	0.0001	0.0011	0.0074	0.0271	0.0654	0.1158	0.1597	0.1771	0.1602	11	
	10	—	—	—	—	—	—	—	—	—	0.0000	0.0002	0.0020	0.0099	0.0308	0.0686	0.1171	0.1593	0.1762	10	
	11	—	—	—	—	—	—	—	—	—	—	0.0000	0.0005	0.0030	0.0120	0.0336	0.0710	0.1185	0.1602	9	
	12	—	—	—	—	—	—	—	—	—	—	—	0.0001	0.0008	0.0039	0.0136	0.0355	0.0727	0.1201	8	
	13	—	—	—	—	—	—	—	—	—	—	—	0.0000	0.0002	0.0010	0.0045	0.0146	0.0366	0.0739	7	
	14	—	—	—	—	—	—	—	—	—	—	—	—	0.0000	0.0002	0.0012	0.0049	0.0150	0.0370	6	
	15	—	—	—	—	—	—	—	—	—	—	—	—	—	0.0000	0.0003	0.0013	0.0049	0.0148	5	
	16	—	—	—	—	—	—	—	—	—	—	—	—	—	—	0.0000	0.0003	0.0013	0.0046	4	
	17	—	—	—	—	—	—	—	—	—	—	—	—	—	—	—	0.0000	0.0002	0.0011	3	
	18	—	—	—	—	—	—	—	—	—	—	—	—	—	—	—	—	0.0000	0.0002	2	
	19	—	—	—	—	—	—	—	—	—	—	—	—	—	—	—	—	—	0.0000	1	
	20	—	—	—	—	—	—	—	—	—	—	—	—	—	—	—	—	—	—	0	20
n	*X*	0.99	0.98	0.97	0.96	0.95	0.94	0.93	0.92	0.91	0.90	0.85	0.80	0.75	0.70	0.65	0.60	0.55	0.50	*X*	*n*

TABLE 7

Table of Poisson Probabilities

For a given value of λ, entry indicates the probability of obtaining a specified value of X.

	λ									
X	**0.1**	**0.2**	**0.3**	**0.4**	**0.5**	**0.6**	**0.7**	**0.8**	**0.9**	**1.0**
0	0.9048	0.8187	0.7408	0.6703	0.6065	0.5488	0.4966	0.4493	0.4066	0.3679
1	0.0905	0.1637	0.2222	0.2681	0.3033	0.3293	0.3476	0.3595	0.3659	0.3679
2	0.0045	0.0164	0.0333	0.0536	0.0758	0.0988	0.1217	0.1438	0.1647	0.1839
3	0.0002	0.0011	0.0033	0.0072	0.0126	0.0198	0.0284	0.0383	0.0494	0.0613
4	0.0000	0.0001	0.0003	0.0007	0.0016	0.0030	0.0050	0.0077	0.0111	0.0153
5	0.0000	0.0000	0.0000	0.0001	0.0002	0.0004	0.0007	0.0012	0.0020	0.0031
6	0.0000	0.0000	0.0000	0.0000	0.0000	0.0000	0.0001	0.0002	0.0003	0.0005
7	0.0000	0.0000	0.0000	0.0000	0.0000	0.0000	0.0000	0.0000	0.0000	0.0001

	λ									
X	**1.1**	**1.2**	**1.3**	**1.4**	**1.5**	**1.6**	**1.7**	**1.8**	**1.9**	**2.0**
0	0.3329	0.3012	0.2725	0.2466	0.2231	0.2019	0.1827	0.1653	0.1496	0.1353
1	0.3662	0.3614	0.3543	0.3452	0.3347	0.3230	0.3106	0.2975	0.2842	0.2707
2	0.2014	0.2169	0.2303	0.2417	0.2510	0.2584	0.2640	0.2678	0.2700	0.2707
3	0.0738	0.0867	0.0998	0.1128	0.1255	0.1378	0.1496	0.1607	0.1710	0.1804
4	0.0203	0.0260	0.0324	0.0395	0.0471	0.0551	0.636	0.0723	0.0812	0.0902
5	0.0045	0.0062	0.0084	0.0111	0.0141	0.0176	0.0216	0.0260	0.0309	0.0361
6	0.0008	0.0012	0.0018	0.0026	0.0035	0.0047	0.0061	0.0078	0.0098	0.0120
7	0.0001	0.0002	0.0003	0.0005	0.0008	0.0011	0.0015	0.0020	0.0027	0.0034
8	0.0000	0.0000	0.0001	0.0001	0.0001	0.0002	0.0003	0.0005	0.0006	0.0009
9	0.0000	0.0000	0.0000	0.0000	0.0000	0.0000	0.0001	0.0001	0.0001	0.0002

	λ									
X	**2.1**	**2.2**	**2.3**	**2.4**	**2.5**	**2.6**	**2.7**	**2.8**	**2.9**	**3.0**
0	0.1225	0.1108	0.1003	0.0907	0.0821	0.0743	0.0672	0.0608	0.0550	0.0498
1	0.2572	0.2438	0.2306	0.2177	0.2052	0.1931	0.1815	0.1703	0.1596	0.1494
2	0.2700	0.2681	0.2652	0.2613	0.2565	0.2510	0.2450	0.2384	0.2314	0.2240
3	0.1890	0.1966	0.2033	0.2090	0.2138	0.2176	0.2205	0.2225	0.2237	0.2240
4	0.0992	0.1082	0.1169	0.1254	0.1336	0.1414	0.1488	0.1557	0.1622	0.1680
5	0.0417	0.0476	0.0538	0.0602	0.0668	0.0735	0.0804	0.0872	0.0940	0.1008
6	0.0146	0.0174	0.0206	0.0241	0.0278	0.0319	0.0362	0.0407	0.0455	0.0504
7	0.0044	0.0055	0.0068	0.0083	0.0099	0.0118	0.0139	0.0163	0.0188	0.0216
8	0.0011	0.0015	0.0019	0.0025	0.0031	0.0038	0.0047	0.0057	0.0068	0.0081
9	0.0003	0.0004	0.0005	0.0007	0.0009	0.0011	0.0014	0.0018	0.0022	0.0027
10	0.0001	0.0001	0.0001	0.0002	0.0002	0.0003	0.0004	0.0005	0.0006	0.0008
11	0.0000	0.0000	0.0000	0.0000	0.0000	0.0001	0.0001	0.0001	0.0002	0.0002
12	0.0000	0.0000	0.0000	0.0000	0.0000	0.0000	0.0000	0.0000	0.0000	0.0001

	λ									
X	**3.1**	**3.2**	**3.3**	**3.4**	**3.5**	**3.6**	**3.7**	**3.8**	**3.9**	**4.0**
0	0.0450	0.0408	0.0369	0.0334	0.0302	0.0273	0.0247	0.0224	0.0202	0.0183
1	0.1397	0.1340	0.1217	0.1135	0.1057	0.0984	0.0915	0.0850	0.0789	0.0733
2	0.2165	0.2087	0.2008	0.1929	0.1850	0.1771	0.1692	0.1615	0.1539	0.1465
3	0.2237	0.2226	0.2209	0.2186	0.2158	0.2125	0.2087	0.2046	0.2001	0.1954
4	0.1734	0.1781	0.1823	0.1858	0.1888	0.1912	0.1931	0.1944	0.1951	0.1954
5	0.1075	0.1140	0.1203	0.1264	0.1322	0.1377	0.1429	0.1477	0.1522	0.1563
6	0.0555	0.0608	0.0662	0.0716	0.0771	0.0826	0.0881	0.0936	0.0989	0.1042
7	0.0246	0.0278	0.0312	0.0348	0.0385	0.0425	0.0466	0.0508	0.0551	0.0595
8	0.0095	0.0111	0.0129	0.0148	0.0169	0.0191	0.0215	0.0241	0.0269	0.0298
9	0.0033	0.0040	0.0047	0.0056	0.0066	0.0076	0.0089	0.0102	0.0116	0.0132
10	0.0010	0.0013	0.0016	0.0019	0.0023	0.0028	0.0033	0.0039	0.0045	0.0053
11	0.0003	0.0004	0.0005	0.0006	0.0007	0.0009	0.0011	0.0013	0.0016	0.0019
12	0.0001	0.0001	0.0001	0.0002	0.0002	0.0003	0.0003	0.0004	0.0005	0.0006
13	0.0000	0.0000	0.0000	0.0000	0.0001	0.0001	0.0001	0.0001	0.0002	0.0002
14	0.0000	0.0000	0.0000	0.0000	0.0000	0.0000	0.0000	0.0000	0.0000	0.0001

continued

TABLE 7

Table of Poisson Probabilities (*Continued*)

	λ									
X	4.1	4.2	4.3	4.4	4.5	4.6	4.7	4.8	4.9	5.0
0	0.0166	0.0150	0.0136	0.0123	0.0111	0.0101	0.0091	0.0082	0.0074	0.0067
1	0.0679	0.0630	0.0583	0.0540	0.0500	0.0462	0.0427	0.0395	0.0365	0.0337
2	0.1393	0.1323	0.1254	0.1188	0.1125	0.1063	0.1005	0.0948	0.0894	0.0842
3	0.1904	0.1852	0.1798	0.1743	0.1687	0.1631	0.1574	0.1517	0.1460	0.1404
4	0.1951	0.1944	0.1933	0.1917	0.1898	0.1875	0.1849	0.1820	0.1789	0.1755
5	0.1600	0.1633	0.1662	0.1687	0.1708	0.1725	0.1738	0.1747	0.1753	0.1755
6	0.1093	0.1143	0.1191	0.1237	0.1281	0.1323	0.1362	0.1398	0.1432	0.1462
7	0.0640	0.0686	0.0732	0.0778	0.0824	0.0869	0.0914	0.0959	0.1002	0.1044
8	0.0328	0.0360	0.0393	0.0428	0.0463	0.0500	0.0537	0.0575	0.0614	0.0653
9	0.0150	0.0168	0.0188	0.0209	0.0232	0.0255	0.0280	0.0307	0.0334	0.0363
10	0.0061	0.0071	0.0081	0.0092	0.0104	0.0118	0.0132	0.0147	0.0164	0.0181
11	0.0023	0.0027	0.0032	0.0037	0.0043	0.0049	0.0056	0.0064	0.0073	0.0082
12	0.0008	0.0009	0.0011	0.0014	0.0016	0.0019	0.0022	0.0026	0.0030	0.0034
13	0.0002	0.0003	0.0004	0.0005	0.0006	0.0007	0.0008	0.0009	0.0011	0.0013
14	0.0001	0.0001	0.0001	0.0001	0.0002	0.0002	0.0003	0.0003	0.0004	0.0005
15	0.0000	0.0000	0.0000	0.0000	0.0001	0.0001	0.0001	0.0001	0.0001	0.0002

	λ									
X	5.1	5.2	5.3	5.4	5.5	5.6	5.7	5.8	5.9	6.0
0	0.0061	0.0055	0.0050	0.0045	0.0041	0.0037	0.0033	0.0030	0.0027	0.0025
1	0.0311	0.0287	0.0265	0.0244	0.0225	0.0207	0.0191	0.0176	0.0162	0.0149
2	0.0793	0.0746	0.0701	0.0659	0.0618	0.0580	0.0544	0.0509	0.0477	0.0446
3	0.1348	0.1293	0.1239	0.1185	0.1133	0.1082	0.1033	0.0985	0.0938	0.0892
4	0.1719	0.1681	0.1641	0.1600	0.1558	0.1515	0.1472	0.1428	0.1383	0.1339
5	0.1753	0.1748	0.1740	0.1728	0.1714	0.1697	0.1678	0.1656	0.1632	0.1606
6	0.1490	0.1515	0.1537	0.1555	0.1571	0.1584	0.1594	0.1601	0.1605	0.1606
7	0.1086	0.1125	0.1163	0.1200	0.1234	0.1267	0.1298	0.1326	0.1353	0.1377
8	0.0692	0.0731	0.0771	0.0810	0.0849	0.0887	0.0925	0.0962	0.0998	0.1033
9	0.0392	0.0423	0.0454	0.0486	0.0519	0.0552	0.0586	0.0620	0.0654	0.0688
10	0.0200	0.0220	0.0241	0.0262	0.0285	0.0309	0.0334	0.0359	0.0386	0.0413
11	0.0093	0.0104	0.0116	0.0129	0.0143	0.0157	0.0173	0.0190	0.0207	0.0225
12	0.0039	0.0045	0.0051	0.0058	0.0065	0.0073	0.0082	0.0092	0.0102	0.0113
13	0.0015	0.0018	0.0021	0.0024	0.0028	0.0032	0.0036	0.0041	0.0046	0.0052
14	0.0006	0.0007	0.0008	0.0009	0.0011	0.0013	0.0015	0.0017	0.0019	0.0022
15	0.0002	0.0002	0.0003	0.0003	0.0004	0.0005	0.0006	0.0007	0.0008	0.0009
16	0.0001	0.0001	0.0001	0.0001	0.0001	0.0002	0.0002	0.0002	0.0003	0.0003
17	0.0000	0.0000	0.0000	0.0000	0.0000	0.0000	0.0001	0.0001	0.0001	0.0001

	λ									
X	6.1	6.2	6.3	6.4	6.5	6.6	6.7	6.8	6.9	7.0
0	0.0022	0.0020	0.0018	0.0017	0.0015	0.0014	0.0012	0.0011	0.0010	0.0009
1	0.0137	0.0126	0.0116	0.0106	0.0098	0.0090	0.0082	0.0076	0.0070	0.0064
2	0.0417	0.0390	0.0364	0.0340	0.0318	0.0296	0.0276	0.0258	0.0240	0.0223
3	0.0848	0.0806	0.0765	0.0726	0.0688	0.0652	0.0617	0.0584	0.0552	0.0521
4	0.1294	0.1249	0.1205	0.1162	0.1118	0.1076	0.1034	0.0992	0.0952	0.0912
5	0.1579	0.1549	0.1519	0.1487	0.1454	0.1420	0.1385	0.1349	0.1314	0.1277
6	0.1605	0.1601	0.1595	0.1586	0.1575	0.1562	0.1546	0.1529	0.1511	0.1490
7	0.1399	0.1418	0.1435	0.1450	0.1462	0.1472	0.1480	0.1486	0.1489	0.1490
8	0.1066	0.1099	0.1130	0.1160	0.1188	0.1215	0.1240	0.1263	0.1284	0.1304
9	0.0723	0.0757	0.0791	0.0825	0.0858	0.0891	0.0923	0.0954	0.0985	0.1014
10	0.0441	0.0469	0.0498	0.0528	0.0558	0.0588	0.0618	0.0649	0.0679	0.0710
11	0.0245	0.0265	0.0285	0.0307	0.0330	0.0353	0.0377	0.0401	0.0426	0.0452
12	0.0124	0.0137	0.0150	0.0164	0.0179	0.0194	0.0210	0.0277	0.0245	0.0264
13	0.0058	0.0065	0.0073	0.0081	0.0089	0.0098	0.0108	0.0119	0.0130	0.0142
14	0.0025	0.0029	0.0033	0.0037	0.0041	0.0046	0.0052	0.0058	0.0064	0.0071

continued

TABLE 7

Table of Poisson Probabilities (*Continued*)

	λ									
X	**6.1**	**6.2**	**6.3**	**6.4**	**6.5**	**6.6**	**6.7**	**6.8**	**6.9**	**7.0**
15	0.0010	0.0012	0.0014	0.0016	0.0018	0.0020	0.0023	0.0026	0.0029	0.0033
16	0.0004	0.0005	0.0005	0.0006	0.0007	0.0008	0.0010	0.0011	0.0013	0.0014
17	0.0001	0.0002	0.0002	0.0002	0.0003	0.0003	0.0004	0.0004	0.0005	0.0006
18	0.0000	0.0001	0.0001	0.0001	0.0001	0.0001	0.0001	0.0002	0.0002	0.0002
19	0.0000	0.0000	0.0000	0.0000	0.0000	0.0000	0.0000	0.0001	0.0001	0.0001

	λ									
X	**7.1**	**7.2**	**7.3**	**7.4**	**7.5**	**7.6**	**7.7**	**7.8**	**7.9**	**8.0**
0	0.0008	0.0007	0.0007	0.0006	0.0006	0.0005	0.0005	0.0004	0.0004	0.0003
1	0.0059	0.0054	0.0049	0.0045	0.0041	0.0038	0.0035	0.0032	0.0029	0.0027
2	0.0208	0.0194	0.0180	0.0167	0.0156	0.0145	0.0134	0.0125	0.0116	0.0107
3	0.0492	0.0464	0.0438	0.0413	0.0389	0.0366	0.0345	0.0324	0.0305	0.0286
4	0.0874	0.0836	0.0799	0.0764	0.0729	0.0696	0.0663	0.0632	0.0602	0.0573
5	0.1241	0.1204	0.1167	0.1130	0.1094	0.1057	0.1021	0.0986	0.0951	0.0916
6	0.1468	0.1445	0.1420	0.1394	0.1367	0.1339	0.1311	0.1282	0.1252	0.1221
7	0.1489	0.1486	0.1481	0.1474	0.1465	0.1454	0.1442	0.1428	0.1413	0.1396
8	0.1321	0.1337	0.1351	0.1363	0.1373	0.1382	0.1388	0.1392	0.1395	0.1396
9	0.1042	0.1070	0.1096	0.1121	0.1144	0.1167	0.1187	0.1207	0.1224	0.1241
10	0.0740	0.0770	0.0800	0.0829	0.0858	0.0887	0.0914	0.0941	0.0967	0.0993
11	0.0478	0.0504	0.0531	0.0558	0.0585	0.0613	0.0640	0.0667	0.0695	0.0722
12	0.0283	0.0303	0.0323	0.0344	0.0366	0.0388	0.0411	0.0434	0.0457	0.0481
13	0.0154	0.0168	0.0181	0.0196	0.0211	0.0227	0.0243	0.0260	0.0278	0.0296
14	0.0078	0.0086	0.0095	0.0104	0.0113	0.0123	0.0134	0.0145	0.0157	0.0169
15	0.0037	0.0041	0.0046	0.0051	0.0057	0.0062	0.0069	0.0075	0.0083	0.0090
16	0.0016	0.0019	0.0021	0.0024	0.0026	0.0030	0.0033	0.0037	0.0041	0.0045
17	0.0007	0.0008	0.0009	0.0010	0.0012	0.0013	0.0015	0.0017	0.0019	0.0021
18	0.0003	0.0003	0.0004	0.0004	0.0005	0.0006	0.0006	0.0007	0.0008	0.0009
19	0.0001	0.0001	0.0001	0.0002	0.0002	0.0002	0.0003	0.0003	0.0003	0.0004
20	0.0000	0.0000	0.0001	0.0001	0.0001	0.0001	0.0001	0.0001	0.0001	0.0002
21	0.0000	0.0000	0.0000	0.0000	0.0000	0.0000	0.0000	0.0000	0.0001	0.0001

	λ									
X	**8.1**	**8.2**	**8.3**	**8.4**	**8.5**	**8.6**	**8.7**	**8.8**	**8.9**	**9.0**
0	0.0003	0.0003	0.0002	0.0002	0.0002	0.0002	0.0002	0.0002	0.0001	0.0001
1	0.0025	0.0023	0.0021	0.0019	0.0017	0.0016	0.0014	0.0013	0.0012	0.0011
2	0.0100	0.0092	0.0086	0.0079	0.0074	0.0068	0.0063	0.0058	0.0054	0.0050
3	0.0269	0.0252	0.0237	0.0222	0.0208	0.0195	0.0183	0.0171	0.0160	0.0150
4	0.0544	0.0517	0.0491	0.0466	0.0443	0.0420	0.0398	0.0377	0.0357	0.0337
5	0.0882	0.0849	0.0816	0.0784	0.0752	0.0722	0.0692	0.0663	0.0635	0.0607
6	0.1191	0.1160	0.1128	0.1097	0.1066	0.1034	0.1003	0.0972	0.0941	0.0911
7	0.1378	0.1358	0.1338	0.1317	0.1294	0.1271	0.1247	0.1222	0.1197	0.1171
8	0.1395	0.1392	0.1388	0.1382	0.1375	0.1366	0.1356	0.1344	0.1332	0.1318
9	0.1256	0.1269	0.1280	0.1290	0.1299	0.1306	0.1311	0.1315	0.1317	0.1318
10	0.1017	0.1040	0.1063	0.1084	0.1104	0.1123	0.1140	0.1157	0.1172	0.1186
11	0.0749	0.0776	0.0802	0.0828	0.0853	0.0878	0.0902	0.0925	0.0948	0.0970
12	0.0505	0.0530	0.0555	0.0579	0.0604	0.0629	0.0654	0.0679	0.0703	0.0728
13	0.0315	0.0334	0.0354	0.0374	0.0395	0.0416	0.0438	0.0459	0.0481	0.0504
14	0.0182	0.0196	0.0210	0.0225	0.0240	0.0256	0.0272	0.0289	0.0306	0.0324
15	0.0098	0.0107	0.0116	0.0126	0.0136	0.0147	0.0158	0.0169	0.0182	0.0194
16	0.0050	0.0055	0.0060	0.0066	0.0072	0.0079	0.0086	0.0093	0.0101	0.0109
17	0.0024	0.0026	0.0029	0.0033	0.0036	0.0040	0.0044	0.0048	0.0053	0.0058
18	0.0011	0.0012	0.0014	0.0015	0.0017	0.0019	0.0021	0.0024	0.0026	0.0029
19	0.0005	0.0005	0.0006	0.0007	0.0008	0.0009	0.0010	0.0011	0.0012	0.0014
20	0.0002	0.0002	0.0002	0.0003	0.0003	0.0004	0.0004	0.0005	0.0005	0.0006
21	0.0001	0.0001	0.0001	0.0001	0.0001	0.0002	0.0002	0.0002	0.0002	0.0003
22	0.0000	0.0000	0.0000	0.0000	0.0001	0.0001	0.0001	0.0001	0.0001	0.0001

continued

TABLE 7

Table of Poisson Probabilities (*Continued*)

	λ									
X	**9.1**	**9.2**	**9.3**	**9.4**	**9.5**	**9.6**	**9.7**	**9.8**	**9.9**	**10**
0	0.0001	0.0001	0.0001	0.0001	0.0001	0.0001	0.0001	0.0001	0.0001	0.0000
1	0.0010	0.0009	0.0009	0.0008	0.0007	0.0007	0.0006	0.0005	0.0005	0.0005
2	0.0046	0.0043	0.0040	0.0037	0.0034	0.0031	0.0029	0.0027	0.0025	0.0023
3	0.0140	0.0131	0.0123	0.0115	0.0107	0.0100	0.0093	0.0087	0.0081	0.0076
4	0.0319	0.0302	0.0285	0.0269	0.0254	0.0240	0.0226	0.0213	0.0201	0.0189
5	0.0581	0.0555	0.0530	0.0506	0.0483	0.0460	0.0439	0.0418	0.0398	0.0378
6	0.0881	0.0851	0.0822	0.0793	0.0764	0.0736	0.0709	0.0682	0.0656	0.0631
7	0.1145	0.1118	0.1091	0.1064	0.1037	0.1010	0.0982	0.0955	0.0928	0.0901
8	0.1302	0.1286	0.1269	0.1251	0.1232	0.1212	0.1191	0.1170	0.1148	0.1126
9	0.1317	0.1315	0.1311	0.1306	0.1300	0.1293	0.1284	0.1274	0.1263	0.1251
10	0.1198	0.1210	0.1219	0.1228	0.1235	0.1241	0.1245	0.1249	0.1250	0.1251
11	0.0991	0.1012	0.1031	0.1049	0.1067	0.1083	0.1098	0.1112	0.1125	0.1137
12	0.0752	0.0776	0.0799	0.0822	0.0844	0.0866	0.0888	0.0908	0.0928	0.0948
13	0.0526	0.0549	0.0572	0.0594	0.0617	0.0640	0.0662	0.0685	0.0707	0.0729
14	0.0342	0.0361	0.0380	0.0399	0.0419	0.0439	0.0459	0.0479	0.0500	0.0521
15	0.0208	0.0221	0.0235	0.0250	0.0265	0.0281	0.0297	0.0313	0.0330	0.0347
16	0.0118	0.0127	0.0137	0.0147	0.0157	0.0168	0.0180	0.0192	0.0204	0.0217
17	0.0063	0.0069	0.0075	0.0081	0.0088	0.0095	0.0103	0.0111	0.0119	0.0128
18	0.0032	0.0035	0.0039	0.0042	0.0046	0.0051	0.0055	0.0060	0.0065	0.0071
19	0.0015	0.0017	0.0019	0.0021	0.0023	0.0026	0.0028	0.0031	0.0034	0.0037
20	0.0007	0.0008	0.0009	0.0010	0.0011	0.0012	0.0014	0.0015	0.0017	0.0019
21	0.0003	0.0003	0.0004	0.0004	0.0005	0.0006	0.0006	0.0007	0.0008	0.0009
22	0.0001	0.0001	0.0002	0.0002	0.0002	0.0002	0.0003	0.0003	0.0004	0.0004
23	0.0000	0.0001	0.0001	0.0001	0.0001	0.0001	0.0001	0.0001	0.0002	0.0002
24	0.0000	0.0000	0.0000	0.0000	0.0000	0.0000	0.0000	0.0001	0.0001	0.0001

X	**λ = 20**	**X**	**λ = 20**	**X**	**λ = 20**	**X**	**λ = 20**
0	0.0000	10	0.0058	20	0.0888	30	0.0083
1	0.0000	11	0.0106	21	0.0846	31	0.0054
2	0.0000	12	0.0176	22	0.0769	32	0.0034
3	0.0000	13	0.0271	23	0.0669	33	0.0020
4	0.0000	14	0.0387	24	0.0557	34	0.0012
5	0.0001	15	0.0516	25	0.0446	35	0.0007
6	0.0002	16	0.0646	26	0.0343	36	0.0004
7	0.0005	17	0.0760	27	0.0254	37	0.0002
8	0.0013	18	0.0844	28	0.0181	38	0.0001
9	0.0029	19	0.0888	29	0.0125	39	0.0001

TABLE 8

Lower and Upper Critical Values T_1 of Wilcoxon Rank Sum Test

	α		n_1						
n_2	One-tail	Two-tail	4	5	6	7	8	9	10
	0.05	0.10	11,25						
4	0.025	0.05	10,26						
	0.01	0.02	–,–						
	0.005	0.01	–,–						
	0.05	0.10	12,28	19,36					
5	0.025	0.05	11,29	17,38					
	0.01	0.02	10,30	16,39					
	0.005	0.01	–,–	15,40					
	0.05	0.10	13,31	20,40	28,50				
6	0.025	0.05	12,32	18,42	26,52				
	0.01	0.02	11,33	17,43	24,54				
	0.005	0.01	10,34	16,44	23,55				
	0.05	0.10	14,34	21,44	29,55	39,66			
7	0.025	0.05	13,35	20,45	27,57	36,69			
	0.01	0.02	11,37	18,47	25,59	34,71			
	0.005	0.01	10,38	16,49	24,60	32,73			
	0.05	0.10	15,37	23,47	31,59	41,71	51,85		
8	0.025	0.05	14,38	21,49	29,61	38,74	49,87		
	0.01	0.02	12,40	19,51	27,63	35,77	45,91		
	0.005	0.01	11,41	17,53	25,65	34,78	43,93		
	0.05	0.10	16,40	24,51	33,63	43,76	54,90	66,105	
9	0.025	0.05	14,42	22,53	31,65	40,79	51,93	62,109	
	0.01	0.02	13,43	20,55	28,68	37,82	47,97	59,112	
	0.005	0.01	11,45	18,57	26,70	35,84	45,99	56,115	
	0.05	0.10	17,43	26,54	35,67	45,81	56,96	69,111	82,128
10	0.025	0.05	15,45	23,57	32,70	42,84	53,99	65,115	78,132
	0.01	0.02	13,47	21,59	29,73	39,87	49,103	61,119	74,136
	0.005	0.01	12,48	19,61	27,75	37,89	47,105	58,122	71,139

Source: Adapted from Table 1 of F. Wilcoxon and R. A. Wilcox, Some Rapid Approximate Statistical Procedures *(Pearl River, NY: Lederle Laboratories, 1964), with permission of the American Cyanamid Company.*

TABLE 9

Critical Values of the Studentized Range Q

	UPPER 5% POINTS ($\alpha = 0.05$)																		
	NUMERATOR DEGREES OF FREEDOM																		
Denominator Degrees of Freedom	2	3	4	5	6	7	8	9	10	11	12	13	14	15	16	17	18	19	20
1	18.00	27.00	32.80	37.10	40.40	43.10	45.40	47.40	49.10	50.60	52.00	53.20	54.30	55.40	56.30	57.20	58.00	58.80	59.60
2	6.09	8.30	9.80	10.90	11.70	12.40	13.00	13.50	14.00	14.40	14.70	15.10	15.40	15.70	15.90	16.10	16.40	16.60	16.80
3	4.50	5.91	6.82	7.50	8.04	8.48	8.85	9.18	9.46	9.72	9.95	10.15	10.35	10.52	10.69	10.84	10.98	11.11	11.24
4	3.93	5.04	5.76	6.29	6.71	7.05	7.35	7.60	7.83	8.03	8.21	8.37	8.52	8.66	8.79	8.91	9.03	9.13	9.23
5	3.64	4.60	5.22	5.67	6.03	6.33	6.58	6.80	6.99	7.17	7.32	7.47	7.60	7.72	7.83	7.93	8.03	8.12	8.21
6	3.46	4.34	4.90	5.31	5.63	5.89	6.12	6.32	6.49	6.65	6.79	6.92	7.03	7.14	7.24	7.34	7.43	7.51	7.59
7	3.34	4.16	4.68	5.06	5.36	5.61	5.82	6.00	6.16	6.30	6.43	6.55	6.66	6.76	6.85	6.94	7.02	7.09	7.17
8	3.26	4.04	4.53	4.89	5.17	5.40	5.60	5.77	5.92	6.05	6.18	6.29	6.39	6.48	6.57	6.65	6.73	6.80	6.87
9	3.20	3.95	4.42	4.76	5.02	5.24	5.43	5.60	5.74	5.87	5.98	6.09	6.19	6.28	6.36	6.44	6.51	6.58	6.64
10	3.15	3.88	4.33	4.65	4.91	5.12	5.30	5.46	5.60	5.72	5.83	5.93	6.03	6.11	6.20	6.27	6.34	6.40	6.47
11	3.11	3.82	4.26	4.57	4.82	5.03	5.20	5.35	5.49	5.61	5.71	5.81	5.90	5.99	6.06	6.14	6.20	6.26	6.33
12	3.08	3.77	4.20	4.51	4.75	4.95	5.12	5.27	5.40	5.51	5.62	5.71	5.80	5.88	5.95	6.03	6.09	6.15	6.21
13	3.06	3.73	4.15	4.45	4.69	4.88	5.05	5.19	5.32	5.43	5.53	5.63	5.71	5.79	5.86	5.93	6.00	6.05	6.11
14	3.03	3.70	4.11	4.41	4.64	4.83	4.99	5.13	5.25	5.36	5.46	5.55	5.64	5.72	5.79	5.85	5.92	5.97	6.03
15	3.01	3.67	4.08	4.37	4.60	4.78	4.94	5.08	5.20	5.31	5.40	5.49	5.58	5.65	5.72	5.79	5.85	5.90	5.96
16	3.00	3.65	4.05	4.33	4.56	4.74	4.90	5.03	5.15	5.26	5.35	5.44	5.52	5.59	5.66	5.72	5.79	5.84	5.90
17	2.98	3.63	4.02	4.30	4.52	4.71	4.86	4.99	5.11	5.21	5.31	5.39	5.47	5.55	5.61	5.68	5.74	5.79	5.84
18	2.97	3.61	4.00	4.28	4.49	4.67	4.82	4.96	5.07	5.17	5.27	5.35	5.43	5.50	5.57	5.63	5.69	5.74	5.79
19	2.96	3.59	3.98	4.25	4.47	4.65	4.79	4.92	5.04	5.14	5.23	5.32	5.39	5.46	5.53	5.59	5.65	5.70	5.75
20	2.95	3.58	3.96	4.23	4.45	4.62	4.77	4.90	5.01	5.11	5.20	5.28	5.36	5.43	5.49	5.55	5.61	5.66	5.71
24	2.92	3.53	3.90	4.17	4.37	4.54	4.68	4.81	4.92	5.01	5.10	5.18	5.25	5.32	5.38	5.44	5.50	5.54	5.59
30	2.89	3.49	3.84	4.10	4.30	4.46	4.60	4.72	4.83	4.92	5.00	5.08	5.15	5.21	5.27	5.33	5.38	5.43	5.48
40	2.86	3.44	3.79	4.04	4.23	4.39	4.52	4.63	4.74	4.82	4.91	4.98	5.05	5.11	5.16	5.22	5.27	5.31	5.36
60	2.83	3.40	3.74	3.98	4.16	4.31	4.44	4.55	4.65	4.73	4.81	4.88	4.94	5.00	5.06	5.11	5.16	5.20	5.24
120	2.80	3.36	3.69	3.92	4.10	4.24	4.36	4.48	4.56	4.64	4.72	4.78	4.84	4.90	4.95	5.00	5.05	5.09	5.13
∞	2.77	3.31	3.63	3.86	4.03	4.17	4.29	4.39	4.47	4.55	4.62	4.68	4.74	4.80	4.85	4.89	4.93	4.97	5.01

(continued)

TABLE 9

Critical Values of the Studentized Range Q (*Continued*)

Denominator Degrees of Freedom	UPPER 1% POINTS ($\alpha = 0.01$) NUMERATOR DEGREES OF FREEDOM (*Continued*)																		
	2	3	4	5	6	7	8	9	10	11	12	13	14	15	16	17	18	19	20
1	90.00	135.00	164.00	186.00	202.00	216.00	227.00	237.00	246.00	253.00	260.00	266.00	272.00	277.00	282.00	286.00	290.00	294.00	298.00
2	14.00	19.00	22.30	24.70	26.60	28.20	29.50	30.70	31.70	32.60	33.40	34.10	34.80	35.40	36.00	36.50	37.00	37.50	37.90
3	8.26	10.60	12.20	13.30	14.20	15.00	15.60	16.20	16.70	17.10	17.50	17.90	18.20	18.50	18.80	19.10	19.30	19.50	19.80
4	6.51	8.12	9.17	9.96	10.60	11.10	11.50	11.90	12.30	12.60	12.80	13.10	13.30	13.50	13.70	13.90	14.10	14.20	14.40
5	5.70	6.97	7.80	8.42	8.91	9.32	9.67	9.97	10.24	10.48	10.70	10.89	11.08	11.24	11.40	11.55	11.68	11.81	11.93
6	5.24	6.33	7.03	7.56	7.97	8.32	8.61	8.87	9.10	9.30	9.49	9.65	9.81	9.95	10.08	10.21	10.32	10.43	10.54
7	4.95	5.92	6.54	7.01	7.37	7.68	7.94	8.17	8.37	8.55	8.71	8.86	9.00	9.12	9.24	9.35	9.46	9.55	9.65
8	4.74	5.63	6.20	6.63	6.96	7.24	7.47	7.68	7.87	8.03	8.18	8.31	8.44	8.55	8.66	8.76	8.85	8.94	9.03
9	4.60	5.43	5.96	6.35	6.66	6.91	7.13	7.32	7.49	7.65	7.78	7.91	8.03	8.13	8.23	8.32	8.41	8.49	8.57
10	4.48	5.27	5.77	6.14	6.43	6.67	6.87	7.05	7.21	7.36	7.48	7.60	7.71	7.81	7.91	7.99	8.07	8.15	8.22
11	4.39	5.14	5.62	5.97	6.26	6.48	6.67	6.84	6.99	7.13	7.25	7.36	7.46	7.56	7.65	7.73	7.81	7.88	7.95
12	4.32	5.04	5.50	5.84	6.10	6.32	6.51	6.67	6.81	6.94	7.06	7.17	7.26	7.36	7.44	7.52	7.59	7.66	7.73
13	4.26	4.96	5.40	5.73	5.98	6.19	6.37	6.53	6.67	6.79	6.90	7.01	7.10	7.19	7.27	7.34	7.42	7.48	7.55
14	4.21	4.89	5.32	5.63	5.88	6.08	6.26	6.41	6.54	6.66	6.77	6.87	6.96	7.05	7.12	7.20	7.27	7.33	7.39
15	4.17	4.83	5.25	5.56	5.80	5.99	6.16	6.31	6.44	6.55	6.66	6.76	6.84	6.93	7.00	7.07	7.14	7.20	7.26
16	4.13	4.78	5.19	5.49	5.72	5.92	6.08	6.22	6.35	6.46	6.56	6.66	6.74	6.82	6.90	6.97	7.03	7.09	7.15
17	4.10	4.74	5.14	5.43	5.66	5.85	6.01	6.15	6.27	6.38	6.48	6.57	6.66	6.73	6.80	6.87	6.94	7.00	7.05
18	4.07	4.70	5.09	5.38	5.60	5.79	5.94	6.08	6.20	6.31	6.41	6.50	6.58	6.65	6.72	6.79	6.85	6.91	6.96
19	4.05	4.67	5.05	5.33	5.55	5.73	5.89	6.02	6.14	6.25	6.34	6.43	6.51	6.58	6.65	6.72	6.78	6.84	6.89
20	4.02	4.64	5.02	5.29	5.51	5.69	5.84	5.97	6.09	6.19	6.29	6.37	6.45	6.52	6.59	6.65	6.71	6.76	6.82
24	3.96	4.54	4.91	5.17	5.37	5.54	5.69	5.81	5.92	6.02	6.11	6.19	6.26	6.33	6.39	6.45	6.51	5.56	6.61
30	3.89	4.45	4.80	5.05	5.24	5.40	5.54	5.65	5.76	5.85	5.93	6.01	6.08	6.14	6.20	6.26	6.31	6.36	6.41
40	3.82	4.37	4.70	4.93	5.11	5.27	5.39	5.50	5.60	5.69	5.77	5.84	5.90	5.96	6.02	6.07	6.12	6.17	6.21
60	3.76	4.28	4.60	4.82	4.99	5.13	5.25	5.36	5.45	5.53	5.60	5.67	5.73	5.79	5.84	5.89	5.93	5.98	6.02
120	3.70	4.20	4.50	4.71	4.87	5.01	5.12	5.21	5.30	5.38	5.44	5.51	5.56	5.61	5.66	5.71	5.75	5.79	5.83
∞	3.64	4.12	4.40	4.60	4.76	4.88	4.99	5.08	5.16	5.23	5.29	5.35	5.40	5.45	5.49	5.54	5.57	5.61	5.65

Source: Reprinted from E. S. Pearson and H. O. Hartley, eds., Table 29 of Biometrika Tables for Statisticians, Vol. 1, *3rd ed., 1966, by permission of the* Biometrika *Trustees, London.*

TABLE 10

Critical Values d_L and d_U of the Durbin-Watson Statistic D (Critical Values Are One-Sided)[a]

	α = 0.05										α = 0.01									
	k = 1		k = 2		k = 3		k = 4		k = 5		k = 1		k = 2		k = 3		k = 4		k = 5	
n	d_L	d_U	d_L	d_U	d_L	d_U	d_L	d_U	d_L	d_U	d_L	d_U	d_L	d_U	d_L	d_U	d_L	d_U	d_L	d_U
15	1.08	1.36	.95	1.54	.82	1.75	.69	1.97	.56	2.21	.81	1.07	.70	1.25	.59	1.46	.49	1.70	.39	1.96
16	1.10	1.37	.98	1.54	.86	1.73	.74	1.93	.62	2.15	.84	1.09	.74	1.25	.63	1.44	.53	1.66	.44	1.90
17	1.13	1.38	1.02	1.54	.90	1.71	.78	1.90	.67	2.10	.87	1.10	.77	1.25	.67	1.43	.57	1.63	.48	1.85
18	1.16	1.39	1.05	1.53	.93	1.69	.82	1.87	.71	2.06	.90	1.12	.80	1.26	.71	1.42	.61	1.60	.52	1.80
19	1.18	1.40	1.08	1.53	.97	1.68	.86	1.85	.75	2.02	.93	1.13	.83	1.26	.74	1.41	.65	1.58	.56	1.77
20	1.20	1.41	1.10	1.54	1.00	1.68	.90	1.83	.79	1.99	.95	1.15	.86	1.27	.77	1.41	.68	1.57	.60	1.74
21	1.22	1.42	1.13	1.54	1.03	1.67	.93	1.81	.83	1.96	.97	1.16	.89	1.27	.80	1.41	.72	1.55	.63	1.71
22	1.24	1.43	1.15	1.54	1.05	1.66	.96	1.80	.86	1.94	1.00	1.17	.91	1.28	.83	1.40	.75	1.54	.66	1.69
23	1.26	1.44	1.17	1.54	1.08	1.66	.99	1.79	.90	1.92	1.02	1.19	.94	1.29	.86	1.40	.77	1.53	.70	1.67
24	1.27	1.45	1.19	1.55	1.10	1.66	1.01	1.78	.93	1.90	1.04	1.20	.96	1.30	.88	1.41	.80	1.53	.72	1.66
25	1.29	1.45	1.21	1.55	1.12	1.66	1.04	1.77	.95	1.89	1.05	1.21	.98	1.30	.90	1.41	.83	1.52	.75	1.65
26	1.30	1.46	1.22	1.55	1.14	1.65	1.06	1.76	.98	1.88	1.07	1.22	1.00	1.31	.93	1.41	.85	1.52	.78	1.64
27	1.32	1.47	1.24	1.56	1.16	1.65	1.08	1.76	1.01	1.86	1.09	1.23	1.02	1.32	.95	1.41	.88	1.51	.81	1.63
28	1.33	1.48	1.26	1.56	1.18	1.65	1.10	1.75	1.03	1.85	1.10	1.24	1.04	1.32	.97	1.41	.90	1.51	.83	1.62
29	1.34	1.48	1.27	1.56	1.20	1.65	1.12	1.74	1.05	1.84	1.12	1.25	1.05	1.33	.99	1.42	.92	1.51	.85	1.61
30	1.35	1.49	1.28	1.57	1.21	1.65	1.14	1.74	1.07	1.83	1.13	1.26	1.07	1.34	1.01	1.42	.94	1.51	.88	1.61
31	1.36	1.50	1.30	1.57	1.23	1.65	1.16	1.74	1.09	1.83	1.15	1.27	1.08	1.34	1.02	1.42	.96	1.51	.90	1.60
32	1.37	1.50	1.31	1.57	1.24	1.65	1.18	1.73	1.11	1.82	1.16	1.28	1.10	1.35	1.04	1.43	.98	1.51	.92	1.60
33	1.38	1.51	1.32	1.58	1.26	1.65	1.19	1.73	1.13	1.81	1.17	1.29	1.11	1.36	1.05	1.43	1.00	1.51	.94	1.59
34	1.39	1.51	1.33	1.58	1.27	1.65	1.21	1.73	1.15	1.81	1.18	1.30	1.13	1.36	1.07	1.43	1.01	1.51	.95	1.59
35	1.40	1.52	1.34	1.58	1.28	1.65	1.22	1.73	1.16	1.80	1.19	1.31	1.14	1.37	1.08	1.44	1.03	1.51	.97	1.59
36	1.41	1.52	1.35	1.59	1.29	1.65	1.24	1.73	1.18	1.80	1.21	1.32	1.15	1.38	1.10	1.44	1.04	1.51	.99	1.59
37	1.42	1.53	1.36	1.59	1.31	1.66	1.25	1.72	1.19	1.80	1.22	1.32	1.16	1.38	1.11	1.45	1.06	1.51	1.00	1.59
38	1.43	1.54	1.37	1.59	1.32	1.66	1.26	1.72	1.21	1.79	1.23	1.33	1.18	1.39	1.12	1.45	1.07	1.52	1.02	1.58
39	1.43	1.54	1.38	1.60	1.33	1.66	1.27	1.72	1.22	1.79	1.24	1.34	1.19	1.39	1.14	1.45	1.09	1.52	1.03	1.58
40	1.44	1.54	1.39	1.60	1.34	1.66	1.29	1.72	1.23	1.79	1.25	1.34	1.20	1.40	1.15	1.46	1.10	1.52	1.05	1.58
45	1.48	1.57	1.43	1.62	1.38	1.67	1.34	1.72	1.29	1.78	1.29	1.38	1.24	1.42	1.20	1.48	1.16	1.53	1.11	1.58
50	1.50	1.59	1.46	1.63	1.42	1.67	1.38	1.72	1.34	1.77	1.32	1.40	1.28	1.45	1.24	1.49	1.20	1.54	1.16	1.59
55	1.53	1.60	1.49	1.64	1.45	1.68	1.41	1.72	1.38	1.77	1.36	1.43	1.32	1.47	1.28	1.51	1.25	1.55	1.21	1.59
60	1.55	1.62	1.51	1.65	1.48	1.69	1.44	1.73	1.41	1.77	1.38	1.45	1.35	1.48	1.32	1.52	1.28	1.56	1.25	1.60
65	1.57	1.63	1.54	1.66	1.50	1.70	1.47	1.73	1.44	1.77	1.41	1.47	1.38	1.50	1.35	1.53	1.31	1.57	1.28	1.61
70	1.58	1.64	1.55	1.67	1.52	1.70	1.49	1.74	1.46	1.77	1.43	1.49	1.40	1.52	1.37	1.55	1.34	1.58	1.31	1.61
75	1.60	1.65	1.57	1.68	1.54	1.71	1.51	1.74	1.49	1.77	1.45	1.50	1.42	1.53	1.39	1.56	1.37	1.59	1.34	1.62
80	1.61	1.66	1.59	1.69	1.56	1.72	1.53	1.74	1.51	1.77	1.47	1.52	1.44	1.54	1.42	1.57	1.39	1.60	1.36	1.62
85	1.62	1.67	1.60	1.70	1.57	1.72	1.55	1.75	1.52	1.77	1.48	1.53	1.46	1.55	1.43	1.58	1.41	1.60	1.39	1.63
90	1.63	1.68	1.61	1.70	1.59	1.73	1.57	1.75	1.54	1.78	1.50	1.54	1.47	1.56	1.45	1.59	1.43	1.61	1.41	1.64
95	1.64	1.69	1.62	1.71	1.60	1.73	1.58	1.75	1.56	1.78	1.51	1.55	1.49	1.57	1.47	1.60	1.45	1.62	1.42	1.64
100	1.65	1.69	1.63	1.72	1.61	1.74	1.59	1.76	1.57	1.78	1.52	1.56	1.50	1.58	1.48	1.60	1.46	1.63	1.44	1.65

[a] *n = number of observations; k = number of independent variables.*

Source: This table is reproduced from Biometrika, *41 (1951): 173 and 175, with the permission of the* Biometrika *Trustees.*

TABLE 11

Control Chart Factors

Number of Observations in Sample	d_2	d_3	D_3	D_4	A_2
2	1.128	0.853	0	3.267	1.880
3	1.693	0.888	0	2.575	1.023
4	2.059	0.880	0	2.282	0.729
5	2.326	0.864	0	2.114	0.577
6	2.534	0.848	0	2.004	0.483
7	2.704	0.833	0.076	1.924	0.419
8	2.847	0.820	0.136	1.864	0.373
9	2.970	0.808	0.184	1.816	0.337
10	3.078	0.797	0.223	1.777	0.308
11	3.173	0.787	0.256	1.744	0.285
12	3.258	0.778	0.283	1.717	0.266
13	3.336	0.770	0.307	1.693	0.249
14	3.407	0.763	0.328	1.672	0.235
15	3.472	0.756	0.347	1.653	0.223
16	3.532	0.750	0.363	1.637	0.212
17	3.588	0.744	0.378	1.622	0.203
18	3.640	0.739	0.391	1.609	0.194
19	3.689	0.733	0.404	1.596	0.187
20	3.735	0.729	0.415	1.585	0.180
21	3.778	0.724	0.425	1.575	0.173
22	3.819	0.720	0.435	1.565	0.167
23	3.858	0.716	0.443	1.557	0.162
24	3.895	0.712	0.452	1.548	0.157
25	3.931	0.708	0.459	1.541	0.153

Source: Reprinted from ASTM-STP 15D by kind permission of the American Society for Testing and Materials.

TABLE 12

The Standardized Normal Distribution

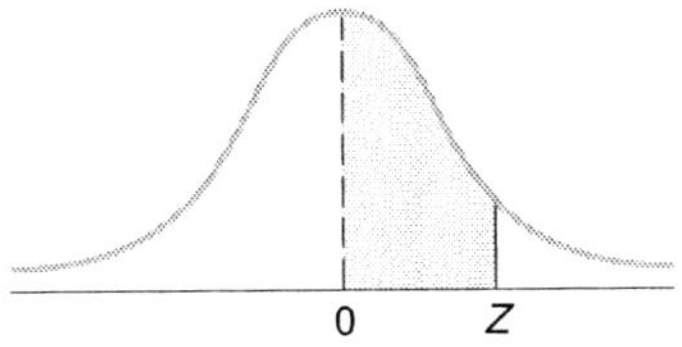

Entry represents area under the standardized normal distribution from the mean to Z

Z	.00	.01	.02	.03	.04	.05	.06	.07	.08	.09
0.0	.0000	.0040	.0080	.0120	.0160	.0199	.0239	.0279	.0319	.0359
0.1	.0398	.0438	.0478	.0517	.0557	.0596	.0636	.0675	.0714	.0753
0.2	.0793	.0832	.0871	.0910	.0948	.0987	.1026	.1064	.1103	.1141
0.3	.1179	.1217	.1255	.1293	.1331	.1368	.1406	.1443	.1480	.1517
0.4	.1554	.1591	.1628	.1664	.1700	.1736	.1772	.1808	.1844	.1879
0.5	.1915	.1950	.1985	.2019	.2054	.2088	.2123	.2157	.2190	.2224
0.6	.2257	.2291	.2324	.2357	.2389	.2422	.2454	.2486	.2518	.2549
0.7	.2580	.2612	.2642	.2673	.2704	.2734	.2764	.2794	.2823	.2852
0.8	.2881	.2910	.2939	.2967	.2995	.3023	.3051	.3078	.3106	.3133
0.9	.3159	.3186	.3212	.3238	.3264	.3289	.3315	.3340	.3365	.3389
1.0	.3413	.3438	.3461	.3485	.3508	.3531	.3554	.3577	.3599	.3621
1.1	.3643	.3665	.3686	.3708	.3729	.3749	.3770	.3790	.3810	.3830
1.2	.3849	.3869	.3888	.3907	.3925	.3944	.3962	.3980	.3997	.4015
1.3	.4032	.4049	.4066	.4082	.4099	.4115	.4131	.4147	.4162	.4177
1.4	.4192	.4207	.4222	.4236	.4251	.4265	.4279	.4292	.4306	.4319
1.5	.4332	.4345	.4357	.4370	.4382	.4394	.4406	.4418	.4429	.4441
1.6	.4452	.4463	.4474	.4484	.4495	.4505	.4515	.4525	.4535	.4545
1.7	.4554	.4564	.4573	.4582	.4591	.4599	.4608	.4616	.4625	.4633
1.8	.4641	.4649	.4656	.4664	.4671	.4678	.4686	.4693	.4699	.4706
1.9	.4713	.4719	.4726	.4732	.4738	.4744	.4750	.4756	.4761	.4767
2.0	.4772	.4778	.4783	.4788	.4793	.4798	.4803	.4808	.4812	.4817
2.1	.4821	.4826	.4830	.4834	.4838	.4842	.4846	.4850	.4854	.4857
2.2	.4861	.4864	.4868	.4871	.4875	.4878	.4881	.4884	.4887	.4890
2.3	.4893	.4896	.4898	.4901	.4904	.4906	.4909	.4911	.4913	.4916
2.4	.4918	.4920	.4922	.4925	.4927	.4929	.4931	.4932	.4934	.4936
2.5	.4938	.4940	.4941	.4943	.4945	.4946	.4948	.4949	.4951	.4952
2.6	.4953	.4955	.4956	.4957	.4959	.4960	.4961	.4962	.4963	.4964
2.7	.4965	.4966	.4967	.4968	.4969	.4970	.4971	.4972	.4973	.4974
2.8	.4974	.4975	.4976	.4977	.4977	.4978	.4979	.4979	.4980	.4981
2.9	.4981	.4982	.4982	.4983	.4984	.4984	.4985	.4985	.4986	.4986
3.0	.49865	.49869	.49874	.49878	.49882	.49886	.49889	.49893	.49897	.49900
3.1	.49903	.49906	.49910	.49913	.49916	.49918	.49921	.49924	.49926	.49929
3.2	.49931	.49934	.49936	.49938	.49940	.49942	.49944	.49946	.49948	.49950
3.3	.49952	.49953	.49955	.49957	.49958	.49960	.49961	.49962	.49964	.49965
3.4	.49966	.49968	.49969	.49970	.49971	.49972	.49973	.49974	.49975	.49976
3.5	.49977	.49978	.49978	.49979	.49980	.49981	.49981	.49982	.49983	.49983
3.6	.49984	.49985	.49985	.49986	.49986	.49987	.49987	.49988	.49988	.49989
3.7	.49989	.49990	.49990	.49990	.49991	.49991	.49992	.49992	.49992	.49992
3.8	.49993	.49993	.49993	.49994	.49994	.49994	.49994	.49995	.49995	.49995
3.9	.49995	.49995	.49996	.49996	.49996	.49996	.49996	.49996	.49997	.49997

CONFIGURING AND CUSTOMIZING MICROSOFT EXCEL FOR USE WITH *STATISTICS FOR MANAGERS USING MICROSOFT® EXCEL 4/E*

1: INTRODUCTION

Use this appendix to verify and adjust the technical and visual interface settings of your copy of Microsoft Excel to best match those used by the authors to produce the Excel results and illustrations presented in this text. This appendix also contains information about adjusting common print and Help system settings.

If you share your copy of Microsoft Excel with other users, be aware that the instructions in this appendix will affect what those users see when they use the shared copy of Microsoft Excel. Make sure to read section 4 carefully if you will be setting up PHStat2 for use with this text.

2: VERIFYING YOUR MICROSOFT EXCEL INSTALLATION

Before using Microsoft Excel with this text, verify that you have a proper licensed version of Microsoft Excel version 97 or later. Open Microsoft Excel and select **Help | About Microsoft Excel**. The first text line in the dialog box will state the version number, build number, and any service release (SR) or service packs (SP) numbers. Record these numbers for later reference. If your version is Excel 97, it must include a SR number of 2 or higher. (You can check the Microsoft Excel Web site for the latest service releases or packs available for your version.)

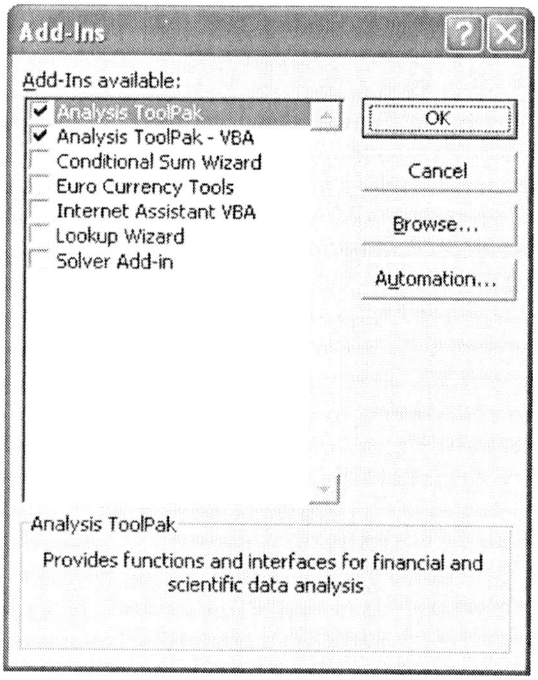

The Excel instructions of this text make extensive use of the Data Analysis ToolPak that Microsoft supplies on the original Microsoft Excel or Office program disk. To verify that the ToolPak has been installed, select **Tools | Add-Ins** and in the Add-Ins dialog box make sure the **Analysis ToolPak** and **Analysis ToolPak - VBA** check boxes are checked in the **Add-Ins available** list. Then click the **OK** button to close the dialog box. (The Add-Ins dialog box for Microsoft Excel 2002 is shown at right. The dialog box in other versions of Excel are similar.)

Should these two add-ins not appear in the Add-Ins list, you will need to exit Microsoft Excel and rerun the Microsoft Excel (or Office) setup program, selecting the add or modify option and then choosing the add-ins, to include them inside your copy of Microsoft Excel. (After doing this, repeat the instructions of the prior paragraph to verify the add-ins installation.)

From *Statistics for Managers Using Microsoft® Excel*, Fourth Edition, David Levine, David Stephan, Timothy C. Krehbiel, Mark Berenson.

3: CONFIGURING THE MICROSOFT EXCEL TECHNICAL SETTINGS

The instructions for using Excel in this text assume that your copy of Excel has been configured with certain technical settings. To verify these settings, select **Tools | Options** and in the Options dialog box:

Select the **Calculation** tab. Verify that the **Automatic** option button of the Calculation group has been selected.

Select the **Edit** tab. Verify that all check boxes *except* the **Fixed decimal**, **Provide feedback with Animation**, and **Enable automatic percent entry** have been selected. (Excel 97 does not contain an Automatic percent entry check box.)

Select the **General** tab. Verify that the **R1C1 reference style** check box is cleared (unchecked) and, if using Excel 97, check the **Macro virus protection** check box. Enter **3** in the **Sheets in new workbook** edit box, select **Arial** from the **Standard font** list box, and select **10** from the **Size** drop-down list box and click the **OK** button.

4: CONFIGURING THE MICROSOFT EXCEL VISUAL INTERFACE

Use the instructions of this section to adjust the visual interface settings of Microsoft Excel so that they best match those used to produce the Excel illustrations in this text. While following these instructions are not a prerequisite for using this text, adjusting the settings as described below will enhance your learning experience by creating greater consistency between what you see on the printed page and the computer display.

General Excel application window settings. To match the visual look of the Excel application window shown in Figure EP1 of the Excel Primer and elsewhere in this text, follow these instructions:

Select **View** and if the **Formula Bar** choice is not checked, select it.

Select **View** and if the **Status Bar** choice is not checked, select it.

Select **View** and if the **Task Pane** choice is checked, clear it (Excel 2002 and later).

Select **View | Toolbars** and if the Standard choice is not checked, select it.

Select **View | Toolbars** and if the Formatting choice is not checked, select it.

If any of these bars are not aligned and snapped to the top of the Excel application window, drag the bar towards the top of the screen until the border of the bar changes to a slender band of small dots. Then release the mouse button. The bar will then snap into place. (If you are using Microsoft Excel 2000, you may need to select **Tools | Customize** and in the Customize dialog box, clear the **Standard and Formatting toolbars share one row** check box and click the **Close** button, in order to allow the tool bars snap to separate rows.)

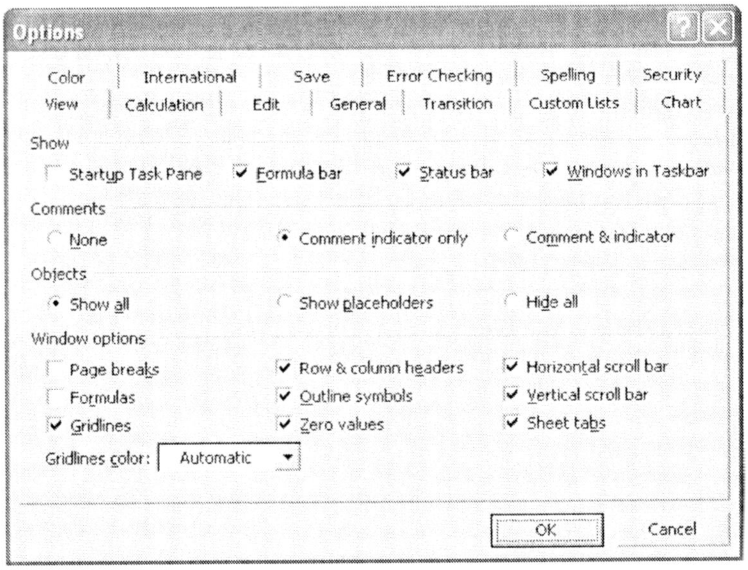

Worksheet area settings. To match the visual look of the worksheet area, shown in numerous illustrations in this text, select **Tools | Options**. In the Options dialog box, select the View tab (shown at right) and select all of the Windows options check boxes *except* **Page breaks** and **Formulas** and then click the **OK** button.

If you find yourself entering worksheet cell formulas at some later time, you may want to revisit the View tab of the Options dialog box and temporarily select the **Formulas** *check box to review and edit the formulas you have entered.*

5: CUSTOMIZING MICROSOFT EXCEL PRINTOUTS

To customize printouts of worksheets and chart sheets, select **File | Page Setup** or click the **Setup** button in the Print Preview window to display the Page Setup dialog box. Useful settings for each of the four tabs of this dialog box are presented below:

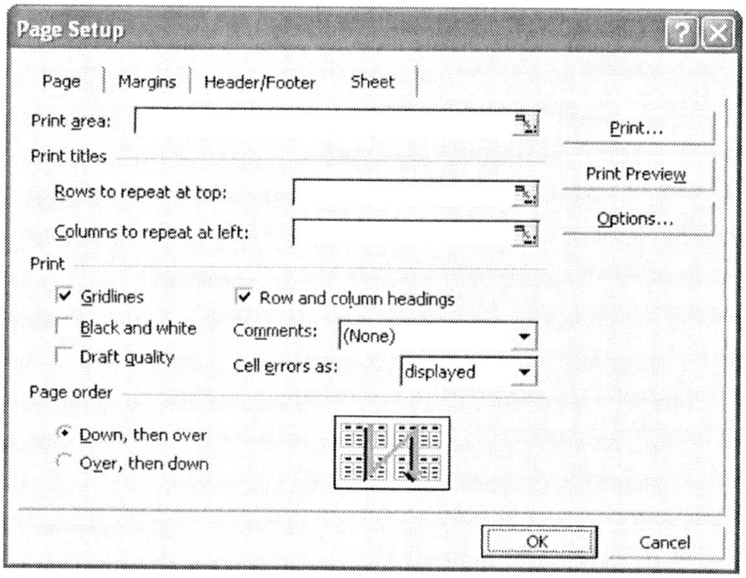

Page tab. Select the **Landscape** option button to fit more columns on a single printed sheet or if your worksheet has a greater width than length. Set the **Portrait** option button to force chart sheets to print their vertical axis aligned with the length of the printed page.

Header/Footer tab. Select a pre-defined format from either the **Header** or **Footer** drop-down list box to add page numbers to your printout.

Sheet Tab (shown at right). With a worksheet active, select the **Gridlines** and **Row and column headings** check boxes of the Print group to produce a printout that will most look like a worksheet displayed onscreen.

Margins tab. Change the values in the **Left**, **Right**, **Top**, and **Bottom** edit boxes to tweak your printout as needed.

After making your entries and selections in the Page Setup dialog box, click the **OK** button to continue using Microsoft Excel.

PHSTAT2 USER'S GUIDE

1: INTRODUCTION

PHStat2 makes operating Microsoft Excel as distraction-free as possible. As a student studying statistics, you can focus solely on mastering statistics now and not worry about having to become an expert user of Excel at the same time. When combined with Microsoft Excel's own Data Analysis ToolPak add-in, just about all statistical methods taught in an introductory statistics course can be illustrated in Microsoft Excel.

PHStat2 executes for you the low-level menu selection and worksheet entry tasks that are associated with implementing statistical analysis in Microsoft Excel. Unlike other add-ins that report results as a series of text labels, hiding the details of using Microsoft Excel, PHStat2 creates actual working Excel worksheets and chart sheets from which you can learn real Excel techniques when you are ready to do so. This makes PHStat2 particularly useful if you are concerned that using a textbook add-in now will leave you unprepared later when you use Microsoft Excel outside your statistics course.

You use PHStat2 to perform a particular analysis by first selecting choices from the PHStat menu and completing entries in a dialog box. PHStat2 generates new worksheets and chart sheets to hold the results of an analysis. Many of these sheets contain formulas that will allow you to change the underlying data and see new results without having to rerun a procedure.

PHStat2 is compatible with all Windows versions of Microsoft Excel, version 97 or later. Specific technical requirements are given in the next section. To use PHStat2, you must first run its setup program, as explained in section 3.

2: TECHNICAL REQUIREMENTS

There are separate requirements for using PHStat2 and running the PHStat2 setup program. The requirements for running the setup program are more exclusive. If you plan to set up PHStat2, make sure to review all of the requirements that follow.

Requirements for using PHStat2:

- Windows 98/98SE/ME/NT 4.0/2000/XP Home/XP Pro computer system.
- Microsoft Excel 97/2000/2002(Office XP)/2003 or later. Excel 97 users must apply the SR-2 or a later free update from Microsoft. PHStat2 is *not* compatible with Microsoft Excel 95 or Macintosh versions of Microsoft Excel.
- Screen resolution settings set to 800 by 600 pixels or 1024 by 748 pixels, *recommended*. PHStat2 will run with *any* screen resolution settings, but setting your system to use Large Fonts or setting your resolution to the minimum 640 by 400 pixels may truncate or obscure PHStat2 message boxes and parts the Microsoft Excel application window.
- Microsoft Excel Data Analysis ToolPak and Analysis ToolPak–VBA installed see the appendix on Configuring and Customizing Microsoft Excel for Use with This Text).
- Microsoft Excel macro security level set to medium (see section 4).
- Up-to-date anti-virus program, *recommended*.

Requirements for running the PHStat2 setup program:

- CD-ROM or DVD-ROM drive.
- Approximately 10 MB hard disk free space while running the setup program and 3 MB hard disk space after program setup. On some older systems, the Windows system files that may get replaced or added during the setup process will require up to 3 MB additional hard disk space.

- Windows user account with administrator or software-installing privileges (Windows NT/2000/XP or networked users only). Note that the typical student or faculty accounts to logon to use networked computers in an academic computer lab do not have this privilege. If you want to setup PHStat2 in such a lab, ask your network or lab technician for assistance.
- Internet access (for downloading updates to Microsoft Excel and PHStat2 as they become available).

3: RUNNING THE PHSTAT2 SETUP PROGRAM

To use PHStat2, you first need to run the PHStat2 setup program. Review the technical requirements of the previous section and, for late-breaking issues, the **PHStat2 readme.rtf** file in the **PHStat2** folder on the CD-ROM that accompanies this text before using the setup program. Having verified the technical requirements of your system and the status of your user account, use **My Computer** or any **Windows Explorer** window to locate the **Setup.exe** program entry in the CD-ROM **PHStat2** folder. Double-click this entry to begin the PHStat2 setup process.

During setup, PHStat2 program files will be copied to your hard disk, Windows system files may be updated, if necessary, and Desktop icons and a Start Menu program group for PHStat2 will be created. As the setup program runs, you will be stepped through a series of dialog boxes in which you need to click the **Next** button to proceed. Important information, such as the terms of the license of use, will be presented and you will have an opportunity to change the default target directory (**\Program Files\PHStat2**) for the PHStat2 files.

When the setup program completes successfully, you may be asked to reboot your system before using PHStat2.

4: GETTING STARTED WITH PHSTAT2

After setting up PHStat2, open Microsoft Excel and verify that the macro security level is set to medium. Select **Tools | Macro | Security** and in the **Security Level** tab of the Security dialog box, select the **Medium** option button and click the **OK** button. Then close Microsoft Excel.

You begin using PHStat2 by either double-clicking the Desktop PHStat2 icon or selecting PHStat2 from the PHStat2 Start Menu program group. As PHStat2 opens, most versions of Microsoft Excel will display a "macros may contain viruses" dialog box. Click the **Enable Macros** button in this dialog box to proceed. When PHStat2 adds a PHStat menu to the Excel menu bar, you are ready to begin work with PHStat2.

To test PHStat2, select the **About PHStat** choice from the PHStat menu. You should see a dialog box that provides version numbers and a copyright date for the version of PHStat2 you have set up. Click the **OK** button to close this dialog box. Select **Probability & Prob. Distributions**, then **Simple & Joint Probabilities** to generate a probabilities worksheet that you can explore.

If you can make these selections successfully and produce a probabilities worksheet, your copy of PHStat2 has been properly set up. (If you have problems, read the **For More Information** section later in this appendix for sources of assistance.)

5: PREPARING DATA FOR ANALYSIS BY PHSTAT2

Many PHStat2 procedures require you to supply worksheet data. For such procedures, prepare your data for analysis by placing it in columns. If you are selecting only part of a column, copy that partial column range to a new column or worksheet. This good practice will allow you to easily verify your data later as well as avoid some common types of user errors.

Due to the limitations of Microsoft Excel, select the worksheet containing the data to be analyzed before selecting the PHStat2 procedure that will use the data. If you forget to do this, you may encounter an error message that refers to an unexpected error or an error in handling a cell range. For procedures that require two or more cell ranges, such as all of the regression procedures, make sure that all your cell ranges are from the same worksheet.

6: WHAT PHSTAT2 IS NOT

PHStat2 is not designed as a commercial statistical package and should not be used as a replacement for products such as SPSS® or SAS. Because PHStat2 emphasizes learning, PHStat2 tries to use the methods of calculation that a learner could follow and would find presented in a textbook that discusses manual calculation. In other cases, PHStat2 uses pre-existing Microsoft Excel programming to produce results that are too complex to manually calculate or present to the learner. Both of these choices will occasionally cause PHStat2 and Excel to produce results not as precise as those produced by commercial packages that use methods of calculation fine-tuned to the limitations of computing technology. While these differences are not significant for most sets of data, real-world data sets with unusual numerical properties or with extreme values could produce significant anomalies when used with PHStat2 and Microsoft Excel. If you are a student, use PHStat2 only with the data discussed in your text or required by your instructor. For such sets of data, the results produced by PHStat2 will allow you to form the proper statistical conclusion about your data.

7: FOR MORE INFORMATION

Read the **PHStat2 readme.rtf** file on the CD-ROM that accompanies this text for late-breaking information about PHStat2 and detailed setup instructions, including technical requirements. Visit the Prentice Hall PHStat Web site at **www.prenhall.com/phstat** for FAQs and the latest news about PHStat2. The Web site is also the place to find updates to PHStat2 as they become available and to e-mail Pearson Education technical support. (Updates are freely available by download by owners of this text who possess the original CD-ROM packaged with the text.)

PREPARING DATA FOR REPORTS AND PRESENTATIONS USING MICROSOFT OFFICE

1: SHARING INFORMATION BETWEEN MICROSOFT EXCEL AND MICROSOFT WORD

In many business situations, the worksheet tables and charts generated in Microsoft Excel need to be included as part of a management report. If you use Microsoft Word to prepare such a report, select the **Edit | Copy** and either **Edit | Paste** or **Edit | Paste Special** commands to share such information between Microsoft Excel and Word. Variations of the Paste Special command allow for simple copying and pasting as well as creating a link between the original information in Microsoft Excel and its pasted copy. Such a link automatically updates the pasted copy in Microsoft Word when changes are made to the original information in Microsoft Excel and can save time when the original information is undergoing constant revision.

Simple copy and paste for worksheet tables. Select the cell range containing the information to be copied and then select **Edit | Copy**. Open the Microsoft Word document to receive the information, click the point in the document where the copied range is to be inserted, and select **Edit | Paste**. This inserts a Microsoft Word table that contains all of the formatted text and numbers of the cell range. During the paste operation, any formulas in the cell range are replaced by their current values.

For example, copying and pasting the contents of cell range A3:D9 of the **Sample** worksheet (See Figure 1 Panel A) in the **Techniques.xls** workbook creates the Word Table shown in Figure 1 Panel B. During this operation the formula in cell B9 and the formulas in columns C and D are replaced by their then-current values.

FIGURE 1

Panel A: Cell range to be copied. Panel B: Word document after paste operation

	A	B	C	D
1	Sample Table			
2				
3	**Objective**	**Total**	**Percentage**	**Cumulative %**
4	IL	42	30.66%	30.66%
5	SC	37	27.01%	57.66%
6	GI	26	18.98%	76.64%
7	MC	20	14.60%	91.24%
8	TK	12	8.76%	100.00%
9	Grand Total	137		

Panel A

Objective	**Total**	**Percentage**	**Cumulative %**
IL	42	30.66%	30.66%
SC	37	27.01%	57.66%
GI	26	18.98%	76.64%
MC	20	14.60%	91.24%
TK	12	8.76%	100.00%
Grand Total	137		

Panel B

Copy and preserve link for worksheet tables. Select the cell range containing the information to be copied and then select **Edit | Copy**. Open the Microsoft Word document to receive the information, click the point in the document where the copied range is to be inserted, and select **Edit | Paste Special**. In the Paste Special dialog box (see Figure 2), select the **Paste link** option button, **Microsoft Excel Worksheet Object** in the **As** list box, and click **OK**.

Other choices in the As list box can be selected and may affect the display, formatting, and printing of the worksheet data in minor ways. (See the Result caption for each and the Microsoft Excel help system for further information.) If you are using a system with an older, slower processor and small memory size, you may want to avoid selecting the Microsoft Excel Worksheet Object as this choice, which allows you to directly edit the contents of the original worksheet without first separately opening Microsoft Excel, may cause performance problems.

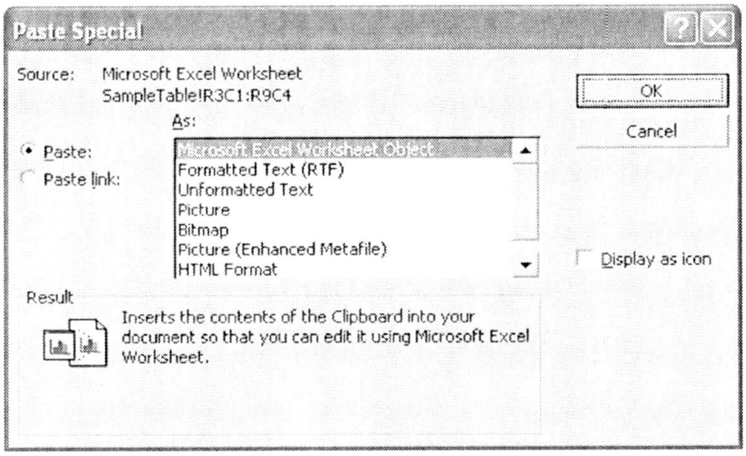

FIGURE 2
Microsoft Excel 2002 Paste Special dialog box for worksheet tables. (The dialog boxes for other Excel versions are similar.)

Copying charts. For best performance, use **Edit** | **Paste Special** for all copying operations involving a Microsoft Excel chart. In the Paste Special dialog box for charts (see Figure 3), select the either the **Paste** or **Paste link** option button, depending on whether or not you wish to preserve a link between the original data and its pasted copy. Then select **Microsoft Excel Chart Object** in the **As** list box and click **OK**. As with copying cell ranges, other choices in the As list box can be selected and may affect the display, formatting, and printing of the chart in minor ways.

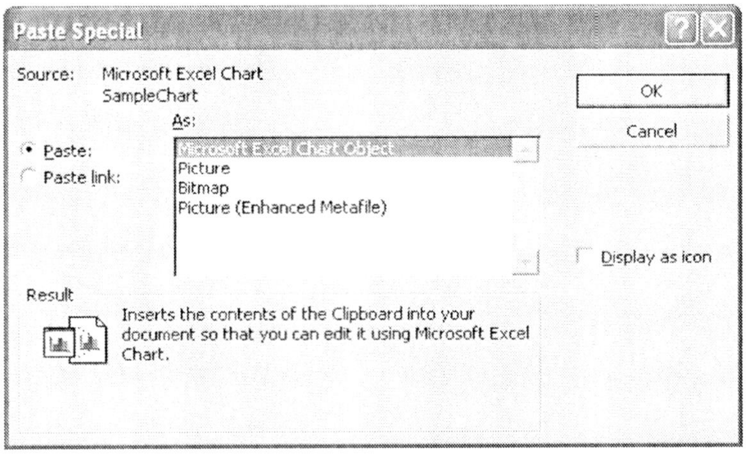

FIGURE 3
Paste Special dialog box for charts

2: USING MICROSOFT EXCEL TABLES AND CHARTS IN A MICROSOFT POWERPOINT PRESENTATION

Just as many business reports require sharing information between Microsoft Excel and Word (see previous section), many Microsoft PowerPoint presentations require the sharing of information between Microsoft Excel and PowerPoint. Use the **Edit** | **Copy** and **Edit** | **Paste** commands to create PowerPoint slides that contain Excel charts or worksheets.

For example, to generate an electronic slide that contains the dot scale diagram of Figure 2 of the "Numerical Descriptive Measures" chapter, first open to the **Figure 3.2** worksheet of the **Chapter 3.xls** workbook in Microsoft Excel and then open Microsoft PowerPoint. The initial Microsoft PowerPoint window will vary depending on the version of Office you are using. Figure 4 shows the typical PowerPoint 2002 initial window containing a task pane and a blank title slide for a new presentation.

FIGURE 4
Microsoft PowerPoint initial window

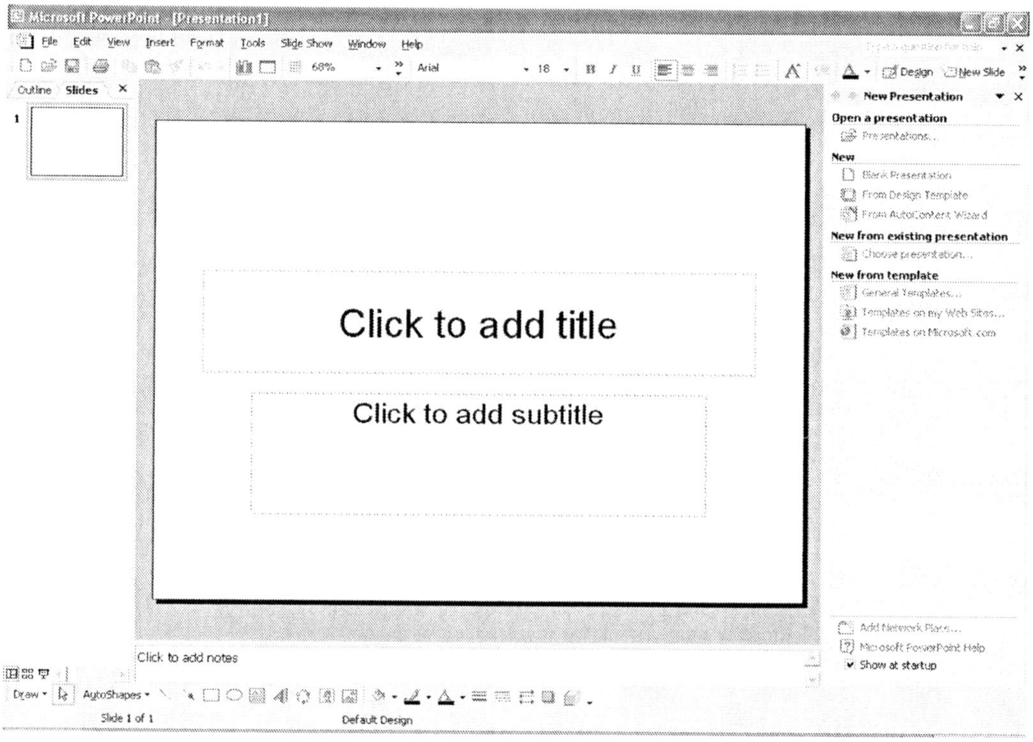

If you are using older versions of PowerPoint, select the **Blank presentation** *option button* from the initial PowerPoint dialog box, or, if you do *not* see a task pane or an initial dialog box, select **File | New** and then select the Blank presentation choice from whatever appears onscreen. Then, if using Excel 2000, select the **General** tab of the New Presentation dialog box and then select **Blank Presentation** and click **OK**. (If using Excel 97, select the **General** tab and then select the **Blank presentation.pot** icon in the list box and click **OK**.)

With the new presentation open, select **Insert | New Slide**. In PowerPoint 2002, the Slide Layout pane appears in the task pane, shown at right. (In earlier PowerPoint versions, a New Slide dialog box with similar contents appears). Right-click the first choice of the **Text and Contents Layouts** section and select **Insert New Slide** from the shortcut menu.

PowerPoint inserts a new slide and makes it available for editing in the editing area as shown in Figure 5 Panel A. Select the frame around the "Click icon to add content" (see Figure 5 Panel B). Switch to Microsoft Excel by pressing **Alt-Tab** until Excel is selected. In Excel, click the dot scale diagram and then select **Edit | Copy**. Return to Microsoft PowerPoint (again use **Alt-Tab**) and select **Edit | Paste** to create the slide shown in Figure 6. To minimize the use of system resources, select the Paste icon that appears under the pasted chart and select **Picture of Chart (smaller file size)** from the pull-down menu (shown at left).

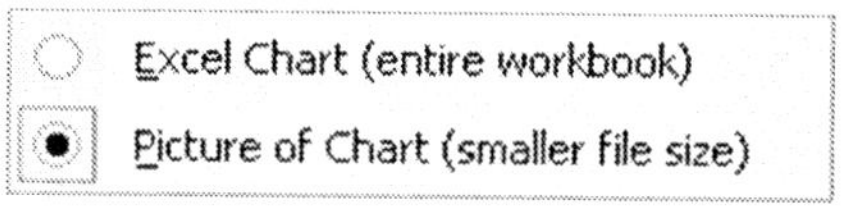

When you paste a chart, be prepared to resize the pasted chart as well as resize or eliminate other areas of the slide. For example, the dot scale diagram as pasted is too small for easy viewing by others. Drag one of the circular chart handles to enlarge the chart. To make more room for the chart, select the "Click to add text" frame and press the **Delete** key. After centering the chart, your slide will look similar to Figure 6 Panel B. Click inside the "Click to add title" frame and enter a title to complete the slide. (If you know that you want only to show a chart on a PowerPoint slide, you can select the "Title And Chart" slide that appears last in the Slide Layout task pane and avoid the adjustments just described.)

Additional slides can be added to the presentation by selecting **Insert | New Slide** in Microsoft PowerPoint and the entire PowerPoint presentation can be saved using the **File | Save As** command.

FIGURE 5
PowerPoint editing area before (Panel A) and after (Panel B) selecting the content area

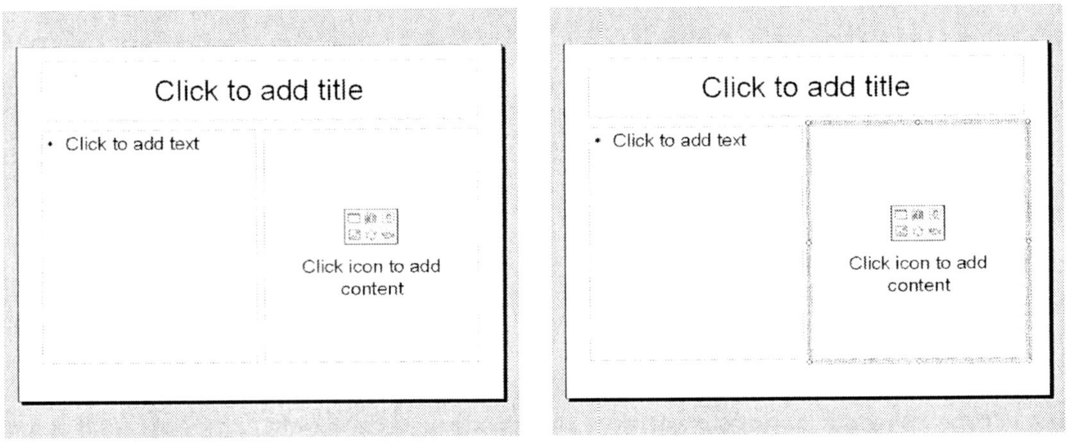

Panel A Panel B

FIGURE 6
Slide after pasting of Excel chart (Panel A) and after resizing the chart (Panel B)

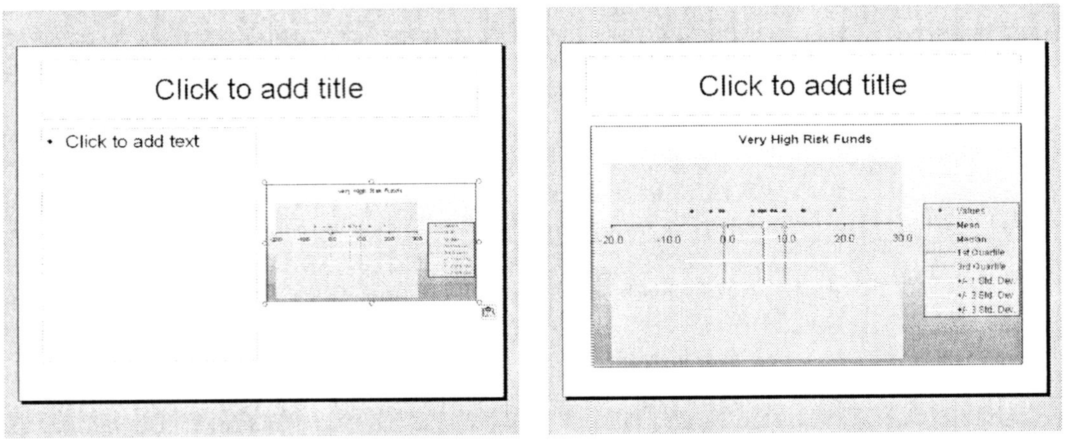

Panel A Panel B

3: PUBLISHING MICROSOFT EXCEL SHEETS AS INTERNET EXPLORER WEB PAGES

Use the **File | Save as Web page** command to save Microsoft Excel 2000 or later worksheets and chart sheets in a form viewable by the Microsoft Internet Explorer web browser. (This command, as described below, is not available in Microsoft Excel 97.) Sheets can be saved with or without a feature Microsoft Excel calls interactivity that allows users to dynamically change the contents of sheets while viewing the sheets in Internet Explorer 4.01 or later. This feature requires that the user/viewer of the interactive sheets have already installed the Microsoft Office Web Components of Microsoft Office (or Excel). As these Web Components are only available to licensed users of Office/Excel—and not to all users of Internet Explorer—most people consider this feature as being of limited value and interactivity is only briefly discussed in this section.

To illustrate the operation of the Save as Web page command, open to the **Figure 12.4** worksheet of the **Chapter 12.xls** workbook. This regression statistics worksheet contains no formulas and no need for the interactivity feature. To publish this worksheet as a Web page, select **File | Save as Web page** and in the (Web) Save As dialog box (see Figure 7), select the **Selection: Sheet** option button, enter **Figure 12.4.htm** to replace the suggested Page.htm in the **File name** edit box, and click the **Save** button.

FIGURE 7
(Web) Save As dialog box

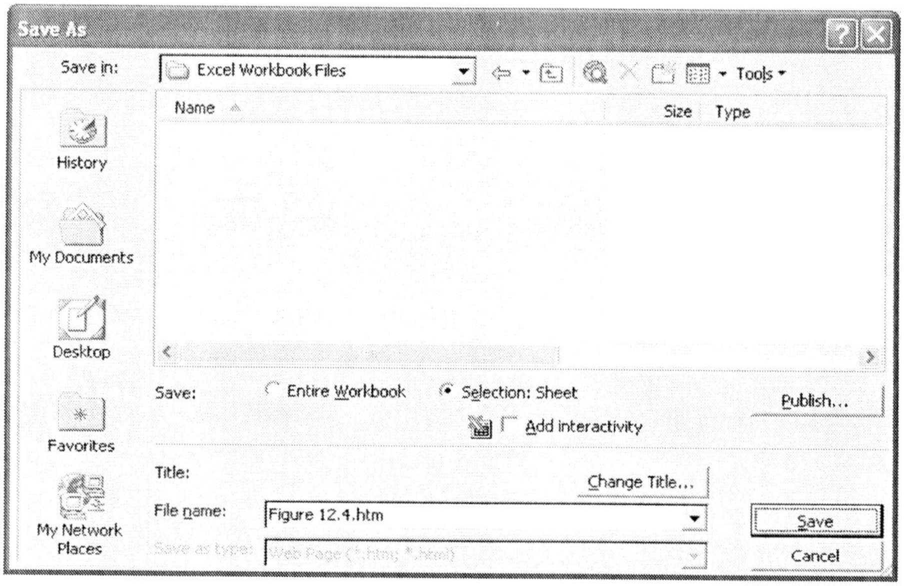

Microsoft Excel generates a formatted html Web page that is a facsimile of the worksheet and that can viewed properly in any copy of Internet Explorer 4.01 or later (see Figure 8). Other users could open this Web page directly in Microsoft Excel to recreate the original Figure 12.4 worksheet.

FIGURE 8
Web page created from Figure 12.4 worksheet

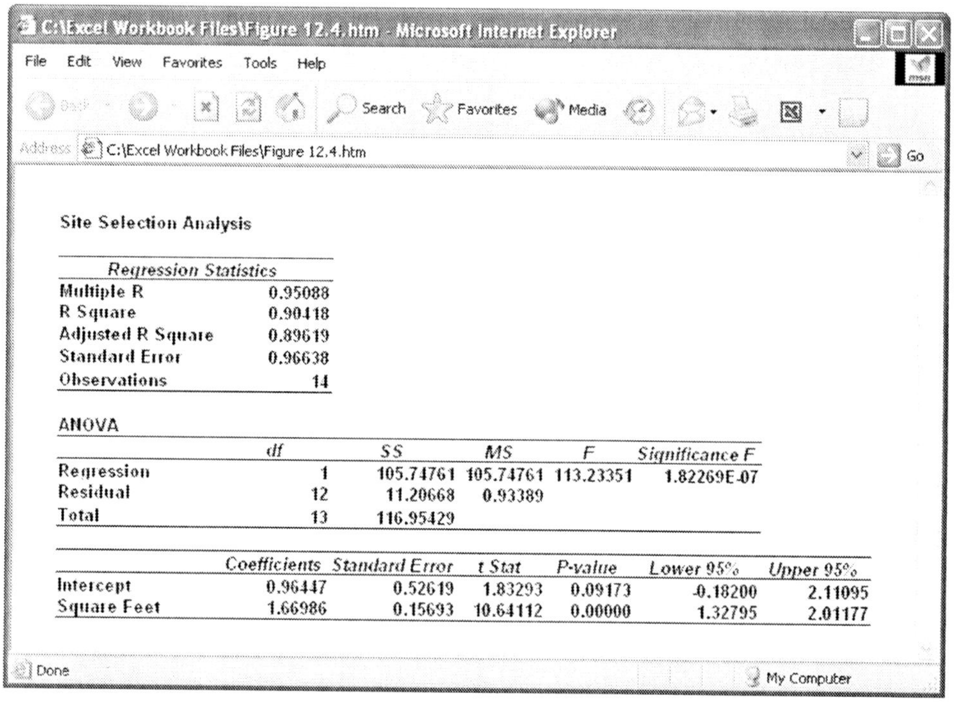

Publishing chart sheets as Web pages. To publish a chart sheet, make the same selections in the (web) Save As dialog box. Microsoft Excel generates a web page that features a graphic snapshot of the chart. Although this snapshot-containing Web page can be opened directly in Microsoft Excel, opening the web page will import only a picture and not the original chart object with its data.

To preserve the original chart and its data, save the chart sheet with interactivity. For example, to save the Figure 12.5 chart sheet as a Web page, select **File | Save as Web page** and in the (Web) Save As dialog box, select the **Selection: Chart** option page, check the **Add interactivity** check box, enter **Figure 12.5.htm** as a replacement value for the suggested Page.htm in the **File name** edit box, and click the **Save** button as shown in Figure 9.

FIGURE 9

(Web) Save As dialog box for Figure 12.5 chart sheet with interactivity

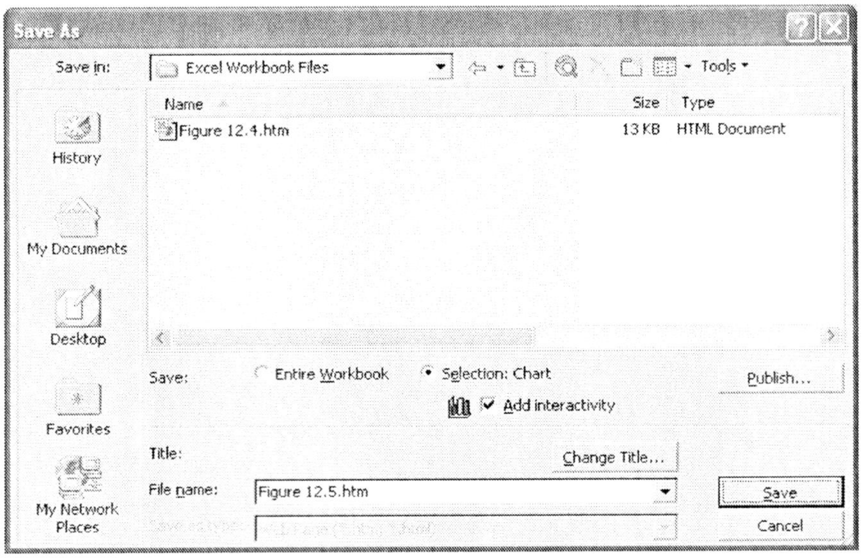

Microsoft Excel generates a formatted html Web page that contains a Microsoft Excel chart as well as a Microsoft Excel worksheet that contains the data for the chart (see Figure 10). This Web page can only be viewed on a system that has both the Microsoft Office Web Components and Internet Explorer 4.01 or later installed. In Figure 10, the toolbar above the worksheet is dimmed, showing that the Web page is in "view-only" mode. On another system, with the proper valid Microsoft Office license, the toolbar would be active and the contents of the worksheet editable.

FIGURE 10

Partial view of Web page (with interactivity) created from Figure 12.5 chart sheet

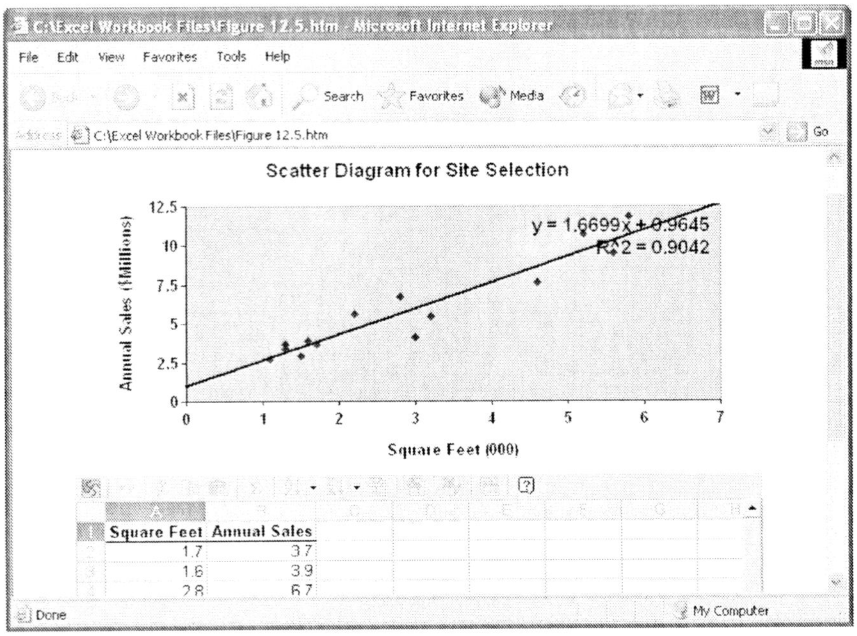

Saving worksheets with interactivity. Worksheets that contain formulas can be saved with the interactivity feature as well. However, this feature works best only with simple worksheets that do not contain formulas that refer to cells on other worksheets. If you attempt to save with interactivity a worksheet with such formulas, such as the **Figure 12.22** worksheet of the **Chapter 12.xls** workbook, the dialog box shown at right appears. If you click the OK button, formulas that contain references to other worksheets (the "external references") will be automatically replaced by their current values during the save operation.

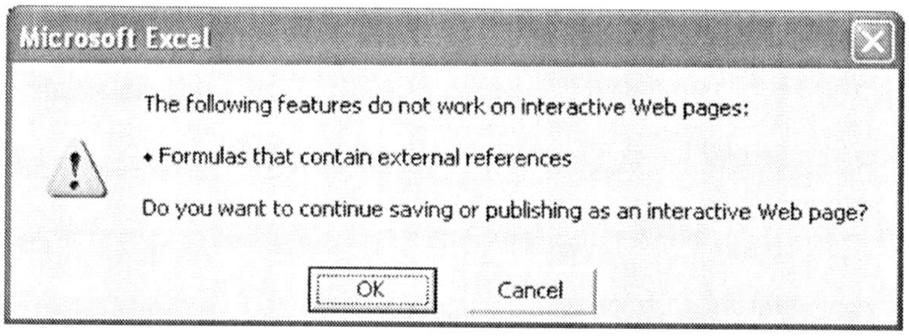

4: RETRIEVING FORMATTED TABLE DATA FROM THE WORLD WIDE WEB USING INTERNET EXPLORER

Many data sets change over time. This is especially true of time-series data, which, by its nature, change as future periods of time elapse. While many printed sources of current data exist, many today turn to the World Wide Web to retrieve, online, up-to-date sets of business, economic, and demographic data.

Finding a Web site of interest. The first step to retrieve data from the Web is locating the Web site or sites that contain the data of interest. One convenient way to do this is to use a **Web search engine**. Web search engines are Web sites that generate a list of clickable links to other Web sites based on search criteria supplied by the user. For example, Figure 11 shows the partial results of a search using the criterion "U.S. Census Bureau data." Not surprisingly, this first Web site listed is the home page of the U.S. Census Bureau Web site. For any particular search, some links listed may be inappropriate or irrelevant, but well-chosen search phrases will increase the likelihood of getting satisfactory results. For example, to search for updated versions of the data sets used in selected end of section or end of chapter problems, try typing the formal name of the data set and/or the listed source of the data.

FIGURE 11

Partial search engine results for phrase "U.S. Census Bureau data"

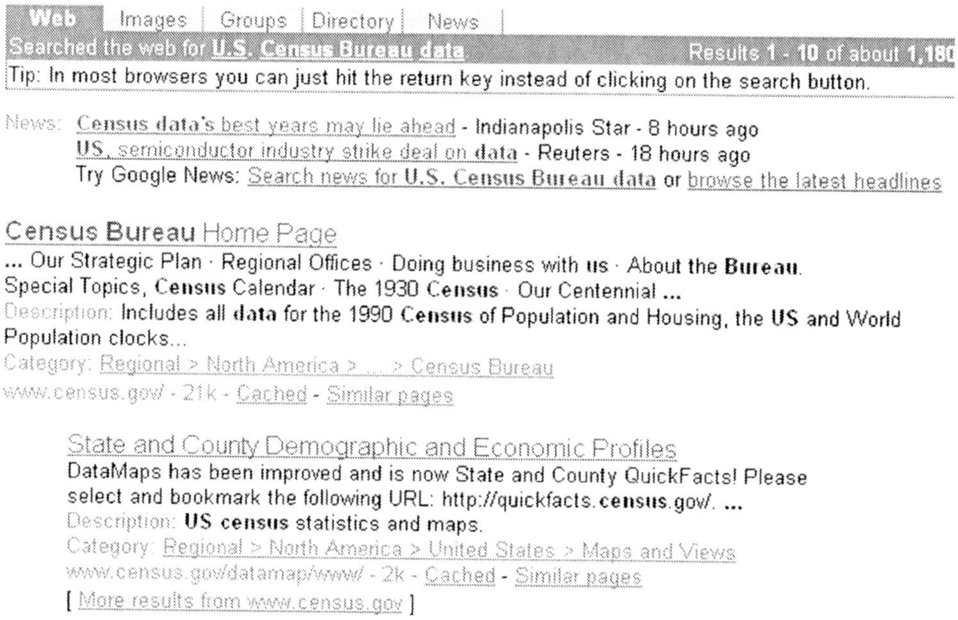

After you link to a Web site that contains the data set of interest, you may need to navigate, or click through, a number of Web pages to locate the link to the data. The **Website Navigation.ppt** PowerPoint presentation, located in the **Instructional Files** folder on the CD-ROM that accompanies this text, illustrates the navigation that was necessary as of mid-2003 to locate historical household income data from the U.S. Census Bureau Web site.

When you navigate to the Web page containing the data set of interest, the data set may be available in a variety of computer file formats. The easiest formats to retrieve are file formats such as the Microsoft Excel workbook format (**xls**) and the comma separated values format (**csv**), that can be downloaded and then directly opened in Microsoft Excel.

Sometimes the data set of interest appears formatted as a table in the Internet Explorer browser window and not as a link to a downloadable file. In such cases you can copy and paste the data directly from the browser into an Excel worksheet. For example, to transfer the "Number of school districts and K-12 enrollment, by type" table from the Web page shown in Figure 12 to an Excel worksheet:

Drag the mouse pointer to select all cells of the table, including the header.

Select **Edit | Copy** in Internet Explorer.

Switch to Microsoft Excel, and with the appropriate worksheet opened, select **Edit | Paste** in Excel.

Adjust the worksheet formatting, including column widths, as is necessary.

Figure 12 Panel B shows the pasted table data after formatting adjustments. Should the data you locate appear only as unformatted columns of text, follow the instructions of the next section to transfer that data into an Excel worksheet.

FIGURE 12

Panel A Table data displayed in Internet Explorer. Panel B Table data after pasting and formatting adjustment

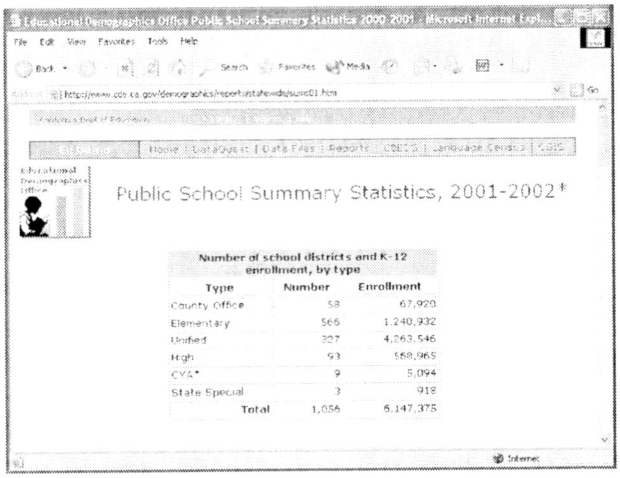

Panel A

	A	B	C
1	**Number of school districts and K-12 enrollment, by type**		
2	**Type**	**Number**	**Enrollment**
3	County Office	58	67,920
4	Elementary	566	1,240,932
5	Unified	327	4,263,546
6	High	93	568,965
7	CYA*	9	5,094
8	State Special	3	918
9	**Total**	1,056	6,147,375

Panel B

5: RETRIEVING UNFORMATTED TEXT DATA FROM THE WORLD WIDE WEB USING INTERNET EXPLORER

Older or more complex data sets, including many historical data sets that appear on the various Web sites administered by agencies of the U.S. federal government, are often presented as unformatted columns of plain text when displayed in Internet Explorer. If such data are not available as a download in a computer file format, you first clean up a saved copy of the Web page and then use the Text Import Wizard to import the text as a proper Excel worksheet.

For example, consider the Web page that in mid-2003 was available at the URL **http://ferret.bls.census.gov/macro/032002/hhinc/new06_000.htm** which contains the U.S. Census Bureau table HINC-06, "Income Distribution to $250,000 or More for Households: 2001." The Web page is typical of many Census Bureau Web pages in that the data is presented as unformatted columns of plain text. To illustrate the multi-step process necessary to transfer the data of that Web page into an Excel worksheet, open Internet Explorer to that URL and select **File | Save As** to save the Web page or skip this initial step by using the saved copy of that Web page, **HINC-06.htm**, that can be found in the **Instructional Files** folder on the CD-ROM that accompanies this text. Then open Microsoft Excel and then open the saved Web page and do these tasks:

Initial cleanup of saved Web page. As a first step, select the **CPS logo graphic** that appears over the first several rows and press the **Delete** key to delete the graphic from the workbook. Select rows **1:11** and then select **Edit | Delete** to delete the notes and table labeling at the top of the worksheet. Scroll to the bottom of worksheet table data and select rows **51:57** and then select **Edit | Delete** to delete the source notes. At this point, the worksheet area will look *like* a true worksheet table of data, although a closer examination of the worksheet will reveal that the "table" consists only of long label values in column A. Save this cleaned up data in Unicode format by doing the following:

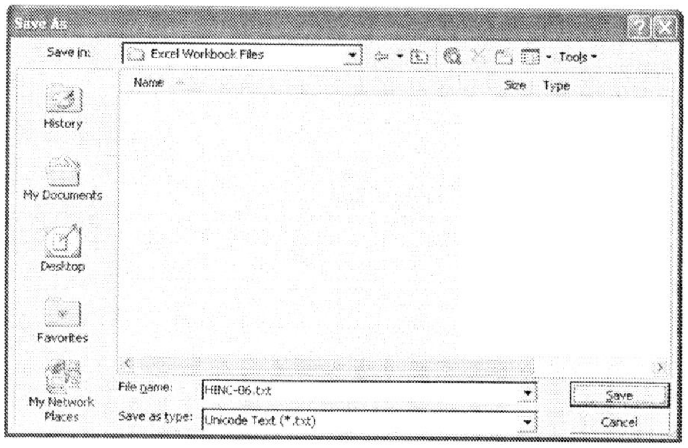

Select **File | Save As**.

In the Save As dialog box (shown at right):

Select **Unicode Text (*.txt)** in the **Save as type** drop-down list box.

Enter a file name (or keep the suggested name) in the **File name** edit box.

Click the **Save** button.

When an informational message box appears warning of possible incompatibilities with the Unicode Text format (shown below), click the **Yes** button to proceed to save the file.

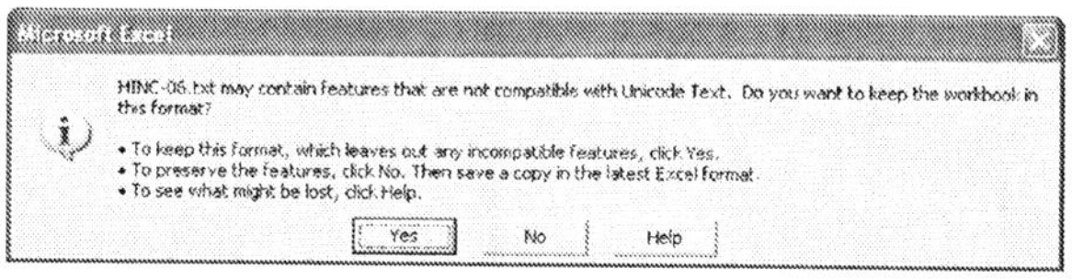

To finish the initial cleanup select **File | Close** to close the worksheet and click the **No** button in the dialog box that asks you if you want to save changes.

Using the Text Import Wizard. Select **File | Open** and open the file saved in the previous step. Be sure to select **Text Files** in the **Files of Type** drop-down list box of the Open dialog box in order to see the saved text file listed.

Opening the file automatically begins the Text Import Wizard. In the Step 1 dialog box (shown below at top), verify that the **Fixed Width** option button is selected and that the **Start import at row** value is 1 and that "All Races" appears aligned with the row 1 label. (If the settings are different, verify that you completed successfully all of the "Initial cleanup of save Web page" task.) Click the **Next** button.

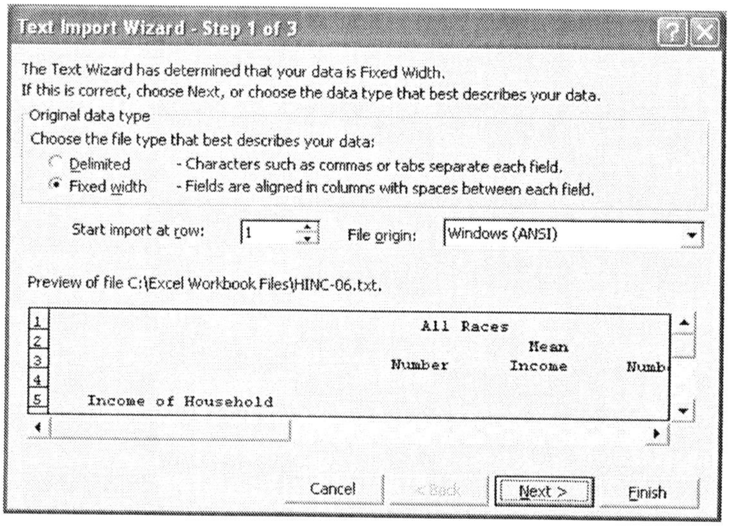

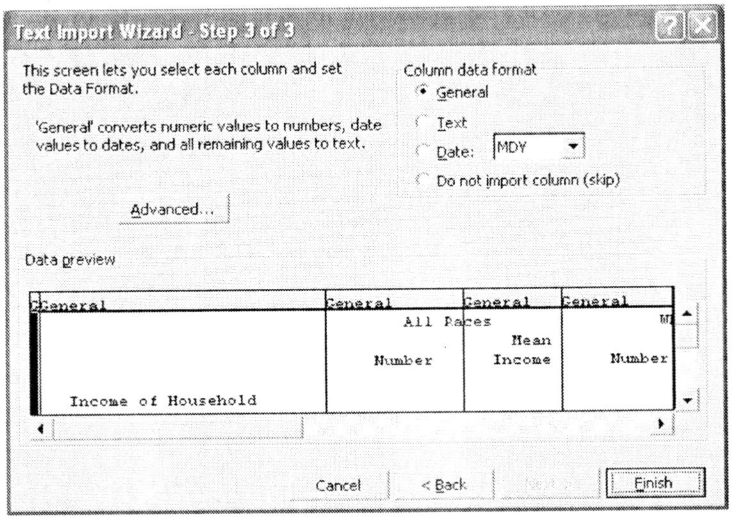

In the Text Import Wizard Step 2 dialog box, click the **Next** button to accept the Wizard's division of the text into worksheet columns. In the Text Import Wizard Step 3 dialog box (shown at bottom right), verify that the **General** Column data format option button is selected and then click the **Finish** button.

In the new worksheet, note that columns A and M contain cells with double quotation mark entries. Delete these unnecessary columns by first selecting column **A**, then selecting **Edit** | **Delete**, then selecting column **L** (the former column M) and selecting **Edit** | **Delete** a second time. Finish by adjusting column width and editing the row 1 category labels and then save the data in Microsoft Excel workbook (**xls**) format.